The Sixth International Conference on Residual Stresses

ICRS - 6

10 - 12 July 2000: Oxford, UK

SPONSORSHIP

Principal Sponsors
AEA Technology plc
MSX International
Philips Analytical
US European Offices of Naval Research & Aerospace

Co-Sponsors
BSSM (UK)
I. Mech. E. (UK)
IoP (UK)
JSMS (Japan)
JSME (Japan)
DGM (Germany)
DVM (Germany)
AWT (Germany)
ASME (USA)
SEM (USA)
FEMS (Europe)
SFZM (France)

The Organising Committee are grateful to the Office of Naval Research International Field Office and European Office of Aerospace Research and Development for their support.

VOLUME 2

IOM Communications

IOM Communications Ltd
1 Carlton House Terrace
London SW1Y 5DB
United Kingdom

Telephone: +44 (0)20 7451 7300 Facsimile: +44 (0)20 7839 2289
Email: admin@materials.org.uk
Internet: http://www.materials.org.uk

IOM Communications Ltd is a wholly owned subsidiary of
The Institute of Materials

Registered Charity No. 1059475
Investors in People

ISBN: I-86125-123-8

Co-ordinated by the Materials Science & Technology Division of the Institute of Materials and organised by IOM Communications Ltd

Printed by Chameleon Press Ltd

June 2000

PREFACE

The Sixth International Conference on Residual Stresses is the first in the series to be held in the UK. Previous conferences were held in Garmisch Partenkirchen, Germany, (1986); Nancy, France (1988); Tokushima, Japan (1991); Baltimore, USA (1994) and Linkoping, Sweden (1997).

These proceedings contain the oral and poster presentations scheduled. They have been grouped into topic areas covering measurement techniques, how residual stresses are produced, the residual stresses that have been recorded in different types of materials, how these stresses are modelled and the effects the stresses may have on material and component performance. It is evident from the papers included that it is a time of rapid advance in the subject. This is due to the combination of developments of new reliable measurement methods and the increased computing power which is becoming available for enabling full three-dimensional elastic-plastic-creep finite element stress analysis to be carried out. In some of the papers these techniques are being used to validate models for the generation of residual stresses and predict how these stress influence performance. It is anticipated that there will be a considerable increase in understanding in the near future which will allow the desirable effects of residual stress to be exploited and the detrimental effects to be minimized.

It is with regret that the death of Professor Jerome B. Cohen has to be announced. He was one of the pioneers of the study of residual stresses by diffraction methods. These proceedings are dedicated to him in view of his contribution to the field. This is outlined in the first paper.

Many people have assisted with the organization of the conference and with the preparation of the proceedings. Grateful thanks are due to The Institute of Materials, the Local Organizing Committee, the International Scientific Board and Oxford University for hosting the meeting. Acknowledgements are also due to AEA Technology for the provision of student bursaries to attend the conference, MSX International for supplying document bags and Philips Analytical and the US European Offices of Naval Research and Aerospace Research and Development in London for financial support.

It is to be hoped that an enjoyable and fruitful meeting will be held.

George A. Webster
Chairman, ICRS-6
May 2000

Professor Jerome B. Cohen
16 July 1932 to 7 November 1999

CONTENTS

Page No.

Page No.

Page No.

POSTERS

Page No.

TECHNICAL ASPECTS OF RESIDUAL STRESS

Page No.

SESSION 6A

RESIDUAL STRESS ANALYSIS IN FIBRE-TEXTURED THIN FILMS; TRANSVERSE ISOTROPY AND GRAIN INTERACTION

M. Leoni, U. Welzel, P. Lamparter and E.J. Mittemeijer
Max Planck Institute for Metals Research
Seestrasse 92, 70174 Stuttgart, Germany

ABSTRACT

Untextured bulk materials usually possess macroscopically isotropic elastic properties. On the other hand, for most thin films transverse isotropy is expected. The usually applied models (as those proposed by Voigt, Reuss, Neerfeld-Hill and Eshelby-Kröner) erroneously predict macroscopic isotropy for an (untextured) thin film. The Vook-Witt assumptions for grain interaction (*J. Appl. Phys.* 36 [7] (1965) 2169) are more suitable for thin films; on this basis the macroscopic elastic constants and the (X-ray) diffraction "ε *versus* $\sin^2\psi$" plots for stressed thin films can be calculated. For columnar-grained, sputtered films (both untextured and textured) the grain interaction model on the basis of the Vook-Witt approach provides a better agreement with the experimental lattice strain data than the classical models.

INTRODUCTION

Nowadays, large-scale production of thin films is mainly based on chemical and physical vapour deposition techniques (indicated by CVD and PVD, respectively). The deposition parameters highly influence the microstructure, including the residual stresses and the crystallographic texture, of the resulting films.

Among the PVD techniques sputtering is a traditional method for the deposition of coatings up to a few micrometers thickness. Sputtered films are often composed of columnar grains with a size in the growth direction which is of the order of the thickness of the film. The distribution of grain orientations in these films is seldom random: the (columnar) grains often present a preferred orientation parallel to the sample normal (the so-called *fibre texture*). This kind of microstructure leads to a mechanical behaviour that reflects transverse isotropy. Thus the macroscopic stiffness/compliance tensors are expected to be consistent with both texture and grain morphology, i.e. they should possess transversely isotropic symmetry (van Leeuwen *et al.* (1)). In this sense the elastic behaviour of a transversely isotropic thin film can be drastically different from that of macroscopically isotropic bulk material.

In order to evaluate the mechanical and the diffraction response of the film, suitable grain interaction models (van Leeuwen *et al.* (1)), describing the stress and strain tensors in all the differently oriented crystallites composing the film, are needed. The grain interaction model should be consistent with the microstructure of the aggregate. In particular, in the case of a thin film, the model should predict macroscopic transverse isotropy both in the absence of texture and when fibre texture occurs (van Leeuwen *et al.* (1); Leoni *et al.* (2); Welzel *et al.* (3)).

Among the various grain interaction models proposed in the literature (Voigt (4), Reuss (5)), the most appropriate for the description of a thin film is that by Vook and Witt (6,7), recently revisited and elaborated for diffraction analysis of stress by van Leeuwen *et al.* (1) and Leoni *et al.* (2). A description of the basics of the Vook-Witt model, in the case of a fibre-textured film, and a first analysis of experimental data taken from a sputtered copper film, are presented here (a more complete evaluation of the experimental data will be published elsewhere (Leoni *et al.* (8))).

GRAIN INTERACTION IN FIBRE-TEXTURED FILMS

Reference frames

Three Cartesian coordinate systems (reference frames) will be used in the following:

- the crystal system C; for cubic crystals, the axes are chosen along the a, b and c axes in the lattice;
- the specimen system S of which the S_3 axis is perpendicular to the specimen surface and of which the S_1 and S_2 axes are in the surface plane;
- the laboratory system L. The lattice strain is measured along the L_3 axis, parallel to the diffraction vector.

Every symbol of a quantity defined in a particular coordinate system has a superscript indicating the reference frame used for the representation. The transformation of coordinates from one to another frame of reference ($\mathrm{Y} \rightarrow \mathrm{X}$) is described by rotation matrices A^{XY} of which the elements (direction cosines) will be indicated as a_{ij}^{XY}.

Macroscopic mechanical response for a transversely isotropic thin film

The film is adherent to a substrate and is subjected to a plane state of stress. The film is thus unloaded in the direction perpendicular to the surface. The symbol $\langle \Omega_{ij} \rangle$ indicates the macroscopic average over all crystallites composing the thin film of the component Ω_{ij} of the tensor Ω. The absence of macroscopic average stress components normal to the surface can then be expressed as:

$$\langle \sigma_{i3}^{S} \rangle = \langle \sigma_{3i}^{S} \rangle = 0 \tag{1}$$

The film is free to expand along its normal and the average strain along the surface normal is given by:

$$\langle \varepsilon_{33}^{S} \rangle \overset{def}{=} \varepsilon_{\perp}^{S} \tag{2}$$

A rotationally symmetric stress field is supposed to act in the plane of the film:

$$\langle \sigma_{11}^{S} \rangle = \langle \sigma_{22}^{S} \rangle \overset{def}{=} \sigma_{//}^{S} \qquad \langle \sigma_{12}^{S} \rangle = \langle \sigma_{21}^{S} \rangle = 0 \tag{3}$$

Due to the transverse isotropy of the body, the rotational symmetry of the stress field induces a rotational symmetry of the strain field:

$$\langle \varepsilon_{11}^{S} \rangle = \langle \varepsilon_{22}^{S} \rangle \overset{def}{=} \varepsilon_{//}^{S} \qquad \langle \varepsilon_{12}^{S} \rangle = \langle \varepsilon_{21}^{S} \rangle = 0 \tag{4}$$

Once the macroscopic stress and strain are known, a set of macroscopic elastic constants can be evaluated. In the present case only two strain tensor components and one stress tensor component are non zero, which allows evaluation of two macroscopic elastic constants (named A and B; van Leeuwen *et al.* (1)):

$$\varepsilon_{//}^{S} = A\sigma_{//}^{S} \tag{5}$$

$$\varepsilon_{\perp}^{S} = B\sigma_{//}^{S} \tag{6}$$

These two elastic constants suffice to describe the macroscopic behaviour of a transversely isotropic body under a rotationally symmetric, plane stress field. Note that for a general type of loading of a transversely isotropic body five elastic constants are needed to fully describe the elastic behaviour of the body (Voigt (4)).

In order to evaluate the macroscopic stress and strain volume averages needed for actual calculations of A and B on the basis of equations (5) and (6), both a description of the orientation of the crystallites in the body and a grain interaction model must be provided.

The distribution of the orientations for the crystallites composing the film is usually described in the Euler (orientation) space by means of the Orientation Distribution Function (ODF) (Bunge (9), Matthies *et al.* (10,11), Roe and Krigbaum (12)). In the following, the conventions of Roe and Krigbaum (12) will be used. The orientation of the crystallite coordinate system C can be described, with respect to the specimen system S, by means of three Euler angles α, β and γ, defining a vector $g = (\alpha,\beta,\gamma)$ in Euler space; thus each point of the Euler space indicates a possible orientation of the crystallite in the specimen system.

Given an infinitesimal orientation range $dg = \sin(\beta)d\alpha d\beta d\gamma$ around g in Euler space, the ODF, $f(g)$, is defined as:

$$f(g)dg = \frac{dV(g)}{V} \tag{7}$$

representing the volume fraction of crystallites ($dV(g)/V$; V is the total volume of the crystallites) oriented in the infinitesimal range dg around g. The orientation distribution function possesses the symmetry elements both of the sample and of the crystal lattice of the material composing the sample. Now, for the thin film considered here, the average stress $\sigma_{//}^S$ can be calculated as (Leoni *et al.* (2)):

$$\langle\sigma_{11}^S\rangle = \langle\sigma_{22}^S\rangle = \sigma_{//}^S = \frac{1}{8\pi^2}\int_{\gamma=0}^{2\pi}\int_{\beta=0}^{\pi}\int_{\alpha=0}^{2\pi}\sigma_{11}^S f(\alpha,\beta,\gamma)\sin(\beta)d\alpha d\beta d\gamma \tag{8}$$

Analogous expressions hold for $\varepsilon_{//}^S$ and $\varepsilon_{\perp}^S$.

In order to be able to calculate the individual stress/strain tensor components of each crystallite in the S system (e.g. σ_{11}^S for each crystallite; cf. equation (8)), some of these stress/strain components have to be set equal for all crystallites. Such hypotheses on the grain interaction are discussed next.

Grain interaction: Voigt, Reuss and Vook-Witt approaches

For each crystallite composing the film, Hooke's law reads:

$$\varepsilon_{ij}^S = s_{ijkl}^S\sigma_{kl}^S = a_{im}^{SC}a_{jn}^{SC}a_{ko}a_{lp}^{SC}s_{mnop}^C\sigma_{kl}^S \tag{9}$$

This formula represents a set of 6 equations in 12 unknowns (the components of the symmetric σ and ε tensors); s is the single-crystal compliance tensor. In order to evaluate the complete stress and strain tensors for each crystallite in the S system, six additional relations for the stress/strain components are needed. These equations are provided by a grain interaction model. In the case of a thin film, the grain interaction model should be compatible with the microstructure of the film.

The traditional models, proposed by Voigt (4) and Reuss (5), suppose that the strain tensor (Voigt) or the stress tensor (Reuss) are, for all crystallites, the same. In the absence of texture this implies macroscopic mechanical isotropy (Stickforth (13)). According to these models discontinuities occur for the stress and strain fields, respectively, at the interfaces between adjacent crystallites. These grain interaction approaches are obviously incompatible with the microstructure of real bodies, and in particular with that of a columnar-grained thin film which cannot be conceived as a body presenting three-dimensional macroscopic isotropy. Each grain in a film with columnar microstructure is surrounded by other grains only in two dimensions (in-plane directions). The grain interaction in the direction normal to the film surface can be supposed to be weak, and the individual grains may expand freely in that direction (i.e. the stress components in the *S* system perpendicular to the film surface can be assumed to be zero for all crystallites).

The above consideration has led to the Vook-Witt approach for thin films (6,7). The model has been recently revised by van Leeuwen *et al.* (1) and it has been demonstrated to yield a macroscopic transversely isotropic behaviour already in the absence of crystallographic (fibre) texture (see in particular Welzel *et al.* (3)). This approach is thus compatible both with the expected macroscopic response of the film (cf. the considerations pertaining to equations (1)-(4)) and with its microstructure. A summary of the grain interaction parameters for the various models is given in Table 1.

	σ_{11}	σ_{22}	σ_{33}	σ_{12}	σ_{13}	σ_{23}	ε_{11}	ε_{22}	ε_{33}	ε_{12}	ε_{13}	ε_{23}
Voigt							X	X	X	X	X	X
Reuss	X	X	X	X	X	X						
Vook-Witt			0		0	0	X	X		X		

Table 1. Grain interaction parameters for the three models considered here: Voigt, Reuss, Vook-Witt. The stress and strain tensor components in the *S* system imposed to be the same for all crystallites, independently of their orientation, have been indicated by "X". Stress components set to zero have been indicated by "0".

Diffraction response

X-ray diffraction can provide an average macroscopic strain value which is fundamentally different from the one that can be acquired from mechanical testing: only a subset of the grains composing the film contributes to the measured strain in the diffraction experiment, since only the crystallites of which the diffracting planes are perpendicular to the measurement direction are probed, whereas the whole specimen contributes to the measured response in mechanical testing. The diffraction experiment does provide an averaging around the diffraction vector **h** since, from the diffraction point of view, all directions in the diffracting planes are equivalent.

Recognising the distribution of crystallites in Euler space (cf. discussion with respect to the ODF), the lattice strain measured in a diffraction experiment can be written as:

$$\varepsilon_{\varphi,\psi}^{meas} = \frac{\int_0^{2\pi} \varepsilon_{33}^{L} f(g(\mathbf{h},\lambda,\varphi,\psi))d\lambda}{\int_0^{2\pi} f(g(\mathbf{h},\lambda,\varphi,\psi))d\lambda} = \frac{\int_0^{2\pi} a_{3i}^{LS} a_{3j}^{LS} \varepsilon_{ij}^{S} f(g(\mathbf{h},\lambda,\varphi,\psi))d\lambda}{\int_0^{2\pi} f(g(\mathbf{h},\lambda,\varphi,\psi))d\lambda} \tag{10}$$

The angle λ denotes the rotation around the diffraction vector, and the integration with respect to λ takes into account the intrinsic averaging due to the diffraction experiment; the angle φ indicates the rotation of the sample around its normal and the angle ψ indicates the tilt of the sample with respect to L_3. The angles ψ and φ are sufficient for the positioning of the *S* system with respect to the *L* system (they thus correspond to measurement angles).

The usual representation of the ODF in terms of Euler angles cannot be directly used in equation (10): a suitable transformation is necessary (see Leoni *et al.* (2)).

It is common practice to represent equation (10) as a relation between $\varepsilon_{\varphi,\psi}^{meas}$ and $\sin^2\psi$ since, for a macroscopically isotropic sample, the relation is linear (Stickforth (13)). In the case of only macroscopic transverse isotropy a non-linear dependence of $\varepsilon_{\varphi,\psi}^{meas}$ on $\sin^2\psi$ can occur. Then equation (10) is used within a least-squares routine with the macroscopic stress/strain tensor components in the *S* system as fitting parameters.

EXPERIMENTAL

Diffraction measurements were performed on a Philips X'Pert MRD system equipped with a copper tube (45KV, 40mA) in parallel beam geometry. A parallel beam was obtained by means of an incident-beam polycapillary collimator (4x4mm opening) and a flat graphite monochromator in the diffracted beam path was set to select CuKα-radiation. Using a 4-circles goniometer (Eulerian cradle) the stress measurements were conducted in ψ-tilting mode at constant φ; it was verified that the same results were obtained at other φ angles.

The analysed sample was a copper film, of thickness 500nm, sputter-deposited onto a thermally oxidised <510>-silicon wafer utilising a planar dc-magnetron with a copper target (purity 99.95%) in an Ultra High Vacuum chamber (base pressure $2\bullet10^{-10}$ mbar). The magnetron was operated at 100W using precleaned (Messer Griessheim Oxisorb gas cleaning cartridge) Ar 6.0 with a pressure of $3.5\bullet10^{-3}$ mbar as a sputter gas. Immediately before the layer deposition the substrates were cleaned by heating them to 673K and, after cooling down to room temperature, by argon ion bombardment using an ion gun. The film thickness was determined by calibration of the deposition rate using a stylus profilometer (Dektak). For this purpose a sample with a step in height was produced by partial layer removal.

RESULTS AND DISCUSSION

Simulations of the mechanical and the diffraction response were performed for various fibre-textured films (cubic materials) exhibiting largely different degrees of anisotropy, A_i, as indicated by the single-crystal elastic constants (see Leoni *et al.* (2)):

$$A_i = 2\frac{s_{11} - s_{12}}{s_{44}} \qquad (11)$$

The macroscopic elastic constants A and B (equations (5) and (6)) for a fibre-textured copper film (<110> Gaussian fibre texture) are shown as a function of texture pole width in Fig. 1. The values obtained for A and B in the Voigt and Reuss limits are, respectively, the lower and upper limits for the elastic constants A and B calculated using the Vook-Witt model. The arithmetic average of the Reuss and Voigt data (Hill's average (14)) agrees well with the Vook-Witt values. A marked effect of the pole width (indicating the sharpness of the texture) on A and B is observed.

The diffraction response for the $\{hhh\}$ reflections of stressed niobium and nickel films is shown in Fig. 2. The Voigt (for any reflection) and Reuss (for the $\{hhh\}$ and $\{00l\}$ reflections; cf. Brakman (15)) models predict a linear dependence of $\varepsilon_{\psi}^{meas}$ (note that in the present case - plane state of rotational symmetric stress and fibre texture - $\varepsilon_{\varphi,\psi}^{meas}$ is equal to $\varepsilon_{\psi}^{meas}$) on $\sin^2\psi$. Clearly, the Vook-Witt model does not show such linearity. It also follows that the diffraction response according to the Vook-Witt type of grain interaction can be outside the "limits" of the Voigt and Reuss types of grain interaction.

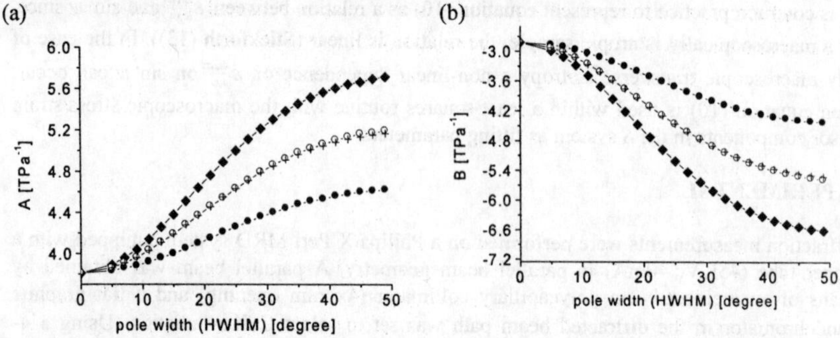

Fig. 1. Dependency of the elastic constants A (a) and B (b) on the texture pole width (described by the half width at half maximum – HWHM – of the pole in Euler space) for an <110> textured copper thin film. The data were calculated according to the Voigt (●), Reuss (◆) and Vook-Witt (O) grain interaction models. The arithmetic average of the Voigt and Reuss values (Hill's average (14)) is also shown (+). Literature single-crystal elastic data, s_{11}= 14.98 TPa^{-1}, s_{12}= -6.29 Tpa^{-1}, s_{44}= 13.26 TPa^{-1} (Meyers and Chawla (16)), were used in the calculation.

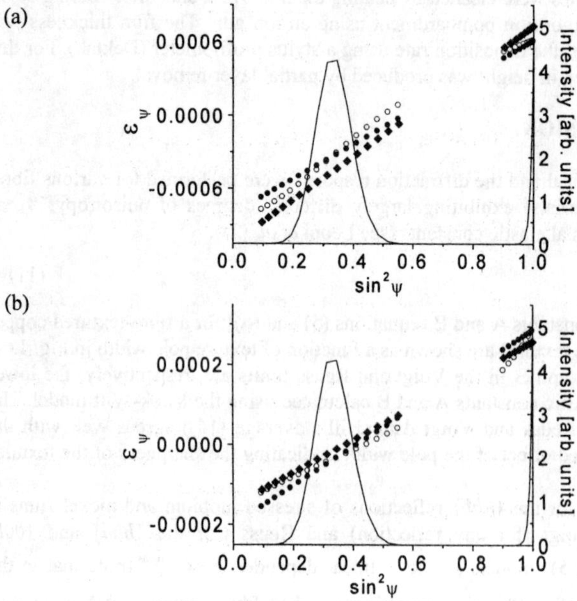

Fig. 2. $\text{Sin}^2\psi$ plots for the {*hhh*} reflection for two different materials, characterised by different values of anisotropy: niobium, A_i = 0.55 (a) and nickel, A_i = 2.51 (b). In both cases a <110> Gaussian fibre texture (5° Half Width at Half Maximum for the pole) is present (elastic constants from Meyers and Chawla (16)). The data were calculated according to the Voigt (●), Reuss (◆) and Vook-Witt (O) grain interaction models whereby a stress of 100MPa has been assumed. The integrated intensity has also been plotted as a function of $\sin^2\psi$ (continuous lines).

The non-linear dependence of $\varepsilon_{\psi}^{meas}$ on $\sin^2\psi$ is also observed for real, measured data; see Fig. 3 pertaining to the {004} reflection for the 500nm-thick copper film.

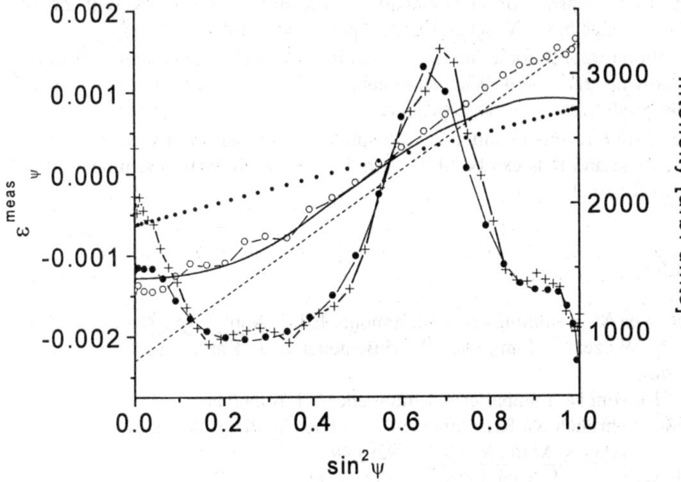

Fig. 3. $\sin^2\psi$ plot for the {004} reflection of the thin copper film sample: experimental raw lattice-strain data (o) and results of the simulation, using a stress, $\sigma_{//}^{S}$ of 180MPa, for the Voigt (dot), Reuss (dash) and Vook-Witt (continuous line) (elastic constants from Meyers and Chawla (16)). The relative integrated intensity, both as measured (●) and as reconstructed from the ODF (orientation distribution function, +), has also been plotted as function of $\sin^2\psi$.

A pronounced curvature is visible for the strain data, followed only by the simulation according to the Vook-Witt type of grain interaction. A good fit occurs up to about $\sin^2\psi \approx 0.65$. The remaining discrepancies are ascribed to an imperfect representation of the true texture by the Orientation Distribution Function (ODF) calculated from a set of measured pole figures for different reflections (the Philips X'Pert Texture software was employed for the calculations; see the differences between calculated and measured intensity as function of $\sin^2\psi$ in Fig. 3). In this context, in particular it should be noted that the data presented in Figure 3 have not (yet) been corrected for any instrumental and/or sample aberration (e.g. sample absorption and instrumental defocusing). A full evaluation of the experimental results including the corrections mentioned will be published soon (Leoni *et al.* (8)).

CONCLUSIONS

- The Vook-Witt approach to grain interaction, in contrast with the traditional Voigt and Reuss approaches, is compatible with the microstructure of a columnar thin film that is either textureless or fibre-textured.
- The macroscopic elastic constants calculated according to the Vook-Witt approach are close to the average of the Voigt and Reuss approaches (Hill's average).
- The diffraction response for a thin film, as exhibited in a $\sin^2\psi$ plot, can be distinctly non-linear following the Vook-Witt approach, for cases where the Voigt and Reuss approaches predict linear $\sin^2\psi$ dependence.
- The experimental results obtained from a sputtered thin copper film show that the $\sin^2\psi$ plots are curved and thus can be fitted with the new Vook-Witt type model but not with the traditional models.

REFERENCES

1. van Leeuwen M, Kamminga J-D, Mittemeijer E J, J. Appl. Phys. 86 (1999) 1904
2. Leoni M, Welzel U, Lamparter P, Mittemeijer E J, Kamminga J-D, Submitted for publication
3. Welzel U, Leoni M, Lamparter P, Mittemeijer E J, In preparation.
4. Voigt W, "Lehrbuch der Kristallphysik", Teubner (Leipzig, Berlin), 1910
5. Reuss A, Z. Angew. Math. Mech. 9 (1929) 49
6. Vook R W, Witt F, J. Appl. Phys. 7 (1965) 2169
7. Witt F, Vook R W, J. Appl. Phys. 39 [6] (1968) 2773
8. Leoni M, Welzel U, Lamparter P, Mittemeijer E J, In preparation.
9. Bunge H-J, "Texture analysis in materials science", Butterworths (London), 1982
10. Matthies S, Wenk H-R, Vinel G W, J. Appl. Cryst. 21 (1988) 285
11. Matthies S, Vinel G W, Helming K, "Standard distributions in texture analysis", Akademie Verlag (Berlin), 1987
12. Roe R-J, Krigbaum W R, J. Chem. Phys. 40 (1964) 2608
13. Stickforth J, Tech. Mitt. Krupp-Forsch.-Ber. 24 [3] (1966) 89
14. Hill R, Proc. Phys. Soc. London 65 (1952) 349
15. Brakman C M, J. Appl. Cryst. 16 (1983) 325
16. Meyers M A, Chawla K K, "Mechanical Metallurgy, Principles and Applications", Prentice-Hall (Englewood Cliffs), 1984

PVD-GRADIENT COATINGS OF TI(C,N) — DEPTH PROFILES OF RESIDUAL STRESSES AND MECHANICAL PERFORMANCE

T. Dümmer, D. Löhe

Institute of Materials Science and Engineering I, Karlsruhe University (TH)
P.O. Box 6980, D-76128 Karlsruhe, Germany

Abstract — Ceramic protective coatings on cutting tools for steel machining are state of the art in industrial applications. Several concepts to improve the efficiency of production processes as for instance high-speed or dry cutting yield increasing demands regarding the wear and corrosion resistance of the protective tool coatings. The generic process characteristics of PVD-coating techniques offer opportunities to tailor the coatings in terms of microstructure and residual stress states by adjusting appropriate process parameters. Besides chemical composition and microstructure the residual stresses in the coatings strongly influence their in-service performance and, are therefore important to assess and to correlate with process parameters. A special approach was employed to non-destructively determine the depth profiles of residual stresses and stress-free lattice parameters present in PVD-Ti(C,N)-compositionally graded coatings by means of depth-resolved X-ray residual stress analysis. The coatings were mechanically tested by recording load-indentation curves using spherical indenters to yield concentric coating fracture. Together with results of residual stress analyses and microscopical characterization of indentation experiments the fracture initiating stresses were determined by FEM-analysis. A positive effect of compressive residual stresses on load-bearing capacity and effective fracture strength of the coating systems clearly turned out. Using a simple fracture criterion the mode-I fracture toughness of the coatings was estimated.

1 INTRODUCTION

In industrial application, cutting, broaching and shaping tools of cemented carbides and high-speed or cold-working steels are commonly supplied with 2 to 7 µm thick wear resistant coatings of for instance TiC, TiN, Ti(C,N) or (Ti,Al)N to increase the tools service life [1...3]. Compositionally graded coatings of Ti(C,N) showing a continuous transition from C-rich Ti(C,N) at the interface to the substrate to N-rich Ti(C,N) at the surface exhibit further increased wear resistance, in particular during interrupted cutting [2] and shaping processes. TiC at the interface yields good adhesion whereas TiN at the surface leads to good wear and corrosion behaviour in case of steel machining. In addition to a tailored microstructural design compressive residual stresses and high hardness of the coatings can further improve the wear and corrosion resistance. However, excessive compressive residual stresses can promote the coatings spalling-off. Therefore, knowledge of the correlation among process parameters, residual stresses and mechanical properties of the coatings is vital. Residual stress analyses on thin coatings are favoured to perform by means of X-ray diffraction [4]. To determine the depth distribution of residual stresses and stress-free lattice parameters present in the graded Ti(C,N)-coatings here investigated a special experimental setup and approach for the evaluation was employed. The procedures are briefly described together with results of residual stress analyses on the coatings. Mechanical properties such as fracture strength and toughness of this kind of coatings can be estimated through indentation tests with spherical [5] and Vickers or Berkovich indenters [6] together with FEM-analyses [7]. The coatings were mechanically tested by recording load-indentation curves using spherical Si_3N_4-indenters with radii of 0.2 and 0.5 mm. At a critical indentation load the induced radial stresses at the coating surface yield concentric cracking in the outer vicinity of the contact zone. From FEM-simulations accounting for the elastic-plastic response of the steel substrate and for the friction in the contact zone the fracture-initiating stresses could be calculated considering the residual stresses of the coatings. Based on a simple fracture criterion the mode-I fracture toughness of the coating material was estimated and is presented here together with the experimental setup and the numerical simulation of the indentation tests.

2 COATINGS INVESTIGATED

Graded PVD-coatings of Ti(C,N) were non-reactively deposited by magnetron sputtering with thicknesses between 4...5.5 µm on the heat treated cold-working steel X210 CrW 12 [8] typically used for broaching tools. The gradient in composition from C-rich Ti(C,N) at the interface to the substrate to N-rich Ti(C,N) at the surface was obtained by moving the substrates underneath a divided target of 150 mm diameter, composed of a semicircular TiC- and TiN-part the movement starting on the TiC-side at the beginning of the deposition process. The coatings were deposited with distances between target and substrate of h = 42 and 59 mm for each distance with gas pressures of p_{Ar} = 0.2, 0.4 and 0.8 Pa using Ar as working gas and no bias-potential. The sputtering power was 1000 W. The substrate preparation was performed according to [8]. During the coating process, the substrate temperature reached approximately 200° to 250° C. The content of retained austenite in the steel substrates upon coating was determined by X-ray diffraction to 9.3 ± 2 vol-%. *Fig. 1* shows a TEM-image of a surface-near cross section of the coating deposited with p_{Ar} = 0.4 Pa at h = 42 mm. A typical columnar microstructure appears with the true cross-sectional diameter of the columns of about 320 nm being determined according to [9].

Fig 1: TEM-image of surface-near cross section of coating deposited with p_{Ar} = 0.4 Pa at h = 42 mm.

3 DEPTH-RESOLVED X-RAY RESIDUAL STRESS ANALYSIS

From peak positions of interference profiles the corresponding lattice spacings of the polycrystalline material can be determined. Due to residual stresses the lattice spacings are changed elastically. From the resulting shifts of peak positions lattice strains in different directions with reference to the specimen and then, based on theory of elasticity, the in-plane macro residual stress state can be determined [10]. In case of the graded coatings of Ti(C,N) investigated here depth distributions of the isotropic in-plane residual stresses $\sigma_\varphi^{RS}(z)$ and of the stress-free lattice parameters $a_0(z)$ over the distance z from the surface are to determine simultaneously from shifts of peak positions. To achieve stable numerical solution of the ill-conditioned problem two requirements have to be met by the measuring procedure. The penetration depth of the X-rays have to be varied in a wide range together with large variation of the measuring direction for the lattice strains and, this two variations should be realized independently from each other. The variation in measuring direction was obtained by registering peak positions at inclination angles of up to $\psi = \pm 88°$ in symmetrical $2\theta/\theta$-configuration. In order to independently vary the penetration depth of the X-rays z* further peak positions at reduced incidence angle α of the primary beam with a priori smaller penetration depth were performed, again to large specimen inclinations of up to $\psi = \pm 80°$. Experimental details are reported in [8] together with the necessary intensity and refraction corrections on the measured results.

The residual stress analyses on the coatings were performed on Ψ-diffractometers using synchrotron radiation of the wavelength $\lambda = 0.150960$ and 0.175779 nm at beamline B2 and G3, respectively, at HASYLAB, DESY, in Hamburg. The {220}-interferences of the cubic Ti(C,N) at peak positions $2\theta \approx 59°$ and 71.5° were registered both, in symmetrical configuration with $\alpha = \theta$ and in asymmetrical configuration with constant incidence angle $\alpha = 2°$. The X-ray values of Young's modulus $E^{\{220\}} = 429$ GPa and of Poisson's ratio $\nu^{\{220\}} = 0.20$ were taken as arithmetic averages of the values for TiC and TiN [10]. In the same way the linear absorption coefficient was determined as $\mu = 787$ and 1187 cm^{-1} [11], the latter for the larger wavelength. Since near the surface the coatings consist of N-rich Ti(C,N), the required refraction correction at the surface was done using the refraction coefficient n = 0.9999843 and 0.9999789 for TiN [11] again, the latter for the larger wavelength.

4 INDENTATION TESTS AND FEM-ANALYSES

The coatings were mechanically tested by recording load-indentation curves. Spherical indenters of Si_3N_4 with tip radii of R = 0.2 and 0.5 mm were used. The coatings were penetrated with both indenter radii at constant feed-rate of 0.005 mm/s during loading and unloading. The maximum loads of the cycles were chosen experimentally which lead to one circular crack observed by optical microscopy. In addition, two higher loading forces were applied yielding increasing number of concentric circular cracks with increasing crack radii. Two rotationally symmetric FEM-models were used to simulate the indentation tests with R = 0.2 and 0.5 mm. Square elements consisting of eight nodes with refinement in the contact area were employed. Special contact elements were used to account for contact friction with the friction coefficient $\mu = 0.2$. The macroscopic elastic constants taken for the indenters of Si_3N_4 and the Ti(C-N)-coatings are E = 320 GPa and $\nu = 0.27$ as well as E = 420 GPa and $\nu = 0.20$. The elastic-plastic response of the steel substrates was determined by quasi-static compression tests on cylindrical specimens with d = 5 mm and l = 10 mm. The true stress-strain response was multi-linear mod-

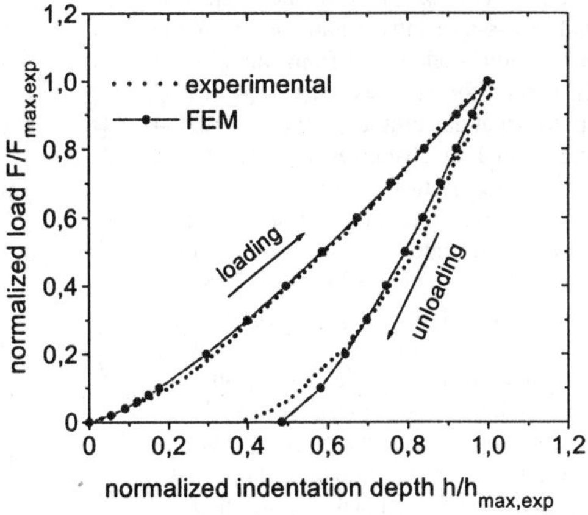

Fig. 2: Simulated and experimentally determined load-indentation curves of uncoated substrate normalized by experimentally determined maximum Load $F_{max,exp}$ and indentation depth $h_{max,exp}$.

eled considering von Mises' yield criterion. The recorded load-indentation curves were corrected for the compliance of the testing device being determined by FEM-analyses. *Fig. 2* shows a simulated and an experimentally determined load-indentation curve of the uncoated substrate clearly demonstrating that the FEM-simulations excellently fit the experimental data; in particular at maximum load where the resulting stress states are taken to determine the fracture stresses of the coatings. The maximum radial stresses at the surface of the coating in the outer vicinity of the contact zone, resulting from superposition of the isotropic in-plane residual stresses and loading stresses, were identified as initiating the observed circular cracks. The crack-initiating load and corresponding radial stress were determined from FEM-calculations in a way that the radial position of the loading-stress maximum meets the radius r_c of the first inner experimentally observed circular crack.

5 RESULTS AND DISCUSSION

i) X-ray residual stress analyses:

Fig. 3 exemplarily shows the {220}-peak positions $2\theta_{\varphi,\psi}$ corrected according to [8] as a function of $\sin^2\psi$ determined on the Ti(C,N)-coating deposited with $p_{Ar} = 0.4$ Pa at h = 42 mm. The top axis of the diagram gives the normalized penetration depth z^*/z_0 of the X-rays, z_0 being the maximum penetration depth at $\psi = 0°$ which contributes 63 % to the diffracted intensity as given in the figure. The curves represent the distribution of the peak positions resulting from the calculated distributions of residual stresses and stress-free lattice parameters. The positive slope of the distributions indicates the presence of compressive residual stresses; the curvature is indicator for gradients in residual stresses and stress-free lattice parameters. The larger values of $2\theta_{\varphi,\psi}$ in case of the asymmetrical configuration with smaller penetration depth z* proofs the gradient in material composition from C-rich to N-rich Ti(C,N) towards the surface, since TiN in the surface-near region has the smaller lattice parameter and therefore shows larger peak positions.

The depth distributions of residual stresses with 63 %-confidence intervals and stress-free lattice parameters of the cubic lattice calculated from this kind of data sets for the six Ti(C,N)-coatings sputtered at gas pressures of $p_{Ar} = 0.2$, 0.4 and 0.8 Pa at distances of h = 42 and 59 mm are plotted in *Fig. 4*. The isotropic in-plane residual stresses are compressive in nature and show negative gradients over the distance z from the surface indicating higher compressive residual stresses at the C-rich interface to the substrate than at the N-rich surface. This finding fits previous results of X-ray residual stress analyses on homogeneous coatings showing higher compressive residual stresses in TiC- than in TiN-coatings [12]. The positive gradients in stress-free lattice parameters result from the larger lattice parameter of TiC ($a_0^{TiC} = 0.4327$ nm) compared to TiN

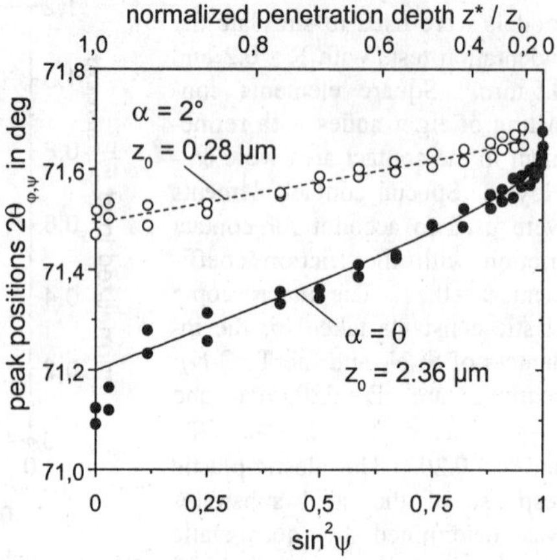

Fig. 3: Measured and recalculated {220}-peak positions vs. $\sin^2\psi$ of coating sputtered with $p_{Ar} = 0.4$ Pa at h = 42 mm.

(a_0^{TiN} = 0.4240 nm). Since neither the lattice parameter of pure TiN nor of TiC is reached at the surface and at the interface to the substrate, respectively, it is to deal with a solid solution of Ti(C,N) over the entire coating thickness.

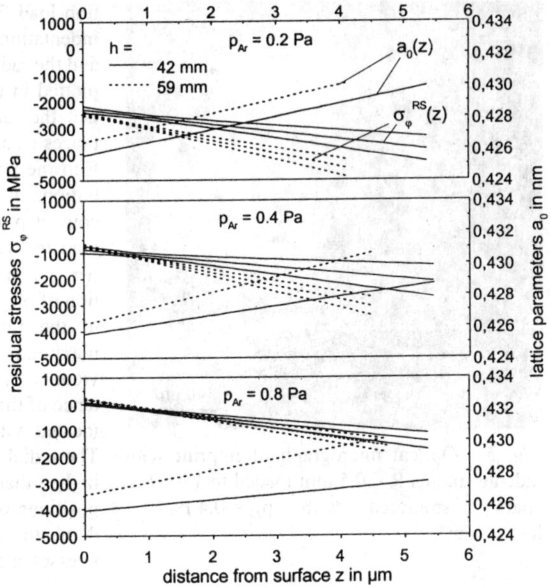

Fig. 4: Depth distributions of residual stresses and stress-free lattice parameters for six coatings sputtered with three gas pressures p_{Ar} and two distances between target and substrate h.

The overall level of compressive residual stresses decrease with increasing gas pressure. This is due to the higher kinetic energy of depositing particles at lower gas pressure yielding larger amounts of lattice defects introduced in the growing coatings which are responsible for the in-plane compressive residual stresses [13]. The distributions of the stress-free lattice parameters are nearly unaffected by variation in gas pressure. Evidently, there is only a small influence of the target distance h on the residual stress distributions, although an increase in target distance is referred to decrease the kinetic energy of the impacting particles resulting in lower overall compressive residual stresses. A closer look on the distributions of the stress-free lattice parameters show larger values with increasing target distance h indicating an enrichment of C in the deposited Ti(C,N). Since TiC and C-rich Ti(C,N) develop higher compressive residual stresses than TiN and N-rich Ti(C,N), respectively, do, this effect evidently compensates the effect of lower particle energy at larger target distance.

ii) indentation tests and FEM-analyses:

The optical micrograph in *Fig. 5* exemplarily shows an imprint corresponding to the indenter radius R = 0.5 mm and a load of 180 N in the coating of thickness s = 4.6 µm sputtered with p_{Ar} = 0.4 Pa at h = 59 mm. The image clearly shows the appearance of concentric ring cracks. At a critical indentation load the tensile radial stresses at the surface in the outer vicinity of the contact zone nucleate the first inner ring crack as also observed by [7] for large R/s-ratio. Experiments showed further ring cracks with larger radii developing as the indentation load raises. From such images of three nominally identical imprints the mean values for radii r_C of the first inner ring crack for each coating and indenter radius were determined. *Fig. 6* shows results of FEM-analyses of indentation tests on Ti(C,N)-coatings on steel substrates with indenter radius R = 0.2 mm (top) and 0.5 mm (bottom). The maximum radial loading stresses σ_{max}^{rr} at the coating surface and maximum shear stresses τ_{max}^{rz} perpendicular to the surface, occuring at about half of coating thickness underneath the surface, are plotted vs. the indenta-

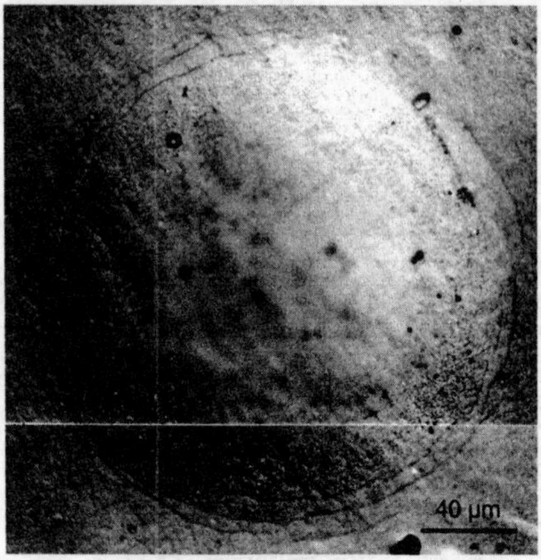

Fig. 5: Optical micrograph of imprint with indenter radius R = 0.5 mm loaded to 180 N in coating sputtered with p_{Ar} = 0.4 Pa at h = 59 mm.

tion load F. The radial distances from the indentation center r of the stress maxima and the radius a_c of the contact zone are also plotted in the figure. For pure elastic contact the radial stresses as well as the distances r and a_c go with the indentation load F to the power of 1/3. This kind of distributions also appears for the elastic-plastic contact plotted in *Fig. 6*. With increasing load the values for a_c approaches those of $r(\sigma_{max}^{rr})$ indicating the increasing contribution of plastic response of the steel substrate to the total deformation. Whereas the maximum radial stresses occur in the outer vicinity of the contact zone the radial distance of the shear stress maximum is always located within the contact area of radius a_c. The radial tensile stresses at the surface are higher than the shear stresses, and at the positions of the shear stress maximum underneath the surface the radial loading stresses are always compressive in nature. Therefore coating failure is clearly expected to be initiated by the radial effective tensile stresses (resulting from superpostion of radial loading stresses and in-plane residual stresses) at the coating surface when exceeding the fracture strength of the coating material.

It is assumed that fracture initiates at flaws at the coating surface and the column boundaries of the coatings' microstructure acting as fracture-initiating flaws being stressed under mode-I condition. The size of the flaws is, according to *Fig. 1*, set as 2a = 320 nm. *Fig. 7 top* shows the related critical loads F_c/R^2 and related radii of the first inner ring cracks r_c/R determined

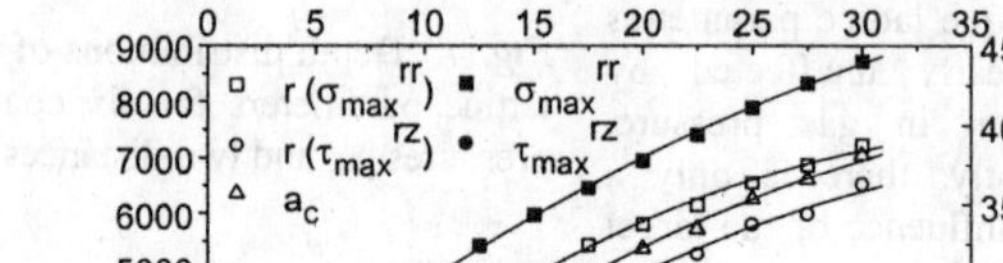

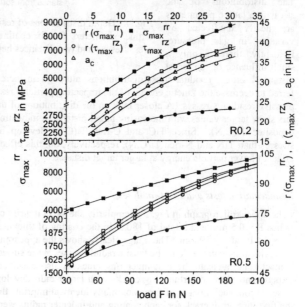

Fig. 6: Maximum radial loading and shear stresses in Ti(C,N)-coating on X210 CrW 12 with radial positions r of the maximum stresses and radius of contact zone a_c vs. load F for indentation test with indenter radius R = 0.2 *(top)* and 0.5 mm *(bottom)* determined from FEM-analyses.

from FEM- and microscopical analyses, respectively, plotted vs. the surface residual stresses for indentation tests on the coatings. For both indenter radii R the critical radii clearly decreases almost linearly with decrease in compressive residual stresses. According to the relationship between F and $r(\sigma_{max}^{rr})$ in *Fig. 6* the critical loads decrease in non-linear fashion with decreasing compressive residual stresses. *Fig. 7 (top)* clearly demonstrates the enhancement in load-bearing capacity of the coating systems with increasing compressive residual stresses. The resulting critical radial loading stresses determined from FEM-analyses are plotted together with the effective critical radial stresses vs. the surface residual stresses in *Fig. 7 bottom*. The critical loading stresses increase almost linearly with increasing compressive residual stresses and can be seen as the effective fracture strength of the coatings enhanced by compressive residual stresses. Using a simple approach based on linear-elastic fracture mechanics the mode-I fracture toughness of the coatings can by determined from the effective critical radial stresses being nearly independent of residual stresses. The fracture-initiating flaws are seen as internal cracks through an infinite plate stressed under mode-I conditions. The mode-I fracture toughness can then be estimated by [14]

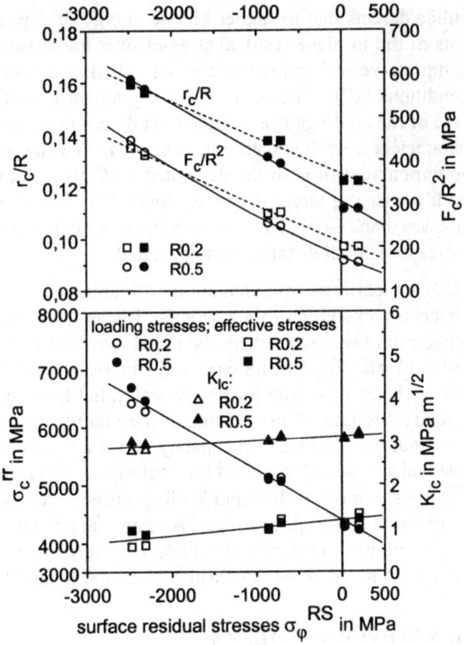

Fig. 7: Related critical radii r_c/R and ralated crirtical loads F_c/R^2 vs. surface residual stresses determined on Ti(C,N)-coatings with two indenter radii R *(top)* and critical radial loading stresses and critical effective radial stresses determined by FEM-analyses together with mode-I fracture toughness vs. surface residual stresses of the coatings *(bottom)*.

$$K_{Ic} = \sigma_c^{\ E} \sqrt{a}\, Y_I \quad \text{with} \quad Y_I = \sqrt{\pi}\,, \tag{1}$$

σ_c^E being the critical effective radial stress. The obtained values for K_{Ic} are plotted in *Fig. 7 bottom*. The resulting values of about 3 MPa m$^{1/2}$ are reasonable for ceramic materials. The slight increase of K_{Ic} with decreasing compressive residual stresses is not significant considering the uncertainties in quantifying the size of the fracture initiating flaws.

6 Conclusions

Compositionally graded wear resistant coatings of Ti(C,N) deposited on the cold-working steel X210 CrW 12 by non-reactiv PVD-magnetron sputtering were investigated by means of depth-resolved X-ray analyses of gradients in residual stresses and stress-free lattice parameters. The observed increase of the overall compressive residual stresses with decreasing gas pressure fits the well accepted model of increasing residual stresses with larger amounts of lattice defects due to higher kinetic energy of depositing particles [13]. The negative gradients of the in-plane residual stresses over the coating thickness agree with findings of higher compressive residual stresses in TiC- than in TiN-coatings when deposited at similar process conditions [12]. The compositional gradient from C-rich to N-rich Ti(C,N) towards the surface of the coatings was detected via determining graded distributions of the stress-free lattice parameters over the coating thickness. Increasing distance between target and substrate yield an enrichment of C in the deposited Ti(C,N) resulting in larger stress-free lattice parameters with increasing target distance. Since C-rich Ti(C,N) develops higher compressive residual stresses than N-rich Ti(C,N) does the expected decrease of compressive residual stresses with increasing target distance was not found.

Mechanical tests by indentation with spherical indenters of 0.2 and 0.5 mm in radius yield concentric cracking of the coatings. It was found that fracture initiated at the surface at a distance from the center where the radial tensile stresses reach a maximum. The crack-initiating critical loads for both indenter radii increase with compressive residual stresses in the coatings. The same is true for the critical radial loading stresses being referred to as the effective fracture strength of the coatings. The increase in critical load and loading stresses clearly turns out the load-bearing capacity and fracture strength being improved by the compressive residual stresses observed in the coatings. The critical effective radial stresses resulting from superposition of residual and loading stresses were almost identical for both indenter radii and nearly similar for all coatings. A simple approach based on linear-elastic fracture mechanics was employed to estimate the mode-I fracture toughness of the coating material. The obtained values for K_{Ic} of about 3 $MPa\,m^{1/2}$ are found to be reasonable for ceramic materials.

ACKNOWLEDGEMENTS

The authors would like to thank Dr. H. Leiste and Dr. M. Stüber at the Institute for Materials Research I, Forschungszentrum Karlsruhe for the deposition of the coatings and for the TEM-investigation. Appreciation is extended to Dr. H. Ehrenberg, Mr. M. Knapp and Dr. T. Wroblewski at HASYLAB, DESY for help at the beamlines. The funding of this work by the Deutsche Forschungsgemeinschaft (DFG) is gratefully appreciated.

REFERENCES

[1] T. Roth, E. Broszeit, K.H. Kloos: *Surf. Coat. Technol.*, 36 (1988) 765-772.

[2] R. Fella, H. Holleck, H. Schulz: *Surf. Coat. Technol.*, 36 (1988) 257-264.

[3] S.J. Bull, D.D. Rickerby, T. Robertson, A. Hendry: *Surf. Coat. Technol.*, 36 (1988) 743-754.

[4] B. Eigenmann, J.L. Lebrun: In *9th International Symposium Measurement of Residual Stresses, Bulletin du Cercle d'Etudes des Métaux, Ecole Nationale Supérieure des Mines de Saint-Etienne* 1993, 2-1 - 2-14.

[5] M.V. Swain, J. Mencík: *Thin Solid Films*, 253 (1994) 204-211.

[6] R. Nowak, C.L. Li, S. Maruno: *J. Mater. Res.*, 12 (1997) 64-69.

[7] E. Weppelmann, M.V. Swain: *Thin Solid Films*, 286 (1996) 111-121.

[8] T. Dümmer, B. Eigenmann, M. Stüber, H. Leiste, D. Löhe, H. Müller, O.Vöhringer: *Z. Metallkd.*, 90 (1999) (10) 780-787; Erratum to T. Dümmer et al.: *Z. Metallkd.*, 90 (1999) (12) 1030.

[9] R.T. DeHoff, F.N. Rhines: *Quantitative Microscopy*, McGraw-Hill Book Company, New York 1968.

[10] B. Eigenmann, E. Macherauch: *Mat.-wiss. u. Werkstofftech*, part I: 26 (1995) 148-160; part II: 26 (1995) 199-216; part III: 27 (1996) 426-437; part IV: 27 (1996) 491-501.

[11] B.L. Henke, E.M. Gullikson, J.C. Davis: *Atomic Data and Nuclear Data Tables*, 54 (1993) 181-342.

[12] T. Leverenz, B. Eigenmann, E. Macherauch, H. Leiste, H. Holleck: *HTM*, 50 (1995) 193-200.

[13] O. Knotek, R. Elsing, G. Krämer, F. Jungblut: *Surf. Coat. Technol.*, 46 (1991) 265-274.

[14] T. Fett, D. Munz: Forschungszentrum Karlsruhe, KfK 5290, Karlsruhe 1994.

[15] H. Schulz: Forschungszentrum Karlsruhe, KfK 4306, Karlsruhe 1987.

THE EFFECT OF RESIDUAL STRESSES ON THE WEAR BEHAVIOR OF TiN FILMS ON ALUMINUM SUBSTRATES

Takao Hanabusa
Tokushima University
Minamijosanjima, Tokushima, Japan

Yasuhiro Miki
Nara Prefectural Institute of Industrial Technology
Kashiwagi, Nara, Japan

Tatsuya Matsue
Niihama National College of Technology
Yakumo, Niihama, Japan

Kazuya Kusaka
Tokushima University
Minamijosanjima, Tokushima, Japan

ABSTRUCT

In the industrial fields, aluminum and aluminum alloys are widely used in mechanical components. However, their application is essentially restricted because of their low strength. If hard coatings are made on a surface of aluminum or aluminum alloys, their application will widely be enlarged. Ceramic coatings on steel substrates are well established in recent material technology to give wear resistance. For example, TiN coatings on cutting tools greatly succeeded in prolongation of tool lives. In the present study, TiN film deposition was tried on a surface of aluminum and aluminum alloy substrates by means of an arc ion plating. The aim is the development of aluminum based materials having strong wear resistance.

Arc current was maintained at 60A for minimizing temperature increase in the substrate during depositing processes. Bias voltage and N_2 gas pressure were changed to examine their role on hardness and residual stress of TiN films. Wear experiment was also conducted with a ball-on-disk type wear testing machine. Vickers hardness test revealed high values (HV=2100 ~ 2400) which depend on both bias voltage and N_2 gas pressure. The TiN films exhibited very high {111} preferred orientation under the condition of high bias voltage of -80V. Residual stresses in the TiN film were measured by the two-exposure X-ray stress measuring method as a function of N_2 gas pressure. Very high compressive residual stresses, -6.3 ~-4.6 GPa, were observed depending on the N_2 gas pressure as well as the hardness of substrate material. Large compressive residual stresses were developed at lower N_2 gas pressure and for higher hardness of the substrate. The depth and the width of wear traces on the surface of specimens were greatly reduced by TiN coatings. Especially, no wear traces appeared on a surface of the film which was deposited at the bias voltage of -80V and the N_2 gas pressure of 1.0 Pa onto Al-Cu alloy specimen.

1 INTRODUCTION

Aluminum alloys are used in a wide range of engineering applications, as parts of precision machines, vehicles, and other mechanical structures as well as electrical devices, because of their excellent properties, i.e., lightness, high electrical and thermal conductivity, high processability, and high recyclability. However, aluminum alloys are inferior to steel regarding their antiwear properties. In this investigation, TiN coatings are tried to deposit on aluminum alloys by an arc ion plating (AIP). There are some examples of TiN coatings on aluminum alloys by an ion beam mixing (IBM). However, the IBM method is restricted to apply coatings on a small and a flat surface. On the other hand, the AIP can often be used to coat films on parts with a large and/or complicated shape.

Film coatings on metal substrates usually generate large stresses because of the mismatched thermal contraction rate between the film and the substrate as they cool from the processing temperature (1,2). In order to produce highly reliable parts covered with such films, hardness, crystal structure, residual stresses and wear resistivity of the film must carefully be investigated. In the present paper, these properties of TiN films coated on aluminum alloys are examined.

2 EXPERIMENTAL METHOD

2.1 PREPARATION OF SUBSTRATE AND DEPOSITION OF TiN FILMS

Three types of aluminum alloy sbstrate, A1050-H24, A5052-H34 and A2017-T451 (JIS) were used in the present experiment. The specimen was 25mm×25mm×5mm in size and was polished by using #600 and #1000 emery papers followed by buff polishing. The surface roughness was 0.12, 0.06 and 0.05 μm (Ra) for A1050, A5052 and A2017, respectively.

The arc ion plating (AIP) system (Type AIP3012, Kobe Steel Co. Ltd.) was used to prepare thin films on aluminum alloy substrates. Figure 1 illustrates a schematic view of the system. Firstly, the chamber was evacuated to below 10^{-2} Pa and then preheated at 573 K and 673 K for 20 min each in order to discharge the gases which sticked to the inner wall as well as the substrate. The system was then cooled down to 373 K and nitrogen gas was injected in the chamber to the prefixed gas pressure (0.5 ～ 2.0 Pa). An arc current of 60 A was selected for preparing TiN films and the bias voltage was varied from 0 to -100 V. Film thickness was controlled to be 3 μm throughout the present investigation.

2.2 X-RAY INVESATIGATION

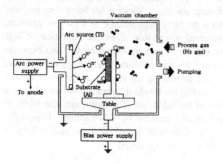

Preferred orientation and residual stresses in the TiN films were investigated by X-ray dif-

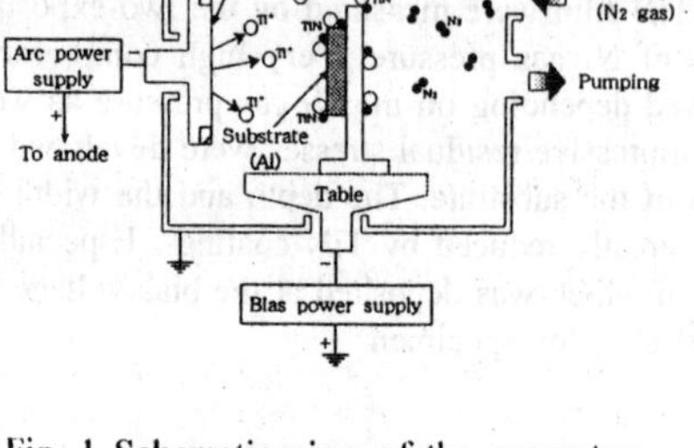

Fig. 1 Schematic view of the apparatus for arc ion plating.

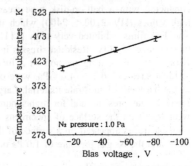

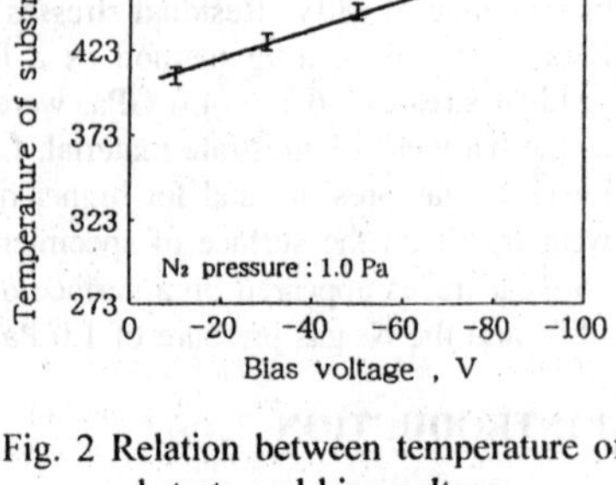

Fig. 2 Relation between temperature of substrate and bias voltage.

fraction with CuKα characteristic X-rays. In the case when {111} plane lies parallel to the film surface and the plane stress state is assumed, lattice strains ε_ψ are represented by the following equation (3);

$$\varepsilon_\psi = (1/2)\, s_{44}\,\sigma \sin^2\psi + \{s_{12} + (1/3)s_0\}\,\sigma \tag{1}$$

where ψ is the angle between the normal of lattice plane and the normal of film surface, $s_0 = s_{11}-s_{12}-s_{44}/2$ and s_{ij} are elastic compliances of single crystal, which are summarized in Table I.

Table I Elastic compliances of TiN single crystal.

s_{11}	s_{12}	s_{44}	(Unit)
2.17	-0.38	5.95	(TPa^{-1})

To measure stresses in the films having {111} texture, the two-exposure method with 222 diffraction was used because diffraction intensity can be obtained at only two ψ-angles, i.e., ψ_1=0° and ψ_2=70.5°. The equation for stress evaluation is

$$\sigma = \frac{2}{s_{44}} \frac{\varepsilon_{\psi 1} - \varepsilon_{\psi 2}}{\sin^2\psi_1 - \sin^2\psi_2} \tag{2}$$

Hardness of the films was also measured using a Vickers micro hardness testing machine with the testing load of 4.9×10^{-2} N. A wear test was also performed by a ball-on-disk type testing machine with the load of 0.5 N.

3 EXPERIMENTAL RESULTS AND DISCUSSION

3.1 EFFECT OF DEPOSITING CONDITION ON SUBSTRATE TEMPERATURE

In the AIP system used in the present investigation, the substrate temperature can not be precisely controled although a heater is mounted behind the sample holder. The substrate temperature changes with depositing conditions such as bias voltage, arc current density, and gas pressure. The main factor is the bias voltage which is applied to the substrate. Large bias voltage applied on the substrate acts as the substrate intensively pulls titanium ions emitted from the target material. Figure 2 shows the increment of substrate temperature with increasing bias voltage under the condition at 1.0 Pa of N_2 gas pressure.

3.2 EFFECT OF BIAS VOLTAGE ON HARDNESS OF FILMS

Figure 3 shows how the Vickers hardness of the substrate changes with bias voltage. Before AIP treatment, hardness of the substrate was 41.6, 73.0 and 131 for A1050, A5052 and A2012, respectively. After the deposition with bias voltage of 0 V, no change in Vickers hardness was observed. However, the hardness of the substrate decreased with increasing bias voltage larger than -30 V, probably due to some tempering effect occured by the bombardment of titanium ions. However, the decreasing ratio was about 10% even if the bias voltage was -80 V, the largest voltage in the present experiment.

Figure 4 shows the relationship between bias voltage and Vickers hardness of the TiN film deposited on A2017 substrate. In contrast with Fig. 3, the hardness of films increased as the bias voltage changes from 0 V to -30 V. The maximum hardness of 2200 ~ 2300

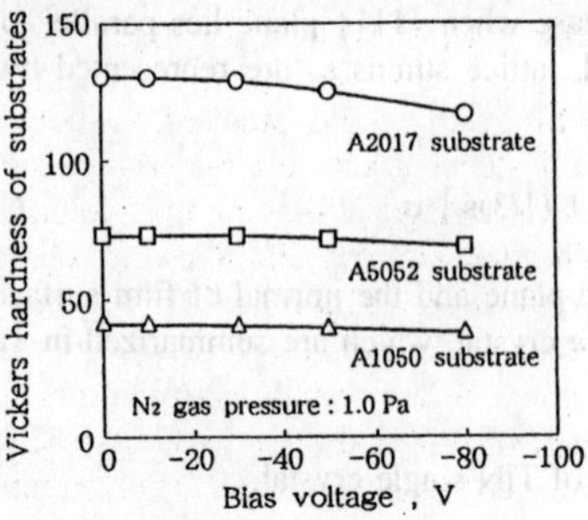

Fig. 3 Relationship betwen Vickers hardness of substrate and bias voltage.

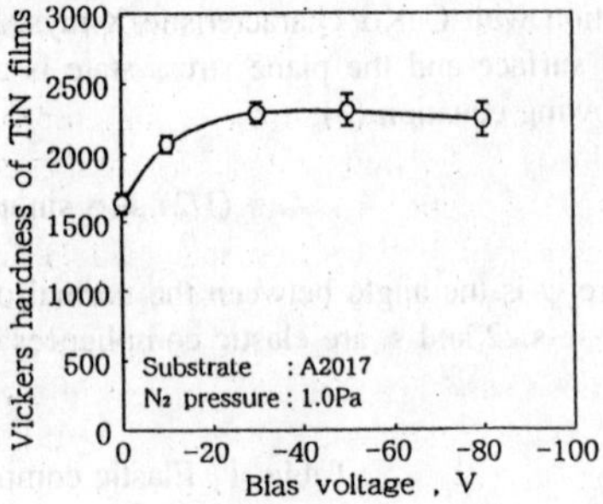

Fig. 4 Relationship between Vickers hardness of TiN films and bias voltage.

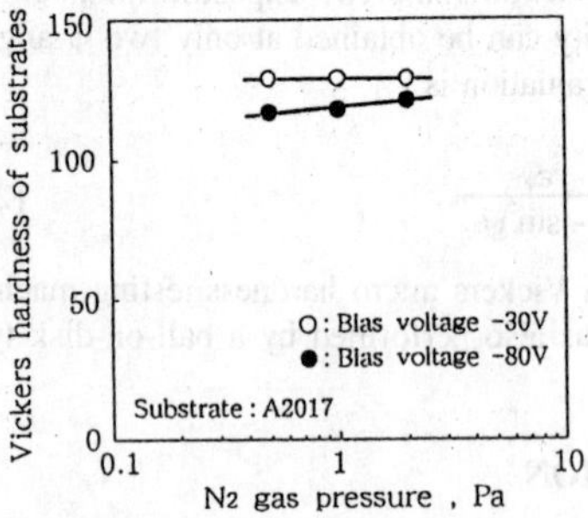

Fig. 5 Relation between Vickers hardness of substrate and N_2 gas pressure.

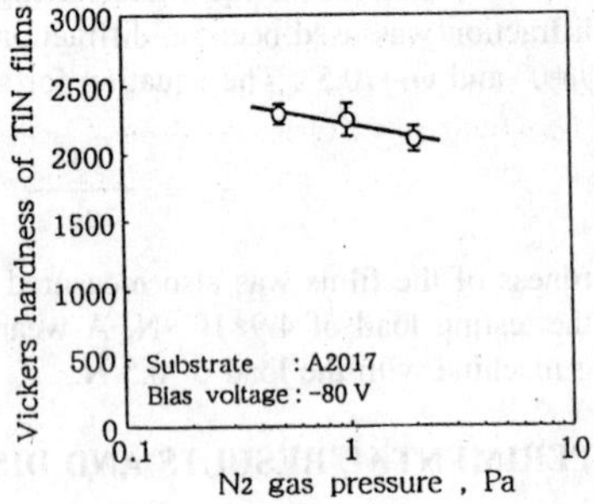

Fig. 6 Relation between Vickers hardness of TiN films and N_2 gas pressure.

was attained at -30 V and thereafter the hardness seems to hold a constant value. Slight decrease in the hardness may occure from tempering effect of the substrate due to high temperature developed in the depositing process. The same results were obtained for the films deposited on A1050 and A5052 substrates.

From the results of Fig. 3 and Fig. 4, we conclude that the bias voltage of -30 V is the optimum condition for getting hard coating films.

3.3 EFFECT OF NITROGEN GAS PRESSURE ON HARDNESS OF FILMS

Vickers hardness of the A2017 substrate was tested for the specimens deposited at -30 V and -80 V in the N_2 gas atmosphere of 0.5 ~ 2.0 Pa. Figure 5 shows a small increase in Vickers hardness of substrates with increasing the gas pressure especially for the bias voltage of -80 V. Therefore, a decrease of the hardness of substrate due to increasing bias voltage can be prevented by increasing N_2 gas pressure, if the high bias voltage is necessary for making films.

Figure 6 shows the results of Vickers hardness of the films which were deposited with the conditions of -80 V of bias voltage and 0.5 ~ 2.0 Pa of N_2 gas pressure. The hardness decreased with increasing gas pressure. The similar result was obtained by Sundgren et. al. who explained their results by the effect of coarsening of TiN grain size in the film (4).

3.4 CRYSTAL ORIENTATION OF TiN FILMS

The crystal orientation of TiN films deposited at 1.0 Pa of N_2 gas pressure was measured by X-ray diffraction using CrKα radiation. Figure 7 shows a very clear appearance that a crystal orientation was strongly dependent on the bias voltage. When the bias voltage is 0 V, medium 220 diffraction and small 111 and 200 difractions from TiN film were observed. As the bias voltage increased to -30 V, all the diffractions from TiN film become very weak. From the film deposited at -80 V, very strong diffraction for TiN 111 and strong diffraction for TiN 222 with wide width were observed. These results mean that (110) and (100) planes preferentially arrange at the bias voltage of 0 V and these preferred orietation diminishes as the bias voltage increases to -30 V and then very sharp (111) orientation develops at -80 V.

Precise inspection for a crystal orientation was mede by mearuring the integrated intensities of TiN 111 diffraction with a function of ψ-angle. If preferred orientation exists in the sample, the integrated intensity is not constant but distributes like as the Gaussian function with varying ψ-angle. We define a double of standard diviation of the Gaussian curve fitted on the integrated intensity distribution as a degree of preferred orientation.

Figure 8 shows that the degree of {111} preferred orientation in a film becomes sharp as the bias voltage increases. Additional experiments revealed that {111} preferred orientation becomes weak with increasing N_2 gas pressure.

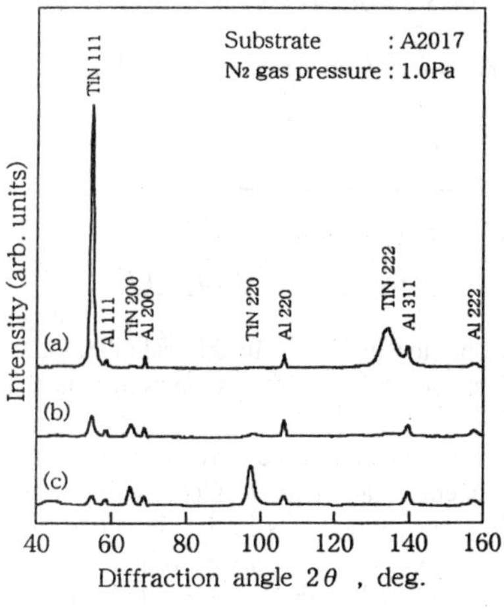

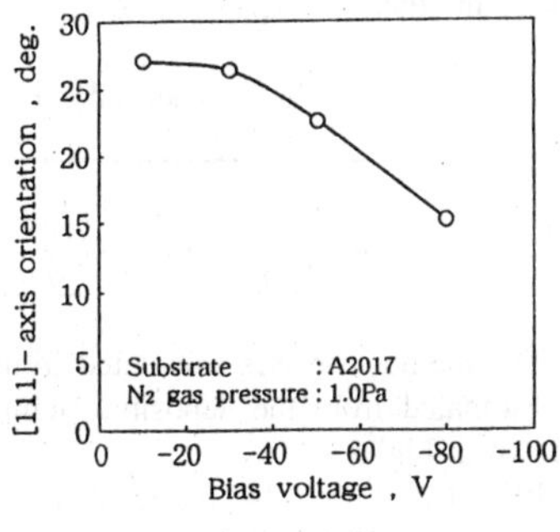

Fig. 8 Relationship between [111] orientation of TiN films and bias voltage.

Fig. 7 X-ray diffraction profiles of specimen (Bias voltage: (a)-80 V, (b)-30 V, (c) 0 V).

3.5 MEASUREMENT OF RESIDUAL STRESS IN TiN FILMS

In general, the diffraction line which appears in high diffraction angle should be used in the X-ray stress measurement. In the present case, however, as can be seen in Fig. 7, there is no diffraction in the 2θ range higher than 134° which corresponds to the diffraction angle of TiN 222. Also, the 222 diffraction coalesces with Al 311 diffraction from the substrate. Therefore, we had to select TiN 111 diffraction which appears at 55.0° in 2θ for the film deposited at -80 V. The measurement for other samples did not succeed because the diffraction intensity for the ψ-angles other than 0° is too weak to get precise diffraction profiles.

In the present investigation, stresses were measured only for the specimens having a sharp {111} preferred orientation. Figure 9 shows the results which reveal very high compressive stress rainging -4.6 to -6.3 GPa. The stress in TiN films depends on N_2 gas pressure so as to linearly decrease with increasing gas pressure. Also they depend on the substrate materials mainly due to their hardness. The residual stress in the film on A2017 substrate is the largest and the one on A1050 substrate is the smallest.

Generally, the residual stress in deposited films originates from the difference in degree of thermal shrinkage in cooling process from the depositing temperature to room temperature. This stress refers to thermal residual stress and is evaluated by the terms of difference of thermal expansion coefficient between the film (α_{TiN}) and the substrate (α_{Al}) and temperature drop ΔT. The thermal strain ε_{th} of the film is represented by

$$\varepsilon_{th} = (\alpha_{TiN} - \alpha_{Al}) \cdot \Delta T. \qquad (3)$$

In the case having {111} preferred orientation, ε_{th} is the strain for the orientation of ψ=90° in eq. (1). Therefore, the thermal stress ε_{th} in the film is evaluated by the following equation:

$$\varepsilon_{th} = \{(2/3)s_{11} + (4/3)s_{12} + (1/6)s_{44})\}^{-1} \cdot (\alpha_{TiN} - \alpha_{Al}) \cdot \Delta T \qquad (4)$$

where the thermal expansion coefficient of TiN and Al are summarized in Table II.

Table II Thermal expansion coefficients.

α_{TiN}	α_{Al}			(Unit)
	A1050	A5052	A2017	
9.35	26.6	25.7	25.0	($\times 10^{-6}$/K)

The thermal stresses calculated from eq. (4) are plotted in Fig. 9. In this calculation, ΔT is estimated from the depositing temperature which depends on N_2 gas pressure, such as shown in Fig. 2.

It is clearly seen that the residual stress measured by X-ray method is three to four times larger than the thermal residual stress. It is general that large residual stress which overcomes the thermal residual stress calculated by eq. (3) develops in the films deposited by physical vapor deposition (5,6). The residual stresses in such films are originated from two reasons. The one is the thermal stress which is referred to the extrinsic stress and the other is the stress referred to the intrinsic stress. The latter is the stress developed in the film itself during depositing process. The reason of intrinsic stress has not been clarified, but it can be thought that the ion bonbardment in the depositing process makes large compressive stress in the film. This is similar to the shot peening effect which causes compressive residual stress in the surface layer of materials.

In addition to the fact of existence of large compressive stress, the residual stress decreases with increasing N_2 gas pressure. Increment of the gas pressure weakens the kinetic energy of ions which plunge into film surface. Therefore, the residual stress becomes lower due to the effect of decreasing bombardment against TiN films.

The second marked point is the dependency of residual stress on the kind of substrate material. The residual stress is largely relating to the hardness of substrate. The 0.2% offset

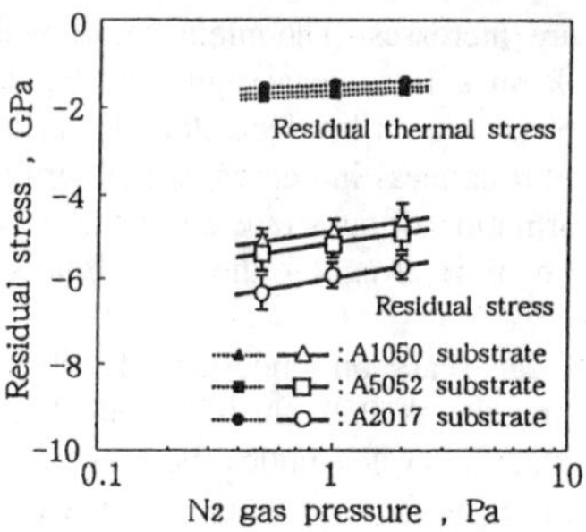

Fig. 9 Relationship between residual stress of TiN films and N_2 gas pressure.

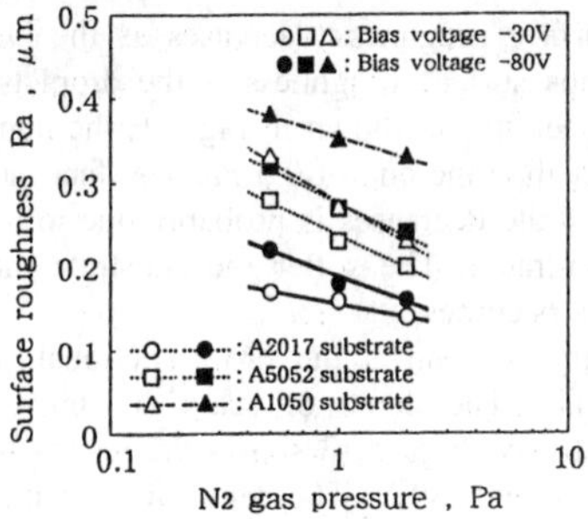

Fig. 10 Relationship between surface roughness of TiN films and N_2 gas pressure.

stress of the A1050, A5052 and A2017 substrate was 0.11, 0.25 and 0.30 GPa, respectively. Stress developed in the film may be large enough to make plastic deformation in the interface layer of the substrate. When the offset stress is small, the substrate easily deforms so as to decrease residual stress in the film.

3.6 WEAR PROPERTY OF TiN FILM/SUBSTRATE SYSTEM

Figure 10 shows surface roughness of the film deposited at the bias voltage of -30 and -80

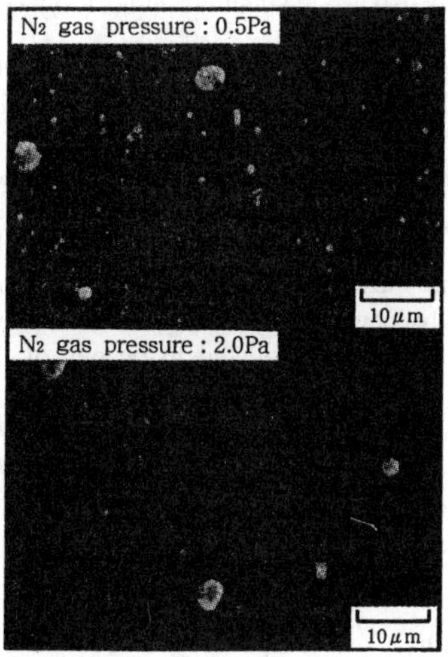

Fig. 11 Surface morphologies of TiN films coated on A2017 substrate (Bias voltage: -80 V).

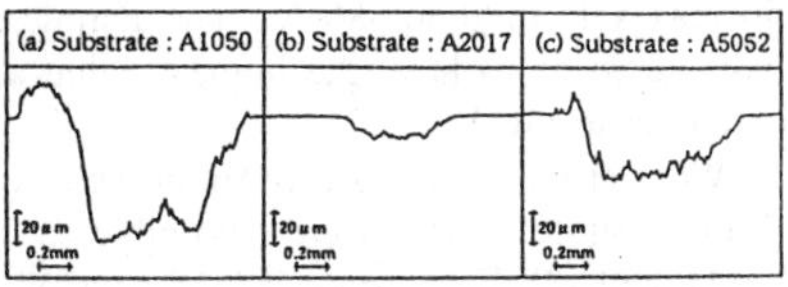

Fig. 12 Surface profiles of wear scars on undeposited substrates.

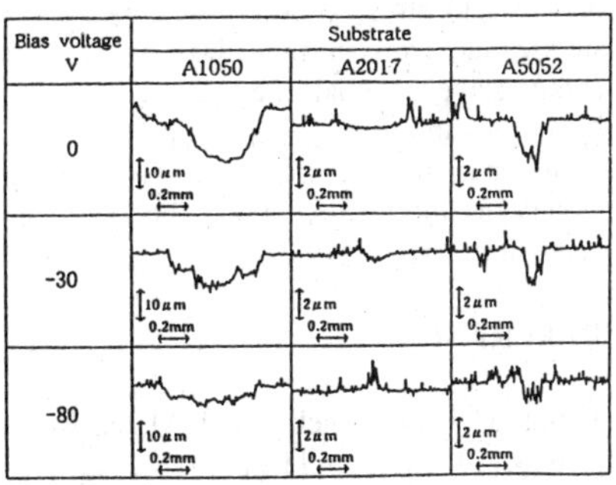

Fig. 13 Surface profiles of wear scars (N_2 gas pressure:1.0 Pa)

V. Surface roughness decreases as the N_2 gas pressure increases. The main cause which develops surface roughness is the droplets which stick on a film surface and the trace of their peeling. As shown in Fig. 11, the number of droplets in the film deposited at 2.0 Pa is smaller than the one of 0.5 Pa. The fact that the surface roughness increases as the hardness of substrate decreases is probably due to irregular deformation of substrate according to ion bombardment. The softer the substrate material is, the more irregular the smoothness of surface becomes.

Figure 12 shows the cross sectional profiles of wear scars on undeposited substrate materials. The depth of scars are 60, 30 and 10 lm for A1050, A5052 and A2017, respectively. Figure 13 shows the results for AIP products deposited under the bias voltage of 0, -30 and -80 V. The depth of scars markedly decreases as the bias voltage increases for all three kinds of substrate. For example, the depth for the sample deposited on A1050, the softest substrate, was about 5 μm which is 1/12 of the depth for uncoated A1050 material. No traces can be seen on the surface of the film deposited on A2017 substrate.

Considering the effect of residual stress on the wear properties, the film deposited on A2017 substrate has the highest compressive residual stress among the films on three kinds of substrate. In other words, the depth of wear scar becomes shallow when higher compressive residual stress exists. Therefore, compressive residual stress is said to be one of the factors promoting wear properties.

4 CONCLUSION

In order to improve wear properties of aluminum and aluminum alloy, TiN film was deposited with an arc ion plating method. The film exhibits high preferred orientation depending on mainly bias voltage: {111} preferred orientation grows as bias voltage increases from 0 to -80 V. The hardness of the film also changes with increasing bias voltage so as to have the highest value at -30 V followed by maintaining almost constant value up to -80 V.

Wear property was greatly improved by TiN deposition and particularly wear scars of the film/substrate system were negligible for a case of the system which deposited at the bias voltage of -80 V and onto A2017 substrate.

Stress measurement was succeeded only for the specimens having sharp {111} preferred orientation. The results show that high compressive stresses much larger than thermal residual stresses were developed in the film and they depended on the hardness and the offset yield stress of substrates, i.e., the stronger the substrate is, the larger the residual stresses develop in the film. As the wear scars are negligible for the film in which compressive residual stresses are large, the residual stress is considered to be one of the factors for improving wear properties.

Summarizing the present results, TiN coating on aluminum and aluminum alloys must be a very useful technique for the parts of precision machine and of the machines which necessitate their lightness.

REFERENCES

1. Sute C J and Cohen J B, J. Mater. Res.,6(1991)950.
2. Noyan I C and Goldsmith C C, Adv. X-Ray Anal., 34(1991)587.
3. Kusaka K, Hanabusa T, Nishida M, Inoko F, Thin Solid Films, 290-291(1996)248.
4. Sundgren J E-, Thin Solid Films, 128(1985)21.
5. Matsue T, Hanabusa T, Ikeuchi Y, Thin Solid Films, 281-281(1996)344.
6. Matsue T, Hanabusa T, Ikeuchi Y, Materials Science Research International, 5(1999)45.

SESSION 6B

DETERMINATION AND EVALUATION OF RESIDUAL STRESSES IN THICK-WALLED CYLINDERS DUE TO AUTOFRETTAGE

H.J. Schindler [1], P. Bertschinger[1], C.H. Nguyen [1], R. Knobel [2]

[1] Swiss Federal Laboratories for Materials Testing and Research (EMPA), Dübendorf, Switzerland; [2] Swiss Ordonance Enterprise (SW), Thun, Switzerland

ABSTRACT

Autofrettage is a treatment to introduce beneficial residual stresses into thick-walled cylinders to improve their performance under repeated loading by internal pressure. In the present investigation the residual stresses are measured and their effect was analysed and discussed. The experimental determination of the residual stress distribution was performed by the crack-compliance-method. The corresponding influence function for thick-walled cylinders, which is needed for the experimental stress measurement by the CC-method, was derived analytically. Besides the residual stresses this method enables one to obtain also the stress-intensity factor as a function of cut depth, which is required in the theoretical fatigue life prediction based on linear-elastic fracture mechanics. Examples of experimental data are presented. To validate the experimental results they are compared with analytical calculations. The agreement between the calculated and measured residual stresses was satisfying. Furthermore the effect of the axial dimension (plane-stress vs. plane strain), which has to be taken into account when using a thin disk for stress measurement by the CC-method, is investigated by a 3D FEM-analysis.

INTRODUCTION

Autofrettage is a well-known and efficient method to introduce beneficial residual stresses in thick-walled cylinders which are loaded in service by internal pressure. Essentially, the treatment consists of an overload by internal pressure such that a major part of the cylinder wall is plastically deformed. After unloading, compressive stresses remain near the inner surface. These stresses are able to prevent or at least retard fatigue crack growth and stress corrosion cracking. Thus, knowledge of the residual stresses is essential to assess the safety and to predict the remaining life of a pipe loaded repeatedly by internal pressure.

The aim of the present investigation was to determine and evaluate the residual stresses in a thick-walled cylinder of 125 mm outer diameter and a length of about 5 m. It was treated by autofrettage several years ago and has been since then in service as a gun-barrel, loaded by hundreds of relatively large load cycles. One of the questions was to what degree the initial residual stresses are still present, since an unknown portion of them is expected to be faded away during service. The original treatment was not known exactly either, so another aim was to get information about the initial pressure and the corresponding initial residual stresses. Regarding these aims, a straightforward measurement technique is the crack- (or cut-) compliance method (CC-method). Its principle is described in [1 – 5] and further literature given therein. In the present paper the application of the CC-method to the case of a thick-walled cylinder is shown and discussed. The scientific challenge of this task was the large size of the test piece, which made prior sectioning necessary, and the geometry, which was new for the CC-method. Since the residual stresses due to autofrettage can be calculated analytically, these tests also offered the possibility to validate the method by comparison between measured and calculated stresses.

MEASUREMENT OBJECT AND PROCEDURE

The cylinder in question has an inner and outer radius of r_i=65mm and r_a=125 mm, respectively, and a length of about 5m. The material is 35 NiCrMoV 12 5 quenched and tempered steel with a yield stress of R_p = 898 N/mm^2 and an ultimate tensile strength of R_m = 988 N/mm^2. The cylinder was in service for several years, loaded by several hundreds of load cycles of about 4000 bar (i.e. 400 N/mm^2). As reported, the pressure of the autofrettage process was chosen such that about two thirds of the cylinder wall thickness should be plastically deformed, while the outer third remained in the elastic state. As shown later, this corresponds theoretically to a pressure of about 6000 bar.

As described in detail in [1-5] the CC-method requires a progressive cut to be introduced along the plane where the residual stresses are to be measured. The main residual stresses due to autofrettage are tangential stresses $\sigma_\varphi(x)$, which require cutting in a radial-axial plane. To enable local radial cutting a relatively thin ring-shaped slice (Fig. 1a) has to be cut off the pipe by two cuts perpendicular to the axis. In the present case a thickness of 43 mm was chosen. Thereby the major part of the axial residual stresses is released, which also affects the tangential residual stresses that are to be determined. This effect has to be accounted for.

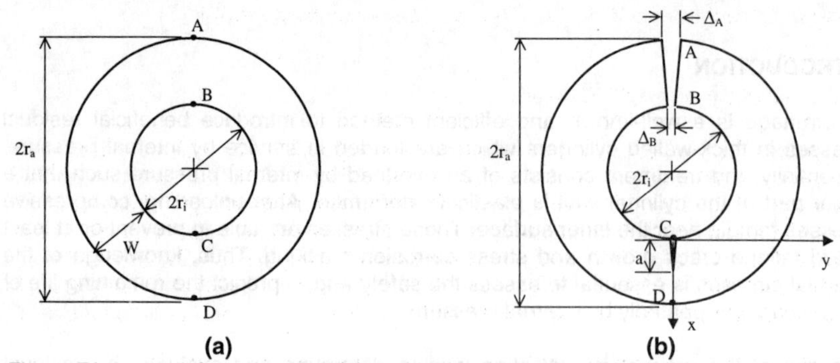

Fig. 1: Ring as cut from the pipe (a) and in the open state (b) (after cutting the section A – B)

To apply the CC-method to the ring as shown in Fig. 1a it is advantageous to separate it first by a cut on section A – B such that an open ring as shown in Fig. 1b results. The advantage is twofold: First, the strain change in the vicinity of section C-D is more significant, thus the measurement is more sensitive, and second, the influence function can be relatively easily estimated on the basis of existing solutions, as shown in the next section. However, by the prior cut of section A – B, a certain portion of the residual stresses in the cross-section C – D is released and must be accounted for afterwards. As shown in the next section, the corresponding portion of the residual stresses can be quantified from measurements of the cut opening displacement at A and B, or by strain measurements at C or D.

Since the accuracy of the CC-method is better in the range of short and medium cut depths, and the residual stresses at the inner part of the wall were of greater interest than those on the outer part, it is preferable to introduce the cut from the inside, along the x –axis as shown in Fig. 1b. The strain was measured by two strain gages, one on the inner surface in a distance of 6 mm from C and the other on the outer surface at D. According to the principle of the CC-method [1 - 5] the stress intensity factor (SIF) due to the residual stresses acting at the cut front, $K_{Irs}(a)$, is obtained by

$$K_{Irs}(a) = \frac{E'}{Z(a)} \frac{d\varepsilon_M}{da} \tag{1}$$

where a is the actual cut depth, ε_M is the strain measured by the above-mentioned strain gages, and Z the influence function. For the strain gage near C the function Z(a) given in [4, 5] for a short edge cut in a rectangular plate can be used with sufficient accuracy for $a \ll r_i$. For the strain gage at D the Z-function was not available, so it was estimated from known functions in related systems (see next section). From $K_{Irs}(a)$ the residual stress distribution $\sigma_{rs}(x)$ can be calculated as described in [2, 5, 6] by inversion of the equation

$$K_{Irs}(a) = \int_0^a h(x,a) \cdot \sigma_{rs}(x) \cdot dx \tag{2}$$

Here h(x,a) denotes the weight function as introduced by Bueckner [7].

ANALYTICAL CONSIDERATIONS

Influence function. Z(a) for the strain gage at location D can be obtained as an approximation relatively easily by combining the influence function for a disk and the one for a rectangular plate. Recalling that the physical meaning of Z is the strain change at D per unit cut extension and unit of K_I, it is obvious that for $r_i \ll W$ it tends towards $Z(a'=W+2r_i+a)$ of a circular disk as given in [4, 5], whereas for $W \ll r_a$ it tends towards Z(a) for a rectangular plate, which also is given in [4, 5]. Without going into the details of the corresponding mathematics, matching of these two solutions leads to

$$Z(a) = 1.7897 \cdot \sqrt{\frac{2\rho - 1 + a/W}{\rho (W-a)^3}} \qquad \text{for } a/W > 0.2(\rho-1)/\rho \tag{3a}$$

$$Z(a) = \frac{B}{(W-a)^{3/2}} \cdot \sqrt{1 - \left(\frac{a/W - A}{A}\right)^2} \qquad \text{for } a/W < 0.2(\rho-1)/\rho \tag{3b}$$

where $A = \dfrac{y_0 x_0 - s x_0^2}{y_0 - 2 s x_0}$ $B = \dfrac{y_0}{\sqrt{1 - \left(\dfrac{a/W - A}{A}\right)^2}}$ $s = 0.8949 \cdot \sqrt{\dfrac{\rho}{2\rho - 1 + \dfrac{0.2(\rho - 1)}{\rho}}}$

$\rho = r_a/W$ $x_0 = 0.2(\rho - 1)/\rho$; $y_0 = Z(a = x_0 W) \cdot W^{3/2} (1 - x_0)^{3/2}$

The functions (3a) and (3b) are shown graphically in Fig. 2.

Stress release due to prior cutting. Prior cutting at section A-B releases the corresponding residual stresses. Because of the condition of axial symmetry of the stresses, the resultant of the released stresses is a pure bending moment M acting on both sides of section A – B and affecting correspondingly the residual stresses in section C - D. According to [8] the tangential stresses in section C – D due to a bending moment M are

$$\sigma_{\varphi B} = -\frac{4M}{N}\left(-\frac{r_i^2 \cdot r_a^2}{\rho^2} \ln\frac{r_a}{r_i} + r_a^2 \cdot \ln\frac{\rho}{r_a} + r_i^2 \cdot \ln\frac{r_i}{\rho} - r_i^2 \right) \quad (4a)$$

where $N = \left(r_a^2 - r_i^2\right)^2 - 4 r_a^2 \cdot r_i^2 \cdot \left(\ln\frac{r_a^2}{r_i^2}\right)^2$ (4b)

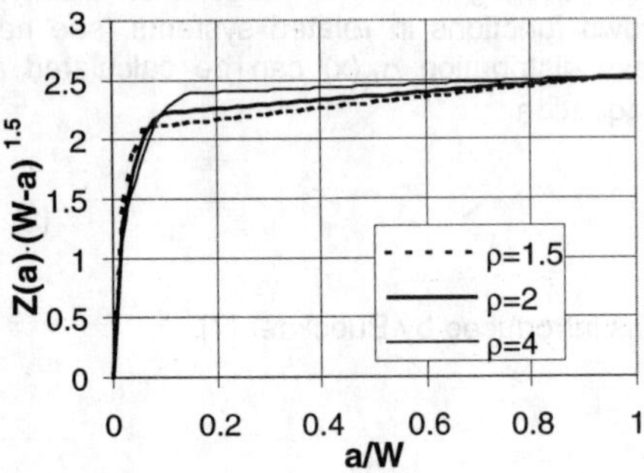

Fig. 2: Z(a) for cylinders for some values of $\rho = r_a/W$

By (4) and a single strain measurement at an arbitrary location x the stress distribution in cross-section C-D due to the stress release on section A-B can be determined. Another, independent possibility to account for this global bending effect due to M is by measuring the cut opening displacements at A and B, Δ_A and Δ_B. The required relation between the stress on C-D and the cut opening displacement can be easily established by the theory of curved beam bending according to [8]. One finds:

$$\Delta_A - 0.394\Delta_B = \frac{1.65 \cdot \pi}{E \cdot W}\left(R_i + 0.606W\right)^2 \cdot \sigma_{\varphi B}(x = 0) \quad (5)$$

Effect of plane stress. When a relatively thin slice is cut off a long cylinder, the state of residual stresses changes from tri-axial to essentially plane stress, which affects the tangential residual stress. Since autofrettage causes plastic deformation under plane strain conditions, the axial stresses after unloading are about $\sigma_a = \nu \cdot \sigma_\varphi$ (with ν being Poisson's ratio). Due to cutting perpendicular to the axis, these stresses are released. This is accompanied by a relaxation of the residual tangential stresses by the amount of $\nu \cdot \sigma_a = \nu^2 \cdot \sigma_\varphi$, which has to be added to the residual stresses measured in the slice.

Combining the above-discussed effects the initial residual stress is obtained as

$$\sigma_{rs/pipe}(x) = (1+\nu^2 \cdot)(\sigma_{rs}(x) + \sigma_{\varphi b}(x)) \quad (6)$$

EXPERIMENTAL DATA

The above defined deformation parameters measured after cutting section A – B were as follows:

- cut opening displacement: $\Delta_A = 1.5$ mm; $\Delta_B = 0.9$ mm (7a)
- global bending strain at D: $\varepsilon_{Db} = 0.000504$ (7b)

By (4) or (5), respectively, the corresponding stress distribution on section C – D can be calculated from either (7a) or (7b). The agreement is better than 10%, thus confirming each other. Being more directly related to the stress, the strain ε_{D0} is used for the stress distribution to be determined. Eq. (4), (7b) and Hooke's law results in

$$M = 3.32 \text{ Nm} \quad (8)$$

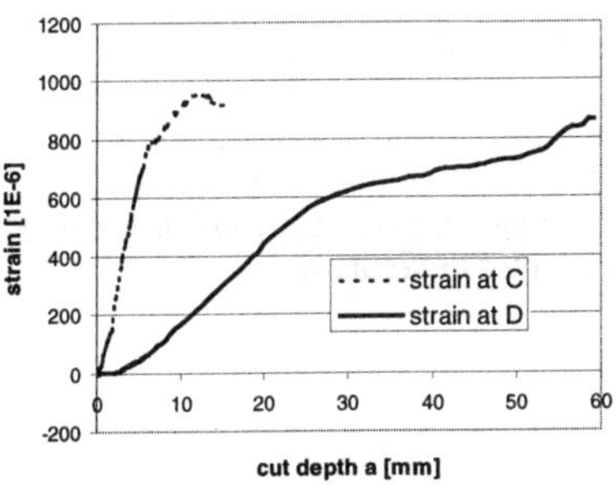

Fig. 3: Strain measured at C and D as a function of cut depth a

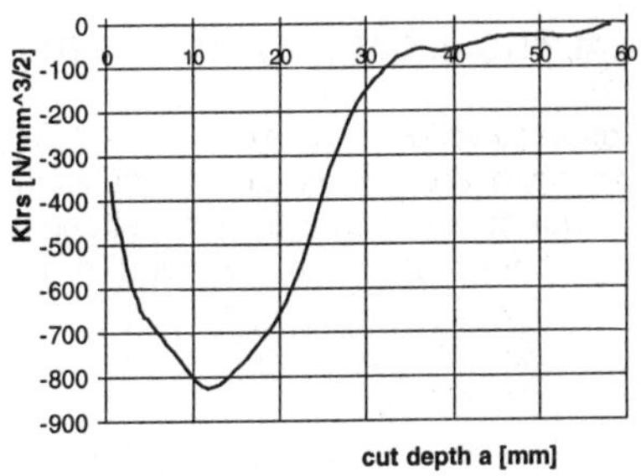

Fig. 4: Stress intensity factor calculated by (1) from curves shown in Fig. 3.

Fig. 3 shows the strain change due to progressive cutting along the x-axis measured by the strain gages at C and D as a function of cut depth. Generally, the higher the slope of these curves, the better the sensitivity of the corresponding measurement location. Accordingly, as expected, the strain gage near C is sensitive in the range of about a<10mm, and the one at D for about a>5mm. The SIF obtained by (1) from these two strain measurements by (1) is shown in Fig. 4, where for a<4mm the influence function Z(a) for a short crack in a rectangular plate was used, and for a>6mm eqs. (3a) and (3b). In the intermediate range, these two curves were matched such that a smooth transition occurs. From the curve shown in Fig. 4 the residual stress distribution $\sigma_{rs}(x)$ was calculated by using (2). Lacking the weight function h(x,a) for this crack configuration, the one for a rectangular plate was used as an approximation. This is justified by the fact that the latter holds for short cracks (i.e. $a<<r_i$) as well as for deep cracks (i.e. $(W-a)<<W$), so it is expected to be sufficiently accurate even in the intermediate range of crack depths. The resulting curve is shown in Fig. 5. The total residual stress in the pipe, which also is shown in Fig. 5, is calculated by (6), using (4) and (8) to account for the global bending effect.

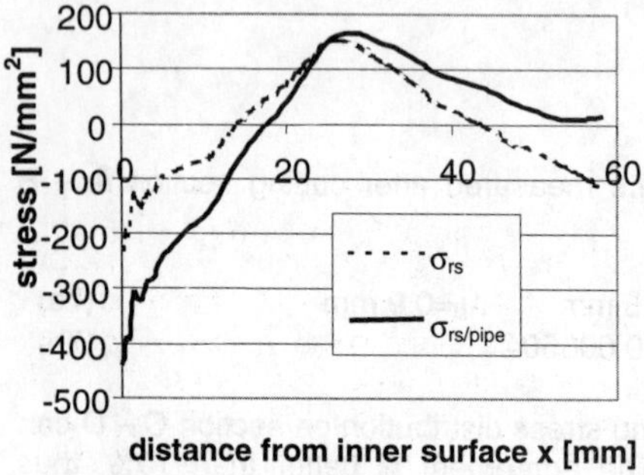

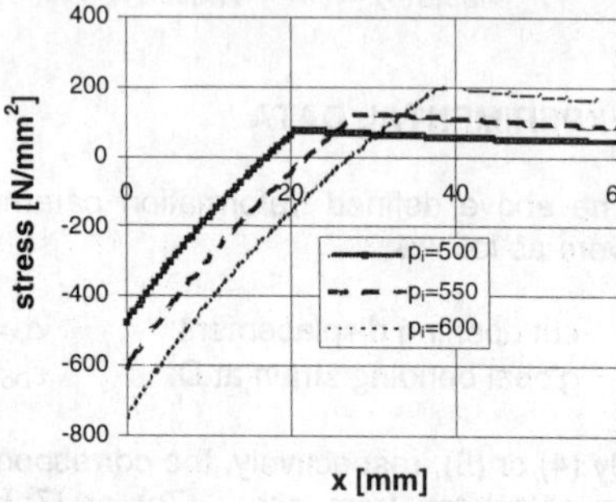

Fig. 5: Residual stress in open ring and total tangential residual stress in the pipe

Fig. 6: Residual stresses analytically calculated for three values of internal pressure p_i (in N/mm^2)

ANALYTICAL CALCULATION OF RESIDUAL STRESSES

In order to validate the experimental procedure the measured stresses are compared with those analytically and numerically calculated. The analytical determination of residual stresses due to autofrettage is rather simple. According to [8] the elastic tangential stresses in a cylinder (Fig. 1a) due to internal pressure p_i are

$$\sigma_\varphi(x) = \frac{R_i \cdot p_i}{R_a^2 - R_i^2} \cdot \left(1 + \frac{R_a^2}{(R_i + x)^2}\right) \tag{9}$$

In the region where Tresca's yield criterion $\sigma_\varphi(x)-\sigma_r(x)<R_p$ is violated, $\sigma_\varphi(x)$ is obtained from

$$\sigma_\varphi(x) = R_p + \sigma_r(x) \tag{10}$$

where the radial stress $\sigma_r(x)$ is obtained from the equilibrium and yield condition, which lead to the integral equation

$$\sigma_r(x) = \frac{-R_i}{R_i + x} \cdot p_i + R_p \cdot \ln\frac{R_i + x}{R_i} - \int_0^x \frac{\sigma_r(x)}{R_i + x} dx \tag{11}$$

The residual stress distribution is obtained by (10), the numerical solution of (11) and subtracting the elastic stresses (9) due to unloading. For the present geometry of the pipe and elastic-perfectly plastic material with a yield stress of R_p = 900 N/mm^2 the resulting curves are shown in Fig. 6 for some values of internal pressure.

Effect of plane stress. To verify the correction made in (6) to account for plane stress, a 3D- finite element stress calculation was carried out. The axial residual stresses under plane stress turned out to be about $\sigma_a=\nu\cdot\sigma_\varphi$ near the inner surface, and about $\sigma_a=\nu\cdot\sigma_\varphi/2$ near the outer surface. As predicted by the above theoretical considerations the residual stresses in the ring are about 10% lower than the ones under plane strain.

DISCUSSION

Comparison with analytical solution. Qualitatively, the agreement between measured and calculated residual stress is good, indicating that there is no fundamental error in the measurement method. Quantitatively an agreement better than about 10 - 20% is not be expected for the following reasons: i) The material is not elastic-perfectly plastic. ii) Tresca's yield criterion is an approximation of the real yield behaviour. iii) After autofrettage, a material layer of some millimetres thickness was removed from the inner surface. Moreover, as discussed above, the weight function used is only an approximation.

As can be seen from the analytical solution, the location of the maximum tensile residual stress corresponds to the original elastic-plastic boundary. Thus, from comparison of Fig. 5 and 6 one can conclude that the pressure used for autofrettage was about 550 N/mm^2 in the present case, thus lower than the two third plastic deformation that the treatment aimed at. Therefrom one can estimate the initial residual stress after autofrettage by the corresponding curve shown in Fig. 6, which is about –600 N/mm^2 at the inner surface. Compared with the measured values, one can conclude that about one third of the initial residual stresses are relaxed due to the service loads.

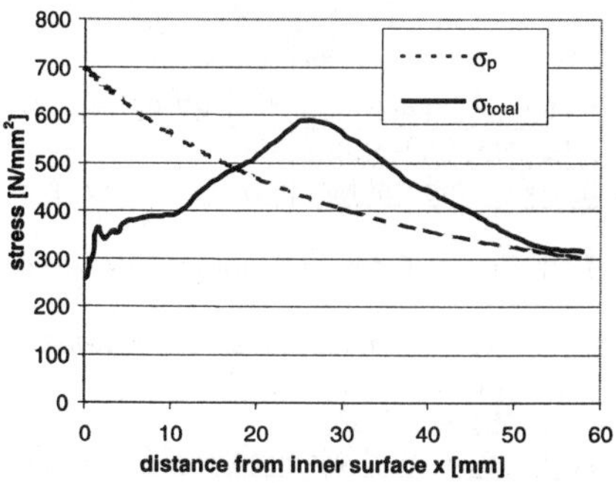

Fig. 7: Comparison of tangential stress due to the service load of p=400N/mm^2 with (σ_{total}) and without (σ_p) measured residual stresses

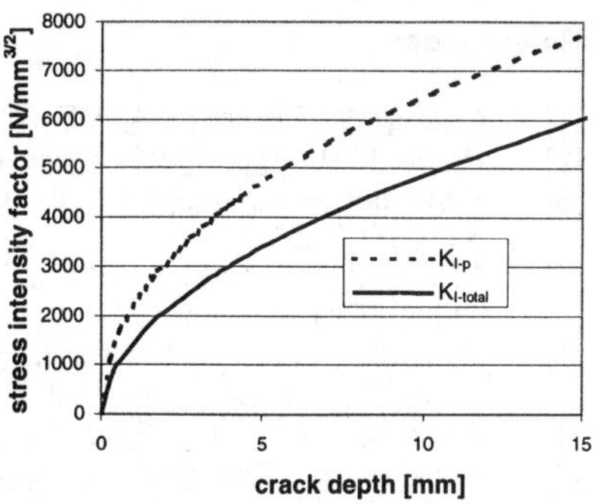

Fig. 8: Comparison of SIF due to internal pressure p=400N/mm^2 with ($K_{I\text{-}total}$) and without ($K_{I\text{-}p}$) residual stresses

Effect of residual stresses. Fig. 7 shows the comparison of the tangential stresses due to the service load of p=400 N/mm^2 with and without the measured residual stresses. Therefrom one can see that the measured residual stresses reduce the maximum tensile stresses near the inner surface, which is crucial for subcritical crack initiation, by more than 50%. The reduction effect of the residual stresses on the SIF of an eventual surface crack is not quite as significant, but still about 33% (Fig. 8). Concerning eventual fatigue crack growth, this reduction results in a retardation of the crack growth rate by about 80%, because according to Paris' law the growth rate depends on the SIF by about the 4th power. Furthermore, as can be seen from Fig. 8, the critical crack size (i.e. the crack depth at the level of fracture toughness, which for the present material is estimated to be about K_{Ic}=4000 $N/mm^{3/2}$) is about twice the one without residual stresses.

CONCLUSIONS

Concerning the method of residual stress determination:

- The CC-method is applicable to measure residual stresses in large pipes
- The weight function for a rectangular plate can be used as an approximation, however, a more exact weight function should be determined to improve the accuracy.

Concerning the physical effects of the residual stresses:

- The majority (about 2/3) of the residual stresses introduced by autofrettage are still present after several years of service.
- They reduce the operating tress at the inner surface by more than 50%
- They reduce the SIF by more than 30%, which corresponds to a retardation of the fatigue growth rate by about 80%.
- The critical crack size is extended by about 100%.
- Due to the reduced crack growth rate, the inspection intervals can be prolonged.

References:

[1] Cheng, W., Finnie, I., ASME J. of Eng. Mat. and Tech., Vol 108, 87-92 (1986)

[2] Prime, M.B., Appl. Mech. Reviews, Vol. 52, No. 2 (1999), 75-96

[3] Schindler, H.J., Cheng, W., Finnie, I., J. Experimental Mechanics, Vol. 37, No. 3 (1997) 272-279

[4] Schindler, H.J. and Landolt R., Proc. of 4th Europ. Conf. on Residual Stresses, Cluny (F) (1996) 509 - 518

[5] Schindler, H.J., Bertschinger, P. Proc. 5th Int. Conf. on Residual Stresses, Linköping, Sweden, 1997, Ed. T. Ericson, et al., Vol. 2, 682-687

[6] Schindler, H.J., Int. J. Fracture, Vol. 74, (1995) R23-R30,

[7] Bückner, H., Zeitschrift für angew. Mathematik und Mechanik (ZAMM), 50 (1970) 529-545

[8] S.P. Timoshenko, J.N. Goodier, Theory of Elasticity, McGraw-Hill, 3rd Ed., (1970)

USE OF THE CRACK COMPLIANCE METHOD FOR THE MEASUREMENT OF RESIDUAL STRESS

D. Nowell, D.A. Hills, and S. Tochilin
Department of Engineering Science, University of Oxford
Parks Road, Oxford, OX1 3PJ, UK

ABSTRACT

The Crack Compliance Method forms a useful complement to established techniques for measurement of residual stress components which vary with depth, but are relatively slowly varying in one direction along the surface of a component. This paper summarises the results of a recent project carried out at Oxford in which a number of simple residual stress fields were measured by crack compliance. These include a plastically bent beam, a shot peened surface, and a T-butt weld. Comparisons are made with neutron diffraction measurements. A number of improvements and enhancements to the method are discussed. In particular, we highlight the importance of taking readings from multiple strain gauges in order to enhance accuracy and discuss the significance of the finite width of the machined slot. Finally, we present some recent results using thumbnail slots in place of through thickness ones. These demonstrate that there is some potential to extend the method to situations where stresses vary in three directions.

INTRODUCTION

The crack compliance method is becoming established as a useful addition to the range of techniques available for measurement of residual stress. In principle, the technique is rather similar to hole drilling: a number of strain gauges are positioned on the specimen or component and a slot is then introduced incrementally (usually by electric discharge machining (EDM)), Fig.1. This allows the residual stresses present to relax and the resulting strain changes at the gauges are recorded. It is then possible to predict the variation with depth of the residual stress component perpendicular to the slot by using a suitable analysis technique. Much early work on the development of the method was carried out by Finnie and his co-workers, e.g. (1), but more recent work has been undertaken by others and a useful review is given by Prime (2). The method is destructive, but is quick and inexpensive and, compared to hole drilling it offers a number of advantages. There is no hoop constraint present to resist relaxation and it is therefore potentially more sensitive than hole drilling. With suitably positioned strain gauges it is possible to measure a residual stress profile through the thickness of a component. As stated above, the method is suitable for measuring a single residual stress component perpendicular to the slot and, with the standard through-slot geometry the method is only suitable for situations where the stress component does not vary along the slot. However, novel slot geometries, such as thumbnails, enable potential extension of the method to overcome these restrictions and some results will be presented later in the paper. The accuracy of the method can be high, but one of the principal sources of error can be the presence of 'multiple solutions', where different residual stress distributions give rise to similar strain changes at the gauge locations. This aspect will also be addressed below.

In a typical experiment we take K sets of strain gauge readings at different depths of slot a_k. We then choose to model the residual stress distribution as a superposition of N basis functions, $p_i(x)$, which may be power series polynomials, Chebyshev Polynomials etc. Each basis function is multiplied by a weight, α_i, as yet unknown, so that the residual stress distribution may be written as

$$\sigma_{yy}(x,0) = \sum_{i=0}^{N-1} \alpha_i p_i(x) \tag{1}$$

The strain change, $\Delta\varepsilon$, recorded at gauge location S_j may then be written as a weighted superposition of the changes due to each of the basis functions. Thus,

$$\Delta\varepsilon(S_j, a_k) = \frac{1}{E^*} \sum_{i=0}^{N-1} \alpha_i C_i(S_j, a_k) \tag{2}$$

where $E^*=E$ in plane stress and $E^*=E/(1-\nu^2)$ in plane strain, ν being Poisson's ratio, and the function $C_i(S_j,a_k)$ represents the strain change caused at location S_j when a crack of length a_k is introduced into a residual stress distribution given by basis function $p_i(x)$. The function $C_i(S_j,a_k)$ is termed the compliance function by Finnie (1). It is then possible to determine the unknown weights α_i by using least squares analysis to give the best fit to the experimental data. Thus, for $K>N$, with J strain gauges.

$$\frac{\partial}{\partial \alpha_i} \sum_{k=1}^{K} \left(\Delta\varepsilon_{jk} - \sum_{l=0}^{N-1} C_{ljk} \right)^2 = 0 \qquad i = 0,\ldots..,N-1 \qquad j = 1,\ldots...,J \tag{3}$$

Evaluation of the compliance functions is frequently the most demanding step in the analysis and a number of methods have been employed. These include Castagliano's theorem combined with stress intensity factor solutions (1), and finite element methods. In the work described here we have used dislocation density methods (3) or finite elements to calculate the required functions. In this paper we will provide an overview of the work carried out recently at Oxford in collaboration with Imperial College. During the project the crack compliance method has been employed to measure residual stress distributions for a number of simple geometries and the results will be presented below.

EXPERIMENTAL WORK

Experimental measurements of strain changes were carried out in-situ on an EDM machine. Two types of electrode were used: wire with a diameter of 0.1mm and sheet electrode material 0.125mm thick. In both cases a slot of approximately 0.2mm width was produced. A digital depth gauge was employed to record the electrode position (and hence the depth of the slot). Strain changes were recorded using small gauges with a gauge length of 0.2mm. These allowed the gauges to be positioned with the centre of the gauge as close as 0.35mm from the edge of the slot. All data was logged by computer using an A/D card. It is important not to constrain the specimen so that full relaxation of the residual stresses can take place. Hence, where through-thickness cutting was to be employed, the specimen was clamped as a cantilever at one end only. Weight effects were eliminated by attaching sufficient expanded polystyrene to the specimen to give it neutral buoyancy in the electrolyte. Figure 2 shows some typical strain gauge data collected for the case of a plastically bent beam. Gauges 1 and 2 were attached to the top of the specimen, 1.35 mm and 2.2mm respectively from the edge of the slot, whereas gauge 3 was attached to the bottom face of the specimen opposite the slot (Fig.1.). It can readily be seen from Fig.2. that the variation of gauge readings with slot depth is initially rapid for the top face gauges but the readings saturate once the slot depth is approximately equal to the distance of the gauge from the slot. This might be expected, since for deeper slots the gauges are essentially in a region of unloaded material. The bottom face gauge reading continues to vary over the full range of slot depths.

The crack compliance method was used to investigate a number of residual stress fields, including:

(i) A Waspaloy beam bent beyond its elastic limit and released.
(ii) A shot-peened sample of IN718
(iii) A T-butt weld

In addition, stresses in a plastically bent beam were also measured using a thumbnail-shaped electrode and compared to those obtained from the similar through slot experiment.

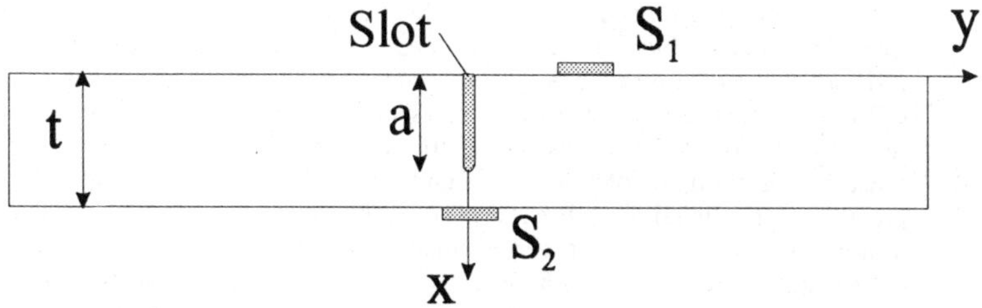

Fig. 1 Typical geometry, showing slot of depth *a* in a component of thickness *t* with two strain guages, S_1 and S_2.

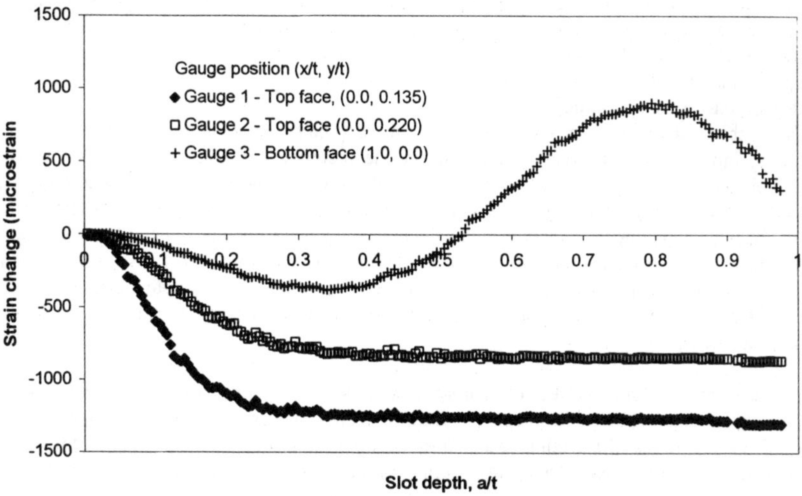

Fig. 2 Strain gauge readings obtained during slitting of plastically bent Waspaloy beam.

ANALYSIS AND RESULTS

In an experimental technique such as the crack compliance method it is important to consider the possible sources of experimental error and the likely errors in the final result. Unfortunately this is not straightforward with crack compliance and the lack of a rigorous means of treating the errors is one of the principle drawbacks of the technique. Errors in the calculated residual stress profile can arise from a number of sources:

(i) Experimental error in the gauge readings. This is generally relatively small and may be minimised by taking a number of readings at each slot depth and averaging them. It can be seen from Fig.2. that the results are reasonably smooth, indicating that error in the gauge readings is small.

(ii) Poor representation of the residual stress profile: In the analysis, the stress profile is assumed to be represented by a linear superposition of basis functions. It is therefore necessary for these functions to be capable of accurately representing the stress field. This can pose a problem, since one does not always know the likely variation of the residual stresses. In practice, a sensible procedure is to choose an appropriate family of basis functions and to repeat the analysis several times with different numbers of functions, N. The results should show little sensitivity to N over a reasonable range.

(iii) Existence of multiple solutions: A significant problem with this type of 'inverse' problem is the possible existence of multiple solutions; several residual stress distributions may give rise to very similar variations of strain with slot depth at the chosen gauge locations. If this is the case, the least squares analysis will not be capable of distinguishing between the possible solutions and an entirely inaccurate solution may be obtained. Nowell et al (4) have shown by means of numerical experiments that the use of multiple strain gauges at different locations on the specimen reduces problems of this nature.

The results presented below were calculated using power series polynomial basis functions of order 5 and were obtained from the experimental strain gauge readings using the least squares technique outlined above. The waspaloy beam was bent in four point bending so as to produce an axial strain of 1% on the top and bottom faces. The applied load was approximately 1.6 times that required to cause initial yielding[1]. Figure 3 shows the calculated residual stress distribution, using results from all 3 strain gauges. Results are compared to those obtained by neutron diffraction (5) and to predictions from simple bending theory, taking into account the work hardening of the material. It can be seen that the crack compliance results agree very well with the neutron results and beam theory prediction close to the surface from which the slot was cut. Agreement is less good for greater depths ($a/t > 0.6$) but this is perhaps to be expected as the top face gauges had saturated at these slot depths and provide little useful information. In effect we are relying purely on the bottom face gauge to obtain a good fit in this region and the possibility of multiple solutions must be considered. More accurate results could probably have been obtained using more than one bottom face gauge.

Figure 4 shows the predicted residual stress distributions obtained from measurements made on a shot-peened INCO 718 plate. At shallow depths, such as are important here, the finite width of the slot is of a similar order to the slot depth. This means that slot width must be taken into account when calculating the compliance functions and approximating the slot as a

---

[1] This figure is larger than the shape factor of the beam (1.5) due to work hardening of the material.

thin crack is no longer appropriate. A number of authors have addressed this problem and provided compliance functions for a finite width slot (e.g. 6,7). Here we employ the results of (7) which considers both flat and round bottomed slots. It is found that, for strain gauges close to the slot, there is little difference between the 'crack' and 'flat-bottomed slot' compliance functions. The round-bottomed slot, however, produces significantly different compliance functions. Two curves are shown in Fig.4: one produced using flat-bottomed slot compliance functions and one using those for a round bottomed slot. The actual experimental slot profile was somewhere between these two assumptions. It will be seen that high compressive stresses are measured close to the surface of the specimen, with some balancing residual tension predicted by the rounded slot compliances. Neutron diffraction measurements of identical samples are currently being undertaken as part of Technical Working Area 20 of the VAMAS project (8). As expected, the measured compressive stresses are of the order of the yield stress of the material.

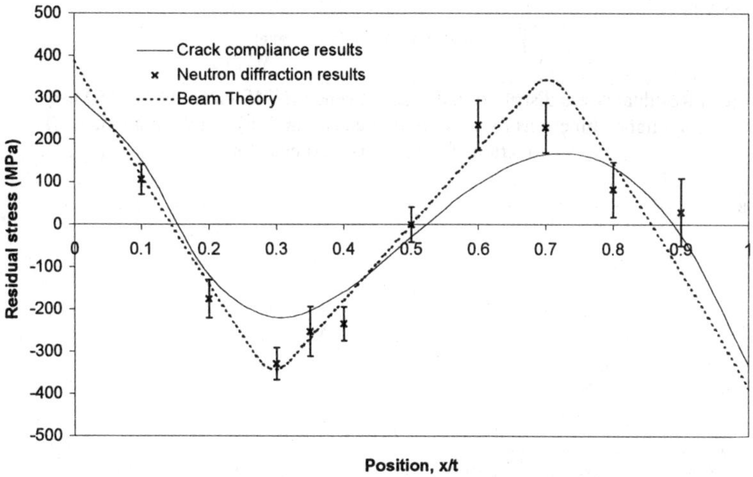

Fig. 3 Residual stress distribution in a plastically bent Waspaloy beam, (i) from experimental results, (ii) measured by neutron diffraction, and (iii) predicted by beam theory.

The third set of measurements were made in the toe of a ferritic T-butt weld (Fig.5.). For this example compliance functions were obtained using the finite element method (9) since the geometry was more complex than can readily be dealt with by the dislocation density method. The results show a high residual tension (≈ 700 MPa) close to the free surface with balancing compression towards the centre of the specimen (Fig. 5). Measurements made by neutron diffraction (10) show a similar trend, although the predicted values are lower. This may be due in part to the volume averaging processes inherent in neutron diffraction measurements.

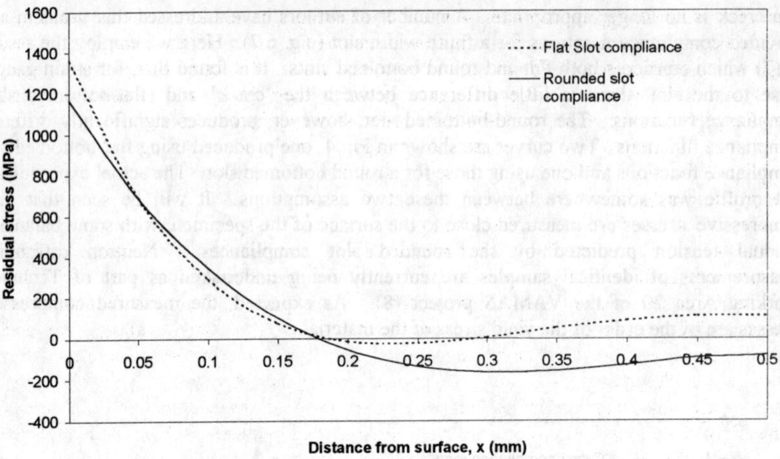

Fig. 4 Residual stress distribution in a shot-peened IN718 plate obtained (i) using compliance functions for a flat-bottomed slot and (ii) using compliance functions for a round-bottomed slot

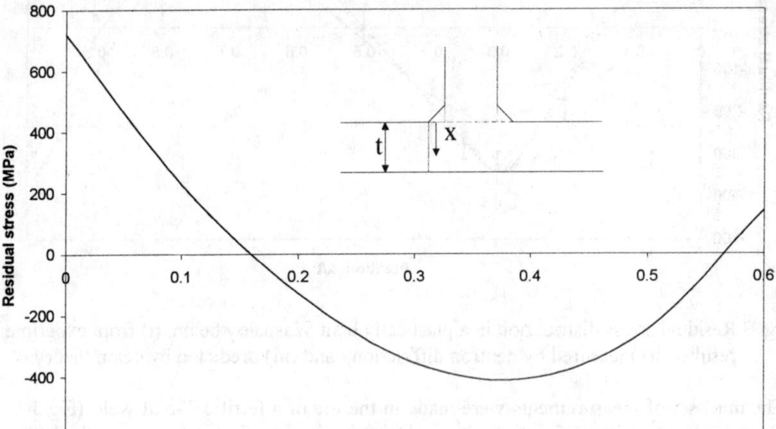

Fig. 5 Residual stress distribution in a Ferritic T-butt weld. Results may be compared with (10).

Finally, Fig.6 shows measurements made on a plastically bent mild steel beam using a semi-circular electrode of radius r = 4.4mm. Compliance functions for this geometry were calculated using the eigenstrain method (11). The predicted residual stresses are compared to those obtained from elastic-perfectly plastic beam theory. In this case a single top-surface gauge was used, situated 0.318*r* from the centre of the slot. The results from the experiment can be seen to be in quite good agreement with beam theory for $a/r < 0.4$. Inaccuracy in the results might be expected for greater depths due to strain gauge saturation.

CONCLUSIONS

The results presented here show that the crack compliance method is capable of producing accurate measurements of the variation of a residual stress component with depth. It is possible to measure entire residual stress profiles through the thickness of a component, or those more localised to the surface (such as produced by shot-peening). Although the method is destructive it is quick and inexpensive and is well suited to situations where the residual stress field is dominated by a single component which is not expected to vary along the length of the slot. Application to situations where residual stresses vary in both directions along the surface may be possible by using novel slot geometries, such as thumbnails. The results reported here, for an experiment carried out with a semi-circular electrode on a plastically bent beam, suggest that further investigation of this possibility would be justified.

Analysis of the likely experimental error present in the results is complicated by the possible existence of 'multiple solutions', where several residual stress fields can give rise to similar variations of strain with slot depth. The use of multiple strain gauges can be employed to minimise this problem. However, the lack of a rigorous treatment of this form of experimental error remains one of the principal drawbacks of the method.

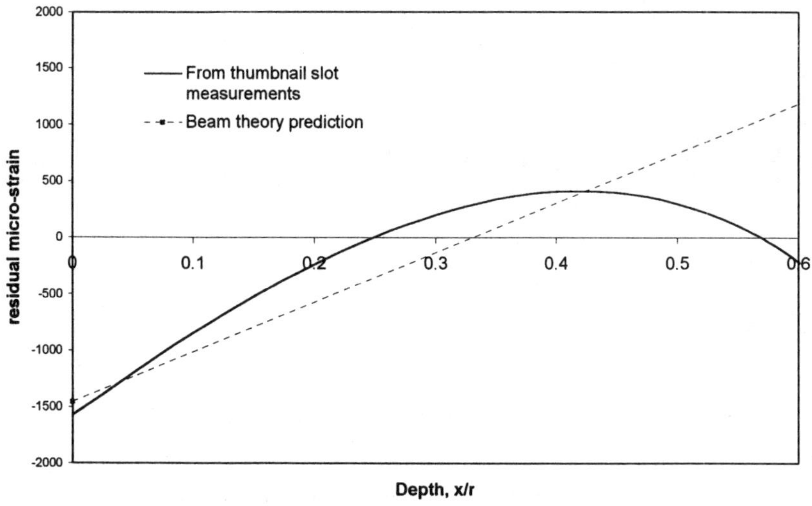

Fig. 6 Residual strains in a plastically bent mild steel beam measured using a thumbnail slot. A semi-circular electrode of radius *r* was employed.

ACKNOWLEDGEMENTS

The work described in this paper was financially supported by the Engineering and Physical Sciences Research Council under grant no. GR/K75507. Neutron diffraction results were obtained by Prof. G.A. Webster and Dr A.N. Ezeilo (Imperial College) under the associated grant GR/L19942.

REFERENCES

1. Cheng, W., and Finnie, I., Proc. 4th Int. Conf. on Residual Stress, Baltimore, June 1994, Soc. Exp. Mech. (Bethel, Connecticut) 1994, p 449.
2. Prime, M.B., Applied Mechanics Review 52, (1999) 75.
3. Nowell, D., Tochilin, S., and Hills, D.A., Proc. 5th Int. Conf. on Residual Stress, Linköping, Sweden, June 1997, Linköping University 1998, p 664.
4. Nowell, D., Tochilin, S., and Hills, D.A., Jnl Strain Analysis, in press (2000).
5. Ezeilo, A.N., and Webster, G.A, Jnl Strain Analysis, in press (2000).
6. Cheng, W. and Finnie, I., Trans ASME: Jnl of Eng Mats and Tech. 115, (1993) 220.
7. Nowell, D., Jnl Strain Analysis 34, (1999) 285.
8. http://www.vamas.org
9. Lei, Y., O'Dowd, N.P., Webster, G.A., and May, P. Imperial College Technical Report, 1999.
10. May, P., Webster, G.A., and O'Dowd, N.P. Proc. 6th Int. Conf. On Residual Stress, Oxford, July 2000, Institute of Materials (London), 2000.
11. Dai, DN, and Hills, D.A., Report No. OUEL 2051/95 University of Oxford, Department of Engineering Science, 1995

EFFECT OF PRIOR PLASTIC DEFORMATION ON THE RELATION BETWEEN RESIDUAL STRESSES AND BARKHAUSEN NOISE

M Lindgren and T Lepistö
Tampere University of Technology
Institute of Materials Science
P.O.Box 589
33101 Tampere, Finland

ABSTRACT

In the present work the effect of prior plastic deformation on the relation between stress vs. Barkhausen noise in mild steel specimens was studied. In the beginning of the tests different amounts of plastic straining was introduced into the specimens. Thereafter, X-ray and Barkhausen measurements were used to monitor the residual stress levels of the specimens. The prestrained specimens were used in tension/compression tests. The load was increased in steps, followed by instantaneous Barkhausen noise measurements. In case of specimens without any prior plastic deformation the linear range of the stress vs. Barkhausen noise curve situated mainly on the compressive side of the stress field. The saturation of the tensile stress level took place at a fairly low stress level. In the prestrained specimens both the saturation tensile stress level and the linear range of the stress vs. Barkhausen noise curve increased. Furthermore, the linear range shifted from the compressive to the tensile stress area. The absolute value of the Barkhausen noise under a certain stress depended on prestraining. This means that if the plastic deformation introduced to the calibration specimen and the real plastic deformation of the actual component including the possible prestraining differ significantly, meaningful errors in the measured residual stress level may occur. The slope of the stress vs. Barkhausen noise curve did not depend on the prestraining. This means the relative values of the residual stresses can be measured even though the amount of prestraining is not known.

INTRODUCTION

Most residual stress measurement methods are not suitable for quality assessment due to their destructive nature, time consuming measurements or too high costs. A potential technique for industrial residual stress measurements is the Barkhausen noise method. Its main advantages are simple to use and cheap equipment, high measuring speed and the information depth of the order of 0.1 mm. The use of the Barkhausen noise in residual stress measurement requires calibration. The calibration specimen is either uniaxially or biaxially loaded and Barkhausen noise values are registered (see for example Ref. 1). The stress vs. Barkhausen noise curve usually contains a linear part and a saturation range at high tensile and compressive stresses. The linear part of the stress vs. Barkhausen noise curve can be used for the residual stress evaluations. The main application area of the Barkhausen noise method is in the field of microstructural variations. It is not widely used or studied in the field of residual stress measurements. Maybe this is why the results found in the literature concerning the relation between (external or residual) stress and the Barkhausen noise are sometimes controversial.

Jagadish et al. (2) have presented results where the Barkhausen noise and the tensile stresses are linearly related, and that the Barkhausen noise saturates already at low compressive stress values. Sengupta and Theiner (3) have observed that stress sensitivity in the tensile stress region in plain carbon steel is not good. Rautioaho et al. (4) have studied stress response of mild steel in normalized and strained condition. They found out that in the normalized condition the stress vs. Barkhausen noise curve saturated already at fairly low tensile stress values (approximately 100 MPa). In strained condition the stress response was stronger and saturation took place at higher tensile stress.

The number of studies dealing with the effect of plastic deformation on the Barkhausen noise is very limited. Karjalainen and Moilanen (5) have studied the effect of plastic deformation on the Barkhausen noise in mild steel specimens using interrupted tensile tests. According to their findings the Barkhausen noise reduces drastically in the loading direction when the yield stress is exceeded. The difference between the Barkhausen noise in the loading and the transverse direction changes significantly. They explain the observed phenomena on the basis of the compressive residual stresses in the loading direction and the tensile residual stresses in the transverse direction.

MATERIALS AND METHODS

Mild steel S235JRG2 was used as a test material in the present study. Its mechanical properties are presented in the Table I. Rectangle specimens with dimensions of 150 mm x 40 mm were cut from a 3 mm thick sheet so that the long side of the specimen was parallel to the rolling direction of the sheet. Tensile testing machine was used to introduce different amounts of plastic deformation into the specimens. Strain was measured with an extensometer placed to the gage section of the specimen. When the predetermined strain level was reached the test was interrupted and the specimen was removed from the testing machine. The strain levels used in the present study are presented in the Fig. 1 together with the measured stress-strain curve of the material.

Barkhausen noise and X-ray diffraction residual stress measurements were carried out for the strained specimens in angles 0°, 30°, 45°, 60° and 90° with respect to the loading direction. After this specimens were put in a closed-loop hydraulic materials testing machine Instron 8800. This time the load was increased in steps. After each loading step the load was kept constant and Barkhausen noise measurements were conducted in different directions. The load range varied from –100 MPa to 300 MPa. The loading sequence was 20 MPa, -20 MPa, 40 MPa, -40 MPa … -100 MPa, 120 MPa, 140 MPa and so on. When loading and Barkhausen measurement sequence was completed the specimen was removed from the testing machine, and Barkhausen noise measurements and X-ray diffraction residual stress measurements were carried out once more in the unloaded condition.

Root mean square (rms) value of the Barkhausen noise burst was measured with commercial equipment Rollscan 200-1 and sensor model 3313. The optimal magnetization and amplification values determined in earlier studies were used (6). The X-ray diffraction measurements were performed with Xstress 3000 equipment using Cr Kα radiation and the standard d vs. $\sin^2\psi$ technique. The full width half maximum (FWHM) of the diffraction peak was also measured.

Table I Mechanical properties of the mild steel.

Yield Stress (MPa)	Tensile Strength (MPa)	Hardness $HV_{0.2}$	Grain size μm
300	420	120	30

RESULTS AND DISCUSSION

Prestraining

The plastic prestraining of the specimens did not introduce any significant residual stresses. The residual stresses measured by X-ray diffraction in loading and transverse direction are presented in the Fig. 2. Strain levels from 0,5 % to 3 % produce small tensile residual stresses to the loading direction while higher strain amplitudes from 5 % to 10 % cause compressive residual stresses. In most studies tensile loading is reported to produce compressive residual stresses (see for example Ref. 7). There are, however, some results indicating also contradictory behavior under small plastic strains. Gurova et al. (8) observed changes from compressive residual stresses to tensile residual stresses with approximately 0.5 % strain in tension. In this study the compressive residual stresses were formed when strain exceeded materials Lüder's strain. Tensile residual stresses may have formed because of microstructural differences between surface and core of the specimen. According to X-ray diffraction measurements there is a small compressive residual stress in the transverse direction at the specimen surface. The compressive stress is assumed to originate from the manufacturing process. It remained virtually unchanged despite of the prestraining.

Barkhausen noise values after prestraining and in as-delivered condition of the material were different. In as-delivered condition the Barkhausen noise value measured in different directions were quite similar. When increasing amount of plastic deformation was introduced to the specimen the Barkhausen noise values became more and more anisotropic. Fig. 3 shows the variation of the Barkhausen noise values in different directions as a function of prestraining compared to the values without any straining. The Barkhausen noise amplitude is reduced in the loading direction and increased in the transverse direction as a function of straining i.e. plastic deformation of the specimen.

The measuring depth of the Barkhausen noise method is bigger than that of X-ray diffraction. Therefore, the depth distribution of residual stresses was measured by X-ray diffraction using electrolytical polishing technique. The measured values of residual stresses were fairly small and the d vs. $\sin^2\psi$ relation turned out to be linear. The present residual stress measurements cannot separate macro and micro residual stresses from each other, and thus the existence of micro residual stresses cannot be excluded. The measured macro residual stresses cannot explain the observed differences in the Barkhausen noise amplitudes.

The full width half maximum of the diffraction peak (FWHM) was also registered in the X-ray diffraction measurements. Parabolic increase of FWHM as a function of plastic deformation was observed. The main reason for this must be the number of dislocations producing local microstrains. Stress fields around dislocations will interact with all suitably oriented moving domain walls (9). When the velocity of moving domain walls is reduced also the amount of Barkhausen noise is reduced. This phenomenon can explain the reduction of the Barkhausen noise in the loading direction but not the increase of Barkhausen noise in the transverse direction.

Step-wise loading

Step-wise loading of non-prestrained specimens showed that the saturation of the Barkhausen noise values took place at very low tensile stress (approximately 40 MPa) value, Fig. 4. The linear part of the stress vs. Barkhausen noise curve, which is used in residual stress measurements, was mostly in the compressive stress range. The saturation compressive stress could not be evaluated as the highest compressive stress used in this study, –100 MPa, was still on the linear part. In prestrained specimens the saturation of the Barkhausen noise amplitude took place at higher tensile stresses and the linear part of the stress vs. Barkhausen noise curve was more in the tensile stress range, Fig. 4. The sudden increase in the rms value of the Barkhausen noise before 300 MPa indicates that yielding at least on the microscopic scale has been taking place at loads which are less than the yield stress measured in a normal tensile test. The starting point and finishing point of the linear part of the stress vs. Barkhausen noise curve and the length of the linear part for different prestraining levels are presented in the Table II.

Table II The starting point and finishing point of the linear part of the stress vs. Barkhausen noise curve and the length of the linear part for different prestraining levels.

Prestraining (%)	Stress level at which the linear part begins (MPa)	Stress level at which the linear part finishes (MPa)	Stress range of the linear part (MPa)
0	< -100	40	140
0.5	< -100	100	200
1	-60	120	180
2	-80	100	180
3	-80	180	260
5	-80	200	280
10	-60	160	220

Barkhausen noise values measured in the transverse direction during loading are presented in the Fig. 5. Because tensile stresses cause compressive stresses in the transverse direction due to Poisson effect, the Barkhausen noise amplitude in the transverse direction reduces with increasing tensile stress. The linear part of the stress vs. Barkhausen noise curve also shifts towards the tensile stress range as a function of prestraining level. In transverse direction the amount of prior plastic deformation does not affect the stress range of the linear part. In this direction the linear stress range is approximately 170 MPa. This behavior is opposite to the one found in the loading direction.

In the present study the prestraining was found to increase the linear range of the stress vs. Barkhausen noise curve even for small amounts of plastic deformation. This increase is beneficial to the residual stress measurements as it increases the sensitivity of the method. Furthermore, the tensile stress at which the Barkhausen noise vs. stress curve became non-linear increased as a function of prestraining. Tensile residual stresses are critical especially in fatigue loaded components. This is why special attention is payed to the measurement of tensile stresses. The present results indicate that prior plastic deformation of a material helps residual stress measurements. The differences in the plastic deformation can lead into large differences in Barkhausen noise vs. stress relation.

The sensitivity of the Barkhausen noise method to the plastic deformation causes certain problems in residual stress measurements if absolute residual stress values are requested. The results show that a value measured in loading direction can correspond to residual stress values in the range of 0-100 MPa depending on the condition of the material i.e. plastic deformation. This finding emphasizes the need of performing the calibration of the method by using specimens which are as similar as possible to the actual component to be measured. If the forming processes of the component produce zones with different amounts of plastic deformation, the absolute values obtained with single calibration curve are not necessarily correct ones.

If only relative values of the residual stress are needed, differences in the plastic deformation do not cause problems. Based on the present results the slope of the linear part of the Barkhausen noise vs. stress curve is independent of the prior plastic deformation. Therefore the variations in residual stresses can be evaluated even though the actual amount of prior plastic deformation is not known.

Figure 6 shows an example of Barkhausen noise results in different directions with prior deformation of 5 %. Barkhausen noise increases in loading direction under tensile stress and decreases under compressive stress. There is a certain stress value under which Barkhausen noise is almost isotropic in all directions. This stress value shifts towards higher tensile stress values as a function of prestraining from –30 MPa without any straining up to approximately 100 MPa with 10 % deformation. This stress value, with nearly equal Barkhausen noise values in all directions, gives a rough estimate of the plastic deformation introduced to the specimen.

CONCLUSIONS

1. Plastic deformation reduced Barkhausen noise amplitude in loading direction and increased it in transverse direction.
2. Prestraining increased the linear range of the stress vs. Barkhausen noise curve and shifted the linear part of the curve towards the tensile stress range.
3. The tensile saturation value in the stress vs. Barkhausen noise curve increased as a function of prior plastic deformation.
4. The slope of the stress vs. Barkhausen noise curve was independent of the amount of prior plastic deformation.

ACKNOWLEDGEMENTS

The financial support of Tekes, the National Technology Agency, and several industrial companies is gratefully acknowledged. Stresstech Inc. is thanked for providing the Barkhausen noise measurement equipment. The help of Mr. J. Sundelin is acknowledged.

REFERENCES

1. Tiitto S, Experimental Techniques 15 (1991) 17
2. Jagadish C, Clapham L, Atherton DL, IEEE Trans Magn 25 (1989) 3452
3. Sengupta AK, Theiner WA, Mater Eval 53 (1995) 554
4. Rautioaho RH, Karjalainen LP, Moilanen M, Proc. of the ICRS2, (1989) 90
5. Karjalainen LP, Moilanen M, NDT Int 12 (1979) 51
6. Rollscan 200 Operating Instructions, Stresstech Inc.
7. Hauk V Ed. 'Structural and residual stress analysis by nondestructive methods' Elsevier, 1997
8. Gurova T, Teodósio JR, Rebello JMA, Monin V, Strain Anal Eng Des 32 (1997) 455
9. Degauque J, Astié B, Kubin LP, J Appl Phys. 50 (1979) 2140

FIGURES

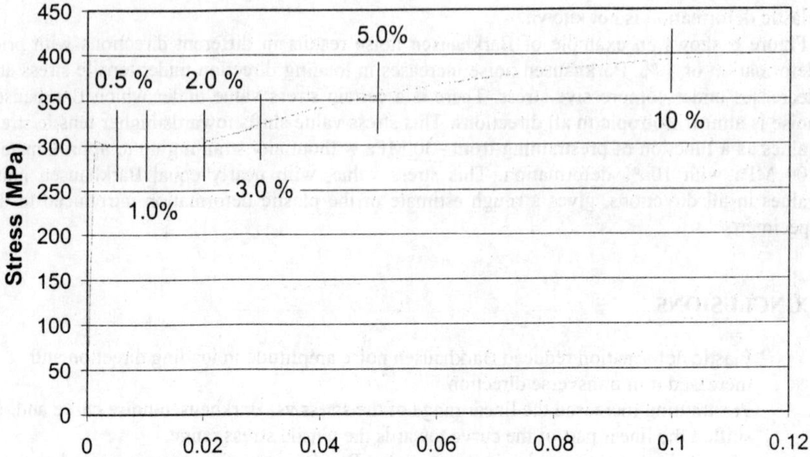

Fig. 1 Strain levels in first loading with respect to the stress-strain curve of the material

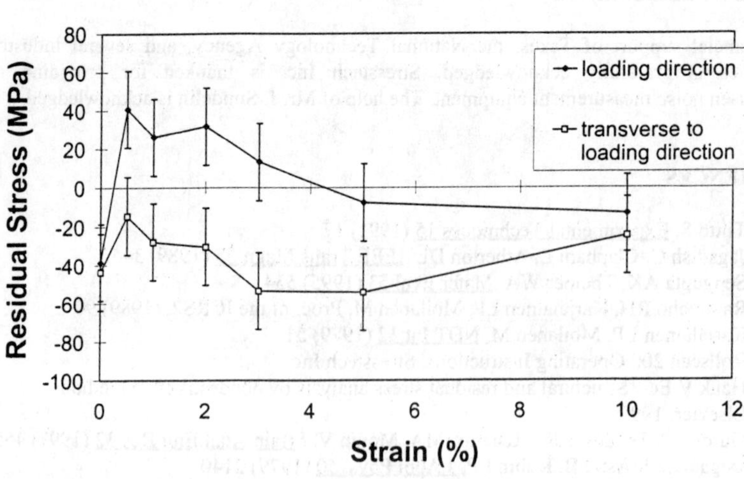

Fig. 2 Residual stresses in loading direction and in direction transverse to loading after different amounts of strain.

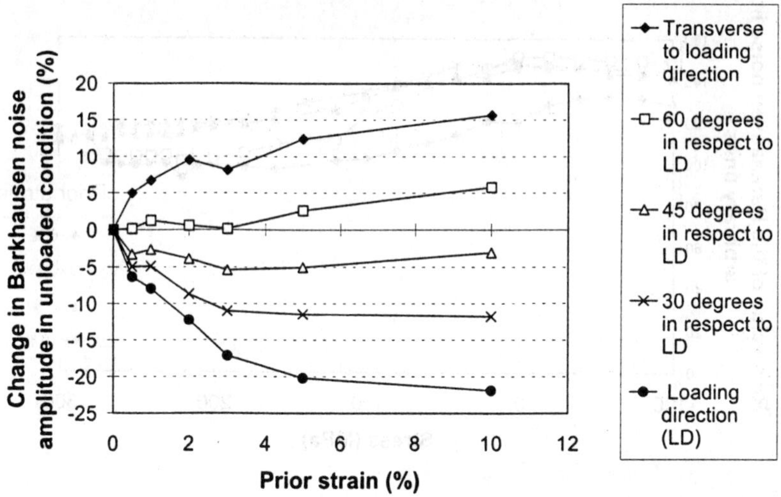

Fig. 3 Barkhausen noise results in different directions as a function of prestraining.

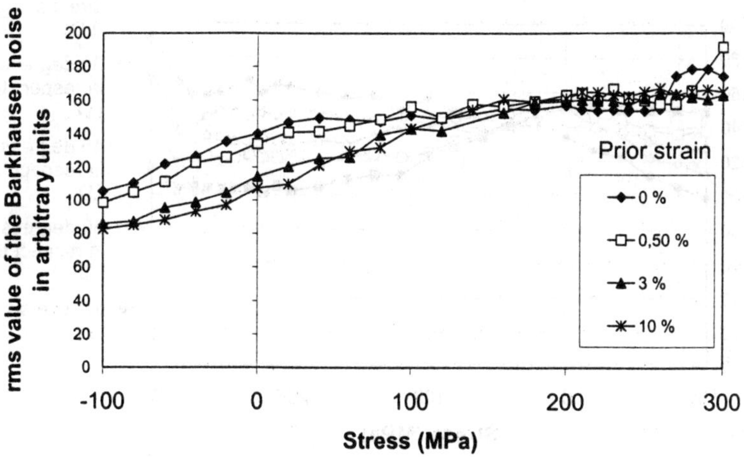

Fig. 4 Barkhausen noise values under stress in loading direction. Results for specimens with different prestraining.

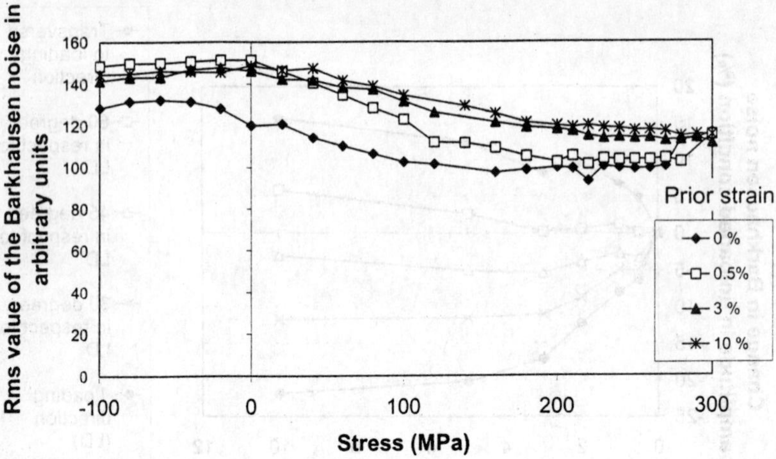

Fig. 5 Barkhausen noise values under stress in transverse direction. Results for specimens with different prestraining.

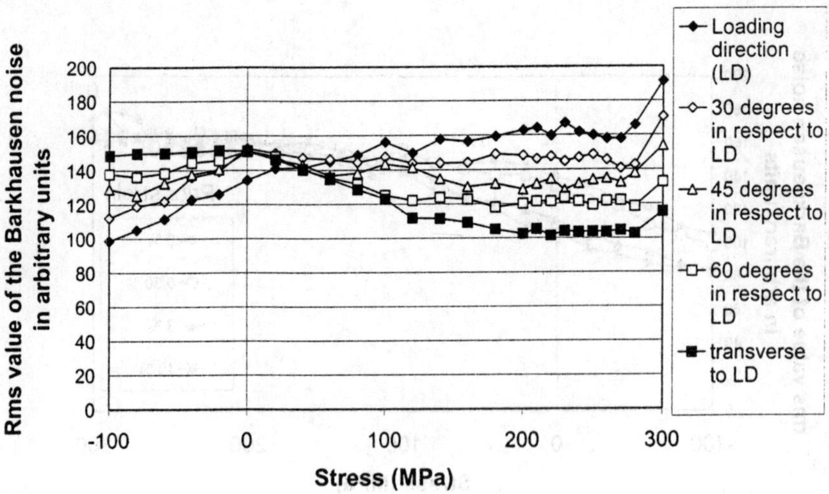

Fig. 6 Barkhausen noise values in different directions under loading. Specimen with 5 % prestraining.

SESSION 6C

CORROSION FATIGUE OF DIFFERENTLY SURFACE TREATED STEEL SAE1045

R Herzog
CC Gießerei Kassel, Volkswagen AG, Germany
B Scholtes
Institut für Werkstofftechnik, University of Kassel, Germany
H Wohlfahrt
Institut für Schweißtechnik, University of Braunschweig, Germany

ABSTRACT

Surface layer analyses and corrosion fatigue tests were carried out on differently surface treated samples of steel SAE 1045, in order to study the influence of machining induced surface layer properties on the corrosion fatigue behaviour and the corresponding damage processes.

For active corrosion fatigue the machining condition of the surface has an important influence on lifetime of components, and the length of the crack propagation phase is decisive. Time of crack formation as well as crack density (number of cracks per unit of area) are mainly determined by roughness of the surfaces. The crack propagation, however, is characteristically influenced by all surface layer properties treated in this paper.

INTRODUCTION

The corrosion fatigue behaviour of metallic components is influenced by a great number of parameters, apart from the corrosion system itself. Also the machining condition of the component's surface belongs to this. A surface layer property which is important for the dynamic strength is the near surface residual stress condition, the influence of which on the fatigue strength in air has been often examined and is therefore well-known. The influence of machining residual stresses on the corrosion fatigue, however, is often questioned, above all dealing with electro-chemical active systems (Spähn (1)). Therefore the influence of machining surface properties and especially machining residual stresses on the corrosion fatigue behaviour of steel SAE 1045 in artificial sea water was systematically examined (Herzog (2)).

MATERIAL INVESTIGATED AND EXPERIMENTAL DETAILS

Steel SAE 1045 has been examined in a quenched and tempered condition. For producing the desired surface conditions, technically relevant machining methods and parameters were applied: grinding with corundum, grinding with cubic boron nitride (with and without prestress) and shot peening.

In order to vary macro- and micro-residual stresses, hardness as well as roughness of the surface layers, and to separate their influence on the damage process of corrosion fatigue, different machining versions and also combined machining methods were examined.

On the finished samples corrosion fatigue tests were carried out using bending fatigue loading in artificial seawater. Computer controlled ψ - diffractometers were used for the residual stress analyses before and during interruptions of the loading process. The interference lines of

{211}- lattice planes of the ferrite were measured by CrKα - radiation. 2Θ - intervals were scanned for 11 ψ-angles at a range of -45° ≤ ψ ≤ 45° and the positions of diffraction peaks were determined according to the gravity line method. The calculation of the residual stresses occured following the $\sin^2 \psi$- method (Macherauch, Müller (3)). Characteristic values of roughness R_a, R_z, R_t, and R_{max} according to DIN 4768 were determined. Furthermore, the crack density (number of cracks per cm^2), the crack lengths and depths as well as the shapes of the cracks were determined in samples which were damaged by corrosion fatigue. Further details about the material (heat treatment and strength) as well as about the processing and about the surface layer analysis are listed in (Herzog (2)).

EXPERIMENTAL RESULTS

Fig. 1 shows the residual stress and half-width distributions measured in the surface layers of differently treated samples before loading. In the upper part of the diagram, for all manufacturing methods, the residual stress components in the longitudinal direction are plotted, which corresponds to the feed direction of grinding and the loading direction of corrosion fatigue tests. Differences between residual stresses in the transverse direction are only small for the ground samples and therefore they do not have to be taken into further consideration. The machining methods and parameters were chosen in such a way that, on the one hand, at a constant surface roughness in surface layers of the same thickness compressive residual stresses of different amounts were produced and, on the other hand, that at the same residual stress level compressive residual stresses were present in surface layers of a different thickness. The half-width distributions point out that all ground samples were strain hardened only in a very thin surface layer by machining and the shot peened samples have undergone a remarkably stronger strain hardening process in thicker surface layers.

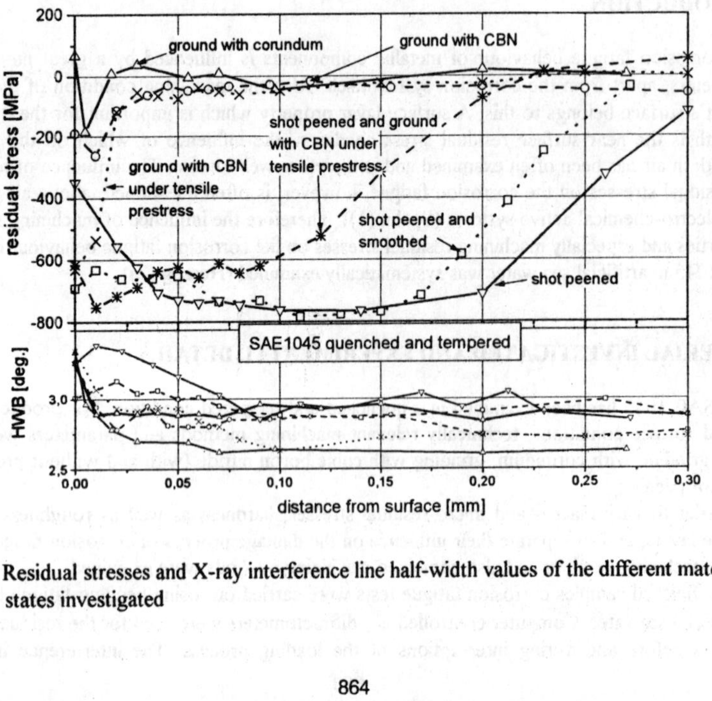

Fig. 1: Residual stresses and X-ray interference line half-width values of the different material states investigated

	R_{max} [µm]	R_t [µm]	R_z [µm]	R_a [µm]
ground with corundum	10.5	11.5	8.1	1.4
ground with CBN	13.3	14.3	10.6	1.6
shot peened	29.3	31.5	22.9	3.2
shot peened and smoothed	5.4	5.6	4.3	0.5

Table 1: Roughness values of differently treated SAE 1045-specimens

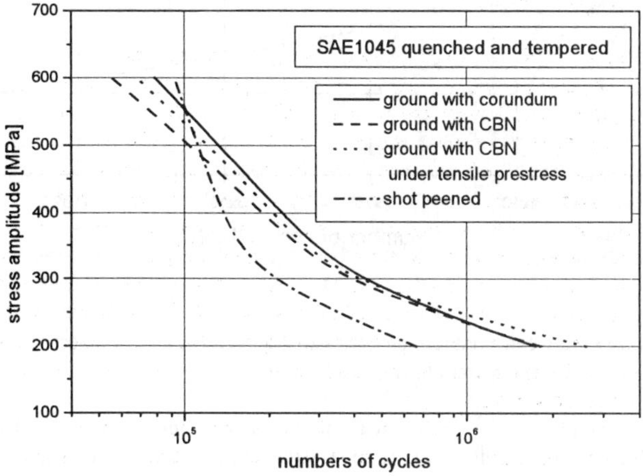

Fig. 2: Numbers of cycles to crack initiation of the different materials states investigated for bending fatigue in artificial sea water

The characteristic values of roughness, which are listed in table 1, show that the surface qualities are nearly the same for all ground samples, the shot peened samples are remarkably rougher than the ground ones, and the grinding and electrolytical polishing of the shot peened samples led to the desired smooth surface.

Figs. 2 and 3 show the results of the corrosion fatigue tests. The instrumentation of the bending fatigue machine enabled gathering of the bending moment during the total loading process. The crack formation and the crack propagation result in a reduction of sample stiffness, which is proportional to the bending moment, transmitted by the sample. Up to a bending moment reduction of 2.5% this value is mainly controlled by the formation of cracks. Therefore the number of load cycles, where a bending moment reduction of 2.5% was present, was defined as the number of cycles for crack initiation N_S (see Fig. 2). The bending moment reduction at further loading can mainly be referred to the growth of cracks present and only to a small amount to the formation of further cracks. Thus the difference between the number of load cycles $N_B - N_S$ (N_B number of cycles to fracture) corresponds to the phase of crack propagation. The corresponding numbers of load cycles of each variant, which are based on the values calculated according to the arcsin $\sqrt{P}$ - transformation, are shown in Fig. 3. Thus, by means of the diagrams 2 and 3, it is possible to separately discuss the effect of the surface layer properties on crack formation and on crack propagation.

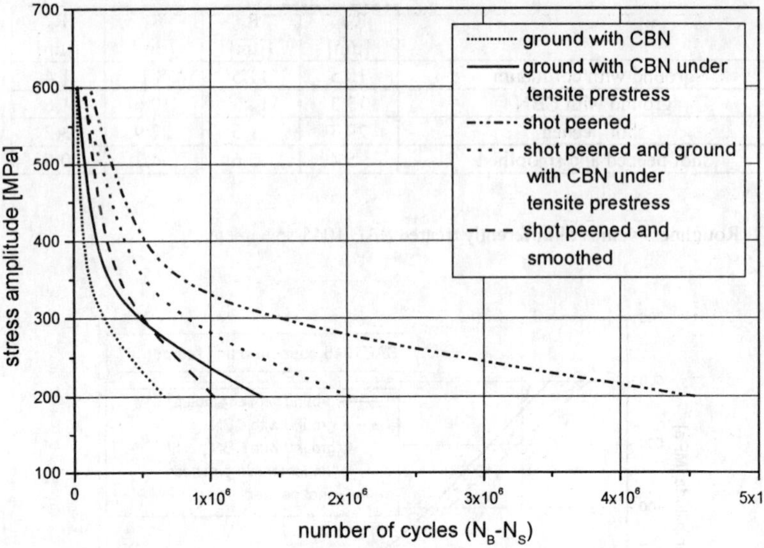

Fig. 3: Difference between numbers of cycles to fracture N_B and numbers of cycles to crack initiation N_S for the material states investigated

Fig. 4, as an example for the three machining states "corundum -ground, CBN-ground and shot peened", shows the results of the residual stress stability examinations and the determined crack densities as a function of the number of loading cycles. All samples were loaded in the same way by bending fatigue with a loading stress of 300 MPa. During loading intervals surface residual stresses were measured and cracks, which showed a length of at least 50 µm, were counted in the test areas on the upper and lower side of the samples. A remarkable influence of the machining condition on the crack density was noted. The greatest values are always observed on the shot peened samples at any particular time. From the crack densities, however, differences between the ground versions cannot be determined. But they become obvious, when the crack lengths are taken into consideration (Herzog (2)).

Fig. 5, for a shot peened sample which was loaded with a loading amplitude of 300 MPa, shows the typical crack propagation. Such crack propagations have only been found with shot peened samples. Starting from a corrosion pit in the center of an indentation of the shot, the cracks grow perpendicular to the surface. In deeper layers crack branching occurs. The location of the branching was measured on a great number of cracks. The results are shown in Fig. 6. Most of the branchings lie in a distance of 0.09 to 0.13 mm from the surface, which corresponds to the surface distance of the maximum of compressive residual stresses. In layers, which are deeper than 0,2 mm below the surface, nearly no branching can be found.

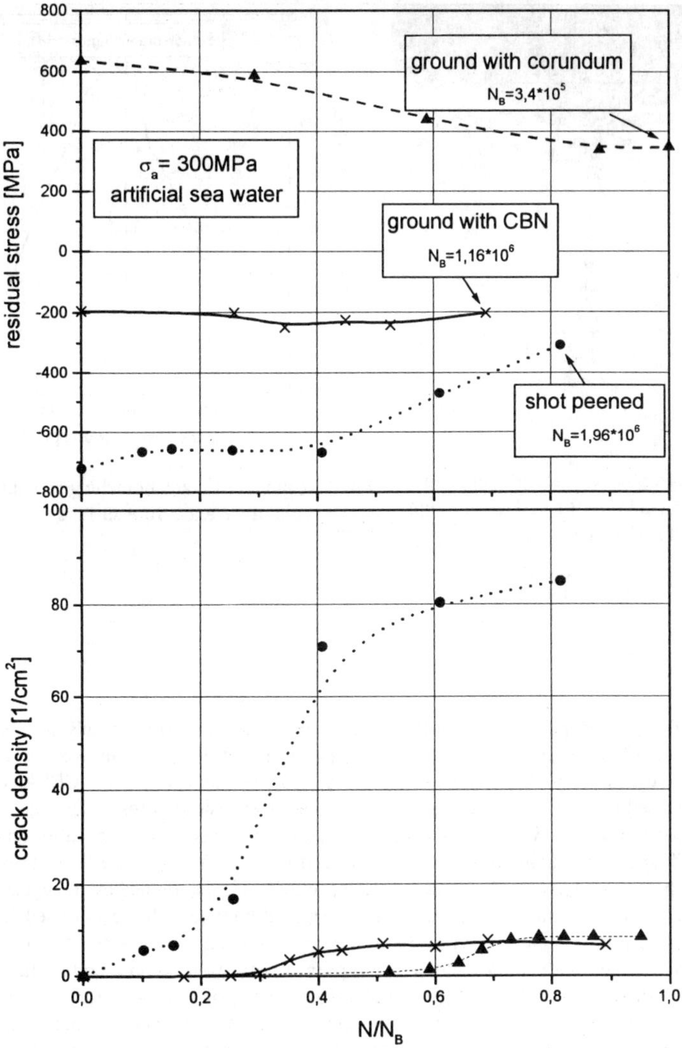

Fig. 4: Surface residual stresses and crack densities as a function of the relative number of cycles N/N_B

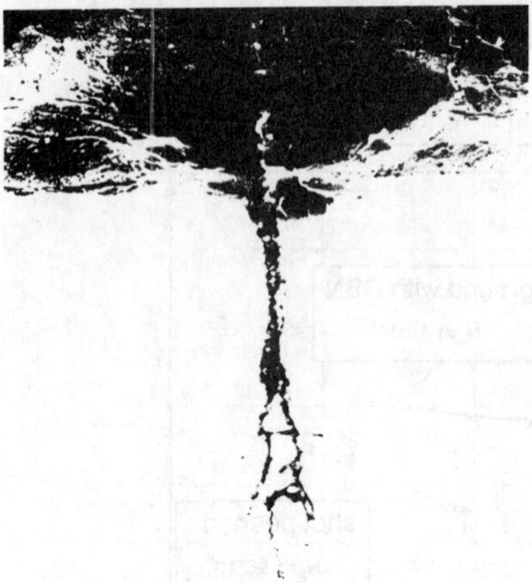

Fig 5: Micrograph of a crack propagating perpendicular to the surface in a shot peened surface layer

0.1 mm

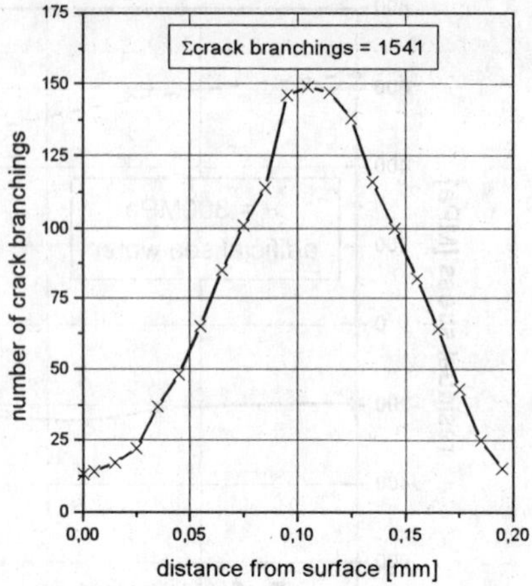

Fig. 6: Amount of crack branching as a function of distance from surface

DISCUSSION

In corrosion fatigue, independently from the initiation mechanism, cracks are only created on the surface. Therefore, for crack formation also the properties of the direct surface and of the immediate surface layer are of special importance. By a comparison between the CBN-ground and the prestressed CBN-ground samples it becomes clear that residual stresses have no influence on the crack formation. Regarding their surface layer properties these states differ only by the amount of surface residual stresses. (See Fig. 1 and table 1). The damage lines shown in Fig.2 are nearly the same. At this early stage of damage, which is determined by the crack formation, there are no differences recognizable. The increased lifetime of the prestressed CBN-ground samples can only be attributed to the longer crack propagation phases. (See Fig. 3). Taking in addition the corundum-ground and shot peened samples into consideration this fact becomes clear. Although there are tensile residual stresses on the surfaces of corundum-ground samples, damage starts later than on the CBN-ground ones. On the shot peened samples, which show remarkable compressive residual stresses, there are initial cracks already in a very early phase of loading. Therefore, not the residual stresses, but the surface roughness is decisive for the time of crack formation. Rough surfaces, for example at shot peened samples, accelerate the creation of corrosion pits, which initiate the crack formation, as shown on the surfaces. Smooth surfaces, however, decelerate the formation of cracks. These observations also correspond with the measured crack densities (Fig. 6).

The effect of the surface layer properties on the crack propagation becomes obvious in Fig. 1 and 3. Already the increase of the amount of compressive residual stresses in thin surface layers leads to a longer crack propagation phase. Increasing the thickness of the surface layer with compressive residual stresses also has a positive effect on the crack propagation.

Thus, one can see that compressive residual stresses obstruct the propagation of cracks in corrosion fatigue and the thickness of the surface layer with compressive residual stresses, on the one hand, as well as the amount of residual stresses, on the other hand, are important for the crack propagation. As increasing the compressive residual stresses in the outer surface layers already leads to a remarkably longer phase of crack propagation, one can follow that residual stresses have a special effect on the growth of short cracks.

Furthermore, one can see from Fig. 3, that the shot peened samples have a noticeably longer phase of crack propagation than those samples which were ground after shot peening. By the grinding process the surface layer with compressive residual stresses becomes thinner than that of the only shot peened samples. Thus, the longer phase of crack propagation of the only shot peened samples becomes clear. However, taking into consideration that the difference between the surface layer thicknesses is only approx. 0.05 mm, it becomes obvious, that there must be other influences, apart from the residual stresses. A remarkable difference between these versions is the surface character. To clarify the question, if the surface roughness also influences the crack propagation, smooth shot peened (additionally ground and polished) samples were investigated. The results show that this treatment has led to a later cracking of the samples (influence of the roughness on the crack formation) but to a remarkably shorter phase of crack propagation. One can conclude that the crack propagation is reduced by a high crack density. Obviously, for individual cracks, the stress intensity is reduced in the case of high crack densities, resulting in a reduction of crack propagation velocity. Similar effects can also be observed in the case of stress corrosion cracking (Goto, Nisitani (4)).

By means of the half-width values of interference lines it becomes clear that by grinding and polishing of shot peened specimens, those material layers were removed which were strengthened by shot peening. The effect of this strengthened surface layer on the crack propagation can be derived from the crack appearance (See Fig. 5). The crack flanks are strongly corroded, up to the depths, in which crack branching occurs. This shows that at first the cracks propagate quickly and only in the material layers in which the cracks branch is the crack propagation stopped. A comparison of the residual stress and half-width distributions with the accumulation curve of the crack branchings shows that there are only crack branching effects in those areas where there are considerable residual stresses and there was only a small amount of crack branching in strengthened areas directly near the surface. With increasing distance from the surface the amount of crack branching increases and then decreases after reaching its maximum. Because the stress intensity range increases with increasing crack length, a reduced crack propagation velocity at greater crack lengths can only be referred to an increased material resistance against crack propagation or a reduction of the effective stress intensity range.

Thus, one can state that the higher material's hardness in the surface layer of shot peened, quenched and tempered samples has not led to a reduction of crack propagation velocity. A retarded crack propagation does only take place in such material layers, which show better toughness properties, together with high compressive residual stresses.

In summary, one can say that regarding active corrosion fatigue the machining condition of the surface has a remarkable influence on the lifetime of components. Time of crack formation as well as crack density (number of cracks per unit of area) are determined by roughness of the surfaces. Cracks are initiated by corrosion pits, whereby surface defects represent a target for corrosion and thus they are starting sites for initial cracks. High roughnesses, as present at shot peened surfaces, accordingly result in a very early crack formation and therefore in high crack densities. In the case of active corrosion fatigue one cannot detect an influence of residual stresses or surface layer strengthening on crack formation.

Regarding active corrosion fatigue the length of the crack propagation phase is lifetime-determining. All surface layer properties treated in this paper have an influence on the crack propagation, whereby the effect of individual parameters is in a complex way dependent on the other surface layer properties. Compressive residual stresses reduce the crack propagation velocity. High values of surface roughness also lead to a reduction in crack propagation, caused by the resulting high number of corrosion pits and initial cracks. Compressive residual stresses play a central part, as they alone obstruct crack propagation and support other mechanisms of influence in this context.

REFERENCES

1. H. Spähn
Beeinträchtigung der Festigkeit durch das Zusammenwirken zeitlich veränderlicher mechanischer Beanspruchungen mit Korrosionsvorgängen
In: D. Munz; Ermüdungsverhalten metallischer Werkstoffe; DGM-Informationsgesellschaft Verlag, Oberursel 1985

2. R. Herzog
Auswirkungen bearbeitungsbedingter Randschichteigenschaften auf das Schwingungsrißkorrosionsverhalten von Ck45 und X35CrMo17
Shaker Verlag, Aachen 1998, ISBN 3-8265-4388-2

3. E. Macherauch, P. Müller
Das $\sin^2\Psi$-Verfahren der röntgenographischen Spannungsmessung
Z. f. angew. Physik 13 (1961), S. 305 – 312

4. M. Goto, H. Nisitani
Crack initiation and propagation behaviour of a heattreated carbon steel in corrosion fatigue
Fatigue Fract. Engng. Mater. Struct. 15 (1992), S. 353 – 363

AN INCREASE IN FATIGUE LIMIT OF A GEAR BY COMPOUND SURFACE TREATMENT

Katsuyuki Matsui[1], Kotoji Ando[2], Hirohito Eto[3] and Yoshitaka Misaki[4]

[1] Post-Graduate Student, Yokohama National University, 79-5, Tokiwadai, Hodogaya, Yokohama, 240-0068, Japan
[2] Department of Energy & Safety Engineering, Yokohama National University
[3] Isuzu Motors Ltd, Kawasakiku, Kawasakishi, Japan
[4] Neturen Ltd, Tamura, Hiratsuka, Japan

ABSTRACT

The fatigue strength of a component is a very important factor for the weight reduction of cars. To increase the fatigue limit of a gear, we studied the effect of compound surface treatment on the fatigue limit, systematically. Six kinds of gears were made of two kinds of steels. The surface treatments adopted were vacuum carburizing(VC), contour induction hardening(CIH) and double shot peening(DSP). By VC, the carbon density at the surface was increased to 0.8% and generation of grain boundary oxidation was prevented completely. By CIH, grain size was refined. By DSP, most retained austenite near the surface was transformed to martensite and the hardness was increased. Also very high compressive residual stress was introduced. By these compound effects, the stress range at the fatigue limit(R=0.1) was increased to 2207MPa. To understand the main factors which control the fatigue limit($R \geqq 0$), regression analysis was made by using our 8 data as to surface treated gear. It is concluded that the main factors which control the stress range at fatigue limit of the gear($R \geqq 0$) σ_{up}(MPa) , are yield stress, maximum compressive residual stress at tooth root in tooth profile direction and average grain size.

1. INTRODUCTION

Due to environmental factors and fuel economy, most vehicles are now required to undergo weight reduction. For this purpose, it is useful to increase the fatigue limit of a vehicle components. Recently, two of this authors proposed new methodology to increase the fatigue limit of vehicle components subjected to $R \geqq 0$ stress, where R is stress ratio[1]. The methodology is: (a)Increase the component hardness HV as much as possible. (b)Introduce a high compressive residual stress near the component surface (should be equal to yield stress, if possible). (c)Make the component grain size finest. To apply this methodology to gears

Table 1 Chemical compositions of materials used(wt.%)

Steel	C	Si	Mn	P	S	Ni	Cr	Cu	Mo
A	0.19	0.06	0.84	0.010	0.019	0.09	0.11	0.09 ·	0.4
B	0.51	0.20	0.74	0.02	0.02	0.04	0.11	0.08	-

Table 2 Gear and compound surface treatment

Gear	I	II	III	IV	V	VI
Steel	A	A	A	A	B	B
Surface Treatment	VC	VC + DSP	VC + CIH	VC + CIH + DSP	C	C + DSP

VC : Vacuum Carburizing, DSP : Double Shot Peening, CIH : Contour Induction Hardening
C : Normal Carburrizing,

successfully, however, there are following five problems to consider: (1)Reduce an abnormal surface structures, such as grain boundary oxidation. (2)Make a finest grain size. (3)Decrease a retained austenite. (4)Increase the surface hardness HV. (5)Introduce a high compressive residual stress near the surface[2]. To solve these problems, the authors adopted following three techniques: (i)Vacuum carburizing. (ii)Contour induction hardening. (iii)Double shot peening[2,3,4]. By compounding these surface treatment, the above five problems (1)~(5) were completely solved, and σ_{up} of gears was increased up to 2207MPa[5]. Finally, to confirm the advisability of our methodology (a)~(c), we studied the correlation between σ_{up} and HV, the maximum compressive residual stress σ_{rmax} and the grain size d_y systematically[5]. Consequently, our methodology proved highly useful.

2. MATERIALS, SAMPLES AND TEST METHOD

Two kinds of steels were used for this study. Chemical compositions of these steels were listed in Table 1. Both steels were quenched and tempered to hardness level of HV≒200. Then, they were machined to the gear [module:3.0, pressure angle:$14^0 30'$, number of tooth:36, helix angle and hand:17^0 right hand, over ball diameter:123.584mm]. Altogether six kinds of gears were made. Gears I ~IV were made of steel A, and the gear V and VI were made of steel B. The surface treatment techniques adopted are Vacuum Carburizing(VC), Contour Induction Hardening(CIH) and Double Shot Peening(DSP). After the machining, the gears were surface-treated with these treatments combined. Table 2 shows the compound surface treatments of each gear. For example, Gear IV was first vacuum carburized, then contour induction hardened and finally double shot peened.

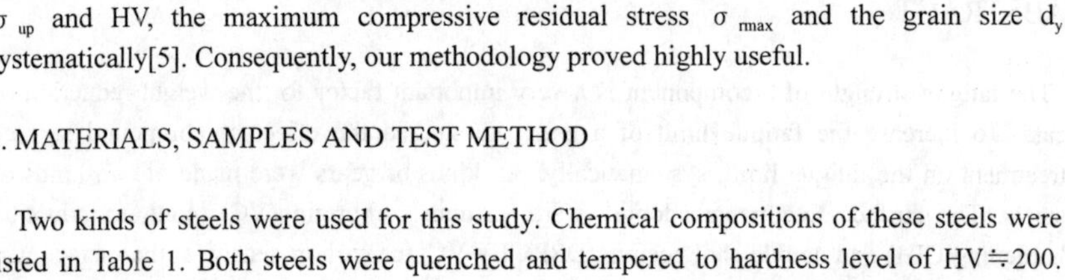

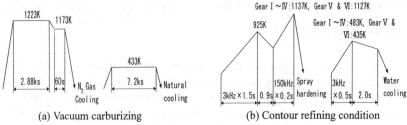

(a) Vacuum carburizing (b) Contour refining condition

Fig. 1 Surface refining conditions

Table 3 Double shot peening conditions

	Primary peening	Secondry peening
Air pressure	490kPa	392kPa
Nozzle dia.	Φ10mm	Φ4mm
Shot dia.	Φ0.6mm	Φ0.08mm
Shot hardness	Approx.700HV	Approx.700HV
Arc height	0.35mm(C)	0.26mm(N)

The gears I ~IV were vacuum carburized to C≒0.8wt% first. The vacuum carburizing conditions are: pressure in furnace=6.67x10^{-2}kPa, temperature=1223K, atomospher=C_3H_8gas, carburizing time=2.88ks. After being carburized, the gear was cooled to 1173K and subsequently quenched using N_2 gas of 5x10^2kPa. The contour induction hardening conditions are: frequency for pre-heat=3KHz, power for pre-heat=1000kW, frequency for main-heat=150kHz, and power for main-heat=600lW. The processes of vacuum carburzing and contour induction hardening are shown in Fig.1, schematically. The double shot peening conditions are listed in Table 3. Two kinds of shots were used: ϕ 0.6mm shot for primary shot peening and ϕ 0.08mm shot for secondary shot peening. The shot size in this sequence is the key to introducing an appropriate compressive residual stress in Gear[2].

To measure the residual stress and the volume fraction of the retained austenite(γ_R), a micro X-ray stress measuring apparatus was used. The gear surface was masked with ϕ 5mm window, and was polished to a specified depth using electrolytic polishing method. The X-ray conditions are: X-ray spectrum = Cr-K beam and X-ray beam injection diameter = ϕ 2mm. The residual stress was calculated with 2θ-$\sin^2\phi$ method, and γ_R was calculated using Ia/(Ia+Im), where Ia and Im are intensity of retained austenaito and intensity of martensite, respectively. A gear fatigue testing system is shown in Fig.2, schematically. The gear was fixed by mounting rod tightly. The test was done using an electro-hydraulic testing machine in air under the test conditions of stress ratio(R=0.1), 10Hz frequency and sin wave load cycle.

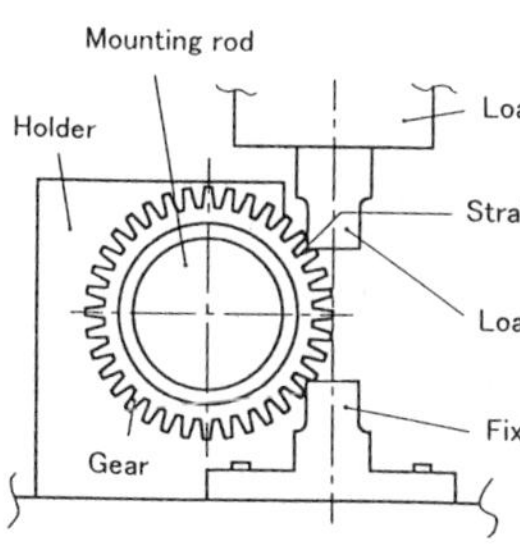

Fig.2 Bending fatigue test method

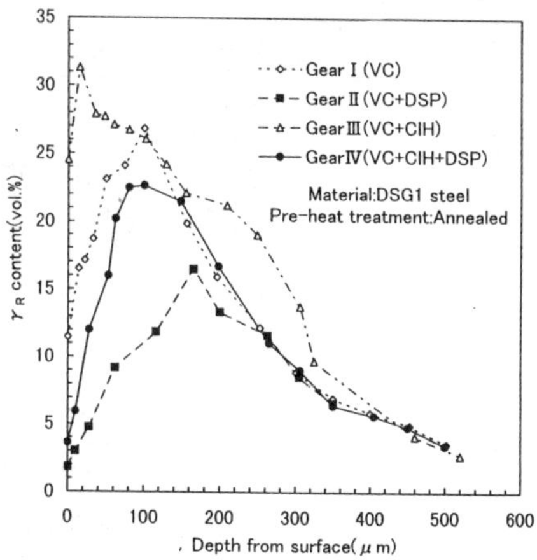

Fig.3 γ_R content distribution of tooth root

3. TEST RESULTS AND DISCUSSION

3.1. Retained austenite

Fig.3 shows the distribution of γ_R. The symbol ◇ shows γ_R of gear I. The γ_R at the surface is 11.5% and the maximum γ_R is 26.8%. The symbol ■ shows γ_R of gear II. The γ_R at the surfaces is very low(1.8%) and the maximum one is 16.5%. The gear II γ_R was reduced considerably as compared to gear I. This γ_R reduction is attributed to double shot peening. The gear III γ_R is shown with the symbol △ in Fig.3. The γ_R at the surface and the maximum are 24.5% and 31.3%, respectively, showing extremely high value. Gear IV γ_R at the surface and the maximum are 3.4% and 21.2%, respectively. Similar to gear II, gear IV γ_R was reduced drastically meaning that the retained austenite was transformed to martensite by strain transformation caused by double shot peening[5].

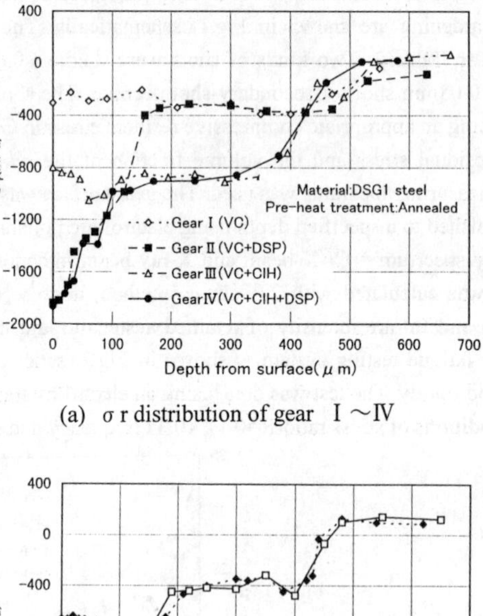

(a) σ r distribution of gear I ~IV

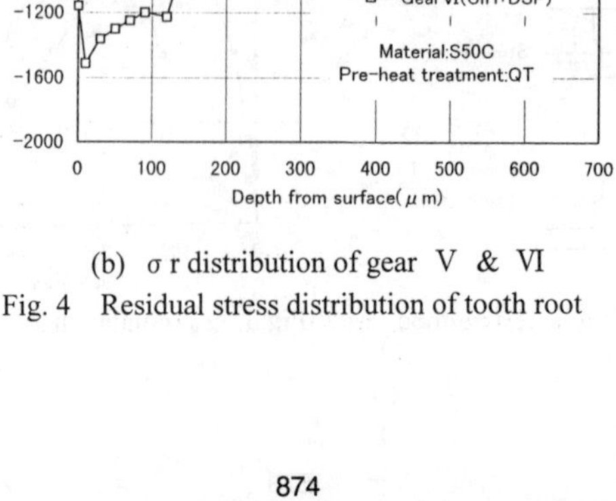

(b) σ r distribution of gear V & VI

Fig. 4 Residual stress distribution of tooth root

3.2. Residual Stress Distribution

Fig.4(a) shows the residual stress distributions of gears Ⅰ～Ⅳ. The symbol ◇ shows the residual stress distribution of gear I with the residual stress at surface(σ_0) about 300MPa and the maximum compressive residual stress(σ_{rmax}) about 400MPa, respectively. Both values are not so high. Symbol ■ shows the residual stress distribution of gear Ⅱ. The maximum compressive residual stress was introduced at the surface with the value 1838MPa. This σ_{rmax} is a surprisingly high value. Symbol △ shows the residual stress distribution of gearⅢ. The σ_0 and σ_{rmax} are 801MPa and 1054MPa, respectively. In gear Ⅳ, the maximum residual stress was also introduced at the surface with the value of 1862MPa. Even 300 μ m below the surface a very high compressive residual stress of 900MPa existed. Fig.4(a) shows that extensively high residual stress were introduced in gears Ⅱ and Ⅳ for the following reason: the retained austenite was transformed to martensite by double shot peening, resulting possibly in quite a large compressive residual stress.

Fig.4(b) shows the residual stress distributions in gears Ⅴ and Ⅵ. Gear Ⅴ(▲), σ_0 is only 662MPa and the σ_{rmax} is 810MPa. Gear Ⅵ(●), σ_0 and σ_{rmax} are 1159MPa and 1346MPa, respectively. These compressive residual stresses are very higher than those of the gear Ⅴ. The only possible cause for gear Ⅵ high values is double shot peening since no retained austenite was realized in gear Ⅴ[4]. On the other hand, the residual stresses in the gear Ⅵ is not enough high compared with that in the gear Ⅳ. The occurrence of transformation made a difference in these residual stress values. Fig.4(c) shows the residual stress distributions in two gears of type Ⅱ, before and after fatigue test. Before the fatigue test, the compressive residual stress at the surface σ_0 was 1838MPa. After the test, the stresses were reduced to 1540MPa and 1627MPa, respectively. However, the residual stresses 50 μ m or beyond below the surface before and after the test remained the same. Tange et al [3] measured the residual stress distribution of coil spring before and after the fatigue test(R=0.15 and N=10^6cycles). Their report says that maximum compressive residual stress before the test was about 1500MPa, and the compressive residual stress distribution after the test did not changed.

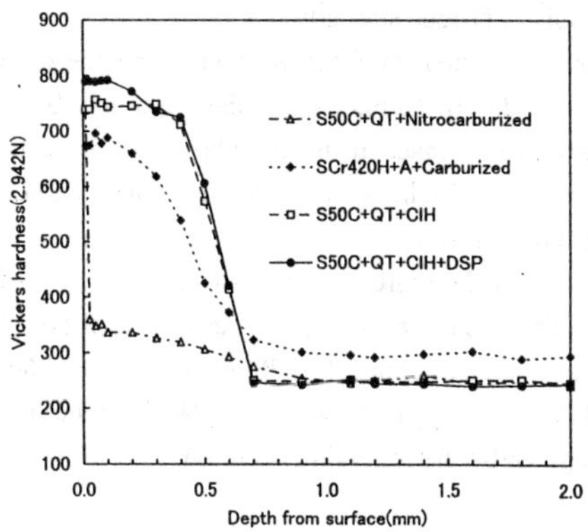

Fig. 5 Hardness distribution of tooth root in gear Ⅰ～Ⅳ

3.3. Hardness distribution

Fig. 5 shows the hardness distributions of gears Ⅰ~Ⅳ. The symbols ◇ and △ show the HV distributions of gears Ⅰ and Ⅲ, respectively. The highest HV of gears Ⅰ and Ⅲ are 735HV and 893HV, respectively. However, the highest HV of the gears Ⅱ and Ⅳ are 1040HV and 1067HV respectively, showing much higher HV than those of gears Ⅰ and Ⅲ. This result is attributed to the strain induced martensite transformation as previously mentioned. The hardness distributions of gears Ⅴ and Ⅵ was abbreviated because of space reason. The highest HV of gear Ⅴ is 757HV and that of gear Ⅵ is 792HV. The gear Ⅴ was not shot peened while gear Ⅵ was double shot peened. Despite of existence or non-existence of the peening treatment, there was only a little difference in HV. This resulted from the fact that there was no retained austenite in gear Ⅴ[4].

3.4. Fatigue Strength

Fig.6(a) shows S-N curves of gears Ⅰ, Ⅱ and Ⅳ. The symbols ◇, ■ and ● show the S-N curve of gears Ⅰ, Ⅱ and Ⅳ, respectively. The gear Ⅲ was not fatigue tested. The stress range at the fatigue limit σ_{up} of gear Ⅰ is 883MPa, while that of gear Ⅱ achieved an increase of about 118% up to 1931MPa, and a further increase of 150% to 2207MPa was realized with gear Ⅳ. These surprising increase in the fatigue limit are attributed to the following two reasons: (a) The carbon density at the surface of these gears is about 0.8%, and the retained austenite near the surface was reduced considerably by strain induced martensite transformation. (b) The hardness near the surface is over 1000HV. The high HV material contains high resistance to initiation and propagation of stage I fatigue crack.

Fig.6(b) shows S-N curves of gears Ⅴ(▲) and Ⅵ(●). The stress range of the fatigue limit σ_{up} of gear Ⅴ is 1256MPa, while that of gear Ⅵ is an increase of 38% to 1710MPa. Both gears showed similar HVs as shown in Fig.5. It can be said that the difference in the fatigue limit resulted from the different compressive residual stress distribution of both gears. The conclusion is that double shot peening played a key role in increasing the fatigue limit[2,3,4].

3.5.Regressionion analysis of fatigue strength

The fatigue tests were conducted on 8 kinds of gears by these authors[5]. All tests were made under the R≒0.1 condition. To understand the important factors to increase the fatigue limit, a regression analysis was made using the above 8 data with special attention to the following three parameters: (a) Yield stress converted from HV. (b) Maximum compressive residual stress σ_{rmax}. (c) Grain size d_γ.

The information required for the regression analysis(HV, σ_{rmax} and d_γ) of 5 gears out of 8 is included in this paper. The yield stress σ_Y was estimated from HV: σ_Y =3.27HV(MPa). Fig.7 shows correlation between σ_{up} and $\{0.478(\sigma_Y+\sigma_{rmax}) +1.363d_\gamma^{-1/2} -894\}$. From fig.7, it can be seen that $\{0.478(\sigma_Y+\sigma_{rmax}) +1.363d_\gamma^{-1/2} -894\}$ is an important parameter to increase fatigue limit and σ_{up} is given by the following equation.

$$\sigma_{up} = 0.478(\sigma_Y+\sigma_{rmax}) +1.363d_\gamma^{-1/2} -894 \qquad \text{---- (1)}$$

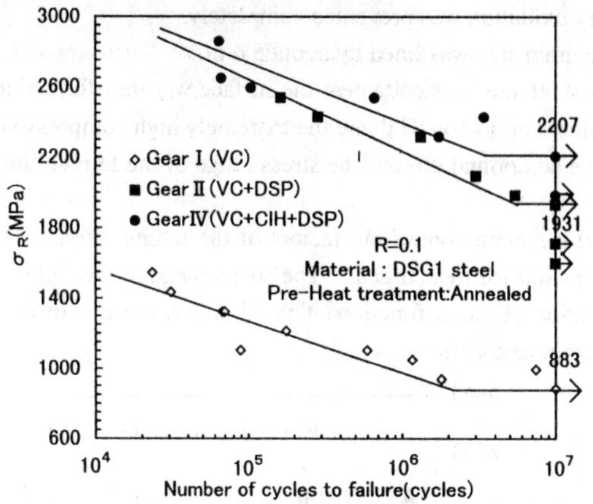

(a) S-N diagram of gear I , II & IV

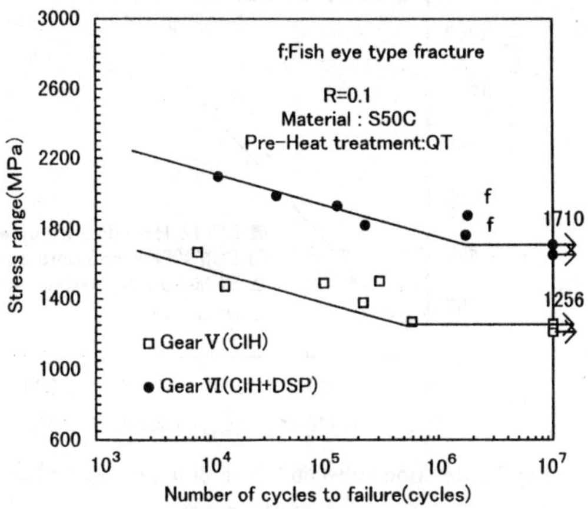

(b) S-N diagram of gear V & VI

Fig.6 S-N diagram of gears

4. CONCLUSION

To increase a fatigue limit of gears, the authors studied the effectiveness of the compound surface treatment systematically. The surface treatments adopted are Vacuum Carburizing(VC), Contour Induction Hardening(CIH) and Double Shot Peening(DSP).

1) With VC, the carbon density at the surface was increased up to 0.8%, and the generation

of grain boundary oxidation was prevented completely.

2) With CIH, the grain size was fined by about 5 μ m.

3) With DSP, most retained austenite near the surface was transformed to martensite, resulting in increased hardness up to 1067HV and the extremely high compressive residual stress.

4) With the above compound effects, the stress range of the fatigue limit was increased up to 2207MPa.

5) To understand the main controlling factors of the fatigue limit, a regression analysis was made on 8 data on surface treated gears. The stress range of the fatigue limit of gears σ_{up} is give by the equation (1) as a function of yield stress, the maximum compressive residual stress and an average grain size.

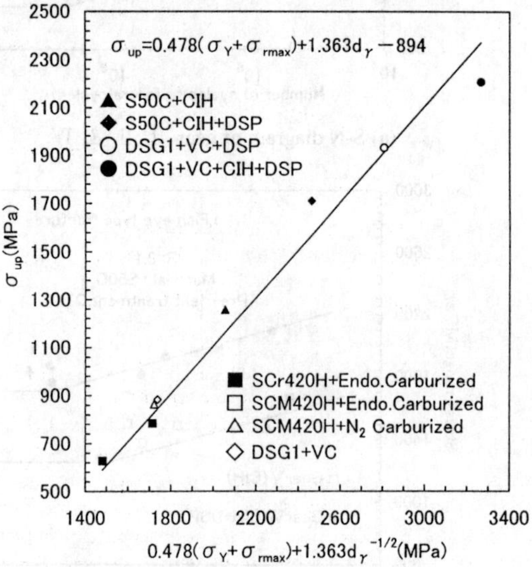

Fig.7 Relation between [0.478($\sigma_Y + \sigma_{rmax}$) +1.363$d_\gamma^{-1/2}$] and σ up of gears

REFERENCE

1).H.Ishigami, K.Matsui, A.Tange and K.Ando: Journal High Pressure Institute.(Acceped).

2).H.Ishigami, K.Matsui, Y.Jin and K.Ando: Fatigue Fact. Engng. Mat. Struct.(Accepted).

3).A.Tange and K.Ando: Proceedings of Sympojium(10th) on Fracture and Fracture Mechnics. 1999, P.6(Kyoto,Japan).

4).K.Matsui, H.Eto, K.Kawasaki, Y.Misaka and K.Ando: Transactions Japan Society Mechanical Engineers. 637-65(1999)P.1942.

5).K.Matsui, H.Eto, K.Yukitake, Y.Misaka and K.Ando: Transactions Japan Society Mechanical Engineers (Submitted).

EFFECT OF GRINDING STRATEGY ON ACCUMULATION OF DAMAGE IN RAILS: NEUTRON DIFFRACTION INVESTIGATION OF RESIDUAL STRESSES IN TRANSVERSE AND OBLIQUE CUT RAIL SLICES

Thomas Gnäupel-Herold
Department of Materials and Nuclear Engineering
University of Maryland, College Park, MD, U.S.A.
and
Center for Neutron Research
National Institute of Standards and Technology
Gaithersburg, MD 20899, U. S. A.

Henry J. Prask
Center for Neutron Research
National Institute of Standards and Technology
Gaithersburg, MD 20899, U. S. A.

J. Magiera
Cracow Inst. of Technology, Cracow, Poland.

ABSTRACT

In rail integrity and safety assessment wear is still the principal rail life limiting factor. Crack failure induced by long-term rolling contact fatigue is also of considerable importance. A main source of such service-induced damage is the concentration of very high contact stresses on the rail which leads to subsurface plastic deformation. The immediate damage effects are fatigue crack initiation and growth accompanied by the transport of material due to plastic flow into the high wear rate gage face. Therefore, considerable attention has been paid to profile control and grinding as a means of controlled decrease of contact stresses as well as relocation of the contact path on the rail. Three-dimensional fatigue modeling indicates that without grinding the depth at which the maximum damage occurs remains constant. On the other hand, the optimal grinding wear rate is able to shift, with increasing tonnage, the location of the zone with maximum damage to greater depths below the initial surface. In this work we examine how the grinding strategy and the service history affect the build-up of residual stress in five different rails. Measurements were made on transverse and oblique cut slices. The geometry of the samples was chosen both to limit neutron absorption and to provide data for the computational reconstruction of the original three-dimensional stress state prior to slicing. Examples for reconstructed stresses will be shown and the influence of grinding will be discussed.

INTRODUCTION

Over the past 20 years the development of high strength alloys and the use of lubrication has lead to a significant prolongation of rail wear life (1-3). Although wear remains the principal life-limiting factor the focus of attention with respect to rail safety and integrity has shifted to crack failure induced by long-term rolling contact fatigue. A main source of such service-induced damage is the concentration of very high contact stresses on the rail which leads to subsurface plastic deformation with accumulation of residual stresses of the order of the yield stress. The immediate damage effects are fatigue crack initiation and growth. Secondary damage effects are initiated by the feeding of material due to plastic flow into the high wear rate gage face as well as longitudinal corrugations which form a wavy structure on the running surface of the rail.

Considerable attention has been paid to profile control and grinding as means of controlled decrease of contact stresses as well as relocation of the contact path on the rail. Three-dimensional fatigue modeling indicates that without grinding the depth at which the maximum damage rate occurs remains constant. On the other hand, the optimal grinding wear rate is able to shift with increasing tonnage the location of the zone with maximum damage to greater depths below the initial surface. Experimentally determined residual strains and stresses are used as a quantitative measure for the accumulated damage (4-16).

Recently, a numerical method (17) has been developed to reconstruct the three-dimensional residual stress state in the rail prior to slicing. The approach is based on a hypothesis that there exists a critical stress state that is established by the highest load to which the rail is subjected. The critical state is not altered by subsequent loads of lower magnitude and similar path, and it is independent of the axial coordinate (4).

In order to apply the plane stress condition as the underlying condition for this method, the method requires sufficiently thin slices taken from the rail. The knowledge of the in-plane strain states in the transverse slice and in the oblique slice whose coordinate frames are rotated with respect to each other allows the calculation of the undisturbed three dimensional stress state. This way, both the axial component of residual stress which was completely lost from the transverse slice when it was removed from the rail sample, as well as Poisson effect losses from in-plane components (17) are obtained. This method is an enhancement of the so called Battelle-3D (5) technique, but requires only one transverse and one oblique cut slice, and can utilize other methods of strain determination such as neutron diffraction, and Moiré interferometry.

Neutron diffraction measures spatially-resolved strain distributions by probing the interatomic distances in crystalline materials (18-22), and has been used previously to determine residual stresses in rails (7, 13-15). The Transverse/Oblique Slice Thermal Moiré (TOSTM) method has also been used recently to attempt to determine stresses in rails (16). However, results with TOSTM in this case do not appear to give stress distributions which fulfill the required macroscopic equilibrium conditions and will, therefore, not be considered further in the present work.

In summary, the purpose of this investigation is to determine the effect of grinding strategies on the distribution and magnitude of service-induced residual stresses. Their importance relies on the fact that they are critical parameters in the estimation of the growth rate of fatigue defects. This information will, ultimately, be used to assess rail inspection frequencies to assure defect detection prior to catastrophic rail failure. The numerical reconstruction of the residual stresses is to be applied to the data obtained from five pairs of rail samples (one each of the transverse and oblique slices) which were taken from a controlled test at the Transportation Technology Center (TTC) in Pueblo, CO.

Specimens

The specimens consisted of five pairs of 6.35 mm thick transverse and oblique cut slices of railroad track which were subjected to 39-ton axle loads at the Transportation Technology

Center's High Tonnage Loop. The 300 HB hardness, steel rails of CFI 136 RE size were subjected to different combinations of grinding strategies and frequencies as summarized in Table 1.

Table 1: Service history and grinding strategy of the railroad slices.

#	Description	Transverse/Oblique
1	Control specimen, no grinding	both
2	FAST* worn profile, ground every 25 MGT**	both
3	Two point contact, ground every 12.5 MGT**	both
4	Two point contact, ground every 25 MGT**	both
5	New rail specimen, not installed in track	both

*FAST = Facility for Accelerated Service Testing

**MGT = Million Gross Tons

Measurement Technique

Neutron diffraction is a technique (18-22) whereby subsurface texture and lattice spacings are measured using Bragg's Law:

$$2\,d \sin\theta = n\,\lambda\,. \tag{1}$$

The lattice spacing d is measured by either varying the wavelength, λ, keeping the diffraction angle, θ, fixed or by varying θ and keeping λ fixed. For the present experiments neutron radiation from a steady state reactor is used. A white neutron beam is diffracted by a [022] oriented copper single crystal (d = 1.2780 Å), at a monochromator diffraction angle which yields neutron wavelengths of 1.68, 0.84 and 0.56 Å (for n = 1,2 and 3 respectively of eqn. 1). Neutrons with a wavelength of 1.68 Å will be diffracted from the Fe(211) (d = 1.17 Å) lattice planes in the steel at a scattering angle of $\approx 90°$. This choice of monochromator angle and sample reflection (hkl) is chosen to obtain the best combination of diffracted intensity, instrument and spatial resolution. The incident beam is collimated by a series of neutron absorbers with apertures to a final size of 3 × 3 mm^2 and led over the center of the sample table of the diffractometer. A schematic of this arrangement is shown in fig. 1. The sample is mounted in a device that allows the sample to be put in different orientations. Close to the rail slice, a vertical aperture (width 3 mm) is mounted. The

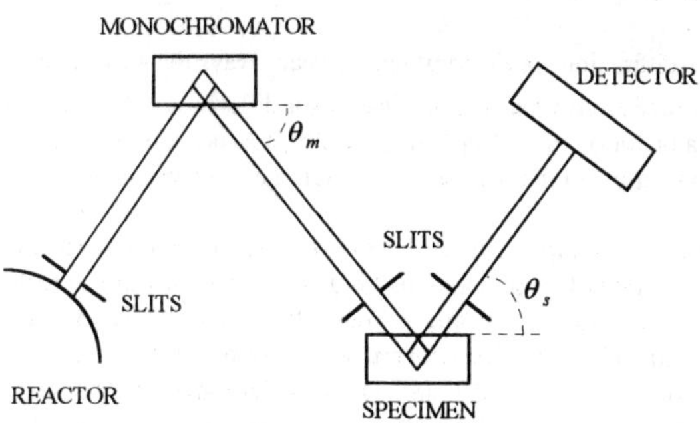

Figure 1. Schematic of the measurement

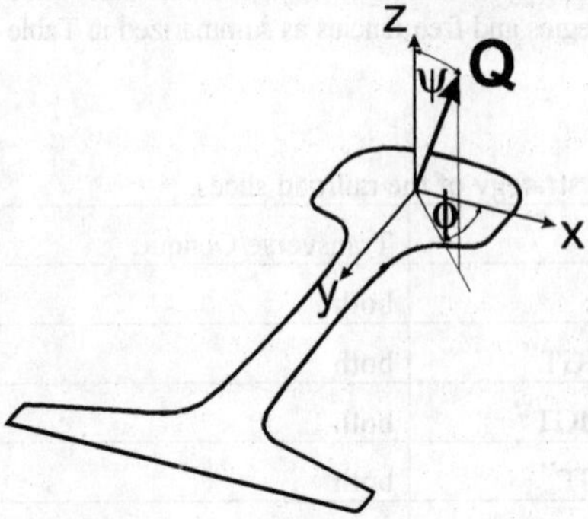

Figure 2: Orientation of the scattering vector Q in the sample coordinate system. The angle ψ is the angle between the z-axis and Q. The angle φ is the angle between the orthogonal projection of Q onto the xy-plane and the x-axis.

combination of incident beam aperture and diffracted beam slit selects a cubic sampling volume of 3 mm × 3 mm × 3 mm. Due to divergence (both horizontally and vertically) in the diffraction geometry the true sampling volume is about equal to 3.4 mm × 3.4 mm × 3.4 mm. The diffraction pattern collected by the position sensitive detector is fitted with a Gaussian/Lorentzian profile. The fitted peak position is then translated into a diffraction angle and subsequently into a *d*-spacing using a set of calibration constants that have been determined in a separate calibration procedure (15).

For a given orientation of the specimen the lattice spacing is measured in a particular direction within the specimen. This direction is expressed by the scattering vector Q, which has the direction of the bisector of the incident and diffracted beams. The angle ψ is defined as the angle between Q and the *z* axis. The angle φ is defined as the angle between the orthogonal projection of Q onto the *x*,*y* plane and the *x* axis (see figure 2).

By measuring the lattice spacing for various orientations in the specimen strain ($\varepsilon = \Delta d/d = (d - d_0)/d_0$) as a function of Q is obtained. In order to determine strains from the *d*-spacings, one needs to know the value of the stress free lattice parameter d_0, which can be obtained from a part of the specimen that is stress free, or from a small coupon of the material that has been extracted from a non-contact area of the specimen. From the measured strains one can calculate the stress field using (20):

$$\varepsilon_{\varphi\psi} = \tfrac{1}{2}s_2(hkl)\begin{bmatrix}(\sigma_{11}\cos^2\varphi + \sigma_{22}\sin^2\varphi + \sigma_{12}\sin 2\varphi)\sin^2\psi + \\ (\sigma_{13}\cos\varphi + \sigma_{23}\sin\varphi)\sin 2\psi + \sigma_{33}\cos^2\psi\end{bmatrix} + s_1(hkl)(\sigma_{11} + \sigma_{22} + \sigma_{33}) \qquad (2)$$

where $s_1(hkl)$ and $\tfrac{1}{2}s_2(hkl)$ are the diffraction elastic constants. In many ways this measurement technique is analogous to X-ray diffraction stress analyses. One major difference is the fact that neutron radiation penetrates about a factor of 1000 deeper into steel than X-rays do. This makes it possible to do stress measurements at positions well below the surface of specimens.

From equation (2) it is clear that all six components of the stress tensor can be obtained by measuring d-spacings in six or more independent orientations of Q. In the present case, samples 1,2, 4, and 5 were measured with Q along *x*, *y* and *z* only. This gives - without any approximations or assumptions (see eqn. (2)) - the three normal stress components: σ_{xx}, σ_{yy}, and σ_{zz}. Specimen 3 was also measured for ψ=90° and φ=30° and 60°. This yields the shear stress σ_{xy}. In order to obtain an areal map of the stresses in the head region, the slices were "covered" by a mesh of measurement locations as indicated in figure 3. For all specimens a complete set of measurements was made with 5 mm between gauge volume centers (transverse slice): 17 points in the x-direction, 9 points in the y-direction. For the oblique slices the y-direction spacing was

$\sqrt{2} \times 5$ mm. To assure that no short-range stress variations were being missed in the 5 mm × 5 mm mesh, specimen 3 was measured again with a 3 mm × 3 mm mesh, 28 x-direction and 13 y-direction points. All gauge volume centers were at 3.17 mm below the surfaces.

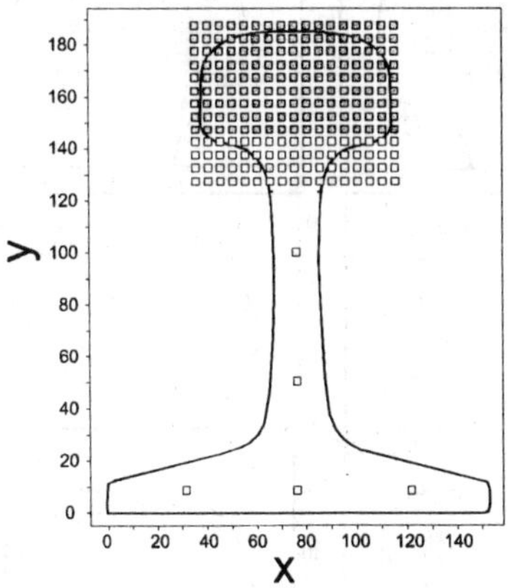

Figure 3: Outline of the unworn transverse slice. The dark gray squares represent the points that were measured on all slices, whereas the light grey points were additionally measured on both the transverse and oblique slice 3. See text for other details.

The relationship between the rail outline and the measurement mesh is established by measuring the position of the unworn slice with respect to the xyz-table. Once this position was determined, reference blocks were fixed on the table. Thus, together with a reference bolt on the sample holder device, a three dimensional fixture was established that allowed the accurate (±0.1 mm) and reproducible alignment of every transverse slice. This procedure was then repeated for the oblique slice. It is clear that this procedure relies on the congruence of the outlines of the worn slices with the unworn slice in their base and web regions. Differences in the head region are not relevant in this context. The accuracy of the positions of the sampling volumes in the worn slices is therefore limited by the shape tolerance of the manufacturing process as well as surface roughness due to corrosion.

The stress free lattice parameter d_0 was obtained from a small coupon ($6 \times 6 \times 12$ mm^3) that was cut off from the extremity of the base region of the unworn slice. The d-spacing obtained from the coupon was used as d_0 value for all slices. Agreement was also achieved with the values for σ_{zz} which were close to zero using this value for d_0. The diffraction elastic constants that were used in this evaluation were: $S_1(110) = -1.3 \times 10^{-6}$ MPa^{-1} and $S_2(110)/2 = 5.83 \times 10^{-6}$ MPa^{-1}. They were calculated from average single crystal elastic constants using a method described in (23). For each measurement point the d-spacings with their respective orientations were entered in equation 2. Equation (2) was then solved in least squares sense for σ_{xx}, σ_{yy}, σ_{zz}, and additionally σ_{xy} for the slices 3.

RESULTS AND CONCLUSIONS

At this point we will summarize the measurement results. Full details are given in ref. (15). The comparison with modeling efforts will be done at a later date when results are available.

From the present measurements we can say the following:

1. As shown in fig. 4 and in previous work (7,13-15), σ_{xx} and σ_{yy} of worn rails show compressive stresses at the top surface of the rail head. These are balanced by tensile stresses in the bulk. This is in agreement with the notion that the top surface has been plastically deformed under the pressure load of the train wheel, not unlike what happens in a process like shot peening.

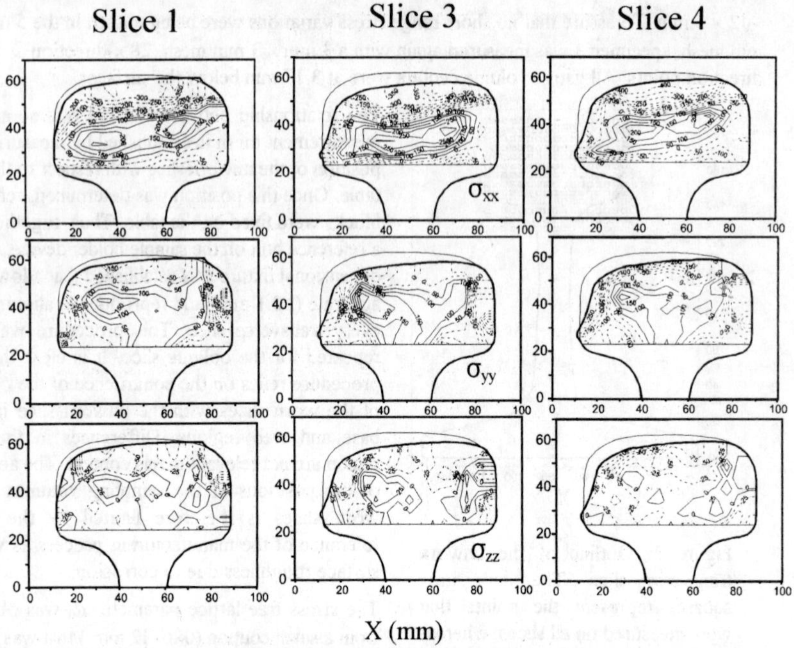

Figure 4. Residual stress contours determined for transverse slices from rails 1,3 and 4. Rails 3 and 4 differ only in the frequency of grinding. The dashed contours correspond to compressive stresses.

2. Comparing the results from specimen #3 with mesh sizes 3×3 mm and 5×5 mm shows that all results can be easily reproduced and that a mesh size of 5×5 mm is sufficient. It can also be concluded that a gauge volume of $3\times3\times3$ mm^3 provides sufficiently high spatial resolution.

3. The comparison between specimen #1 (no grinding) and #3-4 (grinding with different strategies) shows that grinding does shift the zone of maximum residual stresses to greater depths below the initial surface. This supports the idea that a beneficial effect on rail life arises from the relocation of the zone with the most accumulated damage (tensile stresses) to greater depths. This is accompanied by reestablishing the stress balance due to an increasing overlap of zones with stresses of opposite signs.

4. The effect of the grinding interval is an increase of the magnitude of the residual stresses if a more frequent grinding is chosen (Figure 5). Both the compressive and tensile stresses for the x- and y-direction in specimen #3 (ground every 12.5 MGT) are higher than in specimen #4 (ground every 25 MGT).

5. These results suggest that grinding can have a beneficial effect on rail fatigue life. However, the comparison between specimen #1 (no grinding) and specimens #3 and #4

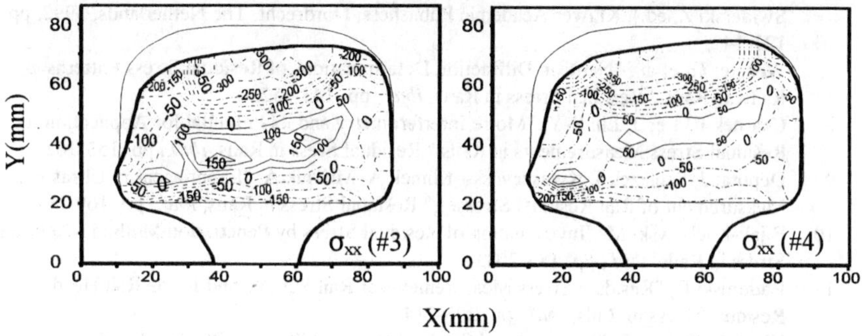

Figure 5. Residual stresses in the x direction for oblique slices of rails 3 and 4.

(ground every 12.5 MGT and 25 MGT, respectively) shows that there exists a best grinding frequency for increasing rail life. This optimal grinding frequency represents the compromise between the shortening of rail life by wear (grinding) and by too frequent grinding on one side, and the effect of prolongation of rail life by limiting fatigue damage on the other side.

ACKNOWLEDGEMENTS

We thank the Office of Research and Development, Federal Railroad Administration (FRA), John A. Volpe National Transportation Systems Center for their support of this work under Project Plan Agreement (PPA) RR-19. We also thank J.E. Gordon for helpful discussions.

REFERENCES

1. Orringer O, "Control of Rail Integrity by Self-Adaptive Scheduling of Rail Tests," DOT Transportation Systems Center, Cambridge, MA, DOT/FRA/ORD-90/05, June 1990.
2. Orringer O, Tang Y, Gordon J, Jeong D, Morris J, Perlman A, "Crack Propagation Life of Detail Fractures in Rails," DOT Transportation Systems Center, Cambridge, MA, DOT/FRA/ORD-88/13, October 1988.
3. Orringer O, "Some Suggestions for Adjusting Rail Rest Schedules to Reflect Track Characteristics, Maintenance, Traffic, and Weather," Proc. Int'l Symp. on Rail Steels - Developments, Performance and Manufacturing, (Bramfitt B, Steele R, Martens J, ed.), AIME Iron and Steel Society, 149-159 (1993).
4. Orkisz J, Holowinski M, "Prediction of Residual Stress in Rails: Practical Benefits from Theoretical Approach," Rail Quality and Maintenance for Modern Railway Operation, (Kalker J, Cannon D, Orringer O, ed.), Kluwer Academic Publishers, Dordrecht, The Netherlands, 1993, pp. 273-296.
5. Groom J, "Determination of Residual Stresses in Rails," Battelle Columbus Laboratories, Columbus, OH, DOT/FRA/ORD-83/05, May 1993.
6. Cundiff C, Rice R, "Comparative Evaluation of Several Alternative Methods for Measuring Rail Residual Stress," Residual Stress in Rails: Effects on Rail Integrity and Railroad Economics - Vol. I: Field Experience and Test Results, (Orringer O, Orkisz J,

Swiderski Z, ed.), Kluwer Academic Publishers, Dordrecht, The Netherlands, 1992, pp. 121-142.
7. Webster G, et al., "Neutron Diffraction Determinations of Residual Stress Patterns in Railway Rails," Residual Stress in Rails, *ibid.*, pp. 143-152.
8. Czarnek R, Lee J, Lin S-Y, "Moire Interferometry and its Potential for Application to Residual Stress Measurements in Rails," Residual Sress in Rails, *ibid.*, pp. 153-167.
9. Deputat J, Szelazek J, Kwaszcynska-Klimek A, Miernik A, "Experiences in Ultrasonic Measurement of Rail Residual Stresses," Residual Stress in Rails, *ibid.*, pp. 169-183.
10. Bijak-Zochowski M, "Investigation of Residual Stress by Penetration Method," Residual Stress in Rails, *ibid.*, pp. 185-203.
11. Radomski R, "Residual Stress Measurements at Rail Surface and Inside Rail Head," Residual Stress in Rails, *ibid.*, pp. 205-214.
12. Wang Y, Chiang F, "Experimental Study of Residual Stress in Rail by Moire' Interferometry," Final Report to U.S. DOT, VNTSC, DOT/FRA/ORD-94/02; FRA-93-24 (1993).
13. Webster P, Mills G, Wang X, Kang W, "Residual Stress Measurements in Rails by Neutron Diffraction", in: J.J. Kalker, D.F. Cannon, O. Orringer (eds.), "Rail Quality and Maintenance for Modern Railway Operation", 307-314, Kluwer Academic Publishers, Dordrecht, The Netherlands, 1993.
14. Brand P, Prask H, Hicho G, "Residual Stress in Steel Railroad Track Measured by means of Neutron Diffraction", Report NISTIR 5912, U.S. Department of Commerce, Technology Administration 1996.
15. Gnäupel-Herold T, Brand P, Prask H, "Neutron Diffraction Investigation of Residual Stresses in Transverse/Oblique Rail Slices Subjected to Different Grinding Strategies," Report NISTIR 6305, U.S. Department of Commerce, Technology Administration 1999.
16. Wang B, Chiang F, Wu S, Experimental Mechanics 39 (1999) 71.
17. Magiera J, Orkisz J, Karmowski W, "Reconstruction of Residual Stresses in Railroad Rails from Measurements Made on Vertical and Oblique Slices," Proc. 4th Int'l. Conf. on Contact Mechanics and Wear of Rail/Wheel Systems, Vancouver, BC, 1994.
18. Choi C, Prask H, Trevino S, J. Appl. Crys 12 (1979) 327.
19. Allen A, Andreani C, Hutchings M, Windsor C, NDT International 14, (1981) 249.
20. Hutchings M, Krawitz A (editors), "Measurement of Residual and Applied Stress Using Neutron Diffraction"; NATO ASI Series (Vol 216E), Kluwer Academic Publishers (Dordrecht/Boston/London), 1992.
21. Allen A, Hutchings M, Windsor C, Andreani C, Adv. Physics 34 (1985) 445.
22. Brand P, Prask H, J. Applied Cryst. 27 (1994) 164.
23. Bollenrath F, Hauk V, Müller E, Z. Metallk. 58 (1967) 76.

SESSION 7A

INVESTIGATION OF THE MICROSTRUCTURE AND THE RESIDUAL STRESS STATE OF A WORN RAILWAY RAIL

E.Wild*, L.Wang*, T. Wroblewski**, A.Pyzalla*
* Hahn-Meitner-Institut Berlin, Glienicker Straße 100, D-14109 Berlin, Germany
** HASYLAB@DESY, Notkestrasse 85, D-22607 Hamburg, Germany

ABSTRACT

On the surface of railway rails microstructural changes develop due to severe loading. These microstructural changes comprise an increase of the dislocation density and a decrease of the domain size, the evolution of peculiar textures as well as martensitic phase transformation in the so-called white etching layer. Here the microstructural changes on the surface of a rail were investigated using X-rays and synchrotron radiation.

1. INTRODUCTION

The increase of axle loads in freight traffic as well as the increase in speed of passenger trains within recent years have lead to an increase of wear of the rails, that appears e.g. in an increase of frequency of structure modifications and defects in the rails' surface layer. Among the structure modifications are riffle bands and the so-called white-etching-layers. These areas have been the subject of a number of investigations since not only the formation of these layers is liable to cause failure of the rail surface but also since from the results of the investigations a better understanding of the microstructural processes of friction and wear is sought for.

The white etching layers have been named according to their resistance towards metallographic etching. They have been shown to reach hardness values up to 1200 HV [1,2]. The composition and crystallographic structure of the white etching layers as well as the process of their formation still is a subject of controversy [3,4,5]. This partially is due to the fact that white etching layers have been reported to appear with a ferritic microstructure in components subjected to high mechanical loading where the occurrence of temperatures enabling austenitisation are unlikely. But, white etching layers also were found with a martensitic structure formed due to a combination of strong plastic deformation and peak temperatures allowing for re-austenitisation and martensitic transformation due to cooling and plastic deformation.

Residual stresses arising in railway rails due to the manufacturing process and due to loading have been the subject of a number of studies and rails even were used as a round robin [e.g. 6-9]. The emphasis of this study is the investigation of the connection between the loading, the microstructural changes with respect to dislocation density as well as texture development and the residual stress distribution. Further new aspects are the determination of the crystallographic structure with a very high local resolution which is now possible due to novel synchrotron radiation techniques.

The rail studied was used by the Deutsche Bahn AG and provided with a record with respect to its loading history.

2. EXPERIMENTAL DETAILS

2.1 LOADING OF THE SAMPLE

The loading of the sample of a rail provided by the Deutsche Bahn AG is characterised in table 1.

Table 1: Loading parameters

Traffic:	36500 tons per day
Arc radius:	6002,35 m
Gauge:	1434 mm
Superelevation:	75 mm
Speed maximum:	280 km/h (Intercity Express ICE train)
Insertion of the rail:	1988
Dismounting of the rail:	August 1997
Stage:	downhill
Turn:	left-turn
Position:	outer rail

2.2 INVESTIGATIONS BY X-RAY DIFFRACTION

Residual stress and texture analyses have been performed by conventional X-ray techniques at the HMI Berlin. The profile analyses were performed using Co-Kα radiation on the (211) reflection. The data were evaluated using the model [10] and the software developed by Prof. Dr. P. Klimanek, TU Freiberg. For residual stress analyses a diffractometer in ψ-configuration was used. The residual stress analyses were performed by the $\sin^2\psi$-method [11].

2.3 INVESTIGATIONS USING SYNCHROTRON RADIATION

In order to investigate the microstructure in those regions showing microstructural alterations [13] a novel technique, developed at HASYLAB, DESY was used. This technique allows the registration of spectra with a very high local resolution by selecting the probed region not from the primary side using a μ-beam but at the secondary side of the sample. Here a large sample area is illuminated and an array of parallel tube like collimators, a so called micro-channel plate (MCP), in front of a position sensitive detector (PSD) suppresses crossfire of radiation scattered from different regions of the specimen. Only radiation parallel to the channel axes reaches the detector yielding an entire image in a single shot. The channels also define the scattering angle 2θ like a Soller collimator does in conventional diffraction experiments. If the arrangement of MCP and PSD is mounted on the 2θ-arm of a diffractometer scans can be performed by variation of the angles of the diffractometer or other parameters. These scans yield an entire image for each value of the scanning variable, while conventional experiments only measure one intensity for each value of a variable yielding one dimensional data set.

Using the imaging method a data set consists of images with more than 1 million pixels. A series of such images yields one spectrum per pixel. Even if the amount of data is reduced by integrating over several pixels or by restricting the analysis to a smaller region of interest (ROI) the number of spectra is still too large to be processed interactively one at a time. Furthermore, there exist strong correlations between spatial and spectral adjacent data making joint processing highly desirable. Therefore, the data was analysed using techniques known from remote sensing, details are given in [12]. The aim of such an analysis is both the determination of the spatial distribution of different microconstituents in the sample as well as the extraction of their spectral properties.

The measurements were performed on the instrument G3 of the HASYLAB@DESY, Hamburg, Germany [12]. In order to avoid fluorescence and while adjusting the penetration depth of the radiation to the depth extension of the white etching layer, an energy of 6.5 keV was chosen. The reflection studied was (110). The step width in 2θ was 0.002°, the 2θ range extended from 56.0° to 56.2° and the time for recording each image was 4 min.

3. RESULTS AND DISCUSSION

3.1 STRUCTURE OF THE WHITE ETCHING LAYER

Fig. 1: White etching layer, optical micrograph
(courtesy of Dr. D. Spaltmann, Prof. Dr. E. Santner, BAM Berlin, Germany)

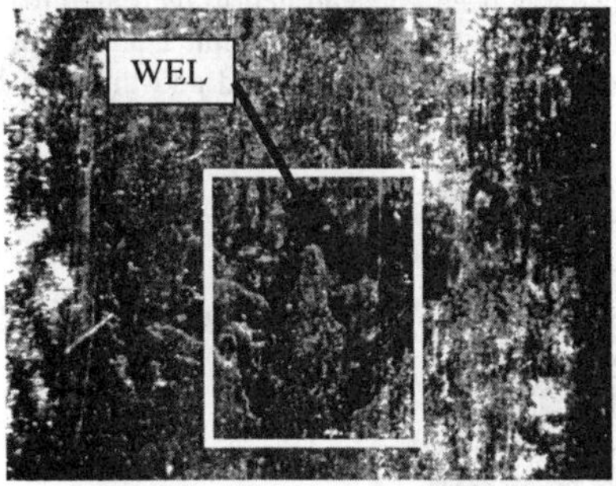

Fig. 2: White etching layer

An optical micrograph of the transverse section of the rail is shown in fig.1. On the top of the rail the white etching layer with its characteristic homogeneous structure is visible. The extension of the white etching layers was observed to be between 2μm and at maximum 10μm. Beneath the white etching layer the microstructure of the steel, which consists of ferrite and pearlite is visible.

The lateral structure of the white etching layer is quite irregular (fig. 2).

Fig. 3 is an eigenimage obtained by

Fig. 3: X-ray diffraction image of a white layer, size of sample area studied: 10mm x 10 mm

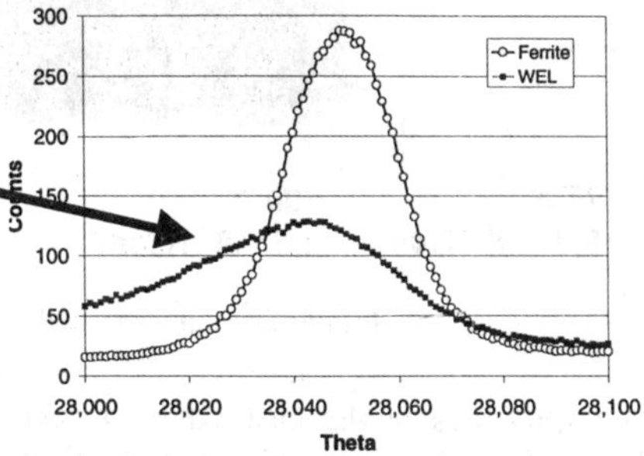

Fig. 4: Reflection profiles corresponding to the dark region and the gray region in fig. 2

applying a spectral transformation (maximum noise fraction transformation) [15] to a series of 101 exposures obtained in an ω - 2 θ - scan around the iron (110) reflection from the rail. It clearly displays the distribution of the white phase in excellent agreement with that found by visual inspection. The distortion of the picture is due to the projection onto the detector having an angle of θ to the sample surface. After the spatial distribution of the white phase had been determined spectral (structural) properties could be extracted. This has been done using a threshold algorithm. Fig. 4 shows spectra obtained by averaging over pixels with gray and black colours respectively in given intervals in fig. 3.
The symmetric profile with the open circles in fig. 4 results from the grey pixels in fig. 3 while the asymmetric flat line with the squares corresponds to the black pixels in the white etching layer (WEL). Each point of the curves is given by the intensity in the original exposure taken at the corresponding angle averaged over those pixels that exhibit a black or grey colour in fig. 3. The curves are representative for the white phase witch appears dark in fig. 3 and the ferrite grey in fig. 3, respectively. In good agreement to X-ray profile analysis the curve obtained for the white etching layer reveals a severe non-symmetric broadening of the reflection. This indicates that the structure of this white etching layer is martensite. The broadening further on hints to a very small crystallite size.

3.2 DISLOCATION DENSITY

A photo of the rails is shown in fig. 5. The white frame indicates the position of the white etching layer discussed before. Obviously the load has been concentrated in the pale area at points 1 and 2 and the white etching layers and the riffle band between point 2 and point 3. The dark area near point 4 on the right side in fig. 5 is strongly corroded and thus can be suspected to be nearly uninfluenced by the loading.

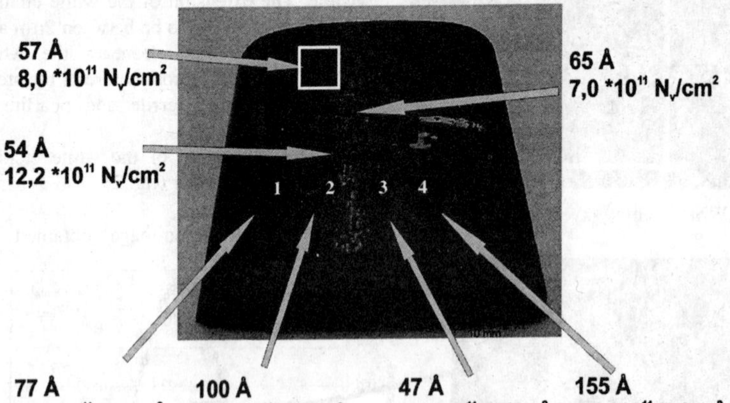

Fig. 5: Domain sizes and dislocation densities

The differences in the load exhibited over the rail also are revealed by the results of diffraction profile analyses, which show structural changes in those areas of the sample subjected to the maximum load. Whereas the dislocation density is only in the order of $4*10^{11}$ N_v/cm^2 in the dark corroded areas it is about three times larger in the riffle bands. In contrast the domain size decreases from 155Å in the dark corroded area to approximately 60 Å in the bright areas and the riffle bands. Thus, with increasing loading the dislocation density due to the strong plastic deformation increases significantly while the domain size decreases considerably.

3.3 TEXTURE

Pole figure analyses on material situated in 10mm distance from the rail surface and pole figure analyses in the dark corroded unloaded area of the rail show that in the initial state the texture of the rail is nearly isotropic. The orientation distribution function obtained on the surface (fig. 6) at point 4 (right side, lower level) hints to a weak <110> - fibre texture in these areas. In position 1 and position 3 a <110> fibre texture with an intermediate stage with a (221) orientation is visible.

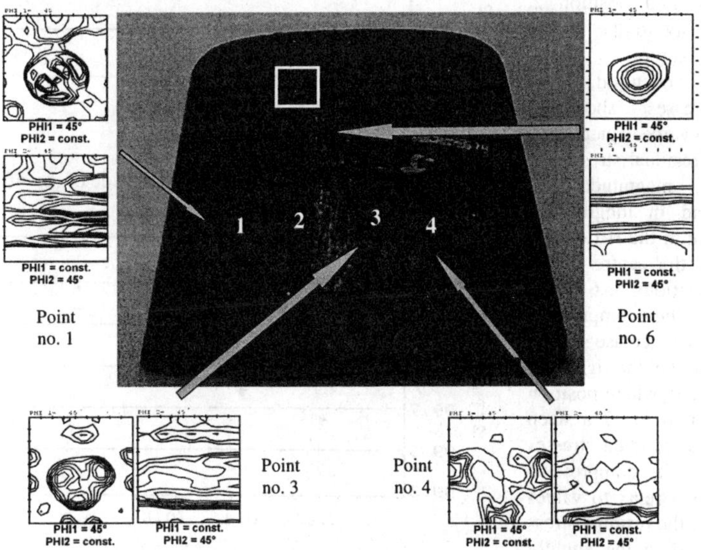

Fig. 6: Texture evolution at positions subject to different loading conditions

The bright area at point 1 (left side, upper level) shows an evolving <111> - fibre texture. By subsequent etching and texture analyses the texture distribution in depth was studied in the riffle band. Obviously with increasing depth the orientation changes from the <111> - fibre texture at the surface to the <110> component determined at position 4. In the riffle bands (left side, lower level and especially at point 6) a sharp and a lot stronger <111> - fibre texture is present. This <111> - fibre texture typically evolves after strong compression of bcc materials and thus is a sensor for the loading in this area.

3.4 RESIDUAL STRESSES

Due to the plastic deformation residual stresses also evolve. They were determined across the rail along two lines crossing the rail in transverse direction as indicated in fig. 7. The residual stresses are compressive in the longitudinal as well as in the transverse direction of the rail. In the areas on the left side of the rail where x = 0 is the residual stresses are low tensile residual stresses (area indicated at the top of fig. 7) or low compressive residual stresses (area indicated at the bottom of fig. 7). In the region between the mark x = 0 and position 2, where according to the profile analyses some plastic deformation occurred, the residual stresses show a tendency towards increasing compressive residual stresses of the same magnitude in transverse and in longitudinal direction. Within the riffle band (pale area in the centre of the rail where positions 5, 6 and 7 are located) the compressive residual stresses increase steeply to a maximum. On the right side of the riffle band where position 3 is indicated in fig. 7 a steep gradient of the residual stresses is visible and the compressive residual stresses relax to values comparable to the residual stress values obtained in the slightly loaded area on the left side of the rail.

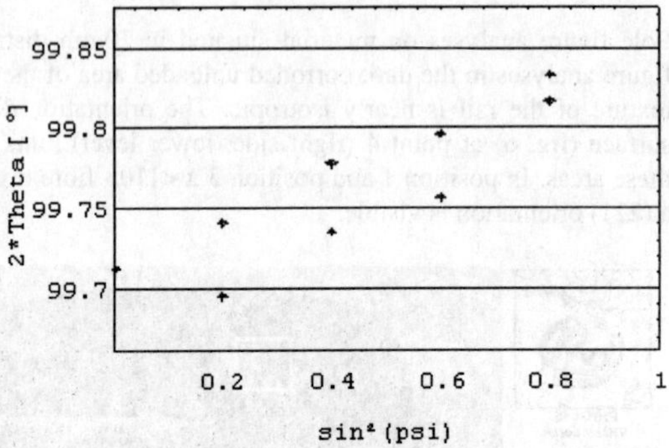

Fig. 8: Typical d-$\sin^2\psi$-curve on the right side of the riffle band

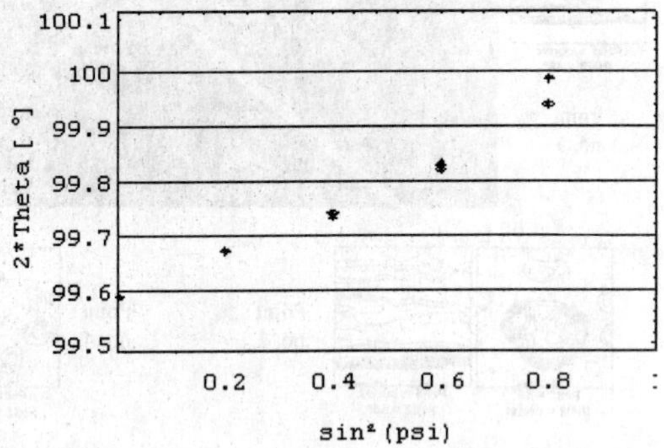

Fig. 9: Typical d-$\sin^2\psi$-curve within in the riffle band

The error bars indicated in fig.7 are due to a splitting of the positive and the negative branches of the d-$\sin^2\psi$-curve caused by shear stresses. These shear stresses are present in both directions. They are especially strong in the area left and right of the riffle band (fig. 8). In those positions where the maximum values of the compressive residual stresses are encountered shear stresses are not present (fig. 9). On the right side of the rail again small shear stress components were detected.

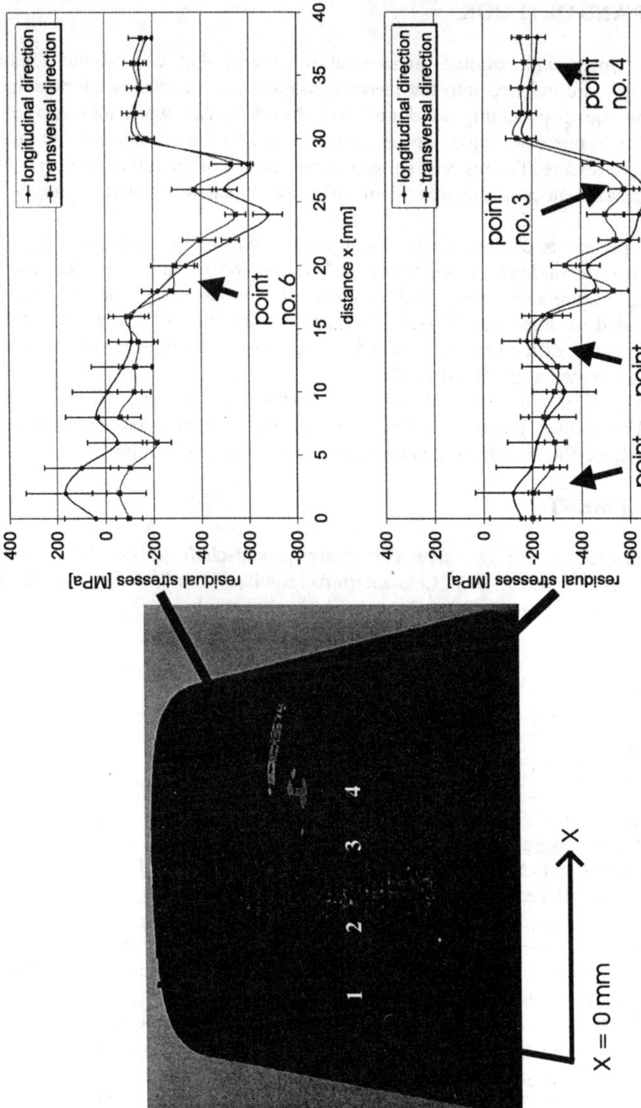

Fig. 7: Residual stress distribution across the rail cross section

4. CONCLUSIONS AND OUTLOOK

X-ray profile, pole figure and residual stress analyses reveal that due to the loading microstructural changes are induced into the piece of rail studied. In those areas that have been subjected to the strongest loading the domain size has decreased while the dislocation density increased. The texture evolving in the areas containing riffles and white etching layers is a sharp <111> - fibre texture. The residual stresses at the surface of the rail are compressive and they reach maximum values in the area where riffle bands and white etching layers are formed.

In addition to the experiments done so far the shear stresses will be quantified further. The residual stress and texture in-depth development will be studied by layer removal due to electrolytic polishing. Future experiments will also include further X-ray imaging studies. These will be expanded to other rails in order to study the structure of the white etching layers. The results of the diffraction studies will be compared to transmission electron microscopy studies performed at the BAM Berlin.

Furthermore, in order to account not only for the structure but also the process of the formation of the white etching layers model experiments are planned in co-operation with groups from the BAM, Berlin, in order to simulate the microstructural evolution.

5. ACKNOWLEDGEMENTS

The authors are indebted to the Deutsche Forschungsgemeinschaft (DFG) for financial support in the framework of the Sfb 605 „Elementarreibereignisse“ and Prof. Dr. Knothe and Mr. Bucher, TU Berlin, as well as the DB AG for supplying the sample.

6. REFERENCES

(1) T.S. Eyre and A. Baxter, Tribology International, 5 (1972) 256
(2) H.G. Feller and K. Walf, Wear, 144 (1991) 153
(3) B.J. Griffith, Journal of Tribology, 109 (1987) 525
(4) V.A. Kislik, Friction and Wear in Machinery, 15 (1962) 153
(5) H. Schlicht, HTM, 28 (1973) Nr.2, 112
(6) D.M.Turley, Materials Science and Engineering 19 (1975) 79
(7) P.J.Webster, X.Wang, G.Mills, G.A. Webster, Physica B 180 & 181 (1992)
(8) C.G.Schilling, G.T.Blake, Exp. Techn. 8 (1994), 25
(9) V.Hauk, H.Kockelmann, HTM 49 (1994) 340
(10) E. Macherauch, P. Müller: Z. angew. Physik 13 (1961), 55
(11) P. Klimanek: ´Röntgendiffraktometrische Subgefügeanalyse an realen Vielkristallen´, Habilitationsschrift, Freiberg (1990)
(12) T. Wroblewski, E. Wild, T. Poeste, A. Pyzalla:„Processing of X-ray diffraction imaging data using remote sensing techniques“, J. Mat. Sci. Letters, in print
(13) T. Wroblewski et al., Nucl. Instrum. Meth. A428 (1999) 570-582
(14) T. Wroblewski, S. Geier, R. Hessmer, M. Schreck and B. Rauschenbach: ´X-ray imaging of polycrystaliline materials´, Rev. Sci. Instrum. 66 (6), June 1995
(15) A. A. Green, M. Berman, P. Switzer, M. D. Craig: IEEE Transactions on Geoscience and Remote Sensing, 26 (1988) 65

STUDY ON SHOT PEENING PROCESSES OF COIL SPRING

AKIRA TANGE
NHK SPRING Co.,Ltd. Suspension Spring Divison
3-10 Fukuura, Kanazawa-Ku, Yokohama, 236-0004 Japan
KOTOJI ANDO
YOKOHAMA NATIONAL UNIVERSITY,
Department of Energy Engineering
79-5 Tokiwadai, Hodogaya-Ku, Yokohama, 240-8501 Japan

ABSTRACT

Automotive Coil Spring is always required to increase fatigue strength for the weight-saving. There are mainly two methods to increase fatigue strength. (a)to increase Vickers hardness, (b) to increase compressive residual stress. For the method(a), since the present Vickers hardness, HV is very high around 600HV, it is difficult to increase the hardness further. On the other hand, if the HV is increased further, the spring will become too sensitive for corrosion fatigue and hydrogen embrittlement. For the method (b), shot peening is a very popular technique to apply compressive residual stress. Based on the above background, we studied the following subjects.

(1) Stress intensity factor of surface cracks by compressive residual stress were calculated. By using the calculated results, it was considered what is the most suitable compressive stress to increase the fatigue life of coil spring.
(2) To apply the most suitable residual stress in coil spring, following four shot-peening techniques were studied, systematically, (2.1)Double shot-peening, (2.2)Stress shot-peening, (2.3)Warm shot peening, and (2.4)Combined shot-peening above.
(3) Fatigue tests were carried out on coil springs which were processed under the above shot-peening techniques. It was found, that (a) the compressive residual stress has a significant effect on fatigue strength and optimum stress distribution can be predicted, (b) proposed combined shot-peening has an excellent effect on increasing the fatigue strength of coil spring.

INTRODUCTION

The requirements for improving the fatigue life of Automotive Suspension Coil Spring have been increasing for designing the spring lighter due to the vehicle's mass saving. Since the fatigue life can be higher as the hardness is higher, the recently designed springs have over 600HV hardness. As the high strength material has higher notch-sensitivity, it was noted that more effective shot peening process could be required eliminating the surface defect[1]. However, the conventional shot peening is not enough to increase the fatigue life of a high strength spring, because the hardness of a spring is sometimes higher than that of shot.

Therefore, several studies on shot peening to high strength materials were reported[(2),(3)]. The Double Shot Peening , say DSP, is now the most popular process to improve the fatigue life of springs . Although the Stress Shot Peening, say SSP, is generally applied to Leaf Springs, the application to Coil Springs has been made recently[(4)]. The Warm Shot Peening, say WSP, is also the recent technology under the productions[(5)]. However, the systematical studies comparing these shot peenings have not been made. The mechanics for improving the fatigue life, is also unknown. In this paper, employing the same coil spring, the relationship between the shot peening process and fatigue life was obtained experimentally. The effects of surface roughness and residual stress distributions on fatigue life were studied. The new shot peening process combined WSP with SSP, say WSSP, is also proposed. It was found that the WSSP can increase the fatigue life of springs substantially.

Experimental Procedures

Spring Materials

Employed spring steel is JIS SUP7(equi. to SAE9260), which is the most popular steel in Japan. The chemical contents(wt.%) are, C:0.59, Mn:0.85, Si:2.05, Cr:0.15, P:0.021, S:0.013.

Springs for Experiments

(a) Spring Specifications

The spring Specifications are, Wire Diameter: ϕ 12.5mm, Mean Diameter of Coil: ϕ 110mm, Effective Number of Coil:5.39, Total Number of Coil:6.89, Free Height of Spring:440mm, Spring Rate:33.3N/mm.

(b) Spring Production Processes and Fatigue test

The Spring Production Processes are, Heating in the air Atmosphere(1223K)→Hot Coiling→ Oil quenching→Tempering(623K×60mins)→Shot Peening Process→Setting→Fatigue Test. The fatigue tests were carried out under the certain deflection with the frequency of 1.5Hz.

(c) Metallurgical Structures and Hardness Distributions

Figure 1 shows the metallurgical structure before shot peening of SUP7 spring. It can be realized that the metallurgical structure is sorbite and that there is slight decarburization at the surface, which may be caused by the heating in the air atmosphere.

Fig. 1 Metallurgical structure for SUP7

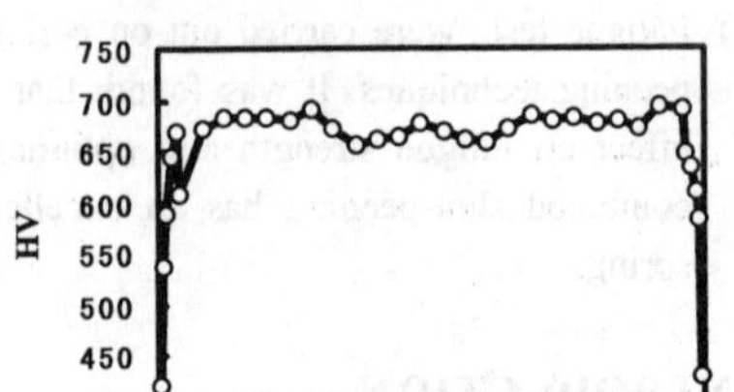

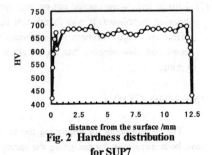

Fig. 2 Hardness distribution for SUP7

Figure 2 shows the hardness distributions. While the average hardness is about 650HV. The surface hardness is decreased to 400-450HmV by reason of decarburization.

(d) Shot Peening methods

Four types of shot peening processes shown below were carried out.

(d-1) Double Shot Peening(DSP)

The DSP would be the most popular shot peening process in the spring manufacture. The Aim of DSP is to have deep residual stress distribution and to obtain higher compressive residual stress around the spring surface. This is to say that the first shot peening is applied by larger shot energy to obtain deeper residual stress and the second shot peening is applied by smaller shot energy to form the surface area in order to increase the surface residual stress. This can be normally achieved by changing the shot size. In this experiments, the DSP conditions are, that the first shot size: ϕ 0.87, shot hardness:690HV, shot speed:76m/s, and, the second shot size: ϕ 0.6, shot hardness:690HV, shot speed:76m/s. In these conditions, the arc height is 0.4mmA and 0.2mmA respectively.

(d-2) Stress Shot Peening(SSP)

The SST was carried out by the following procedures. First, the spring is shot peened under the first shot condition of **(d-1)**. Then, compressing the spring by two plates up to the torsional stress, 735MPa, the first condition of **(d-1)** is applied. The reason why without compressing the spring the shot peening is first applied, is to give the shot peening, to the contact area between the spring and plates. The torsional stress, 735MPa is decided, based on the experimental results where the effect of SSP become larger from this stress level.

(d-3) Warm Double Shot Peening(WDSP)

The warm shot peening is the process where the spring is shot peened at the warm temperature lower than tempering temperature. The yield strength of spring can be tentatively decreased under the warm temperature such as 573K, to make the shot peening process easier and to obtain deeper residual stress distributions. However, since too high a temperature may cause the release of residual stress simultaneously, an optimum temperature exists. In this experiments, based on the Author's former studies(5), the temperature is chosen by 573K. After keeping the spring in the oven at 573K for 20mins, the spring is shot peened under the DSP shot peening condition same as **(d-1)**.

(d-4) Combinations of SSP and WSP(WSSP)

Any experimental studies for the combination of SSP and WSP are not reported. Both the decrease of yield strength and the application of stress can be expected to help the shot peening effect. Therefore, deeper and larger residual stress distributions by WSSP can be expected. The temperature and stress employed here, are 573K and 735MPa. The shot peening is first made without any stress under the same condition of **(d-2)**. Then, giving the stress of 735MPa and heating the spring at 573K for 20mins, the spring is shot peened under the condition of **(d-2)**.

EXPERIMENTAL RESULTS AND ANALYSES

Experimental Results

(a) The relation between shot peening conditions and fatigue life

Figure3 summarizes the fatigue life under each shot peening process. The stress condition is 750±450MPa, which can be presumed to be the highest stress condition in the springs under production. It can be seen from the Figure3 that while the fatigue life of DSP spring is the lowest fatigue life around 100,000cycles, and those of SSP and WDSP spring are the medium level between 200,000 and 300,000cycles, the WSSP spring shows extremely the high fatigue life, where two experimental data show no failure over 1,000,000cycles.Figure 4 shows the S-N diagram, comparing with the one of DSP spring. Although the mean stress can be chosen by the same as the Figure 3, 750MPa, the stress amplitudes are applied by 550 and 650MPa for comparisons. It can be recognized from the Figure 4 that while the DSP spring shows 40,000 to 70,000cycles failure under the stress conditions, 750±550MPa, the WSSP spring shows no failure over 1,000,000cycles under, 750±450MPa and 120,000 to 180,000cycles under 750±550MPa.

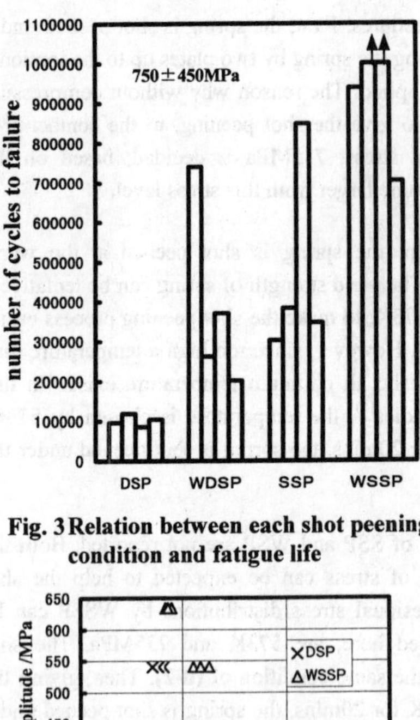

Fig. 3 Relation between each shot peening condition and fatigue life

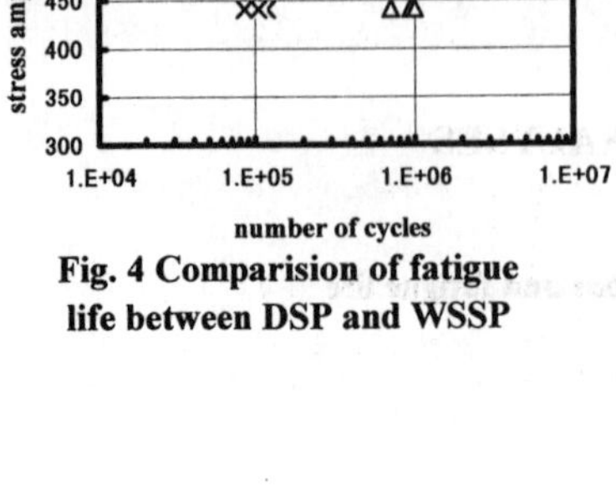

Fig. 4 Comparision of fatigue life between DSP and WSSP

(b) Fractured Surface

Figure 5 shows a typical fatigue fracture surface. It can be seen that the fatigue origin is from the outside surface and the fatigue crack propagates semi-circularly like the normal fatigue fracture. And this fatigue fracture surface corresponds with the maximum principal stress plane. The fatigue crack propagation process is generally said to consist of Stage I where the crack is propagated on the maximum shearing stress plane and Stage II where the crack is propagated on the maximum principal stress plane. Since the Stage I can be seen to be not clear from Figure 5, the most fatigue crack propagation processes can be seen the Stage II.

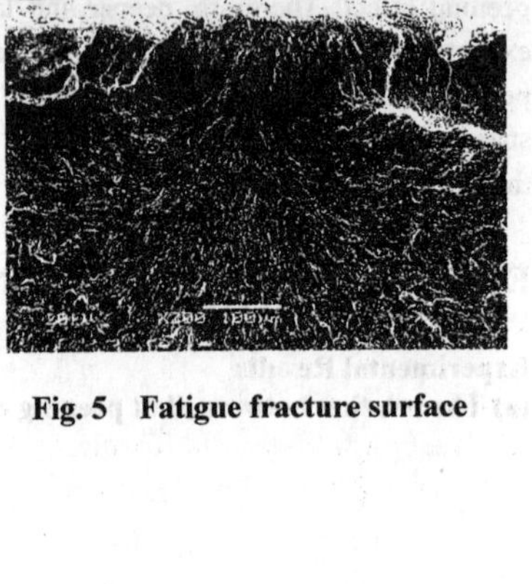

Fig. 5 Fatigue fracture surface

(c) Surface Roughness

The surface roughness can be another factor which can affect to the fatigue life besides the residual stress. Table 1 shows the surface roughness for each shot peening condition. Remarking on the maximum surface roughness, Rmax, while the values of WDSP and WSSP which are the warm forming processes, are 49.3 and 43.8 μ m, the values of DSP and SSP which are the cold forming processes, are 29.3 and 26.2 μ m. This means that the spring surface can be more deformed by the warm processes. In general, the smaller the surface roughness is, the higher the fatigue life is. However, the experimental results shown in the Figure 3 do not meet with this. Therefore, it can be concluded that the effect of surface roughness on fatigue life is rather small.

The value of surface roughness shown in the Table1 are relatively larger at any shot peening conditions. This could be the reason why the Stage I is not clear as shown in the Figure 5.

Table 1 Surface Roughness and Shot Peening Conditions (μ m)

	DSP	WDSP	SSP	WSSP
Rmax	29.8	49.3	26.2	43.8
Rz	24.5	33.5	18.3	27.8

(d) Residual Stress Distributions

Figure 6 shows the residual stress distributions for each shot peening condition. The residual stress is measured by X ray. Considering that the fatigue crack propagation occurs along the maximum principal stress plane, the measurements of residual stress are carried out along the maximum principal stress direction, which is inclined by 45 degree from the axis of coil spring wire at the outside surface of coil.

In most cases, the residual stress is small at the surface, reachs the maximum at the depth of around 0.08mm from the surface, and becomes zero at the depth of around 0.3mm from the surface. Comparing with the fatigue life shown in the Figure 3, the residual stress of DSP spring, which has lowest fatigue life, shows the smallest at both the surface and the peak. The WDSP and SSP spring which have the medium level of fatigue life, the value of residual stress shows the medium at the surface and the peak. Remaking the WSSP spring which has highest fatigue life, the value of residual stress is much higher than the others. This can be concluded that the residual stress distributions have great correlation with the fatigue life.

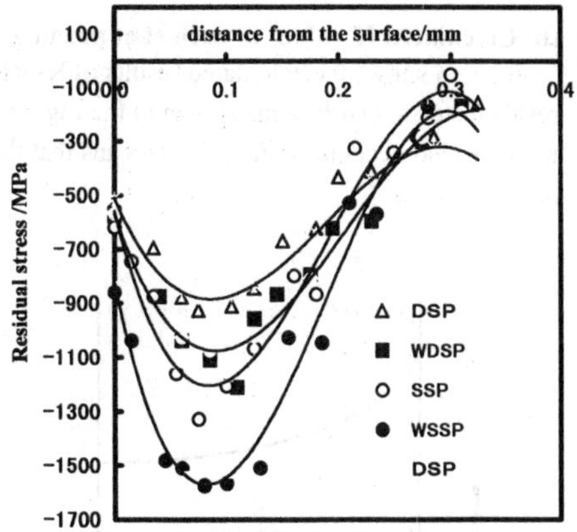

Fig. 6 Residual Stress distributions for each shot peening condition

Estimation of Stress Intensity Factor by Residual Stress Distribution

(a) Analytical Method of K-value by Residual Stress

It is said that the effect of residual stress on improvement of fatigue life can be due to the restraint of crack propagation, especially in the Stage II. In order to know the effect of the residual stress distributions in each shot peening condition on the restraint of crack propagation, the Stress Intensity Factor, K-value, at the surface crack tip is estimated by applying the residual stress distributions as shown in the Figure 6. As for coil spring, the fatigue crack at the Stage II can occur along the 45 degree inclined line in the surface of wire. While the wire diameter is ϕ12.5, the radius of expected crack length is less than 1mm. Therefore, assuming that there are the semicircular crack in the plain plate, Nam et al's method [5], The ASME Boiler and Pressure Vessel Code Sec.X I are applied. As shown in figure 7, this method is to divide the actual stress to the bending, σ b, and tensile σ m, to calculate the K-value at each stress and to sum up each K-value. The K-value is calculated by the following equation (1) and (2) proposed by Ishida.

Tension

$$Ft = K_{I,C} / (\sigma m \sqrt{\pi b}) \quad (1)$$

$$Ft = 1.1362 - 0.3927\mu - 0.345\mu^2 + 0.2623\mu^3 + \lambda(-0.2179 + 0.2354\mu + 0.3773\mu^2 - 0.4189\mu^3) + \lambda^2(5.0486 - 16.7939\mu + 19.986\mu^2 - 8.0212\mu^3) + \lambda^3(-2.6383 + 8.6007\mu - 9.6332\mu^2 + 3.5118\mu^3)$$

Bending

$$Fb = K_{I,C} / (\sigma b \sqrt{\pi b}) \quad (2)$$

$$Fb = 1.1359 - 0.3929\mu - 0.3440\mu^2 + 0.2613\mu^3 + \lambda(-1.5184 + 0.4178\mu + 0.7846\mu^2 - 0.6329\mu^3) + \lambda^2(4.3721 - 13.9152\mu + 16.2550\mu^2 - 6.4894\mu^3) + \lambda^3(-2.9502 + 12.5334\mu - 14.6137\mu^2 + 5.8110\mu^3)$$

$$\mu = b/a, \quad \lambda = b/T$$

where **b** is the depth of crack, **a** is the radius of crack length in the surface, and **t** is thickness.

(b) Calculated K-values in each shot peening condition

Figure 8 shows the calculated results of K-values against the crack depth, based on the residual stress distributions shown in the Figure 6. As the residual stress is compressive, the K-value also becomes minus. This means that the crack can be closed by the compressive residual stress.

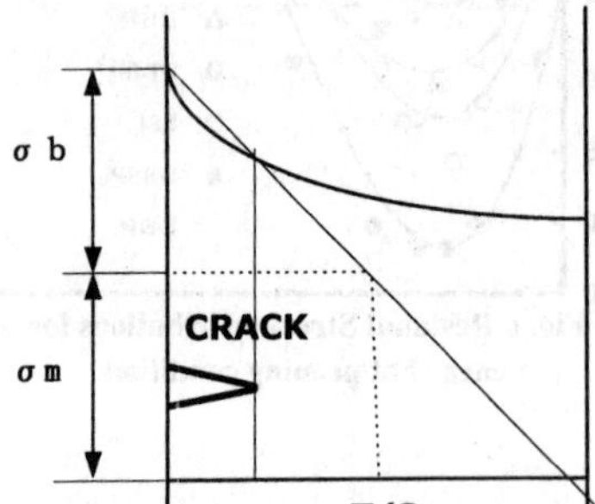

Fig. 7 Divide of stress to bending and tension

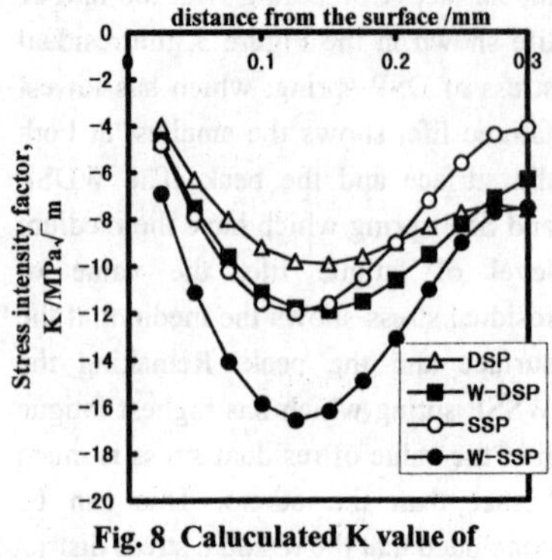

Fig. 8 Calculated K value of semicircular crack tip by useing residual stress distribution

Therefore, the fatigue crack propagation could be delayed when it passes through the compressive residual stress field. For all Shot peening conditions, the K-value is increasing up to 0.13mm crack length and decreasing over 0.13mm crack length. This tendency can be realized to be similar with the shape of residual stress distributions shown in the Figure 6. However, it is noted that the location of the peak is deeper than 0.08mm for residual stress distribution. Comparing each shot peening condition, the K-value of WSSP is much higher than that of other shot peening conditions. This may support the assumption that the restraint of crack propagation due to compressive residual stress can increase the spring fatigue life.

(c) Effect of Surface Residual Stress

It was reported that it is essential for increasing fatigue life to increase the residual stress around the surface(6). In this paper, the WSSP spring of which the surface residual stress was increased, showed prominent improvement of fatigue life. Therefore, as shown in Figure 9, considering the residual stress distribution model where the surface residual stress is ranged between -500MPa, -700MPa, and –900MPa, the K-values are calculated based on the same procedures of Figure 7. Figure 10 shows the results. It can be realized from the figure 10 that the difference of surface residual stress can affect the K-value. The higher the surface residual stress is, the deeper and higher the K-value becomes. This can conclude that it is effective for restraining the crack propagation to make the surface residual stress higher.

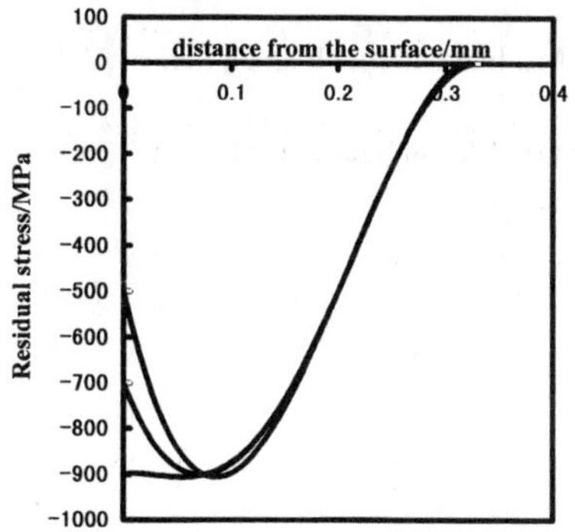

Fig. 9 Residual stress distribution model

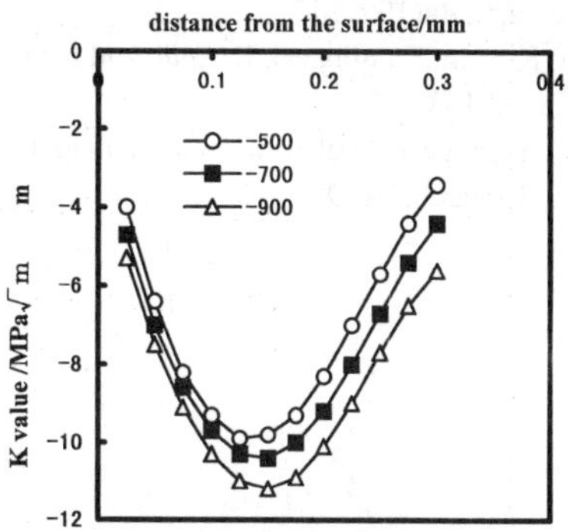

Fig. 10 Effect of surface residual stress distribution on K value

CONCLUSIONS

(1) It was found that comparing with the conventional shot peening process such as DSP, WDSP, and SSP, the newly develcped WSSP shows prominent effect to improve the spring fatigue life. This new shot peening process can be expected to be in production in the near future.

(2) It was realized that there is strong correlation between the fatigue life and the scale of residual stress distribution.

(3) The calculated K-value based on the residual stress distributions showed the same tendency with the residual stress distribution, to support the assumption that the prevention of crack propagation due to compressive residual stress can increase the spring fatigue life.

(4) The effect of the residual stress around the surface on the prevention of crack propagation was studied. It was realized that since higher residual stress in the surface can increase the peak of inside K-value, higher surface residual stress can be helpful to increase the spring fatigue life.

REFERENCES

(1) K.Koyama, R.Kitamura and A.Tange, Transactions of Japan Society for Spring Research, 29(1983),30.

(2) K.Matsui,Y.Eto,K.Kawasaki,Y.Misaka, and K.Ando,JSME,AVol.65, No.637 P1942

(3) H.Ishigami, K.Matsui,Y.Jing, and K.Ando, Study on Reflection and Double Shot-peening to Improve Residual Stress Distribution, Fatigue and Fract. Engng. Mater. Struct. (Submitted)

(4) Eckenhard Muller, DRAHT,44(1993),49.

(5) A.Tange, H.Koyama and H.Tuji, Transactions of Japan Society for Spring Research,44(1999),13.

(6) K.Nam, S.Fujibayai, K.Ando and N.Ogura, JSME International Journal, Series1,Vol 31,no.2,1988,27.

(7) A.Tange,T.Akutsu and N.Takamura,Transactions of Japan Society for Spring Research,36(1991),47.

CHANGE OF STRESS DISTRIBUTION IN THE SURFACE OF SHOT PEENED STEEL DURING FATIGUE PROCESS

S.Ohya, R. Kojima and Y. Hagiwara
Faculty of Engineering
Musashi Institute of Technology
1-28 Tamazutsumi, Setagaya, Tokyo 158-8557, JAPAN

ABSTRACT

In this study, a cantilever rotary bending fatigue tests on shot peened steel specimens were carried out. Actual stress distributions and residual stress distributions on the specimen circumference at maximum tensile stress amplitude to the fatigue failure were, respectively, measured without a pause of fatigue test by *the dynamic x-ray stress analysis* based on single exposure technique.

As the results, actual stress distribution on the specimen circumference was uniform until the macroscopic crack was appeared. After crack initiation, only the actual stress at the crack point greatly changes to compression, and the shape of distribution showed V-shaped. Subsequently, actual stress value at the crack point agreed almost with the residual stress value at the point, when the crack length was larger in size than the width of x-ray irradiation area. On the other hand, the residual stress distribution on the specimen circumference was also uniform, even if the macroscopic crack was appeared. It was confirmed that the fatigue damage in the shot peened surface could not be evaluated from the observation of the change of residual stress distribution.

INTRODUCTION

There are many investigations on improvement effect of shot peening treatment on fatigue strength. It is clear that the residual stress is the same as the mechanically applied mean stress. There are also several investigations on change of compressive residual stress introduced by shot peening in fatigue process. In these investigations, the changes of residual stress in fatigue process were observed using x-ray stress analysis (1-3). However, the change of the compressive residual stress in the surface after fatigue crack initiation is not clarified, because no significant change of residual stress generally occurs during fatigue process.

Recently, authors have developed a *dynamic x-ray stress analysis*, which is to do the *in situ* observation of actual stress in the specimen surface under fatigue test (4-7). It was confirmed that to observe actual stress distribution of the specimen surface at the maximum tensile stress amplitude was effective for the detection of the surface crack (8).

In this study, a cantilever rotary bending fatigue test on shot peened steel specimens were carried out, and actual stress distributions and residual stress distributions on the specimen circumference at several stages of stress cycles to the fatigue failure were, respectively, measured by *the dynamic x-ray stress analysis*. The change of the compressive residual stress introduced by shot peening throughout the fatigue process and the relationship between actual stress and residual stress distributions after crack initiation were discussed.

EXPERIMENTAL PROCEDURE

Specimen

The material of specimens was a plain carbon steel S45C (JIS G 4051). The mechanical properties, as annealed, were yield point σ_y of 417MPa, tensile strength σ_B of 664MPa and elongation δ of 25.8%. The specimens were machined in the shape shown in Fig.1. The specimen has the annular shallow notch in order to fix a position of the crack initiation and fatigue failure. Subsequently, specimens were vacuum annealed for stress relieving at 873K for 10.8ks, and then they were peened only at a part of the annular shallow notch by an impeller type-peening machine using 0.6mm cut wire shots.

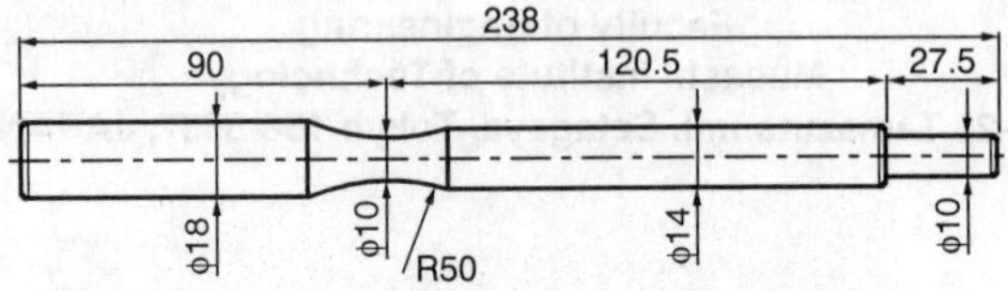

Fig.1 Shape and dimensions of specimen.

Figure 2 shows the depth distributions of the residual stress, the half value breadth of diffraction profile and the hardness. Effective layer of the shot peening on the residual stress is reaching to a depth of about 400μm. The fatigue limit of the peened specimen was about 307MPa, and it has been improved at about 10% in comparison with one of specimen as annealed.

By the way, the x-ray stress constant *K* of the peened surface was experimentally determined by $\sin^2\psi$ method under several applied stress levels, because it was necessary to evaluate quantitatively the surface stress of the peened specimen. The obtained x-ray stress constant *K* was –389MPa/deg. And the linearity between diffraction angle 2θ and $\sin^2\psi$ at all applied stress levels was precisely kept.

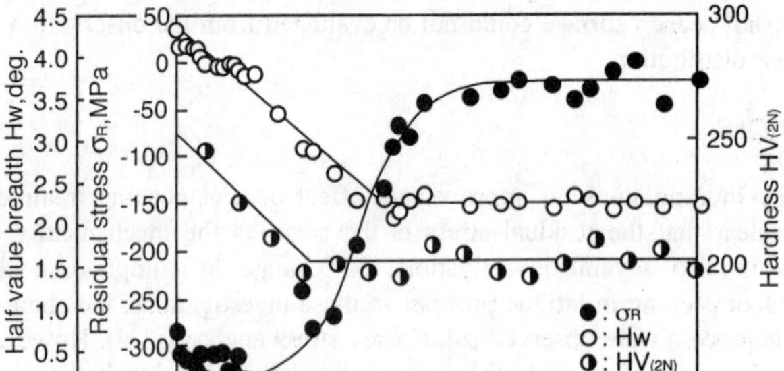

Fig.2 The depth distribution of the x-ray parameters and hardness.

Experimental Equipment

Figure 3 shows the layout of a fatigue test machine and an x-ray stress analyzer. The cantilever rotary bending test machine was adopted to measure the actual stress distributions on specimen circumference at the maximum tensile stress. An x-ray stress analyzer based on the single exposure technique (SET) was mounted on the fatigue test machine. The stress by SET is determined from two diffraction angles $2\theta_1$ and $2\theta_2$ with different ψ angles. This method is effective to perform the rapid stress measurement when a specimen has a good linearity between diffraction angle 2θ and $\sin^2\psi$. In this study, it was expected that the stress could be rapidly measured with high accuracy, because the peened specimen used had a precise linearity of 2θ-$\sin^2\psi$ plots. Another merit of using SET for this experiment is that the measured stress value is not affected by the misalignment between specimen and the analyzer, which may occur during fatigue test (6), (8). This analyzer has two position sensitive proportional counters (PSPC) connected in series to measure simultaneously two diffraction profiles at both $+\eta$ and $-\eta$ sides. And two PSPCs were placed at a short distance from the specimen to increase the intensity of diffracted x-rays. Its distance is 80 mm, and effective detection length of PSPC is 50 mm.

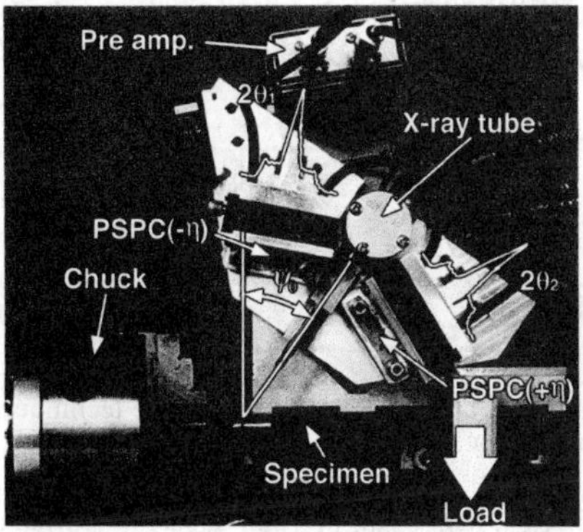

Fig.3 Layout of fatigue test machine, specimen and x-ray stress analyzer.

Measurement of Stress Distribution on Specimen Circumference

The system to measure the actual stress distribution on the specimen circumference at the maximum tensile stress amplitude under fatigue test is shown in Fig.4. The signal processor for PSPC used has 16 memory banks, which a diffraction profile can be stored in one memory bank of 512 channels, and it is possible to switch a bank by the computer. The absolute type rotary encoder of 8bits was coupled to the rotating shaft of fatigue test machine to detect circumferential position of specimen.

The actual stress distributions were measured by following processes.

i) The incidence x-ray beam always irradiates on the upper surface of specimen, because the upper surface is always served the maximum tensile stress during fatigue test.
ii) The specimen circumference is divided equally for sixteen. Sixteen encoder values for the bank switching are input into the computer in advance.
iii) The computer always takes in an output of the rotary encoder after the counting start of the diffracted x-rays, and it is detected which position on the specimen circumference is irradiated by incident x-ray beam at present.
iv) The switching to next bank is carried out, when it reached encoder value for the bank switching. In this interval until next bank switching, the diffracted x-rays are kept on counting, and the diffraction profile is accumulated in the corresponding bank.
v) The bank switching is continuously repeated 16 times during one rotation of specimen. Sixteen diffraction profiles corresponded to each position of circumference are separately stored in each memory bank. However, the intensity of these profiles is not enough to determine exactly diffraction angles.

vi) The operations from iii) to v) are repeated during the preset rotation numbers for collecting diffracted x-rays, and the diffraction profiles are kept on accumulating in each bank, respectively. Subsequently, these are read from the signal processor to the computer. Then, diffraction angles of $2\theta_1$ and $2\theta_2$ are determined in every position on the specimen circumference, and the stresses at sixteen positions are calculated.

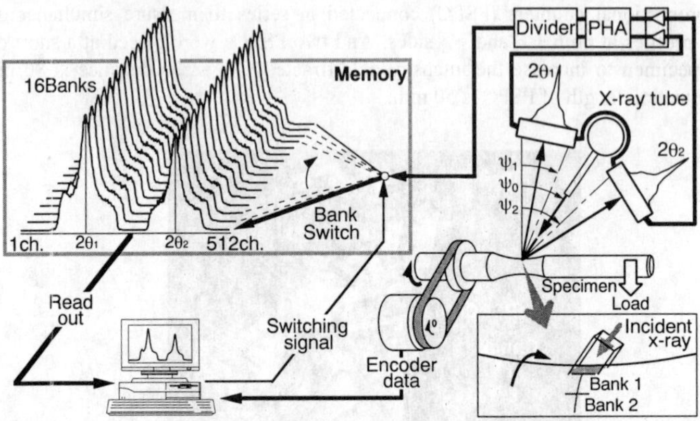

Fig.4 System of x-ray stress analysis by single exposure technique during rotary bending fatigue testing.

In this experiment, the CrKα x-rays beam of 1mm square was irradiated with an incident angle ψ_0 of 35 degrees, and αFe 211 diffraction profiles were measured. In the condition of rotational speed of 980rpm, the rotation numbers for accumulation was set 4000 cycles so that the peak intensity of diffraction profile was over 2000 counts. The 95% confidence limit of the stress calculated from the diffraction profile with peak intensity of 2000 counts was almost 10MPa. In addition, the residual stress distribution was also measured by removing the load during fatigue test.

EXPERIMENTAL RESULTS

The changes of average actual stress and average residual stress at high and low stress amplitudes σ_a of 370 MPa, 330 MPa are shown in Fig.5. The horizontal axis was shown at the ratio of stress cycles N to fatigue life N_f. The average stresses were calculated by using two diffraction angles of the cumulative profile of sixteen diffraction profiles obtained in the distribution measurement. The average compressive residual stresses at either stress amplitude were attenuated at about 30-40% of initial residual stress in the period to the ratio N/N_f of 0.1, because the compressive yielding at the specimen surface was occurred in the compressive range of stress cycle (9). The average actual stress shifts to the tension direction, because it is dependent on the change of average residual stress. Afterward, the behavior of the average actual stress with the increase in the ratio N/N_f was different by the magnitude of the stress amplitude. In the case of high stress amplitudes, the average actual stress gently decreased to failure. However, in the case of low stress amplitudes, it was slightly increased to tension direction throughout the fatigue process. Though the average compressive stress at either stress amplitude was gently attenuated after the ratio N/N_f of 0.1, the specimen surface had the large compressive residual stress of about –200MPa even if just before failure.

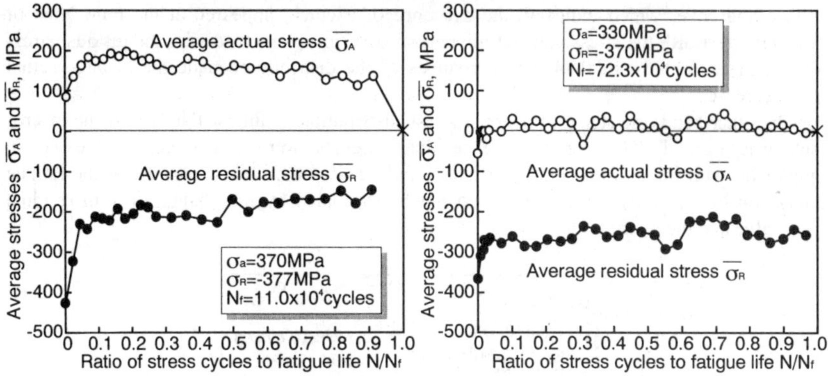

(a) Under stress amplitude of 370MPa (b) Under stress amplitude of 330MPa

Fig.5 Changes of both average actual and residual stresses.

Figure 6 shows an example of the change of actual stress distribtion in the stress amplitude of 340MPa. The actual stress distribution until the ratio N/Nf of 0.88 remained stable. Then, the change in the distribution has appeared as a V-shaped state at the positions A and B of 13 mm and 25 mm, respectively, and the actual stress value at the both positions was large compression. Its fracture surface after the fatigue failure is shown in Fig.7. There were two origins of crack initiation from the appearance of the fracture surface, they agreed well with the positions A and B where the actual stress distribution became the V-groove. These results shows that the position and the period of the crack initiation were detected by a change of the actual stress distribution in fatigue process.

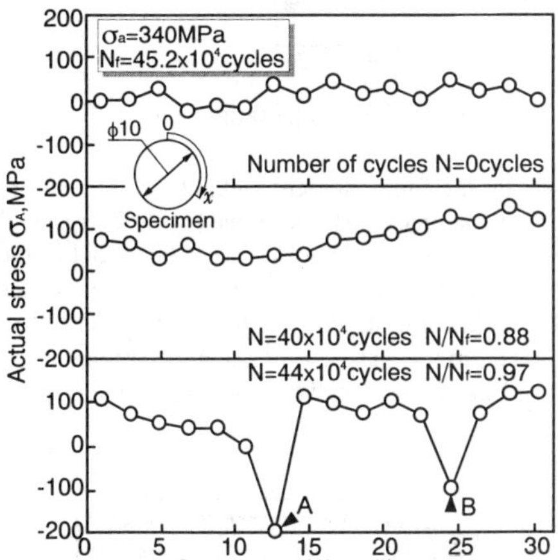

Fig.6 Change in actual stress distributions under fatigue process.

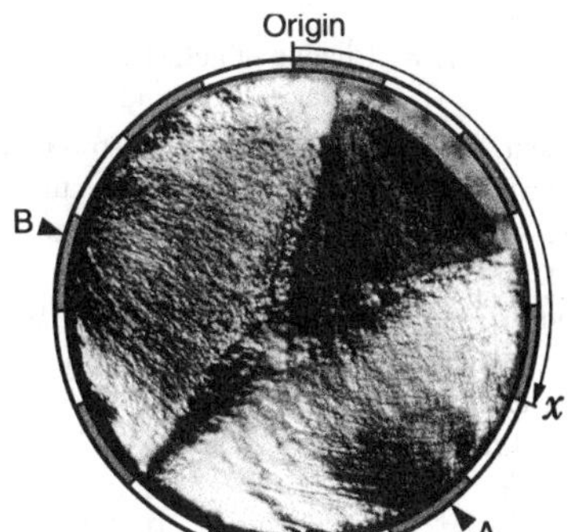

Fig.7 Appearance of fracture surface.

The actual stress distributions measured under the stress amplitude of 370MPa is shown in Fig.8 and the residual stress distribution is also shown. The actual stress distribution with the shallow V-groove, which indicated the existence of a crack, appeared at the ratio N/Nf of 0.86, and afterward, the stress value at the bottom of V-groove agreed with the residual stress value at the ratio N/Nf of 0.94. These changes of the distribution made the average actual stress decrease.

On the other hand, the shape of residual stress distribution is almost flat even if the macro-crack was existed. The compressive residual stresses were not greatly decreased in comparison with initial value until just before failure. It could be confirmed that the fatigue damage on the shot peened surface could not be evaluated by the change of both residual stress value and the distribution.

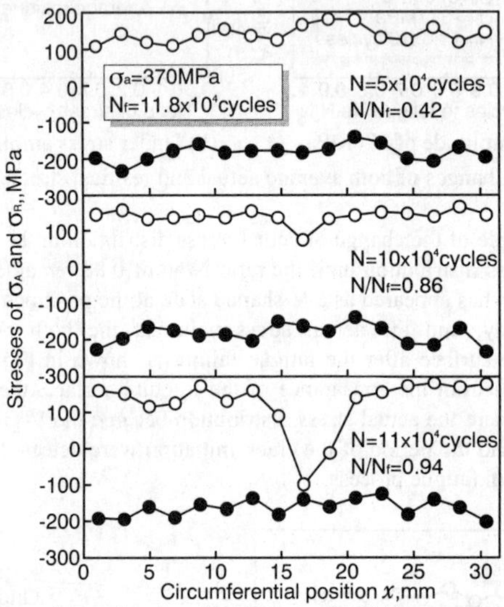

Fig.8 Change of actual and residual stress distribitions under fatigue process.

Next, three-dimensional elastic stress analysis by the finite element method was carried out in order to clarify the reason why actual stress at the crack position agreed with the residual stress at this position. The conditions of FEM analysis were shown in Fig.9. The model of the specimen with semi-elliptic crack in the upper surface of the annular shallow notch was divided using the three-dimensional 10 nodes tetrahedral structure solid element. The load was selected so that the applied stress at the upper surface was 320MPa, and the surface stress distribution around the macr-crack was analyzed under the condition in which there was no initial residual stress.

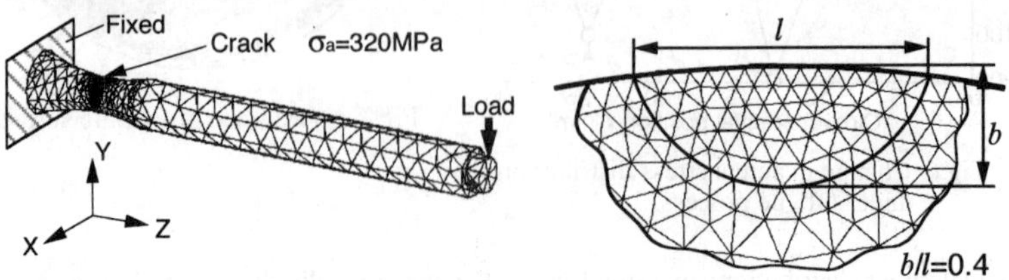

Fig.9 Mesh division of the FEM model.

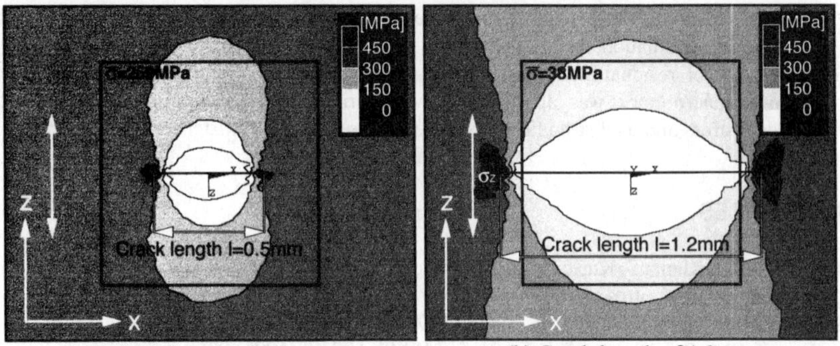

(a) Crack length of 0.5 mm (b) Crack length of 1.2 mm

Fig.10 The stress distribution around a crack analyzed by FEM.

Figure 10 shows the stress distribution around the crack on the specimen surface analyzed by the FEM. The direction of stress value σ_z shown here agreed with one of the stress measured by the x-ray, and the squared frame is shown an x-ray irradiation area of the 1mm x 1mm. In the stress distribution near the crack, there was the oval zone on the crack, which the stress value shows 0MPa or slight compression, and there were also the tensile stress concentration zones at both crack tips. The stress measured by x-ray is a mean value in the irradiation area. As a result of calculating actually, the mean stress in the frame was 259MPa in case of crack length of 0.5mm shown in Fig.10 (a), and it was 38MPa in the case of crack length of 1.2mm shown in Fig10 (b). The stress value approached almost 0MPa, when the crack length was in excess of the width of the irradiation area, because the mean stress value was depended on the proportion of the oval zone relaxed applied stress for the irradiation area. Therefore, the actual stress on the macro-crack must agree almost with the compressive residual stress value at the crack position, if the actual stress distribution is the superposition between the distribution shown in Fig.10 (b) and the uniform compressive residual stress introduced by shot peening.

It is possible to consider similarly the behavior of actual stress, when there are a lot of micro-cracks in the x-ray irradiation area. The decrease of the actual stress and the attenuation of the compressive residual stress will be occurred by increasing a number of the micro cracks. So, the fatigue test by use of the specimen polished surface was carried out to observe the micro crack and slip band. It was confirmed that a number of micro-crack and the total crack length in the irradiation area were increased with increasing the magnitude of stress amplitude. From these results, it was considered that the behavior of both decreasing the average actual stress and the average residual stress shown in Fig.5 (a) was caused by the increase of the micro-crack and initiation of the macro-crack.

CONCLUSION

From these experimental results the following conclusions can be drawn.

(1) The compressive residual stress introduced by shot peening greatly attenuated in the initial stage of fatigue process because of the compressive yielding. Afterwards, its value slightly decreased to fatigue failure because of initiation of micro and macro crack.

(2) The actual stress distribution on the specimen circumference changed in the shape with the V-groove from the smooth form, when the macro-crack was appeared. The bottom of V-groove indicated the crack position, and the actual stress at the bottom agreed almost

with the compressive residual stress value, when the crack length was in excess of the width of the irradiation area.

(3) The shape of residual stress distribution on the specimen circumference was uniform, even if macro-crack was appeared. It was clarified that observation of the average residual stress and its distribution was not useful to detect the existence of macro-cracks.

REFERENCES

1. Kawata Y, Kodama S, Kurita M, J.JSMS, Vol.17 (1968) 1120
2. Zeller R, Residual Stresses (1993) 907
3. Hayashi M, Enomoto K, J.JSMS, Vol.45 (1996) 1107
4. Ohya S, Ohta S, Hasegawa K, Misono S, J.JSMS, Vol.40 (1991) 825
5. Ohya S, Ohta S, Misono S, RESIDUAL STRESSES –III (1991) 957
6. Ohya S, Nishihata H, Yoshioka Y, J.JSMS, Vol.46 (1997) 738
7. Ohya S, Nishihata H, Yoshioka Y, Advances in X-ray Analysis, Vol.40, (1998)
8. Ohya S, Nagahama T, Kojima R, Hagiwara Y, J.JSMS, Vol.48 (1999) 711
9. Kodama S, MECHANICAL BEHAVIOR OF MATERIALS (1971) 111

MEASUREMENTS OF RESIDUAL STRESSES IN THE PROCESSING OF ROLLER BEARINGS

T Berruti, MM Gola,
Department of Mechanics, Politecnico di Torino
Corso Duca degli Abruzzi, 24, 10129 Torino, ITALY

E Bruno, M Mourglia
Avio Bearing Division, SKF Industrie S.p.A.
Via Dante Alighieri 6, 10069 Villar Perosa (To), ITALY

ABSTRACT

Since the residual stresses monitoring has proved to be an essential index to characterise the fatigue life of rolling bearings, more and more customers require a residual stress control on the manufactured components. In the Avio Bearing Division, SKF Industrie S.p.A., Villar Perosa, Italy, the residual stress control has been introduced in the production of the outer ring of an aeronautic roller bearing. In this paper the analysis of the residual stress state of this component will be presented. The diffractometric technique has been used to detect the subsurface residual stress profile in the circumferential direction on the raceway. A previous measurement plan has been set up to verify the possible presence of a trend in the residual stress values over production time (ten months). Afterwards, the residual stress build-up along the different machining phases has been studied.

INTRODUCTION

It is generally recognised that residual stress state beneath the rolling tracks influences the fatigue life of a rolling bearings. Shimizu and al (1) studied the influence of an initial indentation on the rolling contact fatigue of a bearing raceway: they detected near the indentation a ψ - splitting due to microplastic deformations, and surface stresses changing from compressive to tensile due to crack initiation. Maeda and al (2) performed rolling contact fatigue tests on steel balls with subsurface residual tensile stresses in the radial direction, and they noticed the initiation of cracks during the rolling contact tests. Voskamp (3) deeply studied the phenomenon of the rolling contact fatigue in ball bearings; the residual stresses were measured before, during and after fatigue tests, observing how a fatigue crack propagates from tensile residual stress zones and how residual stresses are related to microstructure. The morphological alteration and the residual stress redistribution are described during the fatigue life up to the spalling damage. Voskamp and al (4) applied this analysis based on microstructural-related alterations to systems involving bearings, such as automotive gearboxes. Residual stress diffractometric measurements were performed on gearbox bearings , providing a predictive tool for the fatigue life of the gearbox.

Since the residual stresses monitoring has proved to be an essential index to characterise the fatigue life of a rolling bearing, the customers require to the manufacturer a residual stress control on the manufactured bearings.

In the present paper is presented the study of the residual stress state in the outer ring of a roller bearing. According to the industrial requirement the type of the bearing under study is classified and can not be published. The bearing is a roller bearing, commonly used on commercial aircrafts: it is mounted on the low pressure shaft of the turbine engine.

In service, the outer ring has shown to be the part of the bearing more stressed by fatigue loads. For this reason the customer requires the detection of the circumferential subsurface residual stress profiles on the outer ring raceway. The control criteria for the acceptance of the profiles are defined by the customer in accordance with the manufacturer as the result of fatigue tests on the manufactured ring.

Starting from these industrial requirements the following aspects were analysed:

- the constancy of the subsurface residual stress profile shape over production time;
- the residual stress build up along the manufacturing process;

EXPERIMENTAL SET UP

Measurement apparatus

The residual stress detection is performed using an X-ray diffractometer. The main characteristics of this apparatus are: type Italstructures APD-2000, Ω geometry, Cr tube (35 kV voltage, 40 mA current), scintillation detector, Vanadium filter, opening collimator ϕ 2 mm, spot size of the measurement area ϕ 3 mm. The alignment of the measuring device is tested and the zero-setting is controlled by means of iron powder. Each diffraction peak is detected for a $\Delta\theta$ range of 10 deg, a scan step of 0.2 deg, an exposition time of 10 s; nine peaks are acquired for nine ψ angles (from -40 deg to +40 deg). The residual stress are determined using the $\sin^2\psi$ technique.

Specimens

The specimens (surface ≈ 20X40 mm^2) are cut from the outer rings of the analysed roller bearings. The material is AISI M50 steel. The X-rays mean absorption depth is equal to 4.3 µm. The residual stress is detected (by X-ray diffractometer) in circumferential direction. No curvature correction is applied on the measurement results because of the high ratio (about 50) of the specimen curvature radius on X-ray beam spot radius (Francois and al (5)).

Calibration tests

<u>Bias</u> – The SKF procedure to verify the absence of a bias error in the measurement makes use of two reference specimens certified by SKF Engineering Research Centre, the Netherlands. These reference specimens (surface 20X20 mm^2, material SAE 52000 steel) are cut from two different bearing inner rings and their nominal residual stress values are respectively –210 ±50 MPa and –675 ±50 MPa in circumferential direction.

For each reference specimen, the circumferential residual stress is measured three times; afterwards the bias error is estimated as the difference between the stress nominal value and the mean value of the three stress acquisitions. If the bias is higher than the tolerance $\Delta\sigma_N$ = ±50 MPa, a general maintenance of the diffractometer is required.

During the experimental work here presented, the stress values detected on the reference specimens before and during the measurement activity were always inside the required tolerance $\Delta\sigma_N$.

Precision - The precision was evaluated on a specimen cut from one of the rings under test. Two different measuring conditions were examined.

1) Ten measurements were performed without removing the specimen (from the specimen - holder) in order to detect the circumferential residual stress always at the same point. This analysis allowed to evaluate the "repeatability error" $\Delta\sigma_{r1} = \pm 20$ MPa with a confidence level of 95.5%.
2) Ten measurements for each operator were performed by three different operators. The specimen were removed after each acquisition: this analysis allowed to evaluate the "reproducibility error" $\Delta\sigma_{r2} = \pm 23$ MPa with a confidence level of 95.5%.

After these two acquisitions series, a "precision error" $\Delta\sigma_p$ has been defined, equal to the maximum value between $\Delta\sigma_{r1}$ and $\Delta\sigma_{r2}$.

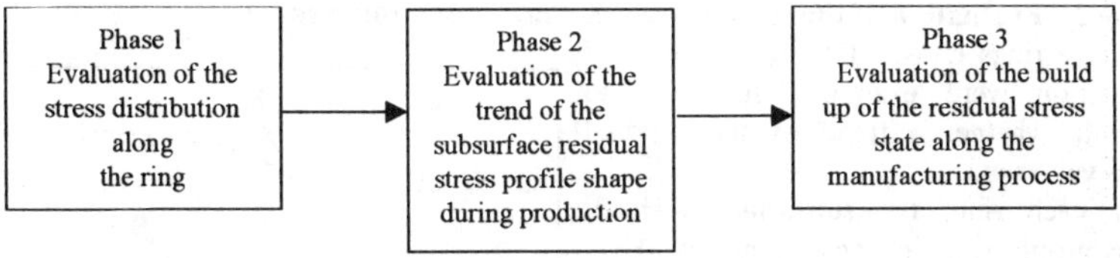

Fig. 1 Measurement phases

MEASUREMENT PHASES

The measurements have been carried on in three different phases summarised in the flowchart of Fig. 1. In phase 1 the study was focused on the evaluation of the variation of the residual stress along the circumferential direction of the ring. The aim was to determine whether the residual stress state detected on a single specimen could be considered representative of the stress state on the whole ring. In phase 2 subsurface residual stress profiles have been detected on sampled rings at the production life (over 10 months) in order to evaluate whether a trend of the residual stress values exists due to variable production conditions. In phase 3 the build up of the residual stress state was evaluated by detecting the subsurface residual stress profile after the different consecutive manufacturing phases;

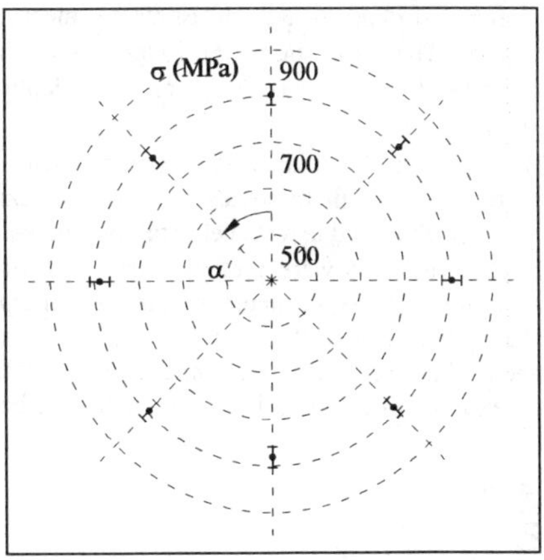

Fig. 2 Ring distribution of the mean residual stress σ (MPa).

Phase 1 – Stress distribution along the ring

The residual stress could vary along the circumferential direction of a ring raceway.

A single ring was examined, and the surface circumferential stress σ (mean of three acquisitions per specimen) was measured on eight specimens cut in six different angular position α (see Fig. 2) along the ring. In Fig. 2 the distribution of σ is plot along the circumferential direction (the error bands are the "precision error" $\Delta\sigma_p$).

As far as it was not found a trend of the σ value along the circumferential position, a statistical normal distribution was supposed for the residual stress σ values along the ring; an error defined as "ring variation error" $\Delta\sigma_r = \pm 45$ MPa was computed from their standard deviation with 95.5% confidence level. The error $\Delta\sigma_r$ will be associated to the residual stress values detected in each sample.

Phase 2 - Evaluation of the subsurface residual stress profile shape

Twelve rings chosen from ten months of production were examined in order to evaluate whether a trend of the residual stress values exists.

For each ring, the subsurface residual stress profile was detected by means of six specimens cut from the ring under test. The following procedure was performed.

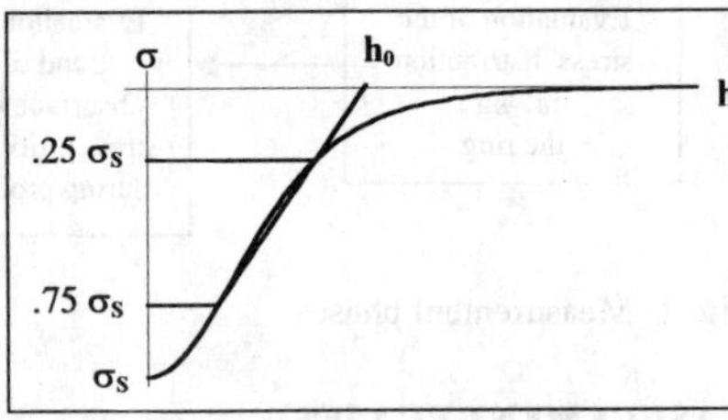

Fig. 3 Characteristics quantities of the subsurface residual stress profile.

1) Each specimen was subjected to an electrolytic removal, in order to obtain six removal depths h_r from 0 to 35 μm. After each removal the effective removal depth h_r was measured by means of a profilometer (Talysurf 10, fidelity 0.5 μm). The error due to the roughness of the surface of the sample, after the removal, varies from $\Delta h = \pm 0.5$ for removal depth $h_r < 10$ μm to $\Delta h = \pm 1$ for removal depth $h_r > 10$ μm.
2) The circumferential residual stress $\sigma \pm \Delta\sigma_r$ was detected on each specimen. Due to the relatively small removals no mathematical correction has been applied for the stress redistribution due to the electrolytic removal.
3) The values σ were plotted versus h in order to obtain the subsurface residual stress profile. The experimental points were interpolated by a Pearson VII curve.

The typical shape of the subsurface residual stress profile detected is sketched in Fig. 3. This shape is characterised by a completely compressive stress distribution and by the location of the maximum of compression stress on the surface of the sample.

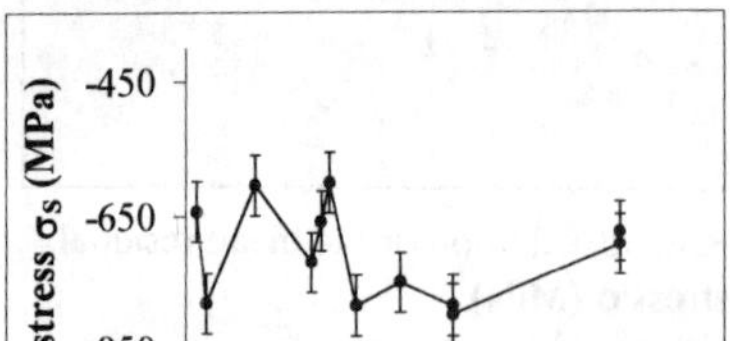

Fig. 4 Surface compressive stress σ_S versus time.

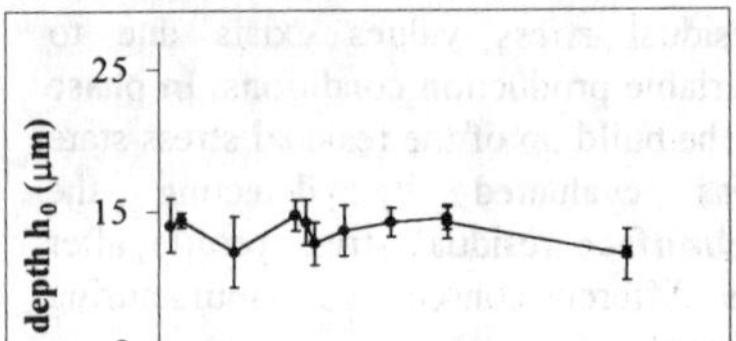

Fig. 5 Zero stress conventional depth h_0 versus time.

As sketched in Fig. 3 the stress profile could be characterised by means of two main quantities: σ_S (surface compressive stress) and h_0 (zero stress conventional depth). The trends of σ_S and h_0 in the twelve rings examined, chosen in different periods of the production, are plotted in Fig. 4 and in Fig. 5. It can be noticed that the quantities of interest σ_S and h_0 don't exhibit a trend overtime.

Phase 3 - Build-up of residual stress state

In order to analyse the different contributions of the mechanical treatments a study about the build-up of the subsurface residual stress profile was performed.

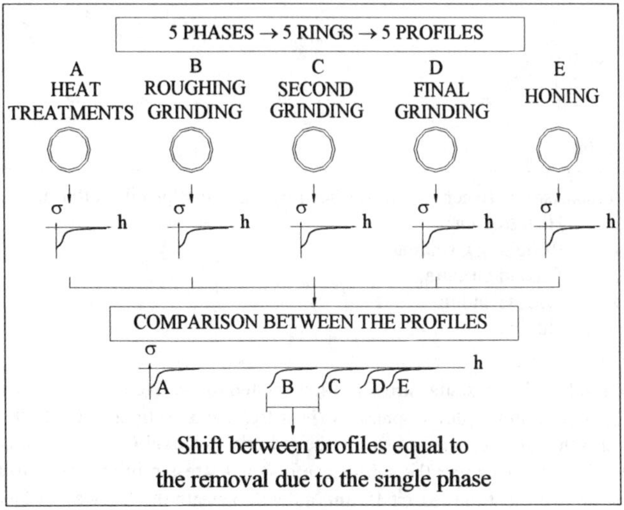

Fig. 6 Analysis plan of the study on the residual stress build-up.

As sketched in Fig. 6, five rings of the same batch were examined at different fabrication phases. The five phases are the following.

- Heat treatments and sand-blasting (phase A): the ring is subjected to austenitizing, quenching, a first tempering, sub-zero treatment, and to other two tempering phases. These thermal treatments are followed by sand-blasting, in order to clean the product by scoriae.
- Raceway rough grinding (phase B).
- Raceway second grinding (phase C).
- Raceway final grinding (phase D).
- Raceway honing (phase E).

The subsurface residual stress profile (6 removal depths) was detected for each ring, as described in the previous paragraph.

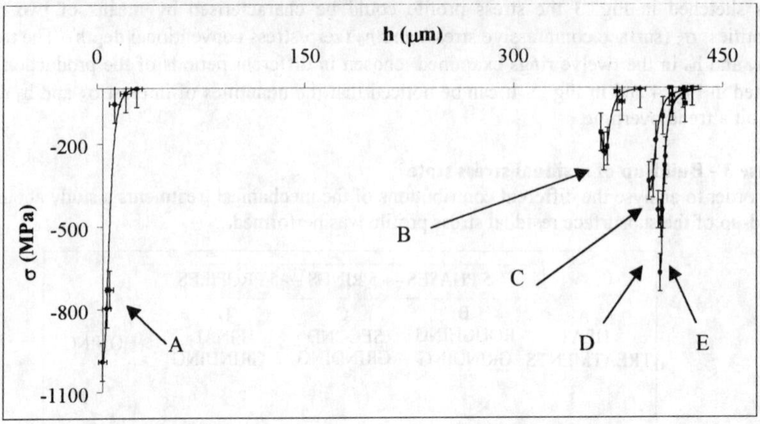

Fig. 7 Comparison between the subsurface residual stress profiles after heat treatment.
A Heat treatment
B Roughing Grinding
C Second Grinding
D Final Grinding
E Honing

In Fig. 7 the subsurface residual stress profiles related to the five different phases are plotted. The residual stress profile due to phase A (heat treatment) extinguishes in the first 15 μm of depth beneath the raceway surface, while the material removal (rough grinding) due to phase B is about 350 μm. Moreover the subsurface residual stress profile related to this machining working phase is present in the first 15 μm of depth beneath the raceway surface. On the other hand the removal due to phase C (second grinding) is about 35 μm. As a consequence, the effects of phases A and B do not influence the residual stress state on the final manufactured ring since they are deleted by the removals due to the following phases. The build up of the final residual stress state is due only to phases C (second grinding), D (final grinding), E (honing).
In Fig. 8 only the last part of the diagram of Fig. 7 (subsurface residual stress profiles related to phases C, D and E) is plotted. The horizontal error bars are the errors in the determination of the removal depth h_r, the vertical error bars are the stress "ring variation error" $\Delta\sigma_r$ (previously defined).

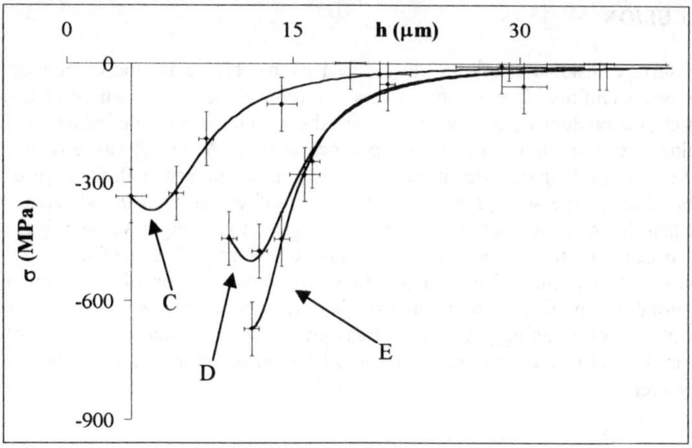

Fig. 8 Comparison between the subsurface residual stress profiles after second grinding.
C Second Grinding
D Final Grinding
E Honing

From the plots of Fig. 8 the following effects can be observed:

- the grinding phases (curves C and D) produces a typical profile shape, with a maximum compressive value beneath the raceway surface;
- the removal due to phases E (honing) changes the profile shape, so that the maximum of the compressive stress is on the surface;
- the high values of residual compression stress are due mostly to the grinding phases C and D, while, if compared to phase C and D, the contribution to the stress level due to honing is quite lower.

In conclusion, the high values of compression stress level are due mostly to grinding while the particular shape profile (i.e. maximum level of compression stress on the surface instead of behind the surface) is due to honing.

In particular, two effects can be noted about honing:

- honing increases the compressive stress state, because of the pressure of the honing stone on the ring raceway (compressive effect).
- honing removes layers of material, with high values of residual compression stress induced by previous machining (removal effect).

CONCLUSION

The subsurface residual stress profile induced by machining on the outer ring of a roller bearing was examined. The residual stress control was performed on rings from different batches chosen randomly from the production, the residual stress state induced in the rings by machining does not show a trend over production time. A typical shape of the subsurface residual stress profile in the circumferential direction was noticed in all the rings examined.

The build-up of the subsurface residual stress profile was then investigated. It has been noticed that the manufacturing phases before the second grinding have no effects on the final profile, because of the material removals due to grinding. The machining phases, which contribute to the build-up of the final subsurface residual stress profile, have proved to be the second grinding, the final grinding and the honing. The high level of compression stress is due mostly to the grinding, while the stress profile shape is due mostly to honing. These results are typical of the ring examined and of the manufacturing process performed by the manufacturer.

REFERENCES

1. Shimizu K, Hirota T, Nagata H, Ishihara T, Miyaji T, Residual Stress - III, Science and Technology, Volume 2 (1991) 1365 - 1370
2. Maeda K, Nakashima H, Tsushima N, Residual Stress - III, Science and Technology, Volume 2 (1991) 1371 - 1376
3. Voskamp A, 'Microstructural Changes during Rolling Contact Fatigue, Metal Fatigue in the Subsurface Region of Deep Groove Ball Bearing Inner Rings', SKF Engineering and Research Centre (Nieuwegein), 1996
4. Voskamp A, Nierlich W, Hengerer F, Evolution (1997) 25 - 31
5. Francois M, Dionnet B, Sprauel JM, Nardou F, J. Appl. Cryst., Volume 28 (1992) 761 - 767.

SESSION 7B

RESIDUAL STRESS IN BUTT WELDMENTS OF 50D STEEL MEASURED BY NEUTRON DIFFRACTION AND MAGNETIC TECHNIQUES

DJ Buttle, W Dalzell, MT Hutchings[1] and AJ Allen[2]
National NDT Centre, AEA Technology Energy, E1 Culham Science Centre, Abingdon, OX14 3ED, UK

ABSTRACT

The residual stress field has been measured in two butt weldments, formed by a single-V and double-V manual metal arc between two plates of BS 4360, 50D steel, using neutron diffraction and two combinations of magnetic techniques. The results are compared and discussed.

INTRODUCTION

Neutron Diffraction (ND) provides the only absolute non-destructive method of determining the triaxial residual stress in depth within components small enough to be taken to a high flux neutron beam reactor (Allen et al (1), Hutchings (2)). Magnetic techniques on the other hand are fully portable and can rapidly measure biaxial stress to a depth of ~6-10 mm in ferromagnetic materials. In this paper a series of measurements of stress made on a single-V and double-V manual metal arc weldment (designated 50D/W1 and 50D/W3 respectively) of BS 4360, 50D steel, using neutron diffraction and magnetic techniques are reported. The results of the techniques are compared in order to make an assessment of the suitability of the magnetic methods for biaxial stress measurements.

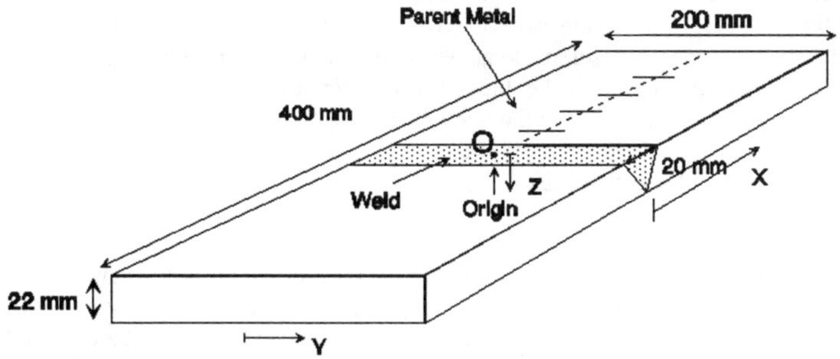

Figure 1. Schematic diagram of the 50D/W1 weldment, with origin and axes used. 50D/W3 has a double V weld. In both cases the Heat Affected Zone extended approximately 5 mm from the edge of the weld material.

[1] *Present Address:- Department of Materials Engineering, The Open University, Oxford Research Unit, Boars Hill, Oxford OX1 5HR..*

[2] *Present Address:- Materials Science and Engineering Laboratory, National Institute of Science and Technology, Gaithersburg, Maryland, USA.*

THE WELDMENT

The butt weldment 50D/W1 is shown schematically in Figure 1, where the origin and axes used are defined. The two 22 mm thick plates were actually at a small angle of ~3° to each other. Most measurements were made on the 'top' faces, that is those at an angle of ~ 177°, on the side of the last weld pass. These faces had a lightly ground finish to facilitate the magnetic measurements. The neutron diffraction measurements were confined to one side of the weld line, whereas the magnetic measurements were made on both sides. However because the weld was slightly proud it was not possible to make magnetic measurements of stress in the weld itself. A second weldment 50D/W3, which had a double-V weld and was of the same dimensions but 23.5 mm thick, was also investigated.

NEUTRON DIFFRACTION MEASUREMENTS

The neutron diffraction measurements were made using the D1A diffractometer at the Institut Laue-Langevin, Grenoble. The wavelength used was 0.1911 nm, monochromated by Ge(511) planes. The Fe(112) reflection was used to measure the lattice strain in the sample. The beam incident on the sample was collimated to ~20' by the combination of the thermal neutron guide and monochromator. A single ^{3}He detector out of the detector bank was used, with a 11' soller collimator between the sample and detector. The gauge volume was 3 x 3 x 3 mm^3, defined by a 3 mm by 3 mm aperture in the incident beam, and a 3 mm wide slit of the full soller height in the diffracted beam.

The sample was mounted on translation slides providing automatic movement in three orthogonal directions. It was mounted with the y axis vertical in order to measure the strains e_x and e_z in the sample x and z directions, and with the x axis vertical in order to measure the strain e_y in the y direction. The principal strains were assumed generally to lie along the symmetry axes of the weldment, and the validity of this assumption was ascertained at one position (15,0,2) in the weldment where the full strain tensor was measured. Scans of strain versus sample angle were also made in two sample orientations. The triaxial strain was measured primarily at positions (x,0,2), along a line perpendicular to the weld line at an average depth of 2 mm below the surface shown dashed in figure 1, and through thickness at one position (15,0,2). The strain values were converted to stress using Modulus E_{112}= 209 GPa and ν=0.29. Zero stress reference angles were determined from average results from an annealed and unannealed 3 mm cube, block and powdered plate material. The uncertainty in this average value is incorporated in the quoted uncertainty bars.

THE MAGNETIC TECHNIQUES

Principles

The magnetic properties of steels and other ferromagnetic materials are sensitive to internal stress levels due to magnetostriction and the consequent magnetoelastic effect. Magnetostriction is the process whereby each magnetic domain is strained along its direction of magnetisation. At minimum energy the magnetisation will align with the crystalline directions - the magnetic easy axes. Consequently a change in the stress level will result in a change in the relative numbers of domains aligned along each of the easy axes so as to reduce the magnetoelastic energy. For example if uniaxial stress is applied, those domains with a component of magnetisation along the stress direction grow by movement of their domain walls. Therefore, internal stress will distort the magnetic hysteresis loop so that there will be changes in parameters such as the coercive field, remanence and permeability, which may be used to measure stress. Although the stress dependence of many magnetic parameters is quite strong there are many other variables, such as hardness, texture, grain size etc. which also affect the measurement (Buttle et al (3)). For this reason reliable methods of stress measurement require a *combination* of magnetic techniques so that the unwanted variables can be eliminated. For most experimental work, calibration of the magnetic parameter against known stress levels is required, although an understanding of the processes involved can enable theoretical formulae to be used to interpolate and extrapolate the calibrations. Magnetic methods are usually rapid, taking just a few minutes.

In the present work the stresses were assumed to be biaxial in the plane of the steel surface. Two combinations of parameters were used:-

(i) Stress Induced Magnetic Anisotropy (SMA) and Magneto Acoustic Emission (MAE), and

(ii) SMA together with Directional Effective Permeability (DEP).

The second combination may readily be incorporated into a single instrument, and is the basis of the AEA Technology MAPS System (Buttle et al (4)).

The SMA Technique

Magnetic anisotropy induced by stress results in the rotation of an induced magnetic field away from the direction in which it was applied (Langman (5)). For example if a magnetic field is applied at some angle with respect to a uniaxial tensile stress in steel, the induced field will rotate towards the tensile axis. No rotation occurs when the magnetic field and stress axes are parallel or orthogonal. To utilise this effect, a sensor coil is inserted between the poles of the magnet, and is aligned so as to link any alternating flux in the direction perpendicular to the applied field in the plane of the component surface. If the oscillating magnetic field is rotated in the steel, the field in the air just above the surface will rotate inducing a corresponding emf across the coil. This is the SMA signal. As the magnet plus coil assembly is rotated through 360° on the steel surface the induced voltage will vary periodically because the rotation of flux will depend upon the angular relationship between the applied field and principal axes. The principal stress directions can be determined from the phase relationship of the SMA with respect to the probe orientation. Also the SMA peak to peak amplitude is almost monotonically related to the size of the stress anisotropy present, giving the difference between the two principal biaxial stresses. Theoretical development has yielded a relationship between the SMA signal and the stress anisotropy enabling the technique to be used for quantitative stress evaluation.

The MAE Technique

If the direction of the magnetostrictive strain changes as a result of abrupt domain wall movement (90° domain walls in steel), elastic waves will be generated. This is Magneto Acoustic Emission, which during the magnetisation process is composed of millions of discrete acoustic emissions which together form a continuous largely incoherent noise signal (Buttle et al (6)). MAE is highly sensitive to stress due to re-distribution of domains as discussed above. MAE signal amplitudes in steel decrease for increasing tension and compression. The MAE signal is normally detected by a piezo-electric transducer while the component under test is subjected to a varying magnetic field. The rms signal as a function of applied cyclic field is measured. The measurement of MAE as a function of probe orientation may be used to determine principal stress axes and, with calibration, stress level information. The penetration for measurement is normally greater than other magnetic methods because the acoustic signal is not attenuated by eddy currents. This has resulted in development of the technique to measure the variation of stress with depth, by changing the magnetic field frequency to vary penetration and using a complex biaxial stress model to invert the data to stress.

The DEP Technique

DEP is measured from impedance changes which are related to the permeability of the material. The impedance of a secondary sensor coil wound on an electromagnet core is monitored while the probe is being rotated. For practical measurement, the impedance signal is divided into in-phase and quadrature components with respect to the drive signal. In the absence of material texture, DEP will be constant and no magnetic anisotropy is measured in a stress free state. However, as discussed above, the presence of stress in the steel will result in an increased permeability parallel to the maximum principal stress axis compared with the permeability in the orthogonal principal stress direction. Therefore in a biaxial stress field, DEP will change sinusoidally as a function of the measuring angle, with maximum and minimum DEP along maximum and minimum stress axes respectively. DEP magnitudes are related to both the principal stress levels enabling, in addition to measurement of principal directions, an absolute measurement of the two stress values to be determined.

MAGNETIC MEASUREMENTS

Measurements using the two combinations of techniques were made at the same points as measured by neutron diffraction. The magnetic data for (i) SMA and MAE, and (ii) SMA and DEP, were converted into biaxial stress levels with uncertainties, using dedicated software together with biaxial calibration maps made from similar material under known applied stress. For all the magnetic measurements the frequency used was ~70 Hz in order to give penetrations of 1 to 2 mm into the surface, similar to the ND measurements. In the case of (ii) SMA and DEP, positions close to the weld were not measured, as DEP is slightly more sensitive to the microstructural variation in the HAZ for which calibration was not available. This was investigated in an earlier study using samples heat treated to contain microstructures simulating those found at various positions with the HAZ.

RESULTS AND DATA COMPARISON

The Variation of Stress away from the Weld

The gauge volume for the neutron measurements was less than that used for MAE and SMA measurements although the penetration depth was slightly more. This appeared to be the best compromise to ensure that as far as possible similar volumes of material were sampled by the magnetic and neutron techniques. The results from the single V plate (50D/W/1) are plotted for ND together with combination (i) in Figure 2 and for combination (ii) in Figures 3 and 4. In these figures, and elsewhere, the numbers 1,2,3 are used for x,y,z, and s is used for σ.

The agreement between the neutron diffraction results and the first combination of magnetic technique stress predictions is very good. As is often the case when using the SMA and MAE techniques in combination, there were two biaxial stress solutions at some of the locations. But in this case it was relatively easy to select the correct solution based on knowledge of the expected signs of the stress components at each position on the weld specimen. Figure 2 shows only this solution for each location. The magnitude of each stress component agrees with reasonable accuracy, the estimated uncertainty usually being sufficient to account for the small disagreement between the magnetic and neutron diffraction results. The mean standard deviation between the magnetic and neutron data sets is 17 MPa. However another source of uncertainty will occur for stresses in excess of 200 MPa (observed at 15 mm position), when these magnetic parameters tend to 'saturate' and sensitivity to stress is reduced.

Biaxial stress levels for the second combination, SMA and DEP shown in Figure 3 for 50D/W/1, do not agree with the neutron data as well as the first combination. The standard deviation between the two data sets is 39 MPa. Measurements could not be made as close to the weld for DEP, because of some sensitivity to changing microstructures within the Heat Effected Zone (HAZ). The rapid measurement capability of the MAPS system is demonstrated in Figure 4 where 150 measurements, collected in one afternoon, are shown as vectors aligned with the maximum stress axis.

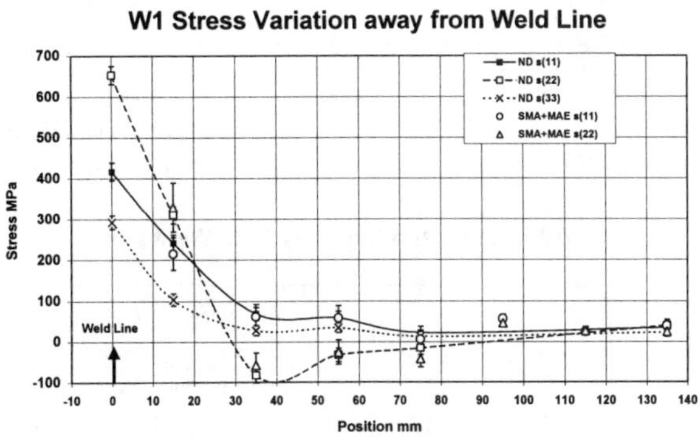

Figure 2. Variation of triaxial stress in 50D/W1 measured by ND at positions (x,0,2) away from the weld centre with 67% confidence uncertainty bars, and of biaxial stress measured by combination (i) SMA & MAE.

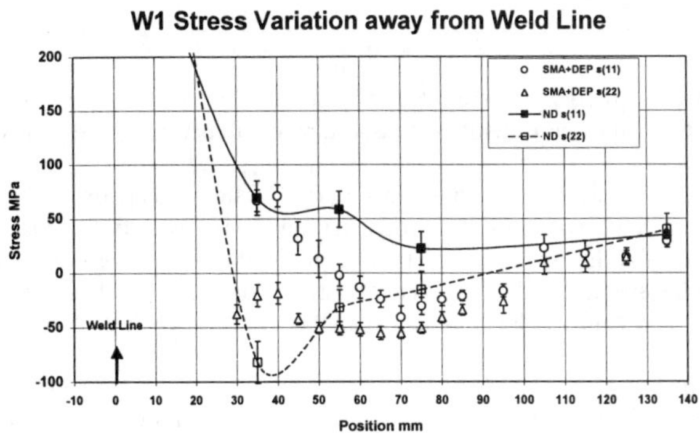

Figure 3. Variation of biaxial stress in 50D/W1 measured by combination (ii) SMA & DEP, compared with the ND data.

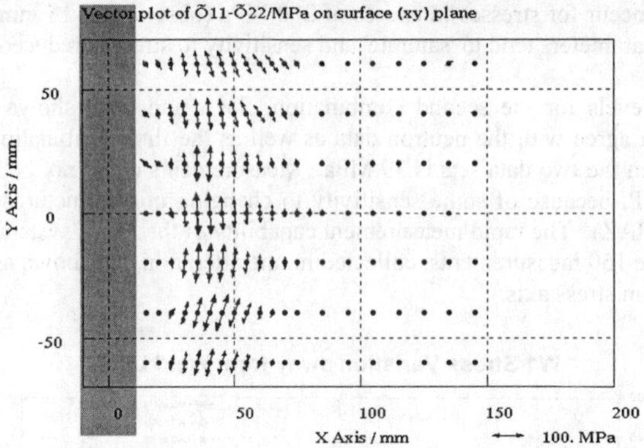

Figure 4. Vector representation of variation of stress differences, σ(11)-σ(22), and orientation of maximum stress axis in 50D/W1 measured by combination (ii) SMA & DEP.

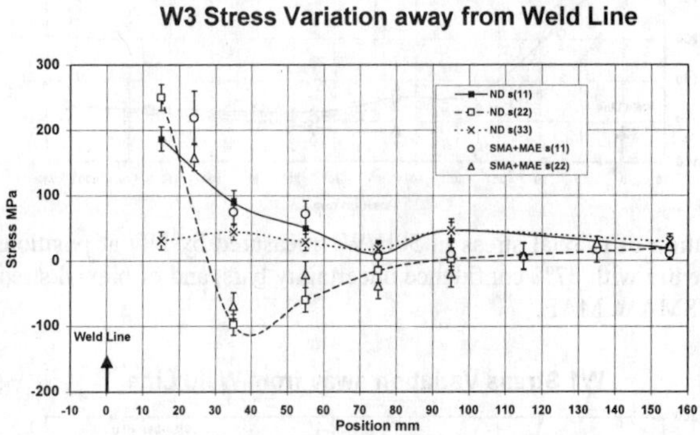

Figure 5. Variation of triaxial stress in 50D/W3 measured by ND at positions (x,0,2) away from the weld centre, and of biaxial stress measured by combination (i) SMA & MAE.

The results for 50D/W/3 are shown plotted in Figure 5. The comparison of the stress levels predicted by the first combination of magnetic techniques with those from neutron diffraction is slightly less good for this specimen. The reason for this is believed to be due to some pitting present on the surface of the specimen at various locations (most severe at the 35 and 55 mm locations). The standard deviation between the two data sets is 23 MPa.

The Strain Tensor

The full strain tensors were measured using ND at one position in each weldment and diagonalised to obtain both the principal strain components and their directions. The following ND results were obtained:

1. For 50D/W1 at position (15,0,2)

   $\varepsilon_{11} = 480 \times 10^{-6}$ with a direction cosine at 24.1°

   $\varepsilon_{22} = 1111 \times 10^{-6}$ with a direction cosine at 23.7°

   $\varepsilon_{33} = -275 \times 10^{-6}$ with a direction cosine at 4.5°

where each of the principal directions (1,2,3) are closest to the (x,y,z) axes.

2. <u>For 50D/W3</u> at position (35,0,2)
   $\varepsilon_{11} = 505 \times 10^{-6}$ with a direction cosine at 1.6°
   $\varepsilon_{22} = -657 \times 10^{-6}$ with a direction cosine at 1.7°
   $\varepsilon_{33} = -221 \times 10^{-6}$ with a direction cosine at 1.4°

The ND results from 50D/W1 thus show the principal directions are rotated almost entirely in the xy (surface) plane by approximately 24°. However the data from 50D/W3 show almost no rotation so that the principal components are almost equal to the components measured along the x, y and z directions. Interestingly SMA measurements on these welded specimens show almost no rotation away from the x and y directions when far from the weld line, but significant rotation as the weld line is approached. For 50D/W/1 the angle of rotation using SMA is found to be 28° in the plane of the surface, close to the 24° found from ND, well within the expected uncertainty for experimental measurement of ±5°. The comparison for 50D/W3 is not in such good agreement, with neutron results suggesting a 1° rotation of the stress tensor compared to 10° found from SMA. However the pitting of the surface could be the cause of the discrepancy.

Depth Profile of Stress

The triaxial strain tensor was measured by neutron diffraction at 3 mm intervals in the z direction through the plate thickness for each plate. The results converted to stress are shown in Figures 6 and 7. MAE measurements were made at the same two locations with a range of 10 magnetic field frequencies between 10 and 180 Hz. In each case the magnet orientated in the x and y directions in turn. In addition MAE measurements were made at locations on each weld far from the weld line to obtain data characteristic of low surface stresses and stress gradients. Thus a total of 80 MAE measurements were made on the two plates.

Biaxial Stress Gradients from MAE and Neutron Diffraction

The biaxial stress gradients in the z direction were obtained from the MAE data by combining the experimental data with theory. Since the theoretical model predicts the ratio between the MAE measured in a complex stress environment to that measured on material containing no stresses, it was necessary to calculate the ratio of MAE values obtained

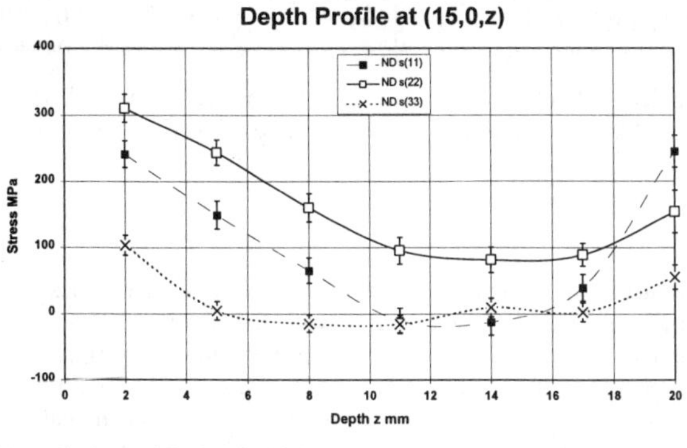

Figure 6. The variation with depth of the stress components along the three symmetry axes for weldment 50D/W1.

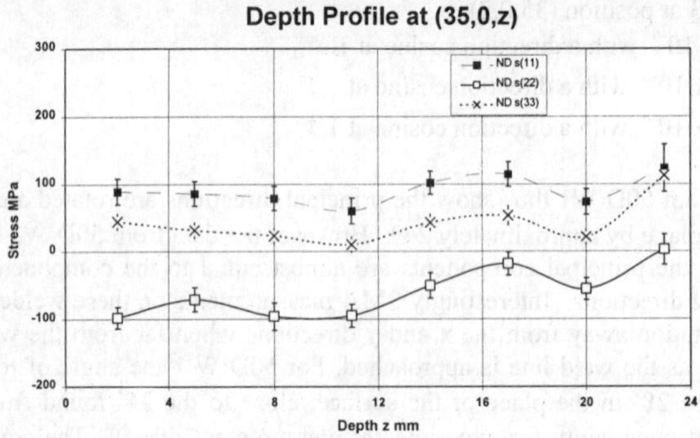

Figure 7. The variation with depth of the stress components along the three symmetry axes for weldment 50D/W3.

at the position close to the weld and at the position far from the weld for each magnetic field frequency used. The theoretical model was incorporated into a FORTRAN programme, which required input of experimental parameters and also the two principal stress levels measured by neutron diffraction at the surface.

The stress gradients to a depth of 10 mm predicted from the MAE experimental data and model, together with values calculated from neutron diffraction data for the first 10 mm depth, are given in Table I. The agreement appears to be very good and demonstrates the ability of the MAE technique to measure how the stress varies as a function of depth into the material. However, the technique does require knowledge of the biaxial stress state at the surface in order to correctly determine the stress levels below the surface.

Stress Gradients	**MAE Results**		**Neutron Diffraction Results**	
	50D/W/1	50D/W/3	50D/W/1	50D/W/3
$\partial\sigma_{xx}/\partial z$ (MPa mm^{-1})	-22 ± 4	3 ± 4	-28 ± 3	-3 ± 2
$\partial\sigma_{yy}/\partial z$ (MPa mm^{-1})	-16 ± 4	-3 ± 4	-24 ± 2	0 ± 10

Table I. Stress gradients along x and y directions determined from MAE data and neutron diffraction data. For MAE uncertainties represent range of possible solutions allowable by least squares fit only.

CONCLUSIONS

The sets of stress values from the two combinations of magnetic techniques show acceptable agreement, given the measurement uncertainties, with the neutron diffraction results. The SMA + MAE combination gives the better agreement but can, in principle, give non-unique stress results. The SMA + DEP combination is the most easily combined into a single instrument (MAPS). This agreement validates the method of analysis and calibration used for the magnetic data, and indicates the power of the portable magnetic techniques for rapid mapping of the biaxial stress field near the surface of ferromagnetic materials.

Acknowledgement

This work was carried out with support from both the AEA Technology HOIS programme and the AEA Technology Growth Programme.

REFERENCES

1. Allen A J et al, Adv. In Phys. **34**, (1985)
2. Hutchings M T, Neutron News **3**, (1992) 14 445
3. Buttle D J, Scruby C B, Briggs G A D, Jakubovics J P, Proc R Soc Lond **A414** (1987) 469
4. Buttle D J, Dalzell W, Gulliver J A, Ravenscroft R A, Scruby C B, Antonelli G, Gori M, Michelis C de and Ruzzier M, Images, contrôle, qualité, Liège 8, (1994), Pub. ISIL.
5. Langman R, NDT International (1982) April 91.
6. Buttle D J, Hutchings. M T, Brit. J. NDT, vol.34, No.4, (1992) April 175-182.

STRESS DETERMINATION BY MICROMAGNETIC TESTING ON TAILORED BLANKS

HK Tönshoff, T Friemuth and H Seegers
Institut für Fertigungstechnik und Spanende Werkzeugmaschinen
University of Hannover
Schlosswenderstr. 5, 30159 Hannover, Germany

ABSTRACT

Welded metal sheets of different ferrous materials, so called tailored blanks, gain increasingly more importance in automotive industry. The forming quality of these sheets is influenced by residual stresses induced nearby the welding zone. The requirements on testing sheets for quality assurance demand a non-destructive method. Micromagnetic testing as a non-destructive monitoring technique is used to determine residual stress in ferromagnetic sheets. Residual stress changes of welded sheets are caused by thermal gradients or phase transformations during processing. Premature failure is often attributed to inappropriate residual stresses. Annealing processes have to be used right after welding to modify the residual stress state. Investigations on the sensitivity of Barkhausen noise analysis are performed. The determined stress state is compared to laboratory methods like X-ray diffraction and metallographical inspection. Different kinds of welding materials are examined.

INTRODUCTION

Microstructure, micro hardness, and residual stresses are important material properties for workpiece behaviour of sheets in forming processes. Quality assurance of sheets requires a fast detection of the material properties. Especially for tailored blanks, sheets welded out of different materials, a non-destructive testing method is necessary to guarantee a high quality standard.

For the scientific testing laboratory X-ray diffraction has proven its high standard to evaluate important material properties. On the one hand this method is known for a high accuracy, but on the other hand much time is used for this investigation. Furthermore, the workpiece often has to be destroyed because only cut-out segments are measurable. For 100% certification during manufacturing only a short time, in this case limited by the the forming cycle, is available for determining material properties. To meet these requirements, a faster non-destructive detection technique is required. One possible testing method is the micromagnetic or Barkhausen noise analysis technique [1]. Due to the sensitivity of the signal on different material properties it has to be correlated to laboratory methods like X-ray investigations and metallographic inspection.

Residual stress as one of the essential material properties plays an important role for the behaviour of welded components in practice. Localised elastic expansion or contraction of the material lattice, as it occurs e.g. in welding, causes residual stresses. The changes usually occur as plastic deformations of the sheets. In later forming operations the forming quality is considerably influenced by these residual stresses. To change the residual stress state different annealing processes could be used after welding.

BARKHAUSEN NOISE

Barkhausen noise analysis or micro magnetic testing is based on the behaviour of ferromagnetic materials in magnetic fields. In ferromagnetic materials domains with different local magnetisation directions are separated by Bloch walls. An increasing external magnetic field causes Bloch wall motions and rotations. As a result, the total magnetisation of the sheet is changing. The magnetisation process is characterised by a hysteresis. Due to the Bloch wall movements single turnarounds of Weiss' domains are required. Analysing the magnetic flux by a coil, this turnarounds are registered as electrical pulses. These pulses are the so called Barkhausen noise.

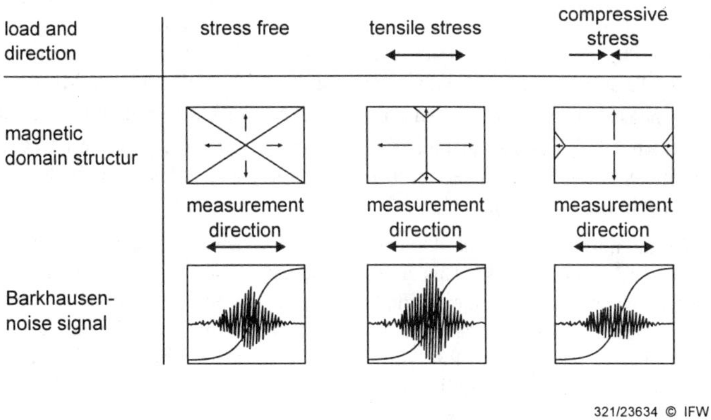

Fig. 1: Influence of Residual stress on the Barkhausen noise signal

It was shown that the magnetic domain structure of ferromagnetic materials and also the Barkhausen noise, is influenced by residual stresses [2, 3]. Compressive residual stress reduces the intensity of the Barkhausen noise whereas tensile stresses increases the max. Barkhausen noise level (Fig. 1) [4, 5]. In addition, the hardness and structure state of the steel sheet influence the Barkhausen noise. To separate the different material characteristics, different quantities have to be analysed for stress determination.

The maximum amplitude of the Barkhausen noise P_{max} is commonly used for residual stress determination. Other values like the peak position and the value of the maximum of the amplitude spectrum can be used for enhanced determination of material properties [6,7]. Especially for excluding changes in micro hardness or microstructure these values have to be analysed and to be taken into consideration for residual stress determination. It has to be pointed out that all Parameters of this testing technique are influenced by the measurement setup. Important parameters are the excitation frequency f_e, the excitation voltage v_e and the used range of the analysing frequency f_a.

EXPERIMENTAL SET-UP

X-ray residual stress investigations were carried out on a Seifert XRD PS two circle diffractometer. Cu Kα radiation was used with a 2 mm point collimator. The well known $\sin^2\Psi$ method was applied with 7 Ψ angles between -45° and +45° [8]. Peak positions were analysed by the centre of gravity method.

For Barkhausen noise analyses a commercial detector system of the American Stress Technologies Inc. (Detector: S1-163) was used. In this detector system the magnetisation unit and the receiver are integrated in one sensor. The Barkhausen noise was evaluated on a separate computer with different statistical programs.

CALIBRATION TEST

Because the residual stress sensitive Barkhausen noise values depend on various material properties, material calibration curves have to be determined for residual stress evaluation [4]. Calibration curves are obtained by measuring the level of Barkhausen noise during compression and tension in one or two directions. In this case only uniaxial tensile forces were applied. The calibration samples were 10 mm wide, 100 mm long, 1 mm thick and consist of H 340 and DC 05 steel with a creep limit of 389 MPa and 195 MPa. Additionally X-ray stress measurements were carried out to correlate stresses measured by X-rays $\sigma_{X\text{-ray}}$ and stresses evaluated by Barkhausen noise analysis σ_{BN}. Therefore, a tension test device was installed in the X-ray diffractometer and the calibration curve for both methods was surveyed simultaneously in the same run.

It has to be taken into account that the calibration curve is determined for a superposition of internal stress and external stress. This stress is also called total load. Based on this diagram a correlation between the laboratory method X-ray investigation and the much faster Barkhausen noise method is possible. But it has to be pointed out that for every different material and also in special cases for every charge, a calibration between the stress level and the Barkhausen noise signal is still necessary. This disadvantage is caused by changes in micro structure or alloying elements.

By using different analysing frequencies, the penetration depth can be varied in a range of several µm up to the mm range depending on the magnetic properties of the used ferromagnetic material. For the magnetic properties of DC 05 (Standard No. 1.0312) and H 340 (Standard No. 1.0548) steel sheets the penetration depth is in the range of 2-28 µm. A frequency of 300 Hz was always used for this investigation.

To improve the quality of the determined residual stress level by Barkhausen noise analysis different evaluation strategies were tested. All these strategies have in common that polynomials of different degrees are used to describe the dependencies. In Fig. 2 the number of parameters of the polynomial which has to be used in the conditional equation is analysed based on the described data. An adequate number of regression coefficients is in the range of 4 coefficients or more. In this range the conditional equation is well defined. For quality assurance the regression coefficient R^2 was used.

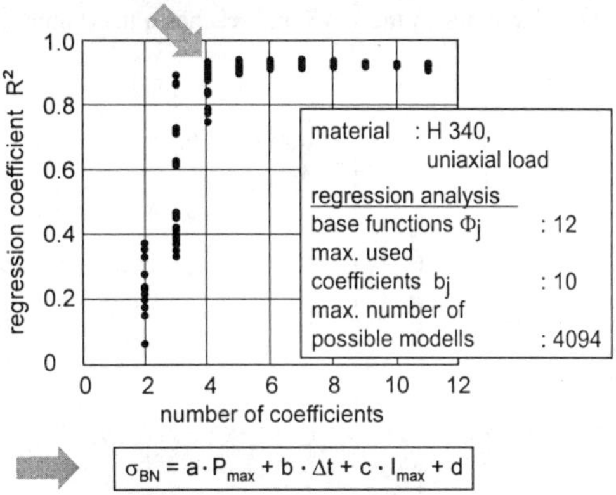

Fig. 2: Evaluation of the correlation polynomial

The residual stresses measured by micromagnetic techniques in this paper are always determined by a polynomial with four coefficients. In particular residual stress evaluation by Barkhausen noise analysis σ_{BN} can be determined by the following equation:

$$\sigma_{BN} = a \cdot P_{\max} + b \cdot \Delta t + c \cdot I_{\max} + d \quad (1)$$

Whereas σ_{BN} is the determined residual stress value, a, b, c, d are the coefficients of calibration measurements, P_{max} is the maximum of the Barkhausen noise amplitude, Δt is the peak shift and I_{max} the maximum of the number of impulses versus the amplitude. It has to be noticed that a constant offset represented by the coefficient d is needed for this equation.

WELDING OF THIN FERROMAGNETIC SHEETS

An important field during manufactoring of tailored blanks is the monitoring of the welding process. The Barkhausen noise analysis presented in this paper was applied to laser beam welding. Inert gas is used to avoid oxidation of the material in the welding zone. Laser beam welding is characterised by a small localised weld seam. For first investigations a CO_2 laser Triagon 6000 manufactured by Wegmann Boasel was applied for welding. The used output power was 2 kW using a feed of 3,5 m/min.

COMPARISON OF LABORATORY METHODS AND BARKHAUSEN NOISE ANALYSIS

For industrial acceptance the Barkhausen noise measurement has to prove its sensitivity to detect changes in the residual stress state of sheets after welding. It has to be compared to well established methods like X-ray residual stress determination and metallographic inspections like microstructure and micro hardness results.

In Fig. 3 a cross-section of the weld seam is displayed. Typical zones of the welding seam can be seen. Next to the primary structure the heat affected zone (HAZ) consisting of a fine and a coarse grained zone is located. A typical dendritic structure occurs in the middle of the weld. The microhardness increases in the HAZ and reaches a maximum in the middle of the weld.

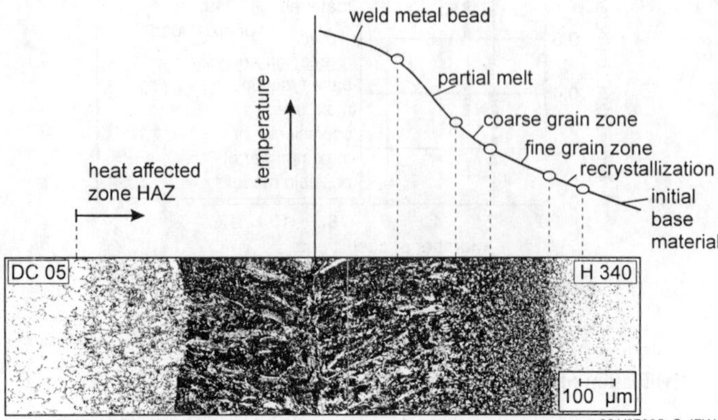

Fig. 3: Cross-section and microhardness of a laser beam welding

The residual stress course perpendicular to the welding seam follows the same tendencies of the microhardness as shown in Fig. 4. High levels for both values are found in the middle of the welding seam. The course of the residual stress is broadened compared to the micro hardness because of the extension of the X-ray measurement area in a range of about 2 mm in diameter. These „classical" values have to be compared with the new evaluation method.

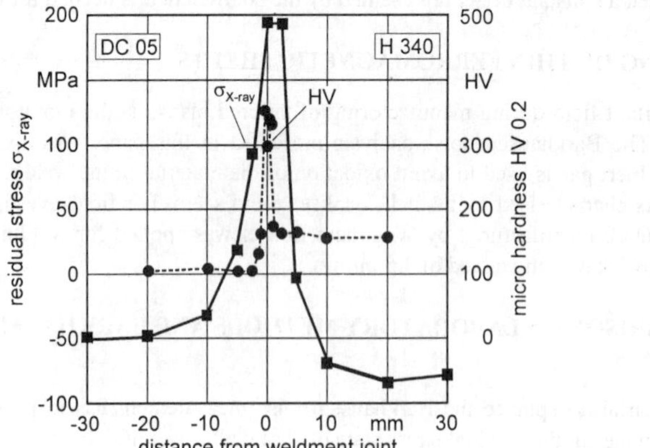

Fig. 4: Residual stress and micro hardness of a laser beam welding evaluated by X-ray analysis and Vickers indentation

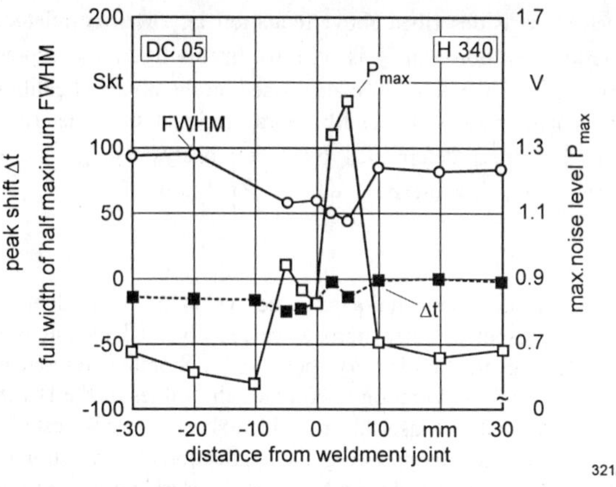

Fig. 5: Barkhausen noise values of a laser beam welding

The parameters found by Barkhausen noise analysis are shown in Fig. 5. Best correlation of one single parameter to the residual stress state is found for the maximum Barkhausen noise level. Other values like FWHM and peak shift are more significant for the material properties of the sheet. In the middle of the welding seam these values show a significant change. The reason is the sensitivity of the Barkhausen noise analysis on every material change even in case of recrystallization, stress relief, annealing or just heat induced dislocation movements. Because of the sensitivity of FWHM and peak shift, it is possible to determine the influence of the microstructure on the maximum noise level and to eliminate this influence for calculating residual stresses.

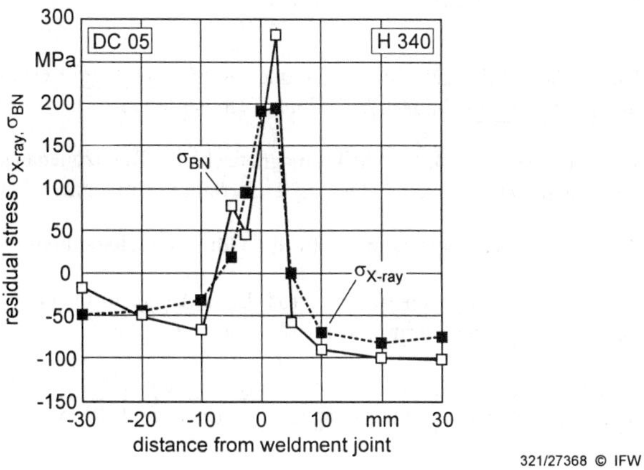

Fig. 6: Comparison of residual stresses evaluated by X-ray and Barkhausen noise analysis

By using the compensation as described above (equation 1), a well correlated residual stress state is found by Barkhausen noise analysis (Fig. 6). In this figure σ_{BN} represents the stress values calculated by equation 1 with coefficients based on the obtained calibration curve. $\sigma_{X\text{-}ray}$ represents the measured stresses obtained by X-ray residual stress determination. A good accordance between the stress determined by X-ray analysis $\sigma_{X\text{-}ray}$ and determined by Barkhausen noise analysis σ_{BN} is achieved.

CONCLUSION

In this paper the Barkhausen noise technique for the evaluation of residual stress of welded ferromagnetic sheets is presented. Characteristic values obtained by the Barkhausen noise signal allow residual stress evaluation in very short time. Laboratory reference tests using X-ray diffraction are necessary for calibration to correlate the values of the Barkhausen noise to residual stresses. For unwelded and laser beam welded sheets, tension tests or sample welds can be used for calibration. Generally speaking, the application of correlation curves allows to determine the residual stress state of welded steel sheets by Barkhausen noise data.

ACKNOWLEDGEMENT

The presented research work is supported by the German Research council (DFG) in a Special Research Department (SFB) 362 named „Fertigen in Feinblech" (manufacturing in sheets).

REFERENCES

1. Heyn H, Decker I, Wohlfahrt H, Proceedings of SPIE: Laser Material Processing: Industrial and Micorelectronics Applications, Vol. 2207, (1994) 198

2. Tiito S, Int. Conf. on Residual Stresses, Soc. Francaise de Metallurgie, Nancy, (1988) 205

3. Theiner WA: Micromagnetic techniques, in Structural and Residual Stress Analysis by Nondestructive Methods, ed. V. Hauk, Elsevier Science B.V. (1997) 564

4. Karpuschewski B: "Mikromagnetische Randzonenanalyse geschliffener einsatzgehärteter Bauteile", Dr.-Ing. Dissertation, University of Hannover, 1995.

5. Kneller E: "Ferromagnetismus", Berlin, Göttingen, Heidelberg, Springer Verlag 1962

6. Tönshoff HK, Karpuschewski B, Prod. Eng., Annals of the German Academic Society for Production Engineering, Vol. II/2 1995, p.203-206

7. Tönshoff HK, Seegers H, Proceedings of the 2nd International Conference on Barkhausen Noise and Micromagnetic Testing, 25-26.10.1999, Newcastle Upon Tyne, United Kingdom

8. Macherauch E and Müller P, Z. angew. Physik 13 (1961) 305

PROBLEMS IN RESIDUAL STRESS DETERMINATION FOR THICK COMPONENTS

M. E. Fitzpatrick[1], M. J. Kennard[2], and C. J. Small[2]

[1]Department of Materials Engineering, The Open University Walton Hall, Milton Keynes MK7 6AA, UK

[2]Rolls Royce plc, PO Box 31, Derby DE24 8BJ, UK

ABSTRACT

Problems exist in obtaining valid, unambiguous stress measurements for large components, where knowledge of the stress distribution is required over a distance of several centimetres at depths of millimetres or centimetres below the surface. In order to achieve in-depth measurements using layer removal techniques, such as hole drilling or X-ray diffraction combined with material removal, the volume of material removed can critically alter the residual stress distribution which is being measured.

In this study, neutron diffraction was used to provide validation of previous hole-drilling measurements on a superalloy quench probe, which was required owing to discrepancies between the hole drilling results and a predictive finite element (FE) model.

The results from the diffraction experiment do not allow for direct comparison with the other results: it was necessary to section the probe before measurement, and this caused a large relaxation in the levels of residual stress. The results highlight the problems involved in obtaining accurate residual stress data from large components.

INTRODUCTION

A knowledge of the stress distribution in a manufactured component can be critical to the generation of accurate fatigue lifing information. Residual stress fields can affect fatigue lives by acceleration or deceleration of a growing crack (1-3). This has implications for many manufactured components, particularly those which experience a heat treatment during processing; since the cooling rate experienced within a material during a quench will affect both the level of residual stress and also the final microstructure that is obtained.

Residual stress generation during cooling can be modelled using the finite element (FE) method. Knowledge of the variation of yield stress of the material in question as a function of temperature is required, along with the thermal conductivity of the material and the thermal transfer between the component surface and the quenching agent. The model can be critically dependent on the geometry of the component, and on any simplifying assumptions which are used in its creation.

In practice, modelling is only suitable in isolation if the problem studied is well-understood, or a relatively small deviation is being made from an existing application. If this is not the case, the model will require validation, usually by direct measurement of the residual stress in the component. This may be simple in the case of near-surface strains, or in cases where the stress varies over a relatively short distance (say a few millimetres) from the surface of the sample.

Surface strains may be measured simply by the X-ray diffraction method. This method can be entirely non-destructive, relying only upon Bragg reflection of X-rays from the surface. However, the penetrability of X-rays is limited, being typically of the order of a few microns, compared to neutrons which can penetrate several millimetres. This does not mean that profiling is impossible with X-rays, but rather that in order to obtain a stress profile it is necessary to perform electrolytic polishing or some other method of layer removal to expose a surface at the required depth.

In principle, neutron diffraction stress measurement offers a simple non-destructive technique for the determination of residual stress (4-6). Neutrons have high penetrability into most materials, allowing determination of the strains (and hence stress) up to several centimetres below a surface. The principles of the technique are identical to those for X-ray diffraction, although the higher penetrability of neutrons allows more flexibility in the geometry of the measurements.

Problems arise with neutron measurements if the neutrons have to traverse long path lengths within a sample. This can vary significantly depending on the material under study: the attenuation of neutrons by nickel is much greater than by aluminium, meaning that in-depth measurements are more difficult for nickel or nickel-based samples. It is possible, in some cases, to facilitate measurements by removing material from the beam path (7), provided that no change in stress occurs at the actual measurement position, as monitored by strain gauges. Other problems can arise, for example, if the material under study scatters neutrons incoherently to a large degree: although titanium in principle should be easy to measure in depth according to its attenuation, measurements are made difficult by a high degree of incoherent scattering, which greatly reduced the signal/noise ratio of the elastic diffraction peak.

In some cases, then, some sectioning or removal of material from the component may be necessary. Again, this is acceptable if it can be shown that there has not been a significant relaxation at the measurement position; sometimes, however, access to the desired measurement location is impossible without sectioning that causes large changes in the internal stress field.

In the present study, knowledge of the residual stress profile was required in a thick (100 mm) nickel component. It is shown that reliable and accurate stress measurement for such components is not technically feasible with current techniques.

Sample details

Ni-base superalloys have become the sole material used in turbine components for both civil and military jet engines. The performance of the components manufactured from these materials – the turbine blades and discs – is critical to the safety of the aircraft. Knowledge of the performance of these materials is therefore of prime importance, not only for newly-developed materials but also for established alloys which have seen property improvements from refinement of manufacturing processes over their production lifespan.

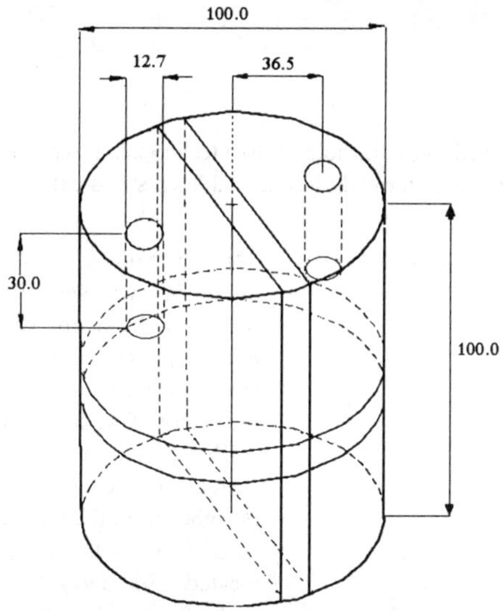

Figure 1: Diagram of the quench probe

One of the key areas for optimizing these materials is that of the heat treatments that are applied to them prior to use. This is important not only from a microstructural viewpoint, in controlling γ' size and distribution, but also in terms of the residual stresses that are generated within the material. It is of critical importance that the evolution of residual stress during heat treatment, particularly during the quenching process, is thoroughly understood.

To this end, several 'quench probes' were prepared from the Alloy 720Li, in the form of cylinders 100 mm long, with a diameter of 100 mm. The cylinders were quenched into oil following a 4-hour heat treatment at a temperature of 1105°C. Each sample had a small (~1 mm diameter and 5 mm depth) thermocouple hole and two larger (~12.7 mm diameter and 30 mm depth) screw mounting holes in one end. The sample is shown in figure 1.

MODEL RESULTS

A finite element (FE) model was developed of the quench process, to predict the stress variation within the probe following the quench. Validation of such a model is required before it can be applied to the modelling of stress development in a real component: direct measurement of the stress can highlight problems with boundary conditions in the model, for example.

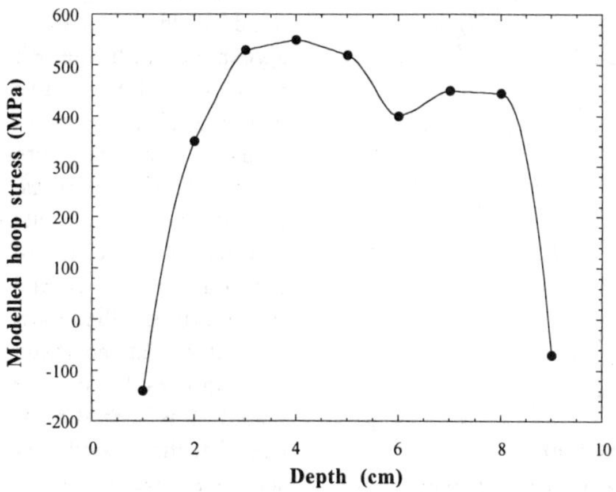

Figure 2: Modelled hoop stress variation

Figure 2 shows the hoop stress variation that was predicted by the FE model. The stresses are the hoop stresses as a function of distance from one end of the cylinder, at a radial position 20 mm from the centre. The distribution along this line is not unusual, showing compressive stress near the surfaces of the probe balanced by tensile stress in the centre.

HOLE DRILLING RESULTS

Initial validation of the FE results was attempted using the hole drilling technique. Deep (*i.e.*, not at-surface) hole drilling measurements were performed. Radial and hoop stress data was obtained from the measurements.

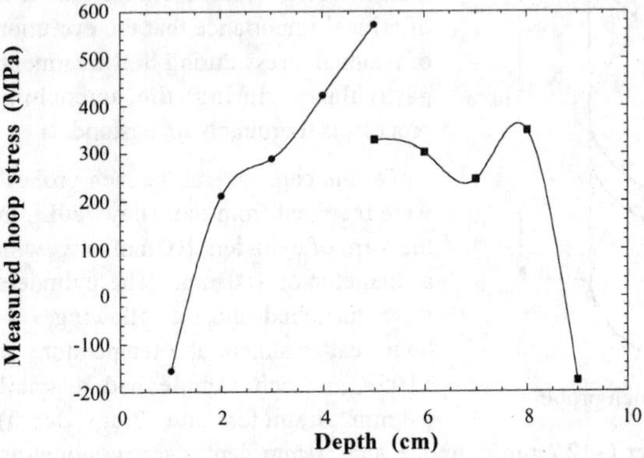

Figure 3: Hoop stress variation measured by hole drilling

Measurements were made in two separate locations, from opposite ends of the probe at positions ~15 mm from the centre. One hole was drilled from the top surface of the cylinder, the other from the bottom surface, with the bores located 180° away from each other. The bores were quite wide, being 30 mm diameter for the outer (nearest to the surface) measurement positions, and 15 mm diameter for the inner measurement positions. It can be appreciated, therefore, that a large volume of material was removed from the probe during the measurements.

Results for the hoop stress in the probe are shown in figure 3. Accuracy figures are not available for these data.

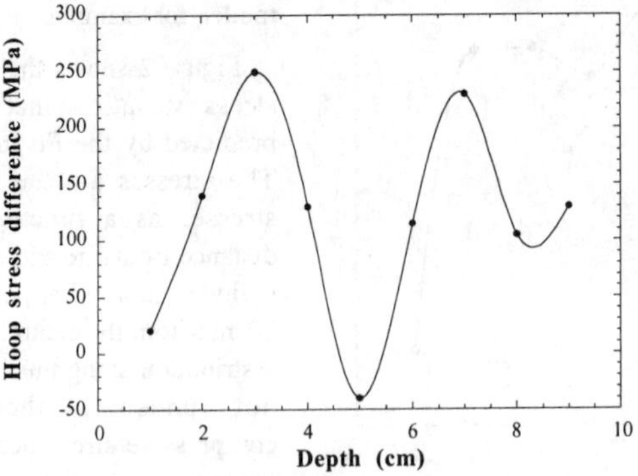

Figure 4: Difference between the two methods (modelled – measured)

Although the general trend of the data is in agreement with the FE results, there are discrepancies in some areas. Measurements were made firstly from the top of the probe (data points on the left side of the graph); the second hole was then drilled from the bottom (data points on the right side of the graph). It is interesting to note that the second data set gives a reading at the centre of the probe which is ~300 MPa lower than the first set. This may be a reflection of the degree to which the removal of material had begun to reduce the stress field which existed in the probe. Although the second data set does show an overall lower stress than the first, this is roughly in keeping with the trend predicted from the FE model (figure 2).

Figure 4 shows the differences between the results obtained by the two methods. Differences of up to 250 MPa can be seen at some points, with a mean difference of around 135 MPa. Hence another measurement technique – neutron diffraction – was used in an attempt to provide validation for either the model or the hole drilling results.

EXPERIMENTAL DETAILS: NEUTRON DIFFRACTION

The neutron diffraction strain measurements were performed on the G5.2 spectrometer at the Orphée reactor facility of the Laboratoire Léon Brillouin, Saclay, France. Full details of the neutron strain measurement method may be found elsewhere (4).

Although neutrons have a high penetrability into most materials, for the quench probe, measurement of the hoop stresses at the required positions would have required very long path lengths within the material, and so prohibitively long counting times. It was necessary, therefore, to cut the probe into sections before the neutron measurements were performed. Two nominally identical probes were sectioned: one was cut into discs, so relaxing the axial strains; the other had a slab removed at the required distance from the centre, with the slab cut parallel to the longitudinal axis of the probe. Cutting the slab was expected to have the effect of relieving the hoop stress direction within it. It was hoped that the strains would therefore be identical in the radial direction for equivalent positions in the slab and disc samples, therefore allowing an overall stress determination to be made.

Strain gauges mounted on the sample surfaces showed very large changes in the residual strains during the machining process, far greater than had been anticipated. This will clearly have had a large effect on the final results.

Furthermore, the neutron diffraction method requires a strain-free reference to which the measured peaks can be compared. In this case a powder sample was used, but, owing to differences in chemical composition or thermal history, it was found that the powder sample was more tensile than all the measured strain points within the sample. Absolute strains could not therefore be determined, and it is therefore more instructive in this case to look at the differences and trends which were observed.

EXPERIMENTAL RESULTS

Previous measurements on nickel superalloy materials at Saclay had indicated that measurement times would be fairly rapid. However, the diffracted intensity was found to be much lower than anticipated, which was attributed to an adverse texture in the quench probe samples compared to those which had been studied before. This restricted the number of results that could be obtained.

As mentioned in the previous section, one probe was sectioned into seven discs, five of 15 mm thickness and two of 12.5 mm thickness. Measurements were made in a total of five samples: four discs and the slab. The four discs correspond to four positions along the axis of the cylinder. Four corresponding positions were measured in the slab sample. Table I shows how these samples correspond to the positions shown in previous figures.

Sample Number	Centre position (mm)	Measured
Disc 1	7.5	√
Disc 2	21.25	√
Disc 3	35	√
Disc 4	50	×
Disc 5	65	√
Disc 6	78.75	×
Disc 7	92.5	×

Table I: Relation of the disc samples to the measurement positions shown in figures 1-3.

Probe symmetry

The probe is cylindrical, with two screw fittings and a thermocouple hole at one end. It was assumed that the stress distribution would be axisymmetric about the centre of the circular cross-section, and measurements were made to validate this.

The strain in Disc 2 was measured at three positions around its circumference, at equal distances from the centre. The results for the three strain directions are shown in figure 5.

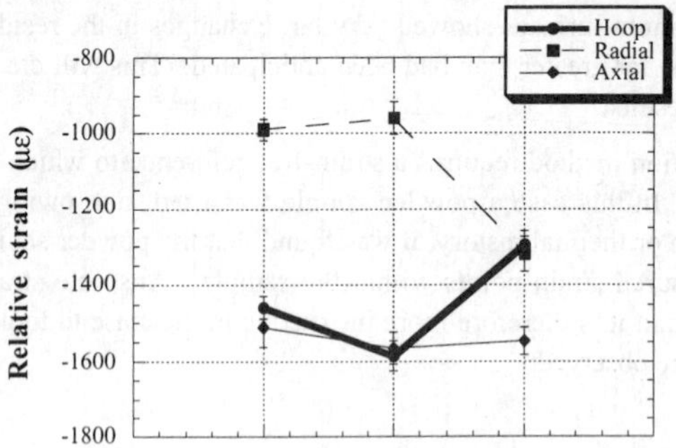

Fig 5: Strain measurements at three positions in disc 2 (S2).

The overall symmetry of the results is clearly poor, with a variation of around 300 με in the radial strains and 200 με in the hoop. The axial strains are more constant, but it may be recalled that these strains were expected to have been relaxed by the machining of the discs, and this may account for the reduced variability. The actual difference in stress owing to these changes is not enormous, being of the order of ~60 MPa, but it was disappointing to find an inherent variability in the stress which was significantly greater than the scatter in the experimental data. It is possible that the steel support bars inserted at one end of the quench probe may have had a greater effect on the stress field than was anticipated. It had not been considered necessary to include these bars in any model of the stress generation in the probe, owing to the reasonable similarity in the properties of the bars compared to the material of the probe itself.

This result does pose problems for the interpretation of other measured strains: the discs were not matched in terms of rotational position relative to the cylinder, so the equivalent positions around the circumference were not known. It is possible, therefore, that this variability could impair any attempt to calculate the stresses from the measured strains, and it is therefore almost certain that the strain variations are of more interest in this case.

Finally, it should be noted that all strain data presented for the probes is negative: this is because, as already mentioned, the reference powder used was not appropriate for the probes, and therefore constitutes a reference only, rather than a zero-stress sample for the experiments.

Strain results

Strains were measured for the samples indicated in Table I.

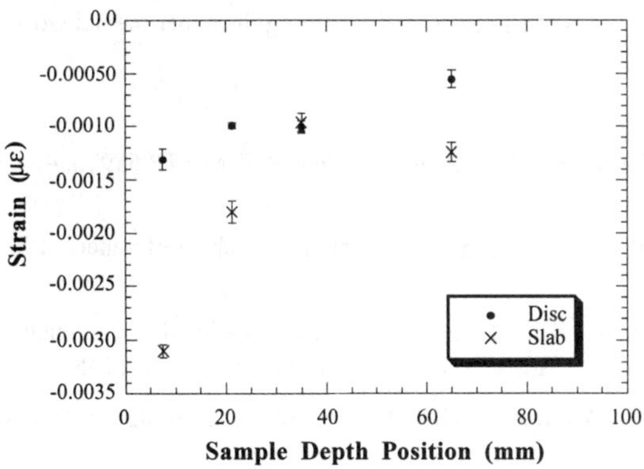

Figure 6: Radial strain variation

The most useful strain variation is probably that shown in figure 6. This shows the measured radial strain variation in the slab sample, along with the corresponding values from the discs, for comparison.

The slab does not suffer from the inter-sample variability which was seen in the discs. The variation of the radial strains can therefore be assumed to be accurate, and also follows the expected pattern seen from the hole drilling and FE model results, varying from relative compression near the end of the probe, and becoming increasingly tensile towards the centre. The magnitude of the variation (estimated from a simple conversion from strain to stress using the elastic modulus) is around 40% lower than that predicted from the FE model. Once again, it is likely that this is an effect of the sectioning of the sample. This can certainly be seen for the disc samples, where the total variation is much smaller than that seen within the slab.

A possible future continuation of the programme would be to extract the strain data from the FE model, and make a direct comparison of this with the neutron diffraction results.

CONCLUSIONS

Neutron diffraction was applied to determine the strain variation in a quenched superalloy, to validate results of an FE model. Despite the widespread use of this and other strain measurement methods, problems still exist when determining the stress variation in large components: neutrons do not have sufficient penetrability and sectioning is invariably necessary if more than ~30 mm of material have to be traversed by the neutron beam. Although this is material-dependent, certainly 30 mm is a suitable upper-bound for nickel alloys. If destructive methods are applied, such as layer removal or hole drilling, the redistribution of the stress field becomes more difficult to compensate for as increasing amounts of material are removed, which can lead to inaccuracies in the measurements.

In this case, the most useful results were obtained from a slab which was cut from the superalloy quench probe. This shows a variation of radial strain which is consistent with the FE model, and can be directly compared with the strain results from this model.

ACKNOWLEDGEMENTS

We wish to thank Dr M. Ceretti of the Laboratoire Léon Brillouin for her help with the neutron diffraction experiments. Funding for the beam time was provided by the Commission of the European Community through the Large Installation Plan. MEF is grateful to Rolls-Royce plc for travel and subsistence funding during the experimental work.

REFERENCES

1. Elber, W.: in 'Fracture Toughness and Slow-Stable Cracking, ASTM STP 559',), 45-58; ASTM, 1974.

2. Rowland, E. S.: in Proc. 10th Sagamore Army Materials Research Conference. 1963, Syracuse University Press, 229-244.

3. Wilks, M. D. B., Nowell, D. and Hills, D. A.: in Fourth International Conference on Residual Stresses. 1994, Society for Experimental Mechanics, Bethel, CT, 1238-1245.

4. Allen, A. J., Hutchings, M. T., Windsor, C. G. and Andreani, C., Advances in Physics 34, (1985) 445 - 473.

5. Hutchings, M. T., Nondestr. Test. Eval. 5, (1990) 395 - 413.

6. Withers, P. J. and Edwards, L., Mater. World 4, (1996) 9-11.

7. Edwards, L., Bouchard, P. J., Dutta, M. and Fitzpatrick, M. E.: in Integrity of High Temperature Welds. 1998, Professional Engineering Publishing, Bury St Edmunds, UK, 181-191.

THE STRESS STATE EVOLUTION MEASURED IN SITU DURING CYCLIC LOADING OF A DUPLEX STAINLESS STEEL

J Johansson and M Odén
Division of Engineering Materials
Department of Mechanical Engineering
Linköping University
S-581 83 Linköping, Sweden

ABSTRACT

In two-phase materials, like duplex stainless steels, microstresses between the two phases are always present due to the difference in physical properties between the two phases. In this study the effect of microstresses on the fatigue behavior during pulsating tension fatigue have been investigated. In several studies, fading of microstresses during fatigue has been reported. However in this study no fading of microstresses was observed. In fact an increase from 50 MPa to 140 MPa of the microstresses in the austenite was observed during the first 100 cycles. This increase in microstresses will influence the fatigue crack initiation. Even if the hardness and yield strength was found to be higher for the austenitic phase compared to the ferritic phase, X-ray stress analysis and transmission electron microscopy show that more plastic deformation occur in the austenitic phase compared to the ferritic phase. The cyclic loading response of the material was thus mainly controlled by the plastic properties of the austenitic phase. Good correlation has been found between the internal stress state and the dislocation substructure evolution during fatigue. It was also found that initial compressive macrostresses in the surface increased from -40 to 50 MPa during the first 10^3 cycles.

INTRODUCTION

Duplex stainless steels, consisting of approximately equal amounts of austenite and ferrite, are today established in a wide product range from chemical tankers, pressure vessels and pipes to heat exchangers, paper machines, and offshore applications. The high strength of the duplex grades enables both weight and cost savings when they are used as corrosion resistant materials in a construction. The use of duplex stainless steels in load carrying applications has increased the demand for thorough knowledge of the fatigue mechanisms in these materials.

The low cycle fatigue behavior of duplex stainless steels has been investigated in great detail by several authors, e.g. ref (1-3). Magnin and Lardon (1) reported that crack initiation was related to the cyclic deformation mechanisms of ferrite at high plastic strain amplitudes ($\varepsilon_{pl} > 10^{-3}$) and to those of austenite at relatively low ε_{pl}. Degallaix et al. (3), on the other hand found that crack initiations were observed exclusively in the ferrite at low strain amplitudes and indifferently in both phases at higher strain amplitudes.

These inconclusive results might be explained by the internal stress state in the material. Residual microstresses are always present in duplex stainless steels due to the difference in coefficient of thermal expansion between the two phases. A large variation in residual thermal stresses, both measured and calculated, has been reported in the literature (4-7), and it is clear that texture effects and plastic relaxation will influence these stresses (6). Johansson et al. (6) have shown that these residual microstresses can change during deformation due to different elastic and plastic properties of the two phases. It is therefore likely that microstresses influence the plastic strain and thus also the cyclic slip localization causing fatigue crack initiation.

In this paper we report on the evolution of the internal stress state of a duplex stainless steel during tension fatigue. The observed stress changes, measured with X-ray diffraction, are correlated to the microstructure evolution, studied by transmission electron microscopy (TEM) and X-ray diffraction texture analysis.

EXPERIMENTAL PROCEDURES

Specimens

The material is a commercial duplex stainless steel of type SAF 2304 provided by Avesta Sheffield AB. The chemical composition is given in Table 1. The steel has been hot and cold rolled to a thickness of 1.5 mm. After the cold rolling, the material was solution treated and quenched from a temperature of 1050°C to avoid precipitation of secondary phases.

The micrograph in Fig. 1 shows, as a result of the rolling, a heavily banded microstructure with austenitic islands in a ferritic matrix. The volume fraction, determined from point counting of each phase, is 45±5% for the ferritic phase and 55±5% for the austenitic phase. For more detailed information about the microstructure, see ref (6).

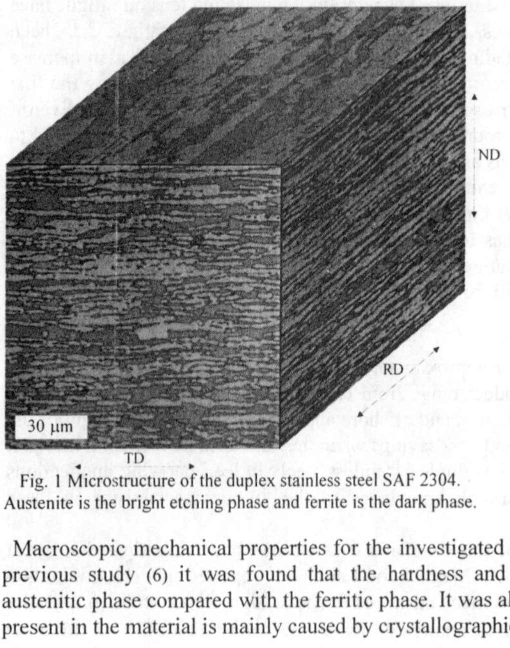

Fig. 1 Microstructure of the duplex stainless steel SAF 2304. Austenite is the bright etching phase and ferrite is the dark phase.

Table 1 Chemical Composition of the Duplex Stainless Steel SAF 2304

Element	Fraction (wt. %)
Fe	Bal.
C	0.022
Si	0.37
Mn	1.5
Cr	22.8
Ni	4.9
Mo	0.31
Cu	0.26
N	0.098

Macroscopic mechanical properties for the investigated material are listed in Table 2. In a previous study (6) it was found that the hardness and yield strength are higher for the austenitic phase compared with the ferritic phase. It was also found that the elastic anisotropy present in the material is mainly caused by crystallographic texture in the ferritic phase.

Table 2 Macroscopic Material Properties of Duplex Stainless Steel SAF 2304, from (6)

Properties	RD	45	TD	Method
Young's modulus [GPa]	196	199	209	Resonance testing
Proof strength Rp0.2 [MPa]	523	530	566	Tensile test
Tensile strength Rm [MPa]	730	713	767	Tensile test
Strain to failure [%]	39	43	38	Tensile test

Flat specimens with a thickness of 1.5 mm, width of 8.0 mm, and gauge length of 70 mm were machined from the sheet with the rolling direction corresponding to the loading axis. After machining, the specimens were ground with 1200-grit SiC paper followed with 6, 3 and 1 μm diamond paste. After mechanical surface treatment, 10 μm was electropolished away from the specimens to avoid grinding stresses at the surface.

Fatigue Testing

Pulsating (R=0.05) stress-controlled fatigue testing was performed in a servohydraulic Instron/MTS testing machine with a maximum capacity of 40 kN. The tests were carried out with a frequency of 1.0 Hz with a maximum load of 500 MPa. The test was interrupted after 10, 10^2, 10^3, 10^4, 10^5 and $3.5 \cdot 10^5$ cycles and the specimens were then moved to a tensile test device constructed to fit on the X-ray diffractometer. The last fatigue cycle was then performed on the diffractometer where phase specific stresses were measured in situ during loading. The stresses were recorded at different load steps, corresponding to 0, 400 and 500 MPa during loading and 100 and 0 MPa during unloading.

Stress Measurements by X-ray Diffraction

An Ω-diffractometer with Cr K_α radiation was used to measure the interplanar spacing of the {211} planes in the ferritic phase and of the {220} planes in the austenitic phase. In order to make three-dimensional (3D) stress analysis possible, lattice displacements were determined in 3 ϕ-directions (0°, 60° and 120°) for 11 ψ-angles between ±50° for the ferrite and between ±42° for the austenite. For a definition of the above angles, see reference (8). The locations of the diffracted peaks were determined by a least squares fit of a pseudo-Voigt function to the data. The unstressed lattice parameters a_0 for each phase in the investigated material were determined previously to be 3.59694±0.00020 Å for austenite and 2.87355±0.00018 Å for ferrite (6). The stress tensor was determined in each phase by a least-squares procedure (9), where the Hill average of the single crystal values given by Inal et. al (10) was used as the X-ray elastic constants. The total stress tensors were than separated into macro- and microstress tensors for each phase (11).

Microstructure Evolution

The microstructure evolution and the dislocation substructure characterization of the fatigued specimens were carried out through TEM studies and XRD-texture measurements.

The crystallographic texture of both phases was determined for the material as received and after 10, 10^3, 10^4, and 10^5 cycles by XRD-texture measurements on a Seifert PTS 3000 diffractometer using Co K_α radiation. Four incomplete pole figures were measured for each phase and orientation distribution functions (ODFs) calculated by the series expansion method (12).

For the TEM studies, disks with a diameter of 3 mm and the foil plane parallel to the tensile axis were punched from both the surface and the interior of the fatigued specimens. The disks were reduced to a thickness of 50-100 μm by mechanical polishing. Foils were finally produced by electropolishing to perforation using a solution of 1000 ml CH_3COOH, 75 ml $HClO_4$ and 45 ml H_2O in a Struers Tenupol-3 electrolytic polishing equipment. The dislocation structures were then examined in a Philips EM400T microscope, operating at 120 kV.

RESULTS AND DISCUSSION

In Fig. 2 the evolution during fatigue of the residual microstresses are shown for the unloaded specimens. The stresses in the rolling direction, which is also the direction of applied load, increase during the first hundred cycles before reaching a saturation stage (Fig. 2a).

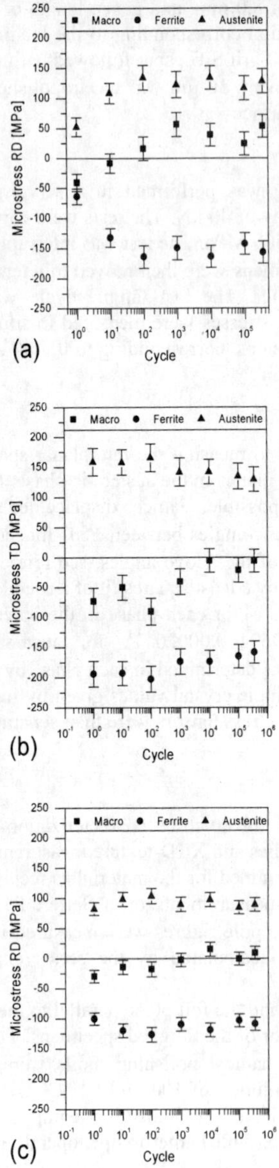

Fig. 2 Evolution of residual microstresses in unloaded specimens during fatigue. (a) shows stresses in the rolling direction, (b) stresses in the transverse direction and, (c) stresses in the normal direction

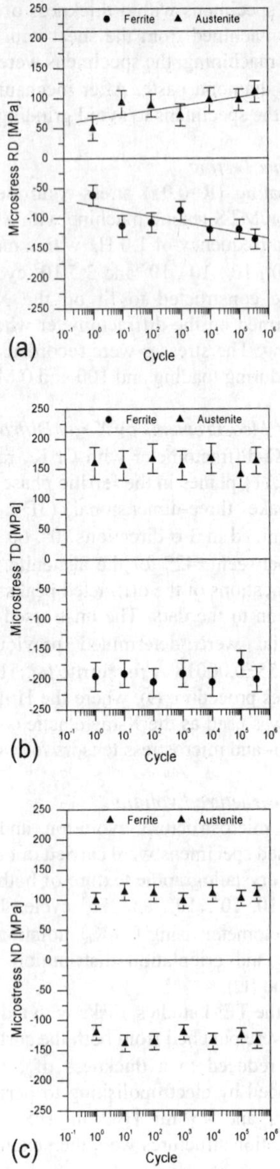

Fig. 3 Evolution of microstresses at maximum applied load during fatigue. (a) shows stresses in the rolling direction, (b) stresses in the transverse direction and, (c) stresses in the normal direction

The microstresses in the other two directions show similar trends but the changes are smaller and fall within the error range (Fig. 2b and 2c). The microstresses measured in situ at maximum applied load increase slightly in the loading direction but follow no significant trends in the other two directions (Fig. 3).

A clearer picture of the load-sharing mechanisms is seen if one studies the hysteresis loop separately for the two phases. In Fig. 4 the measured average total stresses in both phases are plotted as a function of the applied macroscopic total strain for different cycles. One can see that the relative width of the hysteresis loops between the two phases changes during fatigue. While the hysteresis loops in the austenite show minor changes after the very first cycle, there is a trend towards decreasing width of the hysteresis loops in the ferritic phases with increasing number of cycles.

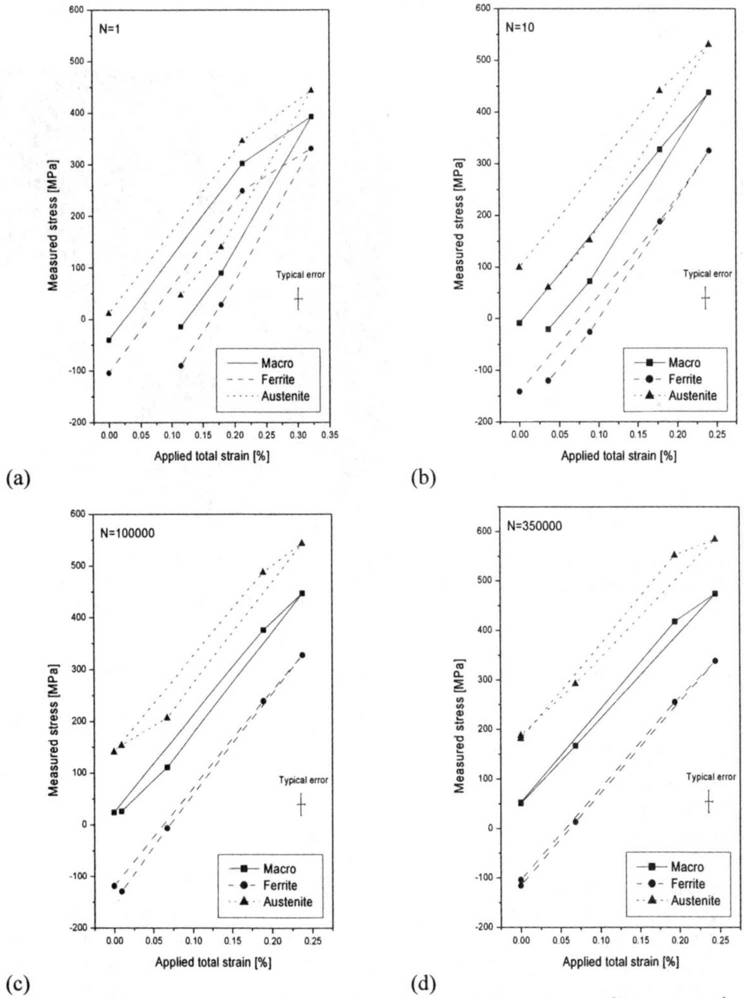

Fig. 4 Hysteresis loops for different load cycles N. (a) N=1, (b) N=10, (c) $N=10^4$, (d) $N=3.5\cdot10^5$

For the as-received material the ferritic phase showed two strong texture components, {001}⟨110⟩ and {011}⟨100⟩, while the austenite showed weaker texture with the strongest component at the {011}⟨111⟩. The evolution of the orientation density during fatigue for the different texture components is plotted in Fig. 5. During fatigue a clear trend towards stronger texture can be noticed in the ferritic phase. It is the rotated cube texture component {001}⟨110⟩ that increases in intensity. The changes in the austenite are insignificant. The texture changes are caused by crystal rotation or formation of new grains with a preferred orientation. For a two-phase material Bunge et al. (13) found that the phase with smaller amount of local plasticity show more pronounced textural changes than the phase with more local plasticity. The ferritic phase, with less plastic activity, is free to deform into the austenite with less interaction than in a single-phase material, but the deformation of the ferrite must be compensated by some 'turbulent' flow of the austenite (13), which leads to an observed weakening of its texture.

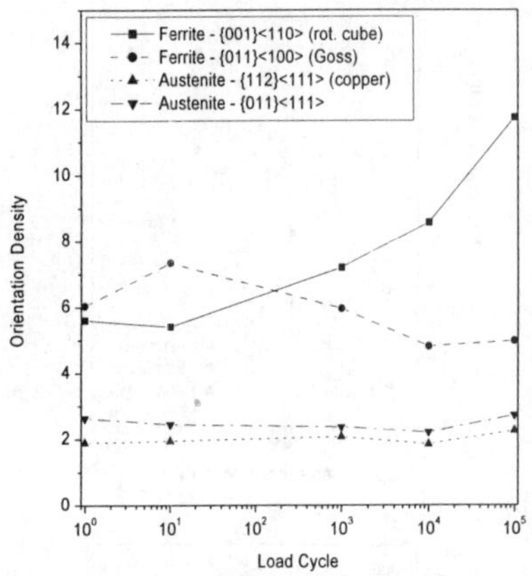

Fig. 5 Evolution of texture components during fatigue in a duplex stainless steel.

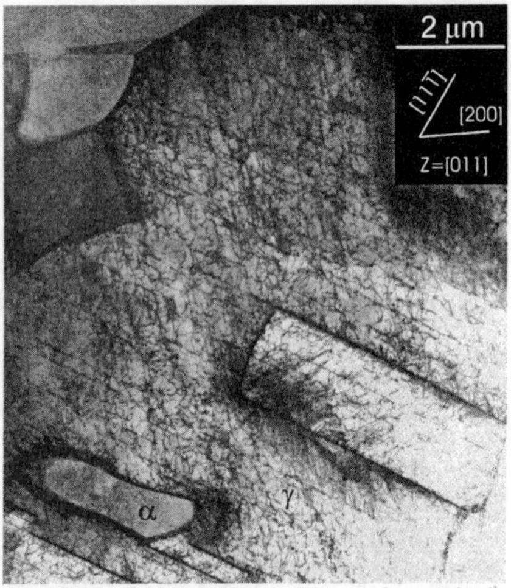

Fig. 6 Bright field transmission electron micrograph of austenitic grain fatigued for $4.2 \cdot 10^5$ cycles. Note the high dislocation density in the vicinity of grain and twin boundaries.

The as-received material showed a low dislocation density in both phases. Annealing twins were common in the austenitic phase due to the low stacking fault energy in this phase. However, after cyclic deformation the dislocation density increased and accumulation of dislocation arrays and small pileups of planar character were observed in the austenitic grains. Meanwhile in the interior ferritic grains, insignificant changes of the dislocation density were observed after $1 \cdot 10^5$ cycles.

After fracture ($4.2 \cdot 10^5$ cycles), a denser dislocation structure was observed in both the ferritic and austenitic phases. In the austenitic phase, a dense distribution of planar arrays within the grains was also found. As shown in Fig. 6, several subsets of straight dislocation segments consistent with the {111}⟨110⟩ slip system are present, together with randomly oriented loops and half-loops. This type of array has been reported to form in the austenitic phase of duplex stainless steels during low cycle fatigue at low strain amplitudes (2, 14, 15). One can also notice a denser dislocation structure close to phase boundaries and twin boundaries. In general, a lower dislocation density was found in the ferritic phase compared to the austenitic phase for the investigated foils. Some ferritic grains showed a substructure with massive pileups at the grain boundaries and a low dislocation density in the interior of the grain, see Fig. 7(a), while others showed a homogeneous distribution of short dislocation segments.

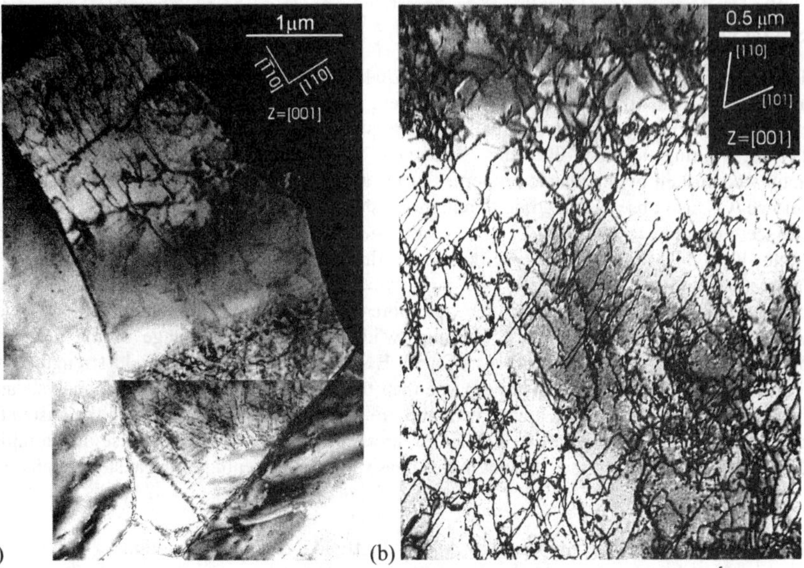

(a) (b)

Fig. 7 (a) Bright field transmission electron micrograph of interior ferritic grain fatigued for $4.2 \cdot 10^5$ cycles.
(b) Bright field transmission electron micrograph of a near-surface ferritic grain fatigued for 10^5 cycles.

The samples taken from the surface region showed a denser dislocation structure in the ferritic grains compared to the samples taken from the center of the fatigued specimen. Fig. 7(b) shows a ferritic grain close to the surface that was fatigued for 10^5 cycles. One can notice formation of dislocation tangles and early formation of dislocation bundles. However, for the austenite no significant difference in dislocation structure was noticed between the near-surface grains and the interior grains. The observed hardening of the surface explains the increase of macrostress from -40 to 50 MPa in the loading direction for unloaded specimens, see Fig. 2.

The X-ray stress measurements show that both phases deform plastically to almost the same degree during the first cycle, see Fig. 4(a). However higher microstresses are found in the austenitic phase after unloading, due to the higher work hardening rate of the austenitic phase, see Fig. 2(a). The compressive microstresses present in the ferritic phase prevent further plastic deformation in this phase, which explains why the widths of the hysteresis loops decrease in the ferritic phase but remain in the austenitic phase, Fig. 4. These results are supported by the TEM investigations, where a denser dislocation structure was observed in the austenitic phase compared to the ferritic phase. In several studies, e.g. (16, 17), fading of microstresses have been reported to occur during fatigue. We did not observe fading in this study when stress-controlled tension-tension fatigue (R=0.05) were performed. In fact, an increase of the microstresses was observed and the reason is the difference in plastic properties between the two phases and the accumulation of a mean plastic strain that takes place in every load cycle. It is obvious that the microstresses influence the cyclic response of the material and must be added to the applied stress when local strains are considered. Since the microstresses are compressive in the softer ferritic phase, the microstresses might act beneficial and delay crack initiation in the ferritic phase. However, if the microstresses are too large, crack initiation from local stress concentrations will instead occur in the austenitic phase.

SUMMARY

The behavior of a duplex stainless steel SAF 2304 during cyclic tension-tension loading with a maximum load of 500 MPa has been studied. A rapid hardening of the austenitic phase contributed to increasing the residual microstresses in the austenitic phase from 50 MPa to 140 MPa during the first 100 cycles. The cyclic loading response of the material was thus mainly controlled by the plastic properties of the austenitic phase. Preferred hardening of the surface was also observed, leading to a higher dislocation density for the ferritic grains in the surface compared to the interior. As a result, an increase of surface residual macrostresses from -40 to 50 MPa was observed during the first 10^3 cycles. After the initial increase of microstress and macrostresses for the early cycles no fading of residual stresses occurred during the following cycles. Evolution of a more intense preferred orientation was observed in the ferritic phase during cyclic loading, while no significant change of the preferred orientation of the austenitic phase was found. Even if the hardness and yield strength were found to be higher for the austenitic phase than the ferritic phase, X-ray stress analysis and transmission electron microscopy show that more plastic deformation occurs in the austenitic phase. A higher load is therefore transferred through the ferritic matrix because of the initial compressive residual stresses present in this phase and the hardening of the austenitic phase.

ACKNOWLEDGEMENTS

The work was financially supported by Avesta Sheffield Research Foundation.

REFERENCES

1. Magnin T, Lardon JM, Mater Sci Eng A104 (1988) 21
2. Mateo A, Llanes L, Itugoyen L, Anglada M, Acta Mater 44 (1996) 1143
3. Degallaix S, Seddouki A, Degallaix G, Nilsson J-O, 'Fatigue 93', Engineering Materials Advisory Services Ltd. (Warley), 1993 p.91
4. Harjo S, Tomota Y, Ono M, Acta Mater 47 (1999) 353
5. Kamachi K, Okada T, Kawano M, Namba S, Ishida T, Tani N, Kubohori T, 'Progress in Science and Engineering of Composites, ICCM-IV', JSCM (Tokyo), 1982 p.1383
6. Johansson J, Odén M, Zeng X-H, Acta. Mater. 47 (1999) 2669
7. Siegmund T, Fischer F, Werner E, Mater. Sci. Eng. A169 (1993) 125
8. Noyan IC, Cohen JB, 'Residual stress measurement by diffraction and interpretation', Springer-Verlag (New York), 1987
9. Winholtz RA, Cohen JB, Aust. J. Phys. 41 (1988) 189
10. Inal K, Lebrun JL, 'ICRS-5', Linköpings universitet (Sweden), 1997 p. 472
11. Noyan IC, Metall. Trans. A 14 (1983) 1907
12. Bunge HJ, Int. Mater. Rev. 32 (1987) 265
13. Bunge HJ, uL-Haq A, Weiland H, 'INFACON 6', SAIMM (Johannesburg), 1992 p.197
14. Kruml TP, J; Obrtlik, K; Degallaix, S, Acta. Mater 45 (1997) 5145
15. Polak J, Kruml T, Degallaix S, Scripta Metall. 29 (1993) 1553
16. Winholtz R, Cohen J, Mater. Sci. Eng. A154 (1992) 155
17. Almer JD, Cohen JB, Moran B, unpublished research (1999).

SESSION 7C

EFFECT OF RESIDUAL STRESSES ON FRACTURE BEHAVIOUR OF ALUMINA BASED COMPOSITES

H Tomaszewski, M. Boniecki and H Węglarz

Institute of Electronic Materials Technology
Wólczyńska 133, 01-919 Warsaw, Poland

ABSTRACT

Alumina based composites containing 10 to 30wt% of second phase particles with higher (ZrO_2+8mol% Y_2O_3) and lower thermal expansion coefficient (SiC) were prepared. In a result, compressive or tensile residual stresses were generated in alumina matrix during cooling from fabrication temperature. The effect of these stresses on fracture behaviour of composites was investigated by testing controlled crack growth during three point bending of single-edge-notched samples. Crack length, *c*, was measured *in situ* using a horizontal light microscope coupled with CCD camera fitted to testing machine. The force, *P*, responsible for a crack length increase, was computer controlled. The stress intensity factor, K_I, was calculated from measured data. The tests showed that ZrO_2 and SiC addition strongly decrease the effect of R-curve in alumina matrix. This phenomenon was explained by analysis of microstructure and residual stresses in ceramics on the base of piezospectroscopic measurements. For some samples of composites studied the tests of crack growth were performed without removing the load. In this case, the time dependent displacement *d* of the sample was measured and recorded together with values of force *P*. The stress intensity factor, K_I, maximal stress intensity factor, K_{Imax}, and resistance to crack initiation, K_{Ii}, were determined from recorded data.

INTRODUCTION

Normally the toughness-curve (T- or R-curve) behaviour is characterised by a change, usually showing an increase in toughness due to material's resistance to crack propagation with crack extension. In many brittle solids it originates from crack tip shielding mechanisms that operate in the crack wake, exerting a crack closure force that decreases the net stress intensity at the crack tip. The R-curve results from the accumulation of this closure force with crack growth, typically reaching a saturation limit. It is well established that the R-curve behaviour of alumina is due to the formation of frictional traction (grain bridges) between opposing crack faces in the crack wake (1). Microstructure variables that are known to control the level of toughening achievable via this mechanism include grain size and shape as well as the magnitude of internal stresses (2) originating from the combination of elastic modulus and thermal mismatch. The residual stresses may be enhanced by addition of the second phase whose thermal expansion coefficient shows the desired degree of mismatch with that of the matrix.

In the present study the effect of SiC and ZrO_2 addition (a phases with lower - α_{SiC}=3.5-4.2x10^{-6} $^oC^{-1}$, α_{Al2O3}=9.0x10^{-6} $^oC^{-1}$ and higher thermal expansion coefficient -α_{ZrO2}=12x10^{-6} $^oC^{-1}$) on residual stress state change in alumina matrix and the resulting altered crack behaviour were investigated.

EXPERIMENTAL PROCEDURE

Alumina ceramics of the following chemical composition: Al_2O_3–99.55wt%, MgO-0.20wt%, Y_2O_3–0.25wt% was used as a matrix. Alumina powder was high purity (4N concentration) with an average grain size below 0.5μm. The starting SiC powder was β-phase with an average particle size about 1μm. Matrix powder was mixed with SiC (0-30wt%) in ethanol and then hot-pressed in carbon dies lined with BN layers under a pressure of 15MPa and a temperature of 1700°C for 1h in argon atmosphere. To the second type of mixtures a ZrO_2+8m% Y_2O_3 powder (MSY8, Mandoval Ltd) with an average grain size of 0.4μm was used. In this case alumina powder mixed with ZrO_2 (0-30wt%) in distilled water was cold pressed and then sintered at 1700°C for 1.5h in high vacuum. Sintered specimens were cut and ground yielding bars having the dimensions of 5x5x45mm (square) or 1.5x6x45mm (rectangular), and one surface was polished. In the central part of the rectangular bar sample (1.5x6x40) a sharp notch was prepared for testing the crack propagation behaviour. The polished surface of the samples was covered with a 150nm thick Al layer to improve the crack path visibility during the test.

The bending strength of composites was determined on square bars with the dimensions 45x5x5mm in three-point bending tests using an universal testing machine (Model 1446, Zwick) with 1mm/min loading speed and 40mm bearing distance.

For measurement of Young's modulus the beams were trimmed to the height of 1mm and then compliance of samples was recorded during loading tests using the same testing machine with 0.1mm/min loading speed and 40mm bearing distance. The values of Young's modulus were determined using the relation given by Fett and Munz (3).

The tests of controlled crack growth were performed in three-point bending with 1μm/min loading speed and 40mm bearing distance using the same testing machine. The crack was initiated and slowly grown by repeated loading and unloading. The crack length, *c*, was measured *in situ* using a special device consisting of horizontal light microscope coupled with a CCD camera fitted to the testing machine. Details of this procedure are described in a second paper presented at this conference (6). The stress intensity factor, K_I, was calculated from crack length, *c*, and force, *P* (3). The data of $K_I=f(c)$ obtained in the range of crack length studied fitted by a linear function of $y=ax+b$ and the slope, *a*, was used as a parameter describing R-curve behaviour. All experiments were done at room temperature in normal air environments.

In several samples the crack growth tests were done without unloading. The time dependent displacement, *d*, of the sample was measured and recorded together with values of force, *P*. By procedure described earlier (4) the maximal stress intensity factor, K_{Imax}, and the resistance to crack initiation, K_{Ii}, were calculated. The crack growth rate $v=dc/dt$ controlled by the stress intensity factor, K_I, was calculated from the time dependent crack length, *c*. Assuming a power-law relation between *v* and K_I; $v=dc/dt=AK_I^n$, the parameters *n* and *A* (or *logA*) were obtained.

Residual stresses within the alumina matrix were measured using the piezospectroscopic technique described earlier (4,6).

Microstructure observations of ceramics studied were performed on polished and thermally etched surfaces by SEM using OPTON DSM 950 microscope. Grain size distribution measurements have also been made.

RESULTS

Al_2O_3-SiC composites

As is generally known (1,2), due to crystallographic and thermal anisotropy of alumina, some grains in the alumina matrix are subjected to compression and play the role of „bridges". Those remaining grains subject to tension are considered as making up the constitutive „matrix". The bridging grains wedged in the microstructure by this internal compressive stress lead to an increase in fracture toughness as the crack grows. According to this statement, the addition of the SiC particles is expected to change the described stress state. The large thermal expansion mismatch between SiC particles and the Al_2O_3 matrix is thought to create additional regions of tension. This expectation has been confirmed by piezospectroscopic measurements. As can be seen from Table I, an increasing content of SiC grains changes the residual stresses in alumina matrix to tensile. This in turn should reduce the effectiveness of grain bridging.

Table I. Residual stresses, σ (MPa), measured in Al_2O_3 grains from alumina matrix as a function of SiC content.

Type of ceramic matrix	SiC content (wt%)			
	0	10	20	30
Alumina	-188.33	+12.52	+77.73	+168.64

- refers to a residual compressive stress (for crystallographic plane *ab* of α-Al_2O_3), + refers to a residual tensile stress

The data of $K_I=f(c)$ obtained in the range of crack length studied were fitted by a linear equation of $y=ax+b$ and the slope, a, was used as a factor describing the tendency of a ceramic towards R-curve behaviour. The dependency of the parameters a and b on SiC content for various composites is listed in Table II. The value of a for a pure alumina matrix is 0.851, which means that the toughness increases strongly namely from 3.6 to about 5.8 $MPam^{1/2}$ as the crack length increases up to 4.0 mm (see Fig.1). The increase in toughness becomes less pronounced as the SiC content increases. For a SiC content of 30wt% in an alumina matrix, the slope parameter decreases almost to zero.

Table II. Linear coefficients a and b (equation of $y=ax+b$) for Al_2O_3-SiC composites as a function of SiC content

SiC content (wt%)	a	b
0	0.851±0,074	2.64±0,09
10	0.378±0.025	3.88±0.08
20	0.224±0.007	4.02±0.02
30	0.061±0.024	4.44±0.11

The negative effect of SiC addition on R-curve behaviour can be related to the observed change of the residual stresses in alumina matrix. However this relation is not so obvious. As can be seen from Table III, the presence of SiC particles in alumina matrix effectively inhibits

Al_2O_3 grain growth. The second argument was found in parallel paper presented at this conference (6). The slope parameter *a* strongly decreases with decreasing Al_2O_3 grain size.

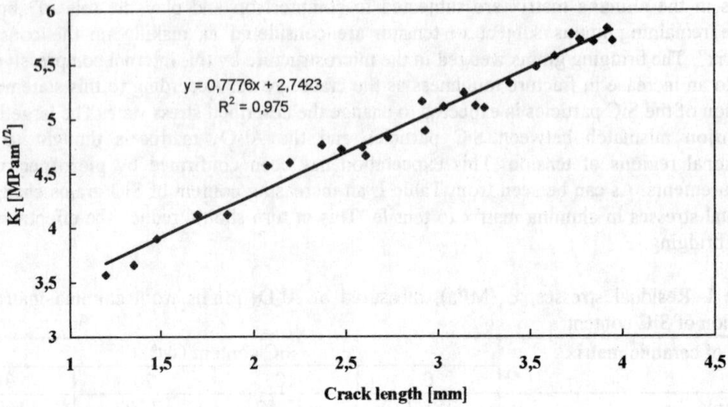

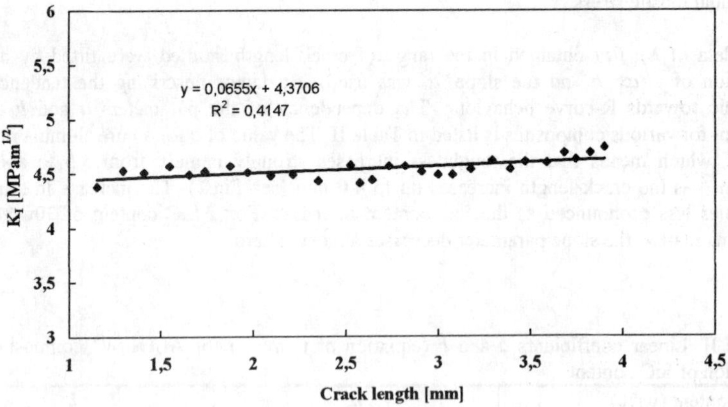

Fig.1. Dependence of K_I on the crack length for an alumina matrix without SiC (top) and for 30wt% SiC content (bottom)

Table III. Mean Al_2O_3 grain size (μm) in alumina matrix as a function of SiC content

Type of ceramic matrix	SiC content (wt%)			
	0	10	20	30
Alumina	4.67±3.91	1.62±0.78	0.96±0.48	0.83±0.27

For several samples of composites the test of crack growth was performed without removing the load. From measured and recorded data, the values of maximal stress intensity factor, K_{Imax}, resistance to crack initiation, K_{Ii}, and crack growth rate parameters n and A were obtained (Table IV). As can be seen, K_{Imax} of the alumina matrix does not increase significantly with increasing SiC addition. However a strong increase of resistance to crack initiation (K_{Ii}) is observed. The increasing values of parameter n show that the initiated crack will propagate with higher rate in alumina matrix with SiC addition than in pure alumina.

Table IV. Maximal stress intensity factor K_{Imax}, resistance to crack initiation K_{Ii}, and crack growth rate parameters n and *logA* for an alumina matrix as a function of SiC content

SiC content (wt%)	K_{Imax} (Mpa m$^{1/2}$)	K_{Ii} (MPa m$^{1/2}$)	Crack growth rate parameters	
			n	*logA*
0	4.78±0.03	3.16±0.06	8.17±0.29	-10.00±0.17
10	4.92±0.06	3.67±0.03	28.83±1.97	-24.07±1.36
20	4.90±0.07	4.10±0.24	36.20±9.97	-28.52±6.08
30	4.86±0.12	4.44±0.19	44.03±12.23	-34.17±8.41

Al_2O_3-ZrO_2 composites

In contrary to SiC, the higher thermal expansion coefficient of ZrO_2 was expected to create additional regions of compression in alumina matrix. It has been confirmed by piezospectroscopic measurements. As can be seen from Table V, an increasing content of ZrO_2 grains changes the residual stresses in alumina matrix to compressive. This change should increase the effectiveness of grain bridging. However controlled crack growth tests showed rapid decrease of R-curve behaviour of composites with increasing zirconia content (Table VI). The slope a equalled 0.665 for alumina matrix decreases to zero for 30wt% zirconia content. This intriguing observation can be related to Al_2O_3 grain size change for composites containing zirconia grains. As it was found (Table VII) zirconia also strongly inhibits alumina grain growth. In a result Al_2O_3 grain size decreases from 18.6μm for alumina matrix to 1.80μm for composites with 30wt% ZrO_2 content.

Table V. Residual stresses, σ (MPa), measured in Al_2O_3 grains from alumina matrix as a function of ZrO_2 content.

Type of ceramic matrix	ZrO_2 content (wt%)			
	0	10	20	30
Alumina	±78.93	-81.68	-148.80	-194.99

Table VI. Linear coefficients a and b (equation of $y=ax+b$) for Al_2O_3-ZrO_2 composites as a function of ZrO_2 content

ZrO_2 content (wt%)	a	b
0	0.665±0,025	3.17±0,08
10	0.067±0.011	3.01±0.12
20	0.031±0.014	2.93±0.02
30	-0.066±0.024	2.76±0.11

Table VII. Mean Al_2O_3 grain size (μm) in alumina matrix as a function of ZrO_2 content

Type of ceramic matrix	ZrO_2 content (wt%)			
	0	10	20	30
Alumina	18.60±8.90	2.07±1.06	2.22±0.88	1.80±0.46

The tests of crack growth performed without removing the load showed that the maximal stress intensity factor, K_{Imax}, of the alumina matrix decreases significantly with increasing ZrO_2 addition (see Table VIII). Decrease of resistance to crack initiation (K_{Ii}) is also observed. Increasing values of parameter n show that the initiated crack will propagate with higher rate in an alumina matrix with ZrO_2 addition than in pure alumina.

Table VIII. Maximal stress intensity factor K_{Imax}, resistance to crack initiation K_{Ii}, and crack growth rate parameters n and $logA$ for an alumina matrix as a function of ZrO_2 content

ZrO_2 content (wt%)	K_{Imax} (MPa m$^{1/2}$)	K_{Ii} (MPa m$^{1/2}$)	Crack growth rate parameters	
			n	$logA$
0	5.02±0.38	3.71±0.21	10.14±2.84	-11.63±0.95
10	3.61±0.20	3.39±0.20	26.62±8.26	-18.88±1.40
20	3.42±0.10	3.24±0.14	28.20±3.21	-18.98±2.43
30	3.32±0.30	3.17±0.18	64.85±1.65	-36.72±0.28

DISCUSSION

Results of parallel work (6) showed that R-curve behaviour of pure alumina strongly decreases with decreasing grain size. This phenomenon can be related to decreasing amount of the bridging grains on a crack path with decreasing Al_2O_3 grain size. For the smallest grain size, where bridging grains are not observed the slope parameter a goes to zero value. The average residual stresses measured by piezospectroscopy also exhibit the similar dependence on grain size. The stress seems to be sufficiently large only for coarser grain sizes to have a significant effect the crack propagation path during fracture. In the case of smaller grain size the average stress is noticeably smaller probably due to diffusional flow relaxing the stresses, which can be related to greater grain boundary diffusivity at the smaller grain (7).

In the case of composites studied both additives change the residual stress state in alumina matrix to tensile (SiC) or compressive (ZrO_2) and cause rapid decrease of the alumina grain size below the range measured in the work (6). Both changes result in decreasing the slope a almost to zero. Decrease the slope a is especially surprising for zirconia addition. It can mean that additional compressive stress fields introduced to alumina matrix by ZrO_2 do not change the amount of the bridging grains responsible for R-curve behaviour. Results obtained point out that the grain size of alumina matrix plays the more important role of in the R-curve phenomenon than residual stresses introduced by a second phase. However to prove this thesis is necessary to prepare the Al_2O_3-SiC and Al_2O_3-ZrO_2 composite samples with the same Al_2O_3 grain sizes that were found for both alumina matrices.

CONCLUSIONS

The aim of this work was to determine the effect of the change in the residual stress state on R-curve properties of alumina ceramics. To facilitate this, SiC particles, having a lower thermal expansion coefficient, α, or ZrO_2 particles with higher α, were added. Tests of controlled crack growth for both types of composite having various SiC or ZrO_2 contents were performed. Data of $K_I=f(c)$ obtained in the range of the crack lengths studied were approximated by a linear equation of $y=ax+b$ and the slope parameter a was used as a factor for describing the R-curve behaviour of composites. A decreasing effect of SiC and ZrO_2 particles content on toughness-crack length dependence was found. The observed changes were related to measurement of alumina grain size and residual stresses. Both additives strongly decreased the matrix grain size. However increasing content of SiC grains changed the residual stresses in alumina matrix to tensile but ZrO_2 to compressive. Analysis of the results obtained pointed to Al_2O_3 grain size as a stronger parameter than residual stresses in decreasing R-curve behaviour of alumina based composites. The tests of crack growth performed without removing the load showed distinct changes of maximal stress intensity factor, resistance to crack initiation and crack growth rate parameters with increasing SiC and ZrO_2 addition.

REFERENCES

1. Bennison S.J. and Lawn B.R., , Acta Metall., **37** 10 (1989) 2659
2. Chantikul P., Bennison S.J. and Lawn B.R., J.Amer.Ceram.Soc., **73** 8 (1990) 2419
3. Fett T. and Munz D., J. Amer. Ceram. Soc., **75** [4] (1992) 958
4. Tomaszewski H., Strzeszewski J. and Gębicki W., J. Europ. Ceram. Soc., **19** (1999) 67
5. He J. and Clarke D.R., J.Amer.Ceram.Soc., **78** 5 (1995) 1341
6. Tomaszewski H., Boniecki M. and Węglarz H., paper presented at this conference.
7. Ma Q. and Clarke D.R., J.Amer.Ceram.Soc., 77 4 (1994) 298

ALTERATION OF RESIDUAL STRESSES IN TiN AND TiC FILMS DUE TO ANNEALING TREATMENTS

T. MATSUE*, T. HANABUSA and Y. IKEUCHI***
***Niihama National College of Technology**
7-1 Yagumo-cho Niihama 792-8580, Japan
****Faculty of Engineering, Tokushima University**
2-1 Jyosanjima-cho Tokushima 770-8506, Japan

ABSTRACT

The structure and residual stresses of TiN and TiC films deposited on a steel substrate were investigated by X-ray diffraction. TiN films approximately 4μm thick were deposited on one side of the substrate by multi-arc physical vapor deposition (TiN_{PVD} and TiC_{PVD} film) and thermal chemical vapor deposition (TiN_{CVD} film). The TiN_{PVD} and the TiC_{PVD} films had a compressive residual stresses of -8.8GPa and -7.8GPa, respectively. These residual stresses decreased on increasing the annealing temperature, and decreased to the level of the thermal residual stress after annealing at temperature of 1073K. The TiN_{CVD} films had a compressive residual stress of -1.8GPa. The residual stresses did not change by annealing at temperatures below 1073K, but they increased with increasing annealing temperatures above 1073K. By X-ray photoelectron spectroscopy (XPS), we determined the ratio of nitrogen (or carbon) to titanium (N or C/Ti) of the TiN_{PVD}, TiC_{PVD} and TiN_{CVD} films after the annealing treatments. The results of the XPS analysis showed that the initial value of N/Ti was about 1.08 in the as-deposited TiN_{PVD} and TiN_{CVD} films, and for those samples the ratio of N/Ti did not change after annealing at temperatures below 1073K, but decreased to 1.00 after annealing at temperatures above 1073K. On the other hand, the initial value of C/Ti was about 1.01 in the as-deposited TiC_{PVD} films, and for those samples the ratio of C/Ti did not change after annealing at temperatures below 1273K, but decreased to 0.80 after annealing at temperatures of 1473K.

1. INTRODUCTION

TiN coatings are widely used in industry especially for wear reduction of forming and cutting tools. However, large residual stresses are necessarily enervated in coating films due to mismatch of thermal expansion between the film and the substrate (thermal residual stress) and other reasons (intrinsic stress) [1-3], exerting a great influence on the mechanical properties of coated material. Therefore, it is important to know the state of residual stresses in the film and the substrate. X-ray stress measurement is very useful to investigate these residual stresses in the coatings. Considerable efforts [4, 5] have been made in stress measurement of various ceramic coatings (including TiN and TiC), deepening our understanding about the relationship between the residual stress and process parameters such as deposition temperatures.

We investigate the residual stress states in the TiN films deposited by Multi-Arc physical vapor deposition (TiN_{PVD} and TiC_{PVD} film) and thermal chemical vapor deposition (TiN_{CVD} film) using the X-ray stress measuring method. By X-ray photoelectron spectroscopy (XPS), we determined the ratio of nitrogen (or carbon) to titanium (N or C/Ti) after the annealing. A comparison was made between the residual stresses in the TiN_{PVD}, TiC_{PVD} and TiN_{CVD} films and the ratio of N or C/Ti after annealing.

2. EXPERIMENTAL DETAILS

2.1. Materials

Spring steel (SUP3:JIS) plates measuring 12mm×20mm×4mm were used as a substrate. Before deposition the substrate was ground to a surface roughness of 0.05μm R_a, and then annealed for 1 hour at 873K. Residual stresses in the annealed substrate ranged from -5MPa to 10MPa.

The TiN_{PVD}, TiC_{PVD} and TiN_{CVD} films were deposited on one side of the substrate by a Multi-Arc PVD and a thermal CVD. The films were approximately 4μm in thickness. Table I shows the conditions of TiN depositon.

Table I Conditions of TiN deposition.

Name of specimen	Film thickness (μm)	Deposition temperature (K)	Coating method
TiN_{PVD}	4	523	PVD
TiC_{PVD}			
TiN_{CVD}		973	CVD

Table II X-ray measurement conditions.

Material	TiN • TiC
Characteristic X-ray	CuKα
Tube voltage	40kV
Tube current	20 mA
X-ray optics	Para-forcusing
Filter	Nickel
Diffraction for stress mesurement (2θ,deg.)	TiN420(CVD, 108.7) TiN222(PVD, 78) TiC222(PVD, 76)
Irradiated area	2 ×8mm^2

2.2. X-ray Stress Measuring Method

As will be explained in detail in the following a sections, the TiN (TiC_{PVD} and TiN_{CVD}) films exhibit high {111} and {100} orientation, respectively. In such a case, no diffraction intensity appears at any ψ angle except for particular angles ψ defined by the crystal structure combined with crystal orientation. Because the $\sin^2\psi$ method cannot be adopted in this case, residual stresses in the TiN and TiC film were evaluated by the two-exposure method with lattice strains measured in the directions determined by the crystal orientation of the film [6, 7]. When the {111} and the {100} planes of the cubic lattice lie a parallel to the surface, we find that the TiN (222) diffraction appears at $\psi = 0^\circ$ and 70.5° and the TiN (420) diffraction appears at $\psi_1 = 26.6^\circ$ and $\psi_2 = 63.4^\circ$ [6-8]. In a both cases, ψ is the angle between the normal of the specimen surface and the normal of the diffraction plane. In this case, if we assume an equal-axial plane stress state, the following equation can be used for evaluating residual stress σ,

$$\sigma = \frac{1}{s_{44}/2} \cdot \frac{d_{\psi 1} - d_{\psi 2}}{d_0} \cdot \frac{1}{\sin^2\psi_1 - \sin^2\psi_2} \qquad (1)$$

where s_{44} (TiN : s_{44}=5.95[TPa^{-1}][9], TiC : s_{44}=5.61[TPa^{-1}][10]) are the single-crystal elastic constants of TiN and TiC. d_0 is the spacing of the same planes in the absence of stress. $d_{\psi 1}$ and $d_{\psi 2}$ are the strains calculated by the Bragg law from the 2θ values of TiN (222) and TiN (420) diffraction at the above two ψ angles. Table II shows the X-ray measurement conditions.

2.3. X-ray Photoelectron Spectroscopy (XPS) Analysis

The ratio of N or C/Ti was determined by X-ray photoelectron spectroscopy (XPS) depth profile analysis using a Perkin Elmer Phi 1600E [Mgkα]. The XPS analysis was performed after Ar sputter etching on TiN and TiC film surface. The depth profile of the spectra of N-1*s* (or C-1*s*) and that of Ti-2*p* peaks were measured by the XPS analysis. We calculated the ratio of N or C/Ti by comparing the areas of the N-1*s* (or C-1*s*) peaks with that of the Ti-2*p* peak after background corrections.

2.4. Annealing Treatment

In order to investigate how the structure and the residual stress in the film is changed by heat-cool cycles, the specimens were annealed in a vacuum furnace at temperatures of 473, 673, 873, 1073, 1273 and 1473 K. The duration of each temperature was 60 minutes. After annealing treatment, specimens were cooled down to a room temperature.

3. EXPERIMENTAL RESULTS

3.1. Crystal Orientation of TiN Film

Figure1(a) shows an example of the X-ray diffraction pattern from TiN_{PVD} film. Because of the highly oriented {111} structure of the TiN_{PVD} film, only two very high intensity peaks of TiN (111) and (222) diffractions were detected by θ-2θ scanning for both the as-deposited and the annealed TiN_{PVD} film. The results revealed that the peak intensities of (111) and (222) diffractions after annealing were higher than those of the as-deposited films. Figure 1(b) shows the integrated intensity distribution against ψ angles for the TiN (222) diffraction of the TiN_{PVD} film. The {111} of the TiN crystals orients parallel to the surface normal of the substrate within ± 10 degrees. These results mean that the TiN_{PVD} film exhibited high {111} orientation. The diffraction pattern and intensity distribution against ψ angles of TiC_{PVD} film showed the same tendency as the results for TiN_{PVD} film.

Figure 2(a) shows examples of the X-ray diffraction pattern from the TiN_{CVD} film. Because of the high {100} orientation of the TiN_{CVD} film, only two diffraction peaks, (200)

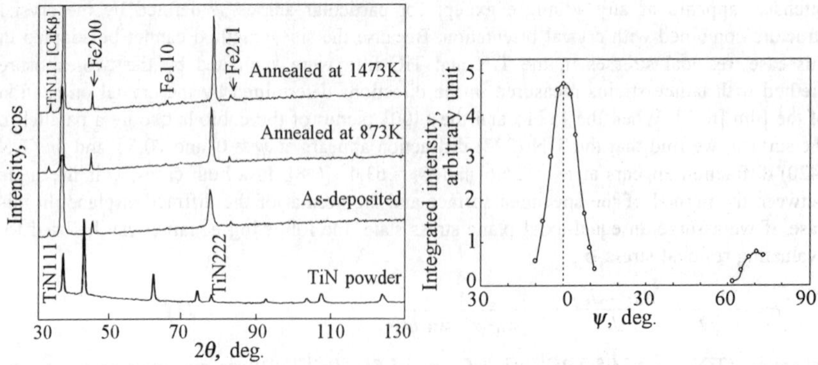

(a) Diffraction pattern (b)Distribution of integrated intensity

Fig. 1(a) Change in diffraction pattern of TiN_{PVD} film an as-deposited and after annealing at 873K and 1473K with CuKα radiation, (b) integrated intensity distribution against ψ angles of TiN (222) reflection in the as-deposited TiN_{PVD} film.

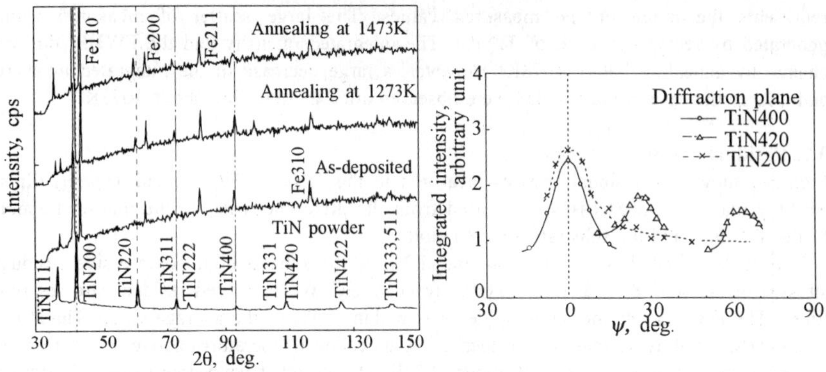

(a) Diffraction pattern (b)Distribution of integrated intensity

Fig. 2(a) Change in diffraction pattern of TiN_{CVD} film an as-deposited and after annealing at 1273 K and 1473 K with CuKα radiation, (b) integrated intensity distribution against ψ angles of TiN (200), (400) and (420) reflections in the as-deposited TiN_{PVD} film.

and (400) were detected in θ-2θ scanning for both the as-deposited and the annealed TiN_{CVD} films. The peak intensity of the (200) and (400) reflections did not change by annealing below 1073K. However, many diffraction peaks including the (200) and (400) reflections appeared after annealing at 1273K. The intensity of all these peaks from the TiN film decreased after annealing at 1473K. When the {100} plane of the cubic lattice lies parallel to the surface, the TiN (420) reflection appears at $\psi = 26.6^\circ$ and 63.4°. Figure 2(b) shows the distribution of integrated intensity in the TiN_{CVD} film as a function of ψ-angles. The TiN (400) and the TiN (420) reflactions appeared within a few degrees around $\psi = 0^\circ$, 27° and 63°, respectively. The TiN (200) shows a peak around $\psi = 0^\circ$ and a gentle decrease with ψ-angles, i.e., a small TiN (200) reflection appeared even after a large increase in ψ. These results mean that the TiN_{CVD} film is mainly composed of {100} oriented crystal, i.e., the {100} crystal axis of the TiN crystals coincides with the normal of the TiN film surface, but small parts of the crystal are randomly oriented.

Figure 3 shows the change in integrated intensities and the change in the full width at half-maximum intensity (FWHM) with an annealing temperature. Figure 3(a) was obtained from the (222) reflection of the TiN_{PVD} films. A small increase in the integrated intensity and a relatively large decrease in the FWHM were obtained with increasing annealing temperature. The annealing treatment caused little increase in the integrated intensity of the TiN films. The increase was so small that it is thought that the TiN crystals underwent no recrystallization. A relatively large decrease in the FWHM was obtained with increasing annealing treatment. Therefore, a decrease in the typeIII of residual stress or growth of TiN crystal grains occurred in the film. Figure 3(b) was obtained from the (222) reflection of TiC_{PVD} films. A small increase in the integrated intensity was seen with increasing annealing temperature. However, after annealing at 1273K, a large decrease in the integrated intensity was observed. On the other hand, the FWHM did not change by annealing below 873K. But, a large decrease in the FWHM was obtained after annealing at 1073K. Figure 3(c) was obtained from the TiN (200) reflection of TiN_{CVD} films. Each of the points in the figure shows the average value of measurements of five times. For annealing at 1273K, the measured values scatter largely as shown by the error bar, which represents the range of the measured values. The large scatter of measured value generated by recrystallization of TiN[7]. The integrated intensity and the FWHM did not change by annealing below 1073K. However, a large decrease in the integrated intensity and a large increase in the FWHM were observed after an annealing above 1073K.

3.2. Residual Stress

Figure 4 shows the residual stresses measured in the TiN_{PVD}, TiC_{PVD} and TiN_{CVD} films. The thermal residual stresses calculated from the differences in the thermal contraction of the TiN film and the substrate are also plotted.

The as-deposited TiN_{PVD}, TiC_{PVD} and TiN_{CVD} films have high compressive residual stresses of about -8.8, -7.8 and -1.8GPa, respectively. We measured residual stresses five times. The range of the measured values was within $\pm 5\%$ of the average value. The stress in the TiN_{PVD} films decreased with increasing annealing temperatures above 473K, reaches to the thermal residual stress level above 1073K. On the other hand, those residual stresses in the TiN_{CVD} films did not change after annealing at temperatures below 1073K. The compressive residual stresses in the TiN_{PVD} and the TiN_{CVD} films increased by annealing above 1073K.

The stress in the TiC_{PVD} films decreased with increasing annealing temperatures above 673K, reaching a minimum level of about -2.0GPa at 1273K. Compressive residual stresses in the TiC_{PVD} films increased by annealing at 1473K.

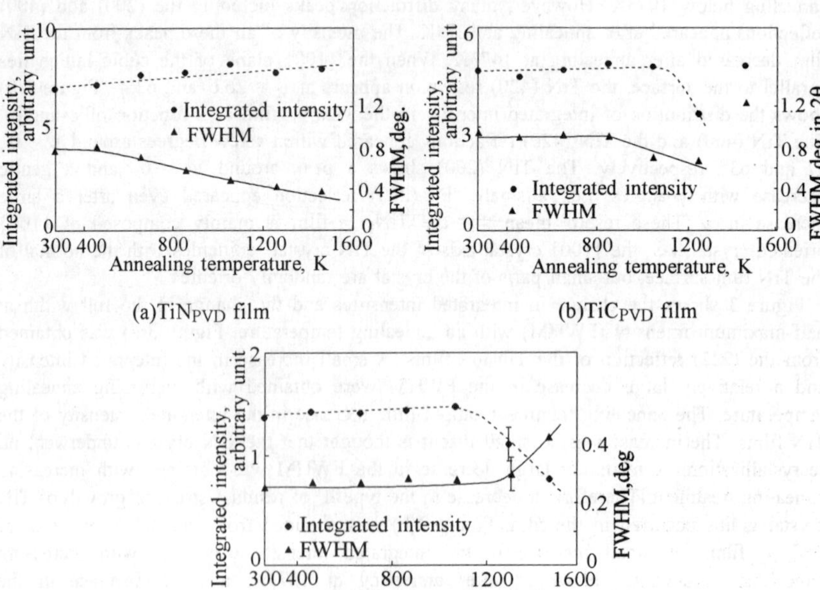

(a)TiN_{PVD} film (b)TiC_{PVD} film

(c)TiN_{CVD} film

Fig. 3 Changes in integrated intensity and FWHM with increasing annealing temperatures, TiN_{PVD}(a) and TiC_{PVD}(b) film with TiN222 reflection, TiN_{CVD} (c) film with TiN200 reflection.

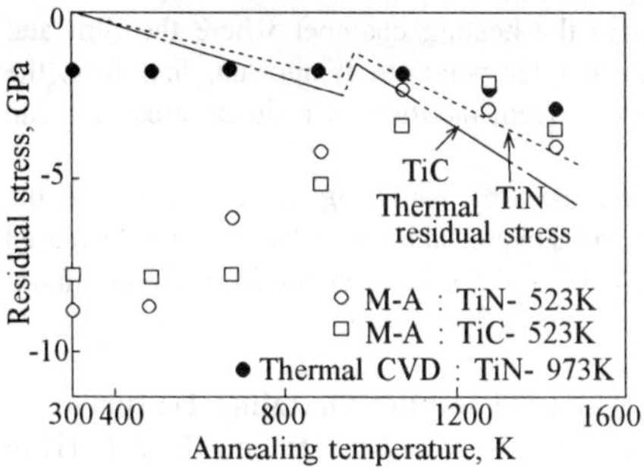

Fig. 4 Changes in residual stress of the TiN_{PVD} and TiN_{CVD} films with annealing treatment.

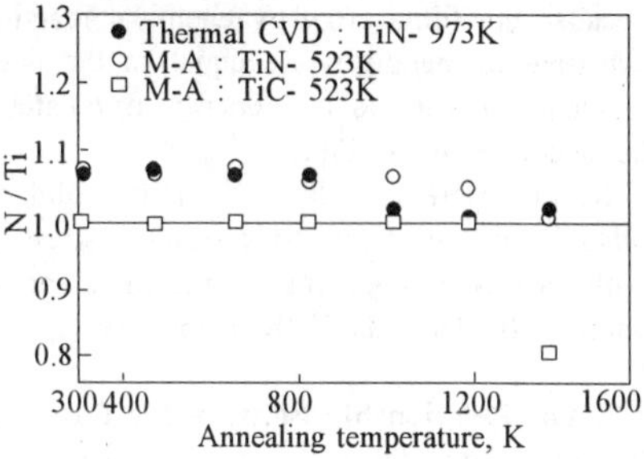

Fig. 5 Changes in N/Ti ratio of the TiN_{PVD} and TiN_{CVD} film with increasing annealing temperature.

4. DISCUSSION

4.1. Effect of Thermal Residual Stress

The development of the residual stress in the film depends on the deposition conditions, such as temperature, ion bombardment (in PVD method) and environment. Mismatched thermal contraction between the film and the substrate generates thermal residual stress after cooling from the depositing temperature to room temperature. Assuming that there is no stress at the depositing temperature, the thermal residual stress is given by

$$\sigma_{th} = \frac{E_F}{1-\nu_F}\left\{\int_{T1}^{T2} (\alpha_F - \alpha_{①})\, dT + \Delta\varepsilon + \int_{T3}^{T4} (\alpha_F - \alpha_{③}) dT \right\} \qquad (2)$$

where E_F and ν_F are, respectively, Young's modulus (E_{TiN}=429GPa[7] and E_{TiC}=449GPa [11]) and Poisson's ratio (ν_{TiN}= 0.19[7] and ν_{TiC}= 0.191[11]) of the film. α_F (α_{TiN}= 9.35×10^{-6} K^{-1} [6] and α_{TiC}= 7.6×10^{-6} K^{-1} [11]) is the coefficient of thermal expansion of the film. The E_F , ν_F and α_F values are assumed to be constant. When the substrate is carbon steel, the α_{sub} changes with temperature, and the volume changes owing to the phase transformation from austenite to ferrite. The cooling process of the substrate material is divided into three regions, i.e. ①ferrite ($\alpha_{sub①}$= 13.9×10^{-6} K^{-1}, below 950K), ② transforming ($\Delta\varepsilon$ =1.54×10^{-3}, between ①and③) and ③austenite ($\alpha_{sub③}$=22.4×10^{-6} K^{-1}, above 1000K(T_3)) regions. From an expansion of Eq.(2), the thermal residual stress is calculated [6]. T_1 is room temperature.

The as-deposited TiN_{PVD}, TiC_{PVD} and TiN_{CVD} films have high compressive residual stresses of about -8.8, -7.8 and -1.8GPa, respectively. Compressive residual stress in the TiN_{PVD} and TiC_{PVD} film are one order of magnitude larger than the thermal residual stress (-0.57GPa and -0.87GPa) calculated by Eq.(2) using T_2 =523K. On the other hand, the stress value in the TiN_{CVD} was the same as the thermal residual stress (-1.6GPa, T_2 =973K) which is derived from the deposition temperature of 973K. High compressive stresses in the TiN_{PVD} films seem to have been generated not only by the stress calculated by Eq.(2) but also by an ion bombardment of the film surface during the deposition process. However, the thermal CVD method has no effect on atomic peening during the deposition process because the films grow by chemical reaction in the heating chamber where the film and substrate temperatures are equal to the deposition temperature. It appears, therefore, the residual stress in the TiN_{CVD} film originates solely from the thermal residual stress and can be calculated by an Eq.(2).

Residual stress in the TiN_{CVD} film did not change by annealing up to 1073K. On the other hand, the compressive residual stress in the TiN_{PVD} and the TiC_{PVD} films decreased with increasing annealing temperatures above 473K and 673K, after reaching the minimum value at 1073K and 1273K, respectively.

4.2. The Relationship Between the Ratio of N or C/Ti and the Annealing Treatment

Figure 5 shows the changes in the ratio of nitrogen (or carbon) to titanium (N or C/Ti) in TiN_{PVD}, TiC_{PVD} and TiN_{CVD} films. By X-ray photoelectron spectroscopy (XPS), we determined the ratio N or C/Ti after annealing at various temperatures. The results of the XPS analysis showed that the initial value of N/Ti was about 1.08 in the as-deposited TiN_{PVD} films. The ratio of N/Ti in the TiN_{PVD} films kept its initial value (1.08) until annealing up to 1273K, followed by a decrease to 1.00 after annealing at 1473K. On the other hand, the ratio of N/Ti in the TiN_{CVD} films was about 1.08 an as-deposited. The ratio of N/Ti did not change by annealing below 1073K, but it decreased to 1.00 by annealing above 1073K. In the case of the TiC_{PVD} films, the initial value of C/Ti was about 1.01 in the as-deposited TiC_{PVD} films. The ratio of C/Ti in the TiC_{PVD} films kept its initial value until annealing up to 1273K, followed by a decrease to 0.80 after annealing at 1473K.

As a result, the decrease of residual stresses in the TiN_{PVD} and the TiC_{PVD} films after annealing below 1073K and 1273K, respectively, were attributed to the relaxation of intrinsic stress generated by an ion bombardment during the deposition process, because the Ti-N,C composition in the TiN_{PVD} and the TiC_{PVD} films did not change after annealing below 1073K and 1273K. On the other hand, in the case of the TiN_{CVD} films, as the Ti-N composition did not change after annealing below 1073K, residual stress in the TiN_{CVD} films did not change after annealing below 1073K.

Compressive residual stresses in both TiN_{PVD} and TiN_{CVD} films increased by annealing above 1073K. These stresses are nearly equal to the thermal residual stresses but the slight difference between them increased with increasing annealing temperatures. This difference may have been caused by stress relaxation during annealing as a result of plastic deformation in the substrate near the interface and the change in Ti-N composition.

5. CONCLUSIONS

Residual stresses in a TiN_{PVD}, TiC_{PVD} and TiN_{CVD} films were measured by the X-ray two-exposure method. We investigated the residual stresses, Ti-N,C composition in the TiN and TiC films.

The TiN_{PVD} and TiC_{PVD} films deposited by multi-arc PVD have a structure with very high {111} orientation. Compressive residual stress was found in the TiN_{PVD} and TiC_{PVD} films, which decreased with increasing deposition temperature. A small increase in integrated intensity and large decrease in FWHM with increasing annealing temperature were obtained for the TiN_{PVD} and TiC_{PVD} films. The TiN_{CVD} film deposited by thermal CVD has a structure with very high {100} orientation and compressive residual stress. The integrated intensity and FWHM did not change after annealing at temperatures below 1073K but a large decrease in the integrated intensity and a large increase in the FWHM were observed after annealing at 1273K. The as-deposited TiN_{PVD}, TiC_{PVD} and TiN_{CVD}

films have high compressive residual stresses of about -8.8, -7.8 and -1.8GPa, respectively. Compressive residual stresses in the TiN_{PVD} and the TiC_{PVD} decreased with increasing annealing temperatures before reaching a minimum value at 1073K and 1273K, respectively. Residual stresses in the TiN_{CVD} films did not change after annealing at temperatures below 1073K. After annealing above 1073K, residual stresses in the TiN_{PVD} and also in the TiN_{CVD} films began to increase to the compressive side along with the thermal residual stress but some differences existed between the measured stress and the thermal residual stress. The ratio of N/Ti was about 1.08 in as-deposited TiN_{PVD} and TiN_{CVD} films, these value did not change by annealing below 1073K, but decreased to 1.00 after annealing above 1073K. The ratio of C/Ti was about 1.01 in as-deposited TiC_{PVD} films, these value did not change by annealing below 1273K, but decreased to 0.80 after annealing at 1473K.

REFERENCES

1. Perry A. J, Jagner M, Sproul W. D and Rudnich P. J, Surf. and Coat. Technol., 42 (1990) 49
2. Hobbs M. K, Cooke R. G, Harris B and Reiter H, British Ceram. Proc., 39 (1989) 119
3. Chang G. C and Phucharoen W, Surf. and Coat. Technol., 32 (1987) 307
4. Sue J. A, Surf. and Coat. Technol., 54-55 (1992) 154
5. Bull S. J, Jones A. M and McCabe A. R, Surf. and Coat. Technol., 54-55 (1992) 173
6. Matsue T, Hanabusa T and Ikeuchi Y, Thin Solid Films, 281-282 (1996) 344
7. Matsue T, Hanabusa T and Ikeuchi Y, Materials Science Research International, 5 (1999) 45
8. Cullity B. D, 'Elements of X-Ray Diffraction', Addison-Wesley Co. Inc., Massachusetts (1978) p. 75
9. Perry A. J, Thin Solid Films, 170, (1989) 63
10. Hellwege K. -H, 'LANDOLT-BÖRNSTEIN', 11 Springerverlag (1979) p.30
11. Sloof W. G, Delhez R, Keijser H, Mittemeijer E. J, J. Mat. Sci., 22 (1987) 1701

THERMAL RELAXATION OF RESIDUAL STRESSES IN THICK SECTION TYPE 316 STAINLESS STEEL GIRTH WELDS

PJ Bouchard[1], SK Bate[2], D George[3], RH Leggatt[4] and AG Youtsos[5]
[1]British Energy, Barnett Way, Barnwood, Gloucester GL4 3RS, UK
[2]AEA Technology, Risley, Warrington, Cheshire, WA3 6AT, UK
[3]University of Bristol, Queens Building, University Walk, Bristol, BS8 1TR, UK
[4]TWI, Abington Hall, Abington, Cambridge CB1 6AL, UK
[5]CEC Joint Research Centre, PO Box 2, 1755 ZG Petten, The Netherlands

ABSTRACT

Thermal relaxation of residual stress in thick section girth welds has been quantified by both measurement and analysis. Two girth welds, joining pairs of ex-service AISI type 316H austenitic stainless steel forgings (432 mm outside diameter, 65 mm thick), were used to measure the stress relaxation effect of a post-weld heat treatment at 750°C for 2½ hours, and the effect of thermal ageing at 550°C for various time increments up to a total time period of 8384 hours. Distributions of residual stress were measured before and after the thermal treatments by diverse techniques including surface hole drilling, deep hole drilling, neutron diffraction, X-ray diffraction and by destructive sectioning. A third welded component was used to characterise material properties for numerical analysis. Alternative analytical approaches were applied to predict the spatial distribution of as-welded residual stress, and to estimate creep stress relaxation. In this paper, the predicted stress fields are compared with measured values before and after each thermal treatment. Good overall agreement is demonstrated between the measured stresses after heat treatment and finite element predictions based on mean RCC-MR creep law data. However, the evidence of stress relaxation during the early hours of relaxation at 550°C is contradictory.

INTRODUCTION

Reheat cracking (RC) at austenitic stainless steel welds during high temperature operation is associated with the thermal relaxation of residual stress, when the creep ductility of the heat affected zone (HAZ) is insufficient to accommodate accumulated creep strains. A total of 261 incidents of RC in operating UK nuclear power plant has been reported in a recent review (1). Over 250 of these observations were associated with heavy section (> 60mm thick) AISI Type 316H stainless steel welds. From a review of inspection data it was concluded that RC initiation developed after 10,000 to 50,000 hours operation in the temperature range 510°C-550°C.

PWHT of stainless steel welds to relieve residual stresses is not required by construction codes because of detrimental metallurgical effects. A full solution heat treatment is sometimes applied to shop-welded components, but this is rarely feasible for field welds, either owing to the adverse effects of high temperature on adjacent welds, or the development of unacceptable temperature and stress gradients. An intermediate PWHT at 750°C has been applied to certain Type 316H field welds and repairs in power generation plant which have a high risk of RC during service operation. This temperature is low enough to avoid microstructural degradation, but high enough to partially relieve stresses without the risk of RC

A ductility exhaustion approach has been developed to predict the initiation of RC in welded stainless steel components (2). It requires an accurate characterisation of the weld residual stress field, and the way it relaxes by creep at high temperature. Relaxation of residual stress during thermal ageing, or PWHT, depends on the initial residual stress-state in the body (including the multi-axiality), the weld geometry, elastic follow-up effects, the creep behaviour of the weld and parent materials, and the nature of the thermal treatment. Approximate methods are available for estimating creep relaxation under bi-axial stress conditions (3). However, finite element (FE) methods are required to evaluate the relaxation of tri-axial residual stress distributions through the thickness of heavy section welds. Little work has been published comparing FE predictions of weld residual stress creep relaxation with measurements, apart from a study by Fidler (4) for a thick section ferritic weld.

This paper describes how the thermal relaxation of residual stresses in thick section stainless steel girth-welded components has been quantified by a combination of diverse measurement and analysis techniques. Specifically, the effects of a PWHT at 750°C for 2½ hours, and of thermal ageing at 550°C for up to 8384 hours are presented. The work was carried out as part of the EC co-funded collaborative project 'Variation of Residual Stresses in Aged Components', VORSAC (5).

EXPERIMENTAL APPROACH

Three nominally identical girth-welded test specimens, designated components A, B and C, were fabricated from three pairs of ex-service steam headers. The header forgings' material was AISI type 316H austenitic stainless steel (service-aged 65,000 hours at 520-530°C). One end of each header was machined to form a J-preparation. Each pair of headers was then joined using a manual metal arc welding procedure with Type 316L electrodes. The test components had an outer diameter of 432 mm, a measured thickness of about 65 mm, and were machined to a final length of 550mm, see Fig. 1. A typical macro-graph of the butt weld is shown in Fig. 2. Furrther details of the fabrication procedure can be found in (6).

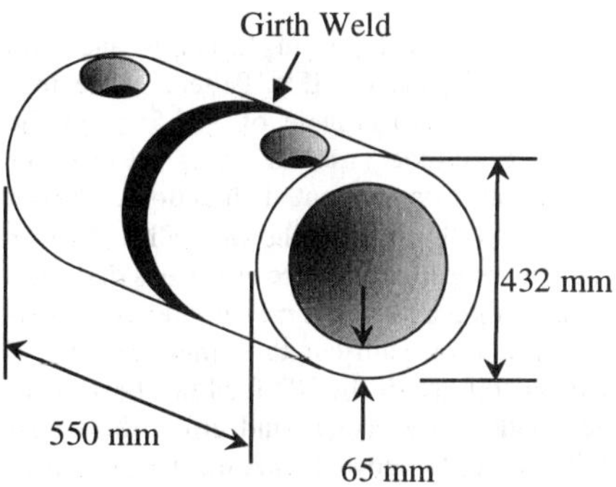

Figure 1 Sketch of Girth Welded Specimens

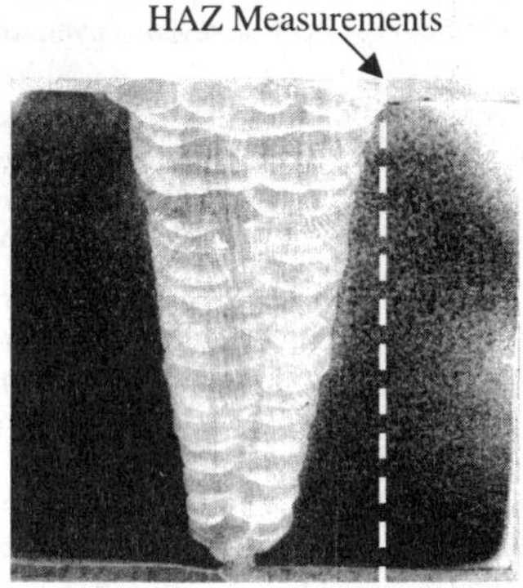

Figure 2 Macro-graph of Test Weld

The effects of two thermal treatments on the relaxation of weld residual stresses were examined: component A was subjected to a low temperature furnace PWHT of 750°C for 2½ hours (based on 1 hour per 25mm thickness), and component B was thermally aged in a furnace at 550°C for 8384 hours. Surface and through-wall weld residual stresses were measured both before and after the heat treatment. Residual stresses were measured prior to ageing (0 hours) and after 182, 2424, 6989 and 8384 hours. Component C was cut-up and used for materials characterisation tests to support FE residual stress simulation studies. The measured properties can be found in the VORSAC project final report (5).

RESIDUAL STRESS MEASUREMENTS

The initial residual stresses in components A and B were measured using surface centre hole drilling, deep hole drilling, X-ray and neutron diffraction methods. The techniques used and measured as-welded results are described in (6). The same techniques were employed to measure residual stresses after thermal treatments, as indicated in Table I.

Measurement	Component A		Component B (hours)				
Techniques	Pre-PWHT	After PWHT	0	182	2424	6989	8384
Surface hole	✓	✓	✓	✓	✓	-	✓
Deep hole	✓	✓	✓	✓	✓	✓	-
X-ray diffraction	✓	✓	✓	✓	-	-	✓
Neutron diffraction	✓	✓	-	-	-	-	-
BRSL	-	✓	-	-	-	-	-

Table I Residual Stress Measurement Techniques Applied

The block sectioning, splitting and layering method (BRSL) was also utilised after PWHT to destructively measure the through-wall residual stresses in component A at the weld centre line (CL) and in the HAZ (Fig. 2). This technique involves machining strain-gauged blocks of material (in hoop and axial stress directions) from the specimen. Membrane and bending components of the through-wall residual stresses are calculated from the measured surface strain changes. Next, the self-balancing non-linear components of the stress distributions are determined from the measured surface strain changes on sawing the blocks in half (splitting), and removing successive thin layers of material from the interior split faces by milling.

Neutron diffraction (ND) residual stress measurements in component A, before and after PWHT, were performed at the Large Component ND Facility of HFR, Petten. A neutron wavelength of 0.28 nm was employed rendering a scattering angle of ~84.5° with the austenitic (111) reflection plane. A large sampling volume (1.8 cm^3) was selected for measurements in the specimen radial, longitudinal and circumferential directions. Seven locations through the wall in the HAZ were measured (≈20 mm from the weld CL). Further measurements were made 6 and 20 mm below the outer specimen surface at various distances from the weld CL. All hoop, longitudinal and radial direction strain measurements at mid-thickness of the specimen wall necessitated a total neutron path length within the steel of about 90 - 95 mm. This proved to be beyond the capabilities of the ND facilities because of path length attenuation and a currently not well understood background effect that shifts results towards pseudo-compression (6). Additional tests showed that the limiting path length for the chosen sampling volume and wavelength was about 70 - 80 mm. However, successful measurements of radial strain relief were achieved (see Figs. 4 and 5 below).

Component A – Measured Effect of PWHT

Measured through-wall residual stresses in the HAZ (Fig. 2) of component A after PWHT are shown in Fig. 3. There is excellent agreement between results from the surface hole, deep hole and BRSL techniques. The maximum tensile stresses are in the hoop direction towards the outer surface, with the deep hole and BRSL methods giving peak measured values of around 120 MPa (36% $\sigma_{parent\ 1\%\ PS}$, or 27% $\sigma_{weld\ 1\%\ PS}$) and the surface centre-hole method a point value stress of 145 MPa. When compared with the measured as-welded stresses (Fig. 3), these results confirm that the PWHT greatly reduced the magnitude of residual stresses through the entire thickness. A similar set of measurements at the weld centre-line (not presented) demonstrated the same effect. However, no firm conclusions could be drawn about the 'relaxation' of outer surface stresses remote from the weld (≥ 50mm from the weld centre-line): axial stresses measured by the surface hole method reduced after PWHT but the corresponding hoop stresses increased; also the X-ray diffraction results showed considerable scatter because of measurement difficulties and suspected skin effects, see (6).

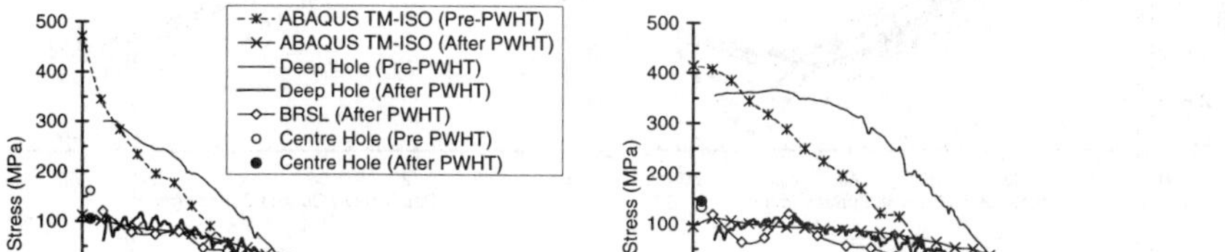

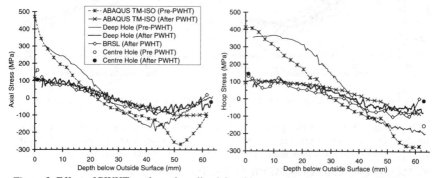

Figure 3 Effect of PWHT on through-wall axial and hoop residual stresses in the HAZ

Apparent radial strains, before and after PWHT, were measured by ND using a common reference value from parent material far from the weld. The results are compared in Fig. 4. The difference in measured radial strains, that is the strain relief, were in good agreement with equivalent results from the FE simulation (ABAQUS TM-ISO model), see Fig. 5. The ND results show that strain relief was positive for most test locations, but became negative at the inner surface. Similar levels of radial strain relief (500-1000 μstrain) at 6mm below the outer surface, were measured up to 60mm from the weld centre-line.

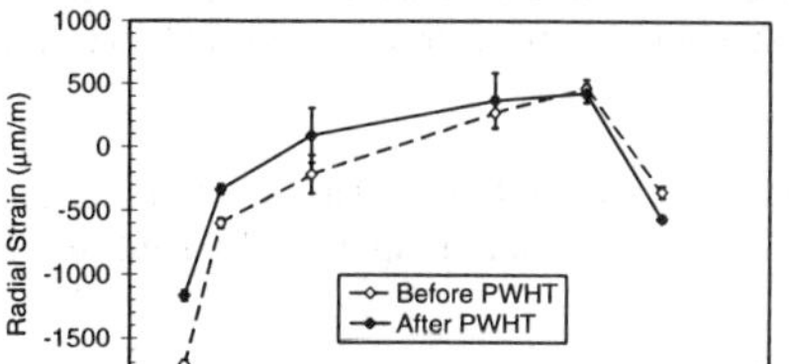

Figure 4 Apparent radial strains in the HAZ measured by neutron diffraction

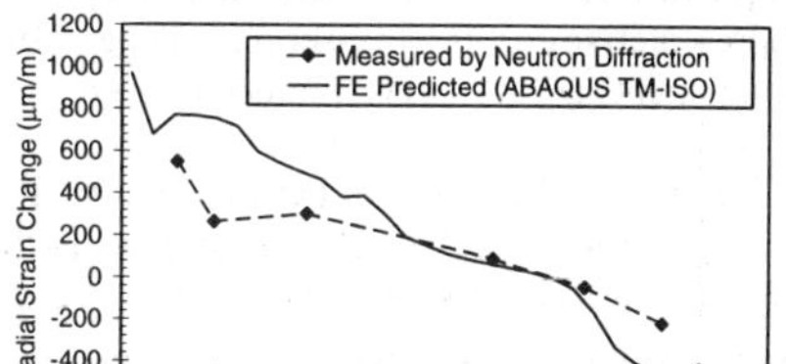

Figure 5 Measured and predicted radial strain relief in the HAZ

Component B – Measured Effect of Thermal Ageing at 550°C

Figure 6 shows the through-wall residual stresses in the HAZ measured by the deep hole technique after 182, 2424 and 6989 hours. The scatter in the results is such that there is no obvious relaxation trend with age; stresses appear to go both up and down with time. Possible reasons for the scatter are circumferential variations and differences in the axial position of the measurements relative to the local weld fusion boundary.

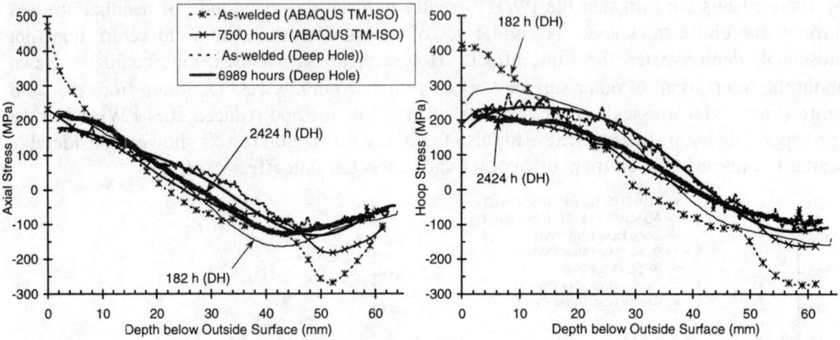

Figure 6 Stress relaxation effect of ageing at 550°C:- through-wall stresses in the HAZ

The variation in stress with ageing time is more readily assessed using the outer surface residual stress measurements. Figs. 7-9 show the results for the weld CL, for the HAZ at the edge of the weld cap (first pass side), and for parent material about 51mm from the weld CL

STRESS RELAXATION - NUMERICAL PREDICTIONS

As-welded residual stresses in the thick-section girth weld were simulated using five FE based approaches and compared with measurements (6). The thermo-mechanical approach using the ABAQUS FE code (7) with 'lumped' weld passes and isotropic parent material hardening (ABAQUS TM-ISO model) predicted residual stresses that correlated reasonably well with measurements. The residual stress field from this analysis was used as the starting condition for ABAQUS creep analyses examining the stress relaxation effects of thermal ageing at 550°C for up to 30,000 hours, and a PWHT at 750°C for 2½ hours. Creep behaviour of the welded joint (weld metal, HAZ and base metal) was modelled using an implementation of mean RCC-MR creep law data (8). These data have been shown to be representative of the ex-service Type 316H stainless steel material used for the test components at low levels of creep damage.

The FE predicted stresses before and after PWHT are shown in Fig. 3. The effect of thermal ageing at 550°C on through-wall stresses in the HAZ is illustrated in Fig. 6, and the influence on outer surface stresses is shown in Figs. 7-9.

STRESS RELAXATION – ANALYTICAL ESTIMATES

Thermal relaxation of residual stresses depends on the initial stress-state (including multi-axiality), the amount of elastic follow-up in the defective section, equilibrium requirements, the time at temperature and the creep behaviour of the weld and parent materials. Analytical methods can be used to estimate relaxation for cases where the geometry and initial stress distribution are simple. For example, the simplified approach given in (3) can be used to quantify creep relaxation for bi-axial residual stresses, provided the stress reduction is less than 20%. The point of maximum principal stress in the weld or parent material is selected for assessment and the reduction in equivalent stress predicted from uni-axial creep data. The corresponding changes in direct components of stress are estimated from the following expression for principal components of inelastic strain:

$$\varepsilon_{c1}=Z(\sigma_{1.0}-0.5\sigma_{2.0})\left\{\frac{1-\dfrac{\overline{\sigma}(t_h)}{\overline{\sigma}_0}}{E}\right\} \qquad (1)$$

where Z is the elastic follow-up factor, $\sigma_{1,0}$ and $\sigma_{2,0}$ are the initial principal stresses, $\overline{\sigma}$ is the equivalent stress with initial value $\overline{\sigma}_0$, t_h is time and E is the elastic modulus. By symmetry a corresponding relationship for ε_{c2} is obtained.

This simplified approach was applied to estimate the stress relaxation at the outer surface of component A after PWHT, and in component B as a function of ageing time. The region of maximum stress in the HAZ was chosen for assessment, using results from the ABAQUS TM-ISO weld simulation (see Table II). Uni-axial stress relaxation of the equivalent stress was calculated using a strain hardening form of the RCC-MR law, and mean values of Z (for the ageing span) based on the FE creep analysis. The relaxed components of stress were then estimated using eqn. 1. The estimated stresses at 20°C are shown in Table II. The estimated thermal ageing results for component B are also plotted in Fig. 8.

	Component A		Component B (hours)				
Stress Component	Pre-PWHT	After PWHT	0	182	2424	6989	8384
Axial[1] (MPa)	471	231	471	387	352	338	336
Hoop[1] (MPa)	415	233	415	358	334	325	323
Equiv.[2] (MPa)	446	111	446	304	244	221	218

[1] Bi-axial relaxation (eqn. 1) [2] Uni-axial relaxation

Table II Simple Estimates of Stress Relaxation in the HAZ at the Outer Surface

Note that it is more difficult to estimate the relaxed through-wall distribution of stress, as the internal stresses cannot be simply related to the surface behaviour owing to the importance of tri-axiality and equilibrium effects.

MEASURED AND PREDICTED RESULTS – EFFECT OF PWHT

Measured and predicted through-wall residual stresses in the HAZ (at the edge of the weld cap, first pass side) before and after PWHT are compared in Fig. 3. All the measured data confirm the accuracy of the ABAQUS TM-ISO (RCC-MR creep) predicted stress-strain state after PWHT, which gives a maximum tensile stress of 111 MPa in the hoop direction and 112 MPa in the axial direction (that is 34% $\sigma_{parent\ 1\%\ PS}$, or 25% $\sigma_{weld\ 1\%\ PS}$). Furthermore, all measurements and the ABAQUS prediction demonstrate that the 750°C PWHT has significantly reduced the weld residual stresses. Similar measured and predicted results were observed at the weld centre line. The estimated axial and hoop components of stress after PWHT (Table II) are seen to be very conservative.

MEASURED AND PREDICTED RESULTS – EFFECT OF AGEING

The deep hole measurements are compared with the ABAQUS TM-ISO mean RCC-MR creep relaxation prediction in Fig. 6. The correlation between predicted and measured stress profiles improves with time, such that there is fairly good agreement between the final aged results. The poor correlation towards the start of life is probably associated with over-prediction of as-welded tensile residual stresses in the HAZ and parent material by the ABAQUS TM-ISO analysis (6). However, the deep hole measurements show no obvious stress relaxation trend with ageing time. This is likely to be caused by the problem of scatter in residual stress measurements (see earlier discussion of deep hole ageing results) masking fairly small changes in stress.

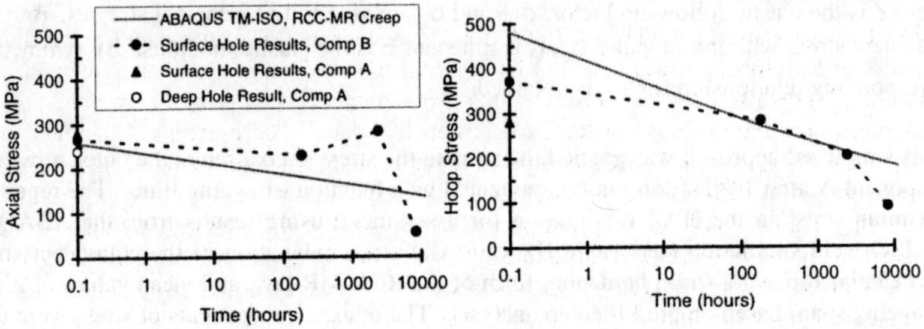

Figure 7 Surface stress relaxation at 550°C at the weld centre line

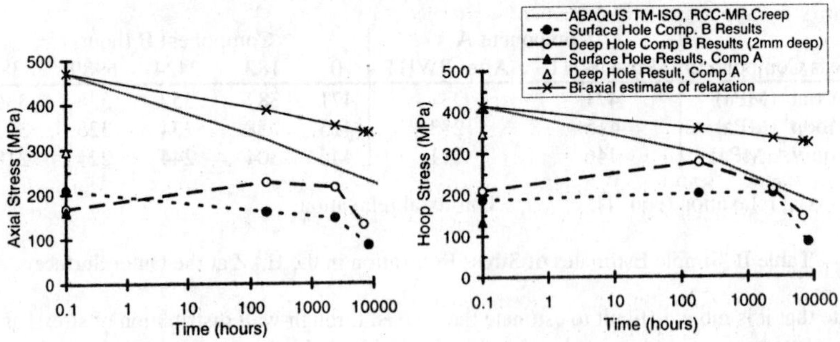

Figure 8 Surface stress relaxation at 550°C in the HAZ (≈24mm from the weld CL)

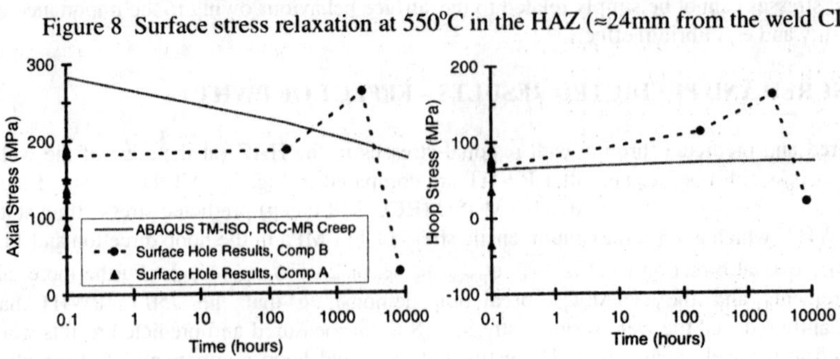

Figure 9 Surface stress relaxation at 550°C in the base material (≈51 mm from weld CL)

Figures 7-9 illustrate the variation in stresses with thermal ageing time for three points on the surface. At the weld centre line, the ABAQUS TM-ISO (RCC-MR creep) predicted stress relaxation behaviour is generally supported by the measurements. The HAZ measurements suggest that stresses increase in the short term, before long-term relaxation. However, this apparent behaviour may be caused by measurement scatter, as indicated by results from component A, which are also plotted. The base material measurements also increase in the short-medium term, whereas the predicted stress levels decrease or remain constant. All the final measurements suggest that long-term relaxation may be faster than predicted by the ABAQUS TM-ISO analysis. The analytical bi-axial estimates of axial and hoop stress relaxation at the outer surface (HAZ location) are seen to be very conservative.

CONCLUDING REMARKS

Residual stresses after a PWHT of 750°C for 2½ hours have been measured using diverse techniques (deep hole, surface hole and BRSL) and found to be in excellent agreement with each other. They also correlate closely with a finite element prediction of as-welded residual stress relaxation, based on mean RCC-MR creep law data. The maximum measured hoop stress in the HAZ was 120 MPa compared with a predicted maximum of 112 MPa. In addition, neutron diffraction measurements of radial strain relief correlated with the prediction. These results demonstrate that the furnace PWHT of 750°C reduced residual stresses from yield magnitude to around 34% of the parent 1% proof stress (or 25% of the weld 1% proof stress). A reasonable correlation between measured and predicted stress relaxation effects of thermal ageing at 550°C has been demonstrated. However, the measured evidence of stress relaxation in the first few hundred hours was contradictory. A large number of measurements are desirable to characterise thermal ageing relaxation in order to quantify the upper and lower bands of scatter and identify any 'rogue' results.

ACKNOWLEDGEMENTS

VORSAC was co-funded by the EC Nuclear Fission Safety Programme, the UK Health and Safety Executive and project partners. The work was performed by AEA Technology, British Energy, BNFL (Magnox), University of Bristol, TWI, Institute de Soudure, VTT Technology, Siemens AG, University of Karlsruhe, University of Ancona and JRC Petten.

REFERENCES

1. Coleman M C, Miller D A, Stevens R A, Proc Int Conf Integrity of High Temperature Welds, PEP Ltd, London (1998) 169
2. Bradford R, I Mech E Conf Trans. Assuring It's Safe, PEP Ltd, London (1998) 287
3. R5 Issue 2, 'Assessment procedure for the high temperature response of structures', British Energy Generation Ltd, (Gloucester UK) 1999
4. Fidler, Int J Pres Ves & Piping 14 (1983) 181
5. VORSAC, 'Variation of Residual Stresses in Ageing Components', EC Contract F14S-CT96-0040 Final Report, (Brussels) 2000
6. Bate S K, Bouchard P J, Flewitt P E J, George D, Leggatt R H, Youtsos A G, Proc ICRS6 (2000). This volume.
7. ABAQUS 5.8, Hibbitt, Karlsson & Sorensen Inc., 1997
8. RCC-MR, Design and Construction Rules for Mechanical Components of FBR Nuclear Islands, Section 1, Sub-Section Z, Technical Appendix A3, AFCEN (Paris) 1985

TUBULAR WELDING NUMERICAL SIMULATION : EXPERIMENTAL VALIDATION.

A Razakanaivo and X Desroches
Electricité de France
Division R&D
1, Avenue du Général de Gaulle
92140 Clamart, France

C Bois
Framatome
Tour Framatome
92084 Paris La Défense, France

Y Lejeail* and J Kichenin**
Comissariat à l'Energie Atomique
13108 St Paul Lez Durance*/91191 Gif-sur-Yvette**
France

ABSTRACT

In order to validate welding numerical simulation, an experimental mock-up has been designed. It consists in an austenitic 316L cylinder with a groove which is full-filled, using TIG process, with thirteen passes of welding. This experimental device is quite representative of an industrial welding process in nuclear field. The experimental program includes an important plan of measurement which allows to get several experimental data associated to the process and which are useful to validate numerical simulation. These data are thermal transient, displacement, strain and residual stress measurement.
2D-axisymmetrical numerical simulations of the process are carried on. The results of several models are compared with experimental data.

INTRODUCTION

Commissariat à l'Energie Atomique (CEA), Electricité de France (EDF) and Framatome have led for a few years a research program on welding finite-element simulation. The purpose is the determination of the residual stresses associated to welding processes in PWR nuclear components. To optimise and validate models and numerical methods developed by the three companies, an experimental object was realised : it is the welding of an austenitic tubular mock-up by TIG process. It is designed so as to get several experimental data characterising the process : temperature and strain all along the process, residual displacement and stress after the welding passes.

After the development of the adequate device, numerical simulations of the process are carried on. These calculations are done using the f.e.m. codes Castem2000 (CEA), Code_Aster (EDF) and Sysweld (Framatome). The first calculations treated in this paper are calculations for which thermal modelling is adjusted on thermal transient data. Actually this adjustment is not so obvious for processes for which there are no measurement and for which only the welding parameters are available. The predictive simulations of the process using only the classical welding parameters will constitute the aim of the next step of the work and will be discussed in an another paper.

The first section of this paper deals with the description of the experimental device. The numerical calculations are presented afterwards : description of modelling, comparison of results. These calculations include a bench marking between the partners on the simulation of the first five passes and a complete calculation of the thirteen welding passes.

EXPERIMENTAL DEVICE.

Description of the mock-up

The installation realised by FRAMATOME concerns the welding of an austenitic 316L tubular mock-up, designed to furnish several experimental data characterising the process. The structure is an axisymmetrical cylinder with a midspan groove machined around the outer wall. The length of the cylinder is L0 =560 mm, its inner radius is r0 = 110 mm, and thickness is e0 = 12.9 mm (see Figure 1). The maximum depth of the groove is d0 = 9.9 mm, its maximum width is w0 = 19 mm. The structure is horizontally clamped at one end to a rotating plate, the other end is free. A pulsed TIG welding process is used to fill the groove under inert gas protection. Both cylinder and deposit materials are austenitic 316L steel. The deposit thread yields from a fixed device at constant velocity V_{thread}. The rotating plate allows a constant angular velocity around the cylinder axis which induces a velocity process of V_{source} (see Table I). Thirteen passes are completed : for each pass the initial azimuth is shifted in order to avoid ovalization of the cylinder. No pass is initiated unless the groove temperature has dropped beneath 100°C. The welding parameters are given in table I.

pass	I (A)	U (V)	thread diameter (mm)	V_{thread} (mm/s)	V_{source} (mm/s)
1	200	11	1	30	1.6
2→13	200	11.5	1	13	1.6

Table I : welding parameters.

The structure is provided with sensors measuring temperatures and displacements all along the process. The sensors are fixed along three meridian lines at 0, 120 and 240 degrees on both sides of the groove. The Chromel Alumel thermocouples are fixed at about 1 and 3 mm from the groove edge. The groove opening is measured with micrometers via rigid arms which allow to shift the micrometers away from the welding electromagnetic field. Measurements characterising the residual displacements are also realised : measurements of the groove width and the distance between two marked points. Topographical mapping realised at the end of each pass allows to obtain the stacking of the passes. (see figure 2). There are also residual stresses measurements which are performed with an X-ray method when the cylinder is at room temperature after passes 5, 9 and 13. A sequence of spots is prepared along 0 and 240 degrees lines, on both sides of the groove. The same spots are used for each series of measurements. These measurements are also completed by center hole method measurements at the end of the 13th pass. Furthermore in order to have indications on the bead shape, a preliminary mock-up made of interrupted passes (13) was realised, with several cross sectional macrography.

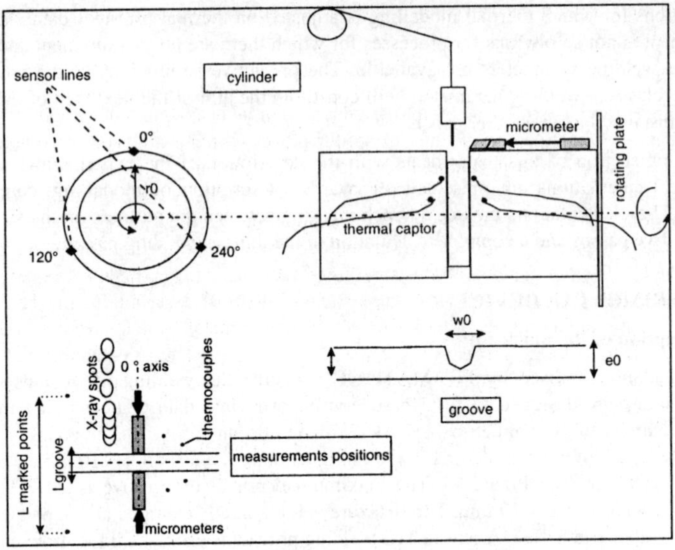

Fig. 1 Experimental device

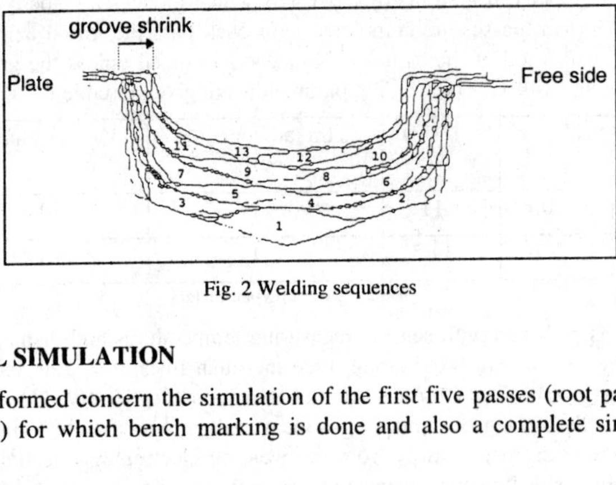

Fig. 2 Welding sequences

NUMERICAL SIMULATION

Calculations performed concern the simulation of the first five passes (root pass and the first four filling runs) for which bench marking is done and also a complete simulation of the thirteen passes.

Modelling characteristics.

Geometrical modelling.

The thermo-mechanical model is a 2D-axisymmetrical model. This two-dimensional idealisation of the problem represents each weld bead as a ring instantaneously heated up to the melting point and cooled uniformly. In fact, during the welding, the metal ahead of the welding torch is more slowly heated by the approaching torch and continues by diffusion to be heated after the torch passage. The initial mesh includes the whole tube with the groove and all the weld beads. Each pass is constructed using the knowledge of the volume of the deposited metal (determined from the welding parameters) and of the shape of the bead with the help of the macrography.

Thermal model

The TIG heat input is simulated by introducing a volumic heat source density in the deposited metal. The time variation and the intensity of the power source is adjusted by comparison with thermal cycle results and the molten zone area (macrography). This is done by Framatome using the finite element code Systus. The adjustments are firstly done on a three-dimensional configuration. These three-dimensional simulations represent the stationary state corresponding to a circular surfacic power source moving at the surface of a plate. Reasonable agreement has been obtained with measured thermal transient. The results are then applied to the axisymmetrical configuration. With the axisymmetrical assumption, the heat flux is a volume density applied in every lattice of the deposited metal. Adjustments are done for the root pass and for a lonely current pass, the 13th one. The modelling parameters associated to this particular current pass are used afterwards just as they are for the other current passes.

In the thermal calculation, all the material properties are temperature dependent. An enthalpy model is used, the latent heat of melting – solidification is taken into account and defined on a 100°C interval around 1400°C. We assume that austenitic base metal and weld metal are identical. A fictitious high thermal conductivity is assigned to the bead to homogenise the temperature in the melted pool. Convection (with static air at room temperature) and radiation exchange are taken into account. The cooling stages between two passes are roughly respected. This interpass time is about 2000 s, which corresponds approximately to a final temperature of the piece of about 100°C, excepted for passes n°5, n°9 and n°13 for which the tube is cooled till the room temperature. The influence of all the future deposited beads, which don't yet exist but which are part of the mesh is kept as low as possible by imposing low values of the thermal conductivity in the corresponding elements.

Figure 3 and 4 shows thermal transient for the root pass and the 2nd pass (*p* and *f* correspond respectively to the plate and free side). Thermal computations are in good agreement with experiment especially for the root pass. Slight differences are observed for the second pass. It is reminded that the simulation of this pass is done with parameters adjusted on the 13th pass while the configuration of the two beads is not the same.

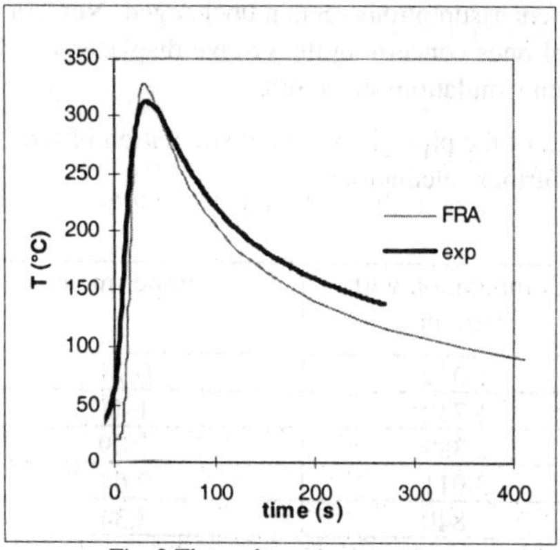

Fig. 3 Thermal transient pass 1

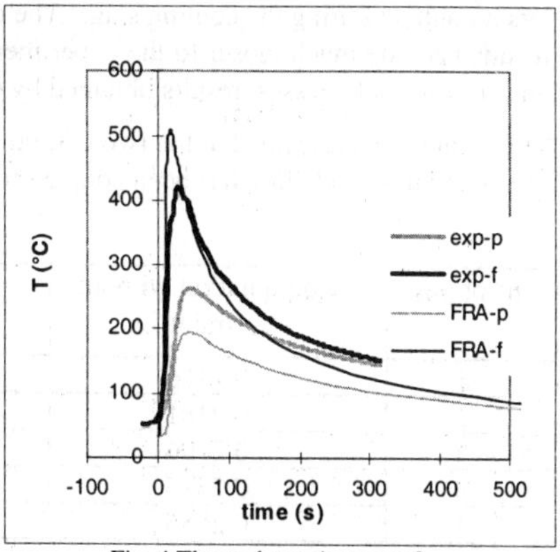

Fig. 4 Thermal transient pass 2

Mechanical model.

Mechanical calculations are performed after the thermal calculations, thermal history being the only mechanical loading. The coupling between thermal and mechanical problem is a weak coupling with the assumption that the influence of the mechanical phenomena on the thermal ones may be neglected.

The mechanical behaviour was assumed to be isotropic with isotropic hardening. Mechanical parameters are determined from tensile curves taken from a EDF/CEA database (1) for 316L(N) steel. This database includes test results for different strain rates and for temperatures between 20 and 1200°C. Tensile curves are extrapolated for higher temperatures. In the mesh, all the weld beads are initially modelled. But they are made fictitious and don't disturb stress and displacement fields of the surrounding metal thanks to the choice of a low elastic modulus (1MPa). During one bead deposit, the bead, initially fictitious, recovers its real material characteristics when it reaches the melting point. Above the melting point, hardening restoration phenomenon is taken into account. This restoration is total and cancels all the strain-hardening cumulated at high temperatures. Computations are conducted assuming large deformations.

Mechanical restraint effect.

In the first computation the pipe was considered free of motion : just one node is connected in the axial direction to ensure numerical stability. Mechanical behaviour is elasto-plastic with isotropic hardening. In term of groove displacement, table 2 shows that numerical simulation underestimates the groove shrink. At the fifth pass, the ratio between experimental and numerical value is about 13. This phenomenon is quite easy to explain : in an axisymmetric computation, the bead is deposited instantaneously over all the groove, which allows the pipe to expand or to contract freely in the axial direction. In the experiment, the heat source move progressively inside the groove. The heating stage being very short, the zone ahead of the weld is still cold and restrains the welded zone. In the groove area, the component cannot expand freely during this stage. This restraint decrease and tend to vanish in the cooling stage, because of the heat diffusion and the source displacement. To simulate this 3D-effect, we conducted another computation : an axial restraint is imposed to the extremity of the pipe during the heating stage. This restraint prevents then the pipe to expand during the heating but lets it contract during the cooling stage. The others assumptions remain unchanged. Numerical results become much closer to the experimental ones concerning the groove displacement. In term of residual stresses, results obtained by both simulations are similar.

The axial restraint applied at the two extremities of the pipe gives a good simulation of the 3D effect and this modelling has been adopted for further calculations.

n° of pass	Computation without restraint	Computation with restraint	Experiment
1	0.1476	1.079	0.74
2	0.2181	1.742	1.41
3	0.2196	2.384	2.09
4	0.2315	3.011	2.64
5	0.2655	3.840	3.34

Table II mechanical restraint effect on the groove shrink.

Benchmark on the first five passes

Using the modelling previously described, a numerical benchmark is performed between the four partners. Differences between calculations come essentially from the modelling of the beads and the mechanical behaviour law. The mesh of the deposited metal may actually be done in different ways and we wanted to know the influence of the bead modelling : the more complex way is to model a geometry as close as possible as the one given by macrography, ie taking into account curved passes (EDF). Another rougher way is to model passes using polygonal forms (Framatome). Finally the simplest way consists in using rectangular forms (CEA1). The two last ways, especially the last one, do not require the knowledge of the exact form of each bead, which is generally the case. In every case the surface of each bead mesh respect the experimental deposited metal volume. The thermal adjustment which is done with polygonal forms is used unchanged in the model using curved forms. But since rectangular forms are very different from the mesh used for thermal adjustment, an another thermal adjustment is required. Furthermore, instead of using an uniform source a gaussian power density is used in order to obtain a better description of the molten zone. A viscoplastic mechanical behaviour is also compared to the elastoplastic one. Except these characteristics the others are quite equivalent. Table III summarises the calculations.

	Weld pass shape	thermal model	mechanical model
Framatome	polygonal	uniform source	elasto-plastic
EDF	curve	uniform source	elasto-plastic
CEA 1	rectangular	gaussian source	elasto-plastic
CEA 2	curve	uniform source	visco-plastic (no hardening restoration)

Table III calculations characteristics.

Figure 5 shows the thermal transient corresponding to the 2nd pass. Figure 6 shows the groove shrink after each pass. A good agreement between numerical and experimental results can be observed up to the third pass and even the fifth for some model. For residual stresses, even if comparisons between calculation and experiment are difficult due to experimental scatter, and especially because of the existence of compressive initial residual stress in the tube, the computations give a good trend of the experiment (RX). Indeed this initial compressive stress is not taken into account in computations. The residual stresses are maximal in the heat-affected zone and are tensile stresses due to the bending effect. They decrease quite rapidly and vanish at 100 mm from the weld area.

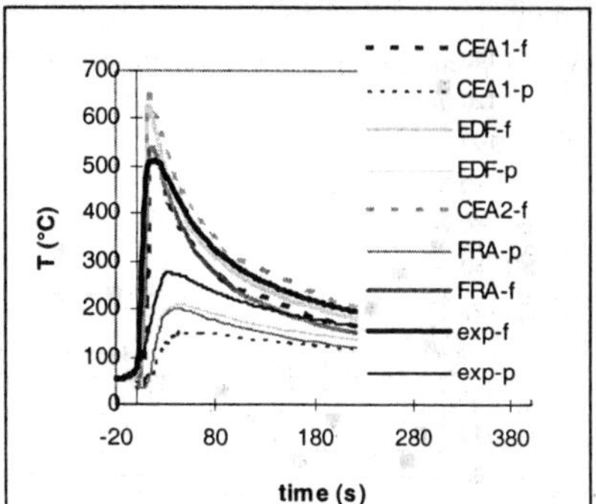

Fig. 5 Thermal transient pass 2

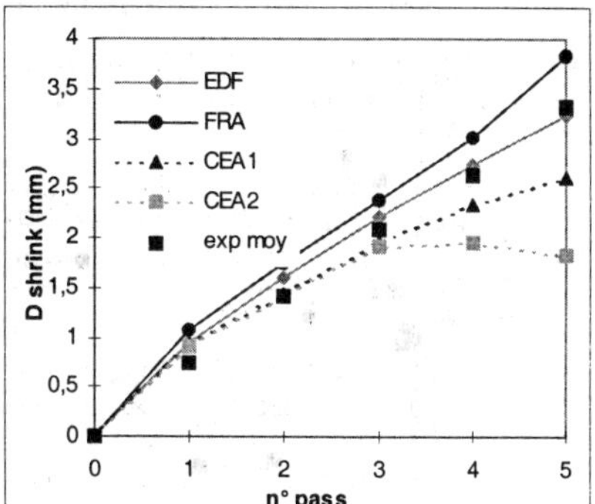

Fig. 6 Groove shrink

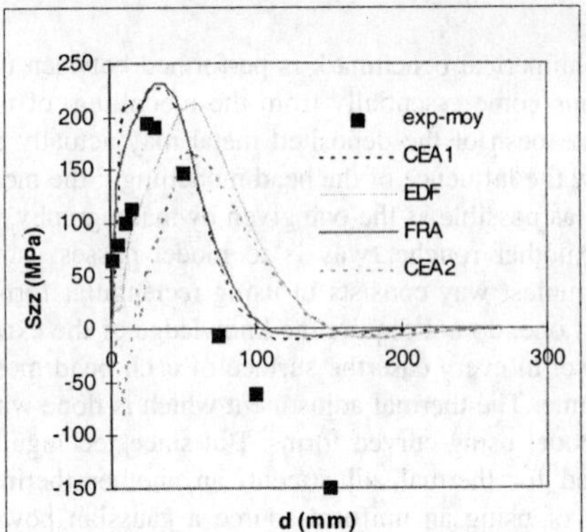

Fig. 7 Longitudinal residual stress

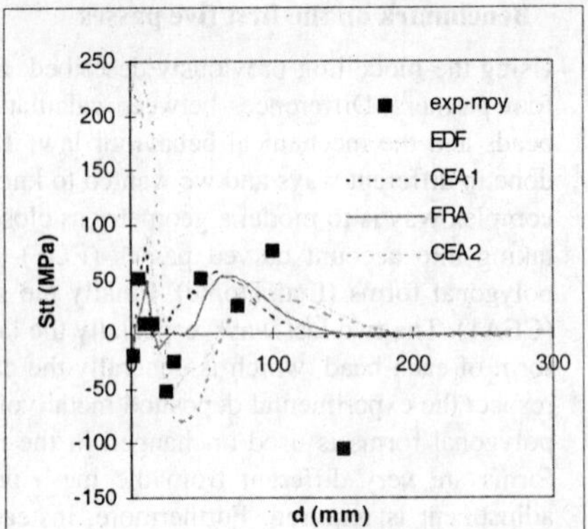

Fig. 8 Circumferential residual stress

The modelling developed allows quite a good simulation of the process. Quite good agreement between numerical and experimental results are obtained. It seems that there are few effects of the weld pass shape on thermal cycle, deformations and residual stresses. The use of a viscoplastic behaviour seems here to have an effect on deformation and residual stress results. Nevertheless, as the modelling parameters use for this case are quite different from the other (no hardening restoration, small deformation), further analysis is required.

Computation on thirteen passes

Simulation of the complete process (thirteen passes) has been carried out. Calculation presented here is done by EDF with Code_Aster using the more complex configuration. Quite a good agreement in term of σ_R is obtained between the numerical and the experimental results after the 9th and the 13th pass. Figure below gives the residual stresses after the thirteen pass. Concerning the groove shrink we have good agreement between experiments and computations till the 5th pass. Afterwards, modelling underestimates the shrink. The use of another mechanical behaviour like viscoplastic law may facilitate the plastic flow at medium and low temperature and increase then the groove displacement.

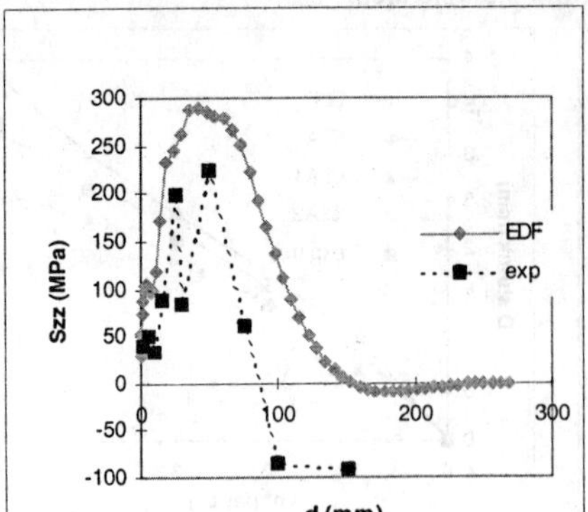

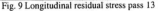

Fig. 9 Longitudinal residual stress pass 13

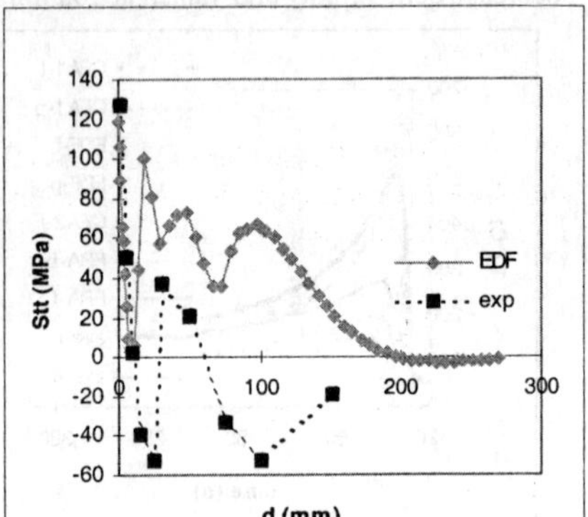

Fig. 10 Circumferential residual stress

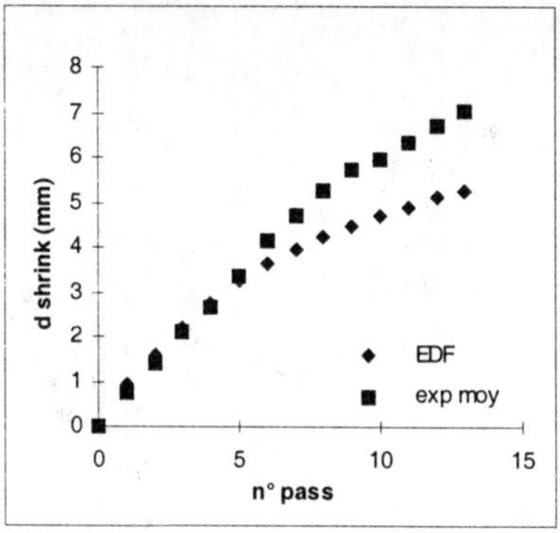

Fig. 11 Groove shrink

CONCLUSION

This program has led to the development of an experimental device which allows to validate and improve methodology in welding simulation. It especially allows to settle a 2D-axisymmetrical model which leads the three finite element codes Castem2000, Code_Aster and Sysweld to a good simulation of the welding process. The specificity of this model is to take into account the 3D mechanical restrain effect. Numerical results of thermal transient, residual strains and residual stresses fit well with experimental results. This result is of importance because even if 3D computations are possible, they remain difficult to carry through, especially for multipass configuration, because of the size and the complexity of the problems considered.

The use of a simple geometrical modelling of the beads gives satisfying enough results. It means that the knowledge of the shape of the weld beads should not be required.

The final step is to develop and to realise " predictive " calculations using classical available " welder " parameters.

Reference

1. Felsen M.F., Grehier J., Lehmann D, "Base de données sur l'acier inoxydable 17-12 au molybdène et azote contrôlé. Caractéristiques de traction – Première partie : présentation des données", Internal report.

POSTERS

A NEW TECHNOLOGY FOR RESIDUAL STRESSES REMOVAL

YU Ragozin and YU Antonov
Machines' Dynamics and Strength Department
Perm State Technical University
29a Komsomolsky Avenue, Perm 614600, Russia

ABSTRACT

Presented in the paper is a physically proved technology for residual stresses relief, differing in principle from all technologies offered before: application of this new technology allows us to minimize the energy and time expense during the treatment of products by hundreds of times.

INTRODUCTION

The appearance of residual macrostresses causes the change of many properties of a material. In the majority of cases they change for the worse. Thus, on account of the total influence of residual stresses and operating (external) stresses the possibility of the early fracture of machines, units, and components appears during the operation process. Under the influence of residual stresses the emergence of a volume stressed condition, making easier the cracking process, is possible. Residual stresses stimulate corrosion-oxidation processes and also the diffusion processes taken place in materials during operation under the high temperatures. It follows from the above that reduction of the level on or full relief of residual stresses should cause a sharp increase in bearing ability of machines, components and units in many cases. At present several methods of reduction and full relief of residual stresses are used. Thermal, mechanical and vibration methods are the most widespread among them. Unfortunately, all these methods have essential disadvantages. For example, the most widespread thermal method is connected with a loss of quality, and furthermore, it requires too much time and energy. Mechanical method is not applicable for the details of complex forms, and besides, it is too laborious. Finally, vibration method allows only partial relief of residual stresses, and furthermore, it has low effectiveness for many materials.

A new method of residual stress relief deprived of the above disadvantages is presented in this paper. A new technology, allowing us to realize a full residual stress relief for the whole volume of a product without changing the strength characteristics, but with the minimum expense of time and energy, was created on the basis of this method.

PHYSICAL FUNDAMENTALS OF NEW RESIDUAL STRESS RELIEF METHOD

Theoretical investigation by Ragozin (1,2) showed that each crystalline material has a quite definite discrete spectrum of atom vibration frequencies in its lattice. The type of dislocation typical of the given solid structure determines the last spectrum, and theoretically it can be calculated for any material. If we apply to a crystal the energy equal to $W_i = h\nu_i$ (W_i - threshold energy level, h - Plank's constant value, ν_i - vibration frequency of i - mode in discrete spectrum), then the energy will be selectively absorbed by the crystal lattice, which will cause a sharp increase of the amplitude of atomic vibrations of the i -mode. Thus, it is a question of possibility of one-phonon processes in crystals. Similar processes were discovered earlier Shull (3), Pelah (4), Gobert (5) in some materials during inelastic neutron dispersion. Therefore the comparison of energy values selectively absorbed by neutrons or giving by them back to the phonons, with theoretically calculated threshold energy level W_i was of particular interest. Such comparisons made for aluminum and copper proved the coincidence of the above volumes and allowed an assumption that it is possible to influence the level of residual stresses affecting the material by means of impulses with the energy W_i. It was obviously seen that in the case of a positive result we shall obtain a method of residual stress relief which has no analogues from the point of view of energy and time expenses.

The direct experimental test of this assumption was carried out on a construction steel of the 40XHMA grade. The values of threshold energy levels W_i for iron (and its alloys) are presented in the Table I. The Table includes also the values W_i for other industrially important metals.

Table I. Threshold energy levels for some metals

Metal	W_i, MJ/m³							
	1	2	3	4	5	6	7	8
Al	14.5	29.1	31.4	43.2	62.8			
a-Ti	27.8	34.2	34.2	35.6	51.7	55.5	73.5	103.4
a-Fe	47.6	71.4	78.6	104.5	110.7	178.0	224.1	
Mo	37.3	41.2	51.4	59.8	76.2	104.0	160.8	

The methods of W_i definition are described in the paper by Ragozin (1). Samples of steel of 6x12x40 mm size after polishing were subjected to a light hardening in oil at a temperature of 860°C and then were tempered at a temperature of 160°C. After such thermal treatment the samples had rather high level of residual stresses which were determined by the standard X-ray "$\sin^2 \Psi$" method. Since the scattering in the residual stresses values is inevitable, the level of residual stresses was determined on each sample of the batch. Then strictly dosed impulses of electrical energy (from a capacitor) were brought to the samples. All threshold energy values W_i for the given material were included in chosen range of energies. Having measured the level of residual stresses in the samples again, we evaluated the degree of residual stress relief depending on the value of electrical energy delivered. Figure 1 illustrates the final results of this investigation. It can be clearly seen that the value of residual stress decreases at the process of bringing the impulses of energy W_α, W_β, W_γ, W_ε, and under the influence of energy impulse equal to W_δ we can observe complete relief of residual stresses. Value W_δ in our case is the main threshold energy level W_i^κ (corresponding to the main threshold vibration frequency in the discrete spectrum Ragozin (2)) for that structure material. It was shown Ragozin (2) that alloying and thermal treatment has very little influence on the location of energy levels in spectrum, but they are able to change the location of the main threshold level of energy W_i^κ.

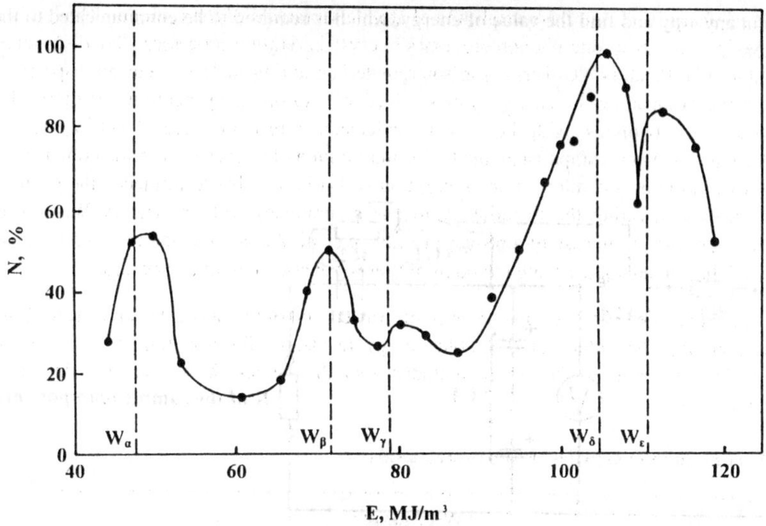

Fig. 1 The degree of residual stress relief N depending on the value of energy supplied E.

Precisely the latter determines the energy capacity of the alloy fracture Ragozin (2, 6), and as it follows from the results obtained in the present paper, it determines also the level of energy required to be brought to the sample (or component) in order to provide the full relief of residual stress in it.

THE NEW TECHNOLOGY AND ITS EFFECTIVENESS

The most effective technology of residual stress relief should provide a full relief of inner stresses over the whole range of products without changing their strength characteristics with the minimum expense of time and energy. The new technology of residual stress relief, the physical fundamentals of which are mentioned above, meets all the mentioned criteria.

There are several variants of technology differing in the way of bringing energy to the sample. The variant of technology with the use of electrical energy accumulated by a capacitor is the most complete among them. Figure 2 illustrates the scheme of electromagnetic installation. Its distinctive peculiarity consists in the application of high-voltage condensers and thyristor start, considerably minimizing the loss of energy in electrical contacts. Installation is applied with the whole series of adjustments required for the mounting of samples practically of any form.

The procedure of residual stress relief is very simple. We calculate the main threshold level of energy W_i^K (for one unit of volume) for the given material. Then determine the volume of a sample in any way and find the value of energy, which is required to be communicated to the capacitor.

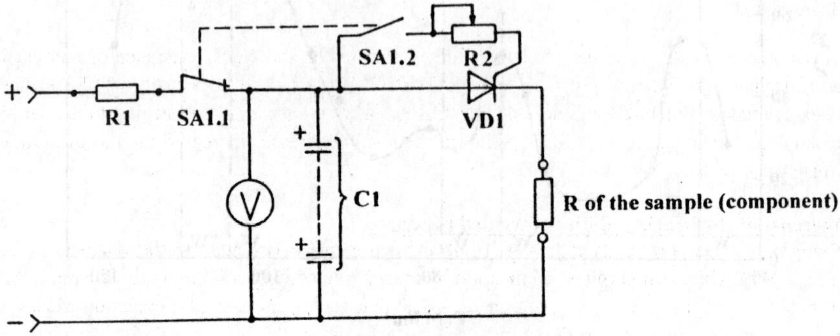

Fig. 2 Electrical scheme of electroimpulse installation.

The voltage on the capacitor will be equal to: $V=\sqrt{2E/C}$, where E is the stored energy, J; C is the capacitance, F; V is the voltage on the capacitor, v. We mount the sample to the equipment. Then we charge the capacitor to the calculated voltage and start the impulse.

The process of definition of the threshold energy level W_i^κ is the most laborious (it requires much time). In principle, it is possible not to define it at all because the expense of energy and time required directly for the process of residual stresses relief are very small. In such case impulses with the energies of all discrete spectrum levels (Table I) should be brought to the sample. For example, for Al and its alloys there are only five impulses, and for α-Fe and its alloys there are also practically five of them. It is clear that the number of these impulses will include also the impulse with the energy W_i^κ for the given material. The examples showing the effectiveness of new technology (refer to Ragozin (7)) are given below.

Increase of durability of hard-faced tools during the treatment of heat-resistant steels. Cutters with brazed plates made of hard alloy BK8 have been tested. Residual stresses of some of them have been relieved by the new technology. Samples of heat-resistant steel of 12X18H9T and 18X3MB were subjected to the treatment. The test conditions were the same for the whole series of cutters. Durability of the tool has been determined according to the size of the edge wear that has been measured along the back face by means of a microscope. The test results showed that durability of cutters increased by 1.4-1.8 times.
Increase of wear and crack resistance of hardened steels. Usually for the manufacturing of tools and bearings steels in a condition after hardening and low tempering are used. Such materials have considerable residual tensile stresses. The effect of residual stresses on the

We investigated the effect of residual stresses on wear-resistance of a hardened instrumental steel of XBF grade. The tests have been conducted on a friction machine according to the "flat block - disc" scheme. Some batches of the samples - blocks (8 x 8 x 30 mm) have been tested. The samples - discs made of the steel X12M with a diameter of 40 mm have been used as a contrabody. The volume wear of a sample - block has been chosen as a criterion of the wear-resistance evaluation. The test results have shown that the samples with relieved residual stresses have a wear-resistance increased 2.6 times. Moreover, the friction coefficient decreased 16%.

In another series of tests the effect of residual stresses on the crack-resistance of hardened and mechanically alloyed powder steel oflTK50H2M grade (with a porosity ~ 12.5%) has been evaluated. Fracture toughness of the steel K_{IC} after the treatment according to the serial technology was equal to ~ 32 MPa. Relief of the residual stresses increased the level of crack - resistance to 30%.

Increase of the bearing ability of welded products.

Pump rods, usually used at the process of oil extraction, are connected together by means of a thread joint. The method of rod connection by means of a contact welding is considered to be more advanced. However, the experiments show that such a method of connection causes a threefold reduction of the rod fatigue limit because of the high level of residual stresses emerged. We have conducted investigations directly on the serial rods of 19 mm made of steel of 20H2M grade. The rods have been subjected to treatment for the relief of residual stresses in the place of welding. The consequent cyclic tests showed that the fatigue limit after such treatment completely restores up to its initial values.

The same problem was solved also in connection with the laser welding of plates made of zirconium alloy (Zr + 1%Nb). Welding of the plates leads to a 50% reduction of the fatigue limit. Additional treatment according to the new technology also restores fatigue properties up to initial values.

Thus, application of the new technology of residual stress relief leads to the significant increase of bearing ability of materials and products. The analyses showed that new technology allows to minimize energy and time expenses by hundred times in comparison with already existing technologies.

REFERENCES

1. Ragozin Yu, I, 8th Eur. Conf. Fract. (ECF 8), Torino, EMAS, 2, 1990, 1150
2. Ragozin Yu, I, Metals, 6, (1996) 69
3. Shull C, G, Wilkinson M.K, Phys. Rev.. 97 (1955) 304
4. Pelah I, et al., Phvs. Rev.. 108 (1957) 1091
5. Gobert G, Jacrot B, J. Phvs. Radium. 19 (1959)
6. Ragozin Yu, I, Proc. 7th Int. Conf. Fract. (ICF 7), Houston, Pergamon Press, 6, 1989, 3731
7. Ragozin Yu, I, Polyanin I,V, Proc. 4th Int. Conf. of Residual Stresses (ICRS 4), Baltimore, Pergamon Press, 1994, 722

DESIGN AND IMPLEMENTATION OF RING-CORE METHOD FOR RESIDUAL STRESS MEASUREMENT

J Siiriäinen *, H Gripenberg, H Hänninen
Helsinki University of Technology
Laboratory of Engineering Materials
Puumiehenkuja 3A, FIN-02150 Espoo
*** Stresstech Oy, Ohjelmakaari 16, FIN-40500 Jyväskylä**

ABSTRACT

The purpose of the study was to improve the measuring possibilities of residual stresses by extending the measuring range deeper into the material than is possible with the present ordinary methods. A measuring device based on the ring-core method was constructed. The ring-core method is based on the same basic principles as the hole drilling method. In the method the existing equilibrium of stresses is disturbed by a step-by-step machined annular groove. When the stresses spontaneously seek a new state of equilibrium, deformations take place in the immediate surroundings of the groove and strains caused by those deformations are registered at the surface by strain gauges in the middle of the groove. The stress distribution as a function of depth can then be derived from the step-by-step collected strain response. The strain response was simulated with FEM analysis.

The annular groove was made by electrical discharge machining (EDM). The measuring method was tested with test bars, which had a uniaxial stress state due to an external tensile force. The bars were stress relief annealed before the test. The results of tests were compared with literature data and the results of the FEM simulation showing that the method agrees with the theory. The measurement scatter was caused by difficulties in electrode positioning, by excessive local warming of the workpiece and by disturbances in the EDM process.

INTRODUCTION

The ring-core method for the measurement of residual stresses is a variation on the hole drilling method and it is not as widely used as the hole drilling method. Compared to the hole drilling method the advantages of the ring-core method are larger relieved strains, increased measurement depth and the fact that the method is not so sensitive to temperature fluctuations in the surroundings, Schajer et al. (1). The measurement is done step-by-step and it is based on the assumptions that one of the principal directions of the residual stress state is in a direction perpendicular to the surface, that no stress exists in this direction and that the residual stress state is biaxial and parallel to the surface, Keil (2). These conditions are generally met only for surfaces and the deeper layers are under a triaxial stress state. Because of the difficulties in measuring the stress component perpendicular to the surface with the current practice it has to be ignored. The annular groove needed to release the stresses can be machined with a suitable cutter, removed by electrolytic polishing or by electrical discharge machining. The depth of the groove in each step has to be known precisely and the machining of the groove has to be done so that it does not alter the existing stress state. The depth of a single step can be greater than in the hole drilling method, e.g., 0.2…0.5 mm/step, thus, allowing less demand for the machining accuracy making it technically easier to achieve.

Instead of drilling a hole in the centre of a strain gauge rosette an annular groove is made around a special strain gauge rosette. The resulting strain relaxation is measured on the surface of the cylindrical core. Figure 1 shows the geometry of a strain gauge rosette and the placement of the rosette in relation to the groove. The maximum depth of the groove is dependent on the dimensions specified for the core.

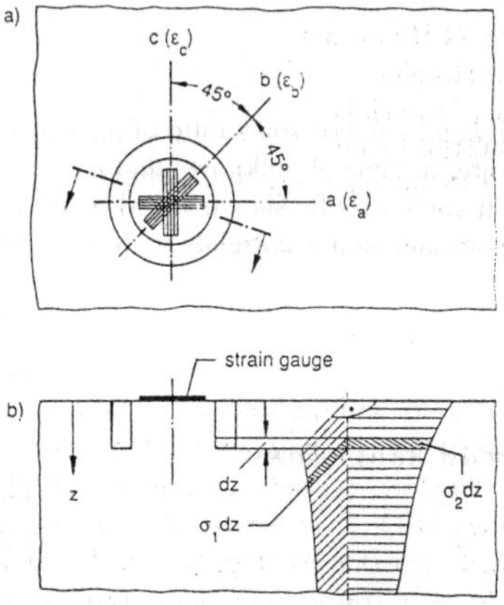

Fig. 1 The ring-core and the strain gage rosette grids indexed as a, b and c. Principal stresses σ_1 and σ_2 and their distributions. Fig. b) is the cross-section of a), Keil (2).

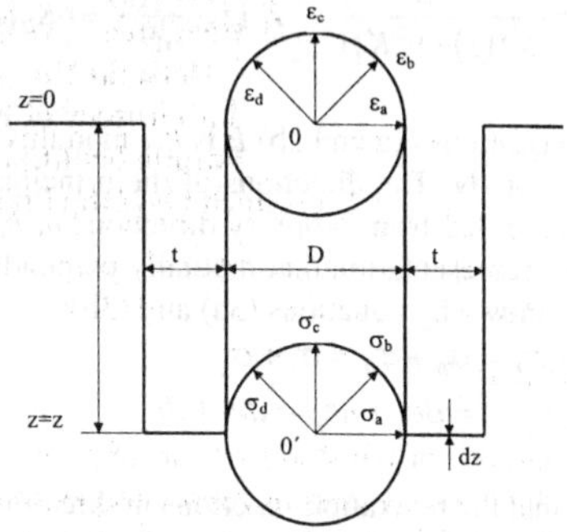

Fig. 2 The relationship between strains measured on the surface and released stresses in depth z.

Theoretical solution

The residual stress state in planes parallel to the surface and perpendicular to the normal, z, of the surface can be described as a function of z. Figure 2 shows a situation where the depth of the groove has increased by an amount of dz from its original depth z. The prevailing stresses are marked by $\sigma_{a,b,c,d}$ and the relieved strains are marked by $d\varepsilon_{a,b,c,d}$. The three strain gages are in directions a, b and c. Direction a is perpendicular to direction c and direction b is perpendicular to direction d. The highest principal stress is σ_1 and it is oriented at an angle α to gauge a. Gauges a, b and c are oriented at 0°, 45° and 90° angles to each other. In general, the change in strain recorded by gauge a can be described as a function of the depth z by the equation:

$$\frac{d\varepsilon_a(z)}{dz} = K_a(z)\varepsilon_a^*(z) \tag{1}$$

In equation (1) $K_a(z)$ is the relaxation function, which describes the effect the strain $\varepsilon^*_a(z)$ has on the strain gauge for increasing depth z. The relaxation function is dependent on the core diameter, the shape of the groove bottom, the strain gauge and the residual stress state. The relaxation functions can be derived from strain gauge measurements carried out on test specimens that are under a known stress or computationally with FE-analysis, König (3). The results from the FE-analysis are then verified with previously mentioned measurements on test specimens.

The principal stresses σ_1 and σ_2 can be calculated from the relaxation functions parallel to the principal stresses and the measured changes in strains, $d\varepsilon_1/dz(z)$ and $d\varepsilon_2/dz(z)$. Equations (2a) and (2b) show this dependence, Wolf et al. (4):

$$\sigma_1 = \frac{E}{K_1^2(z)-\upsilon^2 K_2^2(z)}\left[K_1(z)\frac{d\varepsilon_1(z)}{dz}+\upsilon K_2(z)\frac{d\varepsilon_2(z)}{dz}\right] \tag{2a}$$

$$\sigma_2 = \frac{E}{K_1^2(z)-\upsilon^2 K_2^2(z)}\left[K_1(z)\frac{d\varepsilon_2(z)}{dz}+\upsilon K_2(z)\frac{d\varepsilon_1(z)}{dz}\right]. \tag{2b}$$

In equations (2a and 2b) E is the modulus of elasticity and ν is Poisson's ratio of the material under study. The directions of the principal stresses are, in general, unknown and the strains are recorded from arbitrary directions *a, b, c* and *d*. It can easily be shown based on Mohr's circle representation that mutually perpendicular stresses and strains correlate with each other as is shown by equations (3a) and (3b):

$$\sigma_a+\sigma_c=\sigma_b+\sigma_d=\sigma_1+\sigma_2 \tag{3a}$$

$$d\varepsilon_a+d\varepsilon_c=d\varepsilon_b+d\varepsilon_d=d\varepsilon_1+d\varepsilon_2, \tag{3b}$$

and that the relaxation functions in directions *a, b, c* and *d* are as follows:

$$K_a(z)=K_b(z)=K_1(z) \tag{4a}$$

$$K_c(z)=K_d(z)=K_2(z). \tag{4b}$$

By solving $d\varepsilon_d$ from eq. (3b) and taking eqs (4a) and (4b) into consideration the stresses in directions *a, b* and *c* can be calculated with equations (5a), (5b) and (5c):

$$\sigma_a(z)=\frac{E}{K_1^2(z)-\upsilon^2 K_2^2(z)}\left[K_1(z)\frac{d\varepsilon_a(z)}{dz}+\upsilon K_2(z)\frac{d\varepsilon_c(z)}{dz}\right] \tag{5a}$$

$$\sigma_b(z)=\frac{E}{K_1^2(z)-\upsilon^2 K_2^2(z)}\left[K_1(z)\frac{d\varepsilon_b(z)}{dz}+\upsilon K_2(z)\left(\frac{d\varepsilon_a(z)}{dz}-\frac{d\varepsilon_b(z)}{dz}+\frac{d\varepsilon_c(z)}{dz}\right)\right] \tag{5b}$$

$$\sigma_c(z)=\frac{E}{K_1^2(z)-\upsilon^2 K_2^2(z)}\left[K_1(z)\frac{d\varepsilon_c(z)}{dz}+\upsilon K_2(z)\frac{d\varepsilon_a(z)}{dz}\right]. \tag{5c}$$

In eqs (5a), (5b) and (5c) the numerator of the parenthetical expression has two separate points where it has a value of zero. The first point is on the surface where $z=0$ and, therefore, $K_1=K_2=0$ and the second is deeper and it is zero when the Poisson's ratio and constants have specific values. This fact limits the use of eqs (5a), (5b) and (5c). In practice the eqs are applicable in depths that are reached with current machining methods. With the three stress components calculated the principal stresses together with the principal directions can be calculated from eqs (6a) and (6b). The angle α is calculated with respect to direction a:

$$\sigma_{1,2}=\frac{\sigma_a(z)+\sigma_c(z)}{2}\pm\frac{\sqrt{2}}{2}\sqrt{[\sigma_b(z)-\sigma_a(z)]^2+[\sigma_b(z)-\sigma_c(z)]^2} \tag{6a}$$

$$\alpha=\frac{1}{2}\arctan\frac{2\sigma_b(z)-\sigma(z)_a-\sigma_c(z)}{\sigma_a(z)-\sigma_c(z)} \tag{6b}$$

It can be seen from eqs (5a, b and c) that the determination of the stress state as a function of depth is possible with the strains measured on the surface, when knowing the relaxation functions $K_1(z)$ and $K_2(z)$. These functions have to be derived experimentally or numerically. The relaxation functions are dependent on the residual stress state in the material and they are sensitive to the shape of the groove. This means that the relaxation functions can be simultaneously dependent on the stress state, measuring device and material in question. When the relaxation functions are derived experimentally, a uniaxial stress is introduced to the test specimen and the induced strains are measured. Hooke's law is then applied to these stresses which are parallel to the directions of the principal stresses. The test piece has to be stress free because the residual stresses add to the external load applied to the specimen. By comparing the measured surface strains and the real principal strains the relaxation functions $K_1(z)$ and $K_2(z)$ can be derived. The test piece has to be large enough to prevent the edges of the specimen from affecting the stress field near the groove.

MATERIALS AND METHODS

In the experimental part of the study a measurement system based on the ring-core method was built. Because of the measurement principle in the ring-core method the groove production has to be done without distorting the residual stresses. In mechanical machining induced heat and plastic deformation seriously affect the stresses to be measured. Electrical discharge machining (EDM) was chosen for the groove production to meet the above mentioned demands. The relaxation functions needed in the calculation of stresses were derived experimentally and by FE-analysis. The experimental tests were carried out with different loads and different depths of the groove.

Experimental derivation of the relaxation functions

To maintain the stress in the test specimens and to keep it uniform across the cross-section a special load frame was constructed. After stressing the specimen it was anchored to the frame. Four test specimens were made from low-carbon structural steel (Fe 37). After the specimens were machined they were stress-relieved by annealing at 620°C for two hours. After annealing the specimens were cooled to room temperature together with the furnace. The residual stress in the surface was then measured by X-ray diffraction. Parallel to the longitudinal axis of the specimen the mean stress was 1 MPa and the standard deviation 5 MPa. In the transverse direction the mean stress was 3 MPa and the standard deviation was 8 MPa. This means that the nominal residual stress state was of minor importance. The dimensions of the test specimen were chosen on the basis of the minimum requirements for a ring-core measurement, Keil (2).

The uniform tensile residual stress in the specimen was produced with a tensile-test machine. The specimen was loaded in tension and the surrounding load frame in compression before interlocking them. This configuration produced a tensile stress without any shear stress and minimal elastic offset after removing the specimen set-up from the tensile-test machine. Temperature-compensated strain gauges were attached to the specimen to control the loading of the specimen and to detect distorting bending moments. The stresses in the specimens after loading are listed in Table I. The variation in the stresses can be tolerated because in the relaxation procedure of the ring-core method the measured changes in strain are scaled by the nominal strain. The actual stress in the specimens is determined by the applied strain gages. Because of the linearity of the change the remaining stress could be read straight from the stress-strain curve after removing the specimen from the tensile-test machine. The stress caused by bending was approximately ±2-6 MPa on the specimen surface.

Table I. The nominal stresses in the specimens for the ring-core measurement.

Test specimen	Stress σ_x, MPa
S2a	91
S2b	91
S3	90
S4	87

For the experimental part of this study an EDM apparatus was constructed in order to measure and machine the groove. The equipment has three separate components, a power supply and control unit, machining device and a reservoir for the electrode fluid. A pump attached to the power supply circulates the electrode fluid.

Usually the depth of the groove is measured from the vertical movement of the electrode. In this case the wear of the electrode has to be known since the actual depth of the groove is calculated from the vertical displacement of the electrode and the discharge gap from which the wear is subtracted. The erosion rate of the electrode is highly dependent on the machining parameters and the electrode material. Because of this it is advisable to determine the erosion rate individually for each material. The best way to determine the wear of the electrode is to measure the actual depth of the groove and by dividing the difference between it and the target depth by the number of the steps. This calculation gives the real depth of each step. In practice, the ratio between the material removed from the test piece and the wear of the electrode can be as high as one hundred. This means that the wear of the electrode can be considered to be zero for this experiment. In this particular experiment the wear of the electrode was so slight that it could not be observed with vernier calipers after machining a 5 mm groove. Because of this the wear of the electrode is considered to be negligible.

FE-analysis for derivation of the relaxation functions

The FE-analysis was performed to model the strain response on the surface of the core at different groove depths under the influence of an external load creating a constant stress to the material cross-section. The relaxation functions applicable for the groove geometry under consideration were derived from the calculated strains by solving K_1 and K_2 in equation (1). With the relaxation functions the residual stresses can then be calculated from equations (5a, b and c). The magnitude of the external load was selected to 100 MPa to ensure elastic behaviour of the investigated material by being far enough from the yield point and to keep the specimen dimensions, the load frame dimensions and the force in the tensile test at an acceptable level. For the FE-analysis the actual geometry of the groove was investigated by optical microscopy from samples that had been machined (EDM) with the same parameters as in the actual groove manufacturing. The most important parameter is the radius of curvature between the bottom and the side of the groove as it acts as a stress riser due to the notch effect. The radius of the corner from a groove cross-section with an estimated average radius of 0.5 mm is shown in Figure 3. In practice the corner has always a finite curvature due to the wear of the electrode especially at the corners. However, there is a significant difference in wear between different electrode materials.

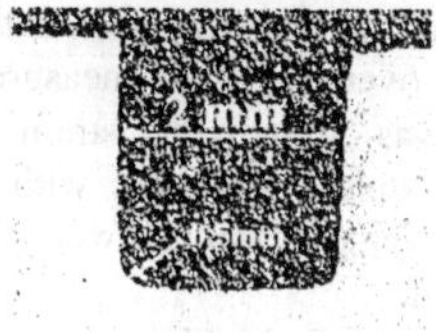

Fig. 3 The cross-section of the groove after EDM.

The FE-analysis was based on a specimen volume with dimensions of 200 x 200 x 25 mm^3. Due to symmetry only a quarter was modelled with the centre of the core on the surface as the origin. The elements used were bilinear solid type (Solid45 3-D structural solid) with internal shape functions on the sides, ANSYS (5). The geometry was well described with this element type without danger of elements interlocking. The details of the FE-model are shown in Figures (4a) and (4b).

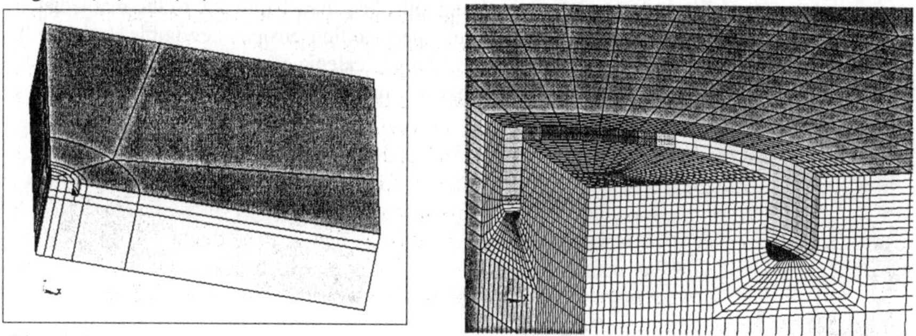

Fig. 4 General view of the FE-model where the interface between the inner and the outer block can be seen. The element mesh with the smallest element size of 0.25 mm.

The groove depth was increased in steps of 0.25 mm in the FE-calculations. The FE-model was loaded with an external, through the cross-section, constant load of 100 MPa, where the direction of the load action is in the x-direction and the growth of the groove is in the z-direction. The dense inner element mesh was constructed as a separate block with radius 0-27 mm connected to the outer less dense mesh through coupled nodal displacements on the boundary between the meshes. This construction reduced the number of elements and the size of the model without loosing accuracy even though reducing computer time. The coupled nodal displacements force the inner block to follow the deformation of the outer block. However, the stresses at the interface are not correctly represented, but the size of the inner block ensured that the disturbances were fading away well outside the outer diameter of the groove. The elastic modulus used was 210 GPa and the Poisson's ratio was 0.3. The strains were collected on the surface (x-y-plane) of the core from the origin to a distance of 3.5 mm in the directions 0° and 90° for every calculation step. These directions are equivalent to the measurement directions a and c in the strain gage of the experimental tensile test. The strain distribution in each gage direction was established as a function of groove depth starting from the origin (z = 0). The dimensions of the three grids in the strain gage in the actual measurements are 2.5 by 5 mm, and the grids are symmetrically centred about the origin. The strain distributions achieved by the FE-model are one dimensional and they can physically be interpreted as the strain of the centre line of the measurement grid. Because the strain is not constant over the grid but varies non-linearly with the distance from the origin, the total strain over the grid is estimated from the graph for every groove increment. In an accurate FE-analysis the total strain is obtained by integrating over the grid area because in the actual strain gage the strain is measured over the whole measurement grid. Based on experimental tests the integration of the strain was omitted. The strain derivatives $d\varepsilon_0/dz$ and $d\varepsilon_{90}/dz$ were calculated from the FE-analysis which combined with equation (1) gave the relaxation functions $K_1(z)$ and $K_2(z)$. Fifth order polynomials were fitted to the discrete changes of the strains with the least square method.

RESULTS

The strains obtained from the FE-analysis on the surface are presented in Figure 5. The relaxation functions $K_1(z)$ and $K_2(z)$ were calculated from the measured strains with the same procedure as in the FE-analysis. Experimentally obtained relaxation functions and functions obtained by FE-analysis are shown in Figure 6. The relaxation function $K_2(z)$ from the FE-analysis is not represented correctly at groove depths less than 1 mm due to the mathematical formulation in the fitting procedure. However, the resulting error is negligible, because the influence of the transverse relaxation function on the calculated principal stress is minor at shallow groove depths. The experimental relaxation functions include measurement results of all the test bars.

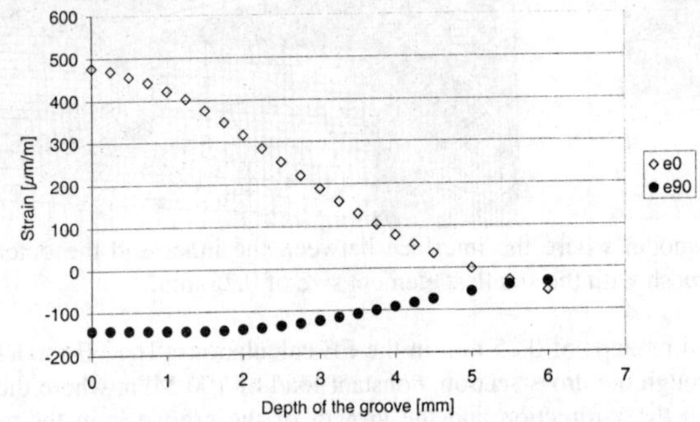

Fig. 5 The strain distributions calculated by the FE-analysis.

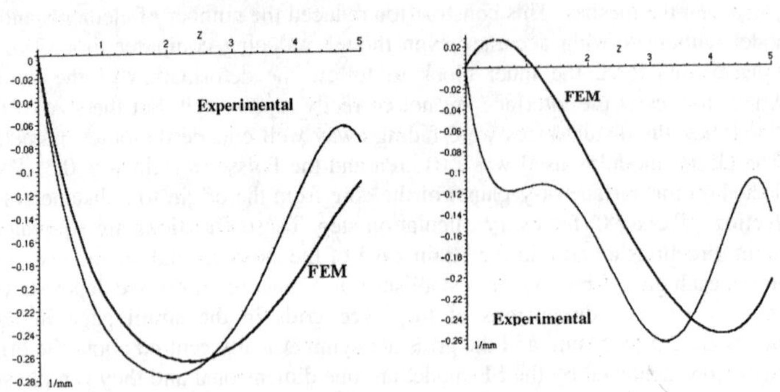

Fig. 6 Comparison between relaxation functions obtained experimentally and with FE-analysis. $K_1(z)$ on the left and $K_2(z)$ on the right.

CONCLUSIONS

The relaxation functions derived in the experimental part have both their respective maximum situated at a shallower groove depth than in the FE-analysis. The strain response in the experiment is sensitive to misalignments at shallow groove depths, such as an inclination of the electrode from the normal of the surface leads to an uneven relaxation of the stresses. The induced residual stresses from the preparation of the measuring point, i.e., grinding the surface for the application of the strain gage can be significant at the first measuring step. The changes in the strain transverse to the loading direction were very small as seen from the FE-analysis, which make them more sensitive to errors in the measurement arrangement than the changes in the longitudinal direction. The conducted tests support the idea that the transverse relaxation function can be omitted at shallow groove depths as it is sensitive to errors and its weight in the calculations is low. Scatter in the performed individual experiments influenced the deduction of the relaxation functions. The experiments prove the applicability of the method for residual stress measurements and give valuable information about the sources of the scatter. By concentrating the research on the observed weaknesses and the ambiguous details the ring-core method can be made an accurate and reliable method for residual stress measurement.

ACKNOWLEGEMENTS

The present study was done under a national project funded by the National Technology Agency of Finland (TEKES) and eight industrial companies in the area of residual stress measurement and modelling.

REFERENCES

1. Schajer, G. S. & Roy, G. & Flaman, M. T. & Lu, J. Hole-Drilling and Ring-Core Methods. In: Lu, J. (ed.). Handbook of Measurement of Residual Stresses. Lilburn, GA 1996, The Fairmont Press Inc. pp. 5-34.
2. Keil, S. Experimental Determination of Residual Stresses with the Ring-Core Method and an On-Line Measuring System. Experimental Techniques 16(1992)5, pp. 17-24.
3. König, G. Ein Beitrag zur Weiterentwicklung teilzerstörender Eigenspannungs-messvervahren, Doctoral Thesis. Staatliche Materialprüfungsanstalt (MPA), Universität Stuttgart 1991. 176 p.
4. Wolf, H. Böhm, W. Das Ring-Kern-Vervahren zur Messung von Eigenspannungen und seine Anwendung bei Turbinen und Generatorwellen. Arch. für Eisenhüttenswesen 3(1971), pp. 195-200.
5. ANSYS Release 5.4, Up 19980310, Ansys Inc.

EFFECTS OF EDM ON SURFACE RESIDUAL STRESSES IN A TMCP STEEL

H Gripenberg, J Siiriäinen *, T Saukkonen, H Hänninen
Helsinki University of Technology
Laboratory of Engineering Materials
Puumiehenkuja 3A, FIN-02150 Espoo
*** Stresstech Oy, Ohjelmakaari 16, FIN-40500 Jyväskylä**

ABSTRACT

The effects of electrodischarge machining (EDM) on the surface integrity were examined by optical and scanning electron microscopy (SEM), microhardness and residual stress measurements in a TMCP steel. The residual stresses in the surface and the underlying region were of special interest, as the EDM creates a "white layer" containing cracks perpendicular to the surface. The residual stresses were examined by the X-ray diffraction method.

The steel plates used were annealed at 620ºC and cooled at a slow rate to stress relieve the samples. The residual stress state was confirmed by X-ray diffraction before the EDM of the surface. The steel plates were machined at three different intensities, described as rough, medium and fine, the last one corresponding to μEDM normally used in industry for the final surface treatment. The specimens were sectioned and electrochemically polished to give a series of decreasing layer thicknesses of the EDM surface. After these preparations the residual stresses were measured.

The compositions of the surface layers due to EDM and the underlying material were analysed with Energy Dispersive X-ray Spectroscopy (EDS). The residual stresses were measured on the EDM surface with X-ray diffraction giving the stress and the principal stress distributions to a depth of at least 0.2 mm for the three machining conditions. The overall objective was the evaluation of the effect of EDM on the surface integrity in terms of the induced residual stress.

INTRODUCTION

In all metallic materials residual stresses are unavoidable as a result of manufacturing processes. This is also the case for EDM, where material is removed by means of repeated spark discharges from a pulsating direct-current power supply with dielectric flow between the workpiece and the tool. The shaped tool (electrode) is fed into the workpiece under servo control, keeping a constant gap between the tool and the workpiece whilst advancing the electrode. A spark discharge then breaks down the dielectric fluid and material is melted and vaporised. The dielectric oil cools and flushes out the vaporised and condensed material whilst re-establishing the gap insulation, Rebelo et al. (1).

Electrical discharge machining (EDM) is widely used in industry especially for giving the final surface finish. EDM is known to affect the material properties to some extent beneath the surface, generating residual stresses due to the uneven heat flow and the resulting metallurgical transformations. Mamalis (2) investigated the residual stresses after EDM and showed their tensile nature, the depth of the zone where they appear, their high magnitude in the surface layers and the increase of their magnitude with an increase in pulse energy.

Rebelo et al. (1) studied the influence of EDM pulse energy on the surface integrity of martensitic steels. In their study they found that a network of cracks was formed, associated with the development of high tensile stresses exceeding the fracture strength of the material. They determined empirical relationships between surface roughness, "white layer" thickness, heat-affected zone thickness, average maximum crack length, depth of maximum value of residual stress and the electric charge, current multiplied by time, for two martensitic steels. The term "white layer" refers to the topmost, by etching apparently unaffected, layer.

The effect of different removal rates on the microstructure for several tool steels was studied by Wendl et al. (3). They showed that the white layer was carburized due to the reaction of the surface with the dielectric fluid during the discharge process. As a result of this an increase in the hardness could be observed. Together with the residual stress and the existing cracks this leads to a considerable loss in toughness that could not be restored by tempering after the EDM.

Residual stress measurement by the ring-core method has traditionally employed mechanical machining of a groove around a strain gage rosette. However, the machined surface deforms plastically due to the mechanical machining process and residual stresses are induced into the material. In an attempt to reduce the amount of residual stress induced by the annular groove production in the ring-core method electrical discharge machining has been used as the machining process for residual stress measurement, Siiriäinen et al. (4).

MATERIALS AND METHODS

The test material, RAEX 560 HSF, was produced by thermo-mechanical controlled processing (TMCP). It is a structural steel manufactured with emphasis on excellent workability, cold formability and weldability. Improvement in these properties leads to economic benefits for manufacturers and end users, by allowing cold working instead of hot working and less preheating in welding, making these steels attractive in the transportation industry and in civil engineering.

The TMCP steel is fine-grained steel that has a low carbon and sulphur content giving good cold workability. TMCP steels are low alloyed, ferritic-pearlitic steels, which have their improved properties due to a complex thermomechanical treatment and not because of alloying. The production technology of controlled rolling and accelerated cooling results in improved strength, good low temperature toughness and ductility. The chemical composition of the studied material is presented in Table I.

TABLE I. The chemical composition of the studied TMCP steel, in weight-%.

	C	Si	Mn	P	S	Al	Nb	V	Ti	N	Mo
RAEX 560 HSF	0.08	0.18	1.51	0.012	0.005	0.037	0.051	0.147	0.002	0.005	0.004

The steel plate was sectioned into rectangular specimens from a 7 mm thick sheet of RAEX 560 HSF steel, so that the longer side coincides with the rolling direction of the steel strip. This is also the direction of the y-axis in the residual stress measurements. The specimen geometry is shown in Figure 1. The encircled area shows the area that has been EDM machined and the place of residual stress measurement. The rectangular shaped specimens were heat treated at 620°C for 15 min to relieve the residual stresses created by the manufacturing processes of the steel sheets. The specimens were heated up with the oven and allowed to cool down slowly along with the oven. The resulting oxide scale was removed by immersing the specimens for 30 min in a 10 % solution of hydrochloric acid, followed by washing in alcohol.

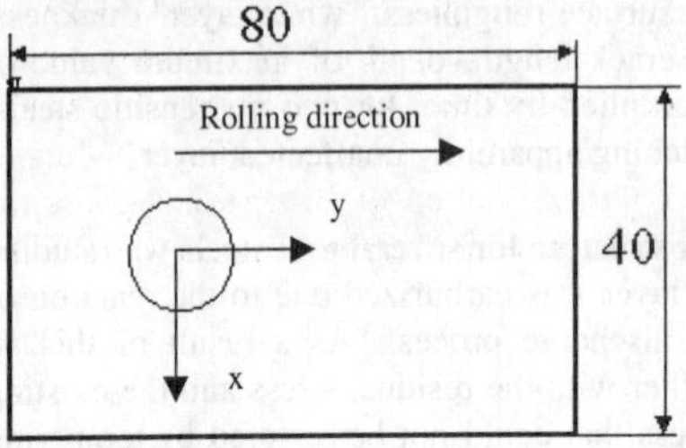

Fig. 1 The specimen and the residual stress co-ordinate system.

Determination of the residual stress profile using X-ray diffraction demands material removal. To avoid disturbances in the residual stress state electrolytic polishing was selected for the material removal. A portable electrolytic polishing unit, Struers Movipol, was used for the material removal as thin layers before the X-ray measurements. In the electrolytic polishing the material is removed by anodic dissolution from the specimen surface in an electrolytic cell, using the electrolyte Struers A2.

Electrical discharge machining

The electrical discharge machining (EDM) of the specimen was done by a system of die-sinking EDM, AGIE Agietron 1U. Three machining conditions were selected for the evaluation of the effects of EDM. The exact values of the parameters, voltage, current, on-time and off-time, for the three conditions con not be stated because of the complex control system in the machine used. The material removal rate and the predefined surface roughness are the parameters that are given to the control system in industrial applications. In this study the surface roughness is the only input parameter. The predefined surface qualities for the test program are shown in Table II.

TABLE II. The predefined surface roughness of the EDM machining.

Surface roughness	Description used in the study	Material removal rate
R_a 0.5 - 1	Fine or μEDM	Slow
R_a 4 - 5	Medium EDM	Medium
R_a 7 - 8	Rough EDM	Fast

The EDM was carried out by machining a circular area of the specimens with a copper electrode of ∅16 mm to a depth of 0.5 mm. The specimens containing an EDM surface were grouped into three series according to the machining intensity. Each EDM surface within a series was electrochemically polished at predetermined steps of material removal, thereby giving a series of specimens with a decreasing layer thickness of EDM surface. After these preparations the residual stresses were measured.

Residual stress measurements

The residual stress measurements were made using the X-ray diffraction technique. The portable X-ray diffraction apparatus used (XSTRESS3000, Stresstech Finland) is equipped with a goniometer comprising an X-ray tube and two position sensitive detectors. The two detectors are positioned symmetrically on both sides of the collimator in the modified ψ-geometry for side inclination. The measurements were performed employing Cr-Kα radiation emitted through a collimator of ∅3 mm. The peak profiles of the Fe {211} reflections were recorded at different ψ-angles; ψ is the angle between the surface normal and the normal of the diffracting lattice planes. The peak shifts in the peak profiles between different ψ-angles were determined by the cross correlation method. Differentiation of Bragg's law gives the relationship between the strain ε present in the deformed crystal and the angular shift in the peak profile $(\theta - \theta_0)$:

$$\varepsilon = \frac{(D - D_0)}{D_0} = -\cot(\theta_0)(\theta - \theta_0). \quad \text{(I)}$$

Because the interest is focused on the stresses rather than on the strains, a conversion of the strain values to stresses is done according to Hooke's law assuming linear elastic and isotropic material behaviour, Noyan et al. (5). The elastic constants used in all the presented residual stress calculations and the measured tensile properties are presented in Table III.

TABLE III. The mechanical properties of the material studied.

	Yield Strength	Tensile Strength	Modulus	Poisson's ratio
RAEX 560 HSF	631 MPa	745 MPa	211 GPa	0.3

Microhardness measurements

The Vickers method was selected for the microhardness measurements, where the test force used was 15 gf. The speed of the indenter was 60 μm/s and the dwell time was 10 s. The microhardness measurements were done on the cross-sections of the specimens, starting from the surface and proceeding to a maximum distance of 0.16 mm into the material. The first indentation was placed as close to the surface edge as the curvature of the edge allowed without reducing the optical accuracy. The following indents were made in a pattern alternating on both sides of the measurement line perpendicular to the surface. The alternations were made to ensure a total distance of three times the diagonal of the indentation pyramid trace between successive measurements. The microhardness profile was also measured after the stress relief heat treatment, to obtain the reference hardness. Then the material hardness profiles were measured from three specimens representing three machining conditions, fine, medium and rough.

EDS analyses

The carbon content distribution in the material was examined by energy dispersive X-ray spectroscopy (EDS). The excitation voltage was 15 kV. Because carbon is a light element the lower border of the energy window covered by EDS makes it difficult to detect carbon in small amounts. The instrument specifications give a resolution of more than 0.3 wt. %. The carbon profiles were determined from the polished cross-sections of the specimen in a similar manner as the hardness profiles. The absolute values of the profiles given are not exact, but the trend can be seen from the shape of the profiles and from their mutual differences.

RESULTS

The effects of EDM on the surface integrity were studied by means of X-ray diffraction, microhardness measurements, EDS analyses and optical and scanning electron microscopy.

Residual stress measurements

After the stress relief heat treatment all specimens were studied with X-ray diffraction to measure their residual stresses; all specimens were in a stress-free condition. The average stress measured was 6 MPa and the standard deviation was 4.3 MPa. The residual stresses were measured in the two orthogonal directions, x and y, displayed in Figure 1. The measured residual stress distributions after the stress relief anneal and after the EDM are presented in Figure 2. The residual stresses were of approximately equal magnitude in both x and y directions for all the machining conditions, as can be seen from Figure 2. The principal stresses were also calculated, and they were found to coincide with the geometrical directions, x and y, of the specimen. Thus, the magnitude of the residual principal stresses can also be seen. The full width half maximum (FWHM) profiles of the X-ray diffraction peaks are shown in Figure 3.

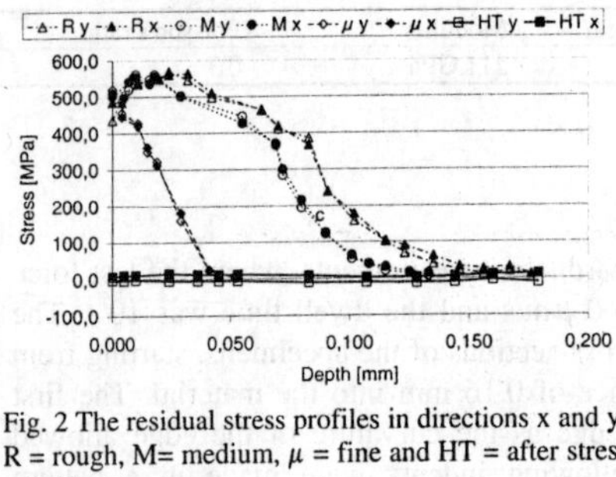

Fig. 2 The residual stress profiles in directions x and y. R = rough, M= medium, μ = fine and HT = after stress relief heat treatment.

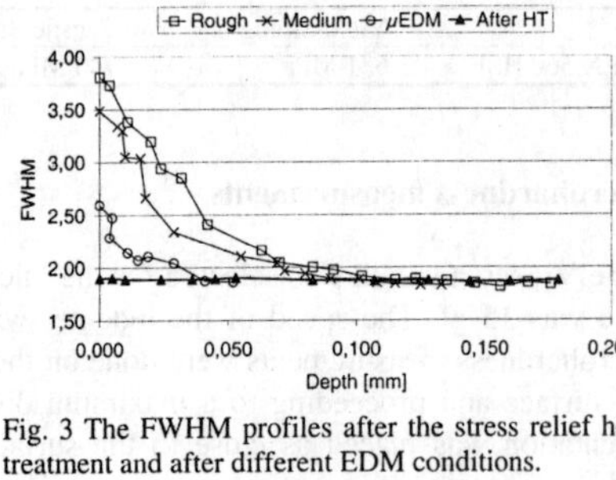

Fig. 3 The FWHM profiles after the stress relief heat treatment and after different EDM conditions.

Microhardness measurements

The microhardness profiles of the base material and the studied machining conditions are presented in Figure 4 and Figure 5. The results show an increase in hardness in the white layer for all machining conditions. The hardness measurements from the white layer are presented with open markers.

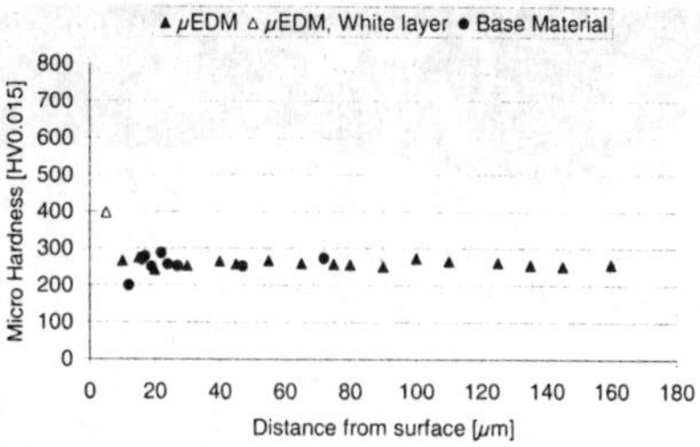

Fig. 4 The microhardness profiles of base material and after μEDM.

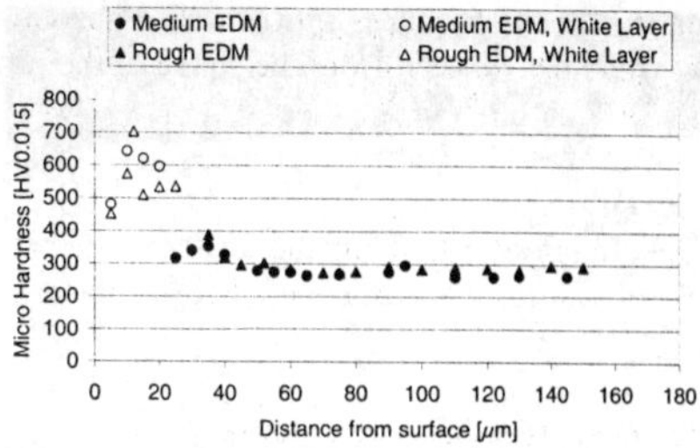

Fig. 5 The microhardness profiles after medium and rough EDM.

EDS results

The carbon content profiles are shown in Figure 6. X-ray intensity maps of a specimen cross-section after rough machining are shown in Figure 7. Changes in the amount of studied elements, C or Fe, appear as a change in the tone value, a brighter area indicating a higher fraction of the studied element and a darker area indicating a smaller fraction of the studied element.

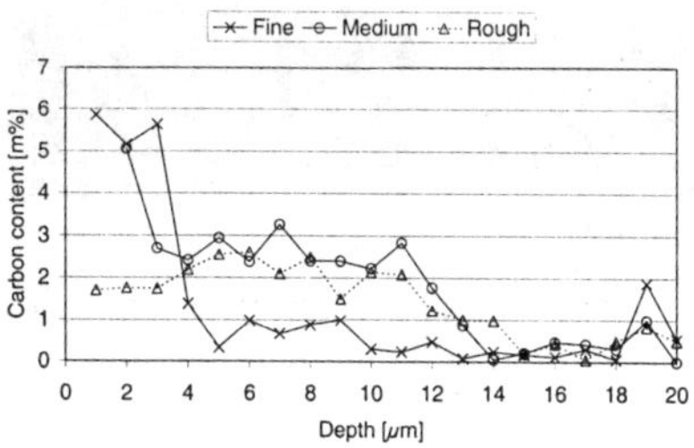

Fig. 6 The depth profiles of carbon content.

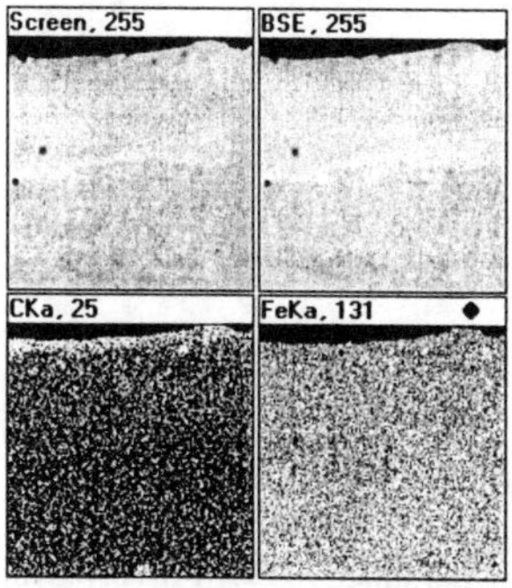

Fig. 7 The X-ray intensity maps of medium energy machining. Surface on the top.

Optical and scanning electron microscopy

Optical and scanning electron microscopy was performed, and the microstructures of the three machining conditions are shown in Figs 8, 9 and 10. The uppermost layer created by the EDM process is referred to as the white layer. It has a high carbon content and it is very hard compared to the base material. The induced high tensile residual stress provokes crack formation in the white layer. Figure 11 shows cracks propagating into the material in a direction perpendicular to the surface.

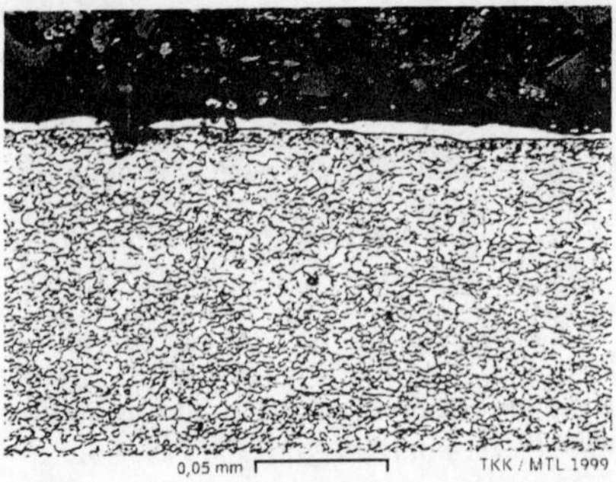

Fig. 8 The microstructure after fine machining.

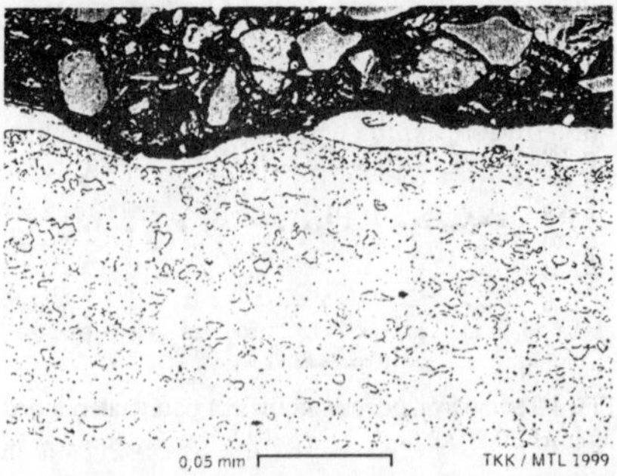

Fig. 9 The microstructure after medium machining.

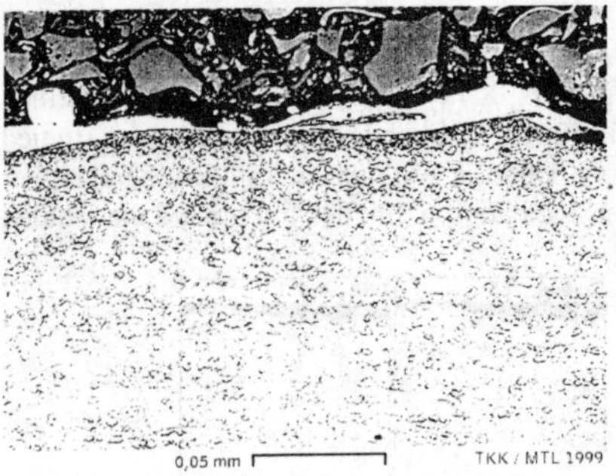

Fig. 10 The microstructure after rough machining.

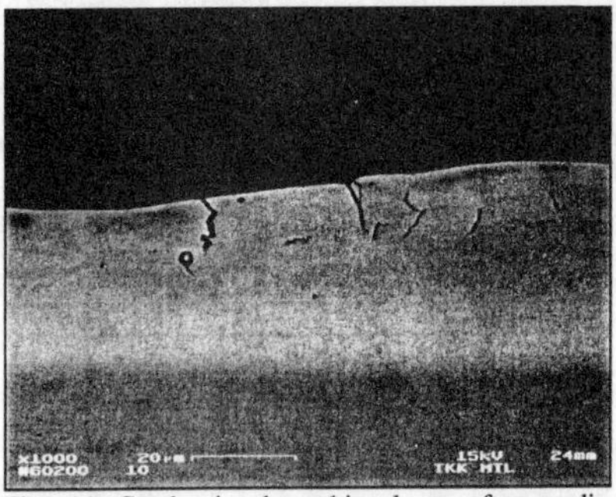

Fig. 11 Cracks in the white layer after medium machining.

DISCUSSION

Economical and productive EDM involves high discharge energies, which is more detrimental to the surface integrity in terms of changes in the material properties. The EDM relies on high thermal interaction between the electrode and the workpiece resulting in changes in both the microstructure and the residual stress.

The residual stresses induced by EDM on the surface are tensile and they have approximately the same magnitude at the surface regardless of machining intensity. However, there is a slight increase in the magnitude for medium and rough machining in the layers close to the surface and the depth of the induced residual stress grows with increasing machining intensity. The increase of the FWHM values close to the surface are due to formation of microstresses and induced plastic deformation.

The hardness profile from machining by μEDM was similar to the reference profile after stress relief heat treatment showing no increase in the hardness on the surface. Medium and rough machining resulted in hardness profiles showing a clear increase in hardness on the surface extending to a depth of 20 μm for medium and 40 μm for rough machining, respectively.

The discontinuous white layer has an alternating thickness, it contains cracks and has a high carbon content. The EDM process increases the carbon content of the surface and the underlying material. Low machining intensity gives a very steep carbon gradient with low penetration depth, whereas higher machining intensity results in a lower carbon content but increases the penetration depth of carbon into the steel. The high carbon content in the surface layer originates from the dissociated dielectric.

CONCLUSIONS

The following conclusions can be made from the studies:

- The discharge energy did not affect the magnitude of residual stress on the surface.
- The penetration depth of the EDM induced residual stress depends on the machining intensity.
- With the fine machining the maximum stress occurs on the surface whereas increasing discharge energy moves the position of the maximum tensile stress into the material.
- In all cases studied, the magnitude of tensile stress decreases from the machined surfaces; the lower the discharge energy the faster the tensile residual stress decreases.
- Due to reactions of the surface with the dielectric fluid the surface is carburized. An increase of the surface hardness can be observed for all machining conditions.
- Low discharge energy causes high carbon content in the surface layers whereas high discharge energy decreases the peak on the surface but increases the penetration depth of carbon.

ACKNOWLEGEMENTS

The present study was done under a national project funded by the National Technology Agency of Finland (TEKES) and eight companies in the area of residual stress measurement and modelling. The authors also wish to thank the Laboratory of Production Engineering at Helsinki University of Technology and especially Mr. Janne Peuraniemi for his expertise in EDM.

REFERECES

1. Rebelo J. C., Morao Dias A., Kremer D., Lebrun J. L. Influence of EDM Pulse Energy on the Surface Integrity of Martensitic Steels. Journal of Materials Processing Technology. 84(1998), pp. 90-96.
2. Mamalis A. G., Vosniakos G. C., Vacevanidis N. M. Residual Stress Distribution and Structural Phenomena of High-Strength Steel Surfaces Due to EDM and Ball-Drop Forming. Annals of the CIRP. 37(1988)1, pp. 531-535.
3. Wendl F., Wupper K.-D. Einfluß der Abschmelzrate beim Elktroerodieren auf Gefügeausbildung und Zähigkeit einiger Werkzeugstähle. Härterei-technische Mitteilungen. 44(1989)4, pp. 197-204.
4. Siiriäinen J., Hänninen H., Gripenberg H. Design and Implementation of the Ring-Core Method for Residual Stress Measurement. This conference.
5. Noyan I. C., Cohen J. B. Residual Stress Measurement by Diffraction and Interpretation. New York 1987, Springer-Verlag Inc. 276 p.

EFFECT OF SECONDARY PHASE ON DIFFRACTION ELASTIC CONSTANTS OF POLYCRYSTALLINE MATERIALS

Keisuke TANAKA, Yoshiaki AKINIWA and Toshimasa ITO
Department of Mechanical Engineering, Nagoya University
Furo-cho, Chikusa-ku, Nagoya 464-8603, Japan

ABSTRACT

The effect of secondary phases on the X-ray elastic constants of sintered alumina was analyzed on the basis of three micromechanical models: Reuss' model, Voigt's model, and the self-consistent model (SC model). The mechanical Young's modulus decreased with decreasing bulk density or increasing porosity, while Poisson's ratio was nearly constant. The experimental value of the X-ray elastic constants, $E'_X/(1+\nu'_X)$ (E'_X=Young's modulus, ν'_X =Poisson's ratio), decreased with decreasing bulk density or increasing porosity. The SC model gave the best estimation for the effect of bulk density on the X-ray elastic constants. The prediction based on the SC model requires the mechanical elastic constants of sintered alumina as a composite and the X-ray elastic constants of diffracting phases. It is not necessary to know the properties of secondary phases. When the mechanical elastic constants of ceramics are not known, the bulk density can be used to estimate the mechanical elastic constants, and then the X-ray elastic constants.

1. INTRODUCTION

Residual stresses have a great influence on the fracture strength of sintered ceramics. The X-ray diffraction method has been successfully used to measure residual stresses in ceramics. Since the strain measured by the diffraction method is the average of the lattice strain in specific grains satisfying the diffraction condition, the elastic constants for the relation between the macrostress and the measured strain are different from the mechanical elastic constants. They are named the X-ray elastic constant or the diffraction elastic constant (1). Precise values of the X-ray elastic constants are required for accurate stress measurements. Sintered ceramics normally contain more than one phase, even if they are called monolithic. For example, sintered alumina consists of the alumina phase, the glassy phase and pores. The X-ray elastic constants of these materials are influenced by the porosity or secondary phases. The measured value of the X-ray elastic constants decreased with decreasing bulk density of alumina (2,3).

In the present paper, sintered ceramics are regarded as multi-phase materials. The micromechanical analysis is presented for the X-ray elastic constant of multi-phase polycrystalline materials. The analysis is applied to predict the effect of the porosity on the X-ray elastic constant of sintered alumina. A simple method is proposed to estimate the effect of porosity on the X-ray elastic constant of sintered alumina.

2. DIFFRACTION ELASTIC CONSTANTS

In the X-ray method, the strain is measured from the change of the X-ray diffraction angle. The stress is calculated from the measured strain by using the X-ray values of the Young's modulus, E_X, and Poisson's ratio, ν_X. The X-ray elastic constants of randomly oriented single-phase polycrystals can be calculated from the single crystal elastic constants by using Kröner's model (4). For the case of single-phase polycrystals, the measured stress is equal to the macrostress.

For the case of multi-phase materials, the mean stress of the diffracting phase is not equal to the macrostress. The X-ray elastic constants of multi-phase materials, E'_X and ν'_X, are used to correlate the lattice strain of the diffracting phase to the macrostress (3). The X-ray elastic constants can be determined experimentally from changes of the slope and the intercept of the linear regression line of the 2θ-$\sin^2\psi$ diagram with the applied stress σ_A as

$$\frac{1+\nu'_X}{E'_X} = -\frac{\cot\theta_0}{2}\frac{\partial}{\partial\sigma_A}\left(\frac{\partial 2\theta}{\partial \sin^2\psi}\right), \tag{1}$$

$$-\frac{\nu'_X}{E'_X} = \frac{\cot\theta_0}{2}\frac{\partial\left(2\theta_{\psi=0}\right)}{\partial\sigma_A}. \tag{2}$$

where $2\theta_0$ is the diffraction angle of the stress-free material.

Secondary phases of sintered ceramics, such as glassy phase and pores, may influence the X-ray elastic constants. The X-ray elastic constants of multi-phase materials are related to those of single-phase polycrystals as (3,5)

$$\frac{1+\nu'_X}{E'_X} = \frac{1+\nu_X}{E_X}\frac{\partial(\sigma_1-\sigma_3)}{\partial\sigma_A}, \tag{3}$$

$$-\frac{\nu'_X}{E'_X} = \frac{1+\nu_X}{E_X}\frac{\partial\sigma_3}{\partial\sigma_A} - \frac{\nu_X}{E_X}\frac{\partial(\sigma_1+\sigma_2+\sigma_3)}{\partial\sigma_A}. \tag{4}$$

where σ_1, σ_2, and σ_3 are the mean value of the principal stress in the diffracting phase under the applied macrostress σ_A. The constant of $(1+\nu'_X)/E'_X$ is particularly significant for the $\sin^2\psi$ method, because the stress is determined by multiplying the inverse of this constant to the slope of the 2θ-$\sin^2\psi$ diagram.

3. MICROMECHANICS OF ELASTIC DEFORMATION OF MULTI-PHASE MATERIALS

3.1. Uniform-stress model (Reuss' Model)

When the stress in the diffracting phase is identical to the macrostress as in Reuss model (6). the X-ray constants of the diffracting phase in the composite are equal to those in single-phase polycrystals, i.e. $E'_X = E_X$ and $\nu'_X = \nu_X$.

3.2. Uniform-strain model (Voigt's Model)

Voigt assumed a uniform strain in each crystal in elastic deformation of polycrystals (7). By assuming that the strains in the matrix and the composite are equal, Hauk and Kockelman (5) derived the following relations.

$$\frac{1+\nu'_X}{E'_X} = \frac{1+\nu_X}{E_X}B, \tag{5}$$

$$-\frac{\nu'_X}{E'_X}=\frac{1+\nu_X}{E_X}\frac{A-B}{3}-\frac{\nu_X}{E_X}A. \tag{6}$$

where

$$A=\frac{E_0(1-2\nu')}{E'(1-2\nu_0)}, \tag{7}$$

$$B=\frac{E_0(1+\nu')}{E'(1+\nu_0)}. \tag{8}$$

where E_0 and ν_0 are the mechanical Young's modulus and Poisson's ratio of the matrix, and E' and ν' are those for composites.

3.3. Self-consistent model

Once the volume fraction, the elastic constants and the shape of all constituting phases are all known, the mean stress in each phase and the elastic constant of the composite can be calculated by Eshelby's inclusion mechanics (8) combined with the mean stress theory by Mori and Tanaka (9). However, the elastic constants and the shape of the glassy phase or other secondary phases in sintered ceramics are usually unknown. In order to determine the mean stress in the diffracting phase as a function of the applied stress, the self-consistent model (10) will be more useful than Eshelby-Mori-Tanaka's model, because the mechanical elastic constants of sintered ceramics, as composites, can be measured experimentally. The results calculated by the above two models are pretty much the same for a variety of multi-phase materials (11).

A spherical particle is embedded in a composite having the composite elastic constants where the particle is the matrix phase. The stress in the particle under the applied stress σ_A in the σ_1 direction is obtained from Eshelby inclusion mechanics and the substitution of the stress in Eq. (3) and (4) gives (3)

$$\frac{1+\nu'_X}{E'_X}=\frac{1+\nu_X}{E_X}B', \tag{9}$$

$$-\frac{\nu'_X}{E'_X}=\frac{1+\nu_X}{E_X}\frac{A'-B'}{3}-\frac{\nu_X}{E_X}A'. \tag{10}$$

where

$$A'=\frac{3(1-\nu')E_0}{(1+\nu')E_0+2(1-2\nu_0)E'}, \tag{11}$$

$$B'=\frac{15(1-\nu'^2)E_0}{2(4-5\nu')(1+\nu')E_0+(7-5\nu')(1+\nu_0)E'}. \tag{12}$$

3.4. Two-phase model

A ceramic model consisting of the matrix phase and pores is here called the two-phase model. Both Voigt's and SC models give (11)

$$E'_X = E_X(1 - f_2), \tag{13}$$

$$\nu'_X = \nu_X. \tag{14}$$

where f_2 is the volume fraction of pores.

4. EXPERIMENTAL PROCEDURE

4.1. Experimental materials

The experimental materials used are four kinds of sintered alumina. Among them, three kinds of alumina were pressurelessly sintered at 1873K. Alumina powder had three different purities: 99%, 96%, and 92% (2). The fourth material is porous alumina (KYOCERA FA10) with a porosity of 0.43. The mechanical elastic constants of materials are shown in Table 1, where the values for 100% are theoretical values calculated from the elastic constants of single crystals of alumina (12) by using Kröner's model (3,4). The other values were experimentally determined. The elastic constants, except Poisson's ratio, of sintered alumina decrease with decreasing purity or bulk density because of the increasing amount of soft secondary phases such as silica phases and pores. Poisson's ratio is nearly constant irrespective of purity.

4.2 X-Ray conditions

The diffraction elastic constants of four kinds of alumina were determined by the X-ray method. Alumina has a trigonal structure with the lattice constants of a=0.4758nm and c=1.2991nm (JCPDS No. 10-173). The diffraction angle of the stress-free material was 152.02 deg. The diffraction of alumina 2.1.10 by Fe-Kα radiation was used to measure the strain. The X-ray equipment has a parallel beam optics and the iso-inclination mechanism (ω -diffractometer). The X-ray elastic constants were determined by the $\sin^2\psi$ method using Eqs. (1) and (2).

The specimens were 54 mm in length with a rectangular cross section of 3.6 mm times 8.8 mm. The X-ray beam was irradiated on the lapped surface of the specimen subjected to four-point bending. The applied strain was monitored by the strain gage glued on the compression surface of the bent specimen, and the applied stress was obtained by multiplying the strain gage output by the mechanical Young's modulus.

5. EXPERIMENTAL RESULTS AND DISCUSSION

5.1 Mechanical elastic constants

As shown in Table 1, the mechanical Young's modulus decreases with decreasing bulk density, while Poisson's ratio remains nearly constant. In the two-phase model, the apparent porosity, f_2', can be obtained from the bulk density ρ of ceramics as

$$f_2' = 1 - \rho / \rho_0. \tag{15}$$

where ρ_0 is the theoretical density of alumina 3.99 Mg/m^3. The following empirical relation for E' (GPa) proposed by Knudesen (13) was found to agree with the experimental results of the present materials.

$$E' = 410\exp(-3.96\, f_2'). \tag{16}$$

5.2 X-Ray elastic constants

Table 2 summarizes the experimental and theoretical values of the X-ray elastic constants for alumina 2.1.10 diffraction. The X-ray elastic constants of single-phase polycrystals were calculated by using Kröner's model (4) from single crystal elastic constants (12). Those values are shown in the column corresponding to 100% purity in the table. In the calculation, Eqs. (5) and (6) were used for Voigt's model and Eqs. (9) and (10) for the SC model. The experimental values of Young's modulus and Poisson's ratio shown in Table 1 were used for the mechanical elastic constants of composites, and the values corresponding to 100% were used for E_0 and ν_0 of the matrix. The prediction based on the SC model agrees very well with the experimental value. Voigt's model gives smaller values than the experimental data, while the two-phase model larger values.

Figure 1 shows the change of the X-ray elastic constant, $E'_X/(1+\nu'_X)$, with the mechanical value. The experimental data on the X-ray value were plotted at the experimentally determined mechanical value. By assuming ν'=0.22, Eqs. (5) and (9) were used to obtain the

Table 1. Mechanical properties of ceramics.

Material	100%	99%	96%	92%	Porous
Bulk density ρ (Mg/m^3)	3.99	3.84	3.71	3.60	2.26
Apparent porosity f_2'	0	0.037	0.070	0.098	0.434
Young's modulus E (GPa)	406	359	324	285	49.2
Poisson's ratio ν	0.232	0.220	0.216	0.222	0.170
E/(1+ν) (GPa)	330	294	266	233	42.1

Table 2. X-ray elastic constants for (2.1.10) diffraction of alumina.

	Material	100%	99%	96%	92%	Porous
Experimental data	$E_X/(1+\nu'_X)$ (GPa)	-	291	284	265	188
	Young's modulus E'_X (GPa)	-	370	349	333	250
	Poisson's ratio ν'_X	-	0.271	0.229	0.255	0.333
Voigt's model	$E_X/(1+\nu'_X)$ (GPa)	312	281	254	223	39.7
	Young's modulus E'_X (GPa)	387	344	310	273	46.8
	Poisson's ratio ν'_X	0.240	0.224	0.220	0.226	0.180
Self-consistent model	$E_X/(1+\nu'_X)$ (GPa)	312	296	283	267	177
	Young's modulus E'_X (GPa)	387	365	349	330	217
	Poisson's ratio ν'_X	0.240	0.234	0.233	0.237	0.221
Two-phase model	$E_X/(1+\nu'_X)$ (GPa)	312	300	290	281	176
	Young's modulus E'_X (GPa)	387	373	360	349	219
	Poisson's ratio ν'_X	0.240	0.240	0.240	0.240	0.240

predictions based on Voigt's and SC models, respectively. For the two-phase model, E' is determined by Eq. (16) as a function of f_2 and $\nu'=0.22$. The corresponding elastic constants were determined by Eqs. (13) and (14). The intersection of three lines corresponds the value for 100% alumina polycrystals. The strain measured by diffraction methods is the strain in crystalline phase only, while the mechanical strain is the sum of the strains of all the constituting phases including crystalline and secondary phases. The secondary phases in sintered alumina, such as glassy phases and pores, are softer than the matrix. The diffraction elastic constants do not change with porosity in Reuss' model, while the diffraction elastic constants decrease by the same amount of the mechanical elastic constants in Voigt's model. The actual behavior of elastic deformation is between Reuss' and Voigt's models and follows the prediction by the SC model. The two-phase model also gives a prediction between Reuss' and Voigt' models.

Figure 2 shows the relation between the X-ray elastic constant and the apparent porosity. The experimental data on $E'_X/(1+\nu'_X)$ were plotted at the apparent porosity shown in Table 1. The predictions for Voigt's and the SC models were obtained by substituting E' determined by Eq. (16) and $\nu'=0.22$ into Eqs. (5) and (9), respectively. The experimental data again agree very well with the prediction based on SC model. Reuss' model gives an upper bound, while Voigt's model a lower bound.

In conclusion, the following method for the estimation of the X-ray elastic constant can be recommended when the experimental data are not available. Once the mechanical elastic constants of ceramics are known, Eqs. (9) and (10) can be used for estimation. When the mechanical elastic constants are not known, the mechanical Young's modulus, E', estimated

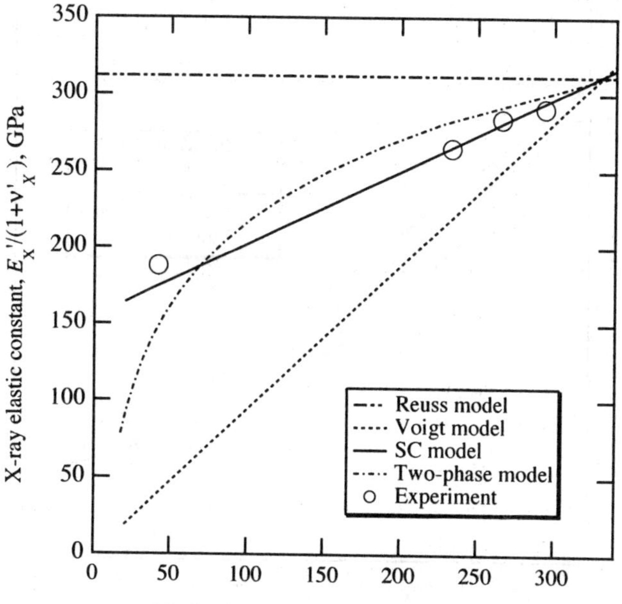

Fig. 1. Relation between X-ray elastic constant and mechanical elastic constant.

from the bulk density by Eq. (16) and $\nu' = 0.22$ can be used for estimation based on the SC model.

The present method based on the SC model can be applied to other engineering materials such as steels and aluminum alloys containing inclusions or precipitates. The diffraction elastic constants of the materials can be different from those calculated from the single crystal elastic constants by Kröner's model, even if the materials do not have preferred orientation. For these cases, Eqs. (9) and (10) are available for theoretical estimation of the diffraction elastic constants from the mechanical elastic constants.

6. CONCLUISONS

The X-ray elastic constants of multi-phase polycrystals were analyzed based on three micromechanical models: Reuss' model, Voigt's model and the self-consistent model (SC model). The theoretical predictions were compared with the experimental data of sintered alumina having various bulk densities. The results are summarized as follows:

(1) The mechanical Young's modulus decreased with decreasing bulk density or increasing porosity, while Poisson's ratio was nearly constant.

(2) The experimental value of X-ray elastic constant, $E'_X/(1+\nu'_X)$ (E'_X=Young's modulus, ν'_X=Poisson's ratio), decreased with decreasing bulk density or increasing porosity.

(3) The X-ray elastic constants determined from SC model were the best estimation of the experimental value. The Reuss' model gave the larger value, while Voigt's model gave smaller

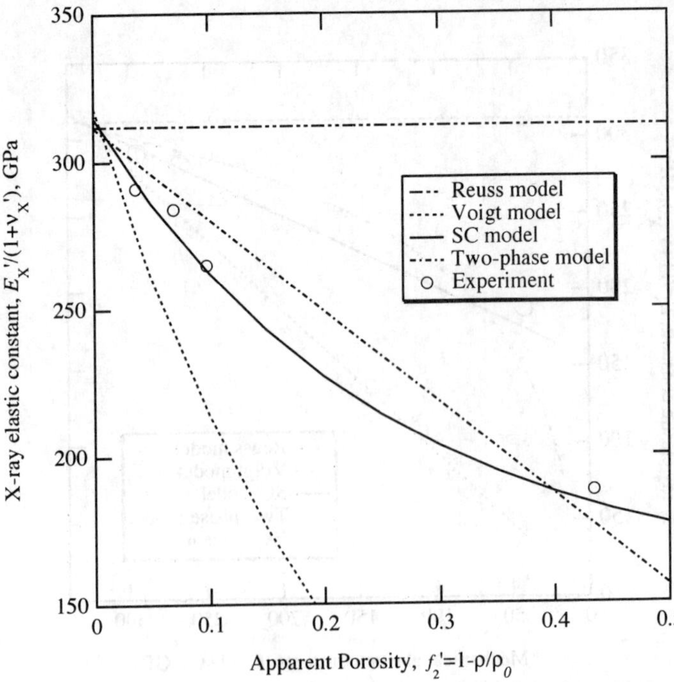

Fig. 2. Change of X-ray elastic constant with apparent porosity.

value.

(4) The estimation based on the SC model requires the mechanical Young's modulus and Poisson's ratio of sintered alumina. The mechanical Young's modulus was estimated from the bulk density, and Poisson's ratio took a nearly constant value of 0.22. Those values can be used for the estimation of the X-ray elastic constants by the SC model, when the experimental data of the mechanical elastic constants are not available.

REFERENCES

1. Noyan C. I., and Cohen B. J., 'Residual stress', Springer-Verlag, (New York) ,1987
2. Suzuki K., and Tanaka K., J. Mat. Sci., Japan 37 (1988) 586.
3. Tanaka K., and Akiniwa Y., JSME Inter. J. A41 (1998) 280.
4. Kröner E., Z. Phys. 151 (1958) 504.
5. Hauk V., and Kockelman H., Z. Metallkde 68 (1977) 719.
6. Reuss A., Z. ang. Math. Mech. 9 (1929) 49.
7. Voigt W., 'Lehrbuch der Kristalphysik', Teubner, Berlin (1928) p. 962.
8. Eshelby D. J., Proc. Roy. Soci., London, Ser. A 241 (1957) 376.
9. Mori T., and Tanaka K., Acta Metall. 21 (1972) 571.
10. Mura T., 'Micromechanics of Defects in Solids', Kluwer Academic Publ., (Dordrecht) 1991
11. Tanaka K., Akiniwa Y., and ITO T., J. Mat. Sci., Japan, 48 (1999) 1352.
12. Trefft E. W., J. Res. Nat. Bur. Stand. 70A (1966) 277.
13. Knudsen R. F., J. Am. Ceram. Soci. 45 (1962) 94.

RESIDUAL STRESS AND ITS GRADIENT IN SHOT-PEENED STEELS MEASURED BY SYNCHROTRON X-RAYS

Y. Yoshioka*, K.Akita **and H. Suzuki**
***Musashi Institute of Technology, yoshioka@me.ese.musashi-tech.ac.jp**
**** Tokyo Metropolitan University, akita-koichi@c.metro-u.ac.jp**

ABSTRACT

Residual stress distributions were measured in steel specimens which had been shot-peened by the use of x-rays from synchrotron radiation source. The measurements were performed in three different wavelengths of x-rays to observe the effect of the x-ray penetration depth on the ε_ψ-$\sin^2\psi$ relations. Since $\sin^2\psi$ diagram with curvature were obtained at the specimen surface and its vicinity, an x-ray stress analytical method ($\cos\psi$ method) which assumed the linear stress gradient with depth was adopted for the residual stress determinations near the surface.

Residual stresses by the $\sin^2\psi$ method are always larger than those by the $\cos\psi$ method near the surface of specimen. When strength on the shot-peened parts is evaluated based on the values of residual stress, an attention should be devoted to this fact.

INTRODUCTION

The distributions of residual stress on shot-peened specimens were usually measured by the $\sin^2\psi$ method [1)-4)]. The typical distribution by this method is that the compressive residual stress generates at the outer surface and it increases with increasing depth from the surface and it decreases gradually and coincides with zero after reaching the maximum compressive value. Such distribution indicates the existence of stress gradient beneath the surface and the $\sin^2\psi$ diagram is sure to curve at higher values of $\sin^2\psi$. Therefore, Bragg angles must be determined up to ψ-tilts of the specimen as high as possible to obtain the most important information close to $\sin^2\psi=1$ and an analytical method taking into account the stress gradient should be adopted in place of the $\sin^2\psi$ method.

One of the authors proposed an analytical method ($\cos\psi$ method) of residual stress taking into account the stress gradient under the assumption of linear stress gradient with depth[5)]. However, determination of stress gradient is experimentally complicated because many factors affect the result such as divergence of incident x-ray beam, increase of irradiated area at higher ψ-tilt angle and so on.

In the present study, synchrotron x-ray sources (SR) as an excellent x-ray source were used to determine the distributions of shot-peened steels more precisely.

STRESS ANALYSIS ON MATERIALS WITH STRESS GRADIENT

We assumed that each stress component has a linear stress gradient with depth, z. The stress at a depth z under a plane stress state, $\sigma_{ji}(z)$, is expressed as follows;

$$\sigma_{ij}(z) = \sigma_{ij0} + A_{ij}\, z \tag{1}$$

where σ_{ij0} is a stress in the surface (z=0) and A_{ij} is a stress gradient. When stresses by eq.(1) are present, we measure the weughted average stress $\langle\sigma_{ij}\rangle$ of σ_{ij} over the penetration depth T as

$$\langle\sigma_{ij}\rangle = \int_0^{z_1} \sigma_{ij}(z)\, I(z)\, dz \Big/ \int_0^{z_1} I(z)\, dz = \sigma_{ij0} + A_{ij}\, W\, T \tag{2}$$

W is the weighted factor and T is the penetration depth of x-rays and T can be defined as follows;

$$T = \frac{\sin^2\theta - \sin^2\psi}{2\mu \sin\theta \cos\psi} = T_1 / \cos\psi + T_2 \cos\psi \tag{3}$$

where $T_1 = -\cos^2\theta / 2\mu \sin\theta$, $T_2 = 1/2\mu \sin\theta$.

Weighted average lattice strain $\langle\varepsilon_{\phi\psi}\rangle$ is expressed as

$$\langle\varepsilon_{\phi\psi}\rangle = \frac{1+\nu}{E}\left[\langle\sigma_{11}\rangle\cos^2\phi + \langle\sigma_{12}\rangle\sin 2\phi + \langle\sigma_{22}\rangle\sin^2\phi\right]\sin^2\psi - \frac{\upsilon}{E}\left[\langle\sigma_{11}\rangle + \langle\sigma_{22}\rangle\right] \tag{4}$$

When average strains were measured at $\phi = 0°$ and 90°, respectively, each strain can be expressed as

$$\begin{aligned}\langle\varepsilon_\psi\rangle(0) &= \frac{1+\nu}{E}\langle\sigma_{11}\rangle\sin^2\psi - \frac{\upsilon}{E}\left[\langle\sigma_{11}\rangle + \langle\sigma_{22}\rangle\right]\\ \langle\varepsilon_\psi\rangle(90) &= \frac{1+\nu}{E}\langle\sigma_{22}\rangle\sin^2\psi - \frac{\upsilon}{E}\left[\langle\sigma_{11}\rangle + \langle\sigma_{22}\rangle\right]\end{aligned} \tag{5}$$

These strains are converted to weighted average diffraction angle as

$$\langle 2\theta_\psi\rangle = -2\tan\theta_0\,\langle\varepsilon_\psi\rangle + 2\,\theta_0 \tag{6}$$

Substituting eqs.(2),(3) and (5) into eq.(6), and adding $\langle 2\theta_\psi\rangle(0)$ to $\langle 2\theta_\psi\rangle(90)$ and rearranging an equation by $(\sigma_{110} + \sigma_{220})$ and $(A_{11} + A_{22})$, we find

$$\langle 2\theta_\psi\rangle(0) + \langle 2\theta_\psi\rangle(90) = (\sigma_{110} + \sigma_{220})\,X_1 + (A_{11} + A_{22})\,X_2 + 4\,\theta_0 \tag{7}$$

where

$$X_1 = -2\tan\theta_0\left[-(1+\nu)/E \cdot \cos^2\psi + (1-\nu)/E\right]$$
$$X_2 = -2\tan\theta_0$$
$$\left[-\frac{1+\nu}{E}T_2\cos^3\psi + \frac{1}{E}\{(1-\nu)T_2 - (1+\nu)T_1\}\cos\psi + \frac{1-\nu}{E}T_1/\cos\psi\right]W$$

In the same manner, subtracting $\langle 2\theta_\psi\rangle(90)$ from $\langle 2\theta_\psi\rangle(0)$, we find

$$\langle 2\theta_\psi\rangle(0) - \langle 2\theta_\psi\rangle(90) = (\sigma_{110} - \sigma_{220})\,X_3 + (A_{11} - A_{22})\,X_4 \tag{8}$$

where $X_3 = -2\tan\theta_0\,(1+\nu)\sin^2\psi / E$, $X_4 = X_3\,(T_2\cos\psi + T_1/\cos\psi)\,W$

Components of stress and stress gradient, σ_{110}, σ_{220}, A_{11} and A_{22} can be determined by the use of least square method. We called this analysis cosψ method.

EXPERIMENTAL

X-ray Source and Stress Measurement

The synchrotron radiation system at the Photon Factory (PF) of the High Energy Accelerator Research Organization, KEK, in Tsukuba, Japan was used as an x-ray source. X-rays between λ=0.25 nm and 0.12 nm are available with the optical system. The divergence angle of the beam source was 1.2 mrad in vertical direction and 12 mrad in horizontal direction. The minimum beam size was 0.55 mm (vertical) and 1.5 mm (horizontal) on the specimen.

Three kinds of diffractions from αFe 211, 220 and 310 were separately measured by adjusting the wavelength. In the present study, we so adjusted the wavelength that an hkl diffraction appears at Bragg angle of 2θ=154°. For example, stresses in the α-Fe(211) plane were measured with a wavelength of 0.2280 nm. This means that three diffraction data with different penetration depth of x-rays can be obtained as tabulated in Table 1 and thus we can synthetically determine residual stress and stress gradient from three kinds of data. A goniometer, with a position-sensitive proportional counter (PSPC) having an effective length of 110 mm, a specimen holder and a beam slit, was prepared for stress measurement. Width of the beam slit for irradiated x-rays was automatically changed to keep irradiation area of x-rays even if ψ angle was tilted. Diffraction angles on each hkl diffraction were measured in seventeen different ψ directions within a range from $\sin^2\psi$=0 to 0.8.

Table 1 Diffraction plane, wavelength and penetration depth of x-rays used.

hkl	Wavelength λ (nm)	Penetration depth (μm)
211	0.22804	6
220	0.19749	9
310	0.17664	12

Material and Preparation of Shot-Peened Specimens

Material of specimen was 800 MPa class high tensile strength steel (HT800) and the size of specimen was 20 x 20 x 50 mm^3. Three kinds of shot-peening process were subjected on the specimen surface so as to have following distribution of residual stress.

a) Compressive residual stress at outer surface exists and it increases with depth. After being reached the maximum value of compressive residual stress, it monotonically diminishes and changes to tensile residual stress. (Case 1)
b) Value of compressive residual stress at surface keeps till some depth and it diminishes. (Case 2)
c) Residual stress at surface is compressive and it monotonically decreases with depth. (Case 3)

RESULTS AND DISCUSSION

Influence of Irradiated Area on the Surface

Since diffraction angles are measured at different ψ directions, x-ray irradiated area on the surface increases in proportion to 1/cos ψ_0 if a size of irradiated x-ray beam is fixed by a slit system. This means that diffraction profile at higher ψ region is to be unsymmetrical because of difference in x-ray path length to the specimen and to the detector. Thus, diffraction angle moves to higher direction and the value of stress is apt to be measured in compressive side. From this point of view, a variable slit system was introduced to hold the constant irradiated area on the surface. Figure 1 shows $\sin^2\psi$ diagrams for verifying the influence of slit. The open circle shows the result measured by the use of the variable slit system and the closed circle shows that by the fixed slit system. As expected, a discrepancy between both measured values increases with the increase of $\sin^2\psi$ and value of stress by the fixed slit system increases in compressive side. Such result indicates that the x-ray irradiated area on the surface should be fixed if the diffraction angle have to be measured at higher ψ angle region.

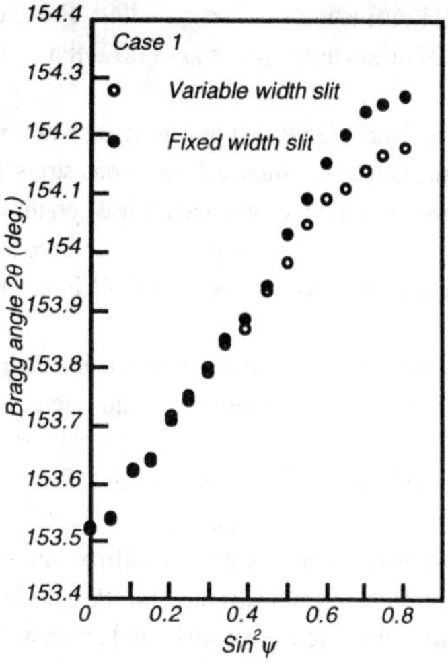

Fig.1 $\sin^2\psi$ diagrams for verifying the influence of slit. Open circle; variable slit. Closed circle: fixed slit.

Residual Stresses on the Surfaces

Residual stresses on longitudinal and transverse direction of each specimen were measured on the three kinds of diffractions and Fig.2a) b) and c) show $\sin^2\psi$ diagrams on the longitudinal direction. Curved relationships are observable on both the case 1 and case 2 specimens. However, approximate linear relationships hold in the $\sin^2\psi$ range from 0 to 0.5 and curves are observed over the range of 0.5 on the case 1 specimen. If Bragg angles were only measured within the $\sin^2\psi$ range of 0.5, the existence of stress gradient is sure to be neglected. On the other hand, since linear relationships between $2\theta_\psi$ and $\sin^2\psi$ are observed on the case 2 specimen, $\sin^2\psi$ method is applicable for the calculation of stress and then stress values on the 211 and 220 difractions were determined as follows;

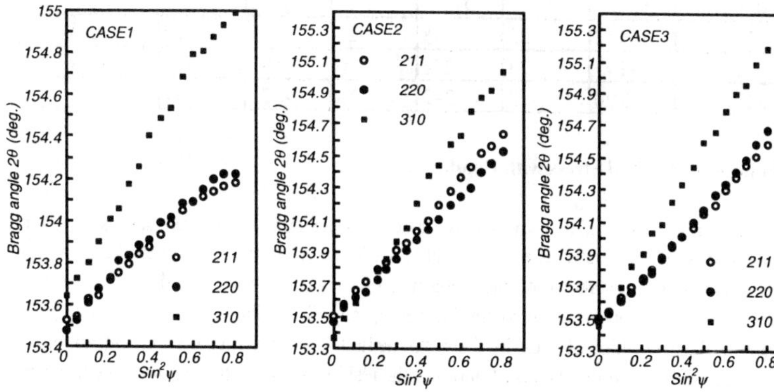

a) Case 1 b) Case 2 c) Case 3

Fig.2 $\sin^2\psi$ diagramas on the surface of shot-peened steel specimens.(longitudinal direction)

211 diffraction σ_{110}= - 499MPa, σ_{220}= - 492MPa
220 diffraction σ_{110}= - 460MPa, σ_{220}= - 468MPa.

An x-ray elastic constant K used was –351 MPa/deg., and this values was converted from the standard value by 'standard for x-ray stress analysis [6]. On the 310 diffraction, stresses were first determined by the use of K value based on the Kroener model, K= -289 MPa/deg. , then,

311 diffraction σ_{110}= - 613MPa, σ_{220}= - 617MPa (Kroener model).

These values of stress are obviously larger than values on the 211 and the 220 diffraction by about 100 MPa, then the stresses were again calculated by the Reuss model, K= - 234 MPa/deg., as.

σ_{110}= - 496MPa, σ_{220}= - 500MPa (Reuss model).

As these values on the 310 diffraction approximately coincide with the 211 and 220 values, K value by Reuss model was used for the calculation of stress for the case 1 and case 3 specimens on the 310 diffraction. Results of stress and gradient determinations are listed in Table 2. Although values on the 211 diffraction almost agree with those on 220 diffraction, values on the 310 diffraction are different from both results. As mentioned above, we made an assumption that each stress component has a linear stress gradient with depth for stress analysis and this assumption formed on the 211 and the 220 diffraction which the penetration depth of x-rays is comparatively small. But the assumption of the linear distribution of stress with depth did not form on the 310 diffraction because the penetration depth is about 12 μm. Therefore, measurement of residual stress distribution was carried out by the use of the 211 diffraction.

Table 2 Calculation results of surface residual stress and gradient for Fig.2a) and c).

	Case 1				Case 2			
Diffraction	σ_{110}	A_{11}	σ_{220}	A_{22}	σ_{110}	A_{11}	σ_{220}	A_{22}
211	-412	-22	-248	-22	-579	10	-507	2
220	-195	-23	-253	-16	-597	15	-529	1
310	-290	-13	-242	-18	-375	-37	-478	-11.2

Distributions of Residual Stress with Depth

After being measured the residual stresses on the outer surface, thin layers were successively removed by electrolytic-polishing and stresses on revealed surface were measured. When the $\sin^2\psi$ relations with curvature were measured, both the $\sin^2\psi$ method and the cos ψ method were adopted for the determination of stress and stress gradient. However, only diffraction data between $\sin^2\psi$=0 and 0.5 were used for the calculation of stress by the $\sin^2\psi$ method. The $\sin^2\psi$ method was only adopted on the case of a linear $\sin^2\psi$ relation. The distributions of the residual stress with depth for three different shot-peened conditions are shown in Figure 3a), b) and c). Results by the $\sin^2\psi$ method almost agree with the distributions expected in the shot-peening process and, generally speaking, the values of compressive residual stress by the cos ψ method are lower than those by the $\sin^2\psi$ method. When a curved $\sin^2\psi$ diagram was obtained, the residual stress which neglected the stress gradient becomes too large or small in comparison with the residual stress that assumed the stress gradient. In particular, the surface residual stress by the cos ψ method is remarkably lower than that by the $\sin^2\psi$ method on the distribution of residual stress such as the case 1 specimen. This is an important problem on the viewpoint of strength evaluation. For example, when the fatigue strength of shot-peened parts are interpreted on the residual stress, the fatigue strength would be over-estimated in the safety side if the influence of stress gradient was neglected by use of the $\sin^2\psi$ method.

CONCLUSIONS

The distributions of residual of the shot-peened steel specimens were measured by the use of x-rays from synchrotron radiation source. Both of the $\sin^2\psi$ method and a method taking account the gradient were adopted for the stress determination. Results shows that large discrepancies were observed on the stress values determined by the both methods. Following results are drawn from experimental results;

1) $\sin^2\psi$ relations with curvature were obtained near the surface of shot-peened specimens. This indicates that the analysis by the $\sin^2\psi$ method is unsuitable for such relations and the use of a method taking account the gradient is desirable for stress determination.
2) The x-ray wavelength as short as possible should be used and the maximum value of $\sin^2\psi$ should be closer to 1 for such materials.
3) X-ray irradiated area on the specimen

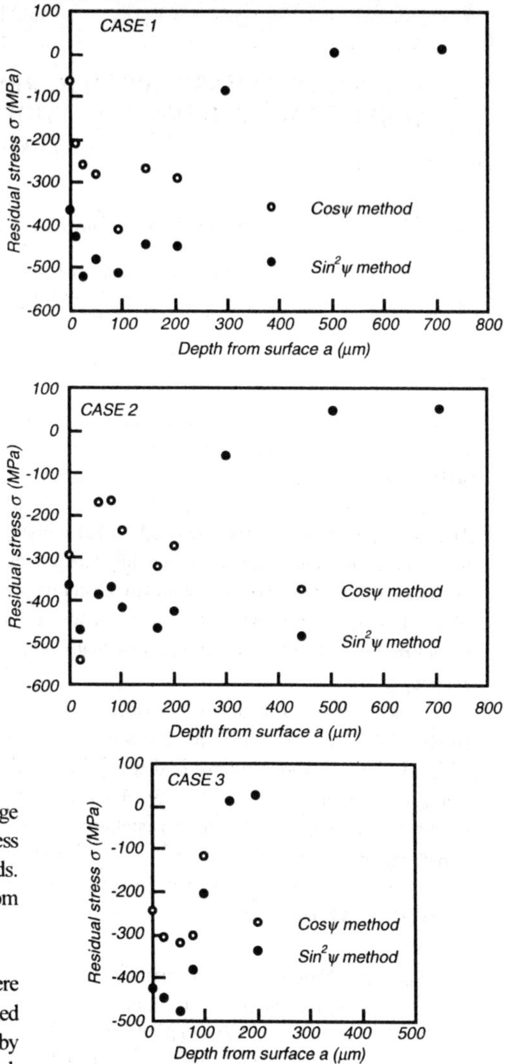

Fig.3 Residual stress distributions in specimens with different shot-peened process.

a) Case 1 (upper)
b) Case 2 (middle)
c) Case 3 (lower)

CHANGE OF PHASE-SPECIFIC RESIDUAL STRESSES OF AN AUSTENITIC-MARTENSITIC TOOL STEEL DURING TENSILE TESTING

J. Moench, A. Kämpfe, A. Sahin and D. Löhe

Institute for Material Science and Engineering I
Karlsruhe University
Kaiserstr. 12
76128 Karlsruhe
Germany

ABSTRACT

Tool-steels with high carbon contents often contain retained austenite after hardening. This has a large influence on the mechanical behaviour of the tool due to the relatively low mechanical resistance of the retained austenite and its ability to transform mechanically induced into martensite. The latter leads to high plastic deformations trough the transformation plasticity at already low loads which cause expensive restoring work or tool exchange.

To characterize the mechanical behaviour of such a two-phase material, investigations which combine tensile tests with simultaneously employed magnetic phase analysis and X-ray residual stress analysis before and after the tensile tests were performed. Introducing the resulting data into a newly developed macroscopic model, it is possible to determine the mechanical response of retained austenite as well as the plastic strains resulting from the transformation.

INTRODUCTION

The austenite-martensite transformation is an important process to increase the strength of steel. However, during the corresponding heat treatment, which consists of austenitisation and quenching, no complete martensitic structure will develop in high carbon steels, for example tool steels. Due to carbon in solid solution, the austenite is chemically stabilized and a part of it remains which is called retained austenite.

When a load is applied to such a two phase structure its behaviour depends strongly on the amount and the deformation behaviour of the retained austenite. It usually possesses a lower yield strength and a larger plastic deformation ability than martensite. Furthermore a part of the retained austenite can be transformed mechanically induced into martensite even at constant temperature. Then due to the transformation plasticity large amounts of strains can occur even at comparatively small loads. The behaviour of the retained austenite may be influenced by a tempering treatment, because the carbon diffusion, enabled at increased temperatures, will change the chemical stability of the retained austenite and the nucleation mechanism for the austenite-martensite transformation.

TASK, MATERIAL, EXPERIMENTAL SET-UP

The aim of the investigation was an analysis of the deformation behaviour of different austenite containing martensitic structures regarding the different deformation of the phases, the transformation behaviour of the retained austenite and its thermal stabilisation by tempering treatments. For that purpose a tool steel with 1% C, 5% Cr, and 1% Mo (German grade X 100 CrMoV 5 1) was used, because here very high retained austenite amounts can be achieved using a suitable austenitisation temperature.
From the forged raw material round hollow specimens (Fig. 1) were prepared. These possess a wall thickness of only 1 mm within the gage length, in order to minimise the residual stresses developing during the following heat treatment. Because of the inhomogeneities within the samples 3 groups with 15 specimens each were used. The first group was austenitized 10 min at 1150 °C and quenched then in 20 °C cold oil, the second was tempered 1 h at 250 °C after the same hardening and similarly the third was tempered 2 h at 300 °C.

At first, the heat treated samples were metallographically examined and then the volume fraction and the residual stresses of the phases were determined with X-ray diffraction (Fig. 2) [1, 2, 3]. With these information the type I residual stresses as well as the averaged type II residual stresses in both phases can be calculated in accordance with the formulas indicated in the figure. For the phase analysis a diffractometer in symmetrical Bragg Brentano arrangement with Mo Kα-radiation was used and three reflections of each phase were analysed. The residual stress determination took place on ψ-diffractometer of the type “Karlsruhe” with Cr Kα-radiation in the range of $-60° \leq \psi \leq 60°$ with 10° steps in each case. For the residual stress analyses on the martensite the {211}-reflections and for that on the retained austenite the {220}-reflections were used.

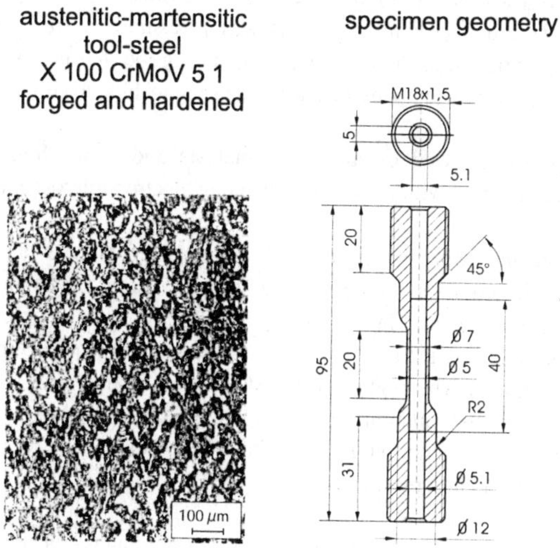

Fig. 1: The microstructure of the hardened state (left) and specimen geometry (right)

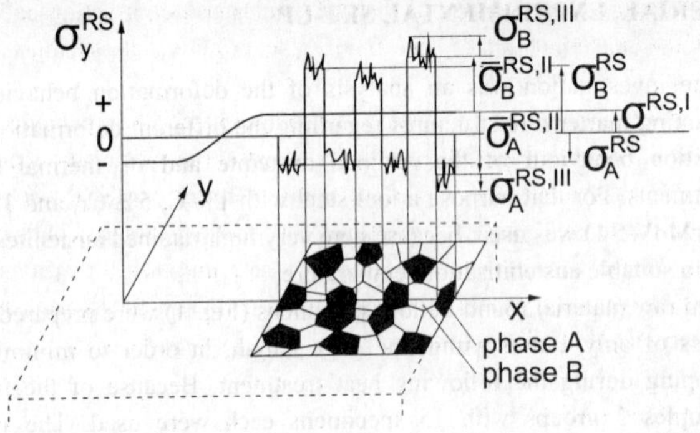

type I residual stresses:

$$\sigma^{RS,I} = \sigma_A^{RS}\, f_A + \sigma_B^{RS}\, f_B$$

with phase contents f_A and f_B

averaged type II residual stresses

phase A: $\bar{\sigma}_A^{RS,II} = \sigma_A^{RS} - \sigma^{RS,I}$

phase B: $\bar{\sigma}_B^{RS,II} = \sigma_B^{RS} - \sigma^{RS,I}$

Fig. 2: Residual stresses in two phase structure

Subsequently, the samples were loaded at room temperature with constant cross head speed $\dot{\varepsilon} = 4.5 \cdot 10^{-5}\, s^{-1}$ until fracture. During this, besides stress and strain the signal of an magnetic inductive single-pole probe (magnetostriction) was measured in situ, which enables the determination of the variation of the phase amounts during the tensile tests. The single-pole probe was a ferritscope of the company Fischer measuring technique GmbH [4].

The tensile tests were followed by an X-ray analysis and a metallographic as well as fractographic characterisation with optical and scanning electron microscope.

In order to evaluate the experimental data of the mechanical tests in such a way that statements about the deformation in the phases as well as the transformation become possible, a macroscopic model is necessary. In this paper a model proposed by Fischmeister and Poech which was developed and verified particularly for tensile tests of martensitic-austenitic model materials [5, 6] was applied. The model was transferred into a small program for this purpose and extended with the transformation phenomenon. The latter consists of isotropic volume expansion because of the different atomic packing of the lattices and an anisotropic plastic deformation, the transformation plasticity.

The model assumes equal stresses in all phases and accounts for the different lateral contractions of the phases, using an effective stress according to von Mises instead of the axial stress component. Therefore, for each point of stress-strain curve the axial stresses, the

radial and circumferential stresses due to the different lateral contraction coefficients of the martensitic and the austenitic phase and finally the effective stress must be determined iteratively.
For the present investigations the "classical" methodology, i.e. the evaluation of the stress-strain curve of the two-phase material from the stress-strain curves of the single phases, was reversed. From the specification of a martensite stress-strain curve (from literature values [6]), the austenite-martensite stress-strain curve, the residual stresses before and after the tensile tests in the phases as well as the variation in phase amounts, the austenite stress-strain curve and the transformation plasticity were determined. For the martensite only elastic deformation was assumed in all sets of samples.

RESULTS AND DISCUSSION

After the heat treatment the residual stresses were small in all of the sets of samples. In hardened samples the volume fraction of retained austenite is about 67 %. During tempering, a small fraction of the retained austenite is chemically destabilised by carbon diffusion into neighbouring martensite, resulting in a corresponding amount of austenite-martensite transformation during cooling from tempering temperature. Hence, volume fractions of approximately 60 % were measured in the tempered samples.

The tensile test curves (Fig. 3) determined after the three heat treatments show clear differences. The yield strength and the tensile strength increase with the degree of tempering, however, the fracture strain rises first from the hardened to the low tempered samples and then drops again. Even though the rate of martensite formation $dV_M/d\varepsilon$ differ strongly regarding hardened and low tempered specimens (see below), the corresponding work hardening rates are almost the same. Contrarily, the work hardening in the high tempered specimens is significantly larger, resulting in a relatively high tensile strength at a relatively low fracture strain.

As shown by the broken lines in Fig. 3, the volume fraction of martensite increases almost linearly during tensile straining. The rate of the mechanically induced martensite formation $dV_M/d\varepsilon$ is reduced from 12 to 4.5 and 3.4 with the tempering degree. In the hardened samples the transformation begins immediately with loading, whereas in the tempered samples it only starts at the onset of macroscopic yielding. Obviously, the martensite nuclei existing after quenching become blocked during the tempering treatment by being occupied by diffusing carbon atoms. On the other hand, from the linear increase of the martensite content observed on the hardened samples especially within the range of the macroscopic yield strength one may assume that no additional martensite nuclei were generated by the beginning plastic deformation.

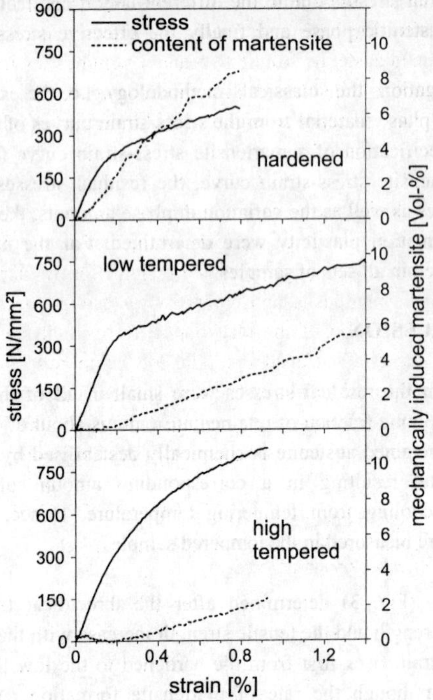

Fig. 3: Stress-strain curves and simultaneously recorded increase of the martensite content for three different types of heat treatment

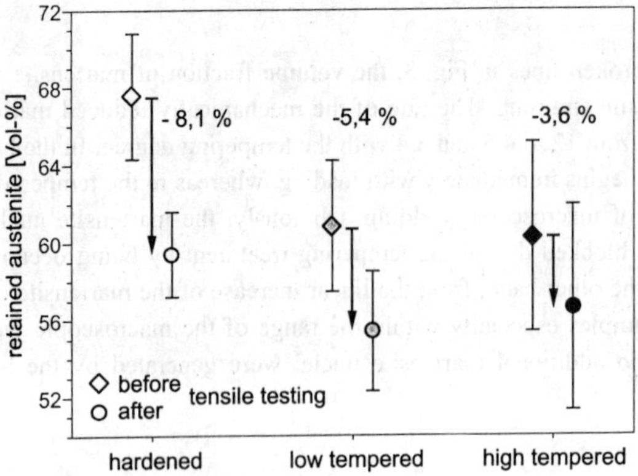

Fig. 4: Average retained austenite contents determined with the X-ray technique before and after tensile testing

A comparison of average retained austenite contents determined by the X-ray diffraction technique before and after the tensile tests (Fig. 4) shows a decrease of the transformed volume fraction of retained austenite from 8 to 5 and 3 volume-% with the tempering degree. This decreasing amount of transformed austenite during tensile testing as well as the increasing yield strength indicates a significant hindering of the austenite-martensite transformation.

Fig. 5 represents the residual stresses before and after the tensile tests. The type I residual stresses are constant within the range of accuracy of the measuring method. On the contrary, the type II residual stresses of the single phases are significantly increased. Tensile residual stresses were found in the martensite and compressive residual stresses were found in the retained austenite. The formation of the phase specific residual stresses is a result of the plastic deformation of the retained austenite. The low tempered samples show the largest changes. This corresponds to the results of the tensile tests. The largest plastic deformations were found after the low tempering heat treatment. Tensile plastic deformations of the retained austenite lead to compressive residual stresses after unloading.

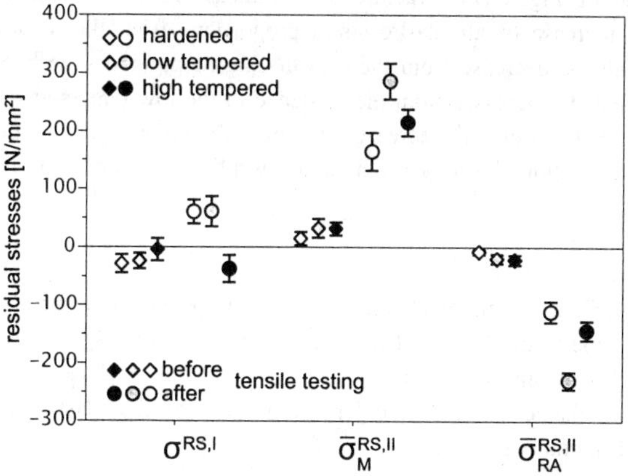

Fig. 5: Type I and type II residual stresses before and after the tensile tests

The modelling of the elastic plastic behaviour of the austenite in the tensile tests for the 3 heat treatments shows a pronounced increase of the resistance of the retained austenite against plastic deformation. Its yield strength and tensile strength increase with the tempering degree, as shown in Fig. 6 on the left-hand side. There are only small differences regarding the moduli of plasticity.

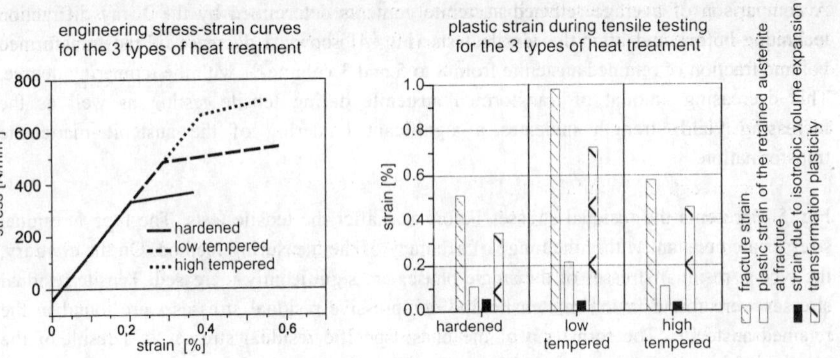

Fig. 6: Results of the modelling of the elastic plastic behaviour of the austenite in the tensile tests

On the right side of Fig. 6 the fracture strains measured are separated into different components. The increase of all plastic strain proportions from the hardened to the low tempered states and the decrease from there to the high tempered state become clear. The transformation plasticity increases from the hardened to the low tempered state even though the volume fraction transformed decreases, because the transformation occurs at higher stresses. The transformation plasticity was assumed as a linear relationship according to

$$d\varepsilon = k \, \sigma \, dV,$$

where $d\varepsilon$ is the differential uniaxial strain, k is a proportionality factor and dV is the differential transformed volume [7]. The proportionality factors k of the 3 experimental groups differ only little from each other.
The transformation plasticity yields the largest fraction of the plastic strain. The other proportions are substantially smaller.

CONCLUSION

During tensile straining of an austenic-martensitic tool steel the volume fraction of austenite transformed into martensite increases almost linearly with the strain. After tempering, the transformation occurs only after macroscopic yielding and the volume fraction transformed decreases as compared to the non-tempered state. The stabilisation of the retained austenite against transformation into martensite is a result of martensite nuclei becoming blocked by carbon atoms diffusing during tempering. Hence, tempering results in a pronounced increase of the flow stress.

The application of a model which assumes equal stresses in the phases and which accounts for their different lateral contractions confirms the stabilisation of the retained austenite by the increase of yield strength and tensile strength. The largest fraction of the plastic strain is always caused by the transformation plasticity. As a consequence of the higher flow stresses, the transformation plasticity in the tempered states is larger than in the non-tempered state, even though the rate of austenite-martensite transformation is much less. Because of these competing influences, the work hardening rate of the three material states investigated do not differ much.

REFERRENCES

1 Macherauch E., Wohlfahrt H., HTM 27 (1972) 230-232

2 Faninger G, Hartmann U, HTM 27 (1972) 233-244

3 Eigenmann B, Macherauch E, Matwiss. u. Werkstofftech. 26 (1995) 148-160, 199-216, Matwiss. u. Werkstofftech. 27 (1996), 426-437, 491-501

4 Neumeier P, Schweißtechnik 39 (1989) 545-548

5 Poesch M H, Fischmeister H, Z. Mkde. 83 (1992) 176-182

6 Poesch M H, Fischmeister H, Z. Mkde. 83 (1992) 379-389

7 Besserdich G, 'Untersuchungen zur Eigenspannungs- und Verzugsausbildung beim Abschrecken von Zylindern aus den Stählen 42CrMo4 und Ck45 unter Berücksichtigung der Umwandlungsplastizität' Diss. (Dr.-Ing.), Universität Karlsruhe (TH), 1995

Development of a New Automated X-Ray Stress Analyzer With its Applications

Masanori KURITA, Le Chi CUONG and Hirotaka NAKAJOU
Nagaoka University of Technology
Kamitomioka、Nagaoka、940-2188 Japan

ABSTRACT

A new automated x-ray stress analyzer was developed to precisely and rapidly measure residual stress and diffraction line broadness. The Gaussian curve, parabola, half-width and centroid methods are provided in this system. In the Gaussian curve method, the broadness of a diffraction line can also be evaluated by using GCP (Gaussian curve parameter). In all these methods, the standard deviations in the peak position and the stress value, which represent the magnitude of the variation in measured values arising from x-ray counting statistics, can be analytically determined simultaneously with the stress. The use of the GUI (Graphical user interface) facilitates the rapid selection of the measurement conditions. This analyzer allows the graphical representation and tabulation of the measurement results.

INTRODUCTION

The method of the x-ray stress measurement is the most effective technique to nondestructively measure residual stress in a small localized surface layer of polycrystalline materials. In this method, the stress is determined from the shift of the peak position of a diffraction line which varies proportionally to the lattice strain of a specimen. The four methods are used to determine the peak position of a diffraction line: the Gaussian curve (1-4), parabola (4-8), half-width (9, 10) and centroid (11) methods. Although the parabola method is most widely used, it can not determine the broadness of a diffraction line, which is often useful to evaluate materials. The Gaussian curve method, on the other hand, can evaluate the broadness of a diffraction line by using GCP (Gaussian curve parameter) proposed by the author (12, 13) together with the stress.

In x-ray stress measurement, since measured values will vary due to x-ray counting statistics, it is important to determine the stress together with its confidence interval to evaluate the reproducibility of the measurement (1, 2, 5, 6, 8, 10, 11, 13-16). Unfortunately, an x-ray stress analyzer that can use the Gaussian curve method and that can determine the stress with its confidence interval is commercially unavailable until now.

A new automated x-ray stress analyzer was developed to precisely and rapidly measure residual stress and diffraction line broadness. The four methods are applicable in this system. In all these methods, the standard deviations in the peak position and the stress value which represent the magnitude of the variation arising from x-ray counting statistics can be analytically determined from a single measurement by using the equations proposed by the author (1, 2, 5, 10, 11, 13-16).

METHODS FOR DETERMINING PEAK POSITION

The location of a diffraction line, called a peak position p, will change proportionally to a lattice strain in crystals, so that applied and residual stresses can be determined from the shift of the peak position of a diffraction line. Therefore, the peak position determination is of principal importance in the x-ray stress measurement. Besides peak positions to determine the stress, the broadness of a diffraction line such as the half-width is used to evaluate materials. Table I gives the four methods for determining the peak position and the broadness of an x-ray diffraction line provided in this system. In Japan, the half-width method is most widely used (9), while the parabola method is widely used in other countries (5-8). On the other hand, we are using the Gaussian curve method (1-4) in our laboratory.

To determine an accurate peak position and broadness of a diffraction line, the measured x-ray counts y or intensity (cps, counts per second) shown in Fig.1 should be corrected for both the background counts y_b and LPA (Lorentz-polarization and absorption) factor (7) as

$$z_i = l_i(y_i - y_{bi}) \tag{1}$$

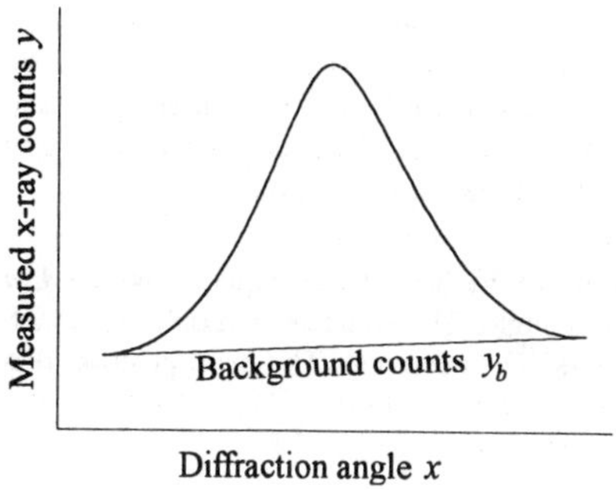

Fig.1 Diffraction line.

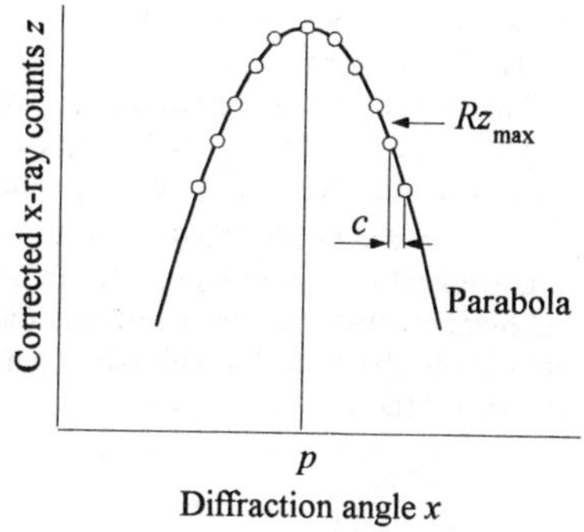

Fig.3 The parabola method.

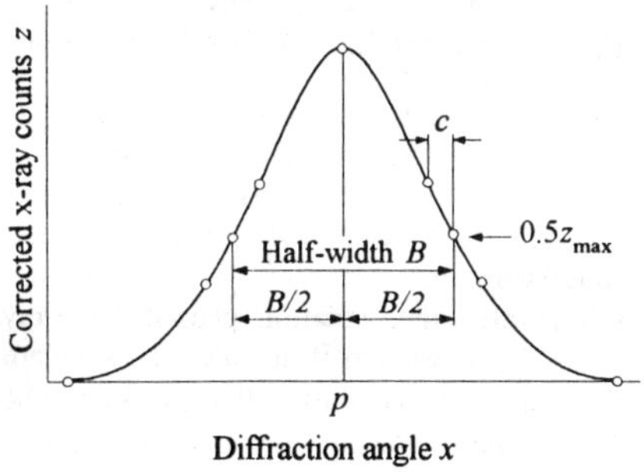

Fig.2 The half-width method.

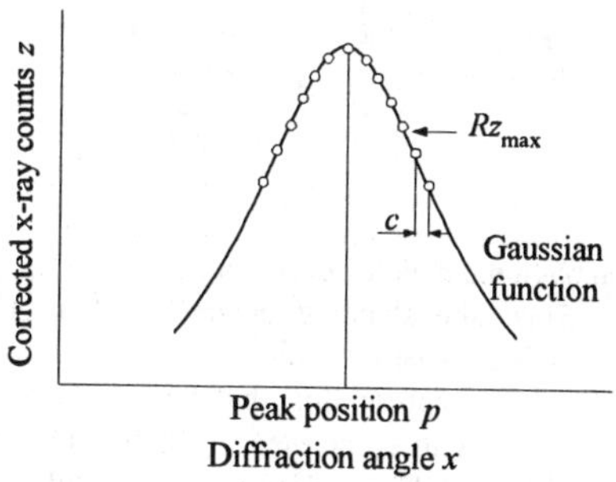

Fig.4 The Gaussian curve method.

Table I Methods for determining peak position and broadness of diffraction line.

Peak position	Broadness	Main user
Gaussian curve method	GCP (Gaussian curve parameter)	Kurita laboratory
Parabola method	-------	USA and other countries
Half-width method	Half-width (Full-width at half maximum intensity)	Japan
Centroid method	Integrated intensity	Rarely used

where z_i is the corrected x-ray counts and l_i is the reciprocal LPA factor. In the parabola and the Gaussian curve methods, however, the background subtraction can be omitted because it has little influence on the peak position and the stress except for materials having extremely high background intensity, so that the peak position p is usually determined from corrected counts z_i given by

$$z_i = l_i y_i \tag{2}$$

In the half-width method, the peak position p is determined as the midpoint of the width B at half maximum intensity (called the half-width) of a diffraction line as shown in Fig.2. In the parabola method shown in Fig.3, the peak position p is determined as the center axis of the parabola approximating the diffraction peak. The Gaussian curve method, as shown in Fig.4, uses a Gaussian function instead of a parabola in the parabola method. In the centroid method, the location of the centroid of the whole diffraction line is used as the peak position.

The Gaussian curve and parabola methods can measure the stress more rapidly than the half-width and centroid methods because the peak position can be determined from several data points (usually 5 to 15) of x-ray counts around the peak of a diffraction line as shown in Figs.3 and 4. In the Gaussian curve method, the Gaussian function g(x) given by

$$z = g(x) = A\exp(-ax^2 + bx) \tag{3}$$

is determined from data points above Rz_{max} by using the method of least squares, where A, a and b are positive constants, and x is the diffraction angle. The constant R usually takes 0.8 and 0.85 in the Gaussian curve and parabola methods, respectively. The peak position p is determined from

$$p = \frac{b}{2a} \tag{4}$$

The detailed determination of a and b by the least squares method to obtain the peak position p from Eq.(4) is omitted here because it is given in the previous papers (1-5).

The broadness of a diffraction line can be evaluated from the standard deviation σ or the variance σ^2 of the Gaussian function approximating a diffraction line. By the definition, the variance σ^2 of the Gaussian function g(x) is calculated from

$$\sigma^2 = \frac{\int_{-\infty}^{+\infty}(x-p)^2 g(x)dx}{\int_{-\infty}^{+\infty} g(x)dx} = \frac{1}{2a} \tag{5}$$

though the detailed derivation (12) of Eq.(5) is omitted here.

Since the standard deviation σ in Eq.(5) will involve the variation caused by x-ray counting statistics similarly to the peak position and the stress and it has also the standard deviation representing the magnitude of the variation in σ, we will call σ in Eq.(5) the Gaussian curve parameter (GCP) α [12, 13] to avoid the confusing term of "the standard deviation of the standard deviation σ". From Eq.(5) the GCP α is given by

$$\text{GCP}\,\alpha = \frac{1}{\sqrt{2a}} \tag{6}$$

To accurately evaluate the broadening of a diffraction line, the background y_b should be subtracted as in Eq.(1). However, the measurement of diffraction lines having various line widths shows that there is a linear relationship between the two kinds of GCP's with and without subtraction of the background (17), so that either GCP can be obtained from the other.

The parabola method, unfortunately, can not determine the standard deviation from Eq.(5), that is, it can not evaluate the broadness of the diffraction line. A distinct advantage of the Gaussian curve method over the parabola method is that the Gaussian curve method can evaluate the broadness of a diffraction line, together with the stress, by using GCP.

A NEW AUTOMATED X-RAY STRESS ANALYZER

An automated x-ray stress analyzer was developed by making use of commercially available x-ray goniometer, x-ray generator and a personal computer. A ST-SMC, which is composed of a scaler-timer (ST) and stepping motor controllers (SMC), was specially designed for this stress analyzer. The scaler-timer measures x-ray counts from the scintillation counter (SC) in a fixed time called the preset time *pt*. The stepping motor controllers drive and control the two stepping motors in the x-ray goniometer.

The ST-SMC is equipped with a built-in CPU to make itself intelligent and to facilitate the control of the SM's and the x-ray counting with the scaler-timer by using the commands from the computer; thus minimizing the computer program for the measurement. The computer program for the measurement was made using the Visual C-language. Commercially available computer application software is also used for the graphical representation and tabulation of the results and real-time monitoring of the measurement. The GUI (Graphical user interface) was used to facilitate the rapid selection of the measurement conditions.

Figures 5 and 6 show the CRT display for the selection of the measurement methods and conditions for ferritic steels. A diffraction line is measured by the fixed-ψ method which is used in a conventional x-ray diffractometer. This system provides the four methods for the peak position determination. Of the iso- and side-inclination methods (18), the iso-inclination method is usually used. The oscillation method is for the measurement of coarse-grained materials. Figure 6 shows the choice of the measurement conditions for the Gaussian curve method. Usually the four ψ angles of 0, 30, 45 and 60 deg. are chosen, but we can choose other ψ angles.

Figure 7 shows a flowchart for the standard stress measurement of ferritic steels by the Gaussian curve method using the iso-inclination method. The stress is calculated from several (usually four) peak positions p at different ψ angles. In the peak position determination, the scanning of the x-ray detector SC to measure x-ray counts y_i starts at a diffraction angle x_0. Measured x-ray counts y_i are corrected for the LPA factor to obtain z_i in Eq.(2). The SC

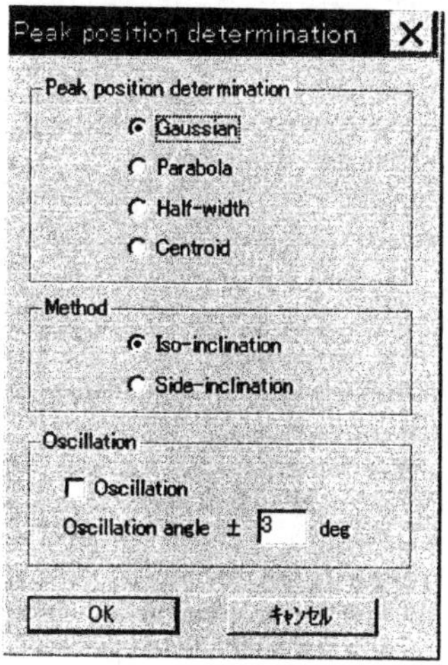

Fig.5 Selection of measurement method.

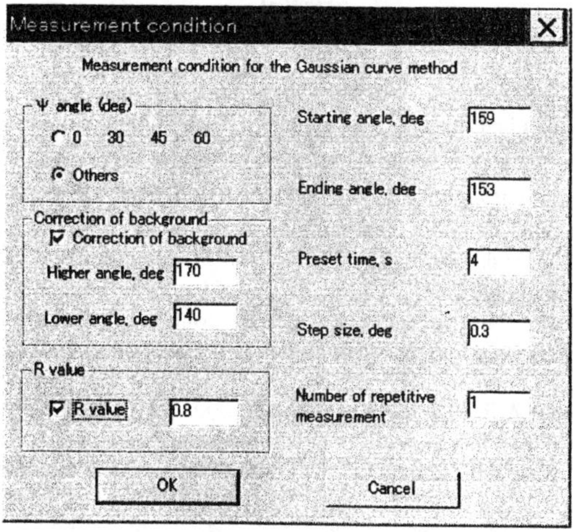

Fig.6 Measurement conditions by Gaussian curve method.

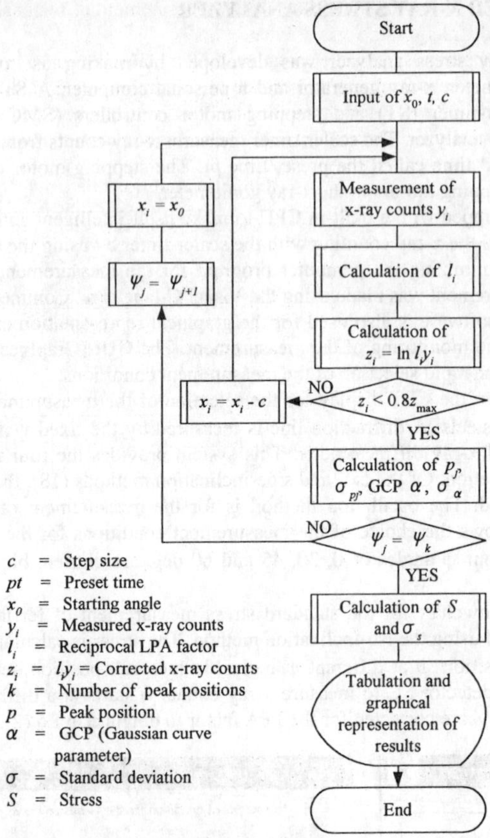

Fig.7 Flowchart of standard stress measurement by the Gaussian curve method.

continues scanning over the diffraction peak and stops immediately after it detects corrected counts z_i smaller than 0.8 z_{max}, then it moves to a next ψ angle to measure next peak position. The peak position p, GCP α and their standard deviations σ_p and σ_α, which represent the magnitude of the variation caused by x-ray counting statistics, are calculated almost at the same time. Immediately after the four peak positions have been measured, the stress S is calculated together with its standard deviation and 95% confidence interval.

MEASUREMENT OF RESIDUAL STRESS AND GCP

Using the automated x-ray stress analyzer developed, the residual stress and GCP of a quenched hardened steel specimen were measured by the Gaussian curve method. For comparison, the residual stress was also measured by the other three methods. A specimen shown in Fig.8 was prepared from structural carbon steel JIS type S50C. The specimen was heated at 850℃ for 1 h and quenched in water. The surface of the specimen was polished with abrasive papers, and the work hardened surface layer was removed electrolytically by about 30 μm. Table II shows the conditions of the measurement of residual stress and GCP. The half-width of the diffraction line was 7.2 deg.

Figure 9 shows the peak position determination by the Gaussian curve method. The SC in the goniometer begins to scan from the higher side of diffraction angle, running over the peak of a diffraction line, and stops scanning immediately after it has detected a x-ray counts z_i below $0.8z_{max}$ to minimize the measurement time. Then, the stepping motor (SM) drives the

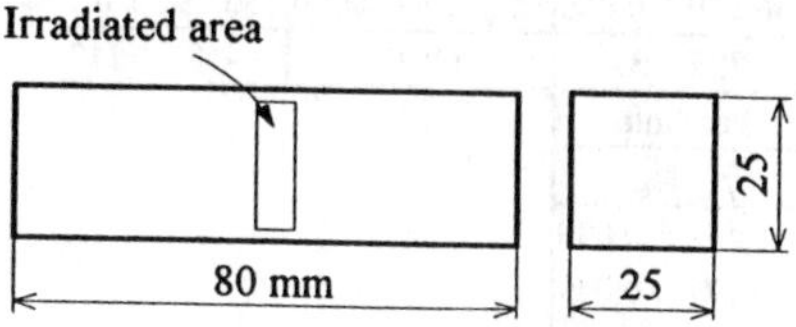

Fig.8 JIS S50C steel specimen.

Table II Conditions of x-ray stress measurement.

Characteristic x-rays	Chromium Kα
Filter	Vanadium foil
Diffraction plane	(211)
Divergent angle of collimator	1°
Tube voltage and current	30 kV, 10 mA
Irradiated area	5 x 20 mm^2
Preset time	4 s
Step size	0.3 °

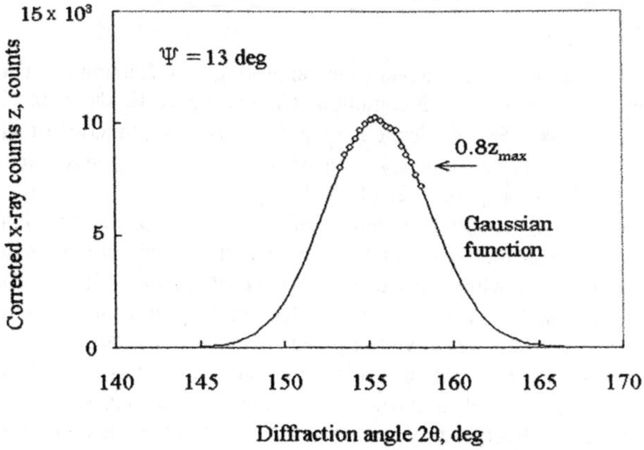

Fig.9 Peak position determination by the Gaussian curve method.

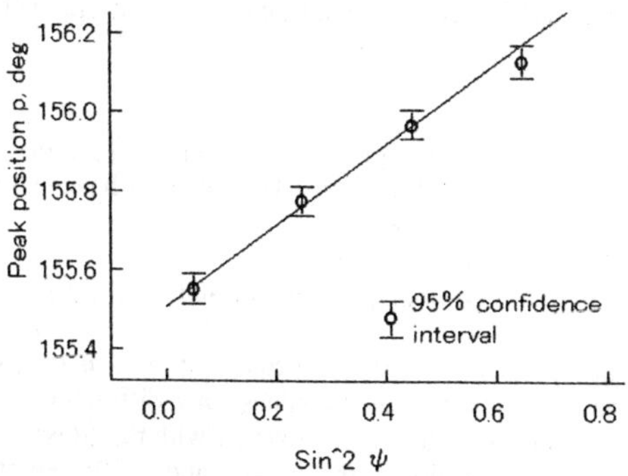

Fig.10 Sin^{2}ψ diagram.

Table III 95% confidence limits of stress S, peak position p and GCP α.

	ψ, deg	$\sin^2\psi$	Gaussian curve method		Parabola	Half-width	Centroid
			p, deg	GCP α, deg	p, deg	p, deg	p, deg
Corrected for background	13	0.05	155.547 ± 0.045	3.113 ± 0.127	155.551 ± 0.043	155.656 ± 0.041	155.989 ± 0.149
	30	0.25	155.735 ± 0.052	3.110 ± 0.158	155.737 ± 0.050	156.021 ± 0.047	156.029 ± 0.163
	42	0.45	155.960 ± 0.048	2.923 ± 0.136	155.964 ± 0.047	156.140 ± 0.041	156.368 ± 0.181
	54	0.65	156.152 ± 0.053	3.057 ± 0.160	156.150 ± 0.050	156.227 ± 0.050	156.296 ± 0.190
	Stress S, MPa		-299 ± 32		-297 ± 31	-269 ± 30	-185 ± 112

	ψ, deg	$\sin^2\psi$	Gaussian curve method		Parabola
			p, deg	GCP α, deg	p, deg
Not corrected for background	13	0.05	155.556 ± 0.032	4.153 ± 0.093	155.558 ± 0.030
	30	0.25	155.778 ± 0.030	4.129 ± 0.083	155.777 ± 0.029
	42	0.45	155.972 ± 0.031	4.007 ± 0.089	155.970 ± 0.030
	54	0.65	156.131 ± 0.035	4.136 ± 0.101	156.135 ± 0.034
	Stress S, MPa		-282 ± 22		-282 ± 21

goniometer to the next ψ angle. The real-time monitoring of diffraction line enables the check of the propriety of the measurement conditions chosen. Figure 10 shows the variation of the peak position p with its 95% confidence interval $\pm 1.96\sigma_p$ as a function of $\sin^2\psi$, that is the $\sin^2\psi$ diagram, where the standard deviation of peak position σ_p was calculated from the equation given in previous papers (1, 2, 14-16).

Table Ⅲ summarizes the 95% confidence limits of the peak position p, GCP and the stress S determined by the four methods. For the Gaussian curve and parabola methods, both the results calculated with and without correction for the background are shown. Table Ⅲ shows that since the background correction has little effect on the peak position and the stress value it can be omitted in the Gaussian curve and parabola methods. In addition, the omission of the background will give the stress with a smaller confidence interval as shown in Table Ⅲ.

The 95% confidence intervals of the stress determined by the Gaussian curve, parabola and half-width methods are almost the same. However, the interval by the centroid method is 3.5 times as large as those of the other three methods. This is because the counting statistics in the foot of a diffraction line will affect strongly the standard deviations of the peak position and the stress in the centroid method (11). Therefore, the centroid method can not be used in practice especially for materials having a broadened diffraction line such as quenched steels.

CONCLUSIONS

[1] A new automated x-ray stress analyzer was developed to rapidly and precisely measure residual stress and diffraction line broadness. This analyzer has the following advantages.

(1) It provides the following methods:

(a) the iso- and side-inclination methods,

(b) the Gaussian curve, parabola, half-width and centroid methods for peak position determination,

(c) the oscillation method for measuring coarse-grained materials.

(2) In the Gsaussian curve method, the broadness of a diffraction line can be evaluated by using GCP (Gaussian curve parameter) together with the stress.

(3) Together with the peak position p, the stress S and GCP, their standard deviations and 95% confidence intervals can also be determined at the same time from a single set of

measurement. Therefore, we can evaluate the reproducibility of the measurement.

(4) The use of the GUI (Graphical user interface) system facilitates the rapid selection of the measurement conditions and the output of the results on the CRT display.

(5) This analyzer enables the real-time monitoring of the measurement, graphical representation and tabulation of the results.

[2] Since the background correction has little effect on the stress in the Gaussian curve and parabola methods, it can be omitted. In addition, the omission of the background correction will give a smaller confidence interval of the stress.

[3] The Gaussian curve, parabola and half-width methods gave almost the same confidence limits of the stress. The centroid method, on the other hand, gave the confidence interval more than three times larger than those determined by the other three methods.

REFERENCES

1. Kurita, M., X-Ray Stress Measurement by the Gaussian Curve Method, Current Japanese Materials Research, Vol.10 (1993), ed. By Tanaka, K., Kodama, S. and Goto, T., pp.135-151, Elsevier Applied Science.
2. Kurita, M., A Statistical Analysis of X-Ray Stress Measurement by the Gaussian Curve Method, Journal of Testing and Evaluation, Vol.9, No.5 (1981), pp.285-291.
3. Kurita, M., A Basic Theory for X-Ray Stress Measurement by Gaussian Curve Method, Journal of JSNDI, Vol.39, No.3 (1990), pp.243-249 [in Japanese].
4. Kurita, M., Simplified Equations for Rapidly Calculating a Parabola and a Gaussian Function by the Least-Squares Method with Engineering Applications, Transactions of the Japan Society of Mechanical Engineers (Series A), Vol.54, No.508, pp.2176-2180 [in Japanese].
5. Kurita, M., Simplified Equations for Peak Position and for its Standard Deviation in X-Ray Stress Measurement, Journal of Testing and Evaluation, Vol.9, No.2 (1981), pp.133-140.
6. Hilley, M. E., Residual Stress Measurement by X-Ray Diffraction – SAE J784a, (1980), pp.50-60, Society of Automotive Engineers.
7. Cullity, B. D., Elements of X-Ray Diffraction, 2nd ed., (1978), pp.447-477, Addison-Wesley.
8. Klug, H. P. and Alexander, L. E., X-Ray Diffraction Procedures For Polycrystalline and Amorphous Materials, 2nd ed., (1974), pp.755-790, John Wiley & Sons.
9. Committee of X-Ray Strength of Materials, Standard Method for X-Ray Stress Measurement, (1997), p.34, Society of the Materials Science Japan [in Japanese].
10. Kurita, M., Statistical Analysis of X-Ray Residual Stress Measurement Using the Half-Width Method, Journal of Testing and Evaluation, Vol.10, No.2 (1982), pp.38-46.
11. Kurita, M., Amano, J. and Sakamoto, I., Statistical Analysis of X-Ray Stress Measurement by Centroid Method, Journal of the Society of Materials Science Japan, Vol.31, No.345 (1982), pp.609-615 [in Japanese].
12. Kurita, M., A New Method for Evaluating X-Ray Diffraction Peak Broadening with Engineering Applications, Advances in X-Ray Analysis, Vol.31 (1988), pp.277-286.
13. Kurita, M. and Hirayama, H., An Estimation of Hardness of Hardened Steels by X-Ray Diffraction Using Gaussian Curve-Fitting Method, Journal of Testing and Evaluation, Vol.12, No.1 (1984), pp.13-19.
14. Kurita, M., Confidence Limits of Stress Values Measured by X-Ray Diffraction, Journal of Testing and Evaluation, Vol.11, No.2 (1983), pp.143-149.
15. Kurita, M. and Uekura, Y., Reproducibility and Confidence Interval of Stress Value Measured by X-Ray Diffraction, Proceedings of the 35th Symposium on X-Ray Studies on Mechanical Behaviour of Materials, (1999), pp.167-172, Society of Materials Science, Japan [in Japanese].
16. Kurita, M., Standard Deviations in X-Ray Stress and Elastic Constants due to Counting Statistics, Advances in X-Ray Analysis, Vol.32 (1989), pp.377-388.
17. Kurita, M. and Ihara, I., Measurement of Hardness of Hardened Steels by X-Ray Diffraction, Journal of the Society of Materials Science Japan, Vol.34, No.379 (1985), pp.449-455 [in Japanese].
18. Committee of X-Ray Strength of Materials, Standard Method for X-Ray Stress Measurement, (1997), pp.26-28, Society of the Materials Science Japan [in Japanese].

Stress Measurements in Silicon Single Crystal by Microbeam Synchrotron X-Rays

Hiroshi SUZUKI*, Koichi AKITA**, Yasuo YOSHIOKA*** and Hiroshi MISAWA**
* Graduate student of Tokyo Metropolitan University
1-1 Minami-Ohsawa, Hchioji, Tokyo 192-0397, JAPAN
** Department of Precision Engineering, Tokyo Metropolitan University
1-1 Minami-Ohsawa, Hchioji, Tokyo 192-0397, JAPAN
*** Department of Energy Science & Engineering, Musashi Institute of Technology
1-28-1 Tamazutsumi, Setagaya, Tokyo, 158-8557, JAPAN

Abstract

X-ray stress measurement in a $\phi 50$ μm region of a silicon single crystal was carried out using synchrotron radiation. The load was applied in three steps using a four-point bending device. In each step, the diffraction angles of three different planes were measured, and the stresses were calculated from the peak shift. The stresses measured by the synchrotron radiation agree well with the applied stresses evaluated using a strain gage. This confirms the possibility of elastic stress measurement of a single crystal in a very small region. Also, the relationship between the setting error of the specimen and stress error was theoretically investigated. It is shown that the effect of misalignment on X-ray stress measurement of single crystal materials is much larger than in the case of polycrystalline materials.

1. Introduction

For the stress measurement of crystalline materials, the X-ray stress measurement method, which measures the lattice strain by X-ray diffraction, is available. This method can be used to measure the stress in bulk materials in the atmosphere. Therefore, this is applicable, for example, in semiconductor devices and micromachines.

In the 1940s~1970s, several articles were devoted to the study of X-ray stress measurement of single crystals and the theoretical background was already established [1]. However, experimental analysis was difficult compared with the case of the stress measurement of polycrystalline materials, because the control of crystal oscillation is required to obtain a perfect diffraction profile; in addition, the measurable diffraction plane is limited and the minimum irradiation area using characteristic X-rays is approximately a $\phi 100$ μm region. However, it seems to be possible to solve these problems using synchrotron radiation with high brilliance and high resolution.

In this study, X-ray stress measurement in a $\phi 50$ μm region of the silicon single crystal was carried out using synchrotron radiation and the possibility of the stress measurement was discussed.

2. Principle

2.1 Theory of X-ray stress measurement of a single crystal

The relationship between stress and strain of a single crystal is expressed as follows [2]. Fig.1(a) shows the crystal system X_i and the laboratory system L_i with respect to the specimen system P_i and the definition of ψ and ϕ angles. Fig.1(b) shows the transformation matrices between each orthonormal coordinate system.

A lattice strain ε_1 in any orientation in the laboratory system is related to the stress components

σ_s in the sample system by the following equation :

$$\varepsilon_l = \gamma S \pi \sigma_s = f(\sigma_{11}, \sigma_{22}, \sigma_{33}, \sigma_{23}, \sigma_{31}, \sigma_{12}) \ , \qquad (1)$$

where γ and π are the components of the transformation matrix from the crystal system to the laboratory system and from the sample system to the crystal system and S is the elastic compliance of the single crystal.

The plane stress condition is assumed in the penetration depth of the X-ray.

$$\sigma_{33} = \sigma_{23} = \sigma_{31} = 0 \qquad (2)$$

From equations (1) and (2), equation (1) is expressed as

$$\varepsilon_l = \gamma S \pi \sigma_s = f(\sigma_{11}, \sigma_{22}, \sigma_{12}) \ . \qquad (3)$$

Therefore, by measuring the strain in three different planes, the stress component σ_s in the sample system can be measured.

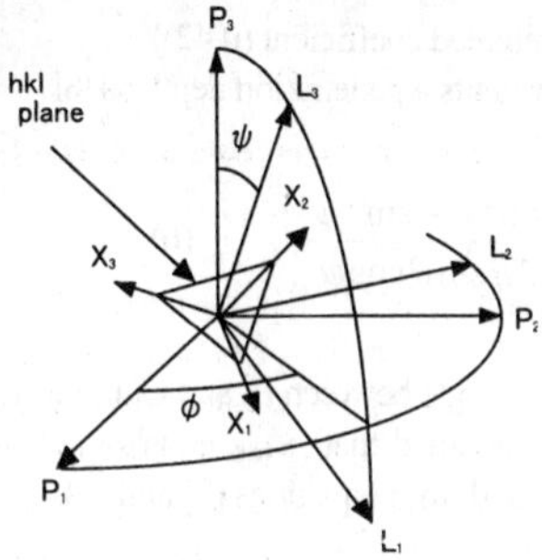

(a) Coordinate system.

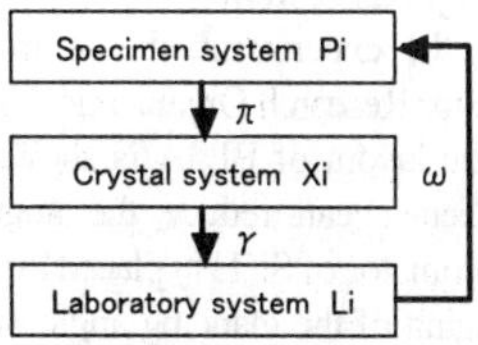

(b) Transformation matrices.

Fig. 1 Three coordinate systems and their transformation matrices and definition of ψ and ϕ.

2.2 The stress on the specimen surface

When a bending stress is applied to the specimen, a stress gradient occurs. As the thickness of the specimen decreases, the stress measured using X-rays gradually starts disagreeing with the result obtained using a strain gage.

The stress on the specimen surface measured using the strain gage is expressed as

$$\sigma_{sg0} = \frac{h_s}{h_s + 2h_{sg} + 2h_a} \sigma_{sg} \ . \qquad (4)$$

(σ_{sg0}: stress on the specimen surface evaluated using the strain gage; σ_{sg}: measured stress using the strain gage; h_s: thickness of the specimen; h_{sg}: thickness of the strain gage; h_a: thickness of adhesive)

The strain measured using X-rays represents a weighted average of the strain from the surface to the penetration depth. Therefore, the strain on the specimen surface evaluated from the X-ray stress measured in this study is expressed as [3].

$$\varepsilon_{hkl0} = \frac{h_s}{h_s + 2WT} \langle \varepsilon_{hkl} \rangle \ . \qquad (5)$$

(ε_{hkl0}: strain of hkl plane on the specimen surface; $<\varepsilon_{hkl}>$: weighted average of the strain of hkl plane;

W: weighted coefficient (0.42))
T represents a penetration depth as [3]

$$T = \frac{\sin^2\theta - \sin^2\psi}{2\mu \sin\theta \cos\psi}. \qquad (6)$$

(ψ: the angle between P_3 and L_3 in Fig.1(a); θ: diffraction angle; μ: linear absorption coefficient)
If it is assumed that ε_{hkl0} equals ε_l expressed by equation (3), the stress on the specimen surface is calculated from equations (3) and (5).

3. Experimental procedure

3.1 The optical system

In the experiment, the beam line 3A (BL3A) in the Photon Factory of the High Energy Accelerator Research Organization, Tsukuba, Japan, was utilized.

The layout of BL3A is shown in Fig.2. The M1 collimating mirror placed 16.2 m from the source center can reduce the angular divergence in the vertical direction. The double-crystal monochromator of Si(111) placed 20.2 m from the source center can vary the energy from 5 to 15 keV by changing of the glancing angle of the monochromator. The second crystal of the monochromator can focus the beam in the horizontal direction. The M2 focusing mirror placed 23.2 m from the source center can focus the beam in the vertical direction. Fig.3 shows a schematic illustration of the crystal oscillating device equipped with a position sensitive proportional counter (PSPC) mounted in the experimental station. The PSPC with a channel number of partitions of 512 ch and detecting window length of 100 mm, was utilized. The distance from the PSPC to the specimens was set at 600 mm in order to obtain a high angular resolution. It is possible to carry out measurements of diffraction angles at the constant angle of 2θ on many diffraction planes, because it is possible to adjust the wavelength using the monochromator. Therefore, even if the diffraction angle is low using the characteristic X-rays, a diffraction line will be diffracted to a high angle. The PSPC was installed at the Bragg angle of 2θ =154 degrees. A $\phi 50$ μm pinhole was used in this study.

3.2 Specimens and loading method

The sample used in this study was a silicon wafer for which the plane orientation was (001) and the orientation in the flat direction was [110]. A specimen, of loading direction [110] and length and width of 40 mm and 5 mm, respectively, was cut from the wafer. A four-point bending device which can be installed on the crystal oscillating device was used in order to apply strain. The inside and outside spans of the load pin were 10 mm and 30 mm, respectively. The preload on the specimen

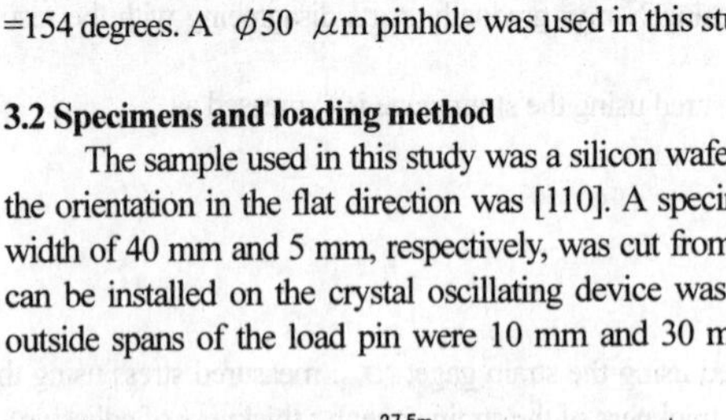

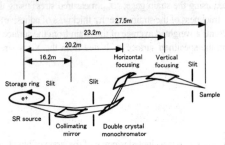

Fig. 2 Layout of beam line BL3A.

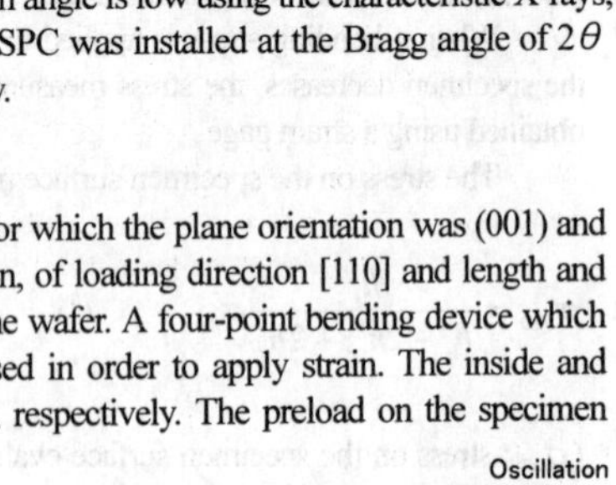

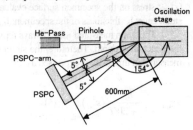

Fig. 3 Layout of the goniometer for X-ray stress measurement.

surface was set at about 15 MPa in order to hold the specimen, and this condition was considered as an initial state. From the initial state, the stress in the three steps was taken as relative stress. In each step, the diffraction angles of three different planes were measured using X-rays, and the stresses were calculated from the peak shift. The mechanical stress applied to the specimen surface was calculated using the output from the strain gage affixed behind the specimen and the stiffness matrices of silicon are shown in Table 1 [4].

3.3 The X-ray stress measurement procedure

First, the combinations of the diffraction planes and the wavelength are decided. Next, the incidence angles of the X-rays, ψ and ϕ, are calculated from the plane index and the loading direction of the specimen. The specimen is set based on ψ and ϕ, and the diffraction profile is measured while oscillating the specimen. The experimental conditions for the diffraction angle are listed in Table 2.

Table 1 Stiffness matrices of silicon [4].

C_{11},GPa	167.4
C_{12},GPa	65.2
C_{44},GPa	79.6

Table 2 Experimental condition of diffraction measurement using synchrotron radiation source.

Diffraction Plane	135	224	2-24
Wavelength, nm	0.179	0.216	0.216
ϕ-Angle, deg.	116.57	90	0
ψ-Angle, deg.	32.31	35.26	35.26
χ-Oscillation Range, deg.	±5(Continuous)		
ψ-Oscillation Range, deg.	±0.1(0.01deg. step)		
Applied Stress, MPa	22, 44, 66		
Pinhole, μm	50		

3.4 The oscillation method of a specimen

Crystal oscillation is required in order to obtain a perfect diffraction profile using the PSPC. As Fig.4 indicates, the biaxial oscillation method, called the "$\chi\psi$ oscillation method," has been used in this study. The axis of χ-oscillation agrees with the direction of incidence X-rays, and the axis of ψ-oscillation agrees with the vertical direction for the χ-rotating axis.

Fig.5 shows the crystal oscillation apparatus developed in this study. The automatic goniometer stage for ψ-oscillation was carried on an automatic rotating stage for χ-oscillation. The height adjuster and ϕ rotating stage were carried on the ψ and χ oscillating attachment. The oscillation conditions in this study are listed in Table 2.

In this study, the crossing and displacement error accuracy was within about 10 μm.

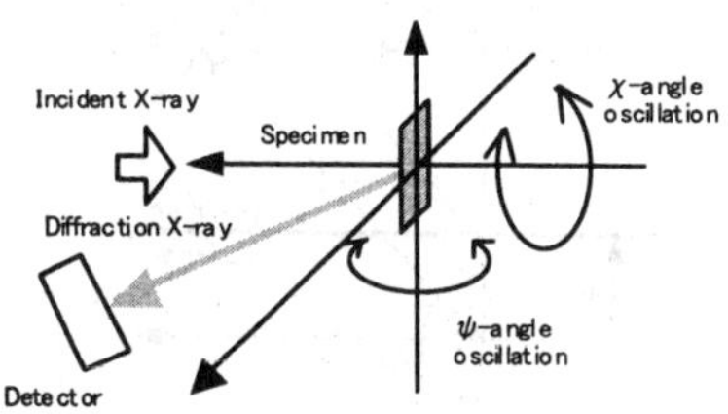

Fig. 4 Oscillating system.

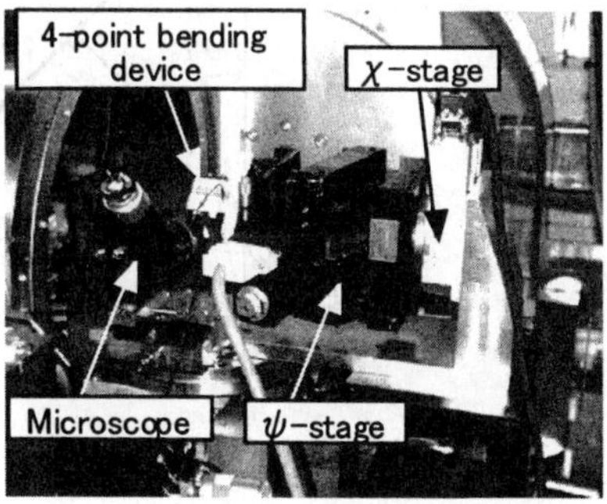

Fig. 5 Overview of crystal oscillating device.

4. The effect of displacement error of specimen on X-ray stress measurement

4.1 Peak shift of X-ray diffraction

In the case of measuring stress using X-rays, the displacement error may affect the stress measurement value. Then, the relationship between the displacement error and the stress error was theoretically investigated. The size of the stress error for the displacement error of the specimen was compared to the cases of stress measurement of a single crystal and stress measurement of polycrystalline materials using the iso-inclination method.

The relationship between the setting error of a specimen and the stress error in the case of stress measurement using iso-inclination with the PSPC is described. As Fig.6(a) indicates, when a displacement error occurs between a stress measurement region and the oscillation center, the diffraction angle detected in the PSPC can be given by

$$2\theta_1 = 2\theta_0 + \frac{L\sin 2\theta_0}{\Delta\alpha\sin(\theta_0+\psi)} + \left\{R_0 + \frac{L\cos 2\theta_0}{\sin(\theta_0+\psi)}\right\}\frac{\tan\left(\frac{\sigma}{K}\sin^2\psi\right)}{\Delta\alpha}. \quad (7)$$

(L: displacement error; R_0: distance from oscillation center to the PSPC; 2α: range of the detecting angle of PSPC; K: X-ray stress constant; $2\theta_0$: the diffraction angle of the unstressed condition; σ: the actual stress; $2\theta_1$: detected diffraction angle)

$\Delta\alpha$ is given as

$$\Delta\alpha = \frac{R_0\tan\alpha}{\alpha}. \quad (8)$$

The relationship between the displacement error of a specimen and the stress error, in the case of X-ray stress measurement of the single crystal using the PSPC, was investigated. As Fig.6(b) indicates, when a displacement error occurs between a stress measurement region and the oscillation center, the diffraction angle detected in the PSPC can be given as

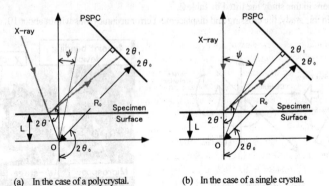

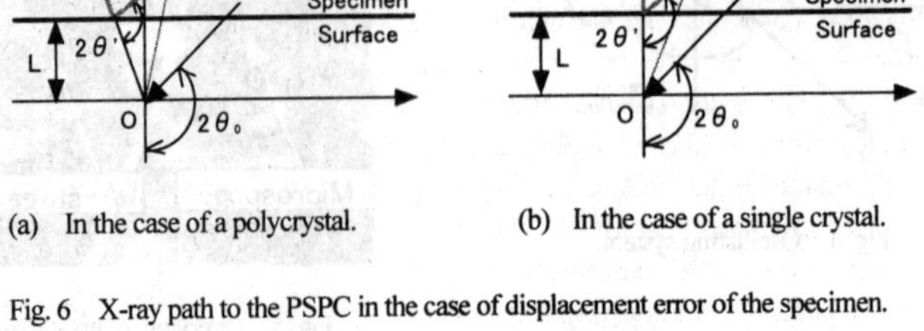

Fig. 6 X-ray path to the PSPC in the case of displacement error of the specimen.

$$2\theta_1 = 2\theta_0 + \frac{L'\sin(180 - 2\theta_0) - (R_0 - L'\cos 2\eta)\tan(2\theta_0 - 2\theta')}{\Delta\alpha}, \quad (9)$$

where $2\theta'$ is the diffraction angle when the stress is σ, and $2\theta_1$ is the detected diffraction angle. L' is given as

$$L' = \frac{L}{\cos(\psi - \eta)}, \quad (10)$$

where ψ is the angle between P_3 and L_3 in Fig.1(a), and $\Delta\alpha$ is similar to equation (8).

4.2 The relation between the setting error and the stress error

The effect of the displacement error for X-ray stress was theoretically investigated. The silicon specimen was assumed as a single crystal material and the combination of measured planes was 135, 224 and 2-24. For polycrystalline materials, the diffraction angle and the stress constant were assumed as 154 degrees and -200~-500 MPa/deg respectively. The stress error for the displacement error was compared in the three following cases.

(1) In the case of stress measurement of polycrystalline materials using the iso-inclination method.
(2) In the case of stress measurement of single crystal materials using characteristic X-rays.
(3) In the case of stress measurement of single crystal materials using synchrotron radiation.

The parameters for stress error calculation are listed in Table 3. The results are shown in Fig.7.

Table 3 Parameters for the calculation of stress error.

		Case (1)	Case (2)	Case (3)
$2\theta_0$, deg.	531family	154	154	154
	422family		121.66	154
R_0, mm		600		
2α, deg.		9.5		
σ, MPa		50		

In the case of (1), the effect of the setting error on the measured stress value was small because the stress error was under 1% for a setting error of 30 μm. In the case of (2) and (3), the stress error values were about 0.78 %/μm and 0.18 %/μm, respectively. The stress error in the case of the stress measurement of the single crystal is over fivefold that for the case of stress measurement of polycrystalline materials. Thus, the effect of the setting error on the measured stress value was large. Therefore, it is necessary to improve the specimen setting accuracy for the center of the optical system in order to improve X-ray stress measurement accuracy of single crystals. The stress error in the case of (2) is 4.3 times that in the case of (3). Therefore, if the diffraction lines of all the measured planes can be diffracted in the high-angle side using a monochromator as in the case of (3), the stress error for the displacement error becomes small, and the measurement accuracy is improved. The case of

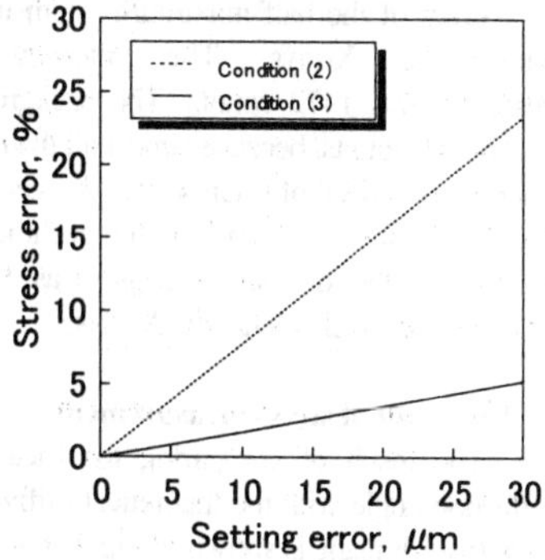

Fig. 7 Result of arranging the stress error at the displacement error.

(3) is similar to the case considered in this study; the setting error must be under about 70 μm, in order for the stress to be within 10 %.

5. Experimental results and discussion

5.1 The diffraction profile

The diffraction profiles of the 135 reflection using characteristic X-rays and synchrotron radiation are shown in Figs.8(a) and (b) respectively.

As Fig.8(a) indicates, in the case of measurement stress using characteristic X-rays, CoKα-rays were used and the irradiation area was ϕ 0.8 mm. The oscillation method is similar to the method used in this study. The measurement condition is similar to that previously reported [5]. The diffraction profile was separated with a 1 degree spacing to two peaks. This was equal to difference in the diffraction angle by CoKα_1 and CoKα_2. The intensity ratio of both diffraction profiles was 2:1, and this was equal to the intensity ratio of Kα_1 to Kα_2. Therefore, it is possible to obtain a perfect diffraction profile using the $\chi\psi$ -oscillation method.

In the case of using synchrotron radiation, monochromatic light is used, so the problem of the double Kα line did not occur and the resultant profile is a monochromatic peak, as shown in Fig.8(b). The half maximum width was about 0.12 degrees, and it was 1/5 for about 0.6 degrees of the half maximum width using characteristic X-rays. The intensity of diffraction was 1472 counts. The background was about 0 counts, because almost all the noise, which is comprised of fluorescence X-rays, was absorbed by the air. Therefore, the accuracy in determining the diffraction angle was better than when using characteristic X-rays.

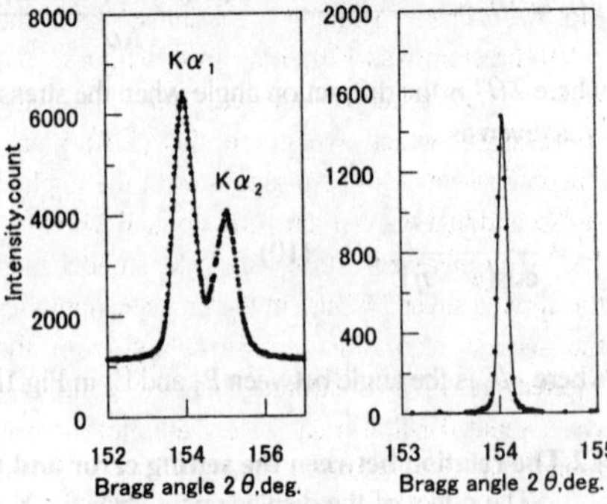

(a) Characteristic X-rays. (b) Synchrotron radiation.

Fig. 8 Comparison of 135 diffraction profile using characteristic X-ray.

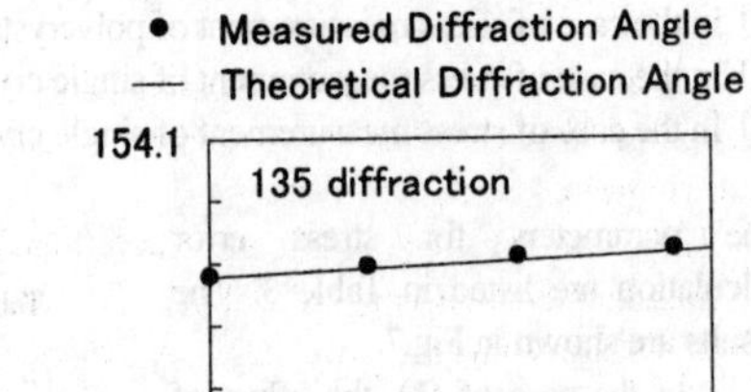

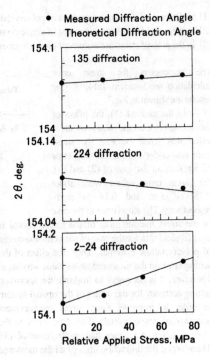

Fig. 9 Comparison of measured and theoretical diffraction angles of three different planes for each applied stress.

5.2 The result of stress measurement

The result of comparing the measured diffraction angle with the theoretical diffraction angle in each plane is shown in Fig.9. The peak shift for the applied stress in each diffraction plane agreed closely with the theoretical value.

The relationship between the measured

stress using SR and the applied stress is shown in Fig.10. The Young's modulus in the [110]-direction was 170 GPa . In this figure, σ_{11} and σ_{22} are principal stresses, and σ_{12} is the shear stress which works on the (110) plane. Theoretical value of σ_{11} agrees with the applied stress, and that of σ_{12} and σ_{22} equal 0 MPa.

The measured stress σ_{11} was smaller than the applied stress 10 MPa in the first step, but after the second step, this almost agreed with the applied stress. The measured stresses σ_{12} and σ_{22} were about 0 MPa in each step, therefore it was found that the measured stresses σ_{12} and σ_{22} agreed with the theoretical values. This comfirmed the possibility of the stress measurement of a single crystal in a ϕ50 μm region using SR.

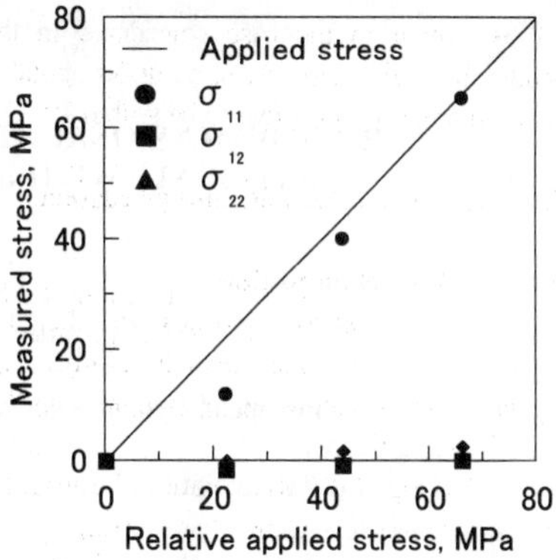

Fig. 10 Result of stress measurement using synchrotron radiation.

6. Conclusions

In this study, X-ray stress measurement in a ϕ5 0 μm region of a silicon single crystal was carried out using SR and the possibility of stress measurement was investigated. At a result, the following conclusions were obtained.

(1) The measured stress almost agreed with the theoretical stress. Therefore, the possibility of stress measurement of a single crystal in a very small region using SR was confirmed.

(2) It is possible that the wavelength can be selected using a monochromator in order to diffract in the high angle where the high-precise strain measurement is possible. Therefore, the precision of the stress measurement is improved.

(3) In the case of the stress measurement of single crystals, the setting position of the sample must be exactly calibrated unlike for the stress measurement of polycrystalline materials. For example, for the measurement conditions used in this study, if the stress error is under 10 %, the precision of the setting of a sample must be within about 70 μm.

Acknowledgments

This work has been performed under the approval of the Photon Factory Program Advisory Committee of the High–Energy Accelerator Research Organization, Japan (Proposal No. 99G037). The authors are indebted to Mr. M. Tanaka and Mr. F. Mori of the Photon Factory, for guidance on how to use the optical system, and Ms. M. Tachibana and Mr. A. Nakamura of Tokyo Metropolitan University, Tokyo, Japan, for assisting with the experiment. This work was supported financially by the Ministry of Education's Res. Grant Program (1999, Commendatory research (A), No. 11750086).

Reference

[1] T. Konaga and K. Honda, JSME, Vol. 73, pp. 972-929 (1970).
[2] T. Hanabusa and H. Fujiwara, JSMS, Vol. 33, pp. 372-377 (1984).
[3] Y. Yoshioka, T. Sasaki and M. Kuramoto, Vol. 34, No. 2, pp. 52-59 (1985).
[4] A. J. Dekker, "Solid Physics" p.351 (1968).
[5] H. Suzuki, K. Akita, H. Misawa, JSME Annual Meeting, No.99-1, Vol. 1, pp. 29-30 (1999).

THREE DIMENSIONAL STRAIN MEASUREMENTS IN BULK MATERIALS WITH HIGH SPATIAL RESOLUTION

U. Lienert*, S. Grigull*, Å. Kvick*,
R.V. Martins*, and H.F. Poulsen**

*European Synchrotron Radiation Facility, BP 220, F-38043
Grenoble Cedex, France
**Risø National Laboratory, DK-4000, Roskilde, Denmark

ABSTRACT

A novel diffraction technique utilizing focussed high energy synchrotron radiation has been developed for local structural characterization within polycrystalline bulk materials. Three dimensional gauge volumes on the micrometer scale are obtained. The technique is non destructive and fast and therefore well suited for *in-situ* measurements during thermo-mechanical processing. The method is presented and the application to the measurement of macrostrains is discussed.

INTRODUCTION

Grains or subgrain domains may be considered as fundamental units of polycrystalline bulk materials subject to the degree of plastic deformation. The length scale of these fundamental units ranges from nano- to millimeters depending on the material and processing.
Macrostresses are defined as at least one dimensional averages over fundamental units whereas microstresses describe the deviations between the fundamental units. Meaningful changes of macrostresses arise on length scales which comprise many fundamental units parallel to dimensions of averaging. However, perpendicular to the averaging directions macrostrain gradients may exist on shorter length scale than given by the fundamental units. Many features within polycrystaline materials such as inclusions, cracks, grain size, or interfaces produce inhomogenities on the micrometer scale and may introduce macro- and microstresses on this length scale. None of the established non-destructive bulk strain scanning techniques provides sufficient spatial resolution to measure such strain fields.

Recently a novel diffraction technique has been developed that provides a three dimensional spatial resolution on the micrometer scale within polycrystalline bulk materials and therefore fills a wide gap between existing techniques, Lienert *et al.* (1, 2). The technique is non destructive and provides fast data acquisition making *in-situ* studies of thermo-mechanical processing possible. This paper focusses on the measurement of macrostrains, applications to the structural characterization of single grains are reported by Juul Jensen *et al.* (3).

The micrometer length scale becomes experimentally accessible by exploitation of the unique brilliance of high energy synchrotron radiation in combination with focussing optics. Two dimensional (2D) detectors reduce the data acquisition time by orders of magnitude. In collaboration with the Materials Research Department, Risø (Denmark), a dedicated experimental station has been constructed at the Materials Science Beamline ID11 of the European Synchrotron Radiation Facility (ESRF) in Grenoble (France). The station, referred to as the 3-Dimensional X-Ray Diffraction (3DXRD) Microscope, is now open for beamtime applications from external users.

PROPERTIES OF HIGH ENERGY X-RAYS

The 3DXRD microscope operates within an energy range from about 40 to 100 keV. Important consequences arise from the small scattering angles 2Θ which are typically 0.1 to 0.2 radians. Samples are therefore generally investigated in transmission geometry. As common to diffraction techniques, the lattice strain ε is deduced from measured peak shifts $\Delta 2\Theta$ by means of the Bragg equation

$$2d \sin \Theta = \lambda \qquad (1)$$

where d is the strained lattice parameter, Θ denotes the Bragg angle and λ is the wavelength of the incoming beam. Because elastic strains are small eq. (1) is differentiated and for angle dispersive measurements (constant wavelength) one obtains

$$\varepsilon = \frac{d - d_0}{d_0} = -\frac{\Delta 2\Theta}{2 \tan \Theta} \approx -\frac{\Delta 2\Theta}{2\Theta} \quad . \qquad (2)$$

Application of eq. (2) requires the knowledge of the strain free lattice constant d_0, and appropriate elastic constants are needed to convert the strain to stress. These are common problems to diffraction techniques and are not discussed here. For practical purposes the $\tan \Theta$ in (2) may be approximated by Θ at high energies. It should be noted that peak broadening due to size effects or microstrain scales with the wavelength and does therefore not complicate the strain determination at small scattering angles. However, constraints arise from instrumental effects such as a beam divergence due to focussing or the absolute error of the measured scattering angle. These effects are discussed in subsequent sections.

The maximum sample thickness is limited by the absorption and typically a transmission of about 10 % still provides sufficient flux and signal-to-noise ratio. The absorption of X-rays is described by a linear attenuation coefficient which decreases roughly with the cube of the wavelength in the absence of absorption edges and increases with $Z^{4.5}$, Z being the atomic number. At 80 keV, 10 % transmission is obtained for 42 mm Al, 13 mm Ti or 5 mm Fe.

FOCUSSING OPTICS

Third generation high energy synchrotron facilities like the ESRF produce high energy X-rays of unprecedented brilliance. Intense beams of micrometer dimension can be prepared by broad band focussing optics. Bent Laue crystals and elliptically shaped multilayer mirrors have been developed to focus high energy X-rays, Schulze *et al.* (4) and Lienert *et al.* (5). A single element provides a line focus, and point focussing is achieved by combination of two elements. A line focus of 1.2 μm height and a point focus of 4×6 μm^2 were achieved. The focal spot size is mainly limited by shape errors of the optical elements and further progress is expected. The typical flux in the focal spot is 10^{11} to 10^{12} ph/sec.

The energy and divergence band width of the focussing optics can be tuned to a corresponding instrumental peak broadening $\Delta\Phi/(2\Theta)$ between 0.1% and 1%. Hence, the lattice strain $(d-d_0)/d_0$ can still be determined to one part in ten thousand if the peak center can be determined within 1% to 10% of the peak width.

EXPERIMENTAL SETUP

The experimental setup is sketched in Fig. 1. The main components are the focussing optics, a precision sample goniometer, an optional optical element that defines the longitudinal resolution, and a 2D detector.

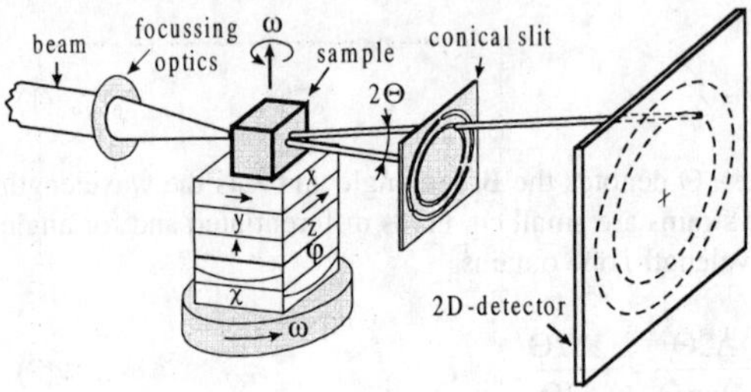

Fig.1: Sketch of the main components of the experimental setup. Distinct spots or continuous diffraction rings are observed on the 2D detector depending on the degree of the plastic deformation and the number of diffracting grains in the effective gauge volume.

The choice of an angle dispersive technique based on 2D detectors has important consequences on the design and operation of the instrument. A pixel number of 1000 by 1000 has proven to be sufficient for many cases, as the effective pixel number in a diffraction peak is increased by azimuthal integration. Spatial distortions can be corrected, but a high reproducibility is compulsory. Several complete diffraction rings can be captured simultaneously on the 2D detector due to the small scattering angles. As a consequence the biaxial strain state in a plane perpendicular to the beam and sections of pole figures may be extracted from a single exposure. Measurement of the complete strain tensor and complete texture characterization only requires sample rotation around a single axis perpendicular to the beam. Hence, only a high concentricity of the rotary table is required to retain the micrometer spatial resolution under sample rotation, as opposed to a small sphere-of-confusion of a Eulerian cradle setup. Typical exposure times of the 2D detector range from tenths of seconds to several seconds.

The actual sample goniometer is based on an air bearing rotary table to achieve the required concentricity. Positioning tables with high dynamical range, *i.e.* high resolution and high maximum speed, are being developed by a combination of incremental encoders and micro-stepping drives. This solution should enable high spatial resolution and averaging by sample oscillation. Samples up to 100 kg can be mounted (with restricted degrees of freedom). The list of auxiliaries includes a stress rig, a torsion cell, and furnaces.

STRAIN MAPPINGS TRANSVERSE TO THE BEAM

The transmission geometry sketched in Fig. 2 renders possible the direct exploitation of the transversal spatial resolution provided by the focussed beam. No further optical element is required between sample and 2D detector but in this case there is no spatial resolution along the beam. Furthermore, the position of scattering grains along the beam is coupled to the radial position of the observed diffraction spot on the 2D detector and an inhomogeneous distribution of scattering grains may be falsely interpreted as peak shifts. The magnitude of this effect is given by the ratio of the sample thickness to the sample-to-detector distance which can be increased by increasing the energy and the detector size. Within these limitations the technique provides a simple and powerful tool for one and two dimensional strain mappings.

As a case study, the depth dependent strain gradient in layered Cu/Ni structures was measured, Lienert *et al.* (5). Reported here are results on a structure consisting of two 90 μm thick electrodeposited Ni/Cu bilayers on a Cu substrate.

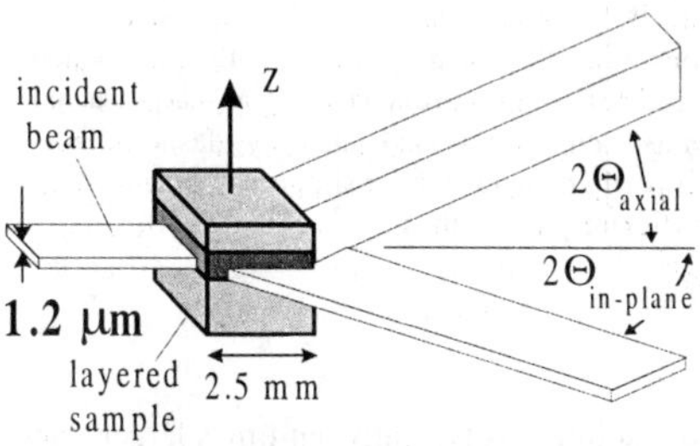

Fig. 2: Scattering geometry of the strain gradient mapping of layered structures. The samples were scanned in the z direction and the axial and in-plane diffraction angles were recorded simultaneously.

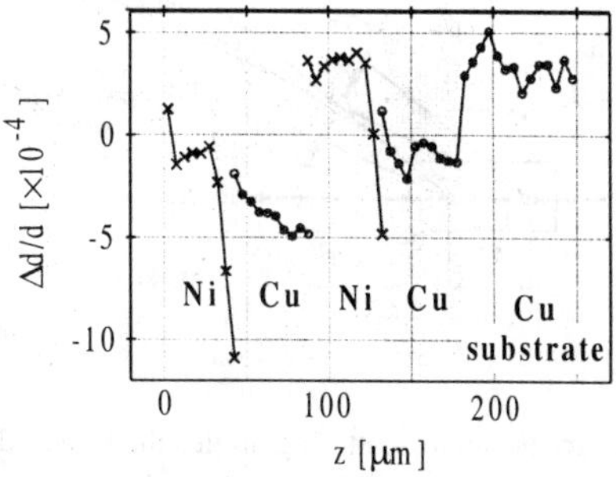

Fig. 3: Residual strain gradients in a structural Cu/Ni multilayer as a function of depth below the surface z. Plotted are the relative d-spacings of the axial 200 reflection. Note the steep gradients at the buried Ni/Cu interfaces.

90 keV X-rays were focussed to a line of 1.2 μm height. The samples were aligned with the interfaces parallel to the beam and scanned in a perpendicular direction obtaining a depth resolution of the same size as the focus height. The longitudinal resolution was not confined but the signal was averaged along the full sample thickness of 2.5 mm where the front and back surface regions contribute only a small amount. The measurement is therefore assumed to reflect true bulk properties. In this way strain gradients across the buried Cu/Ni interfaces were measured, which is not possible by other techniques. The actual strain gradient was recorded by measuring the position of the diffracted beams 2 m behind the sample. Steep strain (and texture) gradients were observed at the Cu/Ni interfaces, particularly within the Ni layers (Fig. 3). The grains within the Ni layers had sub-micron size giving a smooth signal. The strain gradients are suggested to be caused by recrystallisation processes during the electrodeposition.

For applications of the simple transmission geometry using unfocussed high energy X-rays and 2D detectors see *e.g.* Wanner & Dunand (6), Korsunsky *et al.* (7).

LONGITUDINAL SPATIAL RESOLUTION

A three dimensional gauge volume is obtained by the crossed beam technique placing a narrow triangulation slit behind the sample (Fig. 4). The gauge volume is defined by the intersection of the incident beam with the selected diffracted beams.

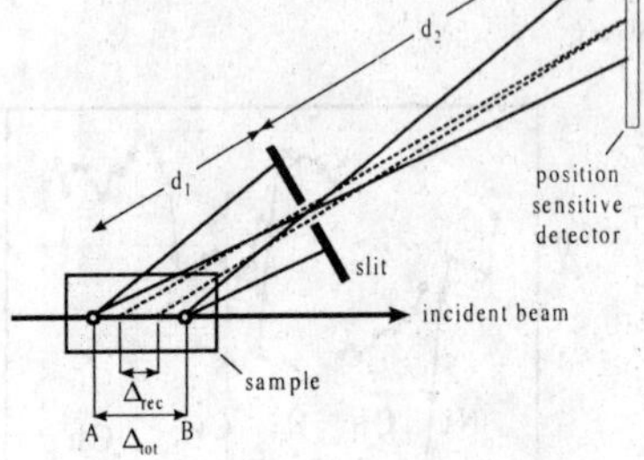

Fig. 4: Sketch of the crossed beam technique. The longitudinal gauge length parallel to the incoming beam is defined by a slit and a position sensitive detector. The finite divergence of the diffracted beams is indicated for local sample volumes A and B. Volume elements between A and B can contribute to the detected signal and constitute the total gauge length Δ_{tot} which increases with the distance d_1. The reconstructed gauge length Δ_{rec} (indicated by dashed lines) primarily depends on the slit gap as long as d_2 is sufficiently larger than d_1.

Due to the small scattering angles the longitudinal resolution is typically ten times larger than the transversal resolution. A good longitudinal resolution can therefore only be obtained for narrow transversal beam dimensions. The size of the samples or sample environment often prevent the slit from being placed close to the sample. Then, a coupling arises between the position and apparent strain of a diffracting grain. It has been demonstrated that this can be taken into account by an appropriate evaluation algorithm, Lienert *et al.* (8). The in-plane strain profile of a shot peened Al sample was measured both with the transversal and longitudinal gauge length. The shot peened Al sample consisted of two pieces of an area of 10×10 mm^2 and 5 mm thickness. Each plate was shot peened on one side and the plates were then mounted to form a 10 mm cube such that the shot peened surfaces faced each other resulting in an internal interface to cancel out both surface and absorption effects in strain measurements (9). Fig. 5 shows that the strain profiles agree apart from the expected resolution broadening.

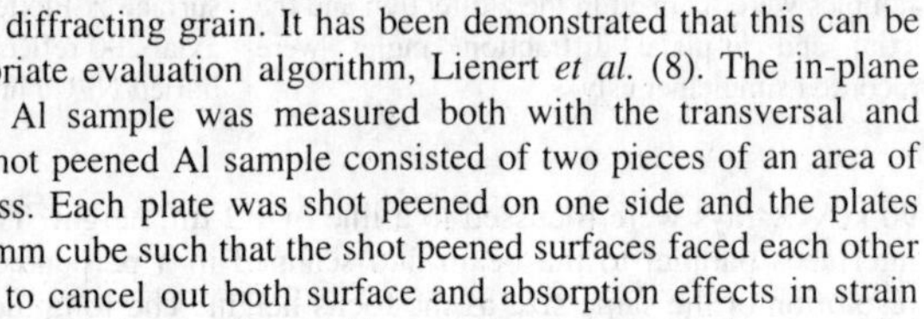

Fig. 5: In-plane 311 strain profile of the shot peened Al sample. q indicates the scattering vector. Plotted are: (a) experimental reference profile (beam parallel to shot peened surfaces)(bold), (b) experimental profile from the reconstruction technique (beam perpendicular to the shot peened surfaces) (circles), and the experimental reference profile convoluted with a Gaussian resolution function of 100 μm FWHM (thin). The insets show the scattering geometry. The shot peened regions are hatched.

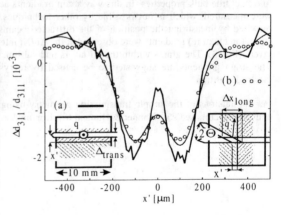

Furthermore, conical slit cells have been developed that enable the simultaneous observation of several diffraction rings from a gauge volume of about 20×20×200 μm^3, Nielsen *et al.* (10). Fig. 6 shows the diffraction pattern obtained from a local volume element within an AlSi alloy sample plastically deformed by torsion. The simple transmission geometry cannot be applied to the rotational symmetry of torsion deformation as integration along the incoming beam averages the strain profile to zero. Experimental details and strain profiles are given by Martins *et al.* (11).

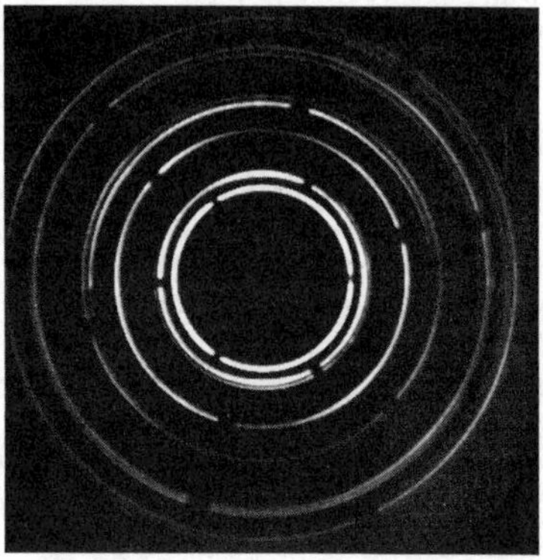

Fig. 6: Diffraction pattern as recorded on a 2D detector from a torsionally deformed AlSi alloy sample. A local scattering volume of 20×20×250 μm^3 was selected by a conical slit cell. The selected reflections are 111, 200, 220, 222, 331 and 422. The azimuthal intensity variation reflects the local texture. Distance pieces, used to assemble the conical slit, can be seen as dark segments in the rings.

Grain averaging

Finally, we address the question under what circumstances meaningful macrostrains can be measured with narrow gauge volumes. The answer will depend on the grain size, texture, geometry of the macrostrain field, nature of existing microstrains, and degree of plastic deformation within the actual sample system. A detailed discussion is beyond the scope of this paper but it seems worthwhile to give rough estimations as differences of orders of magnitude arise due to the use of 2D detectors as compared to diffraction techniques with fixed scattering vector.

As a starting point we consider a gauge volume V_g = 20×20×200 μm^3 which can be confined by a conical slit cell and averaging over a certain number of grains, lets say N > 500. The gauge volume contains at least N grains of an average grain diameter d_{av} of

$$d_{av} = \sqrt[3]{\frac{V_g}{N}} \tag{3}$$

For the chosen parameters we obtain d_{av} = 5.4 μm. We now estimate how many of these grains contribute to the diffraction pattern. Therefore, we assume random orientation, *i.e.* no texture, and introduce an average mosaic spread $\Delta\omega_{gr}$ of the grains. Furthermore, the sample might be oscillated around axes vertical the incoming beam by an amount $\Delta\omega_{osc}$. The described technique using 2D detectors allows the simultaneous observation of n = 5 full diffraction rings. The fraction of contributing grains is approximately given by

$$\frac{\Delta M}{M} = \sum_{1}^{n} \frac{m_{hkl}}{2}\left(\Delta\omega_{gr} + \Delta\omega_{osc}\right) \approx \frac{nm(\Delta\omega_{gr} + \Delta\omega_{osc})}{2} \quad (4)$$

m_{hkl} is the multiplicity factor which is approximated by its average m being 14 for the conical slit cell. A sample oscillation up to $\Delta\omega_{osc} = 0.1$ rad = 6 deg, *i.e.* of the order of the scattering angle, does not increase the transversal gauge length substantially. Even for rather perfect grains with $\Delta\omega_{gr} << \Delta\omega_{osc}$, eq. (4) gives $\Delta M/M = 3.5$ which means that several reflections are observed per grain. If point detectors are used the fraction of observed grains is typically two orders of magnitude smaller requiring a correspondingly larger gauge volume.

Texture and a triaxial microstrain state can be taken into account by measurements at different angular sample settings around an axis perpendicular to the beam. Grains with a mosaic spread larger than the above oscillation range are in general strongly plastically deformed and it is then questionable if averaging over grains is still appropriate or if averaging should take place over the smaller cell blocks.

The gauge volume may be further increased by a translational oscillation in cases where the macrostrain field is homogeneous in at least one direction. We conclude that macrostrain fields should be measurable with the given gauge volume within most materials of grain size below about 10 μm or strongly plastically deformed materials. Finally, it is noted that continuous diffraction rings are not required to obtain meaningful macrostrains. An evaluation procedure of 'spotty' diffraction rings was suggested by Wanner and Dunand (6).

CONCLUSION

A novel diffraction technique has been developed that enables local strain measurements within polycrystalline bulk materials. The technique is based on the combination of high energy synchrotron radiation, focussing optics and two dimensional detectors. Three dimensional gauge volumes on the micrometer scale are achieved at high data acquisition rates. Fast mappings of the complete strain tensor become feasible due to the simultaneous measurement of biaxial strain states. Therefore, a large gap between existing techniques is filled.

The scope of the technique is illustrated by case studies. Routine operation requires adapted instrumentation and software, which is under development. It should be noted that the synchrotron radiation source, focussing optics, and two dimensional detectors are steadily improving. Hence, further improvement of the space, time, and momentum resolution is expected.

We also anticipate the development of three dimensional imaging as demonstrated by micro-tomography. Combining diffraction and imaging on the same instrument would provide the same type of advantages as the electron microscope does, but applied to bulk materials.

ACKNOWLEDGEMENTS

The authors acknowledge the contribution from L. Margulies towards further progress of the project. Support for this work was provided by the Danish Reseach Councils, STVF and SNF (via Dansync).

---

1. Lienert U., Poulsen H.F. and Kvick Å., Proceedings of 40th AIAA Structures, Structural Dynamics, and Materials Conference (St. Louis, MO, USA), 1999, no. A99-24795, p. 2067-2075

2. Lienert U., Poulsen H.F., Martins R.V., Kvick Å., Proceedings of the ECRS-5 conference, 28-30 Sept. 1999, (Noordwijkerhout, The Netherlands), eds. Böttger A.J., Delhez R. and Mittemeijer E.J., J. Mat. Sci. Forum, to be printed

3. Juul Jensen D, Kvick Å, Lauridsen E.M., Lienert U., Margulies L., Nielsen S.F. and Poulsen H.F., to be published in the Proceedings of the MRS 1999 Fall Meeting, *Applications of synchrotron radiation techniques to materials science*, Boston, MA

4. Schulze C., Lienert U., Hanfland M., Lorenzen M., and Zontone F., J. Synchrotron Rad. **5** (1998) p. 77-81

5. Lienert U., Schulze C., Honkimäki V., Tschentscher T., Garbe S., Hignette A., Horsewel A., Lingham M., Poulsen H. F., Thomsen N. B. and Ziegler E., J. Synchrotron Rad. **5** (1998) p. 226-231

6. Wanner A. and Dunand D.C., to be published in the Proceedings of the MRS 1999 Fall Meeting, *Applications of synchrotron radiation techniques to materials science*, Boston, MA

7. Korsunsky A.M., Wells K.E. and Withers P.J., Scripta Materialia **39** (1998) p. 1705-1712

8. Lienert U., Martins R., Grigull S., Pinkerton M., Poulsen H.F., Kvick Å., to be published in the Proceedings of the MRS 1999 Fall Meeting, *Applications of synchrotron radiation techniques to materials science*, Boston, MA

9 Webster P.J., Vaughan G.B.M., Mills G. and Kang W.P., Mater. Sci. Forum vol. 278-281 (1998) p. 323

10. Nielsen S.F., Wolf A., Poulsen H.F., Ohler M., Lienert U., Owen R.A., J. of Synchrotron Rad., to be printed

11 Martins R.V., Grigull S., Lienert U., Margulies L., and Pyzalla A., these proceedings

RESIDUAL STRESS MEASUREMENT WITH HIGH-ENERGY X-RAYS AT THE ADVANCED PHOTON SOURCE

RA Winholtz[1], DR Haeffner[2], REL Green[3], R Varma[3], and D Hammon[3]
[1]*University of Missouri*
[2]**Advanced Photon Source,** ***Argonne National Laboratory***
[3]*Los Alamos National Laboratory*

ABSTRACT
Preliminary measurements with high-energy x-rays from the SRI CAT 1-ID beam line at the Advanced Photon Source show great promise for the measurement of stress and strain using diffraction. Comparisons are made with neutron measurements. Measurements of strains in a 2-mm-thick 304 stainless steel weld show that excellent strain and spatial resolutions are possible. With 200-μm slits, strain resolutions of 1×10^{-5} were achieved.

INTRODUCTION

Neutrons have been used to measure strains and stresses in the interior of engineering materials since about 1980 (1-4). More recently high-energy x-rays from third-generation synchrotron sources have been utilized in a similar way (5-8). Initial measurements of strains with high-energy x-rays from a third-generation synchrotron source were made, and they have shown great promise. Here a comparison is made between these synchrotron x-ray strain measurements and similar strain measurements using reactor neutrons.

EXPERIMENTAL PROCEDURES

Diffraction measurements were made at the Advanced Photon Source of Argonne National Laboratory with intense high-energy synchrotron radiation at the 1-ID-C station of the SRI CAT beam line. A gauge volume was established at the center of the diffractometer with crossed tungsten slits. Strains were measured in the interior of a specimen of 304 stainless steel approximately 25 by 75 mm cut from a 2.2-mm-thick sheet and containing an autogenic weld bead. The weld bead was approximately centered in the 25-mm width and filled a v-notch that had been cut into one side of the specimen along its full 75-mm length. The 531 diffraction peak was observed at approximately 26.2 °2θ. Strains were measured in a variety of directions.

The neutron measurements compared here were made at University of Missouri Research Reactor Center (MURR) on the 2XD powder diffractometer. Measurements were made on a welded cylinder of HP-9-4-30 steel with a diameter of 0.91 m and a wall thickness of 15.2 mm as reported in detail elsewhere (9, 10).

RESULTS

Table I compares the various experimental parameters for the neutron and x-ray measurements. The x-rays, notably, give a much higher strain sensitivity in the results. While the neutrons are able to penetrate a much thicker specimen, the much broader diffraction peak leads to lower strain sensitivity for the measurements, even at a higher Bragg angle. The broad peak results from the need for large divergences in the neutron optics to get sufficient flux on the sample. The x-rays, on the other hand, give a very sharp diffraction peak because of the synchrotron source. In some samples, however, difficulties can arise when insufficient diffracting grains are seen because of the extreme parallelism of the incident x-ray beam.

Another difficulty with the x-rays is the need to work at low 2θ values, giving rise to a gauge volume with one much longer dimension. Here at 26 °2θ, the gauge diagonals have a ratio of four to one. Attempts to work with penetrating x-rays at much larger angles result in a significant reduction in signal intensity due to the small atomic scattering factor compared to lower angles. Neutron scattering is not similarly constrained and roughly cubical gauge volumes are easily achieved by working at 2θ near 90°. When taking the ratio of the gauge volume diagonal to the weld thickness, a relative measure of the spatial resolution, the x-rays come out superior to the neutrons in one dimension and inferior in the other for the comparison here.

Table I. Comparison of Strain Measurements in Welds using Neutrons and High Energy Synchrotron X-rays.

Instrument	2XD Powder Diffractometer MURR	1-ID-C APS
Welded Material	HP-9-4-30 Steel	304 Stainless Steel
Weld Thickness	15 mm	2.2 mm
Slit size	3 mm	0.25 mm
Wavelength	1.76 Å	0.276 Å
$2\theta_p$	98°	26.2°
STD($2\theta_p$)	0.017°	0.00025°
FWHM	1.19°	0.03°
STD($2\theta_p$)/FWHM	0.0145	0.0083
I_{max}	95 counts	198 counts
Gage Volume Diagonals	4.6 x 4.0 mm	0.26 x 1.1 mm
Thickness/Gage Ratio	3.3 / 3.75	8.5 / 2.0
Time to collect peak	2-5 hours	6-10 minutes
Strain Sensitivity δd/d	130 με	10 με

The data collection time for the synchrotron x-rays in these studies was much shorter even though it was collected by point counting while the neutron data was collected with a position sensitive detector. Future use of area detectors for x-ray measurements should improve data collection times by an order of magnitude or more.

CONCLUSIONS

High-brilliance, hard x-rays from advanced synchrotron sources can give much better strain sensitivity and faster data collection than neutrons for diffraction stress measurements in the interior of materials on suitable systems. This is due to the extreme parallelism of the synchrotron beam and the much higher flux. The major detriments to using high-energy x-rays are the long aspect ratio of the gauge volume that results from using the low-angle diffraction peaks available and also the potential difficulties with flight paths in complex geometries. For very deep penetration depths and high atomic number elements, neutrons will have an advantage.

ACKNOWLEDGEMENTS

The use of the Advanced Photon Source was supported by the U.S. Department of Energy, Basic Energy Sciences, Office of Science, under Contract No. W-31-109-ENG-38. Los Alamos participants were supported by the U.S. Department of Energy, Enhanced Surveillance Program, under Contract No. W-7405-ENG-36.

REFERENCES

1. Prask HF, Choi CS, J Nuc Matls 136 (1984)124
2. Schmank MJ, Krawitz AD, Metall Trans 13A (1982)1069
3. Pintschovius L, Jung V, Macherauch E, Vohringer O, Mater Sci Engr 61 (1983) 43
4. Allen AJ, Hutchings MT, Windsor CG, Andreani C, Adv in Phys 34 (1985) 445
5. Daymond MR, Withers PJ, Scripta Mater 35 (1996) 1229
6. Webster PJ, Wang XD, Mills G, Mater Sci Forum 228 (1996) 227
7. Poulson HF, Garbe S, Lorentzen T, Jensen JD, Poulsen FW, Andersen NH, Frello T, Feidenhans'l R, Graafsma H, J Synchrotron Rad 4 (1997) 147
8. Reimers W, Broda M, Brusch G, Dantz D, Liss K-D, Pyzalla A, Schmackers T, Tschentscher T, J Nondestr Eval 17 (1998) 129
9. Winholtz RA, Krawitz AD, Metall Trans 26A (1995) 1287
10. Krawitz AD , Winholtz RA, Mater Sci Engr A185 (1994) 123

X-Ray Stress Measurement of Al_2O_3 Ceramics With a Two-Dimensional Detector

[1)]Yukio HIROSE, [2)]Juwen HE, [1)]Toshihiko SASAKI, [2)]Takeharu MIYANO,
[1)]Department of Materials Science and Engineering, Kanazawa University
Kakuma-machi, Kanazawa 920-1192, JAPAN
[2)]Graduate Student of Kanazawa University
Kakuma-machi, Kanazawa 920-1192, JAPAN

ABSTRACT

This paper describes a study on X-ray stress analysis using a two-dimensional X-ray detector. An Image Plate of the two-dimensional X-ray detector was adopted in this study. The Image Plate enabled us to obtain the whole X-ray diffraction pattern rapidly and accurately, and also to analyze them as digital data by a computer. In this study, X-ray stress measurement method (cos α method) using the Image Plate was applied to sintered Al_2O_3. Residual stress of this material under four point bending was measured by the cos α method. The strain sensitivity for a high stiffness material like a ceramic is not good, and a small change of the diffraction ring recorded on the Image Plate influence on the measurement accuracy. We examine experimental factors which affect the measurement accuracy. The effect of a porosity is also theoretical examined with Eshelby / Mori-Tanaka Model.

INTRODUCTION

An Image Plate (IP)[1][2] is a two-dimensional X-ray detector. A diffraction ring is two-dimensionally recorded and the whole of the diffraction ring was measured. When compared with the usual photograph method, it has high sensitivity. Moreover, because it can record several diffraction rings by a single exposure, the measurement time is shortened. Firstly, it was applied to Al_2O_3 (ceramic material). Secondly, steel (JIS S55C) [3] was also measured as a comparison. However, lower applied loads must be used for the Al_2O_3, because of its low toughness. Therefore, the examination of an X-ray stress measurement condition is necessary because of the poor strain sensitivity. When a high stiffness material is measured by X-rays, a measurement error becomes large because of the poor strain sensitivity due to a small change of the diffraction ring. In this study, X-ray stress measurement method (cos α method) using IP was applied to sintered Al_2O_3. By comparing the result of Al_2O_3 with that of S55C, a validity of stress analysis on this material was examined. The influence of various experimental factors (software oscillation angle, camera length, and diffraction angle) was discussed. The influence of pores in sintered Al_2O_3 during the elastic deformation was compared to a result of the Eshelby/Mori-Tanaka model [4]-[8].

EXPERIMENTAL PROCEDURE

Cosα Method

The X-rays stress measurement method adopting the cos α theory in the experiment is explained in this paragraph. X-ray strains ,ε_{α}, $\varepsilon_{-\alpha}$, $\varepsilon_{\pi+\alpha}$, and $\varepsilon_{\pi-\alpha}$ of a center angle α, $-\alpha$, $\pi+\alpha$ and $\pi-\alpha$ directions shown in Fig.1 is obtained from a diffraction ring by the X-ray stress measurement using IP. The parameter a_1 is defined as an equation (1) with these four X-ray strains. The eq.(1) is also shown as an eq.(2) by stresses σ_{11}- σ_{33} and σ_{13}. An eq.(3) is obtained from the eq.(2) by disregarding a stress factor of Z-direction. The stress σ_{11} is calculated from a slope of relation between a_1 and cos α.

$$a_1 = \frac{1}{2}\left[(\varepsilon_{\alpha} - \varepsilon_{\pi+\alpha}) + (\varepsilon_{-\alpha} - \varepsilon_{\pi-\alpha})\right] \tag{1}$$

$$a_1 = -\left(\frac{1+\nu}{E}\right)\left[(\sigma_{11} - \sigma_{33})\sin 2\psi_0 + 2\sigma_{13}\cos 2\psi_0\right]\sin 2\eta \cos\alpha \tag{2}$$

$$\sigma_{11} = -\left(\frac{E}{1+\nu}\right)\frac{1}{\sin 2\eta}\frac{1}{\sin 2\psi_0}\left(\frac{\partial a_1}{\partial \cos\alpha}\right) \tag{3}$$

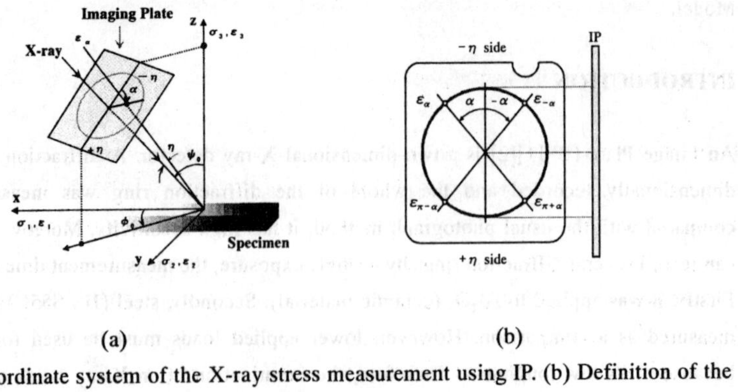

(a) (b)

Fig.1 (a) Coordinate system of the X-ray stress measurement using IP. (b) Definition of the central angle and X-ray strains used for stress calculation.

Table I Mechanical properties.

Test piece	Al_2O_3			S55C
Young's modulus E (GPa)	99.7%	98.5%	92.2%	206
	373	369	285	
Poisson's ratio	0.267	0.269	0.267	0.28

Table II Conditions of X-ray diffraction experiment.

Test piece		Al_2O_3	S55C
Characteristic X-ray		Fe-Kα	Cr-Kα
Diffraction plane		2.1.10	211
Diffraction angle, deg		152.34	156.14
Filter		Mn	V
Tube voltage, kV		30	
Tube current, mA		10	
Collimator ϕ, mm		2	
Incidence angle ψ_0, deg	Specimen	30	
	Fe-Powder	0	
Camera length, mm	Specimen	75	
	Fe-Powder	40	
Exposure time, sec	Specimen	600	180
	Fe-Powder	180	90

Specimens

The test piece used in the experiment is sintered Al_2O_3 with various porosity (3 kinds: 99.7%, 98.5%, and 92.2%). The test piece was pressured at 100MPa, and then sintered at 1273K by normal pressure. The sample dimensions were thickness 4mm, width 10mm, and length 50mm. Mechanical Young's modulus of the samples is listed in Table I. The Young's modulus and poisson's ratio of S55C was shown as a comparison.

X-Ray Stress Measurement Condition

In order to detect applied strain of the test piece, a strain gauge was affixed. The sample was bent by four-point loading (by 5 steps from 0 to 400×10^{-6}). Measurements were repeated five times. X-ray stress measurement conditions are shown in Table II.

X-ray diffraction rings were recorded on IP (IP was manufactured by Fuji Film) by a cassette holder of 5in×5in. The cassette holder was setted to an X-ray diffraction device (Rigaku MSF-2M). The X-ray diffraction data was recorded on a personal computer as a digital data and image processed by software of Rigaku corporation (R-Axis).

A diffraction ring of an iron powder is used to decide a center position of diffraction

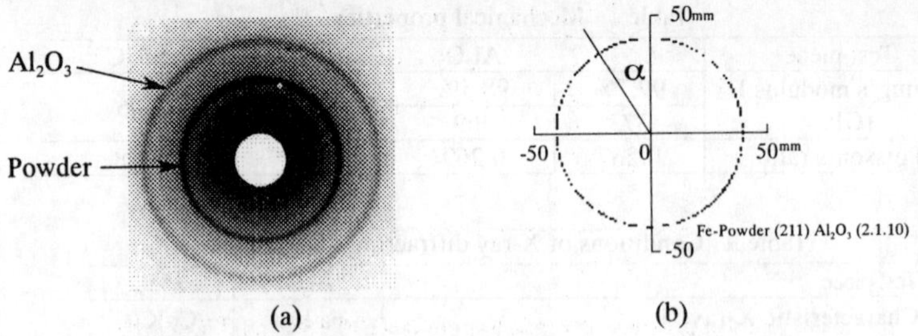

Fig.2 (a) X-ray diffraction rings of Al_2O_3 and iron powder. (b) Peak position of the diffraction ring.

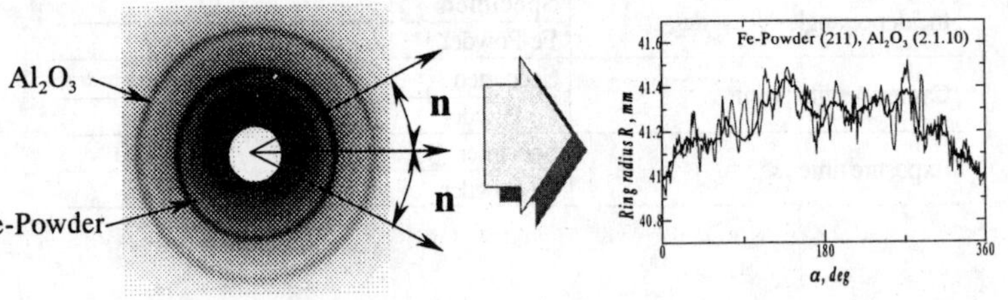

Fig.3 Principle and effect on ring radius of software oscillation.

ring. The distance between powder and specimen was set to 35mm (the distance between powder and IP was 40mm). Two diffraction rings appeared on IP as shown in Fig.2 (a). A peak position of the diffraction ring was decided by using the center position. The obtained peak position is shown in Fig.2 (b).

The Software Oscillation Method

The software oscillation improves the diffraction ring to the excellent one by using image processing. The principle and the effect on a ring radius are shown in Fig.3. The profile in the α-direction is averaged with profiles at n angle(software oscillation angle n) in forward and back. The ring radius of the diffraction ring is smoothed by this method (Fig.3: right). This method can be effectively applied to the stress analysis of Al_2O_3, and its measurement accuracy is improved. However, it is important to select an appropriate software oscillation angle.

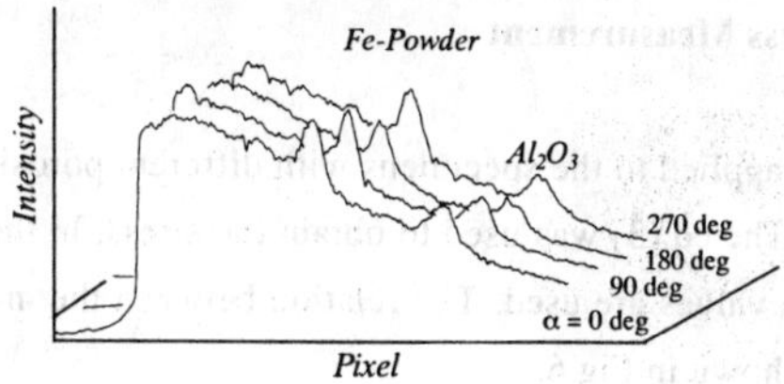

Fig.4 Diffraction profiles of central angle α=0,90,180 and 270degree.

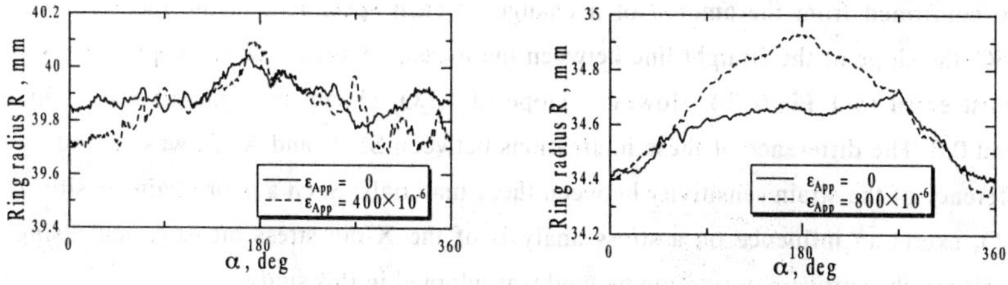

(a) (b)

Fig.5 Ring radius of whole diffraction ring at applied stress was loaded and not loaded. (a) Al_2O_3, (b) S55C

RESULTS AND DISCUSSION

X-Ray Diffraction Ring

Fig.2 (a) shows the diffraction rings of Al_2O_3 and S55C. The inside ring is reflection from an iron powder with camera length 40mm,and the outside diffraction ring from test piece with camera length 75mm.

Fig.4 shows peak profiles of α =0,90,180 and 270 degree. The left peak is the 211 diffraction of the iron powder, and the right peak is 2.1.10 diffraction of Al_2O_3 specimen. Residual stress hardly existed on the surface of the specimen because a peak position of the peak constant in any α-direction.

Fig.5 shows a ring radius of the diffraction ring in all α-directions. When we measure strains of a high stiffness material such as a ceramic, the strain sensitivity is poor and the amount of deformation of the diffraction ring is very small. Furthermore, in the measurements on the Al_2O_3, it was difficult to obtain experimental data due to weak diffraction intensity.

Result of X-Ray Stress Measurement

The bending test was applied to the specimens with different porosity, and stress σ_{11} of each load were measured. The eq.(3) was used to obtain the stress. In the equation, X-ray elastic constants of literature values are used. The relation between the measured stress by X-rays and applied stress is shown in Fig.6.

This relation was also approximated to a straight line by the least square method. The measured stress by X-ray was proportional to the applied stress. Therefore, stress measurement using the IP can be applied to ceramics. The influence of the pores could be also confirmed from the amount of a change of each specimen. In the measurement on S55C, the slope of the straight line between the measured stress and the applied stress was almost equal to 1 Fig.6 (b). However, slope of Al_2O_3 shown in Fig.6 (a) was estimated about 0.8. The difference of these inclinations between S55C and Al_2O_3 was caused by the difference of the strain sensitivity between these materials. Such a poor strain sensitivity of Al_2O_3 exerts an influence on a stress analysis of the X-ray stress measurement using IP. Therefore, the software oscillation method was adopted in this study.

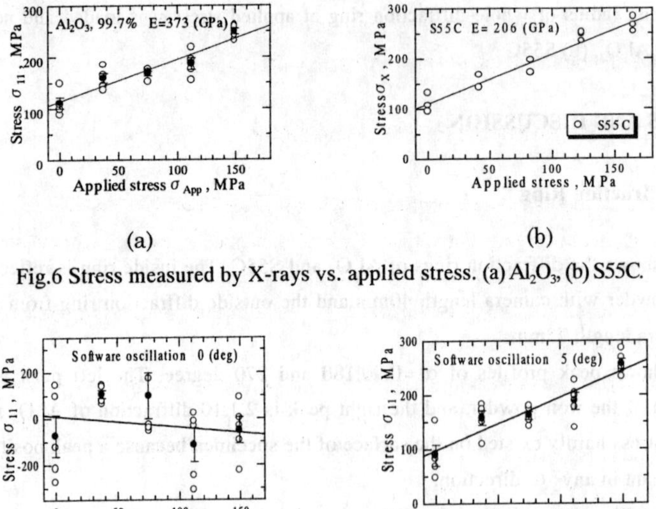

(a) (b)

Fig.6 Stress measured by X-rays vs. applied stress. (a) Al_2O_3, (b) S55C.

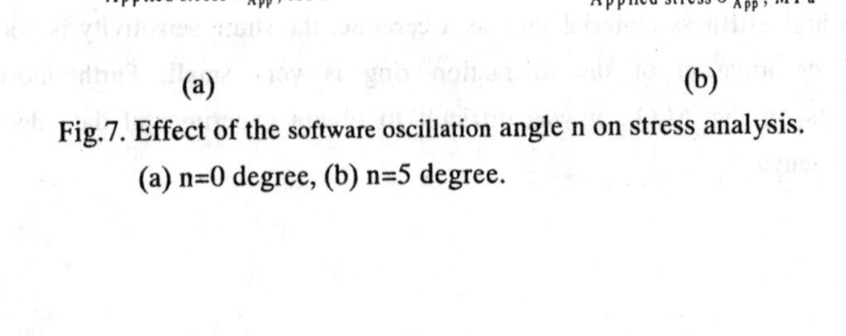

(a) (b)

Fig.7. Effect of the software oscillation angle n on stress analysis.

(a) n=0 degree, (b) n=5 degree.

Influence of Software Oscillation Angle on Stress

The stress value changes according to the software oscillation angle as shown in Fig.7. The software oscillation decreases an unevenness of the stress values. This method can smooth out measurement errors. Therefore, the software oscillation method greatly effects on the measured stress value.

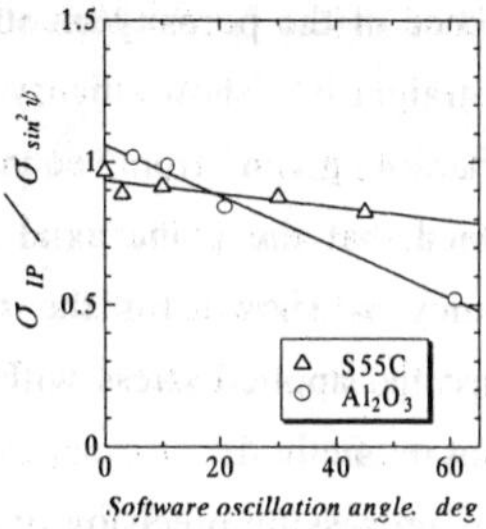

Fig.8 Effect of software oscillation angle on stress values.

Fig.8 shows a change of the measured stress against software oscillation angle n of Al_2O_3 (99.7%) and S55C. The smoothing angle greatly effects on Al_2O_3 than S55C. Lower applied strains must be used to the Al_2O_3 because of its brittleness, so the strain sensitivity of it becomes poor. Hence the distortion of diffraction ring became small. The pore rates of both Al_2O_3 and S55C are different. However, a value of $\sigma_{IP}/\sigma_{sin^2\psi}$ of Al_2O_3 and S55C linearly decreased with increasing of oscillation angle of the software oscillation. According to an approximate by the least square method, the value of $\sigma_{IP}/\sigma_{sin^2\psi}$ of both Al_2O_3 and S55C is almost equal to 1, when the software oscillation angle is 0 degree. Measurement was performed with very high precision. As the result of this experiment, the most suitable smoothing angle of software oscillation is 5 degree.

THEORETICAL EXAMINATION OF POROSITY

An influence of porosity was confirmed by using an Eshelby/Mori-Tanaka model for sintered Al_2O_3 with varying porosities. An eq.(4) stands up by the equivalent inclusion theory of Eshelby and Mori-Tanaka. In the equation, it was assumed that both phases of a matrix and inclusion (second phase) are isotropic elastic body, and second phase is a sphere.

$$\sigma_1^M = (A+2B)\sigma_1^{App} - f\Delta\tilde{\varepsilon}^P - 3B_1 f\Delta\tilde{\varepsilon}_1^P \qquad (4)$$

When the second phase is a pore, equation (5) is written as follows.

$$\sigma_{11}^\mu = (A+2B)\sigma_1^0 \qquad (5)$$

Where, A and B are;

$$A = \frac{K-\alpha(K-K^*)}{3Q}, \quad B = \frac{\mu-\beta(\mu-\mu^*)}{3R}$$

$$K = \frac{E}{3(1-2\nu)}, \quad K^* = \frac{E^*}{3(1-2\nu)}, \quad \alpha = \frac{1+\nu}{3(1-\nu)}, \quad \beta = \frac{2(4-5\nu)}{15(1-\nu)} \qquad (6)$$

The mark " * " means it is a value of the second phase. E and ν means Young's modulus and Poisson's ratio, respectively. *f* is a volume fraction of second phase. The influence of the porosity on stress is shown in Fig.9. The straight line shows theory value based on Micro-Mechanics given from equation (5). Where, we assumed that the plane axial stress state. A similar tendency is shown for the change of each stress against the applied stress with the $\sin^2\psi$ method and the $\cos\alpha$ method.

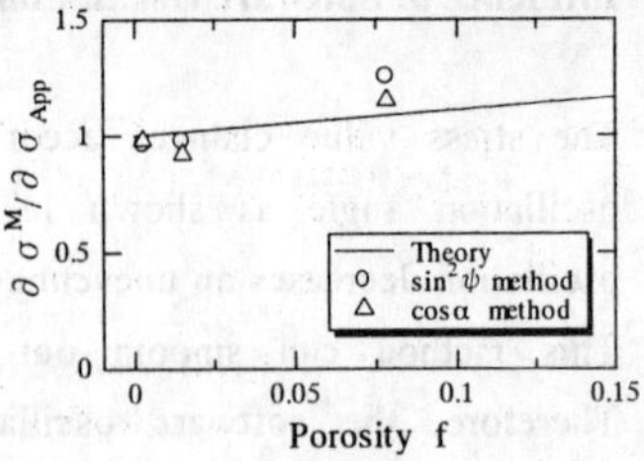

Fig.9 Relation between $\partial\sigma^M/\partial\sigma_{App}$ and volume fraction of Porosity.

The processing precision of the test piece is a little improved against the dispersion, and improvement can be expected by doing the experiment with greater applied stress to the test piece. It is judged that the measurement with IP for ceramics material is possible.

CONCLUSION

In this study, X-rays stress measurement method ($\cos\alpha$ method) using IP was applied to Al_2O_3 for the first time. The results obtained are summarized as follows;

(1) Because the measured stress by X-rays increases with an increasing of the applied stress, X-ray stress measurement using IP can be applied to Al_2O_3.

(2) The software oscillation greatly influences on the measurement. From the experiment, 5 degree of a oscillation angle of the software oscillation was the most suitable for X-ray stress analysis.

(3) The stress of Al_2O_3 changes due to porosity. This tendency of the change corresponded to the result of Eshelby/Mori-Tanaka model.

References

[1]Amemiya Y, Kamiya N, Miyahara J, Applied Physics 55 (1986) 957

[2] Amemiya Y, Kamiya N,.and Satow Y, Nucl.Instr.Meth.246A (1986) 572

[3] Sasaki T and Hirose Y, J. Soc. Mat. Sci, Japan 44 (1995) 1138-1143

[4] Eshelby, J.,D.,Proc.R.Soc.London 241A (1957) 376

[5] Mori T and Tanaka K, Acta. Met.21 (1973) 571

[6] Sasaki T,Rin Z and Hirose Y, Trans. Japan Soc. Mech. Eng.63 (1997)370

[7] Lin S, Yang C, Mura T and Iwakura T, Int.J.Solids Struct.29-14/15 (1992) 1859

[8] Sasaki T, Rin Z and Hirose Y, Trans. Japan Soc. Mech. Eng.62 (1996) 2741

NEUTRON STRAIN SCANNING IN BIMETALLIC TUBES: EXPERIMENTAL AND MONTE CARLO SIMULATION RESULTS

CR Borlado, FJ Mompeán
Instituto de Ciencia de Materiales de Madrid, CSIC,
Campus de Cantoblanco, ES-28049 Madrid, Spain

Ru Lin Peng
Studsvik Neutron Research Laboratory, University of Uppsala,
S-61182 Nyköping, Sweden

J Izquierdo
IBERDROLA, S.A., Hermosilla, 2, ES-28001 Madrid, Spain

ABSTRACT

Neutron diffraction measurements have been carried out on curved components fabricated from bimetallic tubes by cold working. The tubes consist of two layers (an outer one of austenitic steel and an inner one of ferritic steel) with a total wall thickness of 6 mm. Both layers have been scanned at different positions, throughout the material thickness and for three orientations of the component axes with respect to the neutron momentum transfer vector. Due to the complicated geometry of the problem, Bragg peak data have been corrected for non-uniform illumination of gauge volume, neutron absorption and instrumental effects by means of a Monte Carlo simulation which incorporates details of the diffractometer and a realistic model of the specimen. We report on estimations of the stress tensor components as well as on mosaic size and microstress obtained by deconvolution of experimental Bragg peaks using simulated resolution functions.

INTRODUCTION

One of the outstanding features of neutron strain scanning (NSS) is the fact that fabricated components can be explored non-destructively since in most cases the weak neutron-nucleus interaction allows for larger values of beam penetration than electromagnetic probes (1,2). In this paper we apply NSS to the study of stress fields in bimetallic tubes, focusing our attention in the problem of characterizing the stress distribution along cross-sections of both straight and curved parts of U-shaped bends which have been manufactured from the original bimetallic tubes by cold working techniques. After heat treatment, these composite components are used in heat exchangers of oil-burning power plants and interest in the knowledge of residual stress arises from the particular hard conditions in which they operate which bring about stress-induced corrosion and fatigue due to heavy thermal cycling. From a methodological point of view the main ingredients of the problem in our as-manufactured component are a high degree of plastic deformation, a buried but sharply defined interface and a realistic specimen geometry. The study is intended as a first step, which should be followed by the study of the same component once it has been subject to conditioning heat treatment. Similar studies in composite tubes obtained by different fabrication procedures have appeared recently in the literature (3,4).

MATERIALS AND SPECIMENS

The bimetallic tubes were manufactured by Tubacex SA, Alava (Spain) following their patented procedure starting from ASTM A213 T 11 ferritic grade and ASTM A213 TP 347 H austenitic grade steels. The final tubes are obtained by cold rolling to an external diameter of 50.8 mm and 6 mm of minimum wall thickness, corresponding to an internal layer of T 11 steel (thickness: 4 mm) and an outer layer of the TP 347 H material (thickness: 2 mm). Subsequently, they are subject to heat treating cycles to recondition both steels to the specifications of the ASTM A213 standard, straightened and inspected by ultrasound and induced currents to verify that they are free of defects and with adequate bonding between the two steel layers. Metallographic inspection revealed that the interface between the two steel layers is sharp in the micrometer lenght scale. The chemical composition of the materials studied in this paper is shown in Table I. The specimen studied in this work has been produced by Babcok & Wilcox Española, Galindo (Spain) from a batch of tubes manufactured as detailed above. Bending to an U shape has been achieved by cold working and the resulting component has not been subject to any subsequent heat treatment before the neutron diffraction measurements. Figure 1 shows a schematic representation of the specimen. The actual specimen shows thickness decrease near position A (extrados) and increase near position B (intrados) and an estimated ellipticity of nearly 5% through the AB cross section, which is reduced by 15 % with respect to the straight section of the tube. Wide-range neutron diffraction and Rietveld analysis on a sample of the austenitic layer revealed the presence of nearly 5% in volume of a phase whose crystallographic structure is compatible with b.c. tetragonal α'–martensite. X-ray diffraction measurements on the external surface of the austenitic layer revealed strong Bragg peaks compatible with α'–martensite and austenite (in a 4:1 ratio) which disappeared upon heat-treatment of the sample, giving rise to a powder profile corresponding almost enterely to austenite.

NEUTRON STRAIN SCANNING EXPERIMENTS

Neutron diffraction measurements were carried out at The Studsvik Neutron Research Laboratory, Nyköping (Sweden) on the REST dedicated diffractometer (nominal neutron wavelength λ = 1.76 Å from a Si single crystal curved monochromator). The specimen was mounted on an XYZ table in such a way as to ensure that, for every measurement position, the nominal neutron momentum transfer vector was parallel to one of the local radial (r), hoop (h), or axial (t) directions. Typically, the gauge volume was 3 mm^3 and its linear dimensions were chosen so that when it was scanned through the tube wall thickness (in the local radial direction), the spatial resolution along the local radial direction was maximized. The ferritic T11 steel (inner) layer was probed by means of the (211) reflection from b.c.c. α-Fe; the austenitic steel (outer) layer was probed by either the (220) or (311) reflections from f.c.c. γ-Fe. The various interfaces (air-austenite, austenite-ferrite and ferrite-air) for each scan across the tube cross-sections were located by means of scanning the specimen mounted on the XYZ table through the neutron beam and integrating the signal observed in the range of 2θ values covered by REST position sensitive detector (PSD). Data from each measurement were analyzed by non-linear least squares (Gaussian lineshape) to extract the corresponding experimental value of background level, peak center (2θ), peak intensity and Bragg peak full-width-at-half-maximum.

NSS relies on the comparison of the observed (2θ) values with those observed under the closest possible experimental conditions from a "stress-free" sample, $(2\theta)_0$. Then, the well known formula

$$\varepsilon = -\Delta\theta \cot\theta \qquad [1]$$

where $2\Delta\theta = (2\theta) - (2\theta)_0$, can be applied to obtain ε, the lattice strain in the direction of neutron momentum transfer vector at the measurement position. A usually followed procedure to obtain reference "stress-free" values consists of illuminating with the neutron beam a fairly large region of the specimen and relying on the assumption that macrostresses will be cancelled over the resulting large gauge volume. Unfortunately, this procedure may introduce errors due to apparent Bragg peak shifts related to the different wavelength composition around the nominal value λ which is selected when using wider slits. We followed an alternative procedure and obtained from the straight part of the bent tube an annular specimen from which two small tile-shaped samples (length 10 mm) were detached corresponding respectively to the austenitic and ferritic steels. These reference specimens were measured along the three directions (radial, hoop and axial) in their central positions and using the same sets of Bragg reflections and slits as employed in the strain scanning measurements.

The whole set of NSS measurements reported on this paper extended over two reactor cycles (18 days each). Changes in the reactor core fuel arrangement between reactor cycles may bring about changes in the wavelength of the neutrons impinging on the sample. Therefore measurements were taken periodically on standard iron powder samples using the same instrumental set-ups as employed in the NSS measurements to monitor possible significant changes in the incident neutron spectrum.

Neutron beam time availability precludes an extensive measurement of strains along directions intermediate to those chosen as characteristic of our specimen (radial, hoop and axial as indicated in Fig. 1 in our case). This type of measurements was however performed at a single central radial location within the austenitic layer at position A, yielding values for the off-diagonal components of the strain tensor, from which the stress tensor was diagonalized and the principal (local) directions were obtained.

MONTE CARLO SIMULATIONS

In NSS experiments, a combination of experimental effects both related to the instrument and to the sample can contribute to effective Bragg shifts which are not caused by the stress fields. Among these "spurious" effects, non-uniformly illuminated gauge volumes, different neutron absorption and scattering integrated cross-sections for different paths between the scattering centres and the detectors and the spatial dependence within the incident beam of the neutron wavelengths can cause Bragg peak shifts which are comparable in magnitude from those expected from stress fields in most materials (5). For simple specimen geometries, and under carefully chosen instrumental settings, these effects can be modeled and corrected for analytically. However, under more general conditions the analytical approach is not a feasible solution.

To circumvent this problem, we have developed a Monte Carlo code which incorporates the instrumental details along the neutron paths from the reactor tube through monochromator, incident beam slits, sample, scattered beam slits and PSD. Our code evolves from the MSCAT code (6) widely used in the neutron scattering community to simulate multiple-scattering effects. A key point in the use of Monte Carlo codes is the validation of the models incorporated, specially for the monochromator section. For the present work, such validation has been done by extensive testing and comparison with experimental data from clear-cut cases. In particular, the code has been used to simulate successfully the results from the diffractometer resolution tests. With our code, it is possible to simulate the NSS experiments carried out on the bimetallic tube by scanning gauge volumes in the appropriate transmission or reflection geometries through the radial cross section of the specimen. While the experimental data correspond to situations where stress fields and non-ideal coherence length effects are present, the data from the simulations for this particular study case have been obtained assuming single nuclear scattering, no stress fields and sub-resolution Bragg peak widths. Therefore all the variations with respect to the nominal input Bragg angle observed in the simulation results should be considered as arising from experimental effects other than stress fields. Additionally, under these conditions, the lineshape obtained from the simulations is also a very good approximation to the instrumental resolution and we have exploited these results to obtain estimates of the physical mechanisms causing broadening of the Bragg peaks as discussed below.

STRAIN DATA CORRECTION, STRESS AND PRINCIPAL AXES

Under the proviso that Monte Carlo simulation provides an adequate description of the experimental set-up, it is possible to accept that the differences between the simulated Bragg peak positions and the simulation nominal (input) values are the corrections that should be subtracted from the corresponding experimental values to obtain data corrected for 'spurious' experimental effects. Thus, we have corrected our experimental data for positions A, B and D. By using the "stress-free" reference values, and by means of Reuss model (using literature values for the elastic modulus and the Poisson ratio (7)) we have converted the strain values to stresses. The results are shown in Fig. 2.

As previously mentioned the diagonal stress tensor has been determined for the A position in a gauge volume well centered in the austenite layer. The principal stresses are (±15 MPa): -71 MPa (radial direction), 386 MPa (hoop+axial mixed direction) and 260 MPa (axial+hoop mixed direction). The mixed directions are determined by a 15 ° rotation around the retained radial axis. For comparison, the ASTM A213 values for TP 347H grade are 205 MPa for yield strength and 515 MPa for tensile strength.

LINESHAPE ANALYSIS

Extracting information on the relative contributions from mosaic size (coherence domain size) and microstress to the resolution-corrected Bragg peak widths is an ill-posed problem when the only available experimental information is a single diffraction order from a given set of planes. Unfortunately, this situation is the most commonly encounterd one in reactor based dedicated diffractometers. We have explored the possibility to carry out such analysis following the lines suggested by Nandi et al. (8). The initial step of obtaining a set of Fourier expansion coefficients and correcting for the instrumental resolution has been performed by applying Stokes' formulae using FFT expansions for the experimental data and the Monte Carlo simulation results, the latter accounting for most experimental points for the instrumental resolution effects only. A typical set of FFT cosine coefficients, A_n, n=0,1,2,... is shown in Figure 3, together with the corresponding experimental and simulation data. The lower order in the Fourier expansion (n=1,2,3) coefficients are used to obtain an estimate of the mosaic size, M, by means of the initial slope method. Once this magnitude (shown in Figure 4 for our experimental points) is obtained, it can be used to compute in turn an estimate of the r.m.s. microstrain, $<\varepsilon^2>^{1/2}$. For this purpose we have chosen to apply the partition between size (S) and microstrain (ε) broadening effects reflected in the expression:

$$A_n = A_n^{(S)} A_n^{(\varepsilon)} \qquad [2]$$

for the harmonic order, n, corresponding to a mosaic size M/2. Figure 4 shows accordingly the corresponding estimates for $<\varepsilon^2>^{1/2}{}_{M/2}$.

In the absence of experimental data at different diffraction orders which would enable us to verify the correctness of the laws assumed to hold for the $A_n^{(S)}$ and $A_n^{(\varepsilon)}$ coefficients, our estimates for M and $<\varepsilon^2>^{1/2}{}_{M/2}$ should be regarded merely as a basis for a relative comparison between different regions of the specimen rather than as an accurate representation of absolute values.

DISCUSSION AND FURTHER WORK

From Figure 2, it is apparent that our results for stress at the straight part of the tube (position D) show substantial deviations from elastic theory predictions in thick walled bimetallic cylinders since both radial and hoop components exhibit the same overall compressive behaviour. At the austenite-ferrite interface, radial and hoop stress components show continuity within experimental error bars. This situation may reflect a local distortion from cylindrical symmetry induced by the cold working procedure. An additional deviation is observed in the austenitic layer results for positions A and B. While the axial component in position A (extrados) seems to exhibit radial profiles in agreement with the expected springback effect lowering the stresses near the outer surface, the counteracting effect at position B (intrados) is not observed. This position shows good continuity in the radial stress profile for austenite and ferrite, but marked discontinuities in the other two components.

The large amount of plastic deformation brought about by the cold-working procedure is evidenced by a comparison of the domain size and r.m.s. microstrain results (see Figure 4) obtained in A and B positions with respect to the original tube (position D). The domain sizes have been decreased by a factor of 1.5 while increasing the r.m.s. microstrain width parameter by at least a factor of 2 in most points. Therefore, position A reveals itself, in good agreement with standard knowledge, as the potentially more susceptible area for component life-limiting corrosion effects to develop. The outer layers of the austenitic steel seem to be affected by martensite formation revealed in the wide-range diffraction surveys as suggested by the rise observed for most r.m.s. microstrain near the outer tube surface.

To fully assess consistency in our experimental results, a further necessary step in our work would be to incorporate finite element calculation results for this realistic case to our Monte Carlo scattering kernnel. This approach should convert our simulation tool into a predictive one, specially helpful in optimizing the NSS experiment design stage.

ACKNOWLEDGEMENTS

CRB and FJM are grateful to Luis Mompeán for continuous support and many fruitful discussions. Thanks are also due to Mikhail Butman, Martin Grönross and Lars-Erik Karlsson for excellent technical assistance at NFL. CRB was recipient of a CSIC/IBERDROLA S.A. Fellowship. This work was supported by Spanish CICyT Grant No. 2FD97-0301-C02-01 (MAT) and by the European Union TMR-LIP at NFL-Studsvik.

REFERENCES

1. Noyan IC and Cohen JB, 'Residual Stress', Springer Verlag (New York), 1987

2. Hutchings MT and Windsor CG, in Sköld K, and Price DL, (Eds.), 'Methods of Experimental Physics, Volume 23 C: Neutron Scattering', Academic Press (New York), 1986
3. Wang XL, Payzant EA, Taljat B, Hubbard CR, Keisler JR, Jirinec J, Mater Sci Eng A 232 (1997) 31
4. Wang XL, Hoffmann CM, Hsueh CH, Sarma G, Hubbard CR, Appl Phys Lett 75, (1999) 3294
5. Webster PJ, Mills G, Wang XD, Kang, WP, Holden TM: J of Neutron Research 3 (1996) 223
6. Copley JRD, Verkerk P, van Well AA, Fredrikze H: Computer Physics Reports 40 (1986) 337
7. Smithells CJ, 'Metals Reference Book, 5th edition', Butterworths (London), 1976
8. Nandi RK, Kuo HK, Schlosberg W, Wissler G, Cohen JB, Crist Jr. B, J of Applied Cryst 17, (1984) 22

Table I

Chemical composition (weight %) and tensile requirements of steels used in this work

Ferritic grade T11

(Tensile Strength= 415 MPa, Yield Strength= 205 MPa)

C	Mn	Si	P	S	Cr	Mo	Ni
0.01	0.56	0.56	0.015	0.003	1.03	0.46	0.13

Austenitic grade TP347H

(Tensile Strength= 515 MPa, Yield Strength= 205 MPa)

C	Mn	Si	P	S	Cr	Mo	Ni	Nb+Ta
0.043	1.01	0.53	0.033	0.001	17.35	0.33	9.20	0.53

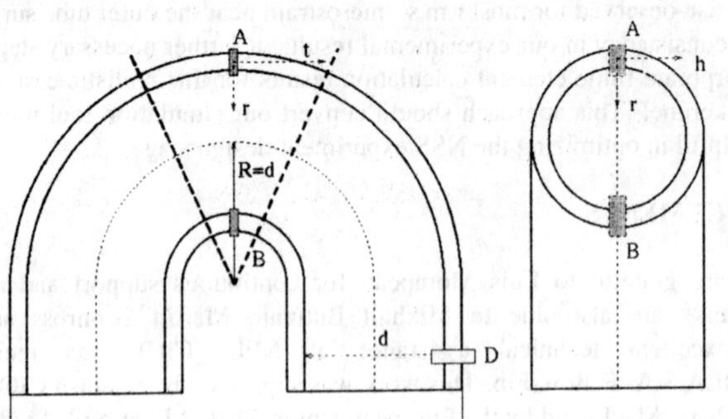

Fig. 1. Schematic of specimen used in this study showing measurement Positions (A, B, D) and orientations (r,t,h).

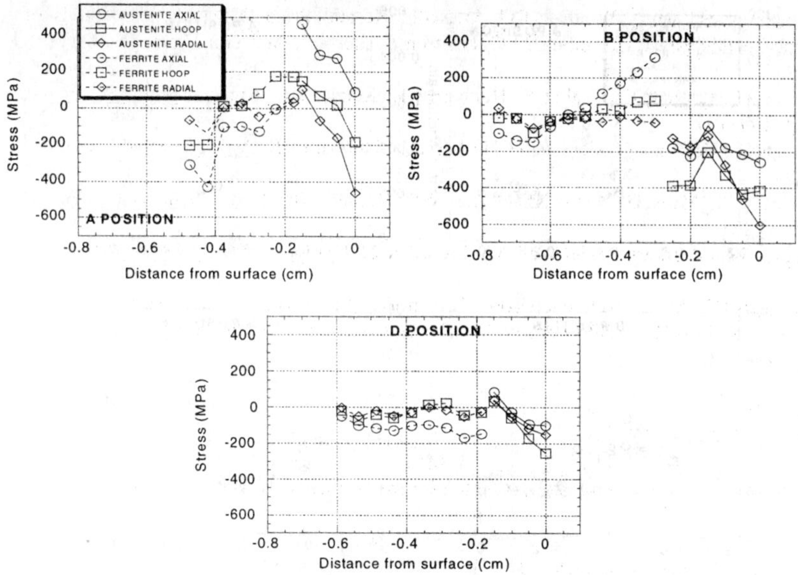

Figure 2. Residual stress components at measured positions and orientations (see Figure 1). The dotted lines joint experimental points in the ferrite layer and the continuous line in the austenitic layer. Distances from surface are measured from the external surface of the tube.

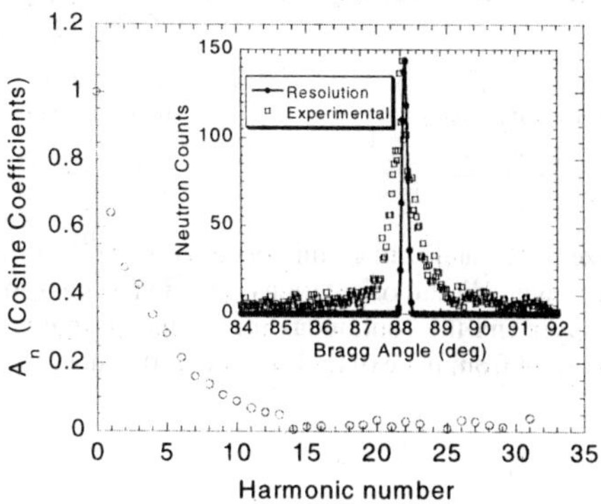

Figure 3. A_n cosine Fourier expansion coefficients for a typical radial orientation at A position in austenite. The inset shows the corresponding experimental data and simulated resolution.

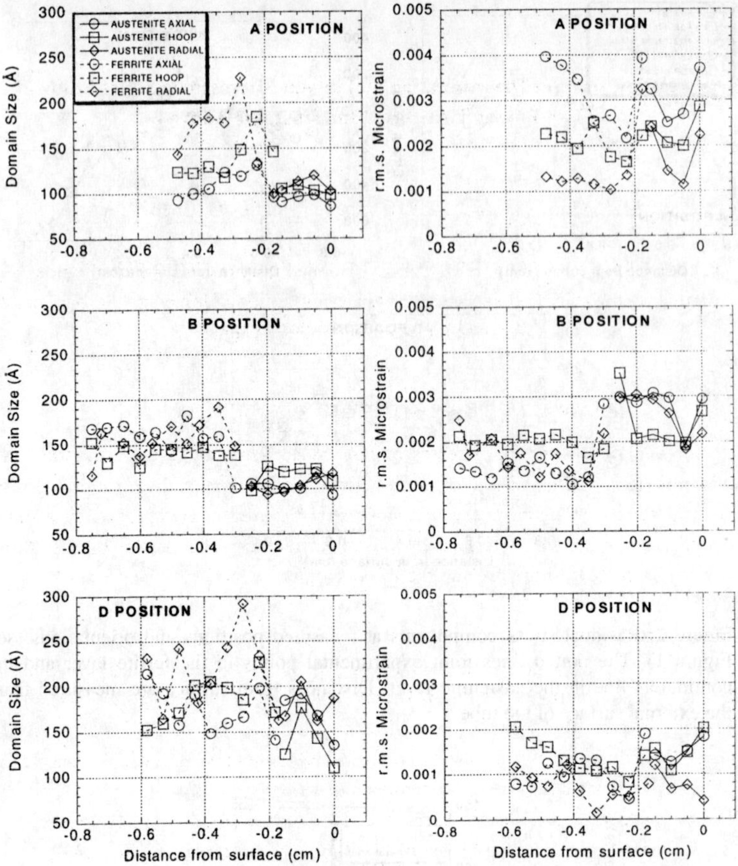

Fig. 4. Domain sizes, M, and r.m.s. microstrains $<\varepsilon^2>^{1/2}{}_{M/2}$ for the different positions (A,B,D, see Figure 1) and orientations. The dotted lines joint experimental points in the ferrite layer and the continuous line in the austenitic layer. Distances from surface are measured from the external surface of the tube.

X-ray Elastic Constant Determination and in-situ Microscopic Stress Study of Two Phases TiAl-Based Intermetallic Alloy

F. A. Guo [(1)&(2)], V. Ji [(1)], Y. G. Zhang [(2)] and C. Q. Chen [(2)]

(1) LM3 ESA CNRS 8006, ENSAM, 151 Bd. de l'Hôpital 75013 Paris France
(2) Department of Materials Science and Engineering, Beijing University Aeronautics & Astronautics, Beijing 100083 China

Abstract: To evaluate the residual stresses in TiAl-based alloys by X-ray diffraction, X-ray elastic constants (REC) of a γ-TiAl alloy were determined experimentally. From these results, the mechanical state of a given phase in a duplex TiAl-based alloy, induced by a uniaxial tensile loading, has been characterized by X-ray diffraction. The reason of the different distribution between the given phase and the macroscopic one has been discussed.

1. INSTRUCTION

The TiAl intermetallic compound has low density, excellent high temperature strength, high specific stiffness and good oxidation resistance compared to the conventional high-temperature alloys[1], and therefore it is expected to be potential light weight heat-resistant material. Extensive studies on the microstructures, plasticity and effects of alloying elements on mechanical properties have been carried out worldwide. However, there are still road-blocks to successful use of two-phase TiAl alloys in structural applications, and one significant barrier is that their room temperature tensile ductility is limited to 2%-3%[2]. It is well known that residual stresses play a role in determining the fracture toughness of materials. So it is necessary to study the distribution and change of the residual stresses in TiAl-based alloys.

The TiAl alloys exhibit generally a two-phase microstructure composed of γ-TiAl and a small fraction of α_2-Ti_3Al phase. Owing to the tetragonal crystal structure of γ phase and the hexagonal crystal structure of α_2 phase, there is a lattice misfit between them. Moreover, slip systems and mobility of dislocations in these two phases are highly different, and mechanical properties of the alloy are in high anisotropy. Therefore, it is expected that deformation is inhomogeneous, and deformation incompatibility across the lamellar interfaces and grain boundaries may occur. Local accumulation and non-uniform distribution of internal strain and stresses introduced by all these effects may relate to brittle fracture behavior, which is a main barrier for the application of the alloys.

The X-ray diffraction stress evaluation method is a non-destructive experimental technique well adapted to evaluate the residual stresses in the metallic materials. Thus, it can be used to study the distribution and change of the residual stresses in TiAl-based alloys. In multiphase materials, however, X-ray diffraction method only allows to measure the mechanical state of one particular phase because the elastic constants of the studied phase are different from that of the aggregate. Therefore, it is necessary to know the elastic constants of the studied phases before measuring the residual stresses of the phases by X-ray diffraction. For a two-phase material. the diffraction method is almost the only method to determine the radiocrystallographic elastic constants (REC) of each phase in-situ. Until now, there is poor information about two-phase TiAl alloy's X-ray elastic constants.

In this paper, a Ti-47%Al-2%Cr-2%Nb alloy has been studied: Fine duplex microstructures with different volume fractions of lamellar grains (consisting of lath colonies of γ-TiAl and α_2-Ti_3Al) and equiaxed γ were obtained. The REC of a given phase were determined in-situ by X-ray diffraction method during a uniaxial tensile test. Volume fractions of two phases were measured from X-ray diffraction scanning spectrum. The phase stresses of the given phase and their distribution were determined using X-ray diffraction technique. The relations between the stresses and the strain, and the peak broadening evaluation and deformation were discussed.

2.EXPERIMENT

A two-phase gamma TiAl alloy with the nominal composition of Ti-47Al-2Cr-2Nb (at.%) was prepared into an ingot by skull melting and casting. The bulk composition of this ingot was determined to be Ti-47.2Al-2.1Cr-1.96Nb.The ingot was hot isostatically pressed, then forged isothermally at 1180°C to a pancake. The samples were cut from the pancake and placed in silica tubes. These tubes were evacuated, filled with argon and subsequently sealed for heat treatments. In order to obtain the duplex microstructures with different volume fractions of lamellar grains and equiaxed γ, different temperatures and annealing times were chosen in γ+ α field, followed by controlled cooling.

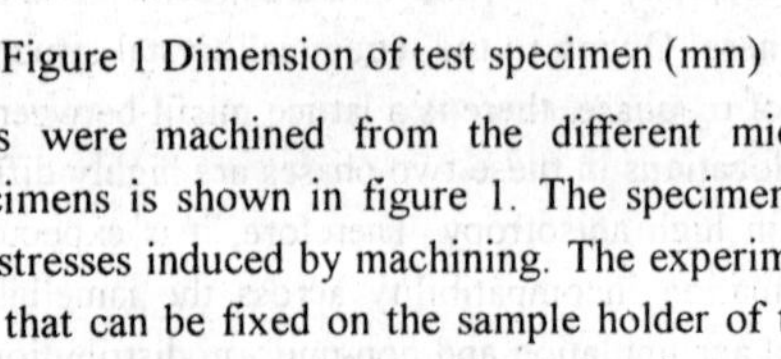

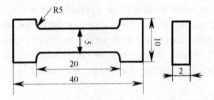

Figure 1 Dimension of test specimen (mm)

The test specimens were machined from the different microstructure samples. The dimension of the specimens is shown in figure 1. The specimens were electro-polished in order to eliminate the stresses induced by machining. The experiments were conducted using a small tensile device that can be fixed on the sample holder of the diffractometer. A strain gage was applied for the measurement of the strain during the test. A load cell that allows the measurements of the stresses applied on the specimen was used. The stresses in γ phase were evaluated by X-ray diffraction with the equipment micro-CGR during step-by-step uniaxial loading. For each step of these mechanical tests, the specimen was strained to a fixed load that remained constant during the X-ray measurements. Thus we know the macroscopic and X-ray stresses of the specimen. Ti-Kα radiation under 25 mA and 25 kV was used for {202} planes of γ phase. The X-ray beam was collimated giving ϕ3mm irradiated spot on the specimen. X-ray diffraction stress analysis has been carried out in loading direction with 15 ψ angles. Classic $\sin^2\psi$ method was used for stress determination. The obtained precision on stress analysis and peak with values are less than 50MPa and 0.3 degrees respectively. The macroscopic tensile experiments were conducted by MTS mechanical property testing machine.

3.RESULTS AND DISCUSSION

3.1 The microstructures and the volume fractions of γ and α_2

The microstructures of the Ti-47Al-2Cr-2Nb alloy used in the present study are shown in figure 2. It can be seen that the microstructures of the four studied specimens are the fine duplex microstructures consisted of equiaxed γ grains and lath colonies ($\gamma+\alpha_2$). The volume fractions of γ and α_2 were measured by X-ray diffraction scanning. The volume fractions of equiaxed γ and lamellar grains, and the volume fractions of γ and α_2 are listed in table Ⅰ.

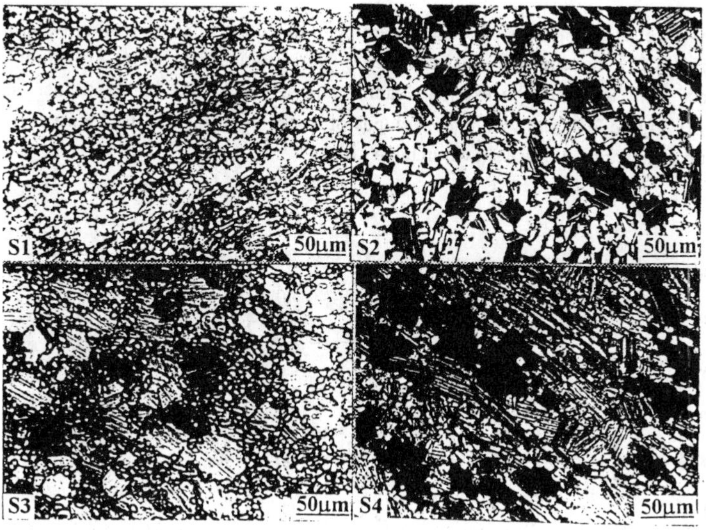

Figure 2 Microstructure of the specimens. S1: 20% lamellar grains + 80% equiaxed γ grains. S2: 50% lamellar grains + 50% equiaxed γ grains. S3: 70% lamellar grains + 30% equiaxed γ grains. S4: 90% lamellar grains + 10% equiaxed γ grains.

It can be seen in table Ⅰ that the volume fractions of α_2 phase varied with the different heat treatment conditions. This is in good agreement with that obtained by Kim using other methods[3]. It should be noted that the volume fraction of the phase α_2 in four studied specimens is too small for evaluating the stresses in the α_2 by X-ray diffraction, because only very low diffracted intensities are obtained, and it is too small to give a reliable diffraction peak. Usually, the necessary volume fraction of a phase for X-ray diffraction stress measurement is no less than 20%[4]. So only the REC and the stresses in the main phase γ have been measured experimentally.

Table I The volume fractions of γ and α_2 analyzed by XRD spectrum, and the volume fractions of equiaxed γ and lamellar grains determined by metallographic imaging

Specimen	S1	S2	S3	S4
volume fraction of equiaxed γ grain	80%	50%	30%	10%
volume fraction of lamellar grain	20%	50%	70%	90%
volume fraction of γ	94.2%	94%	92.9%	91.8%
volume fraction of α_2	5.8%	6%	7.1%	8.2%

3.2 Determination of X-ray elastic constants of phase γ

The X-ray elastic constants of phase γ were determined by uniaxial loading experiments as mentioned in [5]. Specimen 2 and specimen 3 were used for the REC estimation and the confidence limit is 78%. The external loading stresses vs. lattice plane strain is shown in figure 3(a). Figure 3(b) shows $\sin^2\psi$ vs. slopes of the straight lines in the figure 3(a). The X-ray elastic constant results are shown in table II.

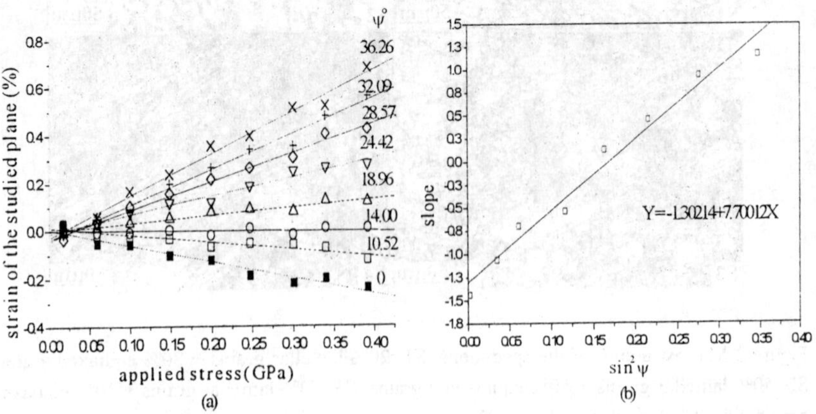

Figure 3 Variation of strain of the studied plane with the applied stresses (a) and the determination of the X-ray elastic constant (b) for {202} lattice planes in phase γ

Table II : The X-ray elastic constants of phase γ

S_1 (MPa^{-1})	$1/2S_2$ (MPa^{-1})	E (202)γ	ν
-1.30214×10^{-6}	7.70012×10^{-6}	156 (GPa)	0.21

It can be seen from the table II that the X-ray elastic constants of γ phase show a pronounced difference compared with that of the macroscopic elastic constants of TiAl alloys (E=176 GPa, ν=0.23 [6]). This is due to the fact that in the X-ray diffraction, only those grains properly oriented for the diffraction contribute to a peak. This orientation selectivity allows us to measure the anisotropic strain of the grains of a particular orientation relative to the stress axes. So REC retains the anisotropic nature of the crystallites. In addition, the mechanical characteristics of a phase in a multiphase material should be largely influenced by the presence of other phase(s), so the obtained mechanical properties of this phase can be different from that of the bulk of one phase material.

3.3 X-ray phase stresses of the γ phase

After determining the X-ray elastic constants of phase γ, the stresses in phase γ under uniaxial tensile can be measured by X-ray diffraction method. The figure 4(a) shows the macroscopic tensile stress-strain curves of four chosen specimens. It can be seen that with the increase of the volume fraction of lamellar grains, the yield strength and the ultimate strength increase. but the elongation decreases. The specimen 2 and specimen 3 have the better yield strength and elongation compared to specimen 1 and 4. This implies that the duplex microstructure with suitable fraction of lath colonies have the good comprehensive properties.

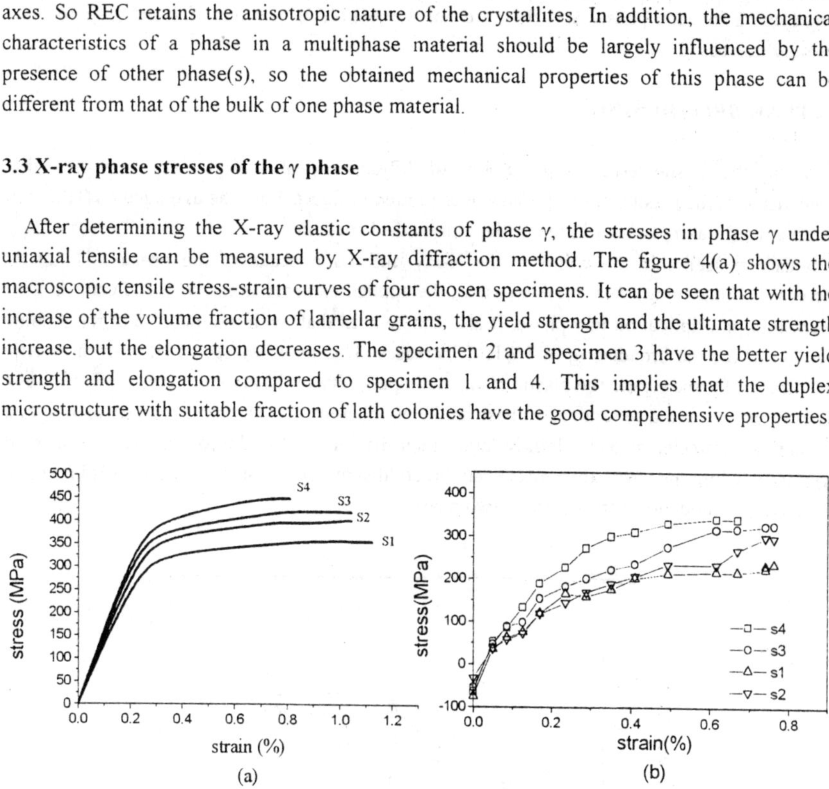

Figure 4 The macroscopic tensile stress-strain curves of four chosen specimens (a) and the stress-strain curves of γ phase of four chosen specimens evaluated by X-ray diffraction under the uniaxial tensile stress (b)

Figure 4(b) shows the stress-strain curves of phase γ of four chosen specimens evaluated by X-ray diffraction under the uniaxial tensile load. It can be seen that with the increase of the strain, the γ phase stress increases, but is less than that of the macroscopic tensile stress at the same strain. The macroscopic yield strength and the ultimate strength of duplex microstructure are higher than that of phase γ. This indicates that with the appearance of the second phase of the intermetallic compounds, the comprehensive properties can be increased. Usually, the key factor in determining the mechanical properties of most intermetallic compounds is the microstructure. The improvement of the strength and toughness of TiAl-based alloys through the use of lamellar microstructures is the well-known example [7].

In figure 4, it can be seen that the stress states in γ are generally different from the average ones. This is because that the elastic constants of the phase γ are different from that of the aggregate, this heterogeneity leads to a localization of the average stress fields, stress free strain exists in each phase, and they are not compatible in the material and lead to local residual stresses.

3.4 PEAK BROADENING

During the tensile testing, the variation of diffraction peak width is a phenomenon that concerns with the plastic strain [8]. The values plotted in figure 5 are the averaged FWHM (full width at half maximum) evolution of the four studied specimens.

It can be seen that the width of the X-ray diffraction peaks of the phase γ is rapidly increased (broadening) with the increase of the applied external stress. This indicates a rapid dislocation multiplication in γ phase. It also can be seen that, with the increase of the volume fraction of α_2, the broadening of FWHM increases. This may be associated with the elastic anisotropy of γ and α_2 and the plastic strain incompatibility of these two phases. In TiAl alloys, a hexagonal α_2 and a tetragonal γ phase are semi-coherent on their close-packed planes, and the lattice parameter of α_2 is slightly larger than that of γ[9]. In addition, the α_2 has six-fold symmetry, while the γ structure lacks even threefold symmetry, resulting in a big difference of plastic accommodation between these two phases.

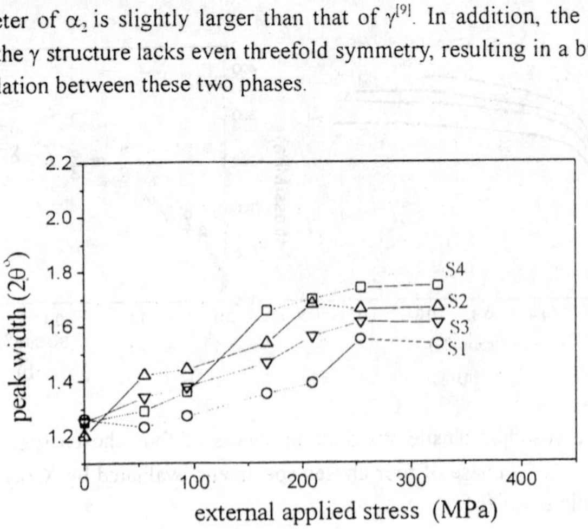

Figure 5:Peak broadening with the external stress

4.CONCLUSIONS

The aim of this study was to determine the X-ray elastic constants of a TiAl-based alloy for X-ray diffraction residual stress analysis, then the stresses in γ phase were conducted by X-ray diffraction technique during a step-by-step uniaxial loading. The peak broadening caused by plastic strain was discussed. This leads to the following results:

1. In the case of multiphase materials, the stresses in a particular phase differ from the macroscopic ones.
2. X-ray diffraction methods can be applied to evaluate the residual stresses of TiAl-based alloys, but it requires the elastic constants of the studied phase.
3. The different stress distribution between the different phases and the peak broadening indicate that incompatible plastic deformation is one of the main reason of the brittleness of TiAl-based alloys at room temperature.

ACKNOWLEDGE

The authors thank the financial support from French-Chinese bilateral common research project No. RA MAX970.

REFERENCE

1 Y. W. Kim, JOM, (1994), vol.46, pp. 30-40.

2 H. Inui, M. H. Oh. Nakamura and M. Yamaguchi, Acta metall.mater., (1992), vol.40, pp.3095-3104.

3 Y. W. Kim, Acta Metall.mater., (1992), vol. 40, pp. 1121-1134.

4 P. Hadmar., L. Barralier and J.M Sprauel, 'Fourth European Conference on Residual Stresses' (June 4-6 1996, Cluny, France), pp. 1043-1051.

5 J. M. Sprauel, 'Détermination des Contraintes Résiduelles Radiocristallographique d'un Acier Inoxydable Austénitique', PhD thesis, University Paris 11 (Paris-Sud-Orsay) 1980.

6 M. .H. Yoo and C. L. Fu, Metall. Trans. A, (1998), vol 29A, pp. 49

7 Y. Kimura and D. P. Pope, 'Structural Intermellics 1997', Edited by M.V.Nathal, et al., The Minerals & Materials Society, 1997, pp.99-105.

8 V. Ji. J. L. Lebrun and P.Sainfort, J. Mater. Sci., (1994), vol. 29, pp. 1553-1557.

9 M. A. Grinfeld, P. M. Hazzledine, B. St, and D. M. Dimiduk, Metall. Trans. A, (1998), vol 29A, pp. 937

PHASE STRESS MEASUREMENT IN STAINLESS SPRAYING LAYER BY X-RAY METHOD

Masayuki Nishida
(Kobe City College of Technology, 8-3, Gakuenhigashimachi, Nishiku,
Kobe 651-2194, JAPAN
E-mail: nishida@kobe-kosen.ac.jp)

Takao Hanabusa
(Tokushima University, 1-2 Minamijousanjima-cho, Tokushima-shi,
Tokushima 770-0814, JAPAN
E-mail: hanabusa@me.tokushima-u.ac.jp)

ABSTRACT

In this study, the X-ray stress measurement technique was used to investigate alterations of bending stress and thermal stress in sprayed layers. Two-phase materials (α-phase and γ-phase) were generated in stainless layer by the laser spraying method.

Bending stresses in the surface layer were measured by X-ray, and thermal stresses were measured by the in-situ thermal stress measurement technique at various stages of thermal cycle treatments.

After annealing, the initial tensile residual stresses existed in α-phase and γ-phase, and those were changed into the compressive state by annealing at 773K for two hours.

From the results of bending stress measurement, stresses measured by the X-ray method were proportional to bending strain in both phases.

In the case of thermal cycle treatment, the interaction between α-phase and γ-phase was confirmed due to the thermal cycling between 273K and 573K. Furthermore, γ-phase was generated the hysteresis loop during the thermal cycling between 273K and 773K.

INTRODUCTION

Thermal spraying is drawing the attention of various industrial fields. This technique is an effective means for making surface modified materials. However, there are some fatal weak points in the coating layer: a porous structure of layers, poor adhesion strength and so on. It is necessary to investigate fundamental characteristics of the sprayed layers to overcome these factors. Especially, the stresses generated in the layer are a very important factor of such diverse problems as the mechanical strength of layers as well as the adhesion of the layer to a substrate.

In this study, the X-ray stress measurement techniques were used to investigate the alterations of the bending stress and the thermal stress in sprayed layers.

Two-phase layers were generated by the laser spraying method. The bending stresses in the surface layer were measured by the X-ray, and thermal stresses were measured by the in-situ thermal stress measurement technique [1] at various stages of the thermal cycle treatments. These techniques are non-destructive for a measurement of surface stresses.

SPECIMEN PREPARATION

In this study, the two-phase spraying layer was prepared by the laser spraying method. The laser spraying method was developed by Shikoku National Industrial Research Institute (Japan). In this method various kinds of wires which are usually used as welding materials can be used, whereas powder materials are often used in the plasma spraying method. A supply of wire materials is available as well as that of powder materials.

Table Ⅰ. Component of the austenitic stainless welding wire (wt.%)

C	Mn	Si	P	S	Cr	Ni
0.04	1.90	0.46	-	-	20.13	9.45

Furthermore, reaction gases can be changed, the spraying particles can be very fine and the porosity which evolves in layers is low [2]. In this investigation, an austenitic stainless welding wire was used as the feed stock. This material was sprayed on the blasted stainless steel substrate (thickness: 6.0 mm) by the laser spraying method (Argon assist gas was used). The thickness of the sprayed layer was about 0.8 mm. The component of this wire is in Table Ⅰ. And Fig. 1 shows the schematic diagram of laser spraying.

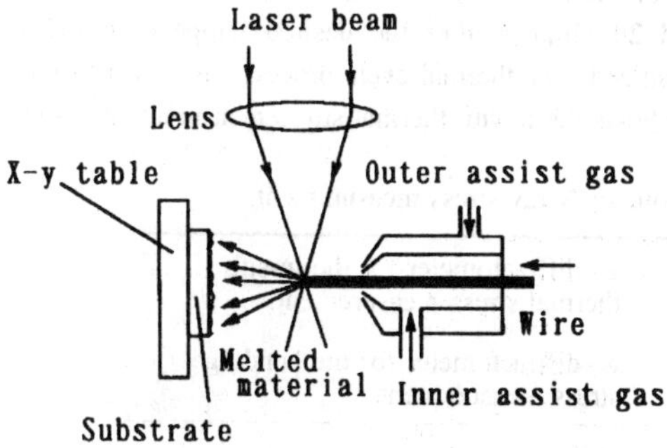

Fig. 1 Schematic diagram of laser spraying.

EXPERIMENTAL PROCEDURE AND CONDITIONS OF X-RAY STRESS MEASUREMENT

In the bending stress measurement, a bending attachment mounted on the measurement stage was used. The tensile or compressive strain caused from bending in the surface layer was measured by a strain gauge attached to the back of specimens. Fig. 2 shows the schematic diagram of the bending attachment.

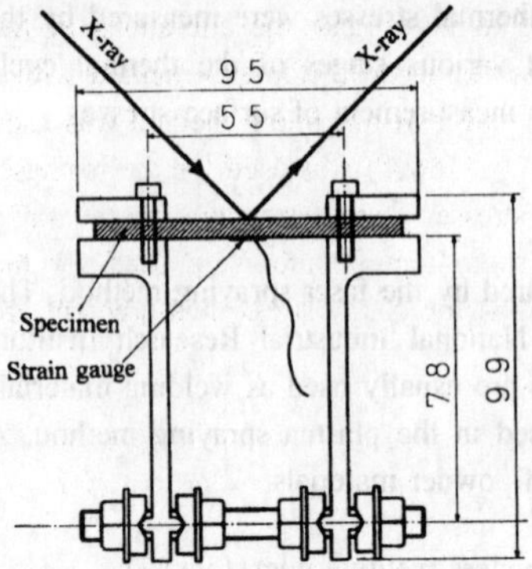

Fig. 2 Schematic diagram of bending attachment.

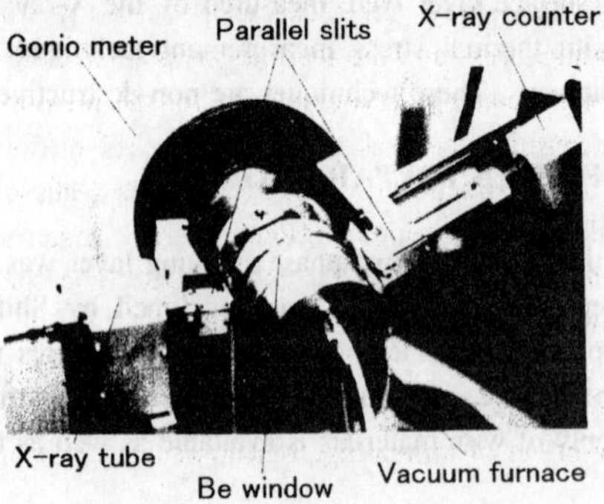

Fig. 3 In-situ thermal stress measurement system.

In the thermal stress measurement, the in-situ thermal stress measurement technique was applied to measure the thermal stress alterations produced by the thermal cycling. In this experiment, the measurement was made in a vacuum furnace (0.27 Pa) mounted on the diffractometer. The computer activated PID controller performed the thermal cycling process. The heating and cooling rate of the specimen was 5 (K/min) in every case. The X-ray stress measurement was started 20 minutes after the desired temperature (373K, 473K, 573K, 673K and 773K) was stabilized. The thermal cycle process was repeated three times between 273K and 773K. Fig. 3 shows the in-situ thermal stress measurement system.

Table Ⅱ. Conditions of X-ray stress measurement.

Method (with the parallel beam slit.)	Ω - diffractometer for the in-situ thermal stress measurement. ϕ - diffractometer for the bending stress measurement.
Characteristic X-ray	CrK α
Bragg reflection plane and diffraction angle (deg.)	α-phase 211, $2\theta_0$=156.4
	γ-phase 220, $2\theta_0$=129.5
Tube voltage (KV)	40
Tube current (mA)	30
ϕ angle ($\sin^2\phi$)	0, 0.1, 0.2, 0.3, 0.4, 0.5

In this study, Crkα characteristic X-ray was used to investigate the alterations of the bending stress and the thermal stress in sprayed layers. The ω-diffractometer method with a parallel beam slit was employed for the measurement. The half-maximum method was used to determine the peak positions. The 211 diffraction ($2\theta_0$=156.4°) was used for the α-phase, the 200 diffraction ($2\theta_0$=129.5°) for the γ-phase. The stresses were determined by the $\sin^2\psi$ method. The elastic constants of bulk materials at room temperature were used for the X-ray elastic constant for convenience. The conditions of the X-ray stress measurement are shown in Table Ⅱ.

EXPERIMENTAL RESULTS AND DISCUSSION

The effect of annealing treatment

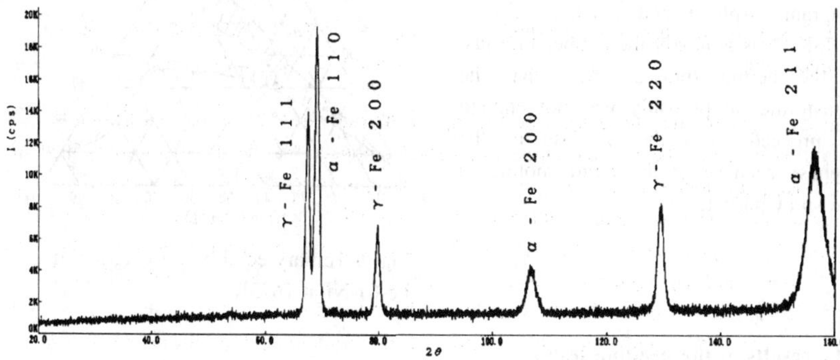

Fig. 4 Peak profile of as-coated layer.

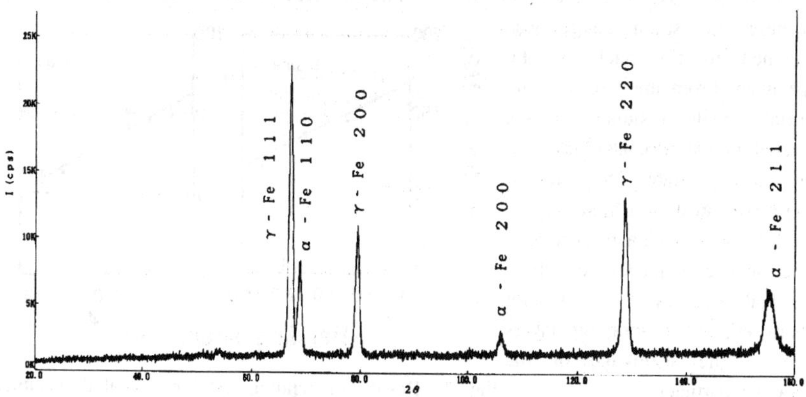

Fig. 5 Peak profile of annealed layer. Annealed at 773K for two hours holding with furnace cooling.

Fig. 4 shows the peak profile of the as-coated layer. As can be seen from this profile, the α-phase and γ-phase are comprised in this layer. The contents of the α-phase and γ-phase were 70% and 30% respectively.

Fig. 5 shows the peak profile of the annealed layer. This specimen was annealed at 773K for two hours with furnace cooling. From this figure, this result shows the simultaneous increase of the γ-phase and the decrease of the α-phase. It seems that the development of the transformation was the cause of these phenomena. In this case, the contents of the α-phase and the γ-phase were 30% and 70% respectively.

These two phase condition may be inferred from the ternary equilibrium diagram at 1673K (Fig. 6). From this diagram, α-phase and γ-phase exist at 1673K. This is nearly the temperature just of the thermal spraying. After that, the transformation probably was not enough to proceed from the α-phase to the γ-phase because of the rapid cooling in the spray particles.

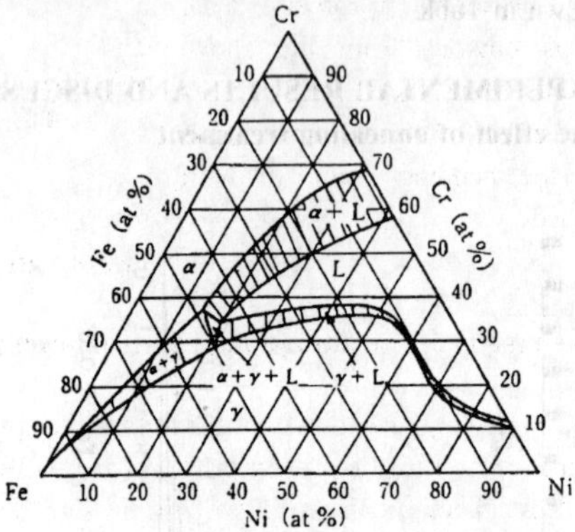

Fig. 6 Ternary equilibrium diagram of Fe-Cr-Ni at 1673K.

The results of the bending tests

Fig. 7 shows the result of X-ray stress measurement for the bending test in the as-coated layer. In the case of this test, the stress value decreases with increasing bending load, because the strain gauge was attached to the back of the specimen. From these results, the initial tensile residual stresses existed in the as-coated layer in the no load state. The ones of α-phase and γ-phase were 150MPa and 30MPa respectively. The tensile tendency of these residual stresses is a general characteristic of spraying layers due to the shrinkage of the spraying particles.

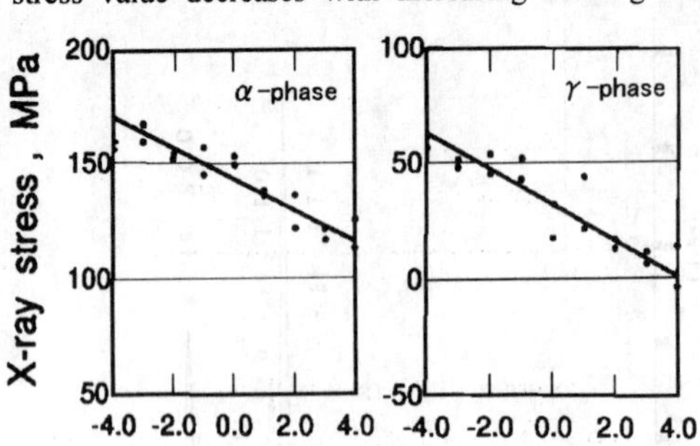

Fig. 7 Results of bending test for as-coated specimen.

Fig. 8 shows the case of the annealed specimen. In this case, tensile residual stresses have changed to the compressive state. These changes of the stress state appear to be due to relaxations of the initial residual stresses and differences of the thermal expansion coefficient between the layer and the substrate. However, in this test the relationship between the α-phase and the γ-phase was not confirmed such as two-phase bulk materials. It seems the large surface roughnesses prevented the measuring of precise data. It is obvious from the above results that the layer stresses measured by X-ray correspond to the bending strain in both phases.

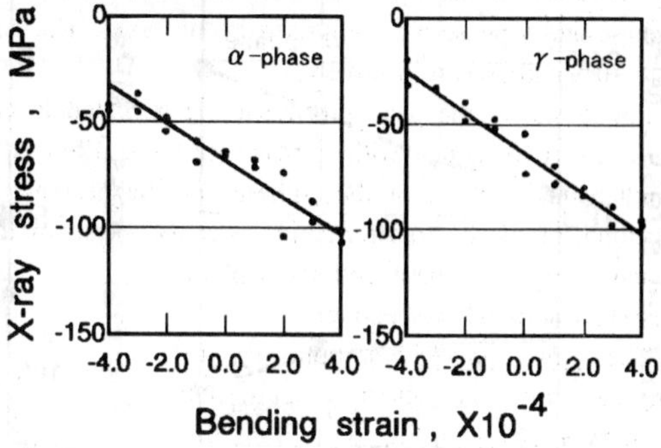

Fig. 8 Result of bending test for annealed specimen.

The results of the alteration in thermal cycling

Fig. 9 and Fig. 10 show the thermal cycling program of two cases. Fig. 9 is between 273K and 573K. Fig. 10 is between 273K and 773K after annealing at 773K for 2 hours.

Fig. 11 shows the results of the in-situ thermal stress measurement during the thermal cycle process between 273K and 573K (in the case of Fig. 9). The plotted points in this figure represent the average of three times measurement, and the irregularity of these data are shown by the error bars. The contents of α-phase and γ-phase were 70% and 30% respectively.

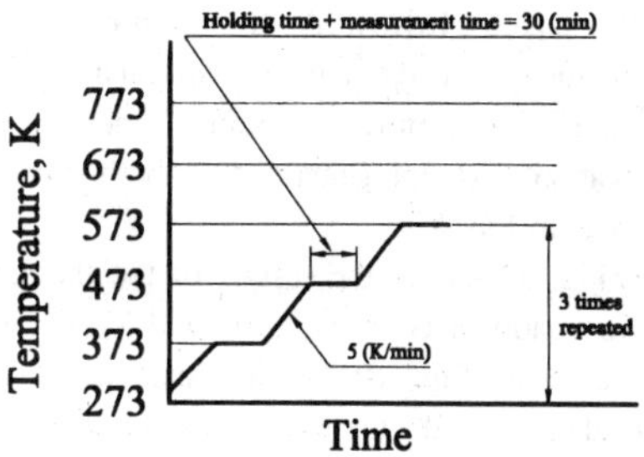

Fig. 9 Program of thermal cycling between 273K and 773K.

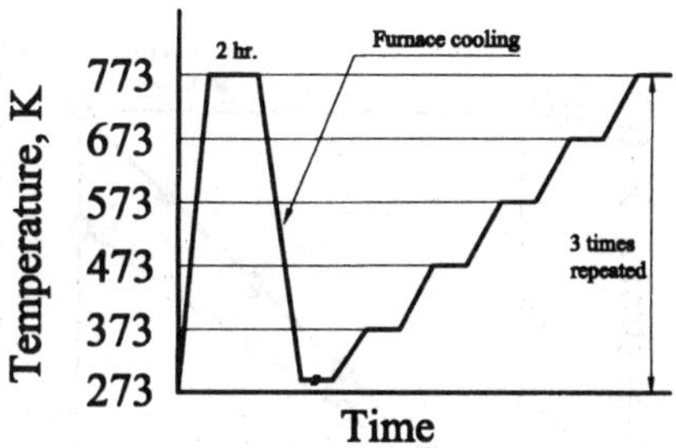

Fig. 10 Program of thermal cycling between 273K and 773K after annealing for 2 hours.

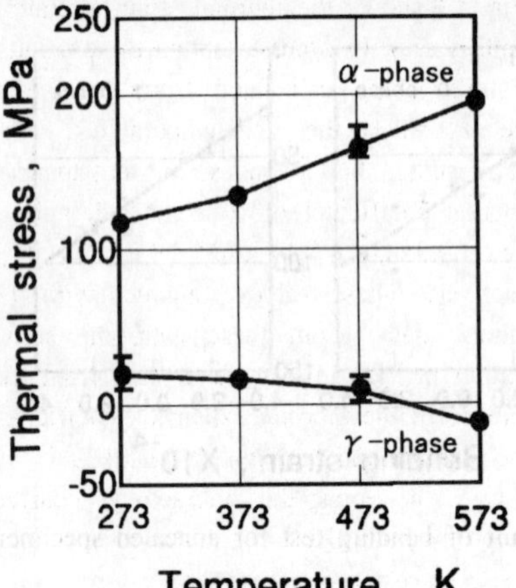

Fig. 11 Thermal stress alteration of α-phase and γ-phase bewteen 273K and 573K.

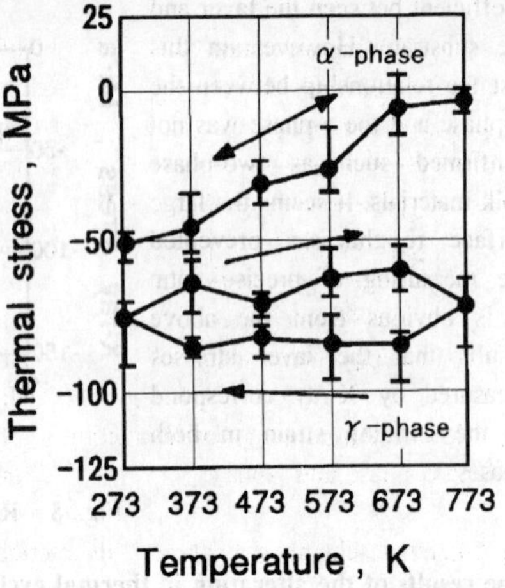

Fig. 12 Thermal stress alteration of α-phase and γ-phase between 273K and 773K. After annealing at 773K for two hours.

In the α-phase, the thermal stress increased with increasing temperature. Conversely, in the γ-phase it decreased with increasing temperature, and then changed into compressive state at 573K. Thermal stress alteration of both cases followed the same route respectively for the temperature raising and dropping. Therefore, it seems the stress relaxation was not generated in both phases such as in Fig. 8.

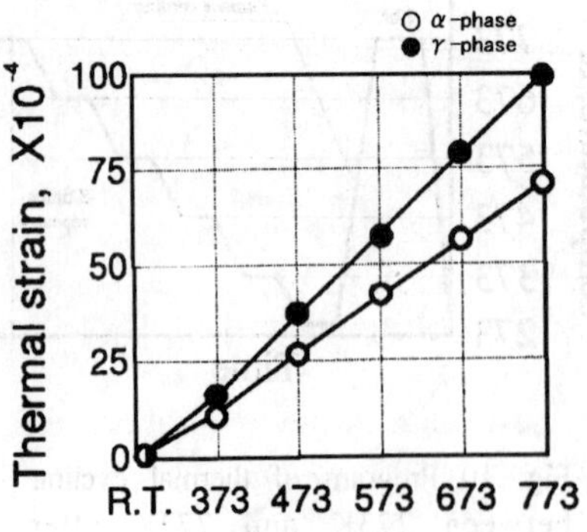

Fig. 13 Thermal strain alterations due to the heating. These strains were calculated form the lattice space of ϕ =0° at each temperature.

Fig. 12 shows the results of the thermal cycle treatment between 273K and 773K (in the case of Fig. 10). This specimen was annealed at 773K for two hours. From these results, it is clear the initial tensile residual stresses were relaxed by the annealing, and then the residual stresses changed into compressive state in both phases at room temperature. In the α-phase, the width of stress alteration between 273K and 773K was below half of the one before the annealing case (see Fig. 6). Especially, the hysteresis loop was generated in the γ-phase.

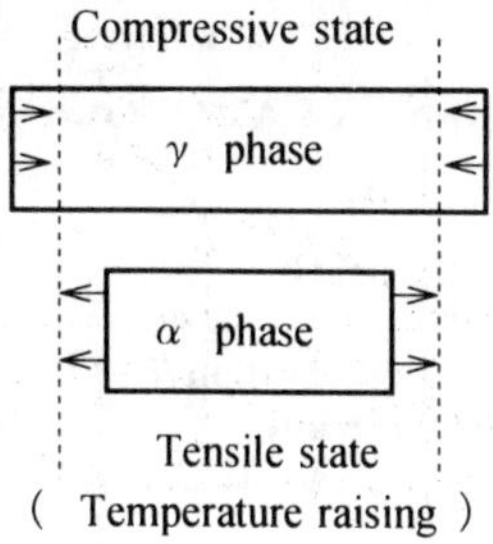

Fig. 14 Schematic diagram of interaction between α-phase and γ-phase.

Fig. 13 shows the thermal strain alteration of both phases. In order to obtain these results, the strains were calculated from the lattice space of $\phi=0°$ at the each temperatures. From these results, the averages of the thermal expansion coefficient of α-phase and γ-phase were 13.5×10^{-6}(/K) and 18.7×10^{-6}(/K), respectively. These values coincided with the handbook data. From these data, the stress alteration in Fig. 11 can be explain from the difference of the thermal expansion coefficient of the α-phase and the γ-phase qualitatively. In this case, it seems the interaction occurred between the both phases. Fig. 14 shows schematic diagram of interaction between α-phase and γ-phase.

However, in the case of Fig. 12, the interaction of the two phases was not confirmed due to the irregular data. Furthermore, the hysteresis loop drawn in the γ-phase case suggests the existence of plastic strain. However, it is not obvious whether the interaction generated between the substrate and the γ-phase or between the α-phase and the γ-phase. It is necessary to inquire further into these phenomena.

CONCLUSIONS

In this investigation, the stress alterations in the sprayed layers were measured by the X-ray method under bending and thermal cycling.

1. The two-phase state (α-phase and γ-phase) existed in the stainless thermal spraying layer. The contents of α-phase and γ-phase were 70% and 30% respectively. After annealing, these contents changed to 30% and 70% respectively.
2. The initial tensile residual stresses existed in the α-phase and γ-phase, and those were changed into the compressive state by the annealing treatment at 773K for two hours.
3. In the bending stress measurement, the measured stresses were proportional to bending strain in the both α-phase and γ-phase. In this case, the relationship between α-phase and γ-phase was not confirmed such as two-phase bulk materials.
4. In the in-situ thermal stress measurement, these residual stresses in the both phases changed to the new states which were influenced by the heating temperature. The interaction between α-phase and γ-phase was confirmed due to the thermal cycling between 273K and 573K. However, those were not confirmed in the other cases.

REFERENCES

[1]M. Nishida, T. Hanabusa, K. Katsumura, J. High Temp. Soc. Jap., Supplement 19(1993)357.

[2]Yoneda, Utsumi, Nakagawa, Matsuda, Katsumura, Arata and Omori, J. High Temp. Soc. Jap., 14(1988)66.

RESIDUAL STRESS ANALYSIS WITH DIFFERENT X-RAY OPTICS

E Auerswald* B Kämpfe* J Bethge B Michel***

***Fraunhofer Institute of Reliability and Microintegration**
Gustav-Meyer-Allee 25, D-13355 Berlin,Germany

****Philips Industrial Electronics B.V.**
Lelyweg 1, 7602 EA Almelo, The Netherlands

ABSTRACT

The authors checked different optical systems for their suitability for the residual stress analysis. The task lies in the field of microsystems. Examples will be given for a chip on board structure. The specimen was measured with an X-ray lens and an X-ray mirror.

INTRODUCTION

The first step of using total external reflection to control X-rays was taken in the first half of the twentieth century. It is the basis of the grazing incidence mirrors commonly used in X-ray telescopes and synchrotron beam lines. But, these mirrors are limited in their application by an extremly small angular acceptance (1).

M. A. Kumakhov and his collaborators introduced the capillary optics by total reflection from the capillary surfaces at very small angles to collimate and / or focus X-ray beams (2). These optics are arrays of hollow glass tubes with different geometries. It is important that the optics have certain properties. First, they should possess a high angular aperture. Second, the capillary or multilayer should create a high energy density on the object on which it is focused. Third, the optics should be able to very effectively transform the diverging radiation into a nearly parallel beam and vice versa and focus a parallel beam on a small spot. Furthermore, the optics should be rather compact and adaptable for various equipments.

In this paper we will report about residual stress analyses with an X-ray lens and an X-ray mirror at samples of microsystems. Experimental results are compared with the Bragg Brentano measurements at the same specimen. In the discussion, such aspects will be included as gain of intensity, reproducibility of the measurements and the influence of an inaccurate position of the specimen on the results of the investigation at the parallel beam technique.

THEORETICAL ASPECTS

THE X-RAY LENS

PHYSICAL BACKGROUND

The technique is based on the concept of reflection. If the angle of incidence is below the so-called critical angle θ_c, total reflection occurs and no intensity is lost in transmission. The critical angle is defined by the ratio between the indices of refraction of two media. Now for the X-rays the index of refraction is very close to unity and thus the critical angle is often only a few minutes of arc.

The complex refractive index for X-rays is usually written:

$$n = 1 - \delta + i\beta \tag{1}$$

β = absorption index

The theoretical expression for the refractivity δ is

$$\delta = \frac{r_e N_g \lambda^2 f}{2\pi} \tag{2}$$

N_g = number of atoms of type g per unit volume
f = atomic scattering factors
r_e = electron radii
λ = X-ray wavelength

Assuming that the absorption can be neglected and that the grazing angles are employed, the refractive index is given by the formula

$$n = 1 - \delta = \cos\theta_c \approx \sqrt{1 - \frac{\theta_c^2}{2}} \tag{3}$$

The critical angle of total reflection is now

$$\theta_c = \sqrt{2\delta} \tag{4}$$

According to this simple theory the reflection coefficient should be exactly equal to unity for all glancing angles up to the critical angle. This means that X-rays entering into a fiber, where total reflection can occur, can propagate inside the fiber by successive reflections without losing any intensity as long as the glancing angle is below the critical angle θ_c (3),(4).

TYPES OF LENSES

Downing (5) and others define two types of lenses, the polycapillary and the monolithic optics. Each lens contains individual channels with a diameters range from a few to tens of micrometers. It depends upon the application.

The main groups of Kumakhov lenses are shown in the Fig. 1a-1d

- widening semilens - transforms a divergent beam into a quasiparallel beam (Fig.1a)
- narrowing semilens - transforms a quasiparallel beam into a convergent one (Fig.1b)
- lens - transforms a divergent beam into a convergent beam (Fig.1c)
- three-sectional lens - consisting of two semilenes with different curvature radii and a straight section smoothly connecting them in the middle (Fig.1d)

The geometry of the lenses such as, for instance length and focal distance is mainly determined by the experimental conditions, the demands to the lens transmission, the focal spot size and the final beam angular divergence. Besides, one must take into account, that the lens transmission is only fulfilled, when all capillaries (both central and peripheral) take part in the beam forming. The peripheral capillary shows more reflections than the central capillary, hence the radiation in the peripheral capillary will be more attenuated. For the radiation to pass effectively, the following conditions should be met:

$$\frac{R \cdot \theta_c^2}{2d} \geq 1 \tag{5}$$

R = capillary curvature radius
θ_c = critical angle

d = mean capillary diameter along the channel (6)

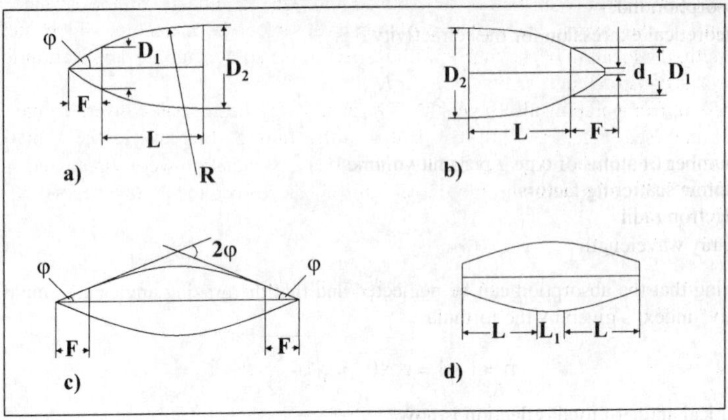

Fig. 1: Types of X-ray lenses

THE X-RAY MIRROR

Some years after the discovery of X-rays, it was suggested that multilayer structures (X-ray mirrors) consisting of elements of different atomic numbers could be used to diffract radiation in the X-ray range. Such structures could also be fabricated artificially. A first periodic structure was produced by depositing copper and gold layers with a period of 10 nm and this produced the diffraction of Mo-K_α-radiation by the superlattice. However, the stability of the mirror remained a problem, because the diffraction efficiency fell to zero over the period of a month. The reason for this was the interdiffusion of the metals and the reduction in the difference between the refractive indices of the two layers. For a long time this was a constant difficulty for multilayer technology. Stable multilayer structures include for example carbon-tungsten, carbon-vanadium, carbon-titanium, carbon-nickel or carbon-iron.
The principal composition of the multilayer X-ray mirror is shown in Fig. 2.

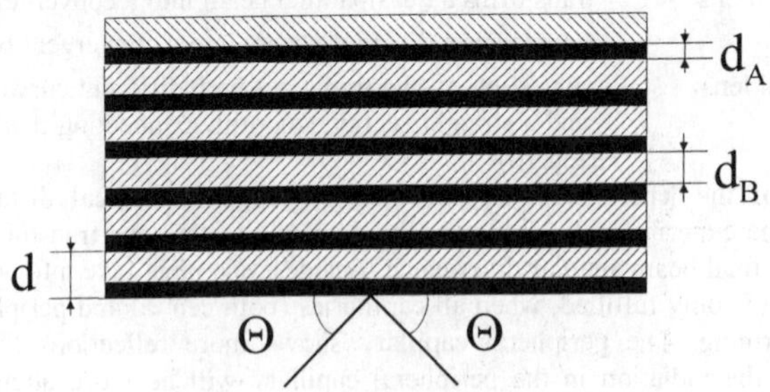

Fig. 2: Multilayer mirror

The multilayer mirrors are differentiated into two basic types, these depending on the optical properties of the layers A and B and consequently on their thickness.
Version 1 - a combination of very thin layers of a heavy metal and a carbon interlayer $d_A \ll d_B$
Version 2 - a combination of two relatively light materials with similar properties $d_A \approx d_B$

With version two, improved spectral properties can be achieved. The diffraction efficiency of the multilayer mirror was mainly determined through the quality of the surface and the uniformity of the layers. The distance of the layers depends on factors which include the wavelength, the location of the mirror with respect to the source and the application for which the mirror is constructed.
When the mirror parabolically bent, the divergent X-ray beam was converted into a quasi-parallel one (see Fig. 3). With the Bragg diffraction at the layers, the radiation was monochromatized and the K_β- and the heterochromatic X-radiation were suppressed.
Using also total reflection, the multilayer mirror can reflect the X-ray beam with a high intensity.

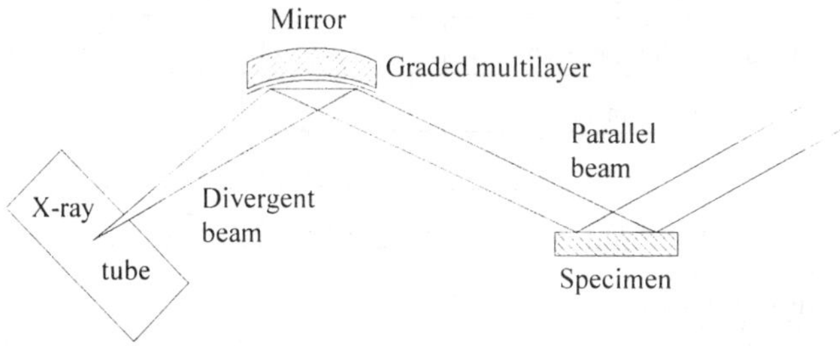

Fig. 3: Beam way with the X-ray mirror (7)

EXPERIMENTS

The residual stress analysis is one main field of our work. We investigate devices, test boards or layered structures from the field of micro systems technology. Therefore we were interested in small radiation beams with a high intensity, also when the specimen was tilted (ω- or ψ-tilting) and turned (φ-turning). The following results were obtained from residual stress analyses of a chip-on-board-structure (COB) using different optics.
COB-structure composition:

ground metallization:	copper	layer thickness 30 μm
reference layer:	nickel phosphide	layer thickness 5 μm
sud gilding:	gold	layer thickness 0.5 μm

The Fig. 4 shows the investigated specimen with the measuring point marked.

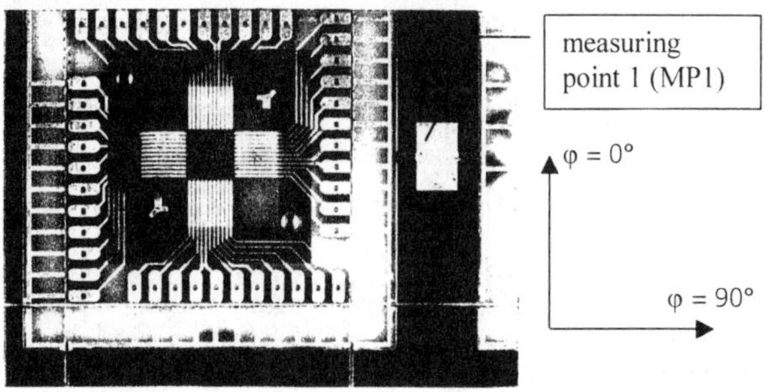

Fig. 4: FR4-board with COB-structure

The residual stress analysis was carried out at measuring point 1 with an X-ray lens, an X-ray mirror and with normal Bragg-Brentano-focussing (variable cross slit). All measurements were done three times to check reproducibility. In Table I the main measuring conditions are concentrated.

Parameter	Value
radiation	Cu-K_α
lattice plane	Au {331}, Cu{420}
step wide	0.03°
measuring time per step	60s or 30s
φ-position	0°, 90°
ψ-position	0°, ± 15° to ± 60°, $\Delta\psi$ = 5°
ω-position	0°, ± 15° to ± 55°, $\Delta\omega$ = 5°

Table I: Measuring conditions

EXPERIMENTS WITH THE X-RAY LENS

For our investigations we used a commercial X-ray equipment (Company Philips). The divergence of the lens for the copper radiation was about 0.3 degrees. A parallel plate collimator was employed for secondary optics. The beam is quasi-parallel in the axial and equatorial directions. The diameter of the reflected beam is about 7 mm, but the variable cross slit is adjustable from 0.1 to 5 mm in vertical and horizontal direction.
The first investigations were made at a stress free tungsten specimen. Because of the parallel radiation technique, two types of tilting for the residual stress analysis are possible. In Fig. 5, the peak shift is represented against the differing tilting angle.

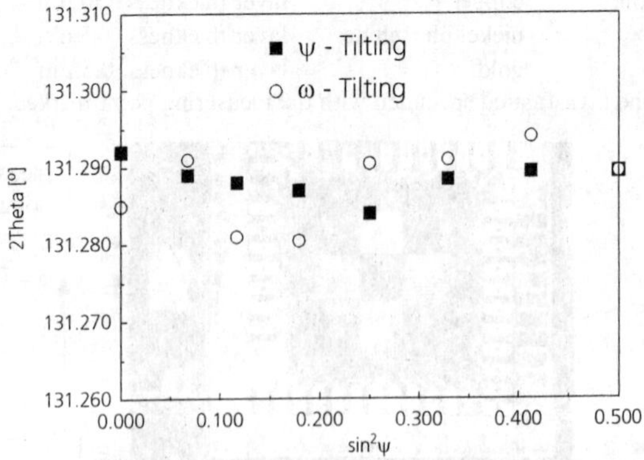

Fig. 5: Course from the reflecting angle on the basis of the tilting method at the tungsten specimen

Fundamental differences were not detected between the two tilting methods. The intensity of the peaks and also the full half width breadth (FHWB) have about the same value (see Table II).

FHWB 2θ [°]	X-ray lens ψ-tilting	X-ray lens ω-tilting
W {321} φ = 0° ω/ψ = 0°	0.498	0.491
W {321} φ = 0° ω/ψ = 45°	0.5055	0.5075

Table II: Comparison of the full half width breadths of the X-ray lens ψ- and ω-tilting

But small differences were determined at COB-structure for example at the Au-lattice plane {331}. When the results of the measurement were compared - X-ray lens with ψ-tilting to X-ray lens with ω-tilting and with the normal BRAGG BRENTANO focussing - it was established that the tension residual stress values of the ω-tilting were the smallest. The reproducibility was very high in all these investigations. The determination of residual stresses with the X-ray lens with ψ-tilting had very small measuring mistakes (see Fig. 6).

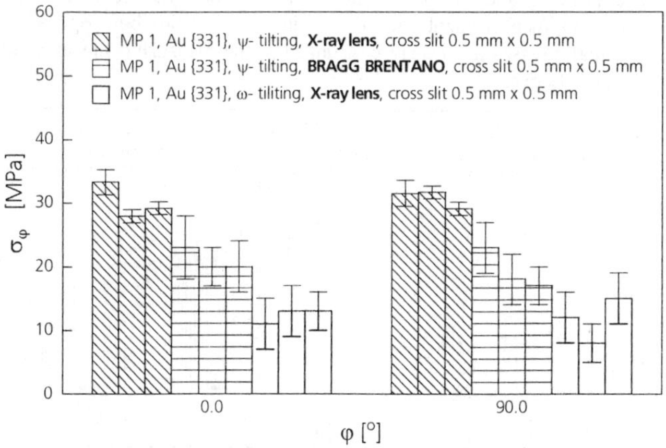

Fig. 6: Residual stress determination using various optics (COB-structure, Au {331})

EXPERIMENTS WITH THE X-RAY MIRROR

A graded multilayer X-ray mirror was specially developed as a plug in PreFix optic modules for the Philips X'Pert-MRD diffraction system. A parallel beam was produced by the mirror with the divergence less than 0.04°. Beam dimensions normally are 1.2 x 20 mm, but with vertical slits the beam can be reduced. For our investigations a small vertical slit with an opening of 0.5 mm was produced. The line focus was necessary for this reflection experiment. So, the residual stress analyses were done with the help of the ω-tilting.

At first also some investigations at the stress free tungsten sample were carried out. As follows from Fig. 7, the measurements with the parallelism at the primary and secondary side are insensitive to 100 μm of a sample shifting perpendicular to the diffractometer axis (z-axis).

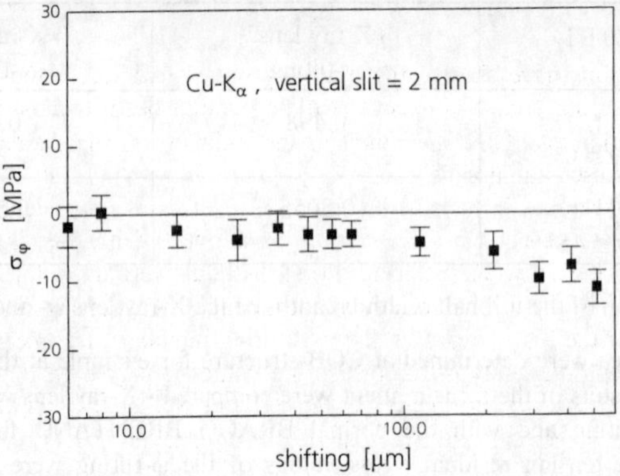

Fig. 7: Stress analysis at the stress free tungsten sample with specific shift in the z-axis

Subsequently compared residual stress to the X-ray lens were determined with X-ray mirror. The measuring conditions and the investigated sample were the same (see Table I). The results of the different measurements are shown in Fig. 8. With both optics, the absolute values of the residual stresses are nearly constant, but the measuring mistakes at the X-ray lens investigations are larger.

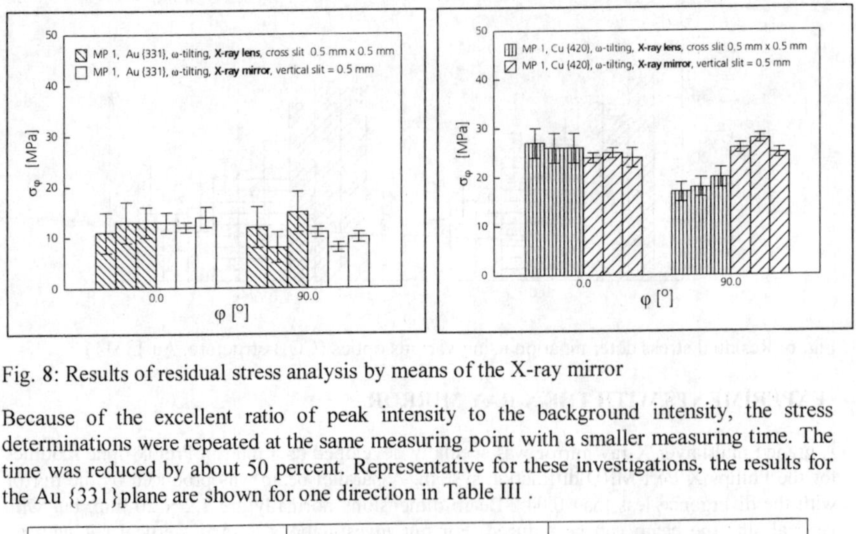

Fig. 8: Results of residual stress analysis by means of the X-ray mirror

Because of the excellent ratio of peak intensity to the background intensity, the stress determinations were repeated at the same measuring point with a smaller measuring time. The time was reduced by about 50 percent. Representative for these investigations, the results for the Au {331}plane are shown for one direction in Table III .

Au {331} $\varphi = 0°$	measuring time 60 s	measuring time 30 s
measurement 1	14 ± 2	12 ± 2
measurement 2	12 ± 1	9 ± 2
measurement 3	13 ± 2	13 ± 2

Table III: Comparison of the residual stress analysis to different measuring times

SUMMARY

Previous investigations have shown, that the new optics realized increasing intensities also when a small measuring area was necessary. The parallel beam technique provided a great advantage for positioning of the specimen in the z-direction. Inaccuracy up to 100 μm is insignificant for the used equipment.
As expected, there were no influences on the residual stresses dependent on the used X-ray optics. The values are nearly the same for different optics with the equal tilting methods. Small differences occurred when differing tilting methods were used, for instance X-ray lens ω- / ψ- tilting (see Fig. 6). One reason of the small differences is possibly the different penetration depth of the X-ray beam by the two tilting methods. The measuring inaccuracies are small and the reproducibility of the measuring values is very high. The new X-ray optics allowed for decreased measuring times (see Table III) as well as the determination of residual stresses using lattice planes at small Bragg angle ($2\theta < 90°$).

REFERENCES

1. Hofman F A,'Polycapillary X-Ray optics for thin film strain and texture analysis', Mat. Res. Soc. Symp. Proc. Vol. 505 1998
2. Kumakhov M A, Komarov F F, 'Multiple reflection from surface X-Ray optics', Physic Reports 191, No. 5 1990
3. Rindby A, 'Applications of fiber technique in the X-Ray region', Nuclear Instruments and Methods in Physics Research A249 (1986)
4. MacDonald C A, 'Applications and measurements of polycapillary X-Ray optics', Journal of X-Ray Science and Technology 6 (1996)
5. Downing R G, Gibson W M, MacDonald C A, 'Polycapillary optics: status, limitations, and prospects', SPIE Vol. 2856, 1996
6. Arkadiev V A, Gruev D I, 'Principal possibilities of Kumakhov lenses', SPIE, Vol. 2278, 1994
7. Philips prospect material
8. Kogan V A, Bethke J, 'X-Ray Optics for materials research', EPDIC 1997

Application of 2-Dimensional Coordinate System Conversion in Stress Measurements With Neutron Diffraction

D. -Q. Wang[a], C. R. Hubbard[a] and S. Spooner[b]
[a] Metals & Ceramics Division
[b] Solid State Division
Oak Ridge National Laboratory
Oak Ridge, TN 37831-6064
USA

ABSTRACT

This paper will present a method and program to precisely calculate the coordinates in a positioner coordinate system from given sample position coordinates with a minimum number of neutron surface scans for three possible circumstances in stress and texture measurement using neutron diffraction, given as follows:

- the coordinates of two points in both systems are known;
- the coordinates of three points in the positioner coordinate system and the angle between two sample surfaces are known;
- the coordinates of four points in the positioner coordinate system are known.

This is achieved by computing a conversion matrix relating the known coordinates in both systems for these three circumstances. Using the conversion matrix, any location in the sample coordinate system can be easily converted into the positioner coordinate system. Although the presentation is based on the two-dimensional case the principle is applicable to three-dimensional study.

1. INTRODUCTION

Two coordinate systems which are commonly used in neutron residual stress mapping are the positioner coordinate system (PCS) and the sample coordinate system (SCS). The former specifies the settings of the XYZ sample positioner, the later the measurement positions within the sample. The locations of interest within the sample are readily specified either from engineering drawings or from practical experience in the SCS. It is more difficult to specify the corresponding positioner coordinates, particularly when the sample coordinate system's axes are not parallel to the direction of the XYZ positioner's axes of movement because of sample mounting constraints and/or complex sample shape. The objective of this report is to describe a method and program to precisely calculate the coordinates in the PCS from given sample position coordinates. This is achieved by computing a conversion matrix relating the known coordinates in the PCS and SCS. The position coordinates in the PCS are obtained by the surface-scanning technique (1-3) or via careful optical measurement with the sample mounted on the goniometer. The coordinates of the same points in the SCS are determined by direct measurement with a caliper or from the engineering drawings. Using the conversion matrix any location in the SCS can be easily converted into the PCS.

For clarity we will present the two-dimensional cases since one can usually align at least one of the three sample axes parallel to one of the positioner axes or the measurements are to be constrained in one plane. Case studies will be discussed for three circumstances for the calculation of the conversion matrixes: (1) the coordinates of two points in both systems are known; (2) the coordinates of three points in the PCS and the angle between the two sample surfaces are known; (3) the coordinates of four points in the PCS are known.

2. DEFINITION OF THE COORDINATE SYSTEMS AND NOTATIONS

There is actually an intermediate coordinate system between the PCS and SCS, called laboratory coordinate system that is used for defining the movement direction of the positioner axes and the position of the sampling volume. However, for the purpose of locating the measurement positions in the sample, only the relation of the coordinates between the PCS and the SCS need to be established. Thus the following discussion will be focused on finding the relation between the SCS and PCS.

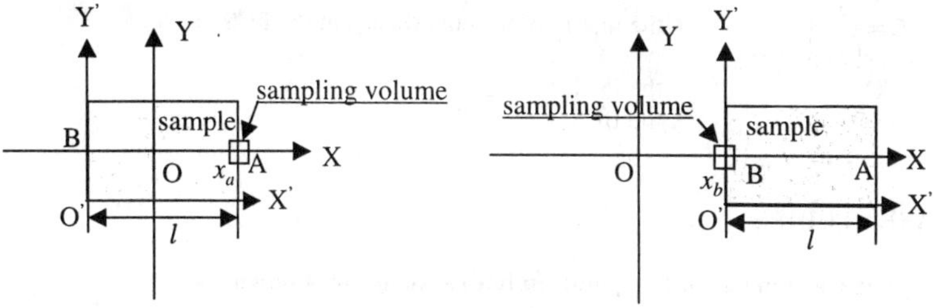

Fig.1 The sense of the coordinates in the PCS is reversed. Note that the coordinate system O-X-Y and the sampling volume are fixed in Fig. 1a (right) and 1b (left). The O-X-Y system is not the PCS. The values of the coordinates of points A and B in the PCS are the readings of the positioner's coordinates with respect to the sampling volume.

Both the PCS and the SCS are left-handed Cartesian systems with the same units (millimeters). Usually the direction or sense of the positioner coordinates is reversed from that in the sample because the sample is moved relative to a fixed gauge volume position defined by the incident and diffracted beam slits. For example, if the sampling volume and the coordinate system O-X-Y are FIXED, and the sample is moved in the positive x direction from where the center of the sampling volume is at point A, to at point B as shown in Fig. 1, then the sample coordinate in the PCS, x_b, is equal to $x_a + l$ (A and B are two fixed points in the sample, l is the length of the sample). Obviously, the value of the coordinate of point A, x_a is smaller than that of point B (x_b).

Notation

g	the shift of the origin of the sample coordinate system along the x-axis with respect to the positioner coordinate system
h	the shift of the origin of the sample coordinate system along the y-axis with respect to the positioner coordinate system
α	the rotation angle of the sample coordinate system with respect to the positioner coordinate system
$x_a, y_a, x_b, y_b...$	the positioner coordinates
$x'_a, y'_a, x'_b, y'_b...$	the sample coordinates
$\boldsymbol{R} = \begin{bmatrix} \cos\alpha & \sin\alpha \\ \cos\alpha & -\sin\alpha \end{bmatrix}$	the conversion matrix for rotation of a left-hand system
$\boldsymbol{T} = \begin{bmatrix} g \\ h \end{bmatrix}$	the matrix for translation of origin
$\boldsymbol{S} = \begin{bmatrix} x' \\ y' \end{bmatrix}$	the matrix of the coordinates in the SCS
$\boldsymbol{L} = \begin{bmatrix} x \\ y \end{bmatrix}$	the matrix of the coordinates in the PCS
OXY	the PCS
O'X'Y'	the BCS

3. CASE STUDIES

Case 1: The coordinates of two points in both systems are known

Assuming that the coordinates of two points, A and B, in both coordinate systems are determined (Fig. 2) as (x_a, y_a), (x'_a, y'_a), (x_b, y_b) and (x'_b, y'_b), then the conversion matrix can be calculated using the equation:

$$\boldsymbol{L} = \boldsymbol{R}\boldsymbol{S} + \boldsymbol{T} \qquad (1)$$

where ***L, R, S*** and ***T*** are the matrixes defined in last section. The coordinates of the two points in the SCS usually can be precisely determined by direct measurement with a caliper or from the engineering drawing. It is often difficult to obtain the coordinates of the two points with the same precision in the positioner coordinate systems because the surface scan technique is accurate only for scans perpendicular to a planar surface.

The problem can be solved by putting a marker cube* at the locations of A and B. One can find the positioner coordinates of the cube center at the locations by surface scanning in two orthogonal directions perpendicular to the cube faces and then precisely calculate the coordinates of the locations of point A and B in both the PCS and the SCS. With the

* Marker cube: a cube attached to the specimen with good neutron diffraction properties, whose dimensions and coordinate in the SCS are precisely known.

coordinates of the two points in both systems, the conversion matrix then is calculated using Eq. (1) with:

$$\sin\alpha = \frac{(x_a - x_b)(y'_a - y'_b) - (x'_a - x'_b)(y_a - y_b)}{(x'_a - x'_b)^2 + (y'_a - y'_b)^2} \tag{2}$$

$$\cos\alpha = \frac{(y_a - y_b)(y'_a - y'_b) + (x_a - x_b)(x'_a - x'_b)}{(x'_a - x'_b)^2 + (y'_a - y'_b)^2} \tag{3}$$

$$g = x_a - x'_a \cos\alpha - y'_a \sin\alpha \tag{4}$$

$$h = y_a - y'_a \cos\alpha - x'_a \sin\alpha \tag{5}$$

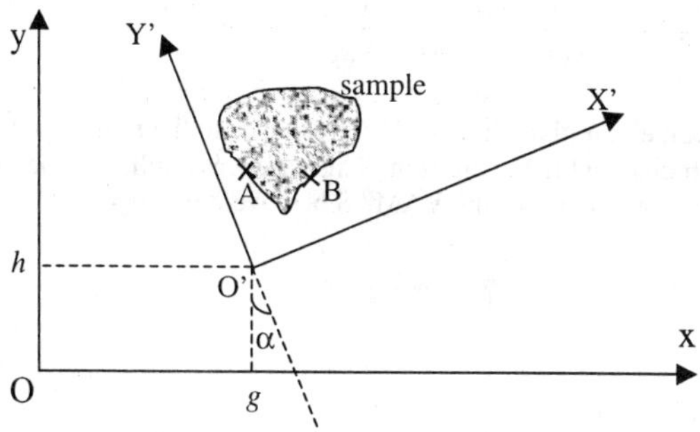

Fig. 2. The coordinates of two points in both systems are known. The shadow area is an image of the section of a sample.

Case 2: The positioner coordinates of three points and the angle between two sample surfaces are known.

This case is suitable for a sample with two planar surfaces at a known intersecting angle, as shown in Fig. 3. It is assumed that the positioner coordinates of three points, A (x_a, y_a), B (x_b, y_b), and C (x_c, y_c) are accurately determined with the surface scanning technique, and the value of the angle, β, between two sample surfaces is measured or obtained from engineering drawings. The line AB should coincide with one of the SCS axes and the origin of the SCS must be located at the intersection of the two surfaces on the sample. The equations for the conversion matrix calculation are:

$$\frac{g - x_a}{x_a - x_b} = \frac{h - y_a}{y_a - y_b} \tag{6}$$

$$g - x_c = k(h - y_c) \tag{7}$$

$$k = \tan[\alpha + 90 - \beta] \tag{8}$$

$$\alpha = \arctan\left(\frac{y_a - y_b}{x_a - x_b}\right) \tag{9}$$

Solving Eq. (6-9), one can obtain:

$$k = \tan\left(\arctan\left(\frac{y_a - y_b}{x_a - x_b}\right) + 90 - \beta\right) \tag{10}$$

$$g = \frac{(x_a - x_b)[k(y_c - y_a) - (x_c - x_a)]}{k(y_a - y_b) - (x_a - x_b)} + x_a \tag{11}$$

$$h = \frac{ky_c(y_a - y_b) - (x_c - x_a)(y_a - y_b) - y_a(x_a - x_b)}{k(y_a - y_b) - (x_a - x_b)} \tag{12}$$

Note that the value of α given in Eq. (8) corresponds to the minimum value and one has to determine which quadrant the angle is in. This case was applied to the experiments for the residual stress measurements of the VAMAS bent weld plate (4).

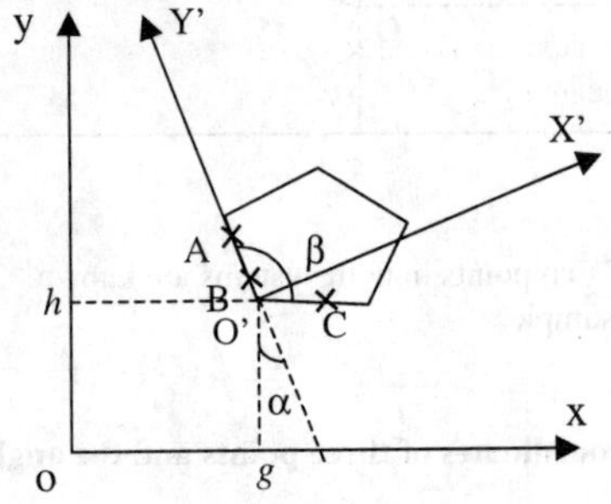

Fig.3. For case 2 the coordinates of three points in the PCS and the angle between two surfaces on the sample are known. The shadow area is an image of the section of a sample.

Case 3: The coordinates of four points in the PCS are known.

This is the case where there are two planar surfaces on the sample, and the angle, β, between the two surfaces, cannot be determined. Four surface scanning measurements have to be carried out to obtain the coordinates of four points in the PCS: A (x_a, y_a), B (x_b, y_b), C (x_c, y_c) and D (x_d, y_d). The four points should be located in the way that there are two points on each surface of the sample, as shown in Fig. 4. The line AB should coincide with one of the SCS axes and the origin of the SCS is located at the intersection of the two surfaces. The equations for the conversion matrix calculation are:

$$\frac{g - x_a}{x_a - x_b} = \frac{h - y_a}{y_a - y_b} \quad (13)$$

$$\frac{g - x_c}{x_c - x_d} = \frac{h - y_c}{y_c - y_d} \quad (14)$$

$$\alpha = \arctan\left[\frac{y_a - y_b}{x_a - x_b}\right] \quad (15)$$

From Eq. (9-11) one can calculate:

$$g = \frac{(x_a - x_b)[(x_c - x_d)(y_a - y_c) - (x_a - x_c)(y_c - y_d)]}{(y_c - y_d)(x_a - x_b) - (x_c - x_d)(y_a - y_b)} + x_a \quad (16)$$

$$h = \frac{y_a(y_c - y_d)(x_a - x_b) - y_c(x_c - x_d)(y_a - y_b) - (x_a - x_c)(y_a - y_b)(y_c - y_d)}{(y_c - y_d)(x_a - x_b) - (x_c - x_d)(y_a - y_b)} \quad (17)$$

Again the value of α given in Eq. (15) corresponds to the minimum value and one has to determine which quadrant the angle is in.

Having obtained the conversion matrixes, ***R*** and ***T***, the positioner coordinates are calculated from the sample positions using Eq. (1).

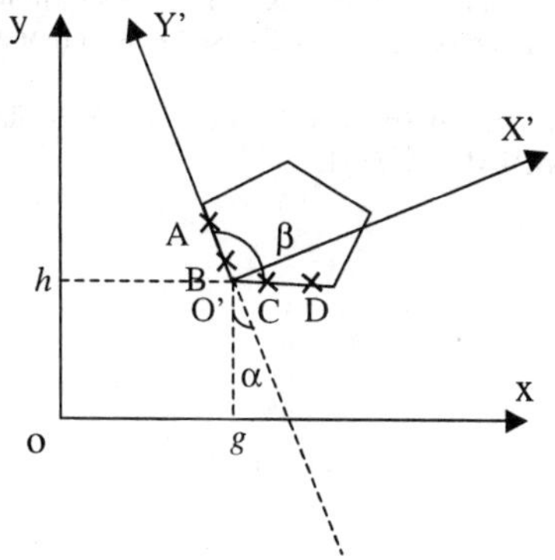

Fig. 4. Four surface scanning measurements are needed for determining the position of the sample if the angle β is unknown. The shadow area is an image of the section of a sample.

4. 2D_CONVERSION: AN EXCEL SPREADSHEET PROGRAM FOR CONVERSION OF THE COORDINATES BETWEEN THE SCS AND THE PCS

The program, "2D_CONVERSION ", was written in Microsoft® Excel 97. Each sheet corresponds to one case. The file name for the program is "2D Conversion" along with three data sets in the file called "2DC samples", one corresponding to each test case. For case 1, the data sheet is "two points". For case 2 the data sheet is "three points" and for case 3 the data sheet is "four points". The program is available upon request.

Acknowledgement

Research sponsored by the Assistant Secretary for Energy Efficiency and Renewable Energy, Office of Transportation Technologies, as part of the High Temperature Materials Laboratory User Program, Oak Ridge National Laboratory, managed by Lockheed Martin Energy Research Corp. for the U.S. Department of Energy under contract number DE-AC05-96OR22464. DQW was supported in part by an appointment to the ORNL Postdoctoral Research Associates Program administered jointly by ORNL and ORISE.

References:

1. Brand P. C. and Prask H. J., "New Methods for the Alignment of Instrumentation for Residual Stress Measurements by Means of Neutron Diffraction", *J. App. Cryst.*, 27(1994) 164-176.
2. Wang D.-Q. and Edward L., "Precise determination of specimen surface position during sub-surface strain scanning by neutron diffraction", Proc. of Fourth European Conference on Residual Stresses, p135-143, France, 1996.
3. Wang D.-Q, Wang X.-L. and Hubbard C. R.,"Precise Determination of Sample Position with a Radial Collimator and/or Slit(s) for Stress Measurements via Neutron Diffraction", in this proceedings.
4. Wang D.-Q, Hubbard C. R. and Spooner S., "Residual stress determination for a ferritic steel weld plate", ORNL/TM-1999/141.

A FOCUSING MONOCHROMATOR OF NEUTRON DIFFRACTOMETER FOR RESIDUAL STRESS ANALYSIS (RESA)

Nobuaki Minakawa, Yukio Morii, and Yutaka Shimojo
Research Group for Neutron Scattering
Advanced Science Research Center
Japan Atomic Energy Research Institute
Tokai-Mura, Naka-Gun, Ibaraki, 319-1195 Japan

ABSTRACT

For residual stress measurement by the neutron diffraction method, a measurement precision less than 10^{-5} nm is required.

The neutron diffractometer for residual stress analysis (RESA) is installed at the thermal guide tube T2-1 port at the JRR-3M in JAERI. We developed a monochromator mechanism to converge neutron beam at a sample position in both horizontal and vertical directions in order to measure residual stress with an high precision and resolution. Five pieces of Si crystals were used. Each one was bent mechanically using piano wire for horizontal focusing and tilted for vertical focusing, that created an adjustable uniform mosaic spread of the crystal from 0.1 to 0.3 degrees. Beam intensity at the sample position was increased with an high resolution.

RESA contains all the mechanism, which can slide the sample table to the horizontal focusing point when changing the wavelength.

INTRODUCTION

By applying a bending stress to the single crystal, the crystal spacing of lattice planes stretches on the crystal periphery.

The internal circumference contracts and a strain of $\Delta d/d$ occurs.
Also, with the radius of curvature an angle difference $\Delta\theta_M$ occurs in the crystal length direction. As for the monochromatic neutron beam, there is focusing in the horizontal plane as shown in Fig. 1. As a result, wavelength λ can be given by the following formula.

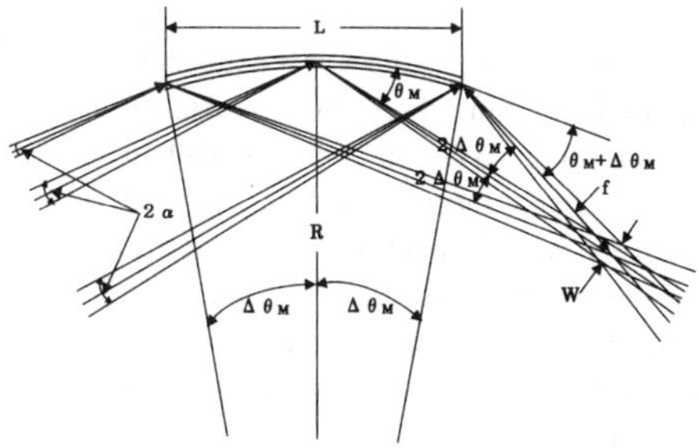

Fig. 1 Principle of Bent Monochromator

$$\lambda = \lambda_0 + \Delta\lambda = 2(d_{0\,hkl} + \Delta d_{hkl}) \sin(\theta_M + \Delta\theta_M) \qquad (1)$$

Also the focal distance f for a parallel neutron beam is obtained from

$$(L/2)\sin\theta_M = 2\Delta\theta_M f \quad (2)$$

$$\therefore f = ((L/2)/2\Delta\theta_M)\sin\theta_M = (R/2)\sin\theta_M \quad (3)$$

where L = the length of monochromator crystal. The incident beam of panchromatic neutrons has some divergence angle α, then if the focusing point for the monochromatic beam has width W, it is possible to show that

$$W = 2\alpha f = R\alpha\sin\theta_M \quad (4)$$

where the radius of curvature of the crystal R can be found from the strain ε measured at the crystal surface by strain gauge.

$$\varepsilon = t/(2R+t) \quad (5)$$

where t = the gauge covering material and the glue thickness from gauge element.

Since plural equipments are installed for one neutron guide tube, the RESA, which is installed in the upper stream, must take neutrons of specific energy as many as possible. Therefore small absorption cross section and high reflection efficiency of the monochromator crystal is required. We chose a silicon single crystal. The schematic drawing of RESA is shown in Fig. 2.

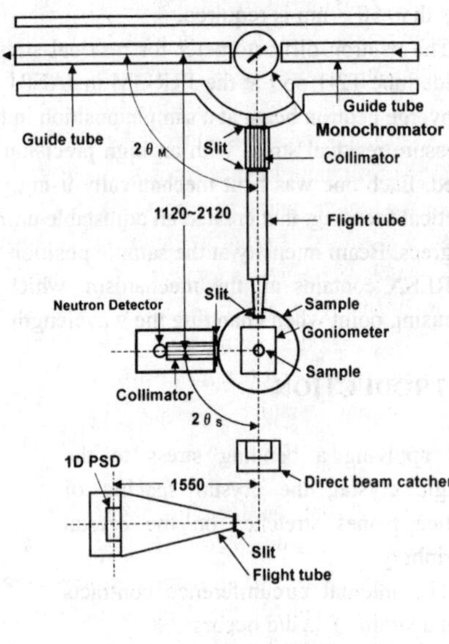

Fig. 2 Schematic drawing of RESA

MECHANISM

The following mechanism is included in the developed monochromator : To obtain a uniform strain $\Delta d/d$ in a crystal and to control mosaic spread, stress was applied by a piano wire in both edges of the crystal. And tilt angle of the each crystal can be adjusted by remote controller for focusing in the vertical direction. In each crystal, the crystallographic axis was adjusted by neutron diffraction to be in the identical direction to the scattering vector. To load five pieces of crystals with equal bending stress, a set a strain gauges was glued to the center of each crystal surface. We used a reflection plane of 100 mm length, 20 mm height, 5 mm thickness, and diffraction planes of (111), (311).

MEASUREMENTS

The strain gauge set to the surface center of the crystals is effective to monitor the bending stress to accompany a time elapse, too. To avoid damaging a crystal by a shock stress in the case of set up in the monochromator shielding tank, the bend strain is adjusted to 450 x 10^{-6} for all of the crystal. The inner crystal reflection intensity distribution of the 5 mm thickness, which experiences a bending stress change, is measured. Scans of θ were made while changing the bending stress.

The measurement was carried out with a high-resolution triple axis neutron spectrometer (TAS-2) whose monochromator was Si(311) crystal disk with a mosaic spread of about 0.1 degrees, 1 mm thickness, and 150 mm diameter. The wavelength used was 0.2 nm. The collimator condition employed the 1st, 2nd, and 3rd collimators of 20 minutes. The beam conditions at the incident and scattered sides both used slits 20 mm width and 20mm height. An attenuator of plastic with 10 mm thickness was put in the position of the incident beam.

After that, the up-and-down elevation was obtained by a high precision Z-axis goniometer of 300 mm range set on the sample table. A focusing-type bent monochromator mechanism was installed onto the Z-axis goniometer table. It scanned in θ from the crystal for the center position. An optimal peak position from the rocking curve was obtained with a Gaussian fitting. A counter rate meter was used to move the other crystal with the beam center and the Z-axis goniometer to produce a maximum count rate with the omega angle adjustment mechanism.

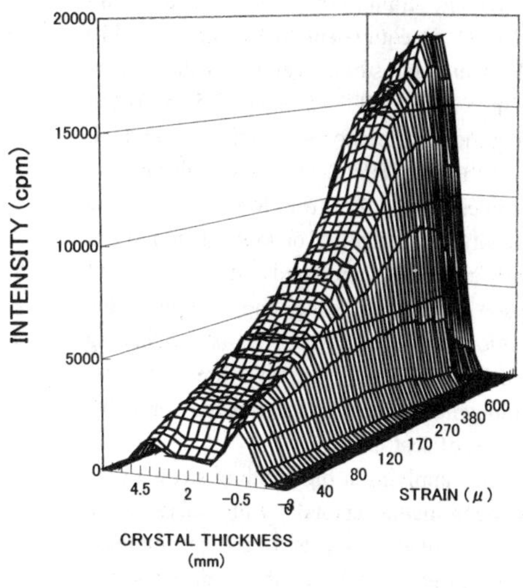

Fig. 3 Strain and Diffraction Intensity

After adjustment of each crystal, the monochromator-shielding tank of RESA is installed to give a neutron wavelength of 0.2 nm. A remote control was used to set up the Ge(111) single crystal with 10 mm width, 10 mm height, and 5 mm thickness. Five pieces of monochromator crystal was focused on the Ge crystal and it was adjusted for angle of elevation. After that, to measure equipment resolution, a Si standard powder sample was measured by neutron diffraction.

As for the equipment condition of RESA, as for the 1st collimator, the critical angle of the neutron guide tube is 0.18 degrees and this value becomes a 1st collimation value. It doesn't use the 2nd collimator, because the mosaic spread of the monochromator crystal is approximately 0.2 degrees. Third collimator has 0.33 degrees in divergence. The neutron detector used a ^{3}He zero dimensional detector.

RESULTS

The scattering neutron intensity changes to the inside of the Si (311) crystal with surface bend strain are shown in Fig. 3. The average strain of the monochromator crystal by bending is shown in Fig. 4.

When finding Δd from the value of the surface strain gauge, it is 7.369 x 10^{-5} nm. However, Δd which was found from the average strain inside the crystal is 43.902 x 10^{-5} nm. The best bending stress is just in front of Si (311) which is 750 x 10^{-6} from the value of the surface strain gauge. However, the average strain in the crystal is about 4480 x 10^{-6} (It is equivalent to the stress of 740 MPa) and radius of curvature R (the surface strain = 450 x 10^{-6}) is about 7.5 m. When using monochromator wavelength around 0.2 nm ($2\theta_M$ = 80°), the focal distance f becomes about 2.4 m from formula (3). The intensity was equal to, or more than about 5 times increased, compared with one slice of crystal when adjusting the sample table position of RESA at 2.4 m and adjusting focusing in the vertical direction. An equipment resolution was achieved below 0.3 degrees of scattering.

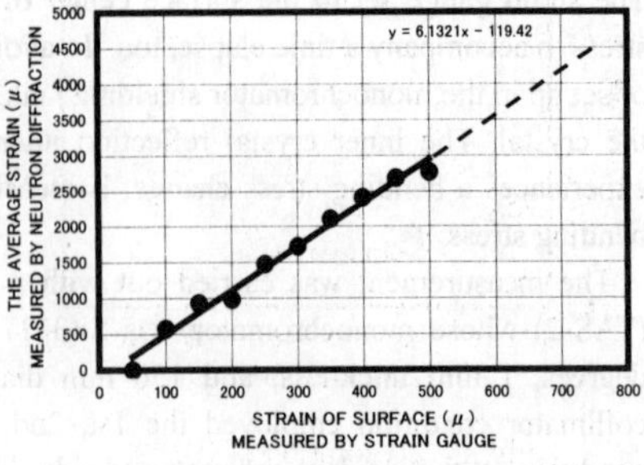

Fig. 4 Average strain measured by neutron diffraction

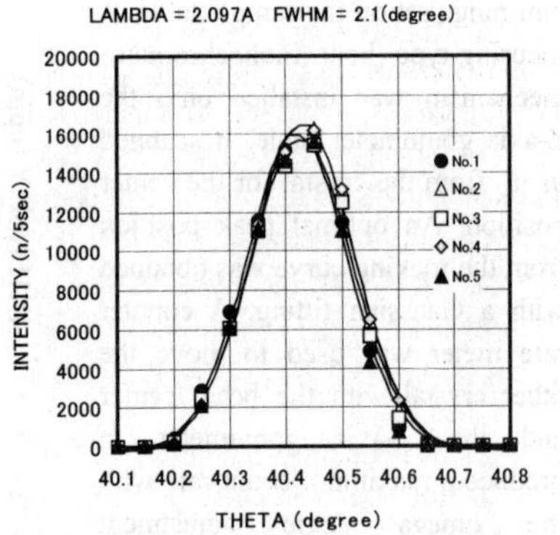

Fig. 5 Rocking curve of 5-crystals on the monochromator mechanism

When applying a big bending stress to the monochromator crystal, with increase in mosaic spread, $\Delta\theta_M$ and $\Delta\lambda$, an increase in integrated intensity is obtained. A rocking curve after five pieces of crystal adjustments is shown in Fig. 5 and the RESA resolution figure is shown in Fig. 6.

CONCLUSIONS

As for the element which decides $\Delta\lambda$, it is contributed by a change in Δd of the lattice spacing by the bending stress and by $\Delta\theta_M$ from the radius of curvature of the crystal.

In RESA a monochromator mechanism has been developed that creates a uniform mosaic spread of the crystal from 0.1 to 0.3 degrees, which is suited to residual stress measurement. Moreover, the sample table can move to the horizontal focusing position on the dancing floor to increase neutron beam intensity at the sample position. Lastly, a phtograph of the monochromator of RESA is shown in Fig. 7.

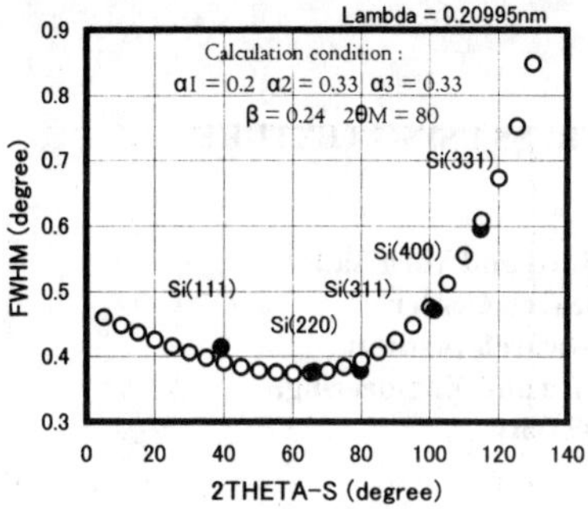

Fig. 6 Resolution of RESA

Fig. 7 RESA's Bent Monochromator

REFERENCES

1. Agamalian M, Christen D K, Drews A R, Glinka C J, Matsuoka H & Wignall G D, Appl Cryst. 31 (1998) 235-240
2. Freund A K, Lect. Notes Phys. 112 (1980) 381-395
3. Fujiwara S, Karasawa Y, Tanaka 1, Minezaki Y, Yonezawa Y & Niimura N, Physica B 241-243 (1998) 207-209
4. Kulda J & Saroun J, Nucl Instrum. Methods A, 379 (1996) 155-166
5. Mikula P, Kruger E, Scherm R & Wagner V, Appl Cryst. 23 (1990) 105-110
6. Mikula P, Kulda J, Lukas P, Strunz P, Saroun J, Vrana M & Wagner V, Report PTB Braunschweig, Germany (1997)
7. Mikula P, Kulda I, Lukas P, Vrana M & Wagner, Nucl Instrum. Methods A 338 (1994) 18-26
8. Mikula P, Lukas P, Saroun J, Wagner V & Kulda J, Physica B 213-214 (1995) 922-925
9. Niimura N, Karasawa Y, Tanaka I, Miyahara J, Takahashi K, Saito H, Koizumi S & Hidaka M, Nucl Instrum. Methods A 349 (1994) 521-525
10. Niimura N, Tanaka I, Karasawa Y & Minakawa N, Physica B 213-214 (1995) 929-931
11. Niimura N, Tanaka I, Minezaki Y, Karasawa Y, Tanaka I, Miki K, Sato M, Hidaka M, Minakawa N & Morii Y, Physica B 213-214 (1995) 786-789
12. Takahashi T & Hashimoto M, Phys. Lett. A 200 (1995) 73-75
13. Tanaka I, Minezaki Y, Harada K & Niimura N, Physica B 241-243 (1998) 227-230

EVALUATION OF INTERNAL STRESS USING TEXTURE

Nobuaki Minakawa, Yukio Morii and Toru Saito[1]
Advanced Science Research Center
Japan Atomic Energy Research Institute
[1]Department of Material Science and Engineering,
Kanazawa University

ABSTRACT

In the process of the manufacturing of first material, the external forces remains in the addition, some form. When manufacturing of material such as the rolling, the forging, the wire drawing, with the external forces, occurrence of the slip, the turn of the grain and grow up a texture. The study of the residual stress is done by a lot of researchers such as Taylor, Barrett from the old days.

We measured a residual stress in the texture to evaluate the residual stress of a primary material and to research how it should deals texture in case of the general inner stress measurement.

Iron steels, aluminum alloy material are often used as the general material. An aluminum alloy material is known as the material that it is easy for the texture to grow. We chose an aluminum material as the measurement sample and used the texture measurement, the standard residual stress measurement, and residual stress measurement of the texture.

INTRODUCTION

We used the neutron diffractometer for residual stress analysis (RESA), which was installed in the thermal neutron guide tube T2-1 port of JRR-3M reactor in JAERI for this measurement. RESA is high resolution type neutron diffractometer which is using the bent crystal of Si(311) for the monochromator.

The measurement sample used the A7075 aluminum alloy material, which is use the test piece of tension test. As for the crystal structure of A7075 is face centered cubic, therefore pure copper-type texture is gotten.

The residual stress of the texture is able to measure the (200) plane of each axis. Because, each [200], [020], and [002] axes has relation of 90°.

SAMPLE

The measurement sample this time used the tension test piece of A7075. A7075 is the precipitation-hardening alloy of $MgZn_2$ compound, being called an extra super duralumin. The chemical ingredient except Al, (5.1 to 6.1 mass% Zn), (2.1 to 2.9 mass% Mg) and (1.2 to 2.0 mass% Cu) Contain based on JIS.

The electric discharge machine cut down a test piece of tension test to the size is 100 mm length, 6 mm width and 3 mm thickness from inside the plank material with 50 mm thickness.

EXPERIMENTS

We used the monochromatic neutron wavelength of 0.208883 nm. The collimation of white incidence neutron beam to the monochromator is 0.18° , which is equivalent to the critical angle of the thermal neutron guide tube. As for the monochromator crystal, the Si(311) single crystal which was controlled by the bending stress was used for 0.23° in the mosaic spread.

The collimation of the incident monochromatic neutron beam to the sample is about 0.3° . The collimator in front of the detector used 0.33° and the incident slit to the sample used a cadmium slit, 15 mm height, 10 mm width. The slit in front of the 3rd collimator used 20 mm height, 10 mm width.

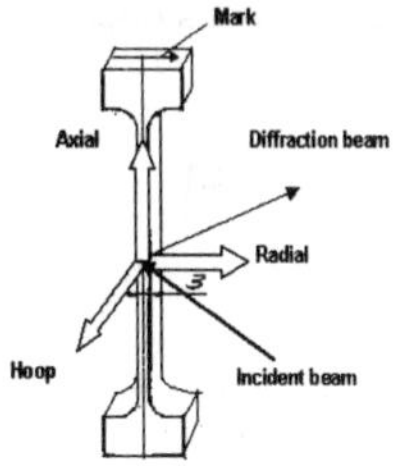

(a) Generally Method

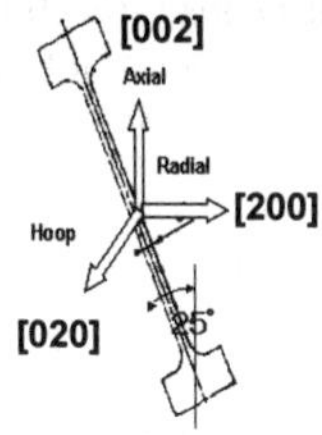

(b) Texture Method

Fig.1 Measurement Direction

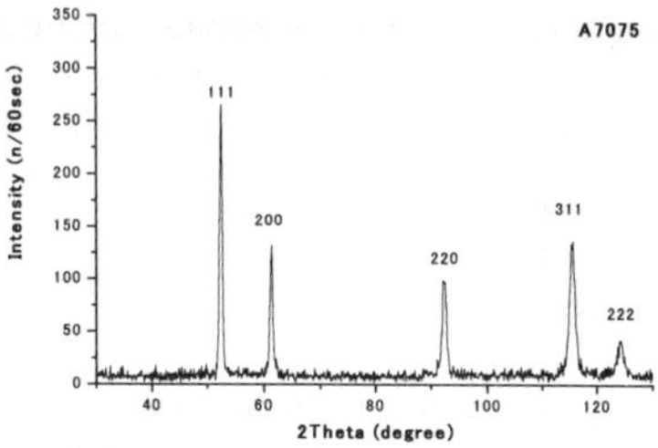

Fig.2 Neutron Diffraction of A7075

A measurement procedure is shown below.

① To know a scattering angle every Miller index of A7075, measured in neutron diffraction.

② To know the texture form of A7075, measured about (111), (200), (220) planes.

We used a 4-circle goniometer for the texture measurement, with the measurement of step angle χ axis at 5° , and φ axis is 10° and measurement time is 30 seconds.

③ To compare with the residual stress of the texture, we measured standard residual stress. As for the measured sample position, the direction of Radial is (χ = 0° ,φ = 0°), the direction of Hoop is (χ = 0° ,φ = 90°), and the direction of Axial is (χ = 90° ,φ = 0°). The direction of Axial is the direction of the roll. The direction of the measurement is shown in Figure 1- (a).

④ We measured a residual stress in the texture. We knew the texture on the (200) plane by the measurement of ② and measured a residual stress about the (200) plane of each axis of [200], [002], [020] which is in the 90° relation. As for the measured sample position, the direction of Radial is (χ = 25° ,φ = 50°), the direction of Hoop is (χ = 25° ,φ = 140°), and the direction of Axial is (χ = 115° ,φ = 50°). The direction of Axial is about equivalent to the direction of the roll. This direction of the measurement is shown in Figure 1- (b).

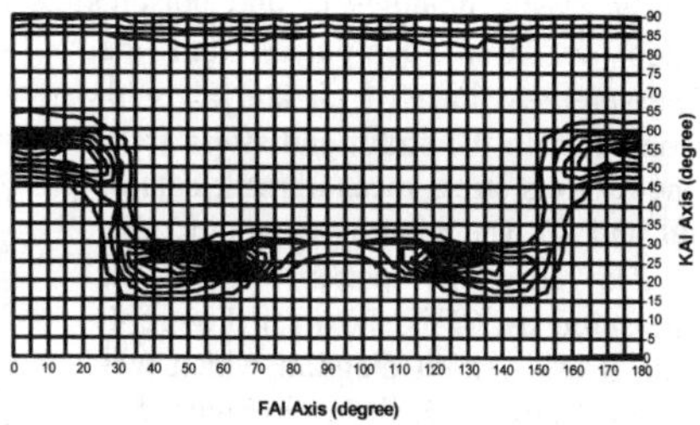

Fig.3 Texture Distribution of A7075(200)

⑤ We measured lattice spacing about the strain free condition of the test specimen. The ideal strain free sample is made a fine powder from identical material. However, it measured neutron diffraction for us all the while rotating a test specimen in the condition which is near the random rotation and it used the lattice spacing which could be gotten as standard lattice spacing $d_{0(hkl)}$.

The stress was calculated using the following formula.

$$\sigma_{R,H,A} = \frac{E}{1+\nu}\left[\varepsilon_{R,H,A} + \frac{\nu}{1-2\nu}\left(\varepsilon_R + \varepsilon_H + \varepsilon_A\right)\right]$$

⑥ The elastic modules E and poison's ratio ν which depends on the mirror index used the tension test machine which is the attachment equipment of RESA to evaluate a stress and measured stress-strain diagram by the neutron diffraction. Stress-strain diagram measured in neutron diffraction to the direction of expansion and the direction of contraction while installing a tension test machine on the sample table of RESA and loading tensile stress.

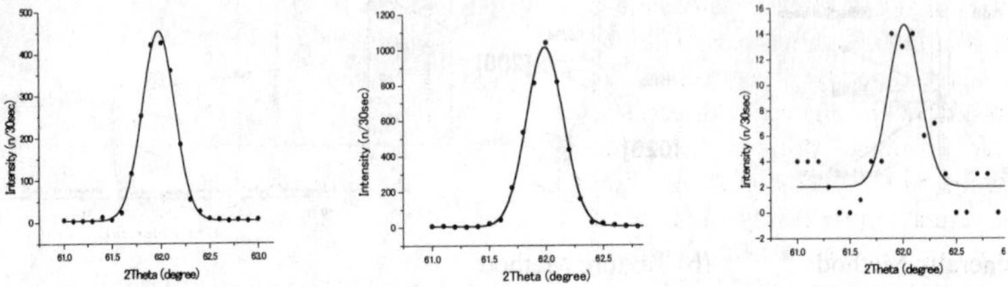

Radial Hoop Axial

Fig.4 Neutron Diffraction Pattern of Sample Rotation

RESULTS

The neutron diffraction pattern which was measured by ① is shown in Figure 2. The graph of 3 dimensional distribution of the texture which was measured by ② is shown in Figure 3. As the result of the texture, it has typical pattern of Aluminum. The standard lattice spacing $d_{0(hkl)}$, elastic modules E, and poison's ratio ν, were computed from the measurement data of ⑤ and ⑥ with computed in the strain and stress from the residual stress measurement data of ③ and ④. The result is shown in Table 1. The diffraction pattern which was measured by ④ is shown in Figure 4. The stress - strain diagram which was measured by ⑥ is shown in Figure 5.

Normal Measurement Method				
	2θs	d (nm)	ε (10^{-6})	σ (Mpa)
Radial(X)	62.017	0.2027348	40.96	14.98
Hoop (Y)	62.013	0.2027442	87.72	17.45
Axial (Z)	62.013	0.2027467	100.06	18.11
Texture Measurement Method				
	2θs	d (nm)	ε (10^{-6})	
Radial(X)	61.996	0.202794	332.61	30.64
Hoop (Y)	61.975	0.2028573	645.26	47.18
Axial (Z)	62.071	0.2025754	-745.11	-26.40

Lambda = 0.208883 $d_{0(200)}$ = 0.202726

E = 70.89 GPa ν = 0.34

Table 1 Calculation of Strain and Stress for A7075(200)

CONSIDERATIONS

For a neutron diffracted pattern of Figure 2, to deal with a calculation of data, a weak peak of Zn is observed, but on the side of a low angle of (220) peak with no quite problem. In the texture pattern of Figure 3, the pattern of the pure copper type is gotten. The standard lattice spacing $d_{0(200)}$ of A7075 is 0.202726 nm.

As for the computation result of the stress measurement by the texture, the direction of Axial shows a negative value from Table 1. This is correct, as Axial direction indicates to be suited to a rolled direction. The measurement value of the each directions, the standard residual stress is about 17 MPa. A residual stress measurement value of a texture shows a value more than approximately three times, as compared with an each directions, standard residual stress value. This residual stress depends on an external force around processing and is a skillful stress, when a texture grows. This primary material of A7075 has residual stress of the maximum about 50 MPa.

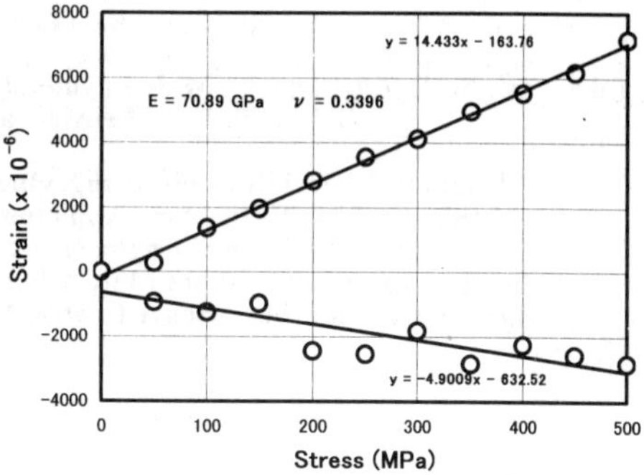

Fig. 5 Stress-Strain Diagram for A7075

CONCLUSIONS

The residual stress value by the external forces depends on the way, the control condition of the manufacture and so on. To evaluate the high precision for the fatigue and the lifetime of the product that is manufactured such as the bend and welding, the internal residual stress which primary manufacture material has cannot be ignored.

The texture exists at all material. As for the material that has big texture, the stress measurement position must be examined. Therefore, to measure texture before measuring a stress is important. Also, after measuring the texture of the test piece of tension test beforehand when measuring tension test, too, it should do tension test.

REFERENCES

1. Barrett C S, Structure of Metals (1952)
2. Hu H, Sperry P R and Beck P A, Trans. AIME, 194 (1952) 76
3. Bunge H J and Roberts W T, J. Appl. Cryst. 2 (1969) 116
4. Bunge H.J, Texture Analysis in Materials Science, Butterworths (1982)
5. Nagashima S, Material Japan 21 (11) (1982) 842
6. Matthies S, Wenk H.R and Vinel G W, J. Appl. Cryst. 21 (1988) 285
7. Kawasaki H, and Iwasaki H, Photon Radiation 5 (3) (1992) 23
8. Kawasaki H, and Iwasaki H, Material Japan 34 (4) (1995) 504
9. Dingley D J and Randle V, J. Mat. Sci. 27 (1992) 4545
10. Engler O and Gottstein G, Steel Research, 63 (1992) 413
11. Matuo M, Kato H, Itoh K, Kokubo I, Inagaki Y and Nagashima S, Texture, JIM(1981)

ENGIN-X: A NEUTRON STRESS DIFFRACTOMETER FOR THE 21ST CENTURY

L. Edwards[1], M. E. Fitzpatrick[1], M. R Daymond[2], M. W. Johnson[2], G. A. Webster[3], N. P. O'Dowd[3], P. J. Webster[4] and P. J. Withers[5].

[1] Dept of Materials Engineering, Open University, Milton Keynes
[2] ISIS Facility, Rutherford Appleton Laboratory, Chilton, Oxon.
[3] Dept of Mechanical Engineering, Imperial College, London,
[4] Institute of Structures and Materials Engineering, Salford University,.
[5] Manchester Materials Science Centre, Manchester University & UMIST.

ABSTRACT

This paper describes ENGIN-X, a neutron diffraction instrument designed for engineering strain measurements, recently funded by the EPSRC. The new instrument, which is being built at ISIS (Rutherford Appleton Laboratory, UK), will achieve an order of magnitude increase in performance over current instruments of this type. In contrast to conventional neutron diffractometers whose designs are compromises, ENGIN–X is designed with the single aim of making engineering strain measurements; essentially the accurate measurement of polycrystalline lattice parameters. This paper explains the outline design methods behind the ENGIN-X design and details the current stage of the design and instrument build. With the large increase in data acquisition rate over present instrumentation inherent in the ENGIN-X design it is vitally important that data handling improvements keep pace with improved data capture rates. Accordingly, the strategy of the software development task accompanying ENGIN-X is also outlined.

INTRODUCTION

Neutron stress measurement is a non-destructive technique that uniquely provides insights into stress fields deep within engineering components and structures. As such, it has become an increasingly important tool within engineering leading to improved manufacturing processes to reduce stress and distortion as well as to the definition of more precise structural integrity lifing procedures. Furthermore, it is the only non destructive means of measuring the stress state deep within engineering components and structures under conditions (temperature, stress, atmosphere, etc.) representative of those which might be experienced in service.

The technique was first developed at Harwell in the late 1970s Allen et al. (1) and has developed significantly over the last 10 years, Stacey et al. (2) Johnson et al. (3), Webster, G.A. et al. (4). Early applications of the technique concentrated on failure analysis, e.g. Smith et al. (5) and the characterisation of residual stress states produced by manufacturing processes e.g. Ozdemir and Edwards (6), with the structural integrity of welds also being particularly prominent e.g. Webster et al. (7).

More recent developments have included strong inputs to the design of advanced materials, Fitzpatrick et al. (8), to engineering design though the validation of finite element simulations, Rudkins et al. (9), and the measurement of direct as well as residual strains in loaded components Edwards et al. (10).

ISIS, the world's brightest pulsed neutron source situated at the Rutherford Appleton Laboratory in the UK currently houses one of the first dedicated neutron stress diffractometers, ENGIN, Johnson et al (3). This paper outlines the development of its successor, ENGIN-X which is designed to produce an order of magnitude improvement in performance over current instruments.

INSTRUMENT DESIGN

The novelty and utility of ENGIN-X rests on three design innovations, which will provide an order of magnitude improvement over the present instrument:

i. designing a figure of merit (FOM) which reflects the true needs of strain measurement
ii. maximising the FOM using an optimally configured super-mirror guide and detector array,
iii. using novel neutron lenses to aid the study of small gauge volumes.

The new ENGIN-X instrument will be a departure from the philosophy of previous diffractometer designs. This is because neutron diffractometers are generally built as 'all-purpose' instruments, with designs that are compromises, balancing competing requirements to measure the intensities, positions and widths of diffraction peaks simultaneously. In the case of ENGIN-X the overriding requirement of the instrument is the accurate measurement of a lattice parameter, at a precisely known location within the component under study. The increased performance of ENGIN-X for lattice parameter determination has been achieved through the design of its neutron optics. Precise determination of measurement location will be achieved using ancillary equipment and novel software approaches.

The first step in this process is to define a figure of merit (FOM). The natural choice is that of 'the inverse of the time taken to measure a lattice spacing to a given accuracy'. This is because it is proportional to the intensity of the source illuminating the instrument, and therefore provides a useful way of comparing the effect of instrument and source performances.

The accuracy with which a lattice parameter is measured is proportional to the error involved in measuring the individual d-spacing of the Bragg peaks recorded in the time-of-flight neutron diffraction pattern. In order to determine a d-spacing from the observed diffraction pattern, the measured data is analysed using a 'least-squares' fitting procedure. It can be shown analytically (e.g. Sivia (11)) that, in the situation of an isolated Gaussian peak, the time (t) taken to measure (with an accuracy of σ) the position of a peak is proportional to $w^2/\{I\ \sigma^2\}$, where w is the width of the peak, and I the intensity recorded in unit time. So that:

$$1/t = k\,I\sigma^2/w^2 = FOM \qquad (1)$$

While Eqn. 1 applies to a Gaussian peak shape, the peak shapes to be found in time-of-flight diffraction instruments based at spallation sources, such as ISIS, are far from Gaussian and the result could not be immediately used.

However the applicability of this FOM to the more general case of an arbitrary peak shape has now been proved by Johnson & Daymond (12) and this result has opened up the possibility of calculating the value of the FOM for a variety of instrument geometries.

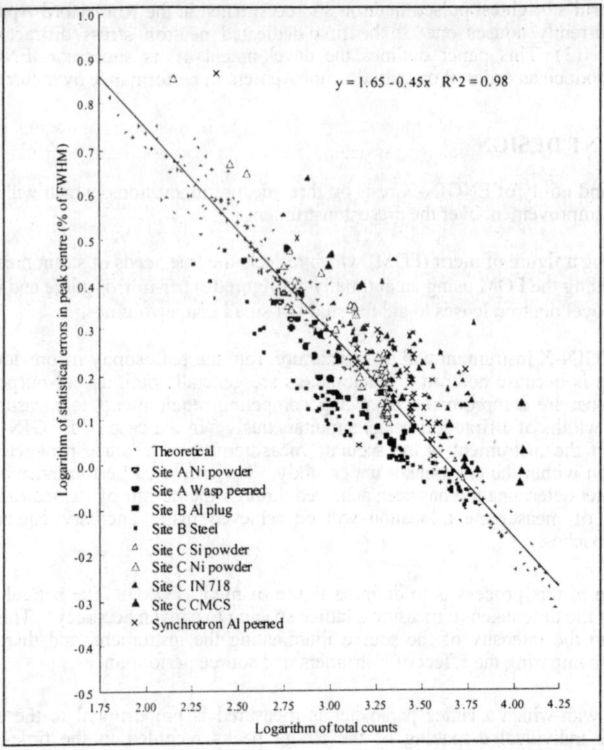

Fig. 1. ln (I.t) vs. ln(σ/w) for a series of diffraction strain measurements.

When applied to different peak shapes the value of *k* will differ from one peak shape to another, but remain constant for a particular shape. The fact that it does not vary too widely is shown from an experimental examination of the variation of the total counts under a peak (It) with the value of (σ/ w). Rearranging (1) we obtain:

$$\ln (\sigma / w) = k' - 0.5 \ln(I\,t) \tag{2}$$

and in Figure 1 we plot the logarithm of (σ/w) *vs.* (It) for a large number of measurements made on a number of different instruments around the world. Despite the fact that the value of k' in equation 2 will differ from one measurement to another, the gradient of the graph (-0.45) is very close to the value in equation 2.

Using the FOM for a single peak, it is straightforward to show that the FOM for a number (n) of peaks is:

$$FOM = \sigma^2 \sum_{j=1}^{n} \frac{I_j}{w_j^2} \tag{3}$$

and combining this with a model including the assumptions given below, the value of the FOM has been calculated as a function of the primary flight path of the diffractometer.

The primary assumptions in the model are:

- Minimum useful wavelength is determined by the resolution of individual peaks
- Maximum useful wavelength is determined by the primary flight path and source frequency
- Angular and time components of resolution are matched
- Top and bottom neutron guide to within 2m of the sample, on the sides it is foreshortened.
- The FOM is inversely proportional to measurement time, (See Equation 3.)

Although the full details of this model are given in Johnson and Daymond (12), we can show here the main result, how the FOM varies with the length of the primary flight path - Fig. 2.

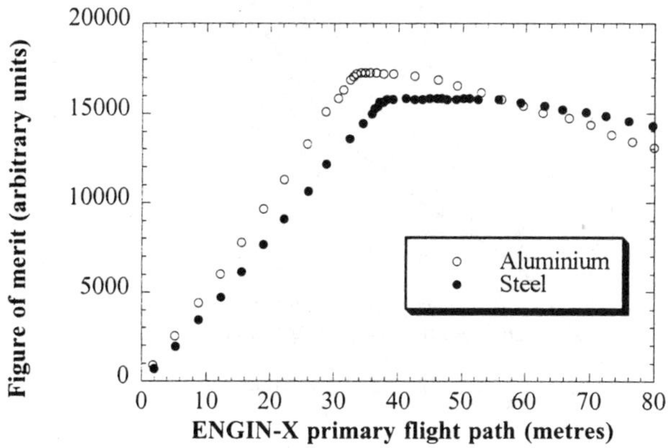

Fig.2 The FOM as a function of ENGIN-X flight path. The two curves are for steel and aluminum.

DESIGNING TO MAXIMISE THE FOM

From the above argument it is clear that the multi-peak FOM (equation 3) must be maximised. This has been achieved by utilising the fact that the detectors in a strain measuring instrument are at 90°. At this scattering angle, the widths (w) of the peaks in the diffraction pattern (and hence FOM) are insensitive to changes in the vertical divergence of the incident beam Johnson et al (3). Thus, while Liouville's theorem dictates that we cannot increase the flux of neutrons per unit solid angle incident on the sample (over that emanating from the moderator), we can increase the total flux of neutrons usefully incident on the sample by increasing the vertical divergence of the beam. This has been achieved by the use of super-mirror guides above and below the incident beam.

Conversely, while the vertical divergence must be increased, the FOM dictates that the horizontal divergence must be minimised. This is because the angular divergence of the neutron beam in the horizontal plane plays a dominant role in defining the widths of the diffraction peaks (w), and while decreasing the horizontal divergence by a factor r lowers the intensity by a similar factor, it also decreases w by r^2, hence *raising* the FOM by a factor r. For the change in incident divergence to have this direct effect on *w*, the secondary divergence (set largely by the detector width) and overall flight path (which affects the time broadening of the diffraction peak) must be matched to the incident divergence.

The above considerations have shown that the FOM is maximised when the primary flight path of the instrument is ~40 - 50m (see Fig2) and the horizontal angular divergence is 0.002 radians. In this case the contributions to peak resolution from time and spatial (angular) components are matched. This divergence has been achieved by foreshortening the *side* walls of the neutron guide at a distance of 12m from the instrument centre. The combined effects of these design features, along with a significant (x2) increase in the detector area, have produced FOM increases over the existing ENGIN instrument varying between x8 and x16, as a function of wavelength (Figure 3).

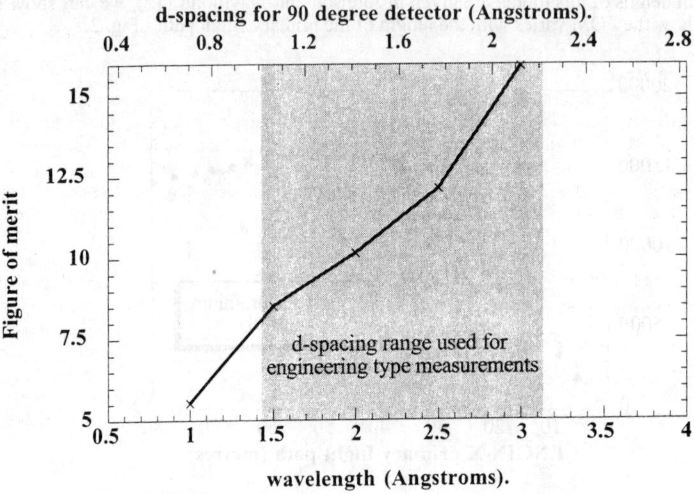

Fig.3 Changes in performance of the existing ENGIN instrument as a function of wavelength.

OTHER DESIGN FEATURES

Five further improvements over the current technology at ISIS are included in the design:

a) an in-shutter guide component
b) a curved guide
c) a 1-d converging guide section (snout)
d) a variable gauge volume capability
e) use of neutron lenses for small gauge volumes.

The in-shutter neutron guide will provide modest, but useful gains by ensuring that the guide is fully illuminated at the longer wavelengths. A glass, super-mirror coated (m = 3) neutron guide with a cross section of 80 x 25 mm will transport neutrons from the neutron shutter to the sample position. From 4 to 38m the guide will be supermirror coated on all four sides, and will curve in the horizontal plane with a radius of 10km. The curvature of the guide will significantly improve the signal to noise ratio of the instrument by removing the high energy neutrons and gamma ray components of the incident neutron beam.

From 38m to the sample position the guide will only be coated on its top and bottom surfaces. This is designed to maintain the vertical divergence of the neutrons incident on the sample, while decreasing the horizontal divergence in such a manner as to maximise the instrument design FOM. From 46m to 48m from the target, the top and bottom of the guide will slope towards each other, further increasing the neutron flux on the sample. Despite the increase in the vertical divergence of the incident neutron beam, this will have no appreciable effect on the resolution of the instrument, due to the 90° scattering geometry. To facilitate the definition of a wide range of gauge volume sizes the incident beam will include variable collimation, both in the beam size and the beam divergence (both horizontally and vertically).

ENGIN-X will use a large radial collimator in the diffracted beam to define the gauge volume. This technology revolutionised strain scanning at pulsed sources and was first designed and implemented by the authors [3]. ENGIN-X will have two sets of radial collimators, each with an add on 'snout' giving 4 gauge dimension options. The main collimators will provide 0.5, 1mm, 2mm and 4mm gauge lengths. The system is designed to enable removal of a collimator completely out of the sample plane to provide space for very bulky samples. Frame definition choppers will allow 25Hz operation which is necessary to define the wavelength range at the proposed 50m flight path (~3.2Å). Operation at max intensity (50Hz) will also be possible using a reduced wavelength range (~1.6Å) where this is required. Due to the use of a curved guide, a T_0 chopper will not be necessary.

A dedicated building and tunnel to protect the guide will be built. Within the building, an area of 6x6m around the sample is shielded and interlocked. This will allow easy positioning of large samples or ancillary equipment. Telescopes for optical alignment of the samples will be placed on support pillars for the building. The sample position will have a (XYZ-ω) sample positioning table, capable of positioning 250kg to better than 50microns. Heavier samples may be accommodated by using the buildings X-Y 2 tonne crane to bear some of the component weight, and using the positioner table for the control of the sample position. A schematic drawing of the main features of the ENGIN-X geometry is given in Figure 4.

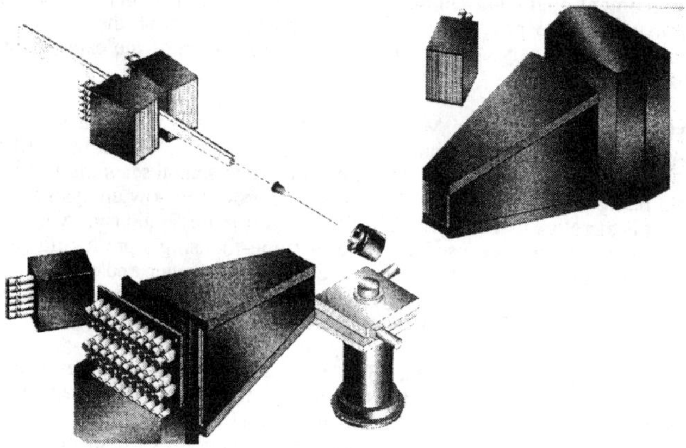

Fig.3 Schematic drawing of current ENGIN-X design geometry.

SOFTWARE DEVELOPMENT

The large increase in data acquisition rate over present instrumentation inherent in the ENGIN-X design means that it is vitally important that data handling improvements are also made. Without software improvements to allow continual monitoring of experimental progress and results, measurements will be made in a conservative manner, and the final information gathered will be less than could be optimally achieved. Specifically the requirements are:

(i) to provide computer aids in setting up the initial measuring strategy,
(ii) to automate as far as possible the routine aspects of the measuring process,
(iii) to complete data analysis in real-time, allowing changes to the measurement strategy,
(iv) to present this information in the most readily understood form.

These requirements lead to the following novel software developments:

Computer Aided Measurement Plan: Commercial CAD packages will be combined with new in-house software to provide a 'Computer-Aided Measuring Plan' (CAMP) during the set up of the experiment. This will allow visualisation of the sample with measurement positions, orientations, depths, and count times marked. Past experience, information on absorption and attenuation effects etc. will be incorporated in these codes so that the measurement procedure can be optimised, maximising the information gained during the experiment. This process will aid the visualisation of the experiment itself, and the detection of component-instrument clashes. A simple user interface to the CAMP will aid the building up of complex 3D scans. Complete integration of ancillary equipment (e.g. positioner, furnaces, stress rig) will ensure that all process variables applicable to the measurement are logged and with the neutron data.

Automated sample alignment and orientation. ENGIN-X will include CCD camera imaging of the view from alignment telescopes, simplifying remote sample manipulation from a single position. Software will be developed to allow 'point and click' determination of the sample position using these images, and the 'intelligent' incorporation of parameters into neutron surface position scans for more precise edge determination.

Automated instrument operation. Following the definition of the experiment within the CAMP, the CAMP will control the progress of the experiment, indicating the status of the present measurement and showing analysed data. Interactive modification of the experimental plan in real time will be possible.

Real time primary data analysis. Multiple detector banks which will, in some cases, be sub-divided to provide greater angular resolution, each provide a value of strain in a different direction. The typical combination of multiple specimen orientations and spatial scanning results in very large amounts of data being produced on a single sample. In order to allow analysis to keep pace with the experiment, it is therefore essential that ENGIN-X incorporate rapid primary data analysis. The data acquisition *hardware* will be used to perform 'time-focusing', producing single combined spectra for entire detectors, reducing the load on the control computer and providing near real-time monitoring of the diffraction spectra. Software 'time-focusing' of data is anticipated to be of a similar time scale to the fastest ENGIN-X measurement times, making this approach essential.

Optimisation of data acquisition times. Once real-time data analysis has been achieved this can be used to assess progress of the measurement plan, and to take intelligent decisions on whether the current measurement plan needs modification. Human judgement tends to overestimate the required measurement time required to obtain a specific accuracy of d-spacing measurement i.e.

signal to noise ratio. The software will therefore enable the measurement plan to be modified in the light of experience gained during earlier parts of the measuring process.

Automated 'first cut' strain analysis. The new ENGIN-X software will facilitate automatic Rietveld analysis of the entire diffraction pattern wherever possible. For many materials of known crystal structure, particularly engineering materials, a Rietveld refinement can be made very quickly, using a 'library' template as a starting point. This approach will be crucial where large numbers of points are measured during spatial scans or rapid variation in time dependent phenomena are under consideration. Data analysis of varying levels of sophistication will be possible. For many specimens strain may be simply calculated from the lattice parameter evaluated by Reitveld analysis at each measurement position. More complex analyses available will include allowance for elastic and/or plastic anisotropy either through modifications to the Rietveld refinement itself or via single peak analyses.

Results visualisation The strains obtained in the analysis will be fed back into the CAMP software allowing strain contour maps to be generated as they are measured. The software will allow the imposition of typical boundary conditions (e.g. zero stress perpendicular to the surface, stress balance along one direction, certain geometrical symmetries) to increase the information provided by these contour maps where appropriate. Similarly, where time dependent processes are under investigation, self scaling, automatically updated plots of strain, peak intensity and peak width as a function of time will be produced.

CONCLUSIONS

This paper describes ENGIN-X a novel purpose designed neutron diffractometer for the measurement of residual and applied stress in engineering materials and components. It has been optimally designed for the measurement of lattice parameter by neutron diffraction and when ENGIN-X and its associated software are commissioned the UK Engineering community will have:

- Access to world class neutron stress measurement
- Software capable of analyzing the data produced by ENGIN-X close to real time

REFERENCES

1. Allen, A, Andreani, C, Hutchings, M T, Windsor C G, NDT Int. 14 (1981) 249
2. Stacey, A, Macgillivary, H J , Webster G A, Webster P J, Ziebeck K R A, J Strain Anal. for Eng Design 20 (1985) 93.
3. Johnson, M W, Edwards, L and Withers, P J, Physica B 234, (1997) 1141
4. Webster GA, Ezeilo, AN, Physica B 234, (1997) 949
5. Smith,D J, Bourke, M A M, Hodgson, A P, Webster G A, Webster P J, J Strain Anal. for Eng Design 27 (1992) 77
6. Ozdemir, A T and Edwards.L, J Strain Anal. for Eng Design 31 (1996) 413
7. Webster, P J, Mills G., Wang X D, Kang W P and Holden, T M, J Strain Anal. for Eng Design 32 (1997) 389
8. Fitzpatrick, M E, Hutchings, M T, Withers, P J, Acta Mat. 45 (1997) 4867-4876
9. Edwards, L, Wang, D Q and Cook, R, *Proc. 5th Int. Conf. on Residual Stresses*, Eds. Ericsson T et al., Linkoping Univ., 1998, ISBN 91 7219 210 7, 1, 343
10. Rudkins N T, Modlen G F, Webster P J, J. Materials Proc. Tech.45 (1994) 287
11. Sivia, DS 'Data Analysis - A Bayesian Tutorial' (Oxford University Press) 1996.
12. Johnson M W & Daymond M R, Rutherford Appleton Laboratory Report, 2000.

RESIDUAL STRAIN/STRESS ANALYSIS BY MEANS OF ENERGY-DISPERSIVE NEUTRON-TRANSMISSION DIFFRACTION

P Mikula, V Wagner*, M Vrána and P Lukáš,
Nuclear Physics Institute, 250 68 Řež near Prague, Czech Republic
***Physikalisch Technische Bundesanstalt, 38116 Braunschweig , Germany**

ABSTRACT
A novel modification of the energy-dispersive neutron-transmission diffraction (EDNTD) method for scanning Bragg diffraction edges which has been implemented on a conventional diffractometer at a steady state reactor is reported. It is demonstrated that the method requiring precise measurements of the intensity-wavelength dependence, which has been used only on time-of-flight instruments can be also simply and succesfully used at steady state sources. Such an intensity-wavelength dependence can be found in a focused convergent beam coming on a sample from a thin bent perfect monochromator, where, though in a limited $\Delta\theta$ range, the monochromatized beam is strongly θ–λ correlated. The presented new technique was in this case tested for a precise scanning of the Bragg diffraction edge and consequently, in scanning of small lattice spacing changes of polycrystalline materials. This EDNTD technique permits us to determine lattice spacing changes $\Delta d/d$ with the sensitivity down to 10^{-5} for small sample volumes and reasonable counting times even at a medium power research reactor. Thus, it can be used for macro- and/or microstrains scanning in polycrystalline materials.

INTRODUCTION

The energy-dispersive neutron-transmission diffraction (EDNTD) method is based on the measurement of a decrease of a beam intensity $I(\lambda)$ transmitted through a sample in a $\Delta\lambda$–range in the vicinity of the Bragg cut-off. The Bragg edge in this case is observed when passing through the limit $\lambda=2d_{hkl}$, (d_{hkl} is the lattice spacing), below which particular reflection planes (*hkl*) begin to scatter neutrons. It means that no angular dependence of scattering is measured and only integrated intensity of this particular reflection can be determined for the transmitted beam for each value of λ. In the last years we have tested three modifications of the high resolution EDNTD based on Bragg diffraction optics which have been developed within the collaboration between NPI Řež and PTB Braunschweig (see refs. Vrána et al (1), Mikula et al (2) and Wagner et al (3)). For the precise measurement of the $I(\lambda)$ scan and thus the determination of the position and the profile of the Bragg edge positioned at $\lambda=2d_{hkl}$, all modifications use the dispersive setting of a double-crystal diffractometer, where cylindrically bent perfect Si-crystals for selection (or analysis) of a quasi-monochromatic beam are used. The most efficient modification of Wagner et al (3) employing a curved Si-analyzer in combination with an one dimensional high-resolution position sensitive detector (1d-PSD) for data acquisition has been routinely used in PTB and NPI as a complementary technique to the Bragg-diffraction-angle analysis (BDAA) method (see refs. Mikula et al (4), (6), (7) and Vrána (5)). However, due to a special diffraction geometry of the analyzer this modification is limited for strain investigations of only Fe samples. The advantage of the new modification presented consists in its simplicity and possibility of adjustment for any Bragg cut-off. However, as refered in Strunz et al (8) and Lukáš et al (9), thanks to a high sensitivity and resolution of the EDNTD-method with respect to microstructural changes, similarly to the peak-profile analysis often used in the case of the BDAA method, edge-profile analysis can also be applied.

EXPERIMENTAL PERFORMANCE

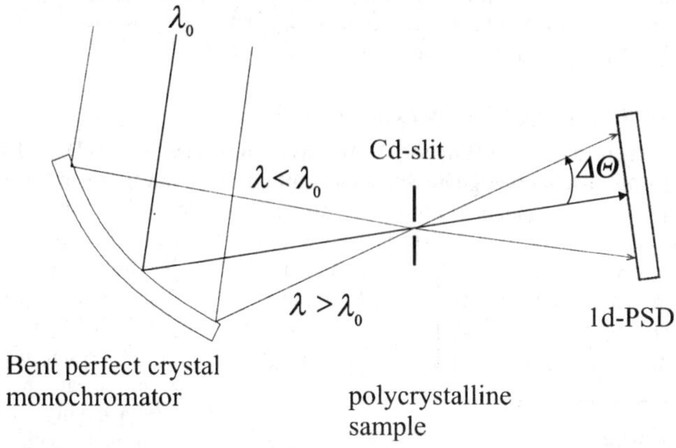

Fig. 1. Schematic sketch of the EDNTD focusing performance of the diffractometer

The simplest EDNTD modification arrangement schematically displayed in Fig. 1 which exploits Bragg diffraction optics basically consists of the following steps and properties (see refs. Vrána et al (5) and Mikula et al (7)):

a. Monochromatic neutrons selected by a horizontally bent monochromator from the white spectrum are focused on a small-width slit (focusing in real space).

b. There is a strong angular-wavelength correlation θ–λ in the beam passing through the slit as

$$\lambda = \lambda_0[1 - \Delta\theta \cdot \cot \theta_M (1 - L_{MS}/2f_M)] . \qquad (1)$$

which can be easily manipulated by changing the monochromator bending radius R_M in coincidence with the monochromator-sample distance L_{MS}. f_M is the focal length of the bent crystal monochromator, $2f_M = R_M \sin \theta_M$.

c. No Soller collimators are used.

d. Intensity $I(\lambda)$ of neutrons transmitted through the sample is measured by a position sensitive detector situated at a distance L_{SD} from the sample which, measures $I(\Delta\theta)$ via $\Delta\theta = x/L_{SD}$.

e. There are small blurring effects Δx_t and Δx_W,

$$\Delta x_t = W , \qquad (2)$$

$$\Delta x_W = W (1+2L_{SD}/f_M), \qquad (3)$$

which come from the effective mosaicity of the bent perfect crystal (determined by its finite thickness D_M and the value of the curvature) and the width of the slit W, respectively. They bring about the θ–λ correlation (1) imperfect and thus have an influence on the smearing Δx of the position of the Bragg edge as seen by PSD.

For evaluation of Δx_t only curvature of the lattice planes of the cylindrically bent crystal was considered. The parameters Δx_t and Δx_W together with the spatial resolution of the detector Δx_D determine the instrumental resolution, which can easily be estimated. The parameter Δx_t

was derived for the case of the monochromator thickness $D_M \geq W/\cos\theta_M$. For $D_M < W/\cos\theta_M$ an effective slit width W_{eff} should be introduced. The parameter Δx_W was derived for the case of an unlimited collimation of the incident polychromatic beam. However, in practice its impact can considerably be reduced for a well collimated beam in a guide tube having a divergence $\Delta\theta_o$. For $\Delta\theta_o \leq 2W/f_M$ we arrive at the estimate $\Delta x_W \leq \Delta\theta_o f_M(1+2L_{SD}/f_M)/2$.

EXPERIMENTAL RESULTS AND DISCUSSION

The test experiment was carried out on the two axis difractometer POLDI of PTB installed at the end of the thermal neutron guide of the medium-power (5 MW) research-reactor FRG-1 in GKSS Geesthacht. As a monochromator, we used a cylindrically bent Si(111) crystal slab of the dimensions of 1x30x200 mm^3 (thickness x width x length) for the take-off angle of $2\theta_M$=28.32° (λ=0.1534 nm). Thanks to remote control of the bending device and thus remote manipulation with the crystal curvature, the optimum focusing conditions could easily be settled, practically for any distance L_{MS} of the slit from the monochromator. The EDNTD profiles of the neutron beam passing through the slit and the polycrystalline samples were scanned by a linear position-sensitive detector ORDELA having the channel width about 0.35 mm and spatial resolution of about 1 mm. In our experiment we used the following performance parameters: L_{MS} = 1 m, L_{SD} = 1.875 m (the sample - detector distance) and R_M = 8.2 m (bending radius of the monochromator) and 1x20 mm^2 or 2x20 mm^2 slits. Due to a high reflection multiplicity and easily accessible neutron wavelength, for the test experiments we used α-Fe(321) edge.

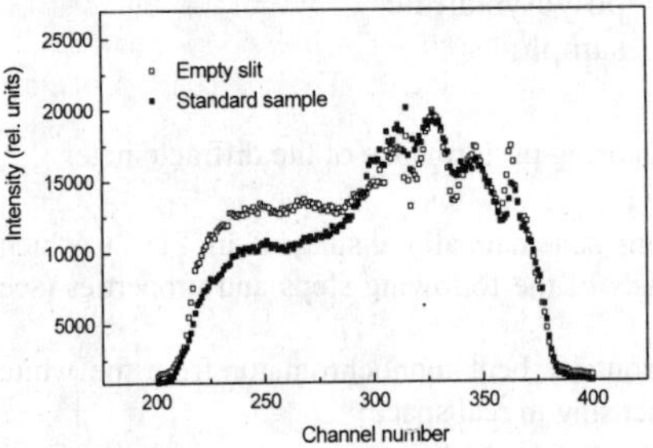

Fig. 2. Spectrum of neutrons (taken in the vicinity of λ=0.15 nm) passing through an empty slit (□) and a standard sample situated behind the slit (■).

Fig. 2 shows two transmission spectra of neutrons passing through the 2x20 mm^2 slit without and with the sample situated behind it. Besides the edge effect for the channel numbers lower than 300, thanks to a good imaging ability of the neutron optical system one also can see inhomogeneities of a distribution of neutrons in the guide tube. After substraction and normalization of intensities we can receive an amplitude of the Bragg edge as shown e.g. in Figs. 3 and 4. However, inspection of Figs. 3 and 4 also reveals the influence of the slit

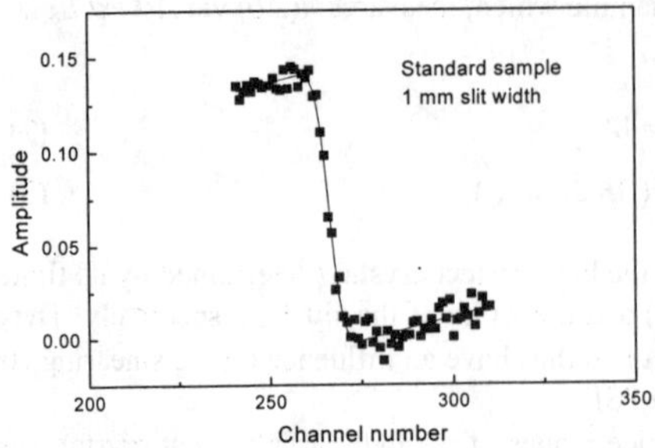

Fig. 3. Bragg edge of an 8 mm thick standard sample of Fe(321); $FWHM$=7.7x10^{-4} rad.

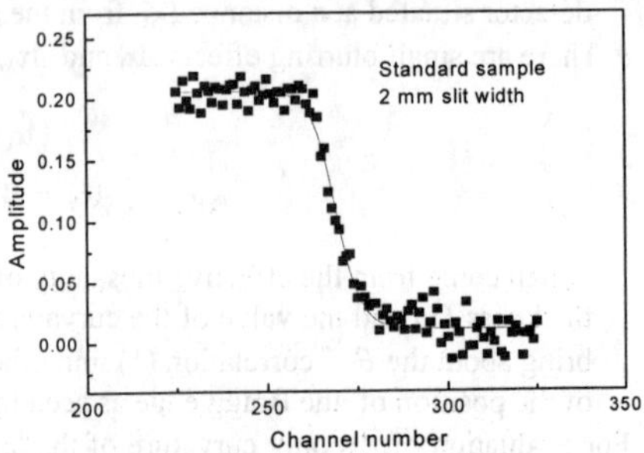

Fig. 4. Bragg edge of an 8 mm thick standard sample of Fe(321); $FWHM$=12.5x10^{-4} rad.

width on the angular resolution as was predicted by the formula (3). For *FWHM*($\delta\theta$) of the edges we assumed the *FWHM* of the Gaussian function in cumulative function used for fitting the shape of the Bragg edge profiles (1 channel corresponds to $\delta\theta$=2x10^{-4} rad). Furthermore, it can be seen from Figs. 3 and 4 that the amplitude of the Bragg edge is dependent on the angular resolution, where the effective mosaicity of the bent perfect monochromator via the slit width W also plays a significant role (see formula (2)). However, the most important parameter of this diffraction performance is the resolution $\delta\lambda/\lambda=\delta d/d$ which is mainly detemined by the width of the slit W, effective mosaicity of the monochromator and finally, by the Bragg angle at the monochromator through the formula

$$\delta d/d = (1/2)\delta\theta \cdot \cot \theta_M). \quad (4)$$

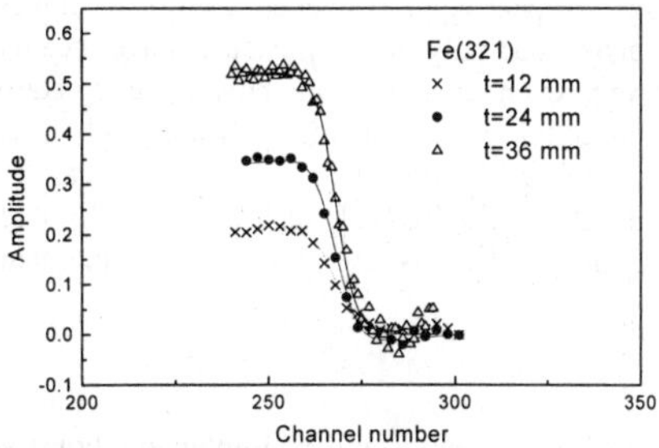

Fig. 5. Bragg diffraction amplitude of Fe(321) for different thickness t of the sample. Slit width W = 2 mm.

Therefore, in our case $\delta d/d$ - resolution is strongly influenced by a rather low angle θ_M at the monochromator (cot θ_M = 3.96).

In the case of the Bragg diffraction edge neutrons fulfilling the condintion $\lambda \leq 2d_{hkl}$ are scattered by a polycrystalline sample out of the incident beam. Then, it is clear that the amplitude of the edge corresponding to $\lambda=2d_{hkl}$ depends on the thickness of the sample as it is demostrated on Fig. 5.

As above mentioned, the EDNTD method can be succesfully used not only for scanning of macrostrains which are derived from the angular shifts of the Bragg edges measurements, but it also offers possibility of precise measurements of the shape of edge profiles. When using a sufficiently high resolution, microstrains can be derived from the edge profile analysis (see ref. Strunz et al (8)). Figs. 6 and 7 demonstrate that this new modification of the EDNTD method can also be used for the evaluation of microstrains (compare *FWHM* and profiles of edges with that of the standard sample in Fig. 3).

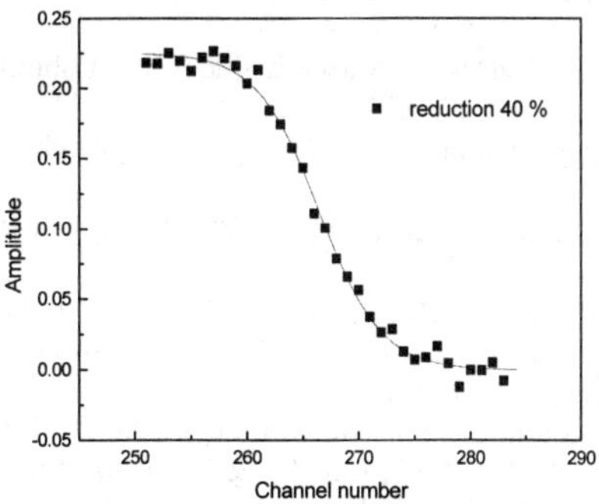

Fig. 6. Bragg edge of the plastically deformed ARMCO steel after thickness reduction of of 40% by cold rolling; *FWHM*=1.4x10^{-3} rad.

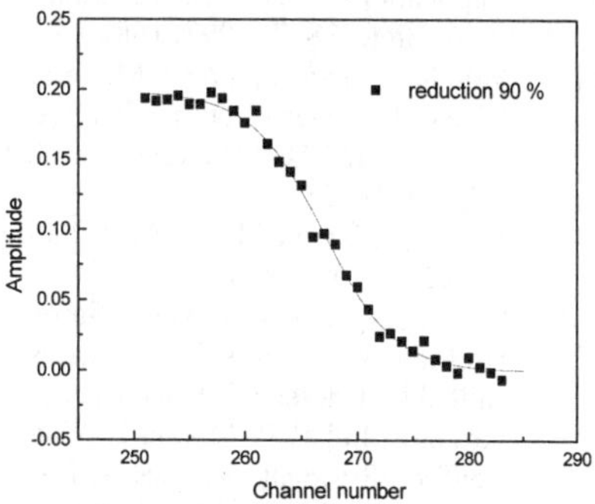

Fig. 7. Bragg edge of the plastically deformed ARMCO steel after thickness reduction of 90% by cold rolling; *FWHM*=1.6x10^{-3} rad.

DISCUSSION

The presented EDNTD focusing performance can easily be installed on any diffractometer having the possibility of changing the monochromator take-off angle; basically, one axis diffractometer could be sufficient. It can provide excellent luminosity and sufficient resolution even for evaluation of microstrains in plastically deformed polycrystalline samples. For this purpose possibly narrow slit (≤1 mm), a thin monochromator slab and a larger monochromator take-off angle which all determine the $\Delta d/d$ - resolution, would be advantageous. In our case, we were limited in the range of monochromator take-off angle and could not use another focusing monochromator with a shorter lattice spacing. When e.g. using θ_M=45°, the $\Delta d/d$ - resolution can easily be improved by a factor of 4 (cot θ_M = 1). In general, depending on the used method, the stress work is usually limited to a rather short θ– or λ–range covered by a single reflection profile or Bragg diffraction edge, respectively. However, using this novel technique, the EDNTD measurements, usually carried out only at the pulsed neutron beams (see e.g. Priesmeyer (10)), can be done effectively even at a medium power steady-state sources. Depending on the reactor power, the cross-section of the transmitted beam can be less than 10 mm^2 for the sample thickness up to 40 mm (for high-flux neutron sources it can be less than 1 mm^2). In this way, it should be pointed out that the EDNTD techniques are limited for measurements of only one strain component parallel to the axis of the incident monochromatized beam.

ACKNOWLEDGEMENTS

Methodological investigations of neutron Bragg diffraction optics and its implementation for high resolution neutron diffractometry and spectrometry are supported by the Grant Agency of the Czech Republic under contract No. 202/97/K038, Grant Agency of the Czech Academy of Sciences under contract No. A1048003 and the TMR-Network ERB FMR XCT 96-0057.

REFERENCES

1. Vrána M, Mikula P, Lukáš P, Šaroun J, Strunz P, Acta Phys. Hungarica **75** (1994) 305
2. Mikula P, Vrána M, Lukáš P, Šaroun J, Strunz P, Wagner V, Alefeld B, Physica B 213&214 (1995) 845
3. Wagner V, Kouřil Z, Lukáš P, Mikula P, Vrána M, In Proc. of 5th Int. Conf. on Applications of Nuclear Techniques "Neutrons in Research and Industry", 9.6.-15.6. 1996, Crete, 2867 (1997) 168
4. Mikula P, Lukáš P, Vrána, M, Klimanek P, Kschidock T, Macek K, Janovec J, Osborn JC, Swallowe GM, Journal de Physique IV 3 (1993) 2183
5. Vrána M, Lukáš P, Mikula P, Kulda J, Nucl. Instrum. Methods in Phys. Research A 338 (1994) 125
6. Mikula P, Vrána M, Lukáš P, Šaroun J, Strunz P, Wagner V, Alefeld B, Physica B 213&214 (1995) 845
7. Mikula P, Vrána M, Lukáš P, Šaroun J, Strunz P, Ullrich HJ, Wagner V, In Proc. of the 5th Int. Conf. on Residual Stresses ICRS-5, June 16-18, 1997, Linköping, Sweden, editted by Ericsson T, Odén M and Andersson A, 2 (1997) 721
8. Strunz P, Lukáš P, Mikula P, Wagner V, Kouřil Z, Vrána M, In Proc. of the 5th Int. Conf. on Residual Stresses ICRS-5, June 16-18, 1997, Linköping, Sweden, editted by Ericsson T, Odén M and Andersson A, Vol. 2 (1997) 688
9. Lukáš P, Kouřil Z, Strunz P, Mikula P, Vrána M, Wagner V, Physica B 234&236 (1997) 956
10. Priesmeyer HG, Larsen J, Meggers K, Journal of Neutron Research 2 (1994) 31

EVALUATION OF RESIDUAL STRESS IN GRAY CAST IRON USING CRICTICALLY REFRACTED LONGITUDINAL (L_{CR}) ULTRASONIC WAVES

MN Srinivasan and K Ramakrishnan
Mechanical Engineering Department
Lamar University
P. O. Box 10904, Beaumont, Texas 77710, USA

ABSTRACT

An ultrasonic technique using critically refracted longitudinal waves (L_{CR}) was employed for determining the magnitude and distribution of residual stresses in gray iron bars. Two sets of samples were prepared from gray cast iron cylinder liners: one set was machined and the other un-machined. Longitudinal ultrasonic wave velocity measurements were then made on all the samples before and after stress relief. Metallographic examination was then carried out on small polished pieces of samples that were cut from all these samples including the measurement of the eutectic cell count. The residual stress development in each sample was analyzed after accounting for the effect of microstructure on L_{CR} velocity.

INTRODUCTION

When they are not properly accounted for, residual stresses can prove to be disastrous. Residual stresses in castings may be induced by unequal cooling rates, volume changes accompanying phase transformations during solid state cooling and mold restraint to contraction, Bray et al (1). The problem of measuring these hidden stresses is usually difficult and requires careful attention being paid to the reliability and accuracy of the results. The X-ray diffraction technique provides accurate and repeatable results under most conditions, but its penetration is relatively low making it possible to measure only the surface effects. Ultrasonic techniques (non-destructive) on the other hand are capable of measuring both bulk and near-surface stresses, since acoustic waves that propagate within the stressed material are utilized.

The physical basis for stress measurements by ultrasound is that of the anharmonicity of the inter-atomic potential. On a microscopic basis, a stress applied to a solid causes a change primarily in the inter-atomic distance, which in turn produces a change in the velocity of sound. This is based on the application of small levels of stress to a metal that will change the velocities of ultrasonic waves in the metal, yielding a linear relationship between the applied stress and change in the velocity, Noronha et al (2). The dimensionless acoustoelastic factor is the ratio of the normalized wave velocity change and the strain in the material, as given by:

$$AEC = \frac{(\frac{\Delta v}{v_0})}{\Delta \varepsilon} \qquad (1)$$

Where AEC is the acoustoelastic constant

$\Delta v = (v - v_0)$

v is the ultrasonic wave velocity in the stressed condition, v_0 is the ultrasonic wave velocity in the stress-free condition of the material, and $\Delta\varepsilon$ is the elastic strain change after stress relieving. The determination of the stress in a casting from a reference level can be determined by the following equation, Bennett et al (3):

$$\sigma = \frac{E}{-(AEC)t}(t - t_0) \qquad (2)$$

where E is the Young's Modulus, t_o is the stress free travel time, and t is the measured travel time in the stressed state. The L_{CR} wave technique (unlike the acoustic birefringence technique) is a bulk wave that can measure internal stresses and needs only one free surface and it is the least affected by material texture or other anisotropy, Chundu (4). Based on the experimental work using both L_{CR} and shear waves, it has been demonstrated, Srinivasan et al (5) that the L_{CR} wave is the most sensitive and convenient ultrasonic stress measuring technique for ductile iron.

EXPERIMENTAL PROCEDURE

The basis of the ultrasonic stress measurement is the acoustoelastic effect, which refers to the changes in the speed of elastic wave propagation in a body that is simultaneously undergoing static elastic deformation. The L_{CR} ultrasonic technique utilizes a high frequency acoustic wave that travels just below the surface of the material. Since this acoustic wave is a bulk wave, this technique is sensitive to the stress field in a finite thickness of the material along the surface. Since the acoustic wave is generated and received at the surface, beam deviations from the expected travel path are not likely. Therefore, travel time measurements obtained with the L_{CR} wave are not affected by reflections. The results thus yield the true longitudinal velocity of the wave in the material. In the method noted above it is assumed that the AEC is a material constant. It is well known, however that the ultrasonic velocity is affected by changes in the microstructure of the material of the object. It would be more appropriate to denote AEC as AEF(acoustoelastic factor) and determine for a given microstructure for calculation of the residual stress. This is particularly relevant for cast iron where the graphite form and the volume fraction can significantly affect the ultrasonic velocity. As such the term AEF is preferred to AEC in this investigation.

Preparation of samples and velocity measurement procedure

Four cylinder liner castings were chosen at random from a lot of about twelve provided by Caterpillar, Inc. Two pieces, each 220 mm long, 25 mm wide and about 10 mm thick were cut from diametrically opposite ends of each cylinder liner. One sample from each set was machined all round so as to get flat bars of about 200 mm length, 20 mm width and 8 mm thickness, with flat, milled edges. The other piece was not machined, but lightly emeried, to remove any rust or surface contamination. Longitudinal ultrasonic wave velocity measurements were then made on the machined samples using the standard pulse-echo method. The instruments and the tools used for the purpose were: a LeCroy oscilloscope with a resolution of 0.11 ns, a Panametrics 5052 UA ultrasonic analyzer (pulser/receiver) and a 2.5MHz longitudinal wave probe. The probes were embedded in clear acrylic shoes, which were machined to allow the correct angle of incidence for critical refraction, Srinivasan et al (5). The mounting assembly for the probes and shoes was held in place using a magnetic clamp and spring device to exert a constant pressure on the assembly.

For the measurement of velocity of the L_{CR} waves, the shoes were initially positioned to touch each other and the travel time through the shoes and the material beneath the shoes was measured. Then the shoe containing the receiver probe was moved through successive chosen increments and the velocity at each successive position was again measured. A plot of the distance between the shoes against the travel time was drawn from this data, which enabled the calculation of the L_{CR} velocity. This is valid over the range of distance between the shoes considered since a straight-line relationship was found between the distance and the travel time. Similar velocity measurements were then made on a Plexiglas (clear glass) block from which wedges were to be machined. Based on the average of a large number of velocity measurements, it was determined that the angle of incidence of the longitudinal wave on the sample should be 37.5^0 for critical refraction. The velocity of the longitudinal waves in the clear acrylic as used was 2730 m/s, Stanley et al (6).

Stress relieving procedure and microstructure evaluation

The samples were subjected to careful thermal stress relieving treatment that consisted of heating to a temperature 600 C, below the eutectoid temperature, at a rate of 20 C/hr from room temperature, holding at 600 C for 8 hr and cooling at a rate of 20 C/hr to room temperature in the furnace. Care was taken to ensure that the furnace was at a uniform temperature in the region where the sample was placed. After ensuring that there was no detectable distortion in the samples due to stress relieving (by comparing the dimensions before and after stress relieving), L_{CR} velocity measurements were made on the samples using the same procedure AEF as before stress relief. Small pieces along the wave travel cut from each of the wave samples were prepared for metallographic examination using the standard procedures of grinding and polishing. They were etched with 2% solution of nitric acid in alcohol and the microstructure was observed using a metallurgical microscope at a magnification of 100. Each sample was re-polished and etched with Stead's reagent and the eutectic cell count in each sample was measured.

RESULTS AND DISCUSSION

It was noted that in almost all the cases there was no linear relationship between the travel distance and travel time, indicating that the L_{CR} velocity varied along the segments measured. In Table I and Table II are shown the L_{CR} velocity in the samples before and after stress relief, respectively. A study of the velocity computed for each successive measurement made in this work on all the samples both flat and curved (as-cast and stress relieved) indicates that the L_{CR} velocity has a much smaller range in the stress relieved flat bars that in the stress relieved curved bars. The probes were placed on the as-cast surface in the curved bars and on the machined surface in the flat bars. Assuming that the stress relieving treatment was effective in all the cases, it is reasonable to relate the ultrasonic velocity in the stress relieved condition to the microstructure, which is the result of solidification and subsequent cooling.

Table V and Table VI show microstructural variations in terms of graphite morphology in all the samples. It is observed that, in general, the as-cast surface has a wide variation in graphite morphology and the graphite is almost always of the random orientation (Type A, B, D) type. On the other hand, the flat bars whose top surfaces are about 4-5 mm below the as-cast surface show predominantly fine graphite of the preferred orientation type. It is therefore reasonable to infer that the solidification rate at the outer surface of the cylinder liners from which the samples were cut, is in general slower than at the underlying layer.

Table I
L_{CR} Velocity in As-cast Curved Bars, m/s

Sample	Positions 1	2	3	4
1	4581	4581	3927	4540
2	2950	4446	4505	3962
3	3226	3728	4579	4118
4	4465	4508	4047	4148

Table II
L_{CR} Velocity in Stress Relieved Curved Bars, m/s

Sample	Positions 1	2	3	4
1	4688	4569	4557	4520
2	3146	3519	3791	3970
3	4688	3731	3914	4091
4	4632	3602	3936	4118

Table III
L_{CR} Velocity in As-machined Flat Bars, m/s

Sample	Positions 1	2	3	4
1	4912	4719	4636	4720
2	4579	4476	4608	4614
3	4596	4688	4600	4614
4	4854	4529	4636	4698

Table IV
L_{CR} Velocity in Stress Relieved FlatBars, m/s

Sample	Positions 1	2	3	4
1	4688	4569	4557	4520
2	3146	3519	3791	3970
3	4688	3731	3914	4091
4	4632	3602	3936	4118

One possible reason for slow cooling at the surface of a centrifugally cast liner is the overheating of the die prior to pouring, due to very short cycle times, allowing sufficient time for the die to cool after knockout and before pouring the metal for the next casting. Another possible reason is that the mold coating offered high resistance to heat flow in the early stages of solidification. The eutectic cell count, which is a measure of the solidification rate is shown for the curved and flat bars in Table VII. It may be seen that except in sample 3, the cell count on the as-cast surface is lower than on the machined surface, indicating that in general the cooling rate at the outer surface of the liner casting is lower than at the underlying layer.

Table V
Graphite Morphology in Curved Bars

Samples	**Segment 1**	**Segment 2**	**Segment 3**	**Segment 4**
1	Medium and fine Type A graphite	Medium and fine Type A graphite	Medium and fine Type A graphite	Medium and fine Type A graphite
2	Fine Type B graphite	Fine Type B and fine Type D graphite	Medium Type D graphite	Medium Type D and fine Type B graphite
3	Medium Type B and Type A graphite	Coarse Type D and medium Type A graphite	Fine Type B and medium Type A graphite	Coarse Type D and fine Type A graphite
4	Medium Type D graphite	Medium Type D graphite	Medium Type D graphite	Medium Type D graphite

Table VI
Graphite Morphology in Flat Bars

Samples	Segment 1	Segment 2	Segment 3	Segment 4
1	Fine Type E graphite	Fine Type E graphite	Fine Type D graphite	Fine Type D and Type E graphite
2	Fine Type E graphite	Fine Type E graphite	Fine Type E graphite	Fine Type E graphite
3	Fine Type E graphite	Fine Type E graphite	Fine Type E graphite	Fine Type E graphite
Sample 4	Fine Type E graphite	Fine Type E graphite	Fine Type E graphite	Fine Type E graphite

Table VII
Eutectic Cell Count, cm^{-3}

Samples	Curved Bar	Flat Bar
1	4290	6690
2	4700	5350
3	5370	6500
4	6740	8690

It is seen from Table II and Table IV that the maximum velocity in the stress relieved curved and flat bars is around 4700-4800 m/s despite differences in the graphite morphology as seen in Table V and Table VI. It appears therefore that the AEF is not greatly affected by the type of graphite (and the eutectic cell count) in the samples examined. However, it is also evident from Table II and Table IV that the L_{CR} velocity can be significantly low in some segments of the samples that have similar type of graphite morphology as in samples that exhibit higher velocity. To resolve this anomaly, the microstructure examination was continued in further detail. It was found that the segments that contributed to low L_{CR} velocity showed significant amount of closely- packed interdendritic porosity. There was good correlation between the reduction in L_{CR} velocity and the severity of interdendritic porosity in the segment concerned.

It is known from theory that when Type A graphite forms, there will be substantial expansion communicated to the liquid during solidification, resulting in low or no porosity. On the other hand, when graphite form changes from Type A to Type B, to Type D, to Type E, the porosity increases in that order, since there is increasing resistance to the transfer of expansion force from graphite to the liquid, due to the steadily increasing intervening austenite dendrite. Table II and Table IV further indicate that the effect of the type of graphite on porosity is more pronounced at the as-cast surface than at the underlying (machined surface) layer. Under ideal conditions, the solidification should progress from the outer surface inwards, implying that the porosity should increase in the inward direction. Apparently, therefore, in the samples from exhibiting severe surface porosity and less sub layer porosity, the solidification at the surface was slower than in the underlying layer, preventing feed metal transfer to the surface.

Measurement of elastic strain change

The elastic strain change in each sample after stress relieving was determined using equation (1). If it is assumed that the stress relieving treatment adopted in this work is effective in removing the residual stress completely, a positive value of $\Delta\varepsilon$ indicates that the residual stress present in the sample before stress relieving is compressive. This is because there is reduced resistance to elastic wave propagation with respect to the ground state when the atoms move closer to each other on account of compression. Likewise, a negative value of $\Delta\varepsilon$ indicates that the residual stress present in the sample before stress relieving is tensile. For a given sample, $\Delta\varepsilon$ is proportional to $[\Delta v/v_0]$ and therefore, it is seen from Table VIII and Table IX that tensile and compressive stresses were present at random at both the surface (as-cast) and underlying layer (machined) of the liner castings. Results for two of the samples are shown in the said tables. The remaining two samples also showed similar results. Compressive residual stress is generally beneficial for good mechanical behavior, particularly in regard to fatigue and stress corrosion resistance. This is one reason why many industrial products are shot peened, to impose a net compressive stress on the surface. Tensile residual stress on the surface however, is generally undesirable, as it can promote premature failure under fatigue loading and stress corrosion conditions.

Table VIII
Sequential Velocity Change-Flat Bars

Sample No./ Position No.	LCR Velocity before stress relief, m/s	LCR Velocity after stress relief, m/s	Change in velocity w.r.t. stress relieved state, %
1/1	4912	4694	+4.64
1/2	4719	4776	-1.19
1/3	4636	4068	+13.96
1/4	4720	4215	+11.98
2/1	4579	4596	-0.37
2/2	4476	4553	-1.69
2/3	4608	4488	+2.67
2/4	4614	4496	+2.62

Table IX
Sequential Velocity Change-Curved Bars

Sample No./ Position No.	LCR Velocity before stress relief, m/s	LCR Velocity after stress relief, m/s	Change in velocity w.r.t. stress relieved state, %
1/1	4581	4688	-2.28
1/2	4581	4569	+0.26
1/3	3927	4557	-13.82
1/4	4540	4520	+0.44
2/1	2950	3146	-6.23
2/2	4446	3519	+26.30
2/3	4505	3791	+18.83
2/4	3962	3970	-0.20

The cylinder liners were cast in permanent molds using the true centrifugal casting process. Since no cores are used in this process, the solidification front moves radially inwards from the outer surface. Based purely on thermal considerations, the area cooling at the highest rate will be in a state of residual compression when the entire casting has solidified and cooled to a lower temperature (e.g. room), Angus (7). This trend is not observed in all zones in the samples examined in the present work. The presence of a strong residual tensile stress on the outer surface of two of the samples (curved samples 1 and 3) indicates that another factor has overridden the thermal factor. It is seen in Table V that the microstructure on the outer surface (as cast, not machined) of both these curved samples consists of significant amount of medium-sized Type A graphite. This suggests that in permanent mold centrifugal casting, if the cooling rate is delayed so much as to promote Type A graphite at the outer surface, instead of finer forms, dangerous tensile stresses are likely to develop in the outer surface. Also, the flat bars, which were machined from initially curved bars, also show significant variation in the graphite morphology on the machined surface (a few millimeters below the as- cast surface) with respect to the as-cast surface. This adds further evidence to support the conclusion, that the solidification conditions were non-uniform in the cylinder liner castings.

It is well known that the modes of solidification are different in cast irons with flake and under cooled graphite. In cast irons with flake and rosette graphite, the austenite-graphite eutectic is lamellar and the expansion of graphite during solidification is fully communicated to the surrounding liquid, reducing the solidification shrinkage to low levels. A side effect of this phenomenon is that the liquid tends to be in tension till the final stages of solidification and this stress is not significantly relieved on complete solidification owing to almost complete elimination of shrinkage cavities. On the other hand, in cast irons with under cooled graphite, the austenite-graphite eutectic is of the 'divorced' type, with graphite forming in the interdendritic regions of austenite, after the austenite dendrites grow to a significant extent. A side effect of this phenomenon is that the expansion force generated by graphite is not fully communicated to the liquid, but is rather shared by the liquid and the already solid austenite dendrites. Thus cast irons with under cooled graphite normally tend to have residual compressive stress on the initially solidified surface, as observed on most other alloys. This trend is evident in Table IV. However, if the solidification pattern shows a tendency to proceed towards flake growth, the residual compressive stress may be expected to decrease and the tendency of residual tensile stress to increase, when the graphite shifts towards flake type. The results seen in Table I and Table IV, support this postulation.

The appearance of flake graphite at the as-cast surface may be attributed to one or more of the following factors. Since sulfur promotes the formation of flake graphite, if the heats of such castings contained significantly higher sulfur, flake or rosette graphite would form instead of under cooled graphite. A more likely reason is that the heat transfer rate at the surface of the castings with flake graphite was significantly lower than in castings with under cooled graphite. One reason for this event is that the mold temperature at the time of pouring the molten metal was too high. This would happen if the permanent mold was preheated too much before pouring the molten metal, or if the operations had been performed on a continuous basis, insufficient time was allowed for the mold to cool after the previous casting was removed, before pouring the metal from the next heat. Slower cooling would also result when the mold coating applied is unusually thick, but this is less likely to occur in practice.

The presence of a residual tensile stress on the as-cast surface of the sample would make it more prone to failures such as cracking or fatigue failure, unless it is fully stress relieved prior to use. In the present work, castings 1 and 3 seem to be more prone to such failure than castings 2 and 4. Thus the ultrasonic technique developed in this project can be used as good diagnostic tool for identifying unacceptable castings in a given lot.

CONCLUSIONS

The present investigation indicates that appreciable residual stress (compressive or tensile) is developed on the outer surface of the as-cast cylinder liner castings examined. The nature and magnitude of the residual stress and its variation in the radial direction are strongly affected by the solidification conditions. The critically refracted longitudinal ultrasonic (L_{CR}) wave velocity change between the as processed and the stress-relieved states is a good measure of the residual stress. However, for the determination for the absolute values of the residual stress, knowledge of the acoustoelastic factor (AEF) is necessary. The L_{CR} technique also has a good potential for nondestructive evaluation of the quality through correlation with the trends in the sign of the residual stress. It was not possible in the present investigation to determine the absolute values of the residual stress, since information is required on the acoustoelastic factor applicable for different combinations of the microstructural features noted in the present investigation, and this generation of database can be planned to be a good scope for future work in this field.

LIST OF SYMBOLS USED

v = ultrasonic wave velocity (L_{CR}) in the stressed condition
v_0 = ultrasonic wave velocity (L_{CR}) in the stress-free condition
$\Delta\varepsilon$ = elastic strain change after stress relieving
E = Young's Modulus
t = measured travel time in the stressed state
t_0 = stress free travel time
σ = Residual stress in a casting
AEC = acoustoelastic constant
AFC = acoustoelastic factor

ACKNOWLEDGEMENT

The authors would like to thank Caterpillar Inc., Mossville, Illinois, for the support provided for this project.

REFERENCES

1. Bray DE, Srinivasan MN, Junghans P, Alagarsamy A, 'Critically Refracted Longitudinal Wave Technique: A new Tool for Measurement of Residual Stresses in Castings', Transactions of the American Foundrymen's Society 99, (1991) 265-267.
2. Noronha PJ, Chapman JR, Wert JJ, 'Residual Stress Measurement and Analysis using Ultrasonic Techniques', Journal of Testing and Evaluation 1, no. 3, (1973) 209-214.
3. Bennett J, 'Microstructure and Residual Stress Evaluation of Ductile Cast Iron using the Critically Refracted Longitudinal (L_{CR}) Propagation Technique', Masters thesis, Texas A&M University, (1993).
4. Chundu SN, 'Residual Stress Measurement in Ductile Cast Iron using Critically Refracted Longitudinal (LCR) Wave Technique', Masters thesis, Texas A&M University, (1991).
5. Srinivasan MN, Bray DE, Chundu SN, Alagarsamy A, 'Ultrasonic Technique for Residual Stress Measurement in Ductile Iron Continuous Cast Round Bars', Journal of Testing and Evaluation 20, no. 5, (1992) 331-334.
6. Stanley RK, Bray DE, Nondestructive Evaluation, McGraw Hill (New York), (1989) 435-438.
7. Angus HT, Cast Iron: Physical and Engineering Properties, Butterworths (Boston), 1976.

STRESS MEASUREMENT BY BARKHAUSEN NOISE METHOD
EFFECT OF HEAT TREATMENTS, DE-MAGNETIZED STATE AND CHEMICAL COMPOSITIONS OF STEELS

Koji Yatsushiro and Masahiko Hihara
Yamanashi Industrial Technology Center,
Kofu, Yamanashi, 400-0055, Japan
Makoto Kuramoto
Polytechnic University,
Sagamihara, Kanagawa, 229-1196, Japan

ABSTRACT
This paper reports the application of the Barkhausen noise method to stress measurement of steels. The studied substances are heat treatment processes, de-magnetized state and chemical compositions. Used steels are JIS-SS400 and S45C. These base metals underwent stress-relief annealing treatment under vacuum at 650°C for 1hour. After the process, S45C was given quenching and tempering treatments. The microstructure was studied by hardness distribution. As a result, remarkable differences were shown in measured values. It is considered that de-magnetization has to be done before the examination. Therefore, the specimens that were given quenching and tempering treatments have always to have the de-carburized layer removed, and be de-magnetized. When this method is used for the specimens tempered over 500°C after the quenching, it is necessary to consider further.

INTRODUCTION
Analyzing of stress and material property is important for evaluation of strength of material in mechanical construction. There are many methods of stress measurement by using X-ray diffraction, ultrasonic wave, acoustic emission, magnetism and so on. In particular, the method that uses the magnetism responds sensitively to the change of the stress and structure. Also, this method has advantages that the measuring time and size of the measuring device can be reduced. Such improvement of the devices, have been already reported in many papers [1),-4)].

Authors tried to use Barkhausen noise method that is one of the stress measurement methods using the magnetism. In summary, we examined the effect of de-carburisation, heat treatment, quenching, tempering and annealing. Moreover, we tried to apply same method in cases where residual magnetization existed, and it was de-magnetized. Afterwards, we investigated relation of applied strain in each case.

EXPERIMENTAL PROCEDURE
Specimen and heat treatments
The steels used were JIS-SS400(Rolled steel for general structure, ISO-E275A) and

S45C(Carbon steel for mechanical structure, ISO-683/1,C45). Specimens were cold rolled steels, the size was: 210mm Length, 25mm Width, 5mm Thickness. All base metals underwent stress- relief annealing treatment under vacuum at 650°C for 1 hour and cooled treatment in furnace. After that, in order to examine characteristics of the materials before and after the heat treatments, the Vickers hardness of cross section of each specimen was measured.

S45C underwent water cooling quenching treatment at 850°C for 1 hour under vacuum, or in Argon atmosphere at 1 atmospheric pressure. Afterward it was tempered under vacuum at 200, 350 and 500°C.

Also, Vickers hardness distribution of two specimens that were held for 0.5 and one hour at quenching under vacuum was measured to examine how holding time influence to Vickers hardness. When the holding time was 0.5 hour, the softened layer was found to the depth of about 300μm from the surface. On the other hand, when the holding time was one hour, the depth of soften range was further extend to about 400μm. Because of this fact, hereafter, holding time for quenching and tempering in this test was determined to be one hour.

Instrument of Barkhausen noise method

Fig.1 shows apparatus of system of instrument used in this study. The apparatus is composed of power source for primary coil, primary exciting coil for detector, secondary coil and Barkhausen noise instrument. In the power source for primary coil, exciting wave was generated by a function generator. Then, electric power was increased with the power amplifier. Barkhausen noise was generated due to magnetized the specimen with primary coil. Unnecessary range of frequency was removed by using band pass filter.

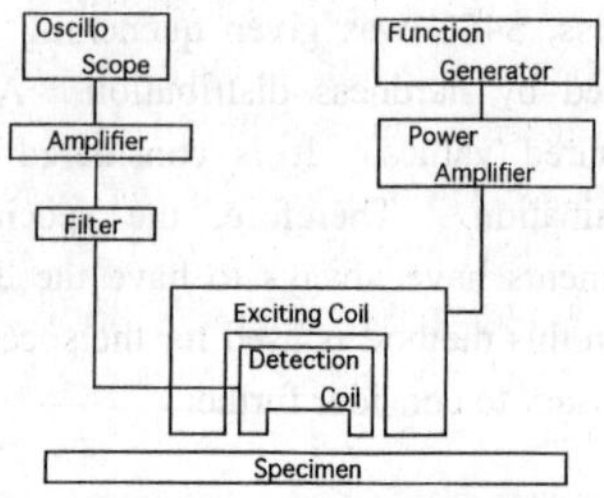

Fig.1 Schematic view of Barkhausen noise measurement

Moreover, as the exciting frequency is easily influenced by secondary detector, it was cut by band pass filter under 10kHz and over 50kHz. Barkhausen noise was measured by the input to digital oscillo-scope after amplification by amplifier. The maximum voltage of Barkhausen noise was used as the parameter of the stress measurement. Fig.2 shows relation of the exciting high frequency and the effective penetration depth.

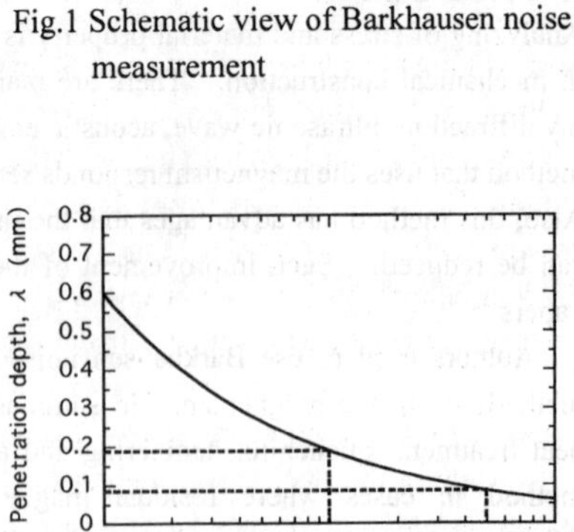

Fig.2 Exciting frequency vs the effective penetration depth.

Apparatus of loading jig

Barkhausen noise was measured by using the four bending load jig and cementing an electric strain gauge on the tensile stress side of the specimen, which gives applied strain. The value was measured five times. The maximum voltage $V_{p\text{-}p(max)}$ of Barkhausen noise measured by digital oscilloscope. We studied the relation of the average value of Barkhausen noise parameter and applied strain.

AC de-magnetizing device

We made AC de-magnetizing equipment. The base metals and stress-relief annealed specimens of SS400 and S45C were de-magnetized. In this experiment, the specimen has been affected somehow by residual magnetization and stress, according to the magnitude of the residual magnetization in the process the magnetic domain was disturbed. We thought this could give different results in the output shown in Barkhausen noise.

Then, the specimen underwent AC de-magnetization, and residual magnetization was removed. The measurement of Barkhausen noise was done after a stable magnetic domain had been attained, and it was compared with before de-magnetization. The relation between intensity of AC magnetic field and the magnetic flux density of the specimen to be de-magnetized, was that when the value of current of AC magnetic field magnified and magnetic flux density has reached the saturation, the de-magnetization was complete.

Experimental results and discussion

Heat treatments and de-carburisation

Fig.3 shows hardness distribution curves of specimens before and after quenching of S45C. A soft layer existed on the depth of about 400μm on surface of specimen after the quenching under vacuum. The quenching treatment in the argon atmosphere was done to improve this phenomenon. However, de-carburized layer was found over a small range, and the depth was not so much improved. But the soft layer still existed to the depth of about 250μm. Therefore, de-carburized layer of specimen surface was removed to the depth of about 500μm by using surface grinding machine. Then the tempering treatment was undertaken at each temperature.

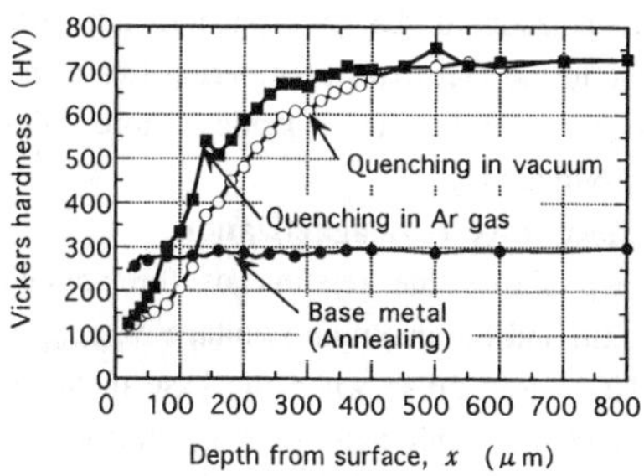

Fig.3 Vickers hardness vs depth from surface of base metal and quenched S45C

Fig. 4 shows Vickers hardness distribution curves of cross sectional specimen of tempered S45C at each temperature. Even in this case, soft layer which was thought due to the de-carburisation existed to the depth of about 50μm. As the tempering temperature became higher, limit of soften layer by de-carburized phenomenon widened. We decided to remove the surface of specimen to the depth of about 100μm by a using surface grinding machine.

Fig.5 shows relation of the time and the temperature of the electric furnace under vacuum at quenching treatment, temperature of the specimen, and the degree of vacuum. The degree of vacuum into furnace was continuously decreased during heat treatment by using rotary and diffusion pump. That is, the temperature in the electric furnace increased and the degree of vacuum decreased. This shows one of the major reasons why de-carburisation occurs. This fact also shows why a little residual air remains in the furnace that can be not removed by the diffusion pump. It is considered that this fact had refined de-carburized layer. Furthermore, the material for quenching was picked out, at the high temperature of 850°C, from the vacuum electric furnace and put into water. At this time, because the material was in contact with air, a bigger de-carburized layer was formed. For the same reason, we considered that this phenomenon was due to the fact that in tempering treatment, higher temperature made more de-carburized layer.

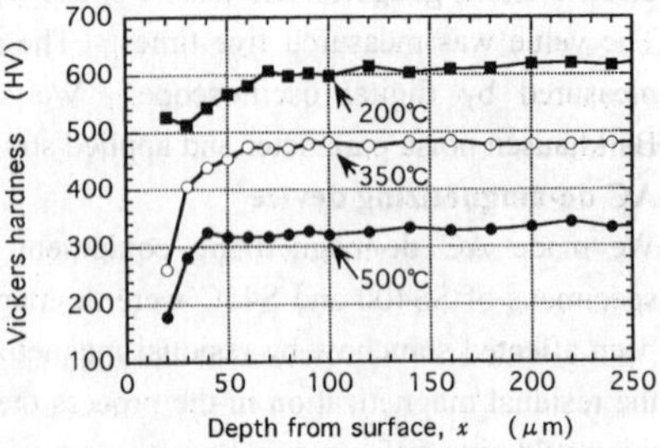

Fig.4 Vickers hardness vs depth from surface of S45C by various tempering temperatures

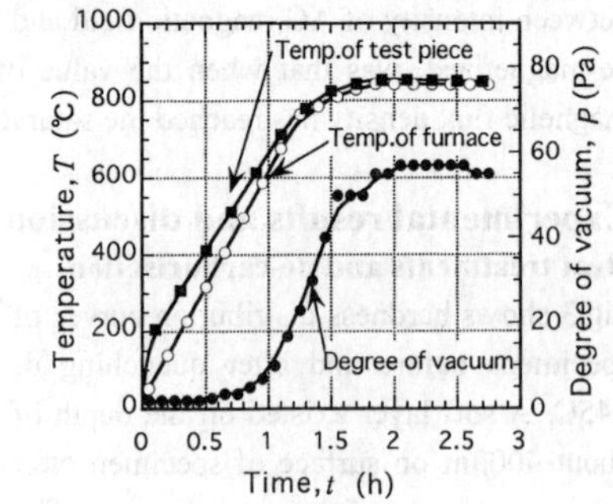

Fig.5 Heat treatment temperature and degree of vacuum vs measuring time

Effect of AC de-magnetization

Fig.6 shows the relation of the applied strain and the maximum voltage $V_{p\text{-}p(max)}$ of Barkhausen noise when the base metal of SS400 had undergone de-magnetization or not. After the de-magnetization strain sensitivity increased considerably compared to before the de-magnetization. Moreover, it was considered that this difference appeared for reason that the base metal before the de-magnetization was measured before grinding. We decided when $V_{p\text{-}p(max)}$ of Barkhausen noise was large the strain sensitivity was high. Also, the same tendency was shown in the S45C.

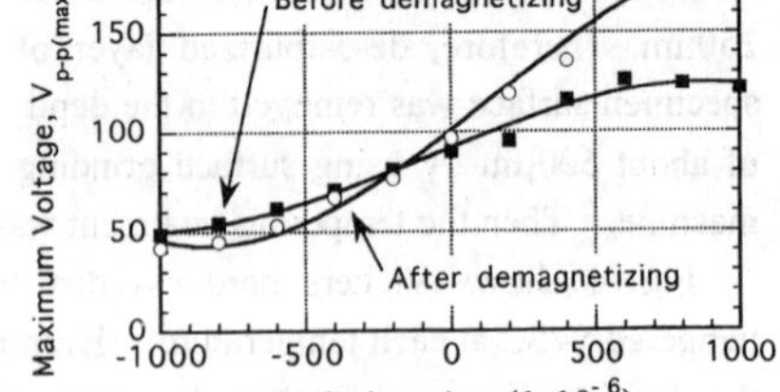

Fig.6 Maximum voltage $V_{p\text{-}p(max)}$ vs applied strain of SS400 specimen before and after de-magnetization

Stress-relief annealing treatment

Fig.7 shows the relation of the applied strain and $V_{p-p(max)}$ when the stress-relief annealed SS400 had undergone the de-magnetization or not. The difference of values was not seen remarkably before and after the de-magnetization. The same tendency was seen in S45C stress-relief annealed specimen.

Fig.8 shows the relation of the applied strain and $V_{p-p(max)}$ of stress-relief annealed SS400 and S45C. SS400 showed higher strain sensitivity than S45C. The difference was due to amount of the carburisation. $V_{p-p(max)}$ over $-500x10^{-6}$ of the applied strain of S45C showed increasing tendency, the strain sensitivity was high. Further, $V_{p-p(max)}$ over $600x10^{-6}$ of the applied strain did not increase, the strain sensitivity was showed no good tendency. SS400 showed the same tendency to the S45C, the change of $V_{p-p(max)}$ was bigger than one of S45C. $V_{p-p(max)}$ on the range of $-500x10^{-6}$~$+600x10^{-6}$ was more sensitive than S45C. The effect of AC de-magnetization in this experiment was large on the base metal before heat treatment, however the stress-relief annealing specimen did not exhibit so large change. It was considered that the residual magnetization was removed by stress-relief annealing, and was removed for reason that de-carburized layer was ground. Further, the penetration depth by the difference of exiting frequency was very shallow to be shown Fig.3.

Effect of de-carburisation

We compared the quenched S45C before the grinding, and after grinding to remove the de-carburized layer. Fig.9 shows the relation maximum voltage $V_{p-p(max)}$ of applied strain and Barkhausen noise in the

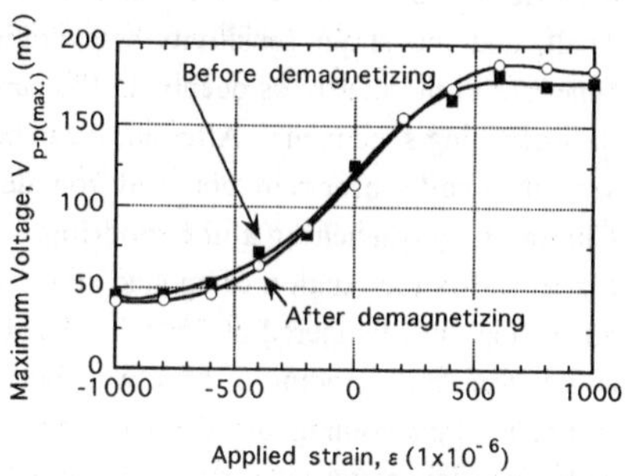

Fig.7 $V_{p-p(max)}$ vs applied strain of stress-relief annealed SS400 before and after de-magnetization

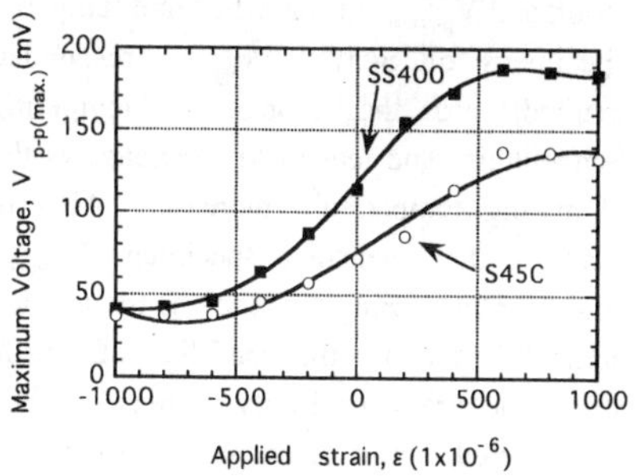

Fig.8 $V_{p-p(max)}$ vs applied strain of stress-relief annealed SS400 and S45C after de-magnetization

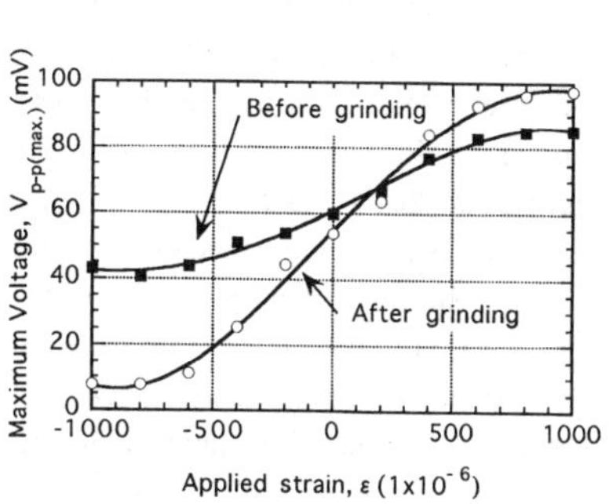

Fig.9 $V_{p-p(max)}$ vs applied strain of quenched S45C before and after grinding

above case. The strain sensitivity was high, when the gradient of $V_{p-p(max)}$ was large to the increase of applied strain. The reaction of $V_{p-p(max)}$ to applied strain before the grinding was small, and the strain sensitivity was not good. The flux from excitation coil did not penetrate in the matrix as deeply, in the case that the surface layer was de-carburized as in the quenching specimen. After all, it can be conjectured that Barkhausen noise values from secondary coil sensor were obtained from de-carburized layer.

Changing by quenching and tempering

Fig.10 shows the relation of applied strain and $V_{p-p(max)}$ of S45C which was ground after the quenching, and tempered at 350°C. There were not much difference in the $V_{p-p(max)}$ after and before the grinding. This was because the de-carburized layer was so thin that magnetic flux, coming out from the coil for magnetization, penetrated through this de-carburized layer and also matrix has been magnetized. Therefore, it was thought that it would not give much effect on the measurements. The same tendency was observed of the materials at different tempering temperatures.

Fig. 11 shows the relation of applied strain and $V_{p-p(max)}$ of quenched and tempered specimens of S45C. $V_{p-p(max)}$ responded markedly to the change of tempering temperature, and tended to increase as the tempering temperature increase. Also in case of the quenched specimen, $V_{p-p(max)}$ showed a increasing tendency as the applied strain. But under the condition of tensile stress, the strain sensitivity decreased, when the applied strain increased. When the applied strain became about 1000×10^{-6}, $V_{p-p(max)}$ reached almost the saturation, and stopped changing. Also in the case of compressive stress, the same situation was observed to the tensile stress. Because the specimen's permeability lowered, Barkhausen noise $V_{p-p(max)}$ reached near saturation. In case of the specimens tempered at 200°C and 350°C, $V_{p-p(max)}$ showed almost straight as applied strain increase. But for higher tensile strain, the strain sensitivity was low. It was the same tendency of quenched specimen. In the case of the tempered specimen at 500°C, under the condition of tensile stress, $V_{p-p(max)}$ showed remarkable increase from about 0×10^{-6}. When the applied strain was

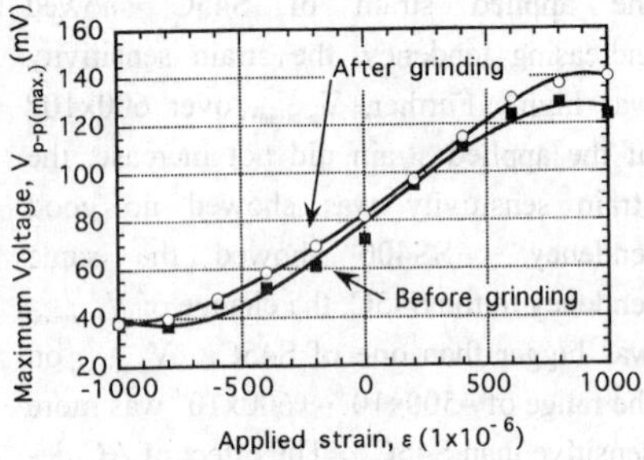

Fig.10 $V_{p-p(max)}$ vs applied strain of quenched and tempered(at 350°C) S45C before and after grinding

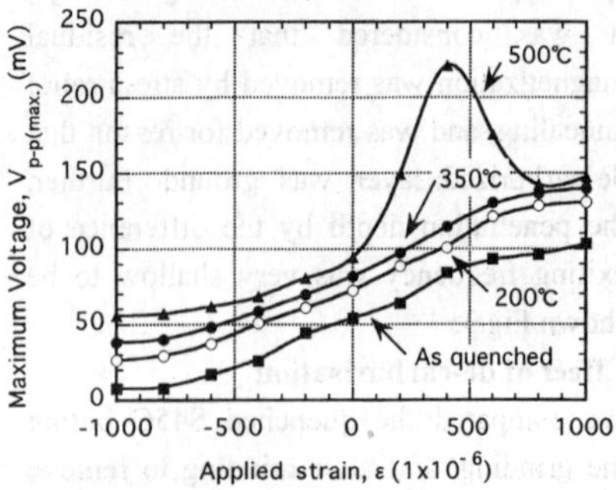

Fig.11 $V_{p-p(max)}$ vs applied strain of S45C, quenched and tempered at various temperatures

$400x10^{-6}$, it showed an abnormal distribution that indicated the maximum point. After that, $V_{p-p(max)}$ showed a tendency of sudden decrease, and it was on the curve of extension line of the compressive stress value side. Over the applied strain, $V_{p-p(max)}$ showed the same tendency in the case of other tempered temperatures. The definite cause of this has not yet been made clear. Also, it was thought that a measurement was possible only in the condition from compressive stress. From all these facts, it has become known that the range of stress measurements is extremely limited.

CONCLUSION

Barkhausen noise had showed sensitive reaction to the change of the steel structure, heat treatment process and others. Therefore, it was very important to monitor the chemical compositions of the steel, and the heat treatment process for the measurement. It was also found out that measurement after AC de-magnetization was extremely important for the correct measurement. The following is the conclusion we have reached.

1) The effect of AC de-magnetization was observed to give an especially large change on the base metal before the heat treatment. This effect was also shown on the stress-relief annealing specimen. On the other hand, not so much change was found on the tempering treatment specimen. But, de-magnetization should be used without fail.
2) In stress measurements, $V_{p-p(max)}$ of the quenched S45C changed considerably, in the case when the de-carburized layer existed, and in the case when the de-carburized layer had been ground. But, when the material was tempered at 200°C and 350°C, de-carburized layer did not influenced to the $V_{p-p(max)}$, that is before and after grinding. But, a unique phenomenon was observed in the specimen when tempered at 500°C. A definite explanation could not be found for this. In such a case as quenching when the surface was greatly de-carburized, it was necessary that a measurement should be taken after the de-carburized layer has been removed.
3) In this study, when the value of applied strain reached $+1000x10^{-6}$ of tensile stress, the magnetic flux reached the magnetism saturation, and the Barkhausen noise $V_{p-p(max)}$ had hardly made any change. On the compressive strain side, when the applied strain exceeded $-1000x10^{-6}$, the specimen's permeability lowered and stopped magnetization. Thereby the Barkhausen noise $V_{p-p(max)}$ reached near saturation. Therefore, the most appropriate range of this Barkhausen noise stress measurement was considered to be about applied strain of range from $-600x10^{-6}$ to $+600x10^{-6}$.

REFERENCE

[1] Furuya Y and Shimada H : J. Japanese Soc. Non-Destructive Inspection, Vol.35, No.8, (1986-8) 592, (In Japanese)

[2] Inaguma T, Sakamoto H and Sugino K : J. Japanese Soc. Non-Destructive Inspection, Vol.46, No10, (1997-10) 761,(In Japanese)

[3] Pasley R L : Mater.Eval., Vol.28,No.7(1970) 157

[4] Rautioaho R and Karjalainen P :J. Magn. Mat., Vol.68,(1987) 314

MEASUREMENT OF RESIDUAL STRESS IN POLYMERIC MATERIALS

A S Maxwell and A Turnbull
Centre for Materials Measurement and Technology
National Physical Laboratory
Teddington
Middlesex, TW11 0LW

ABSTRACT
A comparative evaluation has been made of the effectiveness of the layer-removal and hole-drilling techniques for measurement of residual stress in polymeric materials. A quenched sheet of ABS containing equi-biaxial residual stresses was produced. Residual stresses in the polymer sheet determined from the layer-removal technique were found to be both equi-biaxial and repeatable. In contrast, residual stresses determined by hole-drilling were not equi-biaxial and did not balance through the thickness of the specimen. Although hole-drilling is a more flexible technique than layer-removal, the results obtained are not as reliable.

INTRODUCTION
Thermoplastic polymer mouldings contain residual stresses that are the consequence of differential cooling rates through the thickness of the mould. Although these stresses are commonly found in plastics their magnitude can be extremely difficult to predict as it depends upon a wide range of variables including the mould design, material and processing parameters. These stresses can significantly reduce the life expectancy of the product, increasing the likelihood of dimensional instability and environment stress cracking.

Two techniques that can be used for the measurement of residual stress are the layer-removal and hole-drilling techniques, both well established in the metals industry. Procedures for these two techniques are given in an NPL good practice guide on residual stresses in plastics (1).

The layer-removal technique (2,3) is based on measuring the curvature of flat samples after thin layers have been removed from the surface. In response to removal of a layer, the sample restores equilibrium by warping. The measured curvature as a function of depth can be used to calculate the stress distribution through the thickness of the sample prior to layer removal. The technique has been the primary method used for plastics but is limited to the measurement of residual stress in flat sheets.

Hole-drilling is potentially a more flexible technique as the measurements can be made over a smaller area. However, whilst a standard exists for hole-drilling in metals (4), there has been no detailed study of its application to polymers. The method involves fixing a rosette of strain gauges to the surface of the specimen and drilling a hole precisely through the centre of the rosette. The strains produced at the surface reflect the stress relaxation which has taken place. Using appropriate models, in principle it is possible to calculate the stresses along the two principal axes of the sample using the measured strains.

In previous work (5), comparison between the two techniques was uncertain due to the anisotropy of the stresses in the samples tested. The purpose of this work was to compare the two techniques more directly using specimens containing equi-biaxial stresses.

EXPERIMENTAL

MATERIALS

Specimens containing equi-biaxial residual stresses were produced by heating sheets of ABS in an air-oven at 150°C for 8 hours and then quenching them into iced water at 0°C. The specimens used were flat plates of ABS (Novodur PKT2) 2.6 mm thick which had been prepared by injection moulding. In order to limit the possibility of the plates distorting when quenched, the ABS sheets were held between two aluminium plates. Once quenched the specimens were stored in liquid nitrogen to prevent stress relaxation from occurring.

LAYER-REMOVAL

Using a mill cutter, two rectangular specimens (70 mm x 10 mm x 2.6 mm) were removed from the central region of the ABS plate one parallel and one transverse to the main axis of the plate. The thickness of the specimens were measured prior to layer removal and after each subsequent layer removal. Layers were removed from the specimens using a conventional milling machine with a fly-cutting tool operating at 1600 rpm and at a feed rate of 25 mm/min. During milling, the specimen was fixed and held flat by a vacuum table. The layers removed from the specimen were approximately 0.01 mm thick.

The deformation of the specimens was measured immediately after a layer had been removed using an optical technique (5). The radius of curvature is determined from a circular fit to the measured displacement of the sample at different positions along its length. The residual stresses in the specimen are then calculated in each layer using the equations developed by Treuting and Read (3).

HOLE-DRILLING

A rosette of strain gauges was fixed to the specimen using cyanoacrylate adhesive. The drill was positioned at the centre of the rosette using an optical microscope. In order to minimise induced pressure and heat during drilling, the process is carried out by hand. Holes were drilled in depth increments of about 0.1 mm with a diameter of about 1.7 mm. At each depth, the readings on the strain gauges are allowed to stabilise for about 3 mins before measurements are taken. The residual stresses in the specimen are then calculated at each hole depth using the readings obtained from the strain gauge measurements.

RESULTS

LAYER-REMOVAL

Residual stresses in the ABS specimen were calculated along the principal longitudinal and transverse axes using Treating and Read equations (Figure 1). As can be seen, the residual stresses in the longitudinal and transverse directions are very similar, as would be expected from a plate containing an equi-biaxial stress distribution. In both directions the residual stresses are compressive (negative values) at distances between 0.1 mm and about 0.4 mm from the surface, with a maximum value of 3 MPa, becoming tensile with a maximum value of about 2 MPa towards the centre of the specimen.

In previous work (5), comparison between the two techniques was uncertain due to the anisotropy of the stresses in the samples tested. The purpose of this work was to compare the two techniques more directly using specimens containing equi-biaxial stresses.

EXPERIMENTAL

MATERIALS

Specimens containing equi-biaxial residual stresses were produced by heating sheets of ABS in an air-oven at 150°C for 8 hours and then quenching them into iced water at 0°C. The specimens used were flat plates of ABS (Novodur PKT2) 2.6 mm thick which had been prepared by injection moulding. In order to limit the possibility of the plates distorting when quenched, the ABS sheets were held between two aluminium plates. Once quenched the specimens were stored in liquid nitrogen to prevent stress relaxation from occurring.

LAYER-REMOVAL

Using a mill cutter, two rectangular specimens (70 mm x 10 mm x 2.6 mm) were removed from the central region of the ABS plate one parallel and one transverse to the main axis of the plate. The thickness of the specimens were measured prior to layer removal and after each subsequent layer removal. Layers were removed from the specimens using a conventional milling machine with a fly-cutting tool operating at 1600 rpm and at a feed rate of 25 mm/min. During milling, the specimen was fixed and held flat by a vacuum table. The layers removed from the specimen were approximately 0.01 mm thick.

The deformation of the specimens was measured immediately after a layer had been removed using an optical technique (5). The radius of curvature is determined from a circular fit to the measured displacement of the sample at different positions along its length. The residual stresses in the specimen are then calculated in each layer using the equations developed by Treuting and Read (3).

HOLE-DRILLING

A rosette of strain gauges was fixed to the specimen using cyanoacrylate adhesive. The drill was positioned at the centre of the rosette using an optical microscope. In order to minimise induced pressure and heat during drilling, the process is carried out by hand. Holes were drilled in depth increments of about 0.1 mm with a diameter of about 1.7 mm. At each depth, the readings on the strain gauges are allowed to stabilise for about 3 mins before measurements are taken. The residual stresses in the specimen are then calculated at each hole depth using the readings obtained from the strain gauge measurements.

RESULTS

LAYER-REMOVAL

Residual stresses in the ABS specimen were calculated along the principal longitudinal and transverse axes using Treating and Read equations (Figure 1). As can be seen, the residual stresses in the longitudinal and transverse directions are very similar, as would be expected from a plate containing an equi-biaxial stress distribution. In both directions the residual stresses are compressive (negative values) at distances between 0.1 mm and about 0.4 mm from the surface, with a maximum value of 3 MPa, becoming tensile with a maximum value of about 2 MPa towards the centre of the specimen.

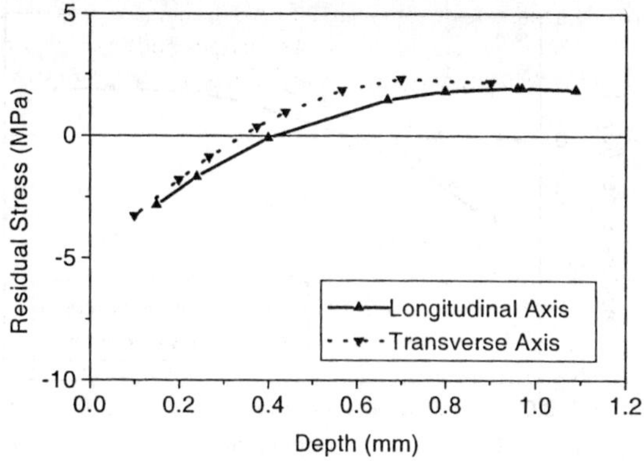

Fig. 1 Residual stresses obtained using the layer-removal technique

HOLE-DRILLING

Hole-drilling tests were conducted on the same biaxial plate from which the layer-removal specimens had been prepared. Strain gauge readings were obtained as a function of the hole depth using the strain gauges situated around the hole. The residual stresses along the two principal axes (Figure 2) were calculated using the procedure described in the ASTM standard. These results indicate that the residual stresses have a maximum compressive stress of 7 MPa at a depth of 0.1 mm and a maximum tensile stress of 5 MPa at a depth of 0.5 mm. The residual stress curve for the longitudinal axis is however considerably higher than that for the transverse axis, behaviour that would not be expected from a specimen with an equi-biaxial stress distribution.

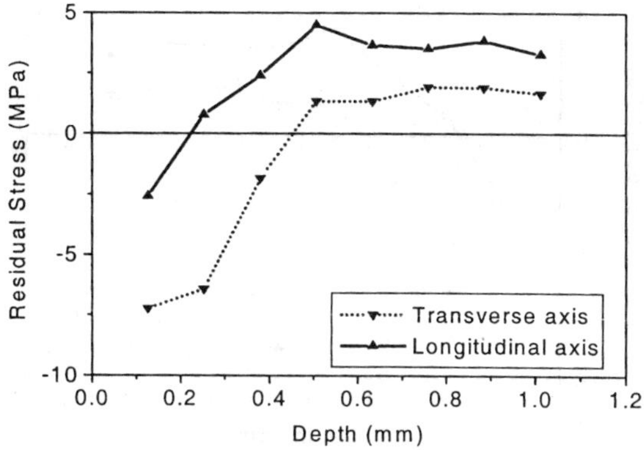

Fig. 2 Residual stresses obtained from the hole-drilling

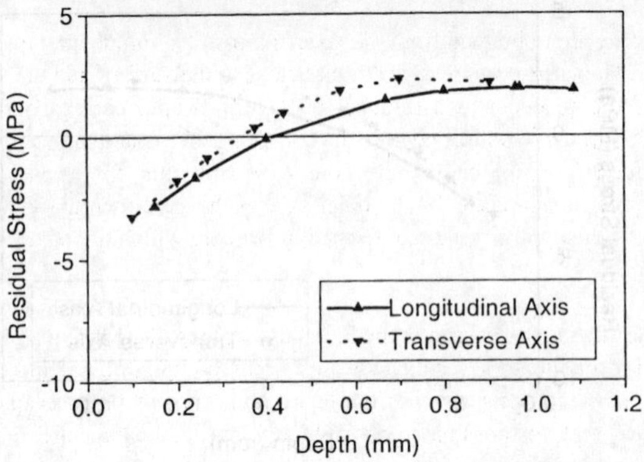

Fig. 1 Residual stresses obtained using the layer-removal technique

HOLE-DRILLING

Hole-drilling tests were conducted on the same biaxial plate from which the layer-removal specimens had been prepared. Strain gauge readings were obtained as a function of the hole depth using the strain gauges situated around the hole. The residual stresses along the two principal axes (Figure 2) were calculated using the procedure described in the ASTM standard. These results indicate that the residual stresses have a maximum compressive stress of 7 MPa at a depth of 0.1 mm and a maximum tensile stress of 5 MPa at a depth of 0.5 mm. The residual stress curve for the longitudinal axis is however considerably higher than that for the transverse axis, behaviour that would not be expected from a specimen with an equi-biaxial stress distribution.

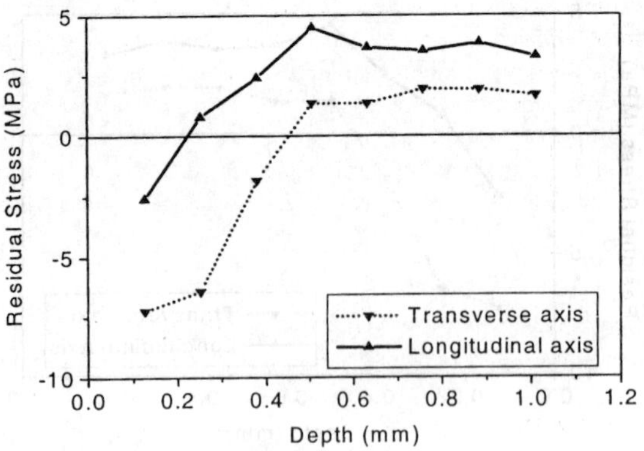

Fig. 2 Residual stresses obtained from the hole-drilling

DISCUSSION

The results that have been obtained from the layer-removal technique are typical of those from a quenched sample. The large compressive stresses close to the surface and the tensile stresses that are observed in the core occur as a result of quenching. Rapid cooling during the quenching process causes the surface to solidify before the core. Once the outer surface of the specimen has solidified subsequent cooling causes the core to shrink due to thermal contraction. This shrinkage is, however, constrained by the outer skin of the specimen that is already solid. As a consequence, tensile residual stresses are formed in the core which are balanced by compressive stresses in the skin.

This skin/core profile is clearly seen in the layer-removal results. Moreover, it can be seen from the layer-removal results that the residual stresses along the longitudinal and transverse axes are almost identical. This is consistent with the equi-biaxial nature of these quenched specimens which shows clearly that it is possible to obtain highly repeatable and consistent results using the layer-removal technique.

Residual stress measurements obtained using the hole-drilling technique also show compressive stresses close to the surface and tensile stress in the core. The profile of the residual stresses obtained using the hole-drilling technique is, however, anomalous because of the gross inequality between tensile and compressive residual stresses through the thickness of the specimen. These results are not realistic as the compressive stresses in the skin should balance with the tensile stresses in the core. Furthermore, it can be seen from the hole-drilling results that the residual stresses along the longitudinal and transverse axes are significantly different. This is inconsistent with the equi-biaxial results that would be expected. It would therefore appear that although the hole-drilling technique is more flexible than the layer-removal technique it is not yet reliable.

CONCLUSIONS

The results demonstrate that the layer-removal technique gives the most consistent results for through-thickness residual stress measurements and this is now being proposed as a standard with the International Organisation for Standardisation (ISO). The hole-drilling technique is potentially more flexible for determining residual stress in complex geometries because the measurements are made over a smaller area. However, the residual stresses obtained using this technique are not those that would be expected from the specimen tested. It would therefore appear that the results obtained from hole-drilling are not as reliable as those obtained from the layer-removal technique. Further work is required to develop the hole-drilling method as an effective tool.

REFERENCES

1. Turnbull A, Maxwell A S, Pillai S, and White J, "Measurement Good Practice Guide - Residual Stress in Polymeric Mouldings", National Physical Laboratory, ISSN 1368-6550, 1998
2. Hindle C R, White J R, Dawson D and Thomas K, Polymer Engineering and Science 32 (1992) 157
3. Treuting R G and Read W T, J. Appl. Phys. 22 (1951) 130
4. ASTM E 837-94a, "Determining Residual Stresses in Extruded or Molded Acrylonitrile-Butadiene-Styrene (ABS) Parts by Immersion in Glacial Acetic Acid"
5. Turnbull A, Maxwell A S, Pillai S, J.Material Sci. 34 (1999) 451-459

DISCUSSION

The results that have been obtained from the layer-removal technique are typical of those from a quenched sample. The large compressive stresses close to the surface and the tensile stresses that are observed in the core occur as a result of quenching. Rapid cooling during the quenching process causes the surface to solidify before the core. Once the outer surface of the specimen has solidified subsequent cooling causes the core to shrink due to thermal contraction. This shrinkage is, however, constrained by the outer skin of the specimen that is already solid. As a consequence, tensile residual stresses are formed in the core which are balanced by compressive stresses in the skin.

This skin/core profile is clearly seen in the layer-removal results. Moreover, it can be seen from the layer-removal results that the residual stresses along the longitudinal and transverse axes are almost identical. This is consistent with the equi-biaxial nature of these quenched specimens which shows clearly that it is possible to obtain highly repeatable and consistent results using the layer-removal technique.

Residual stress measurements obtained using the hole-drilling technique also show compressive stresses close to the surface and tensile stress in the core. The profile of the residual stresses obtained using the hole-drilling technique is, however, anomalous because of the gross inequality between tensile and compressive residual stresses through the thickness of the specimen. These results are not realistic as the compressive stresses in the skin should balance with the tensile stresses in the core. Furthermore, it can be seen from the hole-drilling results that the residual stresses along the longitudinal and transverse axes are significantly different. This is inconsistent with the equi-biaxial results that would be expected. It would therefore appear that although the hole-drilling technique is more flexible than the layer-removal technique it is not yet reliable.

CONCLUSIONS

The results demonstrate that the layer-removal technique gives the most consistent results for through-thickness residual stress measurements and this is now being proposed as a standard with the International Organisation for Standardisation (ISO). The hole-drilling technique is potentially more flexible for determining residual stress in complex geometries because the measurements are made over a smaller area. However, the residual stresses obtained using this technique are not those that would be expected from the specimen tested. It would therefore appear that the results obtained from hole-drilling are not as reliable as those obtained from the layer-removal technique. Further work is required to develop the hole-drilling method as an effective tool.

REFERENCES

1. Turnbull A, Maxwell A S, Pillai S, and White J, "Measurement Good Practice Guide - Residual Stress in Polymeric Mouldings", National Physical Laboratory, ISSN 1368-6550, 1998
2. Hindle C R, White J R, Dawson D and Thomas K, Polymer Engineering and Science 32 (1992) 157
3. Treuting R G and Read W T, J. Appl. Phys. 22 (1951) 130
4. ASTM E 837-94a, "Determining Residual Stresses in Extruded or Molded Acrylonitrile-Butadiene-Styrene (ABS) Parts by Immersion in Glacial Acetic Acid"
5. Turnbull A, Maxwell A S, Pillai S, J.Material Sci. 34 (1999) 451-459

PROPOSAL FOR STANDARD METHOD OF X-RAY STRESS MEASUREMENT OF CERAMICS

Kenji SUZUKI[*1] **and Keisuke TANAKA**[*2]

[*1] Faculty of Education and Human Science, Niigata University, Niigata, 950-2181, Japan
[*2] Department of Mechanical Engineering, Nagoya University, Nagoya, 464-8603, Japan

ABSTRACT

The standard method of X-ray stress measurements of sintered alumina (α-Al_2O_3) and silicon nitride (β-Si_3N_4) is recently proposed in Japan. It is based on the $\sin^2\psi$ method for stress determination. The diffractions recommended for stress measurement is the 2.1.10 diffraction of alumina by Fe-Kα radiation and the 4 1 1 diffraction of silicon nitride by V-Kα radiation. The X-ray elastic constant is estimated from the mechanical elastic constant. The procedure for an accurate stress measurement is described in the standard with several explanatory comments.

1. INTRODUCTION

The residual stress in engineering ceramics is one of the key factors which influence the mechanical properties of ceramics products. The X-ray diffraction method is the most powerful nondestructive method to measure the residual stress in ceramics. The establishment of the standard method has been requested by researchers and engineers in Japan working in the fields of the applications of engineering ceramics.

The X-Ray Committee in the Society of Materials Science, Japan, (JSMS), first published the standard method for X-ray stress measurement in 1973, and have revised it several times to cope with the developments of instrumentation and data processing techniques [1]. This standard method deals with the X-ray stress measurement of ferritic and martensitic steels and austenitic stainless steels. In 2000, a new standard method is drafted for stress measurement in two kinds of sintered ceramics: alumina and silicon nitride. The draft is based on cooperative work by the members of the X-Ray Committee in industries and universities for about ten years. By using round robin specimens, we conducted inter-laboratory measurements of X-ray elastic constants and grinding residual stresses [2].

The standard consists of two parts: the main text and explanatory comments. In this paper, the essence of the main part will be introduced.

2. STANDARD

2-1 Scope

X-ray stress measurement is a method for measuring the surface stress of polycrystalline materials by X-ray diffraction. This standard covers a procedure for X-ray stress measurement of sintered alumina (Al_2O_3) and silicon nitride (Si_3N_4) .

2-2 Method of measurement

This chapter describes the general principle for X-ray stress measurement applicable to any ceramics.

2-2-1 Principle of measurement

X-ray stress measurement is a method of measuring the surface stress from the lattice strain measured as the change in lattice spacing by the X-ray diffraction method.

The $\sin^2\psi$ method is used to obtain the stress value. Figure 1 (a) shows the stress state on the surface, where the stress, σ_x, is to be measured. The stress is determined from the normal strain, ε_ψ, or the diffraction angle, θ_ψ, for the OP direction by the following equation:

$$\sigma_x = \frac{E}{1+\nu}\cdot\frac{\partial\varepsilon_\psi}{\partial(\sin^2\psi)} = \frac{-E}{2(1+\nu)}\cdot\frac{\partial(2\theta_\psi)}{\partial(\sin^2\psi)}\cdot\frac{\pi}{180}\cdot\cot\theta_0 \quad \text{[MPa]} \tag{1}$$

where θ_0 is the diffraction angle of stress-free samples, E is Young's modulus and ν is Poisson's ratio.

The diffraction angle is measured by several values of the inclination angle, ψ, and the data are plotted against $\sin^2\psi$. The relation between $2\theta_\psi$ and $\sin^2\psi$ is linear. Fig. 1

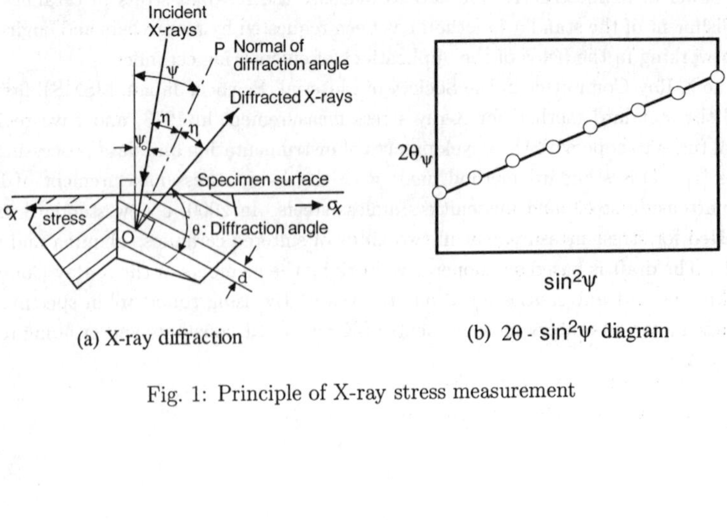

Fig. 1: Principle of X-ray stress measurement

(b) is called 2θ-$\sin^2\psi$ diagram. From the slope, M, of the linear regression line, the stress is determined as

$$\sigma_x = K \cdot M \quad [\text{MPa}] \tag{2}$$

where

$$K = \frac{-E}{2(1+\nu)} \cdot \frac{\pi}{180} \cdot \cot\theta_0 \quad [\text{MPa/deg}] \tag{3}$$

$$M = \frac{\partial(2\theta_\psi)}{\partial(\sin^2\psi)} \quad [\text{deg}] \tag{4}$$

The constant K is called the stress constant.

2-2-2 Method of measurement

2-2-2-1 Characteristic X-ray and diffraction profile

The combination of characteristic X-rays and the diffraction plane is to be selected to satisfy the following items:

1) The diffraction angle 2θ is close to 180 deg.
2) The peak intensity of the diffraction profile is large compared with the background intensity.
3) The diffraction profile is isolated from neighboring profiles.

2-2-2-2 Measurement of diffraction angle

The diffraction angle is determined from diffraction profiles measured by a diffractometer.

2-2-2-3 Slit system

For measurement by a counter, the parallel beam optics should be satisfied by inserting Soller slits at incident and receiving sides. For measurement by a position sensitive detector, a collimator to narrow the divergence is employed or the parallel beam can be used for the incident beam.

2-2-2-4 X-ray detector

To detect X-ray diffractions, a proportional counter can be scanned or a position sensitive proportional counter (PSPC) or a position sensitive detector (PSD) can be used.

2-2-3 Classification of measuring method

2-2-3-1 Classification based on the measurement direction of the diffraction angle

(1) The iso-inclination method (Ω diffractometer)

(2) The side-inclination method (Ψ diffractometer)

2-2-3-2 Classification based on the method of irradiating X-rays

(1) The ψ-fixed method

The normal of the diffraction plane is kept constant during scanning of a detector. The normal of the specimen is scanned by θ, while a detector is scanned by 2θ.

(2) The ψ_0-fixed method

The angle of the incident beam is fixed during scanning of a detector. Only 2θ scanning of a detector is conducted for recording profiles.

2-2-4 Conditions of measurement

2-2-4-1 Voltage and current of the X-ray tube

The voltage must be above 25 kV, and the current should be as large as possible.

2-2-4-2 Incident and receiving slits, and irradiation mask

The divergence angle of incident Soller slits is under one deg. The divergence of receiving slits for a counter method is also under one deg. There are no receiving slits for a position-sensitive detector method. A mask is placed at the outlet of the incident slits to limit the irradiation area (length in the direction of the stress being measured × length perpendicular to it).

2-2-4-3 Incident angle of X-rays

It is recommended to set the inclination angle to seven values corresponding to $\sin^2\psi$ from 0 to 0.6 with an interval of 0.1.

2-2-4-4 Time constants and scanning speed of a detector

(1) For the counter method

(a) Continuous scanning

The product of the time constant and the scanning speed of a detector is less than 2.2 deg.

(b) Step scanning

The step width is less than 0.17 H_w (H_w is the full width at the half maximum). The scanning range is wide enough to determine the background clearly.

(2) For the position-sensitive-detector method

The angle range for one channel in a multi-channel analyzer and the angle range of recording the diffraction follow the recommendations given to step scanning method.

2-2-4-5 Recording diffraction profiles

For precise measurement, the peak intensity of diffracted X-rays, I_P, and the ratio of I_P to the background intensity, I_B, must be high, and the statistical variation must be maintained minimum.

2-2-5 Calculation of stress

2-2-5-1 Correction of measured profiles

Measued X-ray line profiles must be corrected by the modified Lorentz-polarization factor $LP(2\theta)$ and the absorption factor $A(\psi, 2\theta)$. The measured X-ray line profile $\Phi_m(\psi, 2\theta)$ is corrected by the following equation.

$$\Phi(\psi, 2\theta) = \frac{\Phi_m(\psi, 2\theta)}{LP(2\theta) \cdot A(\psi, 2\theta)} \tag{5}$$

where the modified Lorentz-polarization factor $LP(2\theta)$ is given by

$$LP(2\theta) = \frac{1 + \cos^2 2\theta}{\sin^2\theta} \tag{6}$$

The absorption correction is unnecessary for the side-inclination method, while the absorption factor $A(\psi, 2\theta)$ for $+\psi$ inclination for the iso-inclination method is given by

$$\left.\begin{aligned} A(\psi, 2\theta) &= 1 - \frac{\tan\psi}{\tan\theta} && \text{[Fixed } \psi \text{ method]} \\ A(\psi, 2\theta) &= 1 - \frac{\tan(90^\circ + \psi_0 - \theta)}{\tan\theta} && \text{[Fixed } \psi_0 \text{ method]} \end{aligned}\right\} \tag{7}$$

2-2-5-2 Determination of peak position and making $2\theta - \sin^2\psi$ diagram

The half-value-breadth method is the standard method. By plotting the diffraction angle $2\theta_\psi$ as a function of $\sin^2\psi$, the $2\theta_\psi$-$\sin^2\psi$ diagram can be drawn.

2-2-5-3 Stress calulation and error estimation

The stress is determined from the slope, $M = \dfrac{\partial 2\theta_\psi}{\partial \sin^2\psi}$ [deg], of the regression line of $2\theta_\psi$-$\sin^2\psi$ diagram by

$$\sigma_x = K \cdot M \quad \text{[MPa]} \tag{8}$$

$$K = \frac{-E}{2(1+\nu)} \cdot \frac{\pi}{180} \cdot \cot_0 \quad \text{[MPa/deg]} \tag{9}$$

where K is the stress constant.

The stress value and the confidence limit of the stress value are determined by

$$\sigma_x \pm \Delta\sigma_x = K \cdot (M \mp \Delta M) \tag{10}$$

$$M = \frac{\sum_{i=1}^{n}(X_i - \bar{X})(Y_i - \bar{Y})}{\sum_{i=1}^{n}(X_i - \bar{X})^2} = \frac{\sum X_i Y_i - n\bar{X}\bar{Y}}{\sum X_i^2 - n\bar{X}^2} \tag{11}$$

$$\Delta M = t(n-2,\alpha) \cdot \sqrt{\frac{\sum\{Y_i - (A + MX_i)\}^2}{(n-2)\cdot\sum(X_i - \bar{X})^2}} \tag{12}$$

where

$$X_i = \sin^2\psi_i,\ Y_i = 2\theta_{\psi_i},\ \bar{X} = \frac{1}{n}\sum_{i=1}^{n} X_i,\ \bar{Y} = \frac{1}{n}\sum_{i=1}^{n} Y_i,\ A = \bar{Y} - M\bar{X} \tag{13}$$

$t(n-2,\alpha)$ is the t-value for degree of freedom $(n-2)$ with the confidence limit $(1-\alpha)$. The confidence limit is taken as 68.3%. The $\Delta\sigma_x$ indicates the linearity or scatter of the $2\theta_\psi$-$\sin^2\psi$ diagram, and it can be used as an indicator for the evaluation of the measurement.

2-2-5-4 X-ray elastic constant

The constant, $E/(1+\nu)$, in the stress constant K is called the X-ray elastic constant. It is dependent on not only materials, but also on the diffraction plane. It is preferable to use the estimated value which is described later in 2-3-4.

2-2-6 Equipment

2-2-6-1 X-ray generator

2-2-6-2 Diffractometer

(1) Goniometer

(2) Slits, collimator, and filter

2-2-6-3 Detector and recording equipment

2-2-7 Measuring procedure

2-2-7-1 Surface condition

The surface for measurement is preferable to be smooth. When there are stains or damaged layers on the surface, these should be removed before measurement. To avoid the introduction of residual stresses, the surface layer should be finished by buffing with diamond slurry (grain diameter < 1μm).

2-2-7-2 Setting equipment and specimen

The measured surface is placed exactly at the center of a goniometer, and the inclination angle must be set accurately. The direction of the measuring stress should be on the ψ angle plane.

2-2-7-3 Setting measuring conditions

The X-ray power and preset times should be determined as prescribed in 2-2-4. The peak count above the background intensity is to be larger than 1000 counts.

2-2-7-4 Measurement and calculation of stress

The diffraction angle 2θ is determined from corrected X-ray profiles taken at seven different inclination angles by following the prescrived methods in 2-2-5. Plot the data in the $2\theta_\psi$-$\sin^2\psi$ diagram. Draw the linear regression line, and determine M and ΔM. The stress and the confidence limit are determined by multiplying M and ΔM by K, respectively. The stress constant is described in 2-3-5.

2-2-7-5 Calibration of equipment

It is necessary to examine regularly the condition of the equipment. For examination, measure the zero stress of stress-free powders.

2-3 Stress measurement of alumina and silicon nitride

2-3-1 Materials

The materials to be measured are sintered polycrystalline alumina (α-Al_2O_3) and silicon nitride (β-Si_3N_4). It is preferable to satisfy the following conditions.

2-3-1-1 Grain size

The small grain size of specimens is preferred. The number of grains in the irradiated area is large enough to make a continuous diffraction ring. The grain number is larger than # 7 (after JIS G0552), or the grain size is smaller than 30μm for the counter method.

2-3-1-2 Texture

It is preferable that the specimen does not have a strong preferred orientation. A strong texture will induce non-linearity of the 2θ-$\sin^2\psi$ relation.

2-3-1-3 Composition and material history

It is preferable that compositions, sintering conditions and history of the specimen are known. Both the mechanical and X-ray elastic constants may depend on material compositions and sintering conditions.

2-3-1-4 Surface condition

The surface condition of the specimen is preferred to be known. The 2θ-$\sin^2\psi$ diagram will show non-linearity if the specimen has a steep stress gradient such as on the ground surface. For specimens with a large surface roughness, the stress value measured by X-ray method is smaller than the mechanical stress.

2-3-2 Characteristic X-rays and diffraction profile

2-3-2-1 Alumina

The 2.1.10 diffraction by the Fe-Kα characteristic X-ray is recommended. Mn filter is used to eliminate Kβ radiation. For another choice, the 2 2 0 diffraction by the Cr-Kα

characteristic X-ray is available and V filter is used.

2-3-2-2 Silicon nitride

The 4 1 1 diffraction by V-Kα characteristic X-ray is recommended and Ti filter is used. For another choice, the 3 2 3 diffraction by the Cu-Kα characteristic X-ray is available and Ni filter is used.

2-3-3 Determination of diffraction angle

For alumina, the diffraction angle of the 2.1.10 diffraction by Fe-Kα is determined by a 2/5 value breadth method. For alumina, the diffraction angle of the 2 2 0 diffraction by Cr-Kα is determined by the half-value-breadth method.

For silicon nitride, the diffraction angle of the 4 1 1 diffraction by V-Kα is determined by the half-value-breadth method. For silicon nitride, the diffraction angle of the 3 2 3 diffraction by Cu-Kα is determined by the 2/5 value breadth method. When some other methods are employed, the employed method should be indicated in reporting.

2-3-4 X-ray elastic constants

The X-ray elastic constant, $E/(1+\nu)$, can be estimated by the following equations. If the X-ray elastic constant is needed for a particular sample, it can be determined experimentally [3].

2-3-4-1 X-ray elastic constants of alumina

Based on the round robin experiments of X-ray elastic constants, the following methods are recommended for estimation. When the mechanical Young's modulus E' and Poisson's ratio ν' are known, the X-ray elastic constant $E/(1+\nu)$ is obtained from the following equations:

$$\left.\begin{aligned} \frac{E}{1+\nu} &= F_{2.1.10}\frac{E'}{1+\nu'} = 1.12\frac{E'}{1+\nu'} \qquad \text{(for 2.1.10 by Fe - K}\alpha\text{)} \\ \frac{E}{1+\nu} &= F_{220}\frac{E'}{1+\nu'} = 1.07\frac{E'}{1+\nu'} \qquad \text{(for 2 2 0 by Cr - K}\alpha\text{)} \end{aligned}\right\} \tag{14}$$

where F_{hkl} is a coefficient dependent on the diffraction plane.

When the mechanical elastic constants are not known, their approximation can be made by [4]

$$\left.\begin{aligned} E' &= 410\exp\left\{-3.96\left(1-\frac{\rho}{3.99}\right)\right\} \qquad \text{[GPa]} \\ \nu' &= 0.22 \end{aligned}\right\} \tag{15}$$

where ρ (g/cm^3) is the bulk density of the specimen. Equation (14) is not applicable to the specimen of which the bulk density is under 3.2 g/cm^3.

2-3-4-2 X-ray elastic constants of silicon nitride

When mechanical Young's modulus E' and Poisson's ratio ν' are known, the X-ray elastic constant $E/(1+\nu)$ is obtained from the following equations:

$$\left.\begin{aligned} \frac{E}{1+\nu} &= F_{411}\frac{E'}{1+\nu'} = 1.04\frac{E'}{1+\nu'} \qquad \text{(for 4 1 1 by V - K}\alpha\text{)} \\ \frac{E}{1+\nu} &= F_{323}\frac{E'}{1+\nu'} = 1.02\frac{E'}{1+\nu'} \qquad \text{(for 3 2 3 by Cu - K}\alpha\text{)} \end{aligned}\right\} \tag{16}$$

where F_{hkl} is a coefficient dependent on the diffraction plane.

When the mechanical elastic constants are not known, their approximation can be made by [5]

$$\left.\begin{aligned} E' &= 344\exp\left\{-3.31\left(1-\frac{\rho}{3.40}\right)\right\} \quad \text{[GPa]} \\ \nu' &= 0.27 \end{aligned}\right\} \tag{17}$$

where ρ (g/cm^3) is a bulk density of a measured specimen.

2-3-5 Calculation of stress value

The stress constant K is determined by

$$K = \frac{-E}{2(1+\nu)} \cdot \frac{\pi}{180}\cot\theta_0 \quad \text{[MPa]} \tag{18}$$

and the stress value is calculated by Equation (2).

For alumina, the diffraction angle is $2\theta_0 = 152.34°$ for 2.1.10 diffraction by Fe-Kα and $2\theta_0 = 148.73°$ for alumina 2 2 0 diffraction by Cr-Kα. For silicon nitride, the diffraction angle is $2\theta_0 = 152.87°$ for silicon nitride 4 1 1 diffraction by V-Kα and $2\theta_0 = 141.73°$ for silicon nitride 3 2 3 diffraction by Cu-Kα.

When the bulk density of the measured specimen is not known, the following value may be used as an approximation of the stress constant.

$$\left.\begin{aligned} K &= -773 \text{ [MPa/deg]} \quad \text{(for alumina 2.1.10 diffraction by Fe-K}\alpha\text{)} \\ K &= -701 \text{ [MPa/deg]} \quad \text{(for alumina 2 2 0 diffraction by Cr-K}\alpha\text{)} \\ K &= -527 \text{ [MPa/deg]} \quad \text{(for silicon nitride 4 1 1 diffraction by V-K}\alpha\text{)} \\ K &= -733 \text{ [MPa/deg]} \quad \text{(for silicon nitride 3 2 3 diffraction by Cu-K}\alpha\text{)} \end{aligned}\right\} \tag{19}$$

3. REFERENCES

[1] Committee of X-ray Study on Mechanical Behaviour of Materials, 'Standard Method of X-ray Stress Measurement of Iron and Steels', JSMS (1997).

[2] K. Suzuki, Y. Sakaida and K.Tanaka, 'Summary Report of X-ray Stress Measurement of Ceramics by the Ceramic Committee', *124th Committee of X-ray Study on Mechanical Behaviour of Materials, JSMS*, p. 28 (1998).

[3] K. Suzuki and K. Kusaka, 'The Fundamental Principle and Techniques of X-Ray Stress Measurement and Current in the Field (V) Application to Advanced Materials', *J. Soc. of Mater. Sci. Japan*, **48**-3, 308 (1999).

[4] F. P. Knudsen, 'Effect of Porosity on Young's Modulus of Alumina', *J. Am. Ceram. Soc.*, **45**-2, 94 (1962).

[5] T. Hoshide, 'Interrelation Analyses of Mechanical Properties in Commercial Ceramics Using Cataloged Data', *Mater. Sci. Res. Int.*, **4**-3, 179 (1998).

STRAIN FIELD MAPPING IN ALUMINA/COPPER JOINED SPECIMEN

T Pirling[1] and F Saint-Antonin[2]
[1] Institut Laue-Langevin, av. Des Martyrs, BP 156, F-38042 Grenoble Cedex 9, France
[2] CEA/Grenoble, CEREM/DEM/SGM, 17 rue des Martyrs, 38054 Grenoble Cedex 9, France

ABSTRACT

This paper presents the strain field mapping, at room temperature, within a polycrystalline alumina of a brazed alumina/copper specimen obtained from neutron diffraction experiments making use of the high precision strain scanner at the ILL. It has been observed that oscillations of the strain field occurring alternately, with sharp change, from compression to dilatation and back to compression all along the interface and even far from the interface. An interpretation of these 'strain oscillations' is proposed based on the elastic behaviour of alumina and on the brazing cycle.

I- INTRODUCTION

In many applications, ceramics are joined onto metal. For instance, in some electronic chips, the insulator is alumina and the conducting material is copper. Brazing is used to join them. The brazing technique consists of heating the sandwich made of these two materials with an alloy foil placed in between. At the melting point of the foil, the two surfaces are wetted and chemical reactions generally occurred at the solid/liquid interfaces. During the cooling, the two materials are joined as the brazing alloy is solidified.

Due to the difference between the Coefficient of Thermal Expansion (CTE) of the alumina and the metal, residual stresses and plasticity are generated during the cooling process. These residual stresses induce bending and/or deformation of the joined parts. When residual stresses are too high, cracks and/or decohesion occur. Thus, the definition of design rules is a key point for joints fabrication and for in-service lifetime estimation of joints.

In order to design such joints, some empirical rules, reported by Schwartz (1), can be used for simple geometries. But for a more precise description of the cooling effect on the joints resistance, Finite Element Modelling (FEM) of the residual stress field in the brazed parts is widely used. These models require experimental validation before they can be adopted with any confidence for the design of joined components.

The residual stresses can be obtained experimentally by :

- *Stress relaxation techniques:* "residual stress is determined by measuring the elastic strain release that takes place when a specimen is cut into pieces or has a piece removed" as mentioned by Masubuchi (2). This technique is a destructive one and does not allow a direct description of the residual stress field unless associated to FE Modelling of the joint.

- *Dimensional changes on a small sample :* it is possible to record bending or distortions induced by residual stresses on small joined samples. Residual stresses mapping by FEM that matches at best the measured dimensional changes, can be obtained regardless of assumptions concerning the type of brazing behaviour law. A variation of this method called "in-situ brazing recorded in dilatometric apparatus", developed by Lovato et al (3,4,5) is able to get the brazing behaviour law and thus, a more realistic modelling can be performed. These methods give only an indirect residual stress map and the results are strongly dependent on the confidence given to the numerous assumptions made for FEM [Lovato (4)].
- *Diffraction techniques [for instance: Rabin et al (6), Vaidya et al (7), Wang et al (8)]:* X-ray and neutron diffraction techniques allow non-destructive mapping of the stress state inside materials. Both methods use the variation of the lattice parameter of the material as a gauge for the strain. From the strain values, it is possible to determine directly the full stress tensor. X-ray and neutron diffraction are complementary techniques. They differ in size and shape of the sampling volume and size of samples that can be probed.

It should also be added that Rabin et al (6) has performed measurements with Optical Fluorescence Spectroscopy.

Up to now, there are only a few studies in the literature reporting the use of neutron diffraction for residual stress measurements within ceramic/metal bonded specimen [for instance, Rabin et al (6), Vaidya et al (7), Wang et al (8), Youtsos et al (9)]. Most of them report a comparison of the residual stresses measured with results from Finite Element calculations. The tendency today is to compare strain variation instead of stress [7, 8] : this avoids some assumptions needed for the calculation of stresses from the measured strain, which may induce some bias. Anyway, this comparison is not obvious because the gauge volumes used are often quite large compared to the area where the stress distribution is varying. Due to long measuring times and limited access to neutron facilities, often only very few line scans could practically be performed. Nevertheless, the results give an idea of the residual stress distribution even if the results differ from the FE-modelling.

Recently, a new strain scanner has been built at ILL allowing the possibility to perform high precision measurements [Pirling (10,11)].

This paper presents the strain field mapping, at room temperature, within a polycrystalline alumina of a brazed alumina/copper specimen obtained from neutron diffraction experiments.

II- EXPERIMENTAL PROCEDURE

III-a. Sample preparation

The specimen fabrication involved polycrystalline alumina, copper and the brazing alloy. The purity of the alumina is higher than 99.7%: the remaining are sintering aids such as MgO, CaO and SiO_2. The grain size is 5 to 12μm with an average of 7μm. The purity of copper is higher than 99.99%, the oxygen content is lower than 30ppm. The brazing alloy composition in weight % is: 63%Ag-35.25%Cu-1.75%. The brazing alloy solidus temperature is 780°C.

The dimensions of the different materials are :

- Alumina, diameter of 20mm, thickness of 5mm,
- copper: diameter of 20mm, thickness of 2mm,
- brazing alloy: 100μm thickness.

The specimen was brazed in vacuum (about 1 to 10 Pa). The brazing cycle is: heating to 820°C in 2 hours, holding time of 5 minutes at 820°C and cooling to room temperature (RT) in 6.5°/min. Between the solidification temperature of 780°C and RT, the CTE of alumina and copper is respectively $7 \times 10^{-6}.(°C)^{-1}$ and $20 \times 10^{-6}.(°C)^{-1}$. The large thickness of alumina compared to copper makes the assembly very rigid and prevents it from bending otherwise this may have an impact on the diffraction measurements.

III-b. Diffraction set up and neutron diffraction procedure

The experiment was performed on the D1A powder diffractometer of ILL using the strain-scanning equipment. The sample was mounted on an Eulerian-Cradle and measurements were taken in the three principal axis directions. The gauge volume was defined by an aperture of 0.5 mm horizontally and 2 mm high for the axial and radial scans and 2 mm for the tangential scan. The distance to the reference point (centre of the gauge volume) was 45 mm. Additionally, a radial collimator determines the gauge dimension. The collimator has an inner radius of 150 mm and a length of 450 mm. Foils are at in a radial distance of 0.19°. A vertical slit mask, mounted at the big end of the collimator with 1 mm open width for each channel, reduces the gauge size and changes the transfer function of the collimator from triangular shape to a trapezoid. This measure leads to higher accuracy and allows measurements closer to the interface without being influenced by the surface error. A Position Sensitive Detector with an angular resolution of 0.023° allows efficient measurements and gives about 15 points in a peak; enough for a good fit. The measuring time was chosen so that the statistical error of evaluated strains becomes smaller than 100 $\mu\varepsilon$. Measurements were taken in a very narrow grid of 0.25 mm in the outer region where most changes of the strain are expected and in 1 mm steps close to the centre. The reflection used for determination was the Al_2O_3 (311) with 0.2085 nm which appears at 91.746° 2Θ using the wavelength of 0.29911 nm. The reference d0 was taken from a pure Alumina disk of the same dimensions as the brazed one. The average of three measurements in the centre was used and led to 91.763° 2Θ (+/– 0.005°).

III- RESULTS AND DISCUSSION

The results are reported in figure 1 and 2, for the radial strain and in figure 3 and 4, for the tangential strain scanning parallel to the interface at various distances from the interface. The Y axis gives 'μstrain' or '$10^{-6} \times$ strain'.

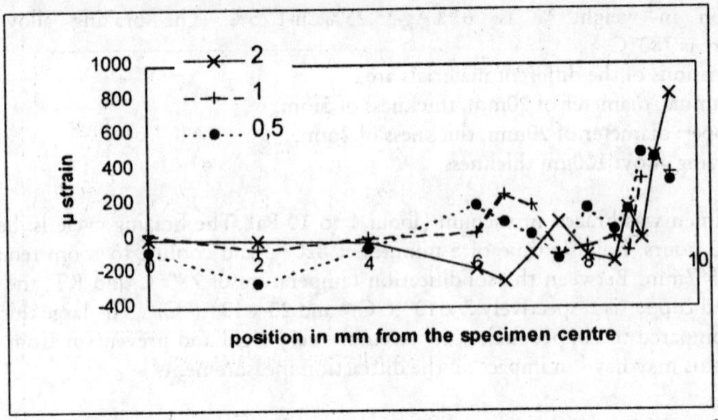

Figure 1 : radial strain along the interface at 0.5, 1 and 2 mm from the interface.

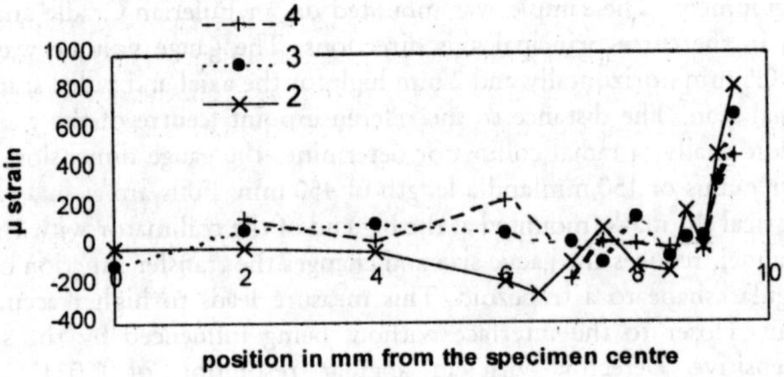

Figure 2 : radial strain along the interface at 2, 3 and 4 mm from the interface.

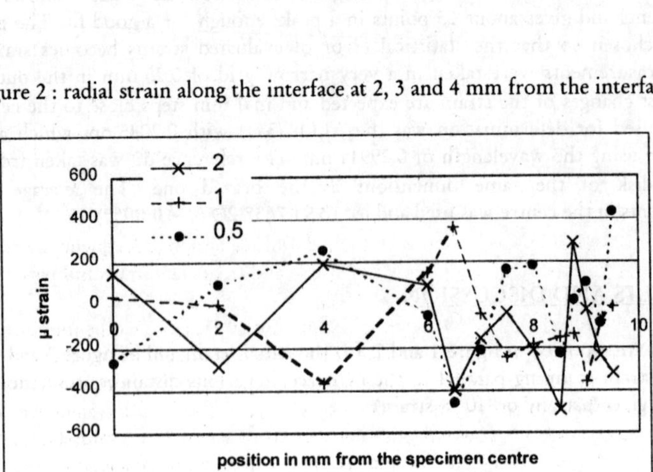

Figure 3: tangential strain along the interface at 0.5, 1 and 2 mm from the interface.

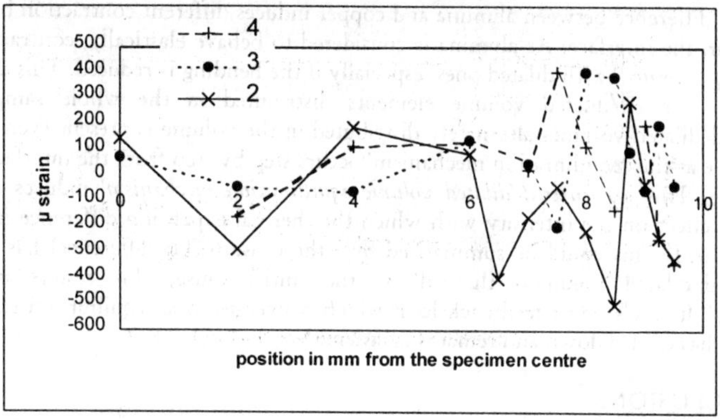

Figure 4: tangential strain along the interface at 2, 3 and 4 mm from the interface.

Whatever the measured distance from the interface, the maximum strain variation is located in the outer part of the specimen. Along the interface, the strain variation can be described as 'strain oscillation' with amplitude and frequency as schematically represented in figure 5 or as a 'sinusoidal damped down curve type' from the outer to the centre part of the specimen. The strain variations are larger than the statistical error that is smaller than 100 μ-strain.

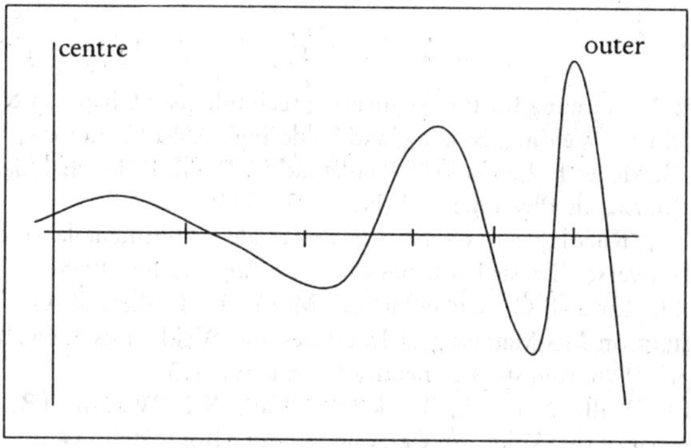

Figure 5: schematic representation with high amplitude and high frequency in the outer region of the sample and, low amplitude and frequency in central part.

The amplitude and frequency of these oscillations are larger close to the interface but they are still existing even far from the interface. The same features could be observed whatever the measuring orientation (tangential, radial or axial). Even less measured points were obtained for axial strains, the same kind of curves were observed by Saint-Antonin et al (12). Thus, the strain field is varying alternatively from tension to compression, especially in the tangential direction (figure 3 and 4). The explanation of the presence of theses oscillation is given in the following paragraph.

The CTE difference between alumina and copper induces different contraction behaviour at, and near, the interface. As alumina is considered to behave elastically, contracted areas must be *'equilibrated'* with dilated ones, especially if the bending is reduced. This difference induces compressed/dilated volume elements distributed in the whole sample. The compressed/dilated volumes alternately distributed in the volume is present even far from the interface as this 'equilibration mechanism' occurs step by step from the interface during the cooling. This *'compressed/dilated volume equilibration mechanism'* induces a sort of retroactive effect on the intensity with which the thermal expansion difference influences the strain field. This could be summarised by : the cause (CTE difference) has an effect (compressed/dilated volumes) that affects the initial cause, this results in 'strain oscillations'. It is a kind of feed back loop which converges to an equilibrium state when the sample has cooled down and remains ... assembled.

IV- CONCLUSIONS

Strain field mapping was performed in alumina of a brazed alumina/copper specimen. It has been observed 'strain oscillations' varying alternately from compression to dilatation and back to compression occurring all along the interface and even far from the interface. This could also be described as a repeat of alternate compressed/dilated volumes which extent is dependent on the relative location from the alumina/copper interface and sample surface.

REFERENCES

1. Schwartz M, 'Brazing for the engineering technologist', Chapman & Hall, 1995, 265.
2. Masubuchi K, 'Welding, Brazing, and Soldering', ASM Handbook, Vol 6, 1993, 1094.
3. Lovato G, Moret F, Le Gallo P, Cailletaud G, Pilvin P, Journal. de Physique IV, C7, Sup. au Journal de Physique III 3 (Nov 1993) 1135.
4. Lovato G, 'Rhéologie des joints brasés: étude expérimentale et détermination par méthode inverse', Thesis Ecole des Mines de Paris, 10 fev. 1995.
5. Burlet H, Lovato G, Chaumat G, Moret F, Cailletaud G, 2nd International Symposium on Mis-Matching of Interfaces and Welds, Eds Schwalbe KH, Koçak M, 24-23 april 1996, Reinstorf-Luneburg (Germany), 423.
6. Rabin BH, Williamson RL, Bruck HA, Wang X-L, Watkins TR, Feng Y-Z, Clarke DR, Journal of the American Ceramic Society 81(6) (1998) 1541.
7. Vaidya RU, Rangaswamy P, Bourke MAM, Butt DP, Acta Materialia 46(6) (1998) 2047.
8. Wang X-L, Hubbard CR, Spooner S, David SA, Rabin BH, Williamson RL, Materials Science and Engineering A211 (1996) 45.
9 Youtsos AG, Schroder J, Timke T, Physica B 234-236 (1997) 959.
10 Pirling T, Proceedings of the sixth European Powder Diffraction Conference EPDIC 6th, Budapest (Hungary), August 1998, in press.
11 Pirling T, European Conference on Residual Stress (ECRS-6), Delft October 1999, submitted.
12 Saint-Antonin F, Pirling T, 'Residual stress measurements in alumina/copper jointed specimen', ILL Experimental Report 5-26-99, august 1999.

DETERMINATION OF RESIDUAL STRESSES WITH PHASE SHIFTING LASER SPECKLE INTERFEROMETRY

R Plaut-Aubry*, M François*, G Montay*, S Branchu*, V Chalvidan** and J Lu*****
*** LAMM , IUT de St.-Nazaire, Bd de l'Université BP 406, 44602 Saint Nazaire – France - E-mail : francois@lamm.univ-nantes.fr**
**** HOLO 3, 7, rue Général Cassagnou, 68300 Saint Louis - France**
***** LASMIS, Univ. Tech. de Troyes, 11, rue M. Curie, BP2060, 10010 Troyes - France**

ABSTRACT

Hole drilling is a widely accepted method for determining residual stresses from relaxation data obtained by a strain gage rosette. Recently, more and more investigations explore the alternative of employing optical techniques to reveal the displacement fields produced by hole drilling (holography, moiré…).

A comparison between strain gage rosette and ESPI (Electronic Speckle Pattern Interferometry) using the phase-shifting technique has been performed. Experiments were executed on shot-peened (2024) aluminium alloy and titanium (TiAl6V4) alloy samples.

ESPI is a non-contact measurement method which does not require any preparation for the samples. The whole displacement field is measured (about several cm²) around the hole with a precision of about 0.1 μm.

Compared with classical interferometry, the main advantages of phase-shifting techniques are the following :

- data treatment is easier to implement on a computer,
- the sign of the displacement is known,
- the information obtained (phase of the interferogram) is directly linked to the displacement field.

INTRODUCTION

Residual stress measurement by optical means has been developing rapidly for about 10 years. The various techniques that can be found in the literature are : double exposure or phase shifting holographic interferometry, shearography, moiré interferometry and more recently, double exposure speckle pattern interferometry. To disturb the stress equilibrium, the hole drilling method is associated with all these techniques.

Holographic interferometry with hole drilling was first used with double exposure technique (1-6). This method, although very accurate, requires the use of holographic films which need to be processed and then replaced with a very high precision. Holographic interferometry can also be used with a phase shifting technique to obtain directly the phase of the hologram (7,8). This makes the analysis of complex patterns easier and allows one to determine the sign of displacement. Compared with other techniques, shearography ("speckle shearing") enables one to determine directly strains and is less sensitive to vibrations ; however, the fringe contrast is lower. Moiré interferometry gives very good quality patterns and uses a CCD (Charge Coupled Device) camera instead of a holographic film (10-12). However, this technique requires a careful and time-consuming surface preparation to glue or engrave a pattern on the drilled area.

Electronic Speckle Pattern Interferometry (ESPI) only needs a very light surface preparation and uses a CCD camera to record speckle patterns. Although this technique gives fringes of lower contrast than holographic interferometry, it is easier to implement and to use. Some authors have been used it with the double exposure scheme (13-15) which major drawback is that the displacement sign cannot be determined without an a priori knowledge of the stress sign or without a system of carrier signal. Another problem is that fringe counting can be difficult when the displacement field is complex as is the case around the hole.

The aim of the present paper is to show that it is possible to use phase shifting ESPI to measure residual stresses with the incremental hole drilling technique.

BACKGROUND

The so-called "symmetric interferometer" is commonly used to measure in-plane displacements with speckle pattern interferometry (16, 19). It can be implemented either with the double exposure technique or the phase shifting scheme. For the latter, a mirror mounted on a piezo-electric translator (PZT) is used to change the optical path length of one of the two arms of the interferometer. A series of pictures with different phases can be obtained for different positions of the mirror. From this series, the phase can be calculated for each point of the field viewed by the camera.

The intensity obtained on one point of the picture is expressed by :

$$I_T = I_1 + I_2 + 2\sqrt{I_1 I_2}\cos(\psi_1 - \psi_2) \tag{1a}$$

where I_1 and I_2 are the intensities given at this point by the two symmetric beams when they are alone. ψ_1 and ψ_2 are the phases of the two beams. After displacement, the intensity becomes :

$$I'_T = I'_1 + I'_2 + 2\sqrt{I'_1 I'_2}\cos(\psi_1 - \psi_2 + \delta\psi) \text{ with} \tag{1b}$$

$$\delta\psi = \frac{4\pi}{\lambda} d \sin\theta \tag{2}$$

$\delta\psi$ is the phase difference due to a displacement d of the considered point along the sensitivity vector. In figure 1, the sensitivity vector is parallel to the x axis. For the phase shifting technique, a minimum of 3 pictures should be taken before displacement (i.e. in the original position) to obtain the phase :

$$\psi_1 - \psi_2 = \operatorname{Arctan}\left(\frac{I_{T3} - I_{T2}}{I_{T1} - I_{T2}}\right) \tag{3a}$$

Where I_{T1}, I_{T2}, I_{T3} are the intensities at a given point for the 3 positions of the PZT. After displacement, another set of 3 pictures should be taken. The new phase of the same pixel is given by :

$$\psi_1 - \psi_2 + \delta\psi = \operatorname{Arctan}\left(\frac{I'_{T3} - I'_{T2}}{I'_{T1} - I'_{T2}}\right) \tag{3b}$$

The phase difference $\delta\psi$ is then obtained by subtracting the two phase values. However, $\delta\psi$ is only known modulo 2π (wrapped). Thus, a direct application of equation (2) to calculate d will give discontinuities in the displacement field. An unwrapping operation should be performed to obtain the displacement value d, assuming that the variations of d are continuous over the picture. The unwrapping algorithm, called "hierarchical spatial unwrapping" was developed by Holo3 (17).

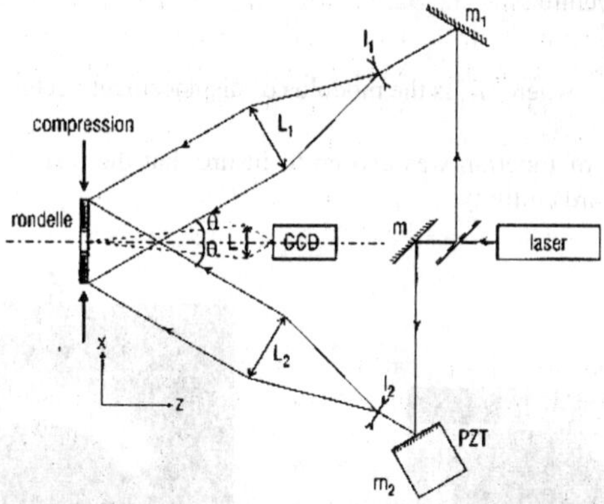

Fig. 1 : Symmetric interferometer with a piezo translator (PZT) (19)

EXPERIMENTS

Measurements were performed on shot-peened 2024 aluminium alloy and TiAl6V4 titanium alloy samples.

Strain gages hole drilling : measurements were performed using CEA 062RE type strain gages, a Vishay P350AF bridge with a commutation box SB-2. Holes were drilled with Vishay RS200 device (18). The drill diameter was 1.6 mm, but due to imperfections in the drilling device, the real diameter of the hole was 1.700 mm in aluminium sample with an ovalisation of 10 μm. In titanium sample, the hole diameter was 1.800 mm with an ovalisation smaller than 10 μm. 20 drilling steps were performed up to a total depth of 1500 μm.

ESPI hole drilling : measurements were performed with a double symmetrical interferometer. Movable mirrors were used to switch from measurements in the x direction and the y direction. The θ angle was equal to 66.5°. A monochrome CCD camera with 512 x 512 pixels enabled one to record the pictures with 256 grey levels. The field covered by the camera was approximately 12 x 12 mm^2. Pictures were acquired and treated by "Fringe Analysis 95" software (20). The specimens were glued on the experiment table so that they do not move during the operation. A thin layer of white painting was sprayed on the surface of the sample to obtain a homogeneous diffuse scattering over the observed surface. Holes were also drilled with Vishay RS200 device and a 1.6 mm diameter drill. The real hole diameter was 1.750 mm with an ovalisation of 50 μm for the aluminium sample and 1.750 mm with an ovalisation of 100 μm for the titanium one. 11 steps were performed up to a total depth of 850 μm. Between each drilling steps, the drilling device was removed to take pictures with the camera.

TREATMENT OF DISPLACEMENT FIELDS

After acquisition and unwrapping, we obtain a series of pictures of the displacement fields in the x direction and another in the y direction (fig. 2 and 3). To avoid unwrapping errors, it is necessary to screen the hole area and also some places where strong light reflections convey no meaningful information. From "Fringe Analysis 95" software, we export the unwrapped pictures into Mathematica® software. The aim of the treatment operations is to find the real centre of the hole and to smooth the noise inherent in speckle patterns. The smoothing is performed by fitting the data with an analytic function using a least square scheme. As the samples are shot-peened, we can assume that the displacement field only depends on the distance r to the hole centre :

$$|\vec{u}| = \sum_n \frac{A_n}{r^n} \quad \text{where } |\vec{u}| \text{ is the modulus of displacement vector and } A_n \text{ a factor} \quad (4)$$

This particular form of function was chosen to insure that the displacement tends towards zero when r tends towards infinity.

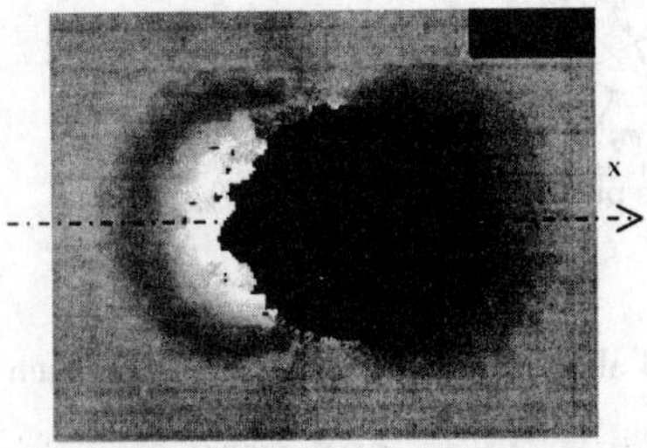

Fig. 2 : displacement field along x axis

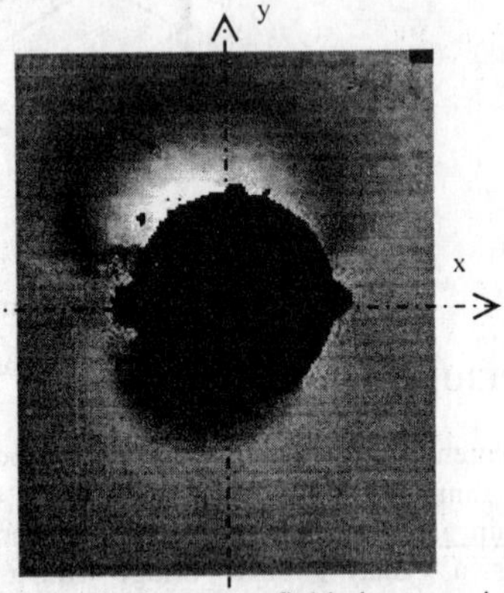

Fig. 3 : displacement field along y axis

The treatment steps, realised with Mathematica® software are the following :

- For each pixel, the displacement vector is obtained from the components of x and y pictures. This is performed for each drilling step.
- 2000 points are taken randomly in the displacement field. For each one, the straight line directed by the displacement vector is determined. As we assume the displacement vector to be purely radial, the intersection point of any couple of lines should be the hole centre. The centroid of the 1000 intersection points is calculated. The same operation is repeated for each drilling step and the centroid of the centroids is considered as the hole centre.
- The hole centre determined in the previous step is taken as the origin of the reference frame.
- 5000 points are taken randomly and for each point, the modulus of the displacement vector is associated to the distance r of the point from the origin.
- The function defined in equation (4) is fitted for each drilling step.

STRESSES CALCULATION

As in the classical hole drilling method, stresses calculation consists in establishing the relationship between the variation of surface strain due to the hole drilling and the residual stress distribution through calibration coefficients. These coefficients can be obtained either experimentally or by a numerical modelisation. In our case, a 2D finite element model is used, taking into account the linear elasticity law of the material, the strain gauge geometry and the hole diameter. For aluminium alloy the Young modulus is 72 GPa and Poisson ratio is 0.34, for titanium alloy, the values are 120 GPa and 0.30 respectively. The calibration coefficient A is determined by using a special loading case (21) :

$$\sigma_{xx} = \sigma_{yy} = \sigma \text{ and } \tau_{xy} = 0 \tag{5}$$

equivalent to a uniform pressure acting on the hole boundary.
The value of B is given by :

$$B = \frac{u_2 - u_1}{2\sigma(r_2 - r_1)} \tag{6}$$

where u_2 and u_1 are the nodal displacements where the measure has been done. B is computed for each depth increment. We can then determine the residual stress state in the material with:

$$\sigma = \frac{\varepsilon}{2B} \tag{7}$$

where $\varepsilon = (\varepsilon_1 + \varepsilon_2 + \varepsilon_3)/3$ is the average strain value on the 3 gauges. For speckle interferometry, as the experimental data is the displacement field, we obtain the stress value directly from equation (6). For the sake of comparison, the displacement was computed for the two extremities of the gage (r = 1.82 mm and r = 3.57 mm).

RESULTS

The stress gradients obtained with speckle pattern interferometry and classical hole drilling method are presented on figures 4 and 5 for each sample. It can be seen that a good agreement is obtained in terms of stress magnitude. However the position of the maximum along the hole depth is slightly shifted of about 50 µm. This can be due to the uncertainty on the drilling origin. The dispersion on the values obtained with ESPI is higher. This can be attributed to the smaller number of depth increments. It should be noted that the shape of the hole in the titanium sample is strongly ovalized in the case of ESPI measurements, probably because of the successive positionings of the drill between each picture.

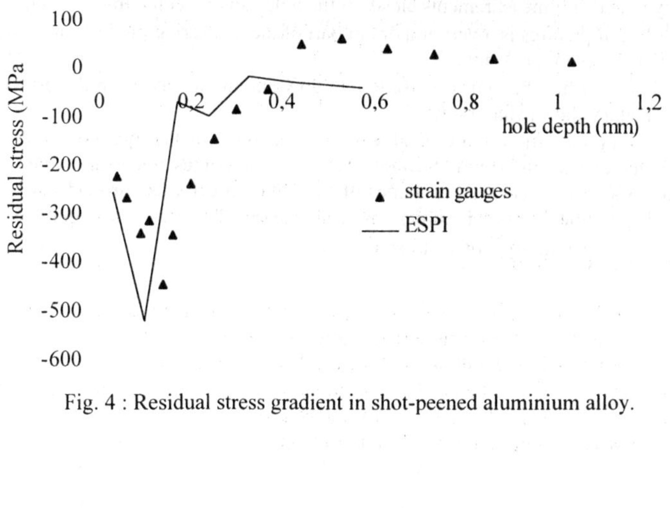

Fig. 4 : Residual stress gradient in shot-peened aluminium alloy.

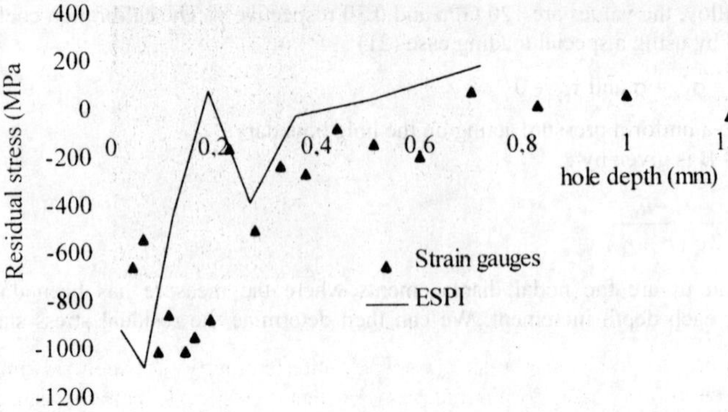

Fig. 5 : Residual stress gradient in shot-peened titanium alloy.

DISCUSSION

The measure of the displacement field by Electronic Speckle Pattern Interferometry with a phase shifting scheme associated to the hole drilling method gives consistent results with the classical hole drilling method in the case of shot-peened metallic specimens. However, some points deserve to be discussed :

- A speckle pattern appears when a laser beam impinges on an optically rough surface (when the roughness is equal or greater than the wavelength of the laser light). Therefore, strains of optically smooth or highly reflecting surfaces cannot be measured directly by ESPI technique. Such surfaces should be prepared by spraying a powder which should be uniform and follow perfectly the displacements.
- The sensitivity of ESPI is lower than that of piezo-resistive strain gauges : 10^{-6} for the latter and 10^{-5} for the former. However, the high redundancy of information and the possibility to perform measurements closer to the hole can overcome this problem.
- The treatment of pictures is a very important part of the measuring process and can lead to large discrepancies in the results.
- It is necessary to filter the optical noise before unwrapping operation. In the present work we used a rectangular median filter.
- The unwrapping operation is a critical step and still requires the operator to choose the starting point of the algorithm. Several trials are sometimes necessary when speckle decorrelation starts to occur. As a matter of fact, the optical noise around the hole may lead to displacement discontinuities as can clearly be seen on figure 6. These discontinuities are a multiple of $\lambda / (2 \sin\theta)$.

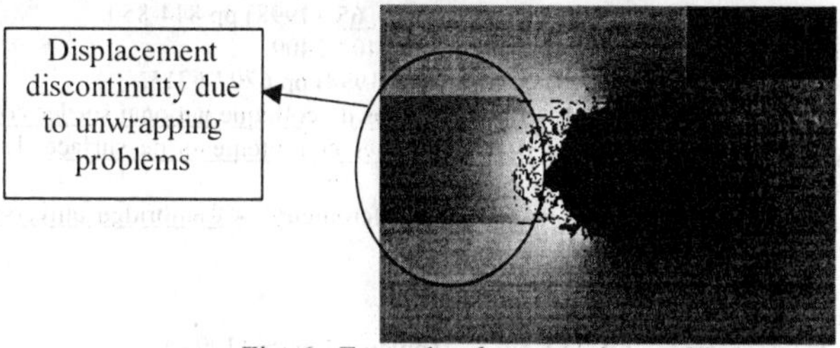

Fig. 6 : Example of unwrapping problem.
The 2π modulation in the phase measured may be difficult to eliminate.

- decorrelation is a recurrent problem in speckle interferometry. Between two images, the roughness of the surface should not vary so that the speckle patterns can correlate. Displacements others than those measured may also produce decorrelation so the specimen should be strongly held during the drilling and measurement operations.

On the other hand, the technique has the following advantages :

- The problem of hole centring with respect to the strain gauges is suppressed.
- The whole displacement field is obtained. This enables to check for systematic errors such as the perpendicularity of the hole axis with respect to the sample surface or stress heterogeneities.
- Most of the time there is no need of surface preparation. If necessary, it remains very simple.
- The cost of optical equipments (camera, laser...) is decreasing rapidly and is today of the same order as extensometric equipments. Furthermore, there is no need of consumable supplies.

From this study, it is possible to conclude that speckle pattern interferometry with a phase shifting scheme is successful to determine the residual stress gradient. However the drill positioning and removing should be automated, which could allow to increase the number of depth increments. Further experiments will be performed, along with improvements in the data treatment.

REFERENCES

1. ANTONOV AA - Svar. Proiz. N°9 (1983), pp 21-23
2. NELSON DV, McCRICKERD JT - Experimental mechanics (December 1986) pp 371-378.
3. MAKINO A, NELSON D - Experimental mechanics (March 1994) pp 66-78.
4. NELSON D, FUCHS E, MAKINO A, WILLIAMS D - Experimental mechanics (March 1994) pp 79-88.
5. LIN ST, HSIEH CT, HU CP - Experimental mechanics (June 1994) pp 141-147.
6. SCHMITT DR, LI Y - Experimental mechanics Vol. 36, No 4, (1996) pp 412-420.
7. LIN ST, HSIEH CT, LEE CK - SPIE Vol. 2577 (1995) pp 226-237
8. HSIEH CT, LIN ST, LEE CK - SPIE Vol. 2577 (1995) pp 238-248.
9. HUNG MYY, LONG KW, ZHANG X, HOVANESIAN JD, HATHAWAY R - SPIE Vol. 955 Industrial Laser Interferometry II (1988).
10. NICOLETTO G - Experimental mechanics (September 1991) pp 252-256.
11. WHU Z, LU J, HAN B - Journal of applied mechanics Vol. 65 (1998), pp 837-843.

12. WHU Z, LU J, HAN B - Journal of applied mechanics Vol. 65, (1998) pp 844-850.
13. ZHANG J - Optical engineering Vol. 37, No 8 (1998) pp 2402-2409.
14. ZHANG J, CHONG TC - Applied Optics Vol. 37, No 28 (1998) pp 6707-6715.
15. MOKHDANI C, INAL K, FRANÇOIS M, VIAL C - Actes du colloque national sur les contraintes résiduelles dans les procédés d'élaboration des céramiques et traitements de surface, Limoges - France. (Septembre 1997)
16. JONES R, WYKES C – "Holographic and speckle interferometry" - Cambridge university press Edition (1989) – Second edition
17. COLON E - HOLO 3, Private communication.
18. VISHAY Micromesures - document Réf. NT 47 E
19. SMIGIELSKY P – "Holographie" - Ed. TEKNEA – Toulouse France (1994.)
20. HOLO 3 – St LOUIS – France
21. LU J, NIKU-LARI A, FLAVENOT JF - Matériaux et technique (déc. 1985) pp 709-718.

A New Approach of Yield Strength Determination using X-Ray Diffraction on Alloy 718

O.Gourbesville *, J.L.Lebrun *, B.Marty **

*LM3, ENSAM Paris, ESA CNRS 8006, 151 Bd de L'Hôpital, 75013 Paris France
**Laboratoire YKOG, SNECMA Gennevilliers, 291 Av d'Argenteuil, 92234 Gennevilliers

Abstract : The aim of this paper is to understand the relations between the microstructure and the mechanical properties of a polycrystalline alloy 718 (NC19FeNb). The X-Ray method allows us to appreciate nanoscopic phenomena like dislocations, distortions and lattices orientations or more macroscopic phenomena like texture or grain size which are representative at the scale of the sample.
Width and shape of X-Ray profile give informations about the density and the distribution of dislocation within the scattering volume. The measure of the integral width allows to estimate a certain aspect of the hardening of the material which is in close relation with the yield strength. Pole figure acquisitions give the scattered intensities in all other space direction described by Ψ and Φ angles. A statistical approach of measured intensities allows to estimate the crystallite size by a new criterion. The calculation of residue between experimental and smoothed intensities gives a quantitative criterion. If the structure is well recrystallised the crystallite size can be assimilated to the grain size.
The knowledge of both X-Ray parameters on a large number of sample which have a known yield strength permitted to establish a phenomenological prediction law of yield strength. This experimental methodology coupled with numerical simulation is applied to industrial forged parts (cross section of turbine disk) to obtain a completely predictive model.

I INTRODUCTION

Turbine disks which hold blades and impart the mechanical torque are extremely loaded at high temperature. An accurate knowledge of the mechanical properties is very important to determine correctly the size and the shape of the disks. They are related to microstructural parameters of material such as bulk hardening, grain size, texture or distribution and amount of precipitates which are introduced during the forging process and thermal treatment.
It is very difficult to quantify these microstructural parameters by classical investigation methods. In particular, the Transmission Electron Microcospy (MET) is difficult to carry out and not very representative at the scale of the piece (turbine disk). B.Marty [1] has shown that X-Ray Diffraction (XRD), in alloy 718, could be used to determine material hardening, grain size and phases proportion (γ, γ' and γ''). The XRD is a non-destructive method and allows to analyse a surface which is more representative at the scale of the piece. Because of the depth of the X-Rays, measure can be edge off by the surface preparation.
Links between the yield strength and the dislocation density in one part (yield strength augmentation by hardening) and grain size in another part (yield strength augmentation if the grain size decrease (Hall and Petch [2]) allow us to establish a phenomenological law.
The goal of this paper is thus to confront this phenomenological law to numerical simulation in order to have a good predictive model which could be introduced in the Metallurgical Post Processor in FORGE 2 ® software.

II METHODOLOGY

II.1 Alloy 718 : NC19FeNb

Alloy 718 is largely used since more than 25 years to manufacture turbine disks in aircraft engineering. It has got a good forgeability, a good creep behaviour until 600°C and it is very stable. Alloy 718 has four main phases : bulk γ, hardening coherent phase γ' (Ll_2) visible as small globular precipitates (<1μm), an hardening semi-coherent phase γ'' (DO_{22}) as lenses precipitates (smaller than γ') and an incoherent phase δ (Doa) visible as its lamellar shape (see figure 1) [1, 3].

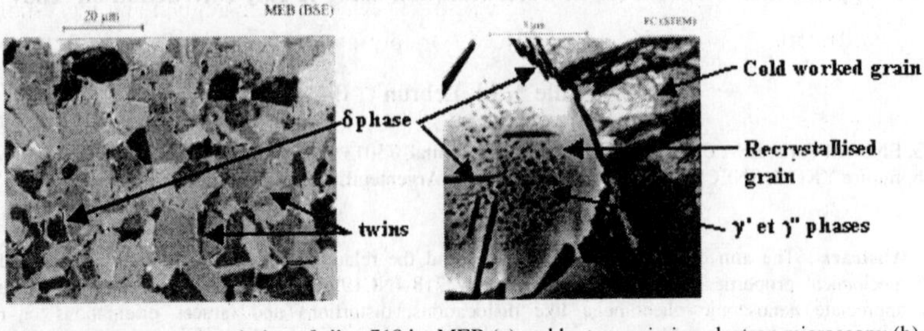

Figure 1 : Microstructure description of alloy 718 by MEB (a) and by transmission electron microscopy (b) [1]

Figure 1.a. shows a polycrystalline material where the average grain size is 20 µm (in this study, grain size will vary from 5 µm to 30 µm). The δ phase surrounds grains and limits their growth. Twins can be frequently observed. In short, alloy 718 presents a complex and heterogeneous microstructure which depends on forging conditions and thermal treatments. This metallurgy is preponderant in mechanical properties control.

II.2 X-Ray profile broadening : hardening of material

In XRD analysis, X-Ray line is the result of constructive interference between diffracted photons by crystalline lattice in accordance with the Bragg's law [4] :

$$2d.\sin\theta=n.\lambda \quad (1)$$

Classical applications of this type of acquisition are the determination of residual stresses in polycrystalline material called "First Order residual stresses". The principle of this well known technique called "$\mathrm{Sin}^2\Psi$ law" is to measure the relative X-Ray line displacement due to the mean variation of the interreticular distance in function of Ψ (angle between the sample perpendicular direction and incident and diffracted beam direction bisector) [5]. Now, more and more studies are devoted to determine stresses at finer scale. In particular, the second order (II order) represents in first approximation the stresses at the grain scales [6, 7]. After recent developments, we can define a new second order (II' order) which determines the stresses distribution inside the grain [8]. The III order rather defines the stress at the scale of the dislocation forest [8, 9] and the IV order those at the scale of the dislocation (Peierls forces) [9].

In this study, we measure the X-Ray line broadening of a polycristal by calculating integral width. The broadening effect is the result of stresses heterogeneities at the grain scale (II and II' order), at the dislocation distribution scale (III order) and at the dislocation scale (IV order). We shall not separate the different contribution. These differents heterogeneities modify locally interreticular distances and contribute to the broadening effect in first approximation.

However, the complex microstructure of Alloy 718 presents difficulties to evaluate easily integral width. Amounts of Fe (19%) and Cr (19%) generate an important fluorescence for each wavelength less than 0.210 nm. The nearness of phases cells parameters doesn't allow us to separate experimentally the contribution of each one. We have to use a mathematical procedure (simplex method [10]) to deconvoluate the γ, γ' and γ" effect.

Thus the material profile can be developed as equation 2 :

$$\textit{Material Profile}(s) = H_1.V_1(s) + H_2.V_2(s) + H_3.V_3(s) + H_4.V_4(s) \qquad (2)$$

Where $H_1.V_1(s)$ and $H_2.V_2(s)$ ($\gamma 1$ et $\gamma 2$) represent respectively the hardened and recrystallised part of γ diffracting volume. $H_3.V_3(s)$ et $H_4.V_4(s)$ represent respectively the contribution of γ' and γ''.

V_i are Voigt function, s reciprocal space position ($\frac{\sin\theta}{\lambda}$) and H_i the height of each line.

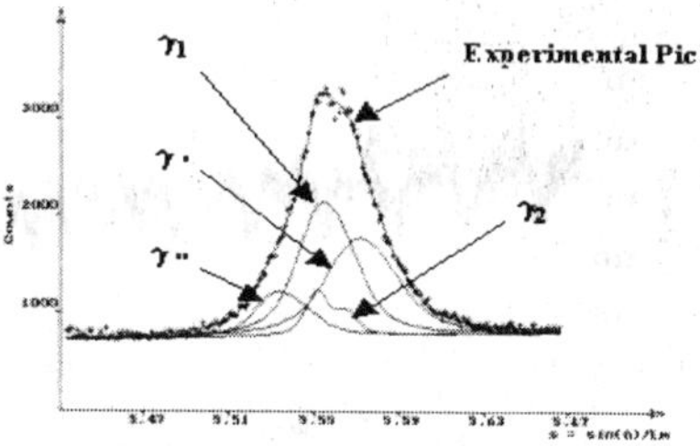

Hardening could be appreciate by three integral widths :

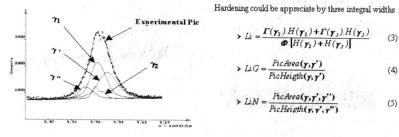

$$\blacktriangleright\ Li = \frac{\Gamma(\gamma_1).H(\gamma_1)+\Gamma(\gamma_2).H(\gamma_2)}{\Phi.[H(\gamma_1)+H(\gamma_2)]} \qquad (3)$$

$$\blacktriangleright\ LiG = \frac{PicArea(\gamma,\gamma')}{PicHeigth(\gamma,\gamma')} \qquad (4)$$

$$\blacktriangleright\ LiN = \frac{PicArea(\gamma,\gamma',\gamma'')}{PicHeigth(\gamma,\gamma',\gamma'')} \qquad (5)$$

Figure 2 : (400) line profile acquisition of alloy 718, results of deconvolution treatment

In these expressions γ is both γ_1 and γ_2, ϕ is a shape parameter (0,74) between Gauss function and Lorentz function.

To quantify the material hardening we will analyse {400} plane with copper wavelength. This choice is a good compromise : δ phase doesn't diffract at this angle and so the profile is only constituted by γ, γ' and γ'' (see **Figure 2**), the fluorescence is not too important and the Bragg angle $2.\theta=117.8°$ permit to have a good consideration of instrumental effect.

II.3 Pole figure acquisition : crystallite size or grain size

Pole Figure acquisition (PF) is a well known technique to determine texture in polycrystalline material. Texture could be defined as the distribution of the grain orientation in a polycrystalline material if we suppose that it is constituted by a finite number of grain. If we want to quantify correctly texture we have to analyse several PF and the number depends on the lattice symmetry and the used method (harmonic method [11] or vector method [12]). In general, it is necessary to acquire at least 2 or 3 PF to calculate the Orientation Distribution Function (ODF).

Also, PF acquisitions could be a very interesting technique to estimate the crystallite size of a polycristal. In 1993, P.Klimanek [13] presented a statistical approach of PF acquisition to determine grain-size both with XRD and neutron diffraction on copper specimens. In this paper we try to explain a new approach of PF acquisition.

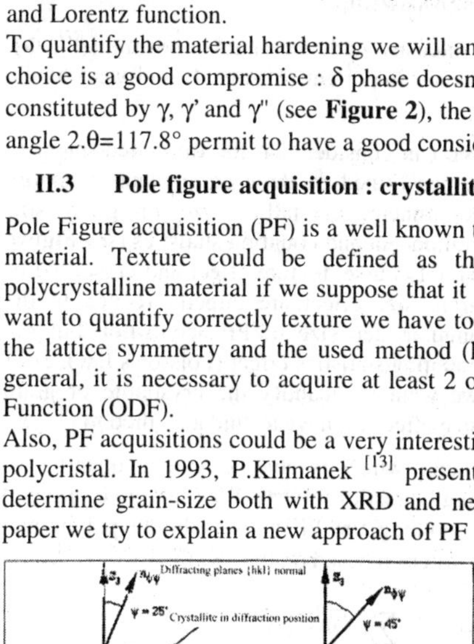

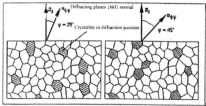

Figure 3 : Crystallite in diffracting position for a couple (Ψ, Φ)

The principle of PF acquisition is to measure diffracted intensities in all space direction described by Ψ and Φ for one {hkl} family (see **Figure 3**). Scattered intensity depends on crystallite number which are in diffracting position inside the irradiated volume for one couple (ψ, Φ). If the crystallographic orientation distribution of the material is isotropic (no texture) and the crystallite size is small, then the scattering volume (diffracted intensity) doesn't vary with (Ψ, Φ). On the contrary, if the material is not textured but the crystallite size is large in relation to irradiating volume, the diffracting volume will strongly vary. To illustrate these considerations we carried out PF acquisitions on samples with different grain size. The irradiated surface is about 7x7 mm² with an incident divergent beam (0.3°) and a penetration depth of about 4 µm for Ψ=0°. A nickel filter and slits length in secondary optics are used. To obtain the desired grain size we applied heat treatment at 1050 °C with different times. The obtained structures are recrystallized solid solution of Fe and Cr in Ni. If the structure is well recrystallised we can assimilate crystallite size to grain size.

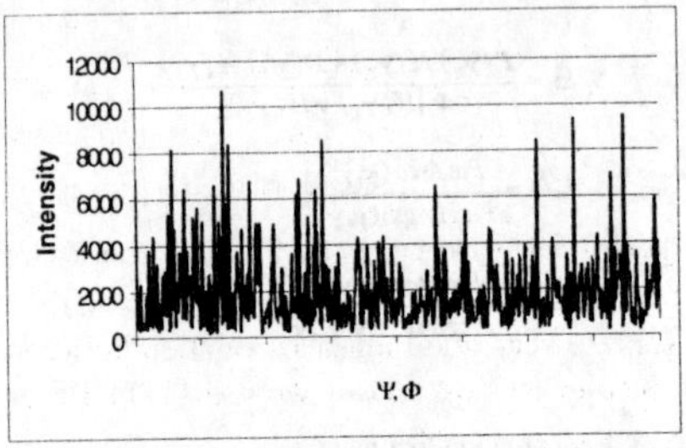

Figure 4 : Linear visualisation of PF acquisition on {200} plane in the case of sample with grain size about 120-150 µm (G=3)

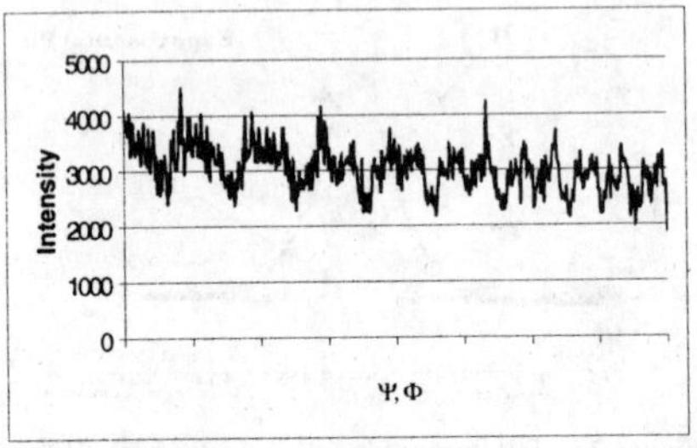

Figure 5 : Linear visualisation of PF acquisition on {200} plane in the case of sample with grain size about 15-20 µm (G=9)

Figure 4 and **Figure 5** show the evolution of intensity with the angular position (Ψ, Φ). When the grain size is important the fluctuations are important (**Figure 4**) and weak if the grain size is small (**Figure 5**).

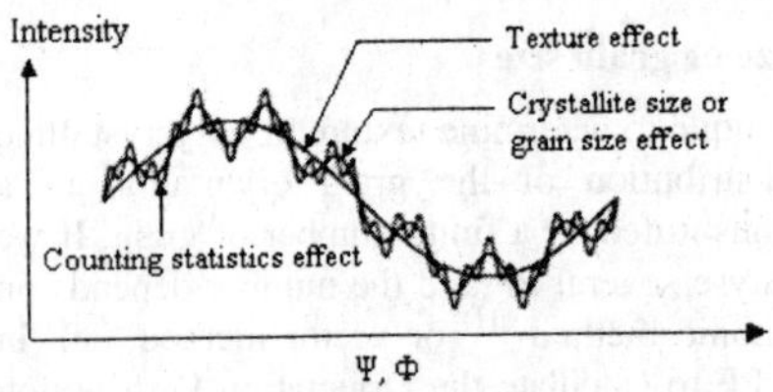

Figure 6 : Analyse of diffracted intensity

We can consider that the diffracted intensity is constituted of three components : texture component, crystallite size or grain size component and counting statistics (see **Figure 6**). Of course, texture effect and crystallite or grain size effect are directly related to the angular step size of PF acquisition but not counting statistics effect (Poisson's law). So if we want to quantify the crystallite or grain size effect we have to find a method to determine the texture component and a parameter which is able to give a quantitative information while taking into account counting statistics effect. We can give a good approximation of the texture component by smoothing the PF with a sliding polynomial function. In a recent paper [14] we introduced $Sp\chi$ criterion based on the "Khi2-law" [15, 16].

$$Sp\chi = \frac{Khi2 - n}{\sqrt{2n}} \quad \text{where} \quad \text{Khi2} = 4 \times \sum_{i}^{n} (\sqrt{Ii} - \sqrt{I\theta})^2$$

Where Ii is experimental intensity, f(θi) smoothed intensity and "n" the number of steps (Ψ, Φ).

Statistic book [16] showed that the variable "2Khi" converges faster toward a normal law, so we will use a new criterion Eta :

$$\text{Eta} = \sqrt{2 \times Khi2} - \sqrt{2 \times n - 1}$$

Sp_χ and Eta are normalised criteria and depend on the acquisition parameters (step size, beam divergence, irradiated area etc…). They give a relative information about the crystallite size but not its absolute size. It will be important to use the same experimental conditions if we want to compare results.

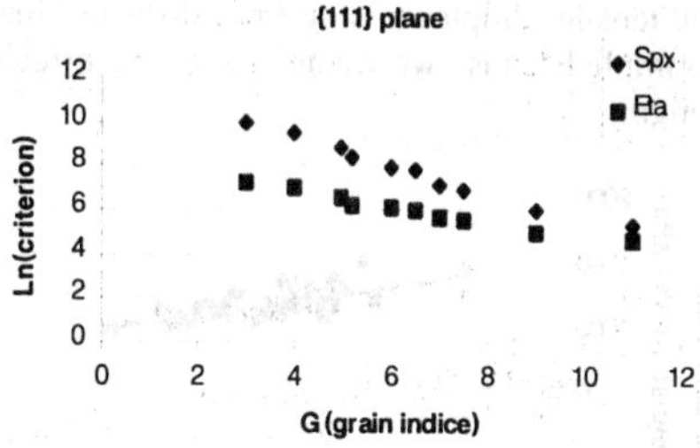

Figure 7 : $Sp\chi$ and Eta evolution versus grain indice quotation for {111} plane

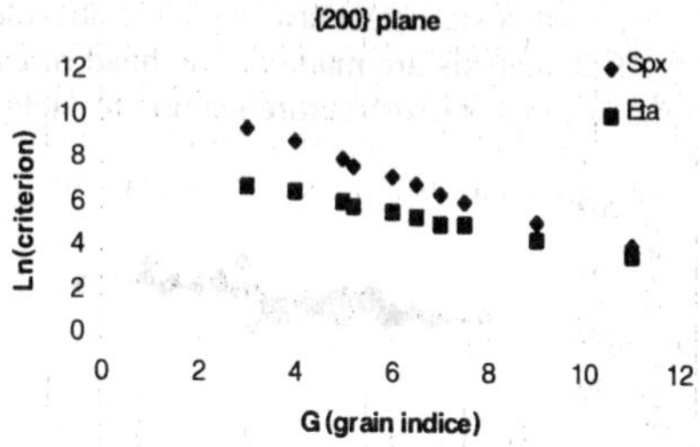

Figure 8 : $Sp\chi$ and Eta evolution versus grain indice quotation for {200} plane

In the case of recrystallised alloy 718, we can observe a very good linear correlation between grain indice quotation and the criteria. The same results are observed if we use {111} PF or {200} PF. Eta increases if the grain size increases.

It might be slightly different if we consider an industrial forged and treated alloy 718. The γ' and γ'' precipitations or the bulk hardening could modify locally crystalline lattice and crystallite size. In future, we are going to carry out heat treatment on these samples to see the effect of γ' and γ'' precipitations and we will try to lead different tests such by forging or cold rolling to evaluate the hardening effect on the criterion.

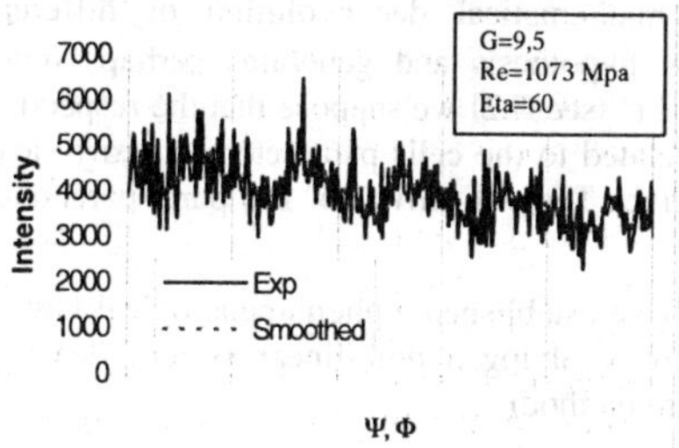

Figure 9 : PF {200} : Diffracted intensity versus (Ψ, Φ) position for an industrial sample (G=9.5)

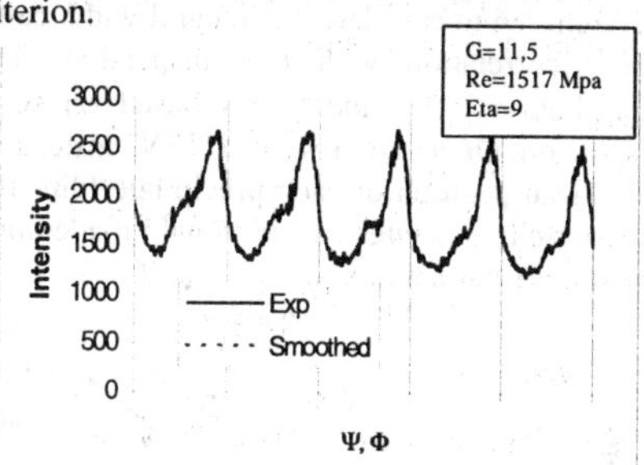

Figure 10 : PF {200} : Diffracted intensity versus (Ψ, Φ) position for an industrial sample (G=11.5)

Figure 9 and **Figure 10** show the experimental and smoothed intensities in function of (Ψ, ϕ) positions respectively for a sample with a grain size about 15 μm and 5-8 μm. Of course, in this case the crystallite size cannot be assimilated to the grain size because of precipitates and hardening. However, criterion seems to be a good quotation for industrial alloy 718 to show microstructural differences. In this case, Eta is a second order parameter of grain size. One after, we will use the {200} PF to determine Eta criterion and the experimental conditions will be identical as those described above.

In general in this study, texture is often weak and it is not taken into account but we will discuss about this difficult point in the last paragraph.

II.4 Phenomenological law

The phenomenological law is based on the knowledge of two XRD parameters : grain size (replaced by crystallite size in second order) and hardening. The variation of precipitates proportion (γ', γ") and of the texture are neglected to establish the law.
To establish a statistical law, we have analysed 60 tensile samples arising from disks turbine. All XRD analysis are made on the head of each sample because we wanted to see the effects of the original microstructure leading to yield strength.

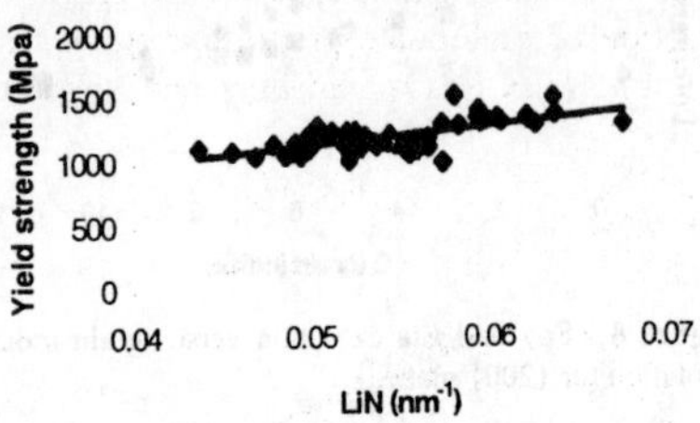

Figure 11 : Correlation between yield strength and the integral width defined in § II.2

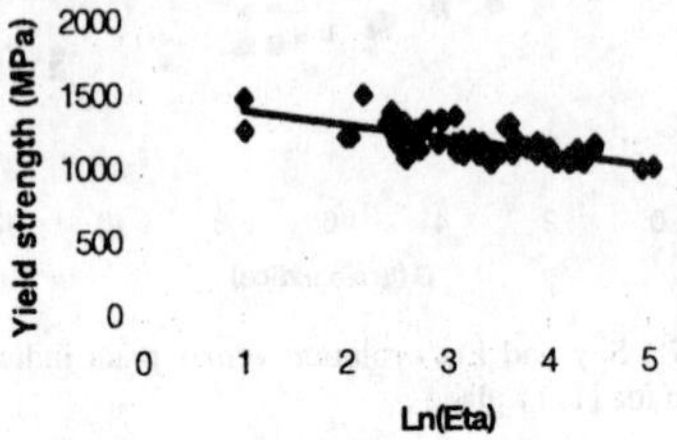

Figure 12 : Correlation between yield strength and the Eta criterion defined in § II.3

Figure 11 and **Figure 12** show the close relations between the yield strength with the hardening estimated by integral width and with the Eta criterion which represents the crystallite size. If the crystallite size increases then yield strength decreases in according with the Hall and Petch law [2]. If the hardening increases then the yield strength increases. We have chosen to correlate the integral width called "LiN" (see II.2) because we have obtained a better correlation with less dispersion. The mathematical deconvolution of different contribution (γ, γ' and γ") is based on several hypothesis and generates perhaps more dispersion. Of course if we use "LiN" instead of "Li" (see II.2) we suppose that the respective line mean position of each precipitate (directly related to the cells parameters) doesn't vary, otherwise it generates an additional broadening effect. Theoretically, "Li" is a purer parameter to estimate hardening.

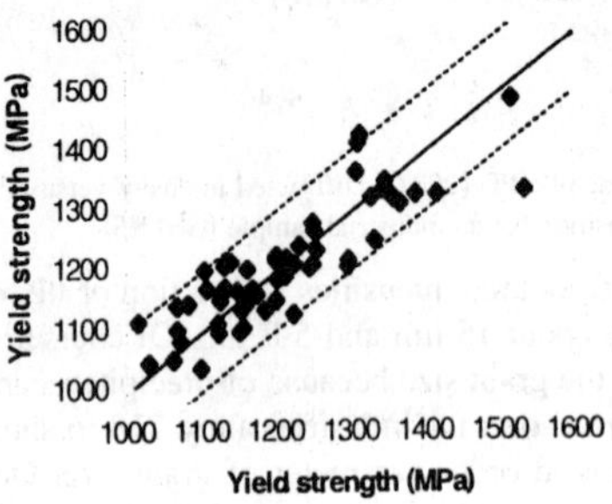

Figure 13 : Correlation between measured yield strength (tensile test) and calculated yield strength (XRD)

We have established a phenomenological law (6) by resolving a multilinear system (least square method).

$$\boldsymbol{R_E^{0.2\%}}_i = \boldsymbol{A \cdot LiN_i + B \cdot Ln(Eta_i) + C} \qquad (6)$$

The dotted lines represent the 95 % confidence interval. By this original experimental approach we are able to estimate the yield strength in ±100 MPa interval in a range of 1000 MPa to 1500 MPa for Alloy 718.

III INDUSTRIAL APPLICATION : Cross section of turbine disk

III.1 Model start-up

The final goal of this work is to confront simulations (FORGE 2) to experimental results in addition to obtain a complete predictive model. For this we carried out X-Ray measurements on a cross section of a turbine disk simulated in FORGE 2. So, it will be possible by using phenomenological law (see equation 6) to know the yield strength on each point of the cross section surface. We can obtain by simulation different metallurgical parameters like dislocations density, grain size, recrystallised fraction or precipitate proportion etc ... In a recent work [14] we have showed a first model linking X-Ray parameters and simulated parameters.

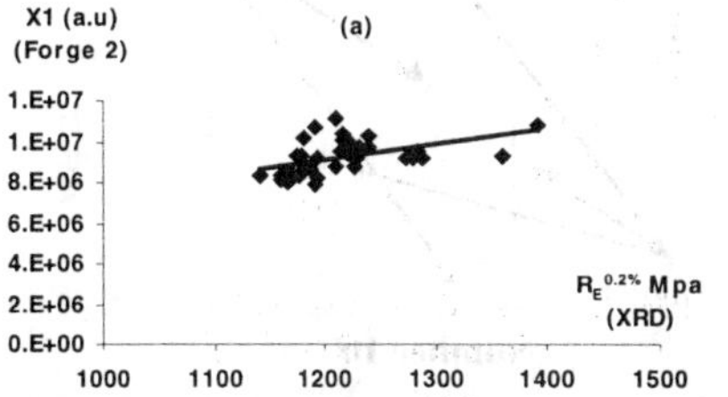

Figure 14 : Correlation between yield strength (XRD) and FORGE 2 parameter (X_1)

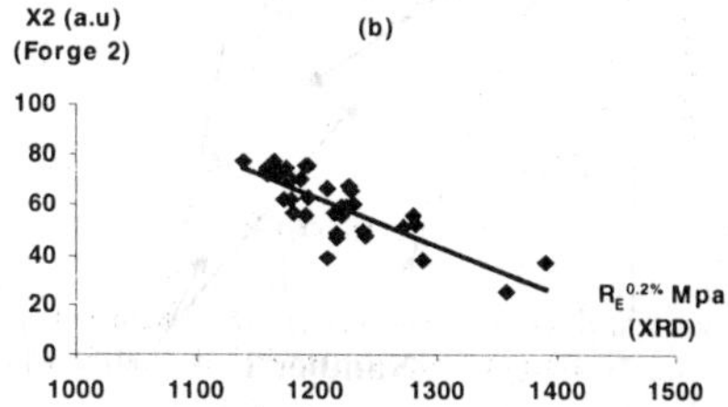

Figure 15 : Correlation between yield strength (XRD) and FORGE 2 parameter (X_2)

These results were extremely cheering and permitted to integrate in FORGE 2 a model based on two parameters X_1 and X_2. X_1 is in close relation with hardening and X_2 depends on cooling time after forging. Consequently, we are able to determine easily the yield strength locally for a turbine disk by numerical simulation. However, we could not compare the results of yield strength determination by XRD and numerical simulation.

III.2 Validation

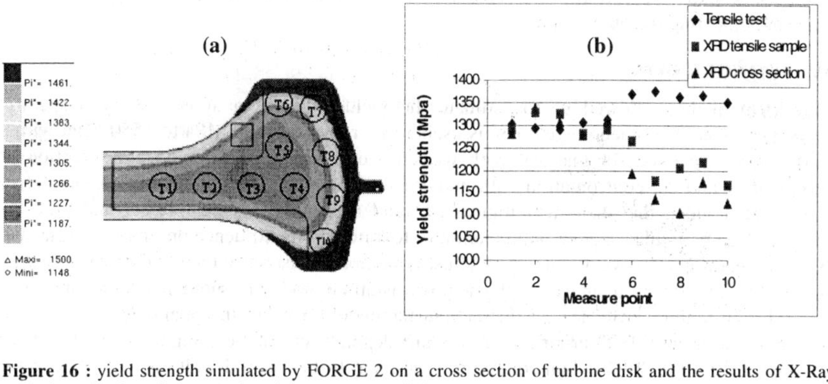

Figure 16 : yield strength simulated by FORGE 2 on a cross section of turbine disk and the results of X-Ray analysis on head tensile tests and on the same area on disk

Figure 16.a. shows the results of simulation on a new forged piece and the corresponding area for tensile test. We can observe on **Figure 16.b.** the evolution of the yield strength determined by tensile test or by XRD on the head of each sample or by XRD on the cross section in function of area. The **Figure 16** shows that the three values are in a good accordance for the first five points but not for the other points. However, if we compare the simulation and the tensile test it seems to be correct. Today, the differences between the XRD values and tensile tests values for the five last points (6, 7, 8, 9 and 10) are not clear. There are several possibilities to explain this effect. The texture could have an influence on the yield strength but it is well known that if the γ" precipitates amount increases the yield strength increases. So we have to take into account these differents contributions.

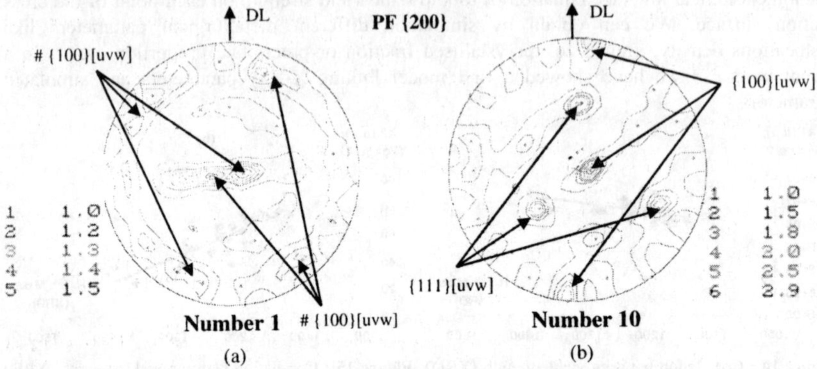

Figure 17 : PF {200} computed by harmonic method for the sample number 1 (a) and number 10 (b)

Today, if we compare poles figures we can observe on {200} PF acquisitions the differences of the texture accuracy and texture sharpness between sample number one (I_{max}=1.5) and number ten (I_{max}=2.9). When the phenomenological law (XRD) gives an under-estimated yield strength, a {111} texture component is present and the {200} component seems to reinforce (see **Figure 17**). At present time, we could observed by simulating with a polycristalline model an increase of about 100 MPa if we considered an isotropic nickel material and another one with a fibre texture {111}. This first result promotes ourselves to continue to study the texture with more accuracy to understand its effect on yield strength without neglecting the other aspects.

IV CONCLUSION

The XRD method allowed us to estimate the yield strength in alloy 718 by a specific procedure. The phenomenological law is usable in a range of 1000 MPa to 1550 MPa with a ±100 MPa dispersion for material with weak texture. The application to cross section of turbine disk and the confrontation with numerical simulation result in a complete predictive model. Of course, the phenomenological law and the model are not perfect and must be improved. In particular, a good appreciation of texture and its influence on yield strength will be developed. For this we are going to adjust a method to discretise the ODF of an industrial material to introduce it in an elasto-plastic polycristalline model. In another way, we are going to study the texture influence on diffraction parameters used in the phenomenological law (integral width and "Eta" criterion). A texture dependence of the integral width has been already observed in 1983 [17] on cold work specimen. If the integral width is measured in the direction of certain preferential orientation it would decrease.

[1] B.Marty, "Etude métallurgique de l'alliage 718 forgé par analyse DRX", Thèse de doctorat, N° 1996-07, ENSAM, 1996
[2] J.Philibert, A.Vignes, Y.Brechet and P.Combrade., "Du minerai au matériau", Masson, p.768, 1998

[3] C.Slama et G.Cizeron, "Etude du comportement structural de l'alliage NC19FeNb", Journal de physique France 7 IV, p.665-688, 1997
[4] A.Guinier, "Théorie et techniques de la radiocristallographie", Dunod, 1964
[5] Norme expérimentale AFNOR, "Méthode d'essais pour l'analyse des contraintes résiduelles par diffraction des rayons X, XP A 09-285, 1999
[6] K.Inal and al., "Stress Analysis in Duplex Steel, X-Ray Diffraction Methodologies of Macro and Pseudo-Macro Stress Analysis in a Textured Duplex Stainless Steel", Scandinavian Journal of Metallurgy, Vol.28, p.139-150, 1999
[7] L.Mcirdi, K.Inal, J.L.Lebrun, "Analysis by X-ray diffraction of the mechanical behaviour of austenitic and ferritic phases of a duplex stainless steel", Advances in X-ray analysis, Vol.42, DENVER, 1998
[8] F.Eberl, J.L.Lebrun, "X-ray Analysis of the mechanical state of a Nickel based multicrystal on the mesoscopic scale : Role of the grain orientation and its boundary", Advances in X-ray analysis, Vol.42, DENVER, 1998
[9] G.Mohamed, thèse de doctorat, université PARIS 13, 1999
[10] D.Taupin, "Probabilities data reduction and error analysis", édition de Physique, p.155-160, 1965
[11] H.J.Bunge and C.Esling, "Quantitative texture analysis", Société française de métallurgie, 1982
[12] A.Vadon, thèse de doctorat, Metz, 1981
[13] P.Klimanek, Grain-size determination by means of X-Ray and neutron high-angle diffraction, Materials science forum, Vol.133-136, pp.921-926, 1993
[14] O.Gourbesville, J.L.Lebrun and B.Marty, Etude par XRD de la microstructure d'un alliage de nickel (Alliage 718) : Relations avec les propriétés mécaniques, in publication, Journal de physique IV, 2000
[15] B.Bourniquel et M.François, Procceeding ICRS4, pp 269-276, 1994
[16] A.Taverne, Connaissance et Maîtrise de la statistique, Les éditions d'organisation, Vol.1 et2, 1984
[17] J.S.Kallend and Y.C.Huang, The determination of the orientation dependence of the stored energy of cold work, ICOTOM 7, Holland, pp 783-786, 1983

SELF CONSISTENT MODEL AND FEM METHODS USED FOR STRESS PREDICTION

A.Baczmanski[1], C. Braham[2], D.Gigout[3], A.Lodini[3] and K. Wierzbanowski[1]

[1]WFTJ, Akademia Górniczo-Hutnicza, al. Mickiewicza 30, 30-059 Kraków, Poland
[2]LMMM,URA-CNRS 1219, Ecole Nationale Supérieure d'Arts et Métiers, 151, Bd de l'Hopital, 75013 Paris, France
[3]LACM,IFTS, Université de Reims Champagne-Ardenne, 7, Bd J. Delautre, 08000 Charleville-Mézières, France

ABSTRACT

A self-consistent model of elastoplastic deformation was used for prediction of tensile test for a two phase steel. The theoretical stresses were compared with the experimental results obtained by X-ray diffraction and from mechanical tests. The parameters of elastoplastic deformation were determined for both phases.
The finite element method (FEM) was applied to evaluate the stress state for the sample subjected to a punching process. For calculations the average properties of the material were assumed.

INTRODUCTION

Different complementary models can be used for prediction of the residual stresses in polycrystalline materials. The finite element method (FEM) is the well known method used for modelling of heterogeneous stress state for a complicated sample shape and different types of deformations. The prediction is based on the phenomenological parameters characterising elastoplastic properties of the material. The polycrystal is treated as the continuous body and the crystallographic character of the grains is not taken into account. The advantage of this method is the possibility of calculation of the heterogeneous macrostress state for a complicated sample shape.

The complementary methods for prediction of internal stress evolution are the Eshelby type models in which the ellipsoidal inclusion embedded in the homogenous matrix is considered. This type of calculation is very convenient for prediction of the second order stresses, i.e., stresses characterising interactions between polycrystalline grains. These types of stresses are very significant for two phase materials after plastic or thermal treatment. In this work the results of the self-consistent model used for elastoplastic deformation are presented. The disadvantage of this type of modelling is a relatively long time of calculation which causes that the modelling for complicated heterogeneous stress states and different sample shapes is not possible.

As the example of Eshelby type modelling the plastically deformed austeno-ferritic steel is studied in order to predict plastic mismatch stresses (second order) between two phases. The X-ray diffraction method was applied for "in situ" tensile test and the stresses were measured independently for each phase. The macrostrain (average for both phases) was controlled by the electrical gauge connected to the surface. The experimental results were compared with the prediction of the elasto-plastic deformation [1,2] model and the stress evolution during plastic deformation was investigated. The influence of the residual stresses on the properties of the material was considered. The elastic limit and parameters characterising hardening process were found by comparing the model with diffraction experiments.

The second aim of this work was the study of stress evolution during the punching process. In this case the stresses are not homogeneous across the sample and the FEM method was used for calculations. The material parameters average for the both phases were taken from experimental tensile test. The Erichsen test, i.e., a deep drawing process with the hemispherical punch was simulated.

SELF CONSISTENT MODEL

The elastoplastic model [1,2] was used for the prediction of tensile deformation. This model treats a given number of polycrystalline grains having different lattice orientations. The calculations are based on the modelisation of the processes occurring inside and between grains. As a result, the internal stresses for different grain orientation and for the whole sample are predicted. The deformation models, used in this work, are based on the prediction of the elastoplastic behaviour of a crystal grain inside the polycrystalline material under applied external stress Σ_{ij}. If the local stress σ_{ij} (at the particular grain) is large enough the plastic deformation occurs due to a slip phenomenon. According to the Schmid's law, the slip can be activated only on this slip system [uvw] (hkl) (the slip direction and plane are specified) for which the resolved shear stress $\sigma_{[uvw](hkl)}$ exceeds some critical value τ_c [1,2], i.e.:

$$\sigma_{[uvw](hkl)} \geq \tau_c \qquad \text{(E1)}$$

During plastic deformation, the multiplication of dislocations and evolution of their spatial distribution inside a grain leads to the hardening of slip systems (τ_c increases with deformation). If we are interested only in the kinetic description of the active slip systems behaviour, their latent hardening can be described with some approximation by a matrix reflecting the interaction between the slip systems (the work hardening matrix). Consequently, the rate of the critical shear stress on the g-th system is equal to [1,2]:

$$\dot{\tau}_c^g = \sum_h H^{gh} \dot{\gamma}^h \qquad \text{(E2)}$$

where: $\dot{\tau}_c^g$ is the rate of the critical stress in the g-th system, $\dot{\gamma}^h$ is the rate of the plastic glide in the h-th system and dot denotes the time derivative.

In practice, the interaction between two active slip systems (g and h) depends on their relative geometrical orientation and they can be divided into two groups, i.e., the W K hardening relations (represented by the H_w terms in the work hardening matrix) and the strong hardening relations (defined as $H_s = A\, H_w$, where A is a anisotropy factor).

To predict the plastic deformation, all the mentioned physical phenomena and quantities should be considered at the grain size scale. Moreover, the influence of the macroscopic quantities (Σ_{ij}, E_{ij} - characterising the sample) on the behaviour of the grain (σ_{ij}, ε_{ij}) must be established. According to Eshelby type of models, the polycrystalline material is approximated by a macrohomogeneous medium at the macroscopic scale and microheterogeneous medium at the microscopic scale. The relation between the local stress rate $\dot{\sigma}^{I}_{ij}$ and the local strain rate $\dot{\varepsilon}^{I}_{ij}$ can be written in the following form [1,2]:

$$\dot{\sigma}^{I}_{ij} = \dot{l}^{I}_{ijkl}\ \dot{\varepsilon}^{I}_{kl} \quad \text{and} \quad l^{I}_{ijkl} = L^{o}_{ijkl} + \Delta l^{I}_{ijkl} \tag{E3}$$

where: $l_{ijkl}{}^{I}$ is the local elastoplastic tangent modulus for the I-th grain and L^{o}_{ijkl} is the macroscopic tangent modulus for a fictionally assumed homogeneous medium.

The relations between local and global strains and stresses can be expressed through:

$$\dot{\varepsilon}^{I} = \boldsymbol{A}^{I}\,\dot{E} \quad \text{and} \quad \dot{\sigma} = \boldsymbol{l}^{I} : \boldsymbol{A}^{I} : (\boldsymbol{L})^{-1}\,\dot{\Sigma} \tag{E4}$$

where: $\boldsymbol{A}^{I} = (\mathbf{I} - \boldsymbol{T}^{II} : \Delta \boldsymbol{l}^{I})^{-1}$ and $\boldsymbol{T}^{II}$ is the interaction tensor calculated assuming the polycrystalline grain as an ellipsoidal inclusion embedded to the homogeneous matrix.

EXPERIMENTAL AND MODEL RESULTS

The X-ray diffraction method was used to determine the internal stresses for the "in situ" deformed samples (tensile test). The interplanar spacing were measured separately for each phase, i.e.:

- $d_{(211)}$ using Cr radiation for α phase,
- $d_{(311)}$ using Mn radiation for γ phase.

From the experimental strains the surface stresses were calculated using the standard $sin^2\psi$ analysis [3,4]. The measured initial stresses of the both phases were an input data for the self-consistent model [1,2]. In calculations, the optimal model parameters of elasto-plastic deformation were chosen in order to fit to the experimentally determined stresses for the α and γ phases respectively (Fig.1) as well to the macrostress obtained from mechanical test (Fig.2). The mechanical tensile curve was obtained as the function of surface macrostress vs. macrostrain measured by the electrical gauge. It should be stated that the surface macrostress is taken as the measured stress applied to the sample shifted down by the value of initial residual stress (average for the both phases) obtained from X-ray diffraction. In Figs 1 and 2, the predicted stresses are compared with the experimental ones. The parameters of elasto-plastic deformation are presented in Table 1.

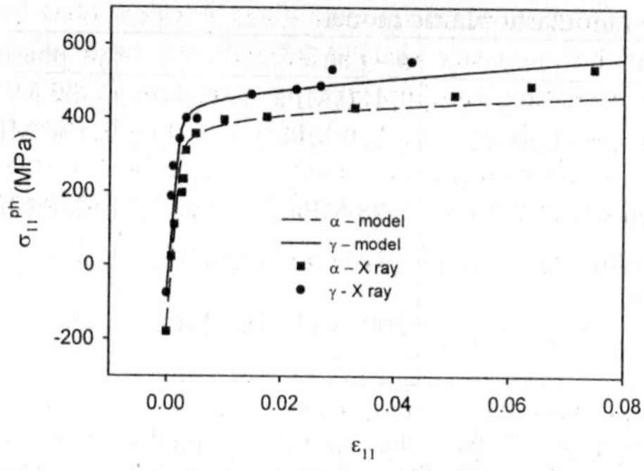

Fig 1. Phase uniaxial stresses σ_{11}^{ph} vs. sample strain ε_{11} is presented for tensile test respectively for α and γ phases. Experimental results determined from shift of diffraction peak (points) are compared with model prediction (lines) calculated for parameters given in Table 1.

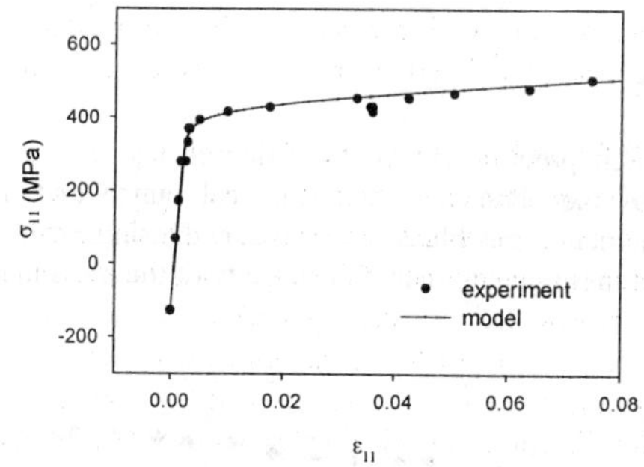

Fig 2. Uniaxial macrostresses σ_{11} vs. sample macrostrain ε_{11} is presented for a tensile test. Experimental surface macrostrain is measured by electrical gauge and the macrostress is the applied stress minus initial surface stress. The model prediction (line) is calculated for parameters given in Table 1.

Table 1. Parameters used for elasto-plastic model

	α - phase	γ - phase
Initial stress	-180 MPa	-80 MPa
Initial critical resolved shear stress τ_o	220 MPa	170 MPa
Hardening matrix:		
H_w - weak component	35 MPa	210 MPa
A - factor of anisotropy	1	1
Elastic constants for grain:		
C_{11} ; C_{12} ; C_{44}	209 ; 111 ; 113 MPa	197 ; 124 ; 122 MPa

The results presented in Figs 1,2 show that the model calculations agree very well with the experimental points for the deformation lower than 3%. For larger deformation the values obtained from X-ray diffraction are over the predicted curves because of relaxation of the surface compressive macrostress due to plastic deformation of the sample. This effect is not seen in the Fig.2. where the experimental macrostress corresponds to the value applied to whole cross section of the sample. The beginning of the curves obtained from X-ray diffraction are sufficient for determination of critical resolved shear stresses τ_o and amplitude of hardening matrixes for the both phases. The self consistent calculations performed for these parameters agree very well with the result of mechanical test in which the relaxation of the surface stress does not occur.

FEM MODELISATION

Using the Abaqus-Explicit program (FEM) the Erichsen test, i.e., a deep drawing with a hemispherical punch was modelled. The hemispherical punch and the blankholder were simulated using rigid elements, the blank was simulated using shell elements. The speed velocity was about 10 times greater than the velocity of the press in order to minimise the

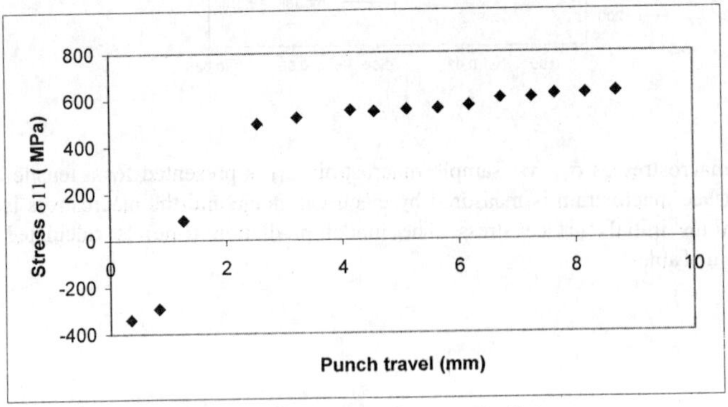

Fig. 3. Results of the FEM prediction with Abaqus –Explicit program.

CPU time cost. The isotropic elasto-plastic parameters were assumed for steel. The behaviour of the sample during punching was predicted and the function of the radial stress (σ_{11}) vs.

magnitude of punching was presented in Fig 3. It is well seen, that the stress is changing rapidly untill the punch travel parameter equal to 3 mm, which corresponds to equivalent deformation of 5%. For this deformation the σ_{11} stress reaches a value of 550 MPa and after it increases very slowly.

CONCLUSIONS

The model parameters were estimated using the stresses measured for α and γ phases respectively . For the optimal parameters the model stresses fit very well to the experimental ones (Figs 1 and 2), especially for the low deformations. In the sample studied the initial compressive stresses (i.e., before tensile test) were found for both phases. This can be explained by the surface macrostress generated during sample preparation. The measured values of initial surface stresses were used as the input data for model calculations.

The macroscopic parameters characterising elastoplastic deformation were obtained from the tensile test. These parameters were the input data for FEM method which was used for the modelisation of the punching deformation.

Acknowledgements:
The presented work was supported by the Komitet Badan Naukowych (Polish Committee of Scientific Research).

BIBLIOGRAPHY

1. Lipinski,P. and Berveiller,M., Int. Journ. of Plasticity, **5**, 149, 1989.
2. Lipinski P., Berveiller M., Reubrez E. and Morreale J., Arch of Appl. Mech., **65**, 291,1995.
3. Noyan, I. C., Cohen, J.B., Residual Stresses - Measured by Diffraction and Interpretation, Springer-Verlag, Berlin, 1987.
4. Baczmanski, A., Wierzbanowski, K., Tarasiuk, J., Ceretti, M. and Lodini,A., Rev. de Metall., **94**, 1467, 1997

PLASTICITY EFFECT ON RESIDUAL STRESS RESULTS USING DIFFERENT HOLE-DRILLING EVALUATION METHODS

M Kornmeier, JP Nobre, J Gibmeier*, B Scholtes* and AM Dias
Departamento de Engenharia Mecânica, University of Coimbra, Polo II, P-3030 Coimbra, Portugal
***Institut für Werkstofftechnik, University Gh Kassel, Mönchebergstr. 3, D-34125 Kassel, Germany**

ABSTRACT
The reliability of the incremental hole-drilling technique for analysing shot-peening residual stresses is investigated, considering the influence of stress gradients and of the plasticity effect. Experimental results obtained on steel samples by different hole-drilling evaluation methods are compared to residual stresses determined by X-ray diffraction. The occurrence of local plastic deformations is reduced by the work hardening effect of the shot-peening treatment, which can be characterised by micro-hardness variation. The performance of different evaluation methods to determine typical shot-peening residual stress gradients is demonstrated for a case where no plasticity effect can be expected. Experimental results are compared to the results obtained from elastic finite element analysis. The influence of the residual stress gradient on the plasticity effect is studied by means of elasto-plastic finite element analysis. Strain relaxation curves taking into account elastic-plastic material behaviour are compared to elastically calculated values. Observed differences depend on the residual stress gradient and, more exactly, on the local ratio of residual stress to yield strength. These differences lead to a depth-dependant overestimation of residual stress values when the evaluation methods for the incremental hole-drilling method are applied. The related error is less pronounced than for the case of constant residual stresses but depends strongly on the in-depth residual stress distribution.

INTRODUCTION

Residual stresses can be accurately determined by the incremental hole-drilling (IHD) method, if the residual stress magnitude does not exceed 60% of the material's yield strength, Beaney et al (1), (2). Higher residual stresses lead to local plastic deformations due to the stress concentration around the drilled hole and affect residual stress evaluation, which is based on linear elastic equations. The resultant overrating of residual stresses depends on various factors, as e.g. the residual stress state and the orientation of the strain gage rosette, Beghini et al (3), and is normally estimated as a function of the ratio of residual stress magnitude to material's yield strength. This so-called plasticity effect was quantified mostly by means of numerical calculations by several authors. According to Beaney (4) for example, an error of +15% can be expected in stress calculation for residual stress magnitudes of 70% yield strength. An overestimation of 20% for residual stresses reaching 90% yield strength was reported by Beghini et al (3). In Gibmeier et al (5), an error of 35% is given for a stress magnitude of 95% yield strength. Such error estimations however afford the exact knowledge of the respective yield strength, which may differ considerably from the bulk material's value after surface treatments, as verified by Nobre et al (6). Furthermore, error estimations were generally realised considering an in-depth uniform stress field. The combined influence of stress gradients and the plasticity effect on the reliability of residual stress distributions obtained by the incremental hole-drilling method was not yet described so far and will be discussed in the present study. The applicability of the method will be examined for the case of highly stressed shot-peened surfaces. Based on an experimental study on shot-peened steel samples described in Nobre et al (6), the influence of different evaluation methods commonly available for in-depth residual stress determination by IHD will be investigated. Residual stresses obtained by X-ray diffraction will be used as reference values. In order to separate the influence of the plasticity effect from the already differing ability of the evaluation methods to determine stress gradients accurately, strain relaxation curves obtained from finite element method (FEM) simulations will be evaluated. The error caused by the plasticity effect will be analysed as a function of depth by comparing the obtained residual stress result to the FEM set values.

INCREMENTAL HOLE-DRILLING EVALUATION METHODS

For the evaluation of in-depth non-uniform residual stresses by the incremental hole-drilling method several calculation procedures have been proposed. In this work, three main calculation procedures are applied and the results compared to each other. The differential method (DM), Schwarz et al (7), is a differential formulation of the incremental strain method proposed by Kelsey (8). It is based on the relationship between surface strain relaxation and hole depth for a known uniform stress field and the correlation of these data with those obtained when drilling a hole in an unknown non-uniform stress field. This method assumes that the incremental strain relaxation at the surface depends mainly on the residual stress in the respective depth increment and neglects additional strain relaxations caused by higher stresses existing in the previous increments. This effect becomes relevant at greater distances to the surface if strong residual stress gradients are present and can lead to flattened stress profiles. Bijak-Zochowski (9) proposed the integral method (IM), developed by, e.g., Schajer (10), to overcome this simplification, taking into account that the strain relief at the material's surface is the accumulated result of the residual stresses originally existing in the zone of each successive increment, along the total hole depth. However, this method, representing the theoretically best solution, is very sensitive to measurement errors. For this reason, the IM should be used with a few large depth increments as reported by Schajer et al (11). Finally, the average stress method (ASM), proposed by Nickola (12) as a simplification of the integral method, defines an equivalent uniform stress to take the influence of the residual stresses in previous increments into account. In this method, the concept of an equivalent uniform stress that produces the same strain increment as the real non-uniform stress field implies that stresses at all given depth increments contribute equally to the strain relief measured at the surface. However, it is neglected that residual stresses existing close to surface contribute much more to the strain relaxation than those in deeper increments. A comparison of these methods can be found in, e.g., Schajer (10), Kockelmann et al (13), Flamman et al (14).

MATERIALS AND EXPERIMENTAL PROCEDURE

Table I Mechanical properties and chemical composition of the materials

Sample – Steel (DIN)	$R_{p0.2}$* [MPa]	R_m* [MPa]	n*	Hardness [HV]	Chemical Composition [% weight]** C	Si	Mn	Cr	Mo	Ni	V
1 – 36NiCrMo6	1120	1220	0.07	380	0.34	<0.4	0.65	1.50	0.22	1.50	
2 – 14NiCr14	445	670	0.17	230	0.14	<0.4	0.55	0.75		3.25	
3 – X42Cr13	425	680	0.21	220	0.38	0.9	0.5	13.6			0.3

(*) uniaxial tensile tests (ASTM E 8) – strain hardening exponent n obtained according to ASTM E 646
(**) producer data

Table I shows the mechanical properties and the chemical composition of the steel alloys used. An identical shot-peening treatment according to the standard MIL-S-13165 C (normal impact, peening medium S170, Almen intensity 14A, 100% coverage) was applied to a series of steel specimens.

For the IHD technique, high-speed drilling equipment and three-element strain gage rosettes (milling guide RS-200 with air turbine and strain gages CEA-06-062UM-120, Measurements Group, Inc.) were used. The surface strain relief was measured in depth increments of 0.02-0.08 mm, up to about 1 mm below the surface. Smaller steps were carried out close to the surface to obtain stress gradients more precisely. The typical hole diameter was about 1.8 mm. Residual stress evaluation was carried out by means of MPA-Stuttgart (DM), H-Drill (IM) and ReStress (ASM) software, using the elastic constants E = 210000 MPa and $\nu = 0.3$.

XRD residual stress analysis was combined with local electrolytic layer removal to obtain residual stress depth profiles. Stress relaxation due to layer removal was not corrected since the affected region was small and no significant relaxation effects could be expected. Lattice deformations of the Fe-{211} planes were measured using CrKα radiation. Residual stresses were calculated for the plain stress condition using the X-ray elastic constants $\frac{1}{2} s_2 = 5.832 \cdot 10^{-6}\,MPa^{-1}$ and $s_1 = -1.272 \cdot 10^{-6}\,MPa^{-1}$.

Furthermore, Vickers micro-hardness (HV 0.1) measurements on the cross section of the samples were used to estimate the local yield strength from micro-hardness distributions, as described in Nobre et al (6), where more details about the experimental procedures can be found.

FINITE ELEMENT MODEL

Incremental strain relaxation curves were calculated by the finite element method using code ABAQUS. The equi-biaxial stress state caused by shot-peening allowed the use of a two-dimensional model with axisymmetric elements to calculate the surface strain relaxation at the strain gage position as a function of the hole depth. In addition, the dimensions of the strain gages were taken into account by integrating the axisymmetric strain field over the strain gage area. The elasto-plastic materials behaviour was described by isotropic hardening starting at a yield stress of 402 MPa. The elastic constants were chosen compatible to the values used for the hole-drilling evaluation. Three different residual stress distributions, with maximum stresses reaching about 95% of the yield strength were considered by using prestressed elements. The yield strength was set constant over the depth. Therefore, the local ratio of residual stress to yield strength, used for discussion, is directly determined by the different stress gradients considered.

RESULTS AND DISCUSSION

In the following, residual stress distributions obtained by incremental hole-drilling, using the three different evaluation methods, will be compared. Experimentally determined strain relaxation curves had to be evaluated with larger depth increments (0.1 mm) than finite element values due to the error sensitivity of the integral method and the average stress method. The evaluation algorithm of the differential method implied a slight strain smoothing, reducing the error sensitivity but also affecting the direct comparability. Finite element results were all evaluated with the same increment size for all methods, using smaller increments near the surface.

Elastic Material Behaviour

In Fig. 1, the efficiency of the different IHD evaluation methods to determine in-depth residual stress gradients is demonstrated. In Fig. 1a), experimentally determined residual stress depth distributions are shown for the shot-peened sample 1. X-ray diffraction reference results, reaching barely 50% of the materials yield strength, allow assessing the accuracy of the IHD evaluation methods when the plasticity effect can be excluded. In Fig. 1b), strain relaxation curves, calculated by elastic FEM analysis for a given FEM stress profile (FEM I), were evaluated. In this case, the residual stress results obtained by the different evaluation methods can be compared directly to the set values without the potential influence of any measurement errors.

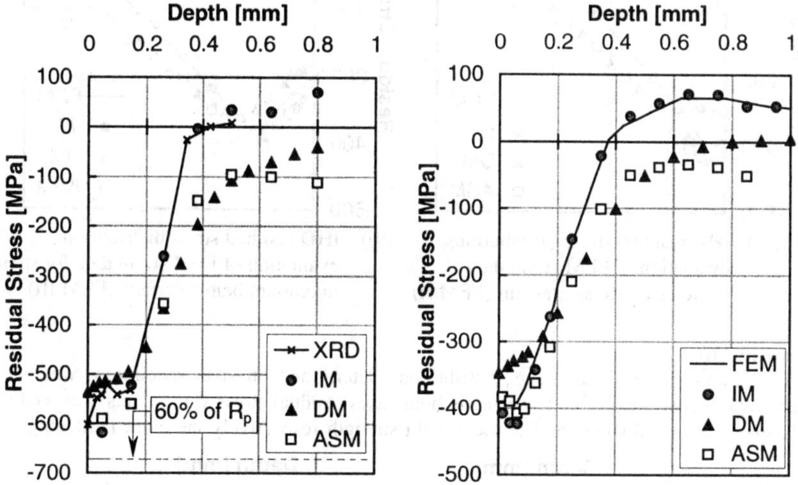

Fig. 1 a) IHD residual stress distributions measured on sample 1 (36NiCrMo6), XRD results as reference values

b) IHD residual stress distributions, evaluation of FEM strain relief data for set stress distribution (FEM I)

For both examples, the following characteristics of the evaluation methods can be observed: Close to the surface the differential method (DM) underestimates the real residual stress magnitude, while the integral method (IM) slightly overrates the real residual stresses. Here, the average stress method (ASM) shows, especially for the finite element example, the best agreement with the set values. With increasing distance from surface, the integral method is clearly the most appropriate calculation procedure. Only this method is able to detect the in-depth distributions accurately. The differential method and the average stress method show a distinct overrating of residual stress values in that case. Both methods still indicate residual stresses of about -100 MPA where XRD respectively FEM set values reach zero residual stress. This can be related basically to the theoretical shortcomings inherent to these methods compared to the integral method, Schajer (10).

The same behaviour of the IHD evaluation methods can be observed when smaller stress gradients (FEM II) and a stress maximum below the surface (FEM III) are analysed. Corresponding evaluations of finite element results (elastic analysis) are shown in Fig. 2 a) and 2 b), respectively. While the residual stress maximum at a depth of 0.2 mm is still quite well detected by all methods, the discrepancies of the results of the differential method, and especially of the average stress method increase with depth. Conversely, the integral method always shows excellent agreement over the whole depth analysed.

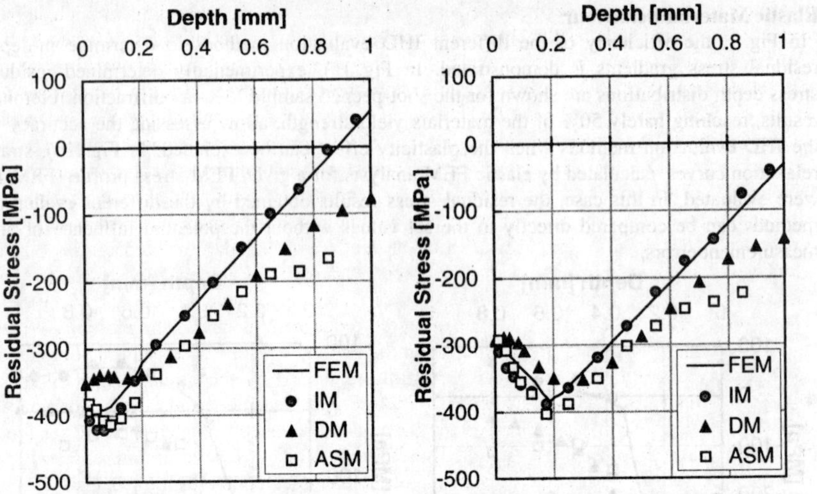

Fig. 2 a) IHD residual stress distributions, evaluation of FEM strain data for reduced stress gradient (FEM II)

b) IHD residual stress distributions, evaluation of FEM strain data for stress maximum below surface (FEM III)

Plasticity effect

Fig. 3 shows two residual stress distributions determined on steel specimens, where the plasticity effect was expected to occur. In both cases residual stress values clearly exceed the bulk materials' yield strength. The local yield strength respectively the work hardening was

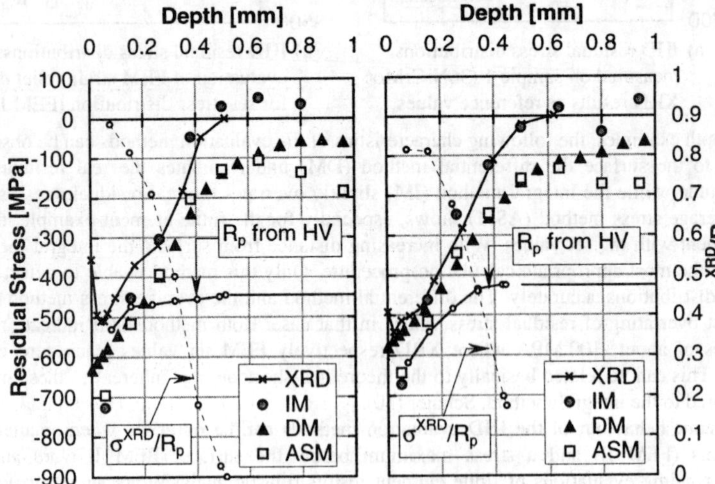

a) Sample 2 b) Sample 3

Fig. 3 Shot-peening residual stress results, work hardening (primary axis) and local ratio of residual stress to estimated local yield strength (secondary axis) quantified by micro-hardness measurements by Nobre et al (6). Revealing a much higher work-hardening, the IHD results obtained for sample 3 appear to be much less affected by the plasticity effect than those in the case of sample 2, where IHD results clearly overestimate the residual stresses detected by XRD. While the differences observed close to the surface for sample 3 could still be explained by the higher uncertainty in determining the first depth increment, the distinct overestimation of the IHD results for specimen 2 must be related to the plasticity effect. For its occurrence, the depth-dependent ratio of local residual stress magnitude to local yield strength seems to be responsible. Such a percentage ratio was estimated from the XRD residual stress values and the respective micro-hardness based local yield strength, Nobre et al (6), as a function of depth, and included in the diagrams on the secondary axis. For specimen 2, this value exceeds 90% of the local yield strength close to the surface. On the other hand, the residual stresses reach only about 80% of the local yield strength in the case of specimen 3, explaining the reduced influence of the plasticity effect. The discrepancies of average stress and differential method's results observed in both cases at greater distances from the surface can be mainly explained by the limited ability of these methods in stress gradient analysis as shown before. On the other hand, at this position an additional influence of the plasticity effect can not be excluded completely. How far local plastic deformations, occurring close to the surface, can affect the entire stress profile, will be analysed by the elasto-plastic FEM simulation of the incremental hole-drilling method.

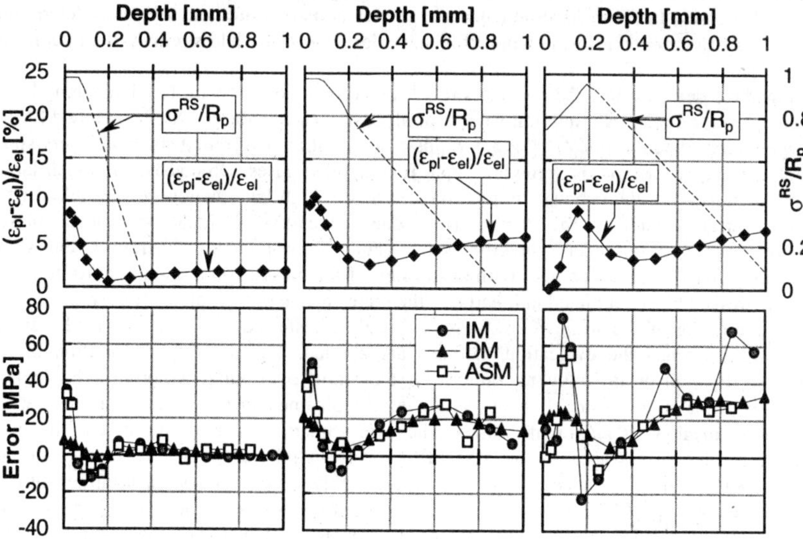

Fig. 4 a) Example FEM I b) Example FEM II c) Example FEM III

The diagrams of Fig. 4 permit to discuss the occurrence of the plasticity effect and its impact on the overestimation of residual stresses. Comparing strain relaxations obtained by elastic (ε_{el}) and by elasto-plastic (ε_{pl}) FEM calculations for the three different residual stress gradients already used before, characteristic differences are obtained. Considering elasto-plastic material behaviour, always higher strain relaxations are observed than for the purely elastic case. This is a direct consequence of locally occurring plastic deformations caused by the stress concentration due to the notch effect of the hole. Hence, representing cause and direct effect of local plasticity, the ratio of residual stress to yield strength (σ^{RS}/R_p) and the relative "overrating" of the strain relaxation ($(\varepsilon_{pl}-\varepsilon_{el})/\varepsilon_{el}$) are shown together in the upper diagrams, as a function of the hole depth. The resulting errors of residual stress evaluation, which is based on mere elastic material behaviour, are given in the diagrams right below for each evaluation method. Here, the error was defined as the difference of residual stress values obtained from evaluating strain curves of elasto-plastic and purely elastic FEM analysis, respectively. This way, these errors are independent of the capacity of each method to determine the present stress gradients correctly and represent exclusively the overrating of the respective residual stress values due to the occurrence of the plasticity effect.

Comparing the results of the three different stress gradients, a clear correlation of the local residual stress level, the overrating of the strain relaxations and, finally, the residual stress error can be noticed. In fact, up to 10% higher strain relaxations than expected for elastic material behaviour are observed in the zones where the residual stress magnitude reaches maximum values. At a closer look, it seems even that the strain overrating is anticipating the evolution of the residual stress level. Especially for case FEM III (Fig. 4.c), the maximum strain overrating is clearly reached before the stress level achieves its maximum value. This can be understood supposing that the stress field right below the actual drilling depth determines mainly the amount of plastic deformation, caused by the stress concentration around the bottom edge of the hole. This influence of the deeper layers can also explain that for the considered stress gradients, the strain overrating stays always smaller than for constant residual stresses. In Gibmeier et al (5), a strain overestimation of about 15% was determined already at 0.1 mm depth for a comparable stress level of 95% yield strength, being constant over depth.

At the hole depths where the residual stress levels drop below 80% of the yield strength, the strain overrating reaches minimum values for all cases. The smallest value is obtained for the steepest stress gradient (FEM I). While in this case, the strain overrating stays on a very small level, it increases again with growing depth for the other cases. Obviously, the much larger depth region where the residual stresses stay on a very high level is now responsible for the strain overrating far from the surface. Here, due to the small residual stress level, plastic deformations will not occur directly at the actual drilling depth. Therefore, the strain overrating must be rather caused by the extension of the plastic zones already existing in the highly stressed layers, initiated indirectly by the mere change of the hole geometry.

The overrating of the strain relaxations is directly transferred into overestimated residual stress values when the evaluation methods are applied. The in-depth distribution of the residual stress error is following quite well the strain overrating evolution. The highest overestimation of the residual stress values is also obtained in the zones where the strain overrating reaches its maximum values. The overestimation of about 40 MPa of the near surface residual stress level in the case FEM I corresponds to about 10% of the nominal residual stress value. In the other cases, where the highly stressed zones reach farther into the material, errors up to 80 MPa (20% of the maximum residual stress level) can be expected due to local plastic deformations. In these cases, a distinct residual stress overestimation also appears in deeper layers. The integral method and the average stress method always show a quite similar behaviour, even if the integral method is characterised by more scattering and hereby higher values, probably due to its higher error sensitivity. The differential method's results seem to be less sensitive to the plasticity effect due to its smoothing characteristics, but still show the same tendencies as the other methods. Furthermore, an interesting phenomenon consists in the oscillating behaviour of the error appearance. Directly after passing the maximum value, the residual stress error rapidly drops to zero and can even shortly reach small negative values. This effect is most pronounced for the integral method, obviously due to its higher error sensitivity.

CONCLUSION

In the present study, the suitability of the incremental hole-drilling (IHD) technique for shot-peening residual stress analysis was investigated. Experimental and FEM results demonstrated that, among the evaluation methods, only the integral method is basically able to characterise the depth distribution for a typical shot-peening residual stress state accurately. The theoretical simplifications of the average stress and the differential method lead to smoothed residual stress depth profiles, allowing a good approximation of the residual stresses only close to the surface.

Comparison with X-ray diffraction results showed furthermore, in good agreement with the evaluation of strain relaxations determined by FEM, that the integral method slightly overestimates the residual stress level close to the surface. On the other hand, the differential method tends systematically to underestimate the residual stress values for the first drilling steps, probably due to the internal smoothing algorithm of the software used.

The plasticity effect, leading to overestimated residual stresses by the hole-drilling method, appeared to be less pronounced than in the case of residual stresses constant with depth. Residual stress measurements by incremental hole-drilling and by X-ray diffraction on shot-peened steel specimens can still agree quite well, even when the residual stress magnitude exceeds the bulk materials' yield strength. This can be mainly attributed to the work hardening of the near surface layers. On the other hand, results of elasto-plastic FEM simulations proved that the lower stress level of the deeper layers leads to smaller local plastic deformations and thus reduces the strain overrating at the surface as well.

For the assessment of the influence of the plasticity effect in the case of residual stress gradients, the local ratio of residual stress to yield strength is a useful criterion. For a residual stress maximum exceeding 95% of the local yield strength, a plasticity related overestimation of the real residual stress value between 10% and 20% was observed for the results of the integral method. With increasing extension of the highly stressed layer close to the surface, higher errors are observed and errors tend to spread into deeper layers.

Finally, for the practical assessment of the reliability of residual stress values obtained by the hole-drilling method in highly stresses surfaces, an estimation of the work hardening effect is essential. Here, the local yield strength can be estimated, e.g., from micro-hardness measurements to assess the relevance of the plasticity effect.

REFERENCES

1. Beaney EM, Procter E, Strain 10 (1974) 7
2. Tech. Note TN-503-4, Vishay - Measurements Group Inc., (1993) 1
3. Beghini M, Bertini L, Raffaelli P, Journal of Testing and Evaluation 22 (6) (1994) 522
4. Beaney EM, Strain 12 (1976) 99
5. Gibmeier J, Kornmeier M, Scholtes B, 5th Europ. Conf. on Residual Stresses (ECRS 5), Delft 1999, in print
6. Nobre JP, Kornmeier M, Dias AM, Scholtes B, 5th Europ. Conf. on Residual Stresses (ECRS 5), Delft 1999, in print
7. Schwarz T, Kockelmann H, HBM-Meßtechnische Briefe 29 (2) (1993) 33
8. Kelsey RA, Proc. Society for Experimental Stress Analysis (SESA) 14 (1) (1956) 181
9. Bijak-Zochowski M, VDI-Berichte 313 (1978) 469
10. Schajer GS, Journal of Eng. Mat. and Tech. (ASME) 110 (4) (1988) Part I 338-Part II 344
11. Schajer GS, Altus E, Journal of Eng. Mat. and Tech. (ASME) 118 (1) (1996), 120
12. Nickola WE, Proc. of Spring Conf. on Exp. Mechanics, New Orleans, SEM, (1986) 47
13. Kockelmann H, Schwarz T, GMA-Bericht 22 (1993) 93
14 Flaman MT, Mills BE, Boag JM, Experimental Techniques 11 (1987) 35

STRESS ANALYSIS AND MICROBEAM X-RAY DIFFRACTION STUDY BY USE OF SYNCHROTRON RADIATION SOURCE

Y.Yoshioka*, T.Sasaki and K.Akita*****
***Musashi Institute of Technology, yoshioka@me.ese.musashi-tech.ac.jp**
****Kanazawa University, sasakit@kenroku.ipc.kanazawa-u.ac.jp**
***** Tokyo Metropolitan University, akita-koichi@c.metro-u.ac.jp**

ABSTRACT

This paper introduces some recent trend of x-ray (residual) stress and microbeam x-ray diffraction analyzes by the use of a synchrotron radiation source (SR) in Japan. In the field of x-ray stress measurement, stresses in several kinds of hkl diffraction could be measured by changing the wavelength of x-rays and a distribution of residual stress near surface could be measured. Since microbeam diffraction profiles with high positional resolution could be obtained by the use of a SR, stress intensity factor range ΔK could be qualitatively estimated from the change in profiles on the fatigue fracture surface and its vicinity. Such results were accomplished by the use of a SR.

INTRODUCTION

The synchrotron radiation source has many advantages as an excellent x-ray source that offers

1) high intensity;
2) a choice of optional wavelength over a narrow width when a monochrometer is used,
3) small divergence.

Stresses on any hkl diffraction can be measured with high accuracy in the higher Bragg angle region by selecting the required x-ray wavelength from a SR in the field of x-ray stress analysis by Yoshioka (1). On the other hand, microbeam x-ray diffraction technique is also powerful tools as well as the x-ray stress analysis in the fields of material evaluation. The theory was established about fifty years ago [Hirsch & Keller (2)] , but the practical use is not always spread because it was difficult to get the high intensity x-ray microbeam with small divergence. However, the situation is being changed by the use of a SR and of an imaging plate which is an area x-ray detector [Miyahara et al (3)]. The SR is the most suitable x-ray source for the microbeam diffraction analysis and the use of imaging plate enabled short exposure time.

The purposes of this paper are to introduce several results on the stress measurements and the microbeam x-ray study by the use of a SR in Japan.

EXPERIMENTAL

X-rays from Synchrotron Radiation Source

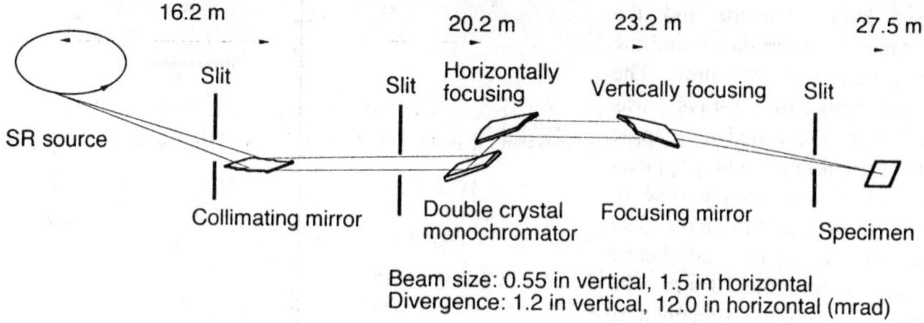

Fig.1 Schematic layout of beam line 3A at Photon Factory of KEK.

The synchrotron radiation system at the Photon Factory (PF) of the High Energy Accelerator Research Organization, KEK, in Tsukuba, Japan was used as an x-ray source. A beam line used was BL-3A and the optical layout used is shown in Fig.1[Kawasaki et al (4)]. It consists of a double Si 111 crystal monochrometer, collimating mirror and focusing mirror. X-rays between λ=0.25 nm and 0.12 nm are available with the optical system. The divergence angle of the beam source was 1.2 mrad in vertical direction and 12 mrad in horizontal direction. The minimum beam size was 0.55 mm (vertical) and 1.5 mm (horizontal) on the specimen

Stress Measurement by SR X-rays

The use of SR enables the measurements at constant Bragg angle 2θ on many diffraction planes, and we adopted a constant Bragg angle of 2θ=154° for all the diffraction planes [Yoshioka (1)]. For example, stresses in the α-Fe(211) plane were measured with a wavelength of 0.2280 nm. A goniometer, with a position-sensitive proportional counter (PSPC) having an effective length of 110 mm, a specimen holder and a beam slit, was prepared for stress measurement as shown in Fig.2. Width of the beam slit is changed to keep irradiation area of x-rays even if ψ angle was tilted.

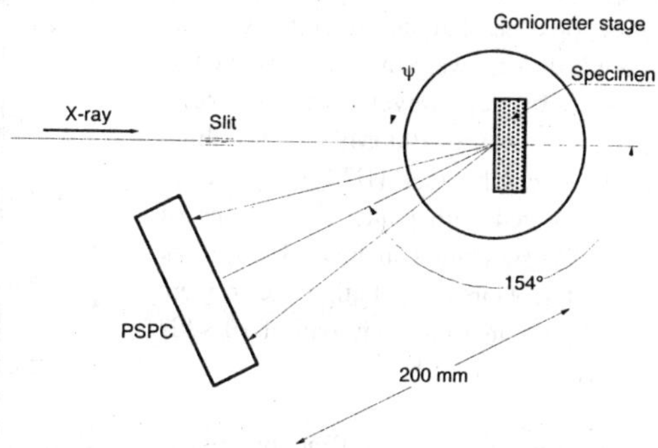

Fig.2 Layout of goniometer for stress measurement.

Microbeam X-ray Diffraction Camera

Figure 3 shows a schematic layout of the microbeam x-ray back reflection camera used. Specimen is to be located at the focusing position of beam line and a 0.2 mm diameter pinhole was set 140 mm up stream from a specimen position. We used an imaging plate (IP) as an area X-ray detector and the distance between the IP and the specimen was 80 mm. The wavelength of X-rays was adjusted so that the Bragg angle 2θ of an hkl diffraction appears at 154° as well as the case of the stress measurement. The diameter of the Debye-Scherrer ring is to be about 78 mm. The beam size on the specimen is about 250 μm and the positional resolution was calculated as 0.41 μm. Positional resolution is superior to that possible with a conventional laboratory x-ray source. When the same optical layout was employed using a laboratory source, the positional resolution was about 2.5 μm.

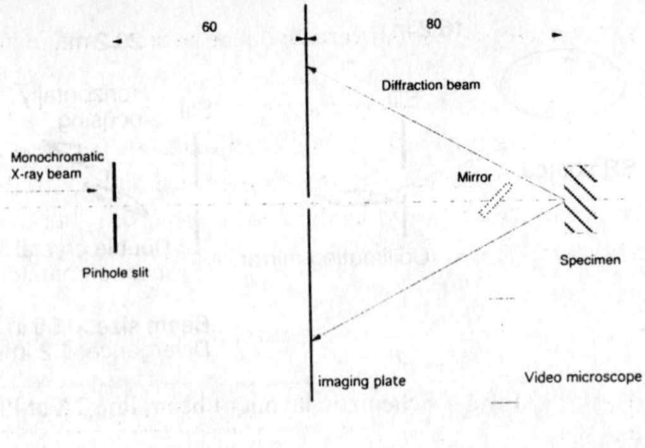

Fig.3 Optical layout of microbeam back-reflection camera.

RESULTS AND DISCUSSION

Stress Measurements on the Surface of Fatigue-Fracture

To estimate the stress intensity factor range ΔK from the distribution of residual stress on the fatigue fracture surface, residual stresses were measured by the use of three different wavelengths of x-rays. Specimens were 1000MPa class high tensile strength steel (HT1000) and all were received with planer dimensions of the ASTM standard 1 inch (25.4mm) thick compact tension type. Fatigue tests were carried out under constant load of 10.8 kN and stress ratio of 0.1.

Combinations of diffraction plane, wavelength and penetration depth of x-rays at ψ=0° are shown in Table 1.

Table 1 Diffraction plane, wavelength and penetration depth.

hkl	Wavelength λ (nm)	Penetration depth (μm)
211	0.22804	6
220	0.19749	9
310	0.17664	12

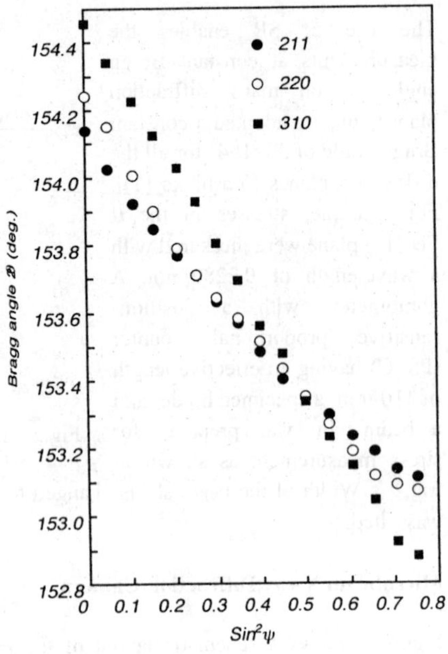

Fig.4 Sin²ψ diagrams on the fatigue fracture surface.

Irradiated area is 5mm in vertical direction and 2 mm in horizontal direction.

An example of $\sin^2\psi$ diagram is shown in Fig.4. The position of measurement was at 22.5 mm of crack length. A nearly straight line between 2θ and $\sin^2\psi$ is obtained on the 310 diffraction but curved relations are observed on both of the 211 and the 220 diffractions. This fact means that the $\sin^2\psi$ method is not applicable, but stress values by the $\sin^2\psi$ method were at first approximately calculated and results are listed in the second column in Table 2. The stress value by the 310 diffraction is too far apart from other values. Then, a stress in outer surface and stress gradient were calculated by a method called cosα method which assumed a linear distribution of stress gradient with depth direction [Yoshioka et al (5)]. Results are shown in the third and fourth columns in Table 2. It is also clear that the value of stress gradient by the 310 diffraction is too smaller than the other results. This fact suggests that the distribution of stress gradient is not linear till the depth of 12 μm where is the penetration depth to the specimen of x-rays used. We, therefore, assumed a quadratic-distribution of gradient and the $\sin^2\psi$ distribution was re-constructed by the use of the quasi-Newton method. A distribution of stress gradient optimized by this process is shown in Fig.5 and this distribution at near surface approximately agrees with the linear distributions assumed for the 211 and the 220 diffractions.

Table 2 Values of stress and its gradient calculated by the various methods.

hkl	Sin²ψ method	Cosψ method (linear)		Cosψ method (quadratic)	
	σ (MPa)	σ_{110} (MPa)	A_{11}(MPa/μm)	σ_{110} (MPa)	σ_{max}(MPa)
211	481	259	132	127	907 at 6 μm
220	557	294	105		
310	629	552	17		

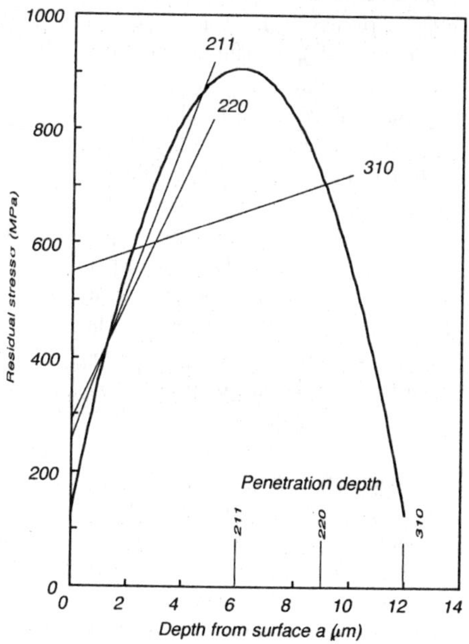

Fig.5 Stress distributions determined from the various methods.

Such measurements and analysis were also performed on the other positions of fatigue-fracture surface and the stress intensity factor range ΔK was estimated.

X-Ray Elastic Constants of Alumina Ceramics

In the case of the x-ray stress measurements on ceramics, many diffraction lines are apt to appear at small angle intervals because lattice constant of ceramics is generally larger than wavelength of x-ray used. It is, therefore, important to use the best combination of characteristic x-rays and a diffraction plane for stress measurements. However, it is not always possible to get the best combination as far as the conventional x-rays from metal target is used because of the specific wavelength available. The capability to choose a wavelength from a SR enables the measurement of any hkl diffraction at higher Bragg angle area. We measured x-ray elastic constants of alumina ceramics on several hkl diffractions by the use of SR. Seven kinds of hkl diffractions, 410, 220, 12 10, 229, 226, 146 and 324, were selected for measurement of $E/(1+\upsilon)(=S_2/2)$. Bending stresses were subjected on the specimen which has a dimension of 60×8×4 mm^3 and diffraction angles were measured at 11 angles from 0 to 45 degrees of ψ-tilt at each step of applied stress.

Figure 6 shows results of measurements (closed circles) and theoretical values based on the Reuss model [Reuss (6), Tanaka et al (7)](open circle). A chain line indicates the mechanical value. The experimental values on the 12 10, 229 and 324 diffraction almost coincide with the theoretical ones. Although disagreements are observed on the other diffraction planes, the largest discrepancy between the experimental value and the theoretical one was about 15 % on the 226 diffraction. The reason why is that the diffraction intensity is smaller in comparison with other ones. Therefore, it is considered that the experimental values approximately coincide with the theoretical values based on the Reuss model within the experimental error. As a result we can calculate an elastic constant for any hkl diffraction suitable when a conventional x-ray source is used.

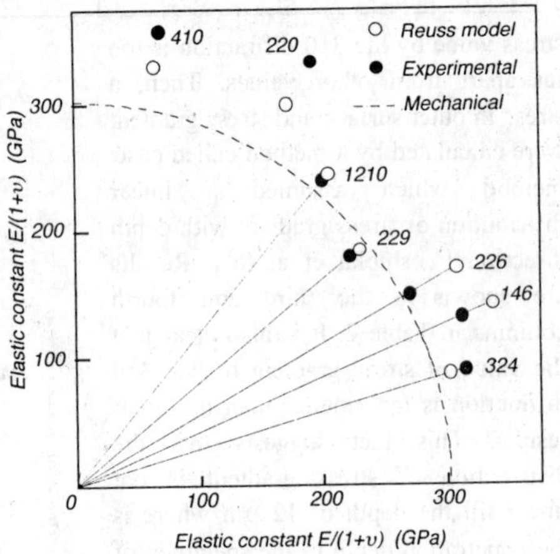

Fig.6 X-ray elastic constants for alumina polycrystal.

Observation of Fatigue Fractured Surface by Microbeam Diffraction Technique

As another estimation of the stress intensity factor range ΔK, we used microbeam x-rays from a SR to obtain a high-resolution x-ray beam and Debye-Scherrer patterns near the fracture surface. Material of compact tension type specimens was 0.15% low carbon steel and fatigue tests were carried out under constant load control. Several positions were chosen at stated intervals in the direction of crack propagation for the measurement of the x-ray pattern. Debye-Scherrer pattern of αFe 211 diffraction was recorded on the imaging plate. The distributions of x-ray parameters beneath the fracture surface were again recorded on the new surfaces revealed by successive electrolytic-polishing.

Figure 7a) shows a Debye-Scherrer Pattern recorded from fracture surface under the condition of the maximum load of 10.8 kN and the stress ratio of 0.05, respectively. A continuous ring is observed, but if this ring was partially enlarged as shown in Fig.7b), it is obviously the existence of many fine spots. This fact shows that crystallites in this region would be polygonally deformed, that is, subgrains would be formed by cyclic stressing. When a conventional microbeam x-ray source was used, such fine spots in a ring were observed beneath the fracture surface region but they were not always observed at the fracture surface because of poor of resolution[Yoshioka et al (8)].

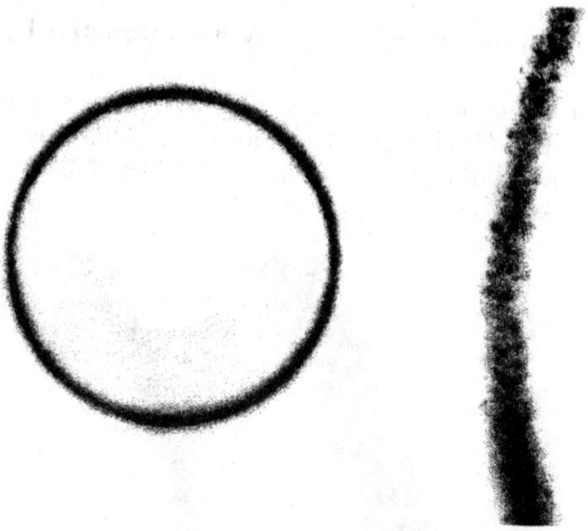

a) b)

Fig.7 Microbeam Debye-Scherrer patterns on fatigue fracture surface. a) Whole pattern. b) Partially enlarged pattern of a).

Figure 8 shows patterns obtained from various positions at depths of 24, 40, 84 and 104 μm, respectively. The number of spots in the ring decreases with the increase of the depth from fatigue fracture surface. The Debye-Scherrer ring gradually separates into several arcs and fine spots in the depths of the fracture surface. Then, such spots in the arcs almost disappear at a depth of 104 μm. This indicates that the effect of cyclic stressing does not reach this depth and this region is outside of the cyclic plastic deformed zone.

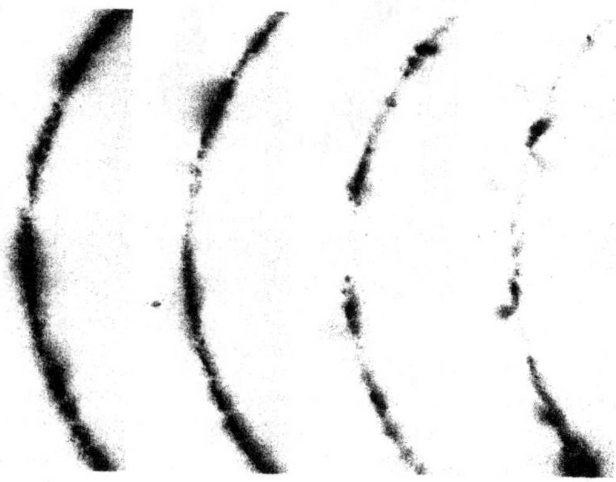

24 μm 40 μm 84 μm 104μm

Fig.8 Debye-Scherrer patterns from various depths from fatigue fracture surface.

The number of spots in each Debye-Scherrer patterns was counted and the number of spots were plotted against the depth from the fracture surface. The number of spots at the position of ΔK=20 MPam$^{1/2}$ monotonically decreases with the depth below the fracture surface. Then it reaches a constant number at a depth of more than 100 μm. The depth is about 500 μm at a position of ΔK=40 MPam$^{1/2}$. These depths nearly agree with depths of cyclic plastic zone calculated from fracture mechanics theory. Therefore, it is possible to estimate the stress intensity factor range ΔK at a fracture surface.

Observation of Microbeam X-Ray diffraction Pattern of Creep Damaged Specimen

Change in microstructure during creep process was observed. Material of specimens was Al-SiC powder alloy and creep load of 45MPa was subjected under the temperature of 300 °C. X-ray conditions were basically the same but Al 311 diffraction by the x-ray wavelength of 0.238 nm was measured.

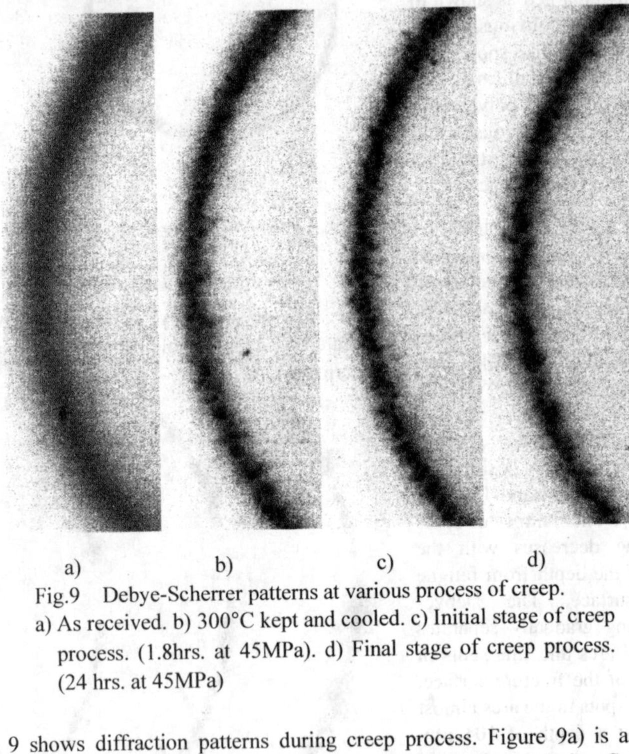

a) b) c) d)

Fig.9 Debye-Scherrer patterns at various process of creep.
a) As received. b) 300°C kept and cooled. c) Initial stage of creep process. (1.8hrs. at 45MPa). d) Final stage of creep process. (24 hrs. at 45MPa)

Figure 9 shows diffraction patterns during creep process. Figure 9a) is a diffraction pattern of as received specimen and a continuous and broadened Debye-Scherror ring influenced by machining was observed. The specimen was kept at 300 °C for 20 hours before creep load and then cooled to the room temperature and a diffraction pattern was measured. The pattern changed from broadened ring in a) to spotty pattern which indicates the strain relief as shown in b). Then, creep load of 45 MPa was applied and kept till fracture. Figure 9c) shows a pattern at the initial stage of creep process. The shape of spots in the ring became to clear than those in b) and the number of spots increased because subgrain size decreased due to increase of creep strain. Figure 9d) shows a pattern at final stage of the creep process. Since the decrease of subgrain size occurred at initial stage, the number of spots was maintained during creep process. However, since micro lattice strain slightly increases during process, the outline of spot may be obscure. It is possible to detect the creep fracture by observing such change in microbeam diffraction pattern.

CONCLUSIONS

In the future, the x-ray diffraction method by SR will be used more extensively to measure the residual stress with high accuracy in engineering field, in particular, advanced materials and failure analysis. Moreover, the microbeam diffraction technique by SR will be surprisingly developed in practical fields because of small divergence and high intensity.

The research described here was performed on beam line 3A(BL-3A) in the Photon Factory, High Energy Accelerator Research Organization, Tsukuba, Japan, under Contract No. 98G265 and was sponsored by the Grant-in-Aid for Scientific Research (C) of the Ministry of Education, Science, Sports and Culture, Japan.

REFERENCES

1. Yoshioka, Y.: Current Japanese Materials Research, 10,109(1993)
2. Hirsch, P.B. & J.N.Keller: ProcPhy.Soc. Sec.B.64, Part 5,369(1951)
3. Miyahara, J. , K.Takahashi et al: Nucl. Instr & Methods A246, 572(1986)
4. Kawasaki, K. et al: Rev. Sci. Instrum, 63, 1023 (1992)
5. Yoshioka, Y., T.Sasaki and M.Kuramoto: Adv.X-Ray Anal. 28,255(1985)
6. Reuss, A.: Z.ang Math. Mech. 9,49(1929)
7. Tanaka, K. et al: J. JSMS, 36 792(1987) (In Japanese)
8. Yoshioka, Y., S.Ohya, K.Hasegawa & S.Yusa; MAT-TEC 93 Improvement of Materials, 257 (1993)

MEASURING AND ANALYSIS OF RESIDUAL STRESSES AFTER DIFFERENT QUENCHING CONDITIONS OF STEELS

Janez Grum, Slavko Božič, Martin Zupančič
University of Ljubljana, Faculty of Mechanical Engineering, University of Ljubljana
Aškerčeva 6, 1000 Ljubljana, Slovenia

ABSTRACT

Increasing demands of users regarding ensurance of the specified mechanical properties and working order of machine parts and products require a search of relations between the composition and microstructure and certain knowledge of residual stresses present based on good knowledge of the quenching process. The paper presents results regarding numerous residual stresses measurements on heat-treatment 42CrMo4 steel specimens with different masses. To measure the residual stresses, the relaxation method was used, involving gradual mechanical removal of the hardened layer in which the deformation of the specimen was measured by resistance strain gauges. The experimental procedure, including also determination of through-hardenability, permits the selection of a suitable quenching process in the adapted concentration of the polymeric water solution taking into account different masses of the samples. The investigations conducted confirmed that variations of the residual stresses after quenching are decisively affected by the quenching conditions described by the cooling curves. In all cases the range of the residual stresses was comparatively small since the maximum values obtained amounted to around 370 MPa, which is a much lower value than that of the yield stress of the material.

Key words: Quenching, Various mases of steels, Cooling rate, Residual stresses, Relaxation method.

INTRODUCTION

Residual internal stresses in a machine part are self-balanced internal stresses which persist in a material due to different thermo-mechanical processes during its machining. Residual stresses are present already in semi-products, which are later treated by various machining processes to make a final machine part. Residual stresses in a workpiece change after each treatment. Changes in residual stresses in the workpiece after individual machining processes depend on the kind of process applied and the conditions under which the process is performed. After each machining process new residual internal stresses are obtained as a result of previous residual stresses before machining and the new stresses introduced. The resulting variation of residual internal stresses depends on the sign and values of the previous residual stresses and the new stresses. Residual stresses occurring after various heat-treatment processes or even thermo-mechanical treatment of blanks/workpieces, where residual stresses are a result of volume changes which are themselves due to temperature differences and to phase transformations between the core and the surface, are very important (1,2).

EXPERIMENTAL PROCEDURE

Selection of steel and quenching agent

For an investigation of the influence of steel mass and of a quenching agent on mechanical properties of steel after heat treatment a very commonly used, alloyed heat-treatment steel, i.e. 42CrMo4 steel according to DIN standard, was selected.

In the investigation of the influence of steel mass and quenching agent on mechanical properties of steel and range of residual stresses after heat treatment, a 15% polymeric water solution of Slovenian manufacturer »Olma«, Ljubljana was used (3,4). The polymeric water solution with a 15% concentration was made of a concentrate of Aquatensid BW. The concentrate is designed for steel hardening as well as for heat treatment of various non-ferrous alloys. It is a result of co-operation between Slovenian manufacturer "Olma" and the world-known manufacturer "Petrofer".

Measuring system

In order to be able to predict microstructure, hardness and strength variations with different specimen masses, a computer-aided experimental set-up for temperature measurement and data processing was elaborated in our laboratory of heat treatment as shown in Fig. 1. The experimental set-up consisted of specimens of various masses in which, at selected measuring points, thermocouples for measurement of cooling curves were inserted (5). The cooling curves were, via a multi-channel temperature converter, transmitted to a PC for subsequent data processing. Thus it is possible to monitor physical phenomena in the boundary layer via cooling curves which were recorded for an individual quenching agent.

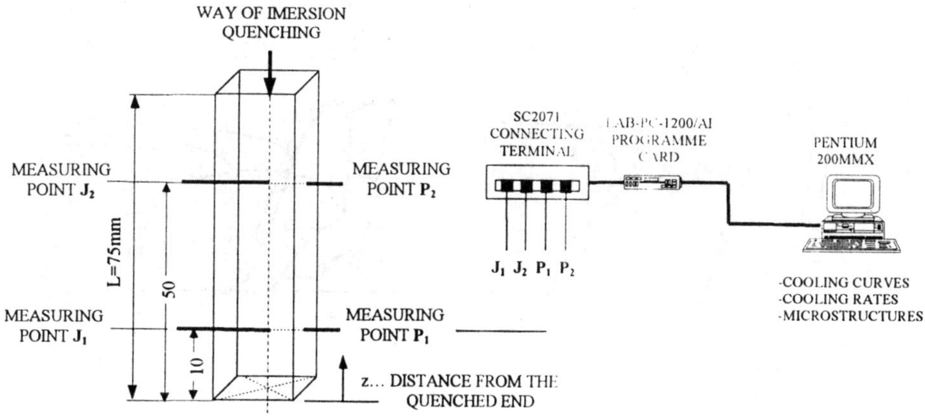

Fig. 1 Experimental set-up for capturing cooling curves for the specimens having different dimensions and being cooled in the 15% polymeric water solution

The data on time-dependent temperature variations, i.e. cooling curves, were then processed by EXCEL 5.0 software package. The results obtained were displayed as diagrams, tables, and column charts. The cooling curves measured at different measuring points of the specimens having different masses permit several displays in diagrams, i.e.

- cooling curves and cooling rates as a function of temperature;
- cooling curves in a continuous cooling transformation (CCT) diagram;
- predicting of portions of individual microstructure phases;
- predicting hardness after quenching of the specimens having different masses in different quenching agents.

EXPERIMENTAL RESULTS

Cooling curves

In our case quenching was limited to prismatic specimens made of the same heat-treatment steel having the same heights (L = 75 mm) but different quadratic cross sections, i.e. 20×20 mm and 35×35 mm. Cold specimens were put in an oven heated up to 600 °C. When this temperature was reached by the surface as well as by the core, they were gradually heated to a hardening temperature of 850 °C. The prismatic specimens had thermocouples inserted at four measuring points. The latter permitted to determine two cooling rates at the characteristic points of the surface and those of the core. The heated prismatic specimens were then carefully transmitted to a cooling medium, i.e. immersed into the 15% polymeric water solution. Fig. 2 shows a continuous cooling diagram (CCT) of the heat-treatment 42CrMo4 steel with superimposed cooling curves for individual measuring points in the prismatic samples having dimensions of 20×20×75 mm and 35×35×75 mm respectively.

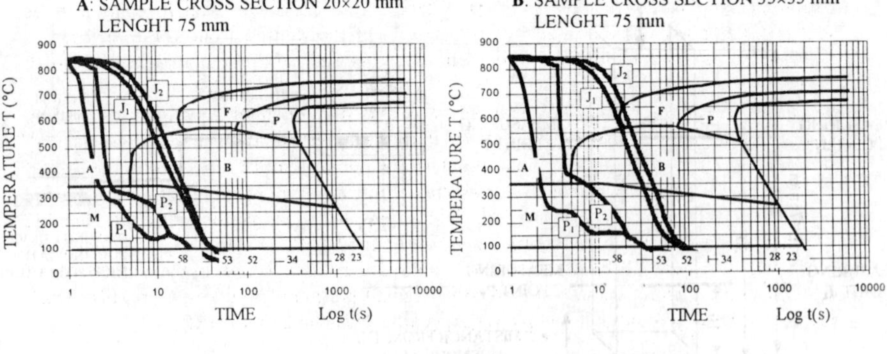

Fig. 2 Continuous cooling transformation (CCT) diagram of the alloyed 42CrMo4 steel with superimposed cooling curves measured at 4 different measuring points of two prismatic samples: 20×20×75 mm (A); 35×35×75 mm (B) in the 15% polymeric water solution at 25°C without agitation

The variations of the cooling curves in the CCT diagrams permit to draw the following conclusions:

- At both surface measuring points of both samples (P_1-P_2) intensive cooling can be observed in the zone of the undercooled austenite and slowed-down quenching precisely at the transition area between the zone of the undercooled austenite and that of the martensitic transformation where a two-phase transformation zone persists until a complete transformation of the undercooled austenite into martensite has been achieved.
- In quenching of the 20×20×75 mm sample, a faster transformation from the zone of the undercooled austenite to the ambient temperature was ensured than in quenching of the 35×35×75 mm sample. In quenching of the greater-mass sample, as expected, at both measuring points greater differences in temperature between the core and the surface were obtained than in quenching of the smaller-mass sample.
- In quenching of the smaller-mass sample at both surface measuring points (P_1-P_2) a martensitic microstructure was obtained. A similar microstructure was obtained also at the surface of the greater-mass sample; but at measuring point P_2 not only the martensitic but also a negligible portion of bainitic microstructure was obtained.
- At measuring point P_1, in both samples, intensive quenching was obtained at the highest temperatures, i.e. at the upper part of the undercooled austenitic zone. Decay of a vapour insulating film, i.e. interruption of film boiling, can be achieved at this measuring point in a very short time, i.e. in one second after the immersion of the sample in the 15% polymeric water solution. At measuring point P_2, which is 50 mm from the lower sample edge, the slowed-down quenching was observed already at the initial cooling stage, i.e. after two seconds with the lower-mass sample and after up to 3.5 seconds with the higher-mass sample. This time interval between the beginning of quenching and the characteristic slowed-down quenching in the initial phase corresponds to the persistence of the vapour insulating film at measuring point P_2.
- Based on the temperatures measured at the individual measuring points, the speed of progression of the wetting front and the time achieved up to the decay of the vapour insulating film in dependence from its distance from the lower sample edges can be calculated respectively. The speed of progression of the wetting front at the lower-mass sample thus amounts to 40 mm/s while with the higher-mass sample it amounts only to 16 mm/s.
- A hardly observable difference between variations of individual superimposed cooling curves at measuring points J_1 and J_2 is thus attributed to a quick through-thickness transition of the wetting front at both samples. The cooling curves measured in the core of the smaller sample with a smaller cross section confirm, as far as temperature stresses are concerned, a favourable variation which ensures a predominantly martensitic-bainitic microstructure showing hardness values higher than 52 HRC. A slightly greater deviation occurs in quenching of the larger sample with a larger cross section in the central area of which bainitic microstructure with a relatively small portion of fine ferrite prevails, which produces the reduction of the sample hardness after quenching to 40 HRC.

Measurement of residual stresses

The so-called Hole Drilling Strain Gauge Method is the most suitable for measurement of internal stresses in various loaded structures. For measurement of residual stresses at a selected point satisfactory conditions for placing a three-legged resistance measuring rosette should be fulfilled. The method is based on measurement of specific deformations in individual directions with regard to the location of the three-legged resistance measuring rosette, which allows subsequent calculation of main stresses and determination of their

location. Advantages of the method are its simplicity and adaptability to different applications since measurements may be performed in a laboratory, in production or even on site.
In the study, measurement of the residual stresses was carried out at three characteristic measuring points of the two samples (Fig. 3):

– calculation of the main residual stresses at measuring point 1, i.e. in the middle of the lower edge where $z = 0$ mm;
– calculation of the main residual stresses at measuring point 2, i.e. at a distance z of 10 mm from the lower edge;
– calculation of the main residual stresses at measuring point 3, i.e. at a distance z of 50 mm from the lower edge.

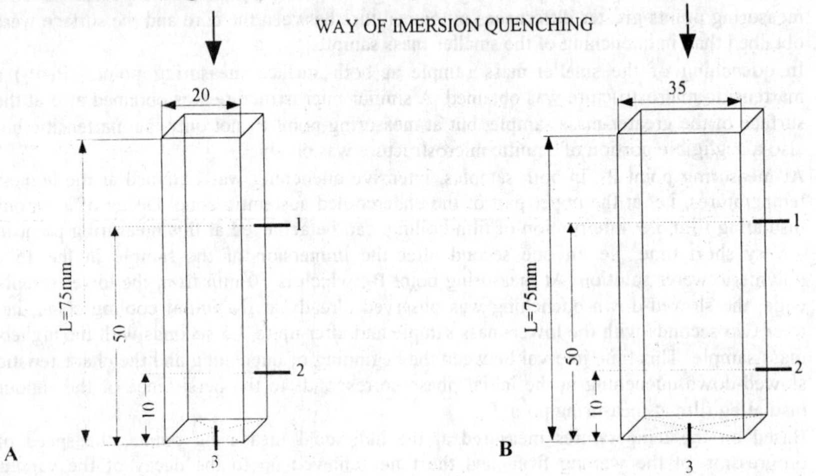

Fig. 3 System of designating the selected measuring points for measurement of the residual stresses at the sample with a cross section of 20×20 mm^2 (A) and at that with a cross section of 35×35 mm^2 (B)

The diagrams in Fig. 4 showing variations of the main stresses at the sample with the smaller cross section, i.e. 20×20 mm^2, indicate very similar values and their variation through the sample thickness.

It is characteristic of all the calculated main stresses σ_1 and σ_2 at all measuring points that they are hardly perceptible at the surface but they increase to the nominal value up to the depth of 0 15 to 0.25 mm. The highest main stress was calculated at measuring point 3, i.e. at the sample front face, which achieves values up to 235 MPa while the minimum calculated main stress is by 50% lower and amounts to 117 MPa. A similar variation of the main stresses can be found also at measuring point 2, i.e. at the lower sample part where the maximum main stress amounts to 198 MPa and the minimum to 98 MPa. A comparison of the main stresses at measuring point 3 and those at measuring point 2 shows a negligible deviation in terms of their values and their through-thickness variation. The deviations of the calculated main stresses σ_1 an σ_2 amount to only around 10% and are lower at measuring point 1, i.e. at the lateral surface at a distance L of 50 mm from the sample front face.

The diagrams in Fig. 5 shows variations of the calculated main stresses at the selected measuring points 1, 2, and 3 through the thickness of the higher-mass sample. Equal measuring points were selected, however, in this case the sample cross-section was much larger and amounted to 35×35 mm^2. This indicates a three-times larger sample cross-section and, consequently, a three-times higher sample mass.

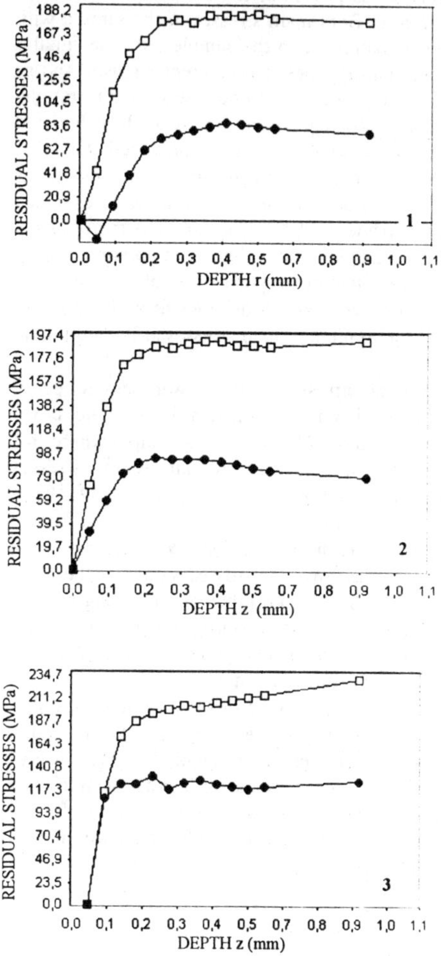

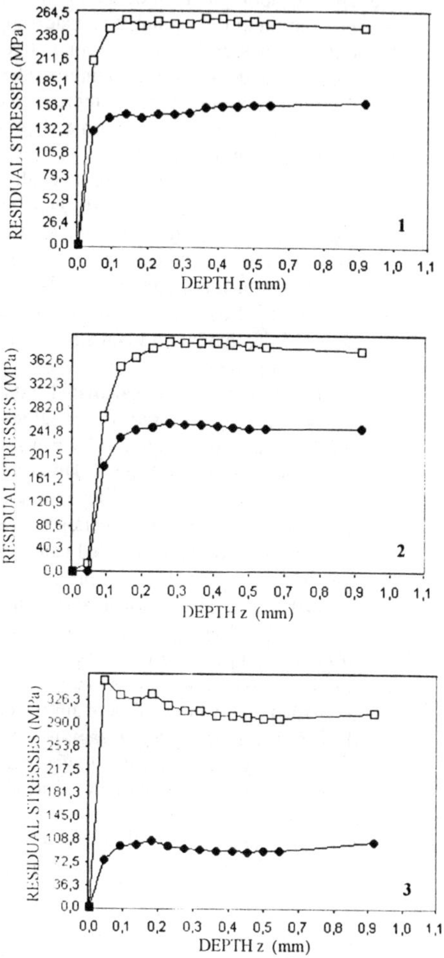

Fig. 4 Variations of the calculated main residual stresses σ_1 in σ_2 at measuring points 1, 2, and 3 after quenching of the 20×20×75 mm samples in the 15% polymeric water solution

Fig. 5 Variation of the calculated main residual stresses σ_1 and σ_2 at measuring points 1, 2, and 3 after quenching of 35×35×75 mm samples in the 15% polymeric water solution

The main residual stresses σ_1 and σ_2 also in the higher-mass sample are inherently tensile regardless of the measuring points selected. It is characteristic of the samples with the larger cross section that the curves of their residual stresses from the surface to the nominal depth, where they achieve the highest value, are steeper. These minimum and maximum main stresses respectively are found already in the depth of 0.05 mm at measuring point 3. The most gently sloping curves of the minimum main stress as well as the maximum main stress are found at measuring point 2 in a depth of 0.2 mm. Both main stresses in the sample with the larger cross section are by around 50% higher than those in the sample with the smaller cross section at the same measuring points. Both main stresses are inherently tensile and as such very unfavourable for dynamically loaded parts, since the latter are subjected to fatigue and will, at the final phase of thermal treatment, also produce failure. Based on the calculated values of the main residual stresses at the six measuring points, it may be concluded that:

- The residual stresses were, in all cases, inherently tensile and are known as transformation-type residual stresses. Such a stress state in the sample is to be expected regarding the cooling curves, which are taken inside the CCT diagram. The range of the residual stresses was relatively small since the maximum values obtained amounted up to 370 MPa, which is a considerably lower value than that of the yield stress of the material.
- The curves of the residual stresses are very alike, yet there are differences in the absolute values of the maximum main stresses as well the minimum main stresses at the individual measuring points.
- A comparison of the calculated main residual stresses at the lower sample edges (measuring point 3) shows lower values of the maximum main residual stresses, i.e. down to 235 N/mm^2, in the 20×20×75 mm sample than in the 35×35×75 mm sample where this value amounts to 335 N/mm^2. The result expected of the calculated main residual stresses was a consequence of smaller temperature differences and a quicker movement of the wetting front in the axial direction of the 20×20×75 mm sample.
- A comparison of the calculated main residual stresses at varying distances from the lower sample edges (measuring points 1 and 2) shows that lower calculated values of the main residual stresses are obtained at measuring point 1 (z = 50 mm) than at measuring point 2 (z = 10 mm). The higher calculated main residual stresses at measuring point 2 correspond to higher temperature differences in the radial direction of this point with regard to the through-cross-sectional temperature difference at measuring point 1.
- The calculated values of the main residual stresses in the 35×35×75 mm sample exceeded those of the 20×20×75 mm sample at both measuring points, i.e. 1 and 2. With the lower-mass sample, as expected, lower main residual stresses were obtained, which was a consequence of good through-hardenability through the whole sample cross-section. The higher calculated values of the main residual stresses in the surface layer of the lower-mass sample were a result of stronger volume changes which coincided with the kinetics of martensitic and two-phase martensitic-bainitic microstructure.

CONCLUSIONS

- In steel hardening it is necessary to select a proper austenitizing temperature and duration considering its initial microstructure in order to ensure a fine and homogeneous austenite microstructure which consequently, after quenching, ensures formation of fine martensite. Quenching of the steel concerned should be such that the actual cooling rate approximates to the critical cooling rate. A proper cooling rate of the steel concerned during quenching, however, may be ensured only if the cooling capacity of the quenching agent and the influence of mass, which have a synergetic effect on microstructure formation after quenching, are well known.

- As far as through-hardening is concerned it may be stated, taking into account the investigations conducted, that the polymeric water solutions containing 15% of Aquatensid ensure favourable quenching rates as well as favourable temperature differences between the surface and the core in a given moment in the sample made of heat-treatment 42CrMo4 steel. The results of the one-factor variance analysis confirm that the sample-quenching process in the 15% polymeric water solution of Aquatensid is reliable and ensures repeatable hardening results.

REFERENCES

1. Liščić B, Steel Heat Treatment, Chapter 8, Steel Heat Treatment Handbook, Eds, Totten G, E, Howes M,A,H, Marcel Dekker, Inc. (New York) 1997, 527
2. Tszeng T,C, Wu W,T, Semiatin L,A, Sensitivity Study of the Process Model for Predicting the Distortion During Heat Treating, Proceedings of Second International Conference on Quenching & Control of Distortion, Eds, Totten G,E, Howes M,A,H, Sjöstrom S,J, Funatani K, Published by ASM International, The Materials Information Society, (Cleveland) 1996, 321
3. Grum J, Božič S, Lavrič R, Influence of Mass of Steel and a Quenching Agent on Mechanical Properties of Steel, Heat Treating, Proceedings of the 18th Conference, Including the Liu Dai Memorial Symposium, ASM International, The Materials Information Society, Eds, Wallis R,A, Walton H,V, (1998) 645
4. Grum J, Božič S, Lavrič R, Effects of quenching agent and mass of steel on their mechanical properties, Proceedings of the 6th Conference on Materials & Technologies, Kovine in zlitine, 33 (1999) 231
5. Grum J, Božič S, Zupančič M, Influence of Quenching Process Parameters on Residual Stresses in Steels, ASM Heat Treating Society, The 3rd International Conference on Quenching and Control of Distortion, Eds, Totten G, E, Liščić B, Tensi H,M, (Prague) 1999, 436

INFLUENCE OF LASER SURFACE REMELTING CONDITIONS ON MICROSTRUCTURE, MICROHARDNESS AND RESIDUAL STRESSES OF GRAY AND NODULAR IRONS

Janez Grum, Roman Šturm, Pavle Žerovnik
Faculty of Mechanical Engineering, University of Ljubljana
Aškerčeva 6, 1000 Ljubljana, Slovenia

Key words: Laser surface hardening, Surface remelting, Residual stresses, Relaxation method, Gray and nodular irons

ABSTRACT

To investigate the residual stresses laser surface remelting, the size and variation of residual stresses were measured as a function of the modified layer depth on flat specimens from different kinds of gray and nodular iron. Optimal laser hardening conditions were chosen, while only the way of guiding the laser beam over the surface of flat specimens was varied. To measure the residual stresses, the relaxation method was used, involving gradual electro-chemical removal of the modified layer in which the deformation of the specimen was measured by resistance strain gauges.
Experimental results have confirmed that surface remelting can be successfully performed also with low power laser sources. They achieve a sufficient depth of the modified layer, desirable microstructure changes and good microhardness profiles of the modified layer.
After laser remelting of different types of gray and nodular irons the measured residual stresses show a similar variation as well as absolute values at different sample travelling speeds and at different kinds of guiding the laser beam across the surface. Residual stresses are in all the cases of tensile type on the surface and then slightly decrease to the depth of 0.1 mm or 0.2 mm when they transform into compressive stresses. The relatively great depth of transformation of tensile into compressive residual stresses confirm that even after fine-grinding it is not possible to achieve the desired stress state in the material with more or less high compressive residual stresses in the surface layer. The results of the research investigation confirm that especially gray iron components, as well as nodular iron components, have to be very carefully designed and carefully machined by grinding in order to avoid notch effects or ultimate failure.

1. INTRODUCTION

Cast iron is commonly used in a wide range of industrial applications thanks to its good castability, good mechanical properties and low price. By varying the chemical composition and microstructure of cast irons it is possible to change their mechanical properties. Cast irons are also distinguished by good wear resistance which can be raised even higher by additional surface heat treatment. With the use of induction hardening, it is possible to ensure a homogeneous microstructure in the thin surface layer, however this is possible only if cast irons have a pearlite matrix. If they have a ferrite-pearlite matrix, a homogeneous microstructure in the hardened surface layer can be achieved only by laser surface remelting. A number of industrial applications have shown that in laser surface remelting it is necessary to pay attention to a favourable distribution of residual stresses in the surface layer of a

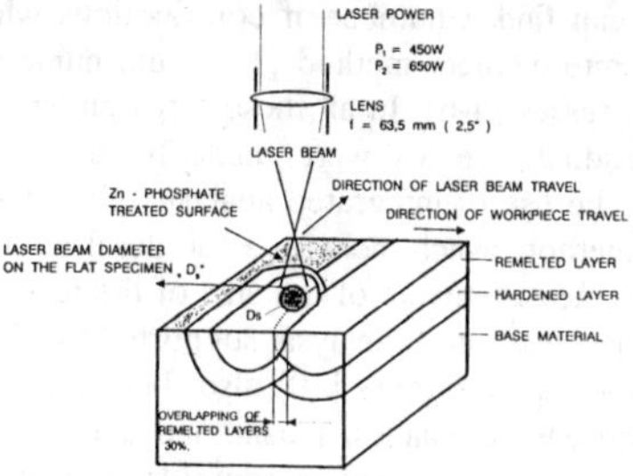

Fig. 1. Laser surface remelting process and description of laser treatment characteristics

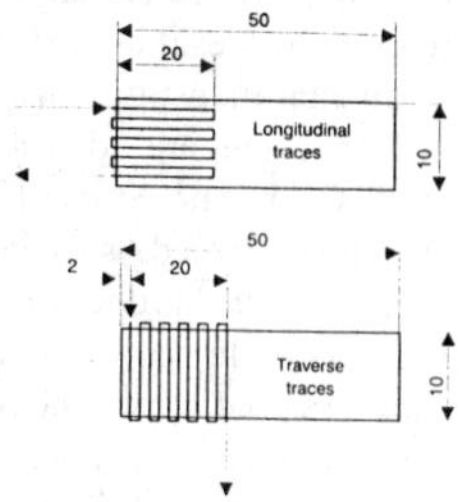

Fig. 2. Specimen geometry and different ways of laser beam travel in laser remelting proces

Figure 1 is a schematic presentation of the laser surface remelting process. The selected laser source was a CO_2 laser with a wavelength of $\lambda = 10.6$ µm. Two laser beam power values were chosen, P = 450 W and P = 650 W. The focusing lens has a focal distance f = 63.5 mm (2,5") and three degrees of defocus $z_{s1} = 10$ mm, $z_{s2} = 12$ mm and $z_{s3} = 14$ mm. The laser beam travelling speed was adjusted to the necessary energy input for surface layer remelting. With respect to the just mentioned parameters we varied travelling speeds form 2 to 42 mm/s in increments of 2mm/s. In this way we ensured different energy inputs into specimen surface and that in the range from 6.8 J/mm2 to 143 J/mm^2. The complete remelting of the specimen surface was ensured by varying the degree of laser trace overlapping which was adjusted by moving the specimen cross-wise to the motion of the laser beam.

Different ways of guiding the laser beam over the specimen surface were selected, i.e. zig-zag in langitudiual direction (a), and zig-zag in traverse direction, with the laser beam turning round outside the flat specimen to achieve more uniform heat transfer in the material. In this way it was possible to achieve different heat conditions in the flat specimen during the heat treatment process as well as during cooling which influence the preheating of the workpiece prior to treatment and the tempering of the created modified microstructure. Figure 2 shows different ways of laser beam travel across the specimen surface and in laser remelting process.

To determine the optimal remelting conditions, heating with a laser beam was performed by making a single trace on the specimen. After the determination of the optimal remelting conditions, the rest of the tests were made so that a 30% overlapping of the remelted traces was ensured. By overlapping traces, we achieved a fully and uniformly remelted specimen surface and a desired depth of the modified layer.

Since

gray and nodular irons due to their different graphite morphologies and different microstructures behave differently in laser remelting, we determined the optimal travelling speed of the laser beam vs. specimen for both kinds of material. It was found that the energy input into the flake graphite gray iron was smaller than in the case of nodular iron in ensuring a smooth remelted surface and optimal surface layer quality. An additional requirement in the given remelting conditions was a required depth of the modified layer which ranged within 0.4 - 0.5 mm. Thus, in the case of gray iron we decided on the travelling speed v_1 =24mm/s with an energy input of E = 16.5 J/mm^2, and in the case of nodular iron on v_2 =12mm/s with an energy input of E = 33 J/mm^2.

The dimensions of the specimens were adapted to the chosen remelting procedure and the requirements of subsequent residual stress measurements. Figure 2 shows the laser beam trace in longitudinal and traverse direction on the flat specimen and the specimen dimensions. After remelting, two adjacent trace overlap by a third of their width, which affects the remelted traces profiles and surface properties.

machine component. In professional literature we can find a number of contributions which deal with calculations of residual stresses by the finite element method [1-3], and numerous reports on experimental investigations of residual stresses [4-6]. In all these research studies, measurements of the size and distribution of residual stresses were made by the X-ray diffraction method. Grum and Šturm [7-9] suggest the use of integrated analysis of the laser-modified layer by the so-called "surface integrity" method which includes a full description of the modified layer by microhardness measurements, measurements of the size of the remelted and hardened layer, complemented by a complete microstructure analysis supported by X-ray phase analysis and residual stress measurements. The same authors [10] also focus attention on selection of those machining conditions that will ensure smallest tensile and compressive residual stresses. Only this carefully selected and integrated treatment can contribute to longer life time of machine components subjected to dynamical loads.

Residual stresses are a result of elasto-plastic deformations induced in the specimen material during the remelting process. The size and magnitude of internal stresses depend on temperature conditions in heating and cooling and physical properties of the specimen material. The contribution discusses the size and distribution of residual stresses after laser remelting a thin surface layer on gray iron 200 and nodular iron 400-12. Residual stresses are induced not only by temperature differences but also result from stresses due to microstructural changes between the surface and the core of the specimen subsequent to cooling down to the ambient temperature. The distribution and size of residual stresses in the remelted thin surface layer depend mostly on melt composition and cooling conditions. Different rates of solidification remelted layer and subsequent cooling of the modified layer are reflected in the volume proportions of the created cementite, residual austenite and martensite in the microstructure. The rate of heating and cooling of the thin surface layer is a function of laser power, beam diameter on the specimen surface and interaction time. In addition, the number of passes of the laser beam over the specimen surface and different degrees of laser trace overlapping were increased to see how this can affect the heat conditions in the specimen. To determine the residual stresses, the relaxation method was used. This is based on measuring the specimen strains during electrochemical material removal of the stressed surface layer.

2. EXPERIMENTAL PROCEDURE

After laser remelting of a thin surface layer of gray and nodular iron, we get a thin modified layer consisting of a remelted and hardened layer. Given that the remelting process was very rapid and the specimen mass sufficiently high, a very rapid cooling was ensured. The actual rates of cooling are considerably higher than the required rates of quenching and are achieved by heat conduction into the remaining cold part of the specimen. Thanks to self-hardening, the process is very clean and simple, which plays an important role in industrial applications. Another important factor in laser heat treating processes is laser light absorptivity in the interaction with the specimen surface. This depends on the laser light wavelength, kind of specimen material and its temperature. Laser light absorptivity of a CO_2 laser with a wavelength of 10.6 μm into metal materials is at ambient temperature only a few per cent and then up to the melting point temperature increases gradually to 50%. Despite that all specimens were chemically treated in a Zn-phosphate bath at a temperature of 50 °C. In this way the absorptivity was increased to 80% and a greater depth of the modified layer and repeatability in terms of its size and quality were achieved.

3. EXPERIMENTAL RESULTS

3.1. Microstructure and Microhardness Analysis of Remelted Layer

A right composition and microstructure scale of the particular phases in the remelted surface layer are important in defining the optimal properties in machine parts. The microstructure in the remelted layer consists of very finely dispersed cementite phase in residual austenite with traces of martensite. The results of the microstructure analysis in the remelted layer have confirmed that the reason that flake graphite gray iron is essentially more sensitive in the terms of selecting optimal remelting conditions is in totally dissolution of graphite and smallest volume fraction of residual austenite. Very rapid cooling rates of the remelted surface layer of gray and nodular irons can, depending on the remelting conditions, produce the folowing effects:

- Incomplete dissolution of graphite nodules in nodular irons;
- Redistribution of larger undissolved graphite nodules due to hydrodynamic forces and buoyancy in the molten pool;
- At a favourable area to volume ratio of graphite flakes in the gray iron it is possible to achieve complete dissolution of the graphite in the pool;
- Furrows on the remelted layer surface of gray iron with flake graphite occur mostly due to too low laser beam travelling speeds, i.e. at too high energy inputs or too high inert gas pressure;
- The occurrence of porosity in gray iron may be attributed to volume changes between the graphite and cementite, as well as to thermal and microstructure stresses immediately after solidification;
- Cracks in the remelted layer run in the direction of the vector of the solidification rate in the interface front between the solid and liquid condition and occur mostly in gray iron.

In the heat affected zone only solid state transformation can be noted. During heating the basic pearlite-ferrite structure transforms into austenite which in cooling, depending on the carbon content, transforms into martensite and ferrite with some residual austenite. Thus in gray iron, the heat affected zone consists of graphite flakes in the martensitic matrix. In the nodular iron, however, the heat affected zone consists of a martensite-ferrite matrix intermingled with graphite nodules. Around the graphite nodules there is a formation of hard martensite shells.

The results of microhardness measurements have confirmed the structure changes in the material and have shown that laser surface melt hardening can be a successful method. Microhardness measurements were made according to Vickers with a weight of 0,3 daN. The hardness of the base material in soft state ranges between 200 to 250 $HV_{0.3}$ and after laser treatment increases onto 800 to 950 $HV_{0.3}$ in remelted layer.

3.2. Residual Stress Measurements

To measure the residual stresses on specimens, we decided to use the relaxation method with electrochemical removal of the stressed layer. By measuring residual stresses by relaxation method on special specimens it is however possible to get a good insight into the effects of particular remelting processes on the state of the material and how this changes with a change in remelting conditions. A result of electro chemical removal of the stressed layer is relaxation and a new mechanical equilibrium state. By measuring the strain in a new equilibrium state of the specimen we can define what was the stress in the removal layer. Measuring the strain of the specimen after different removal times or different removal depths, we can define the residual stress variation as function of the depth of the modified layer.

For the calculation of residual stresses it is necessary to know the history of the removal for a given material. In this way, after a certain time of electro-chemical removal, it is possible to define the depth of the removal as well as the remaining thickness of the specimen, which is necessary for the calculation of the inertia and resistance moment of the specimen. On the basis of the data obtained in this way, we can calculate the size of residual stresses existing along the depth of the specimen. The experimental measuring system for measuring the strains of the specimen after relaxation and the calculation into residual stresses is illustrated in Figure 3.

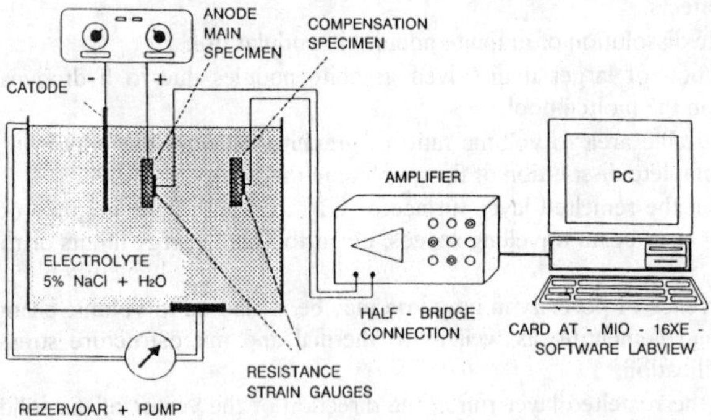

Fig. 3. Measurement of strain in electro-chemical removal of the material

The specimen for measuring residual stresses is connected to the anode whereas the cathode is made of stainless steel. Both electrodes are sunk into electrolyte containing a 5% water solution of NaCl. Uniform density of the electric current between the anode and the cathode is ensured by a forced circulation of electrolyte and simultaneous filtering of the electrolyte. Special care should be given to the choice of the conditions for electro-chemical removal that would ensure uniform removal across the entire surface of the specimen:

– Linear time dependence of the removal to a discussed depth.
– Suitably fast removal rate to keep the measurement procedure as short as possible.

On the basis of previous experiments, an optimal time characteristic of the electro-chemical removal was defined, which was 0.01 mm/min for the current density 0.5A/cm^2 and the size of the gap between the electrodes 3 cm.

The resistance strain gauges on the measuring and compensation resistance strain gauges were connected in a half-bridging connection so that the difference in the stress between them was measured considering the compensation of the temperature dilatation of the material. The measured stresses were amplified in the amplifier and processed with the AT-MIO-16XE-50 hardware card and LabVIEW software package by National Instruments and presented on the screen as the residual stresses/depth profile.

The residual stress variation is very much dependent on the conditions present in the process of remelted layer cooling which can be described by the volume percentage of residual austenite and cementite and concentration gradient of the cementite. With the increase of the amount of residual austenite in the remelted layer, there is a great danger that residual stresses will change the direction and will transform from compressive into tensile. A surface with tensile residual stresses is, however, much more likely to develop cracks, which may propagate and grow into a catastrophic failure.

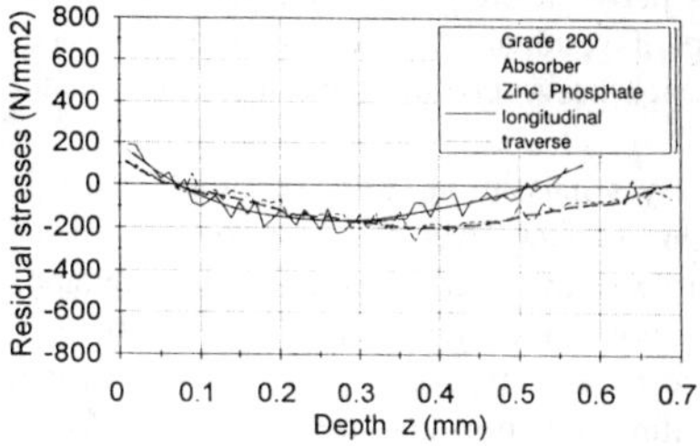

Fig. 4. Residual stresses in gray iron Grade 200 after remelting

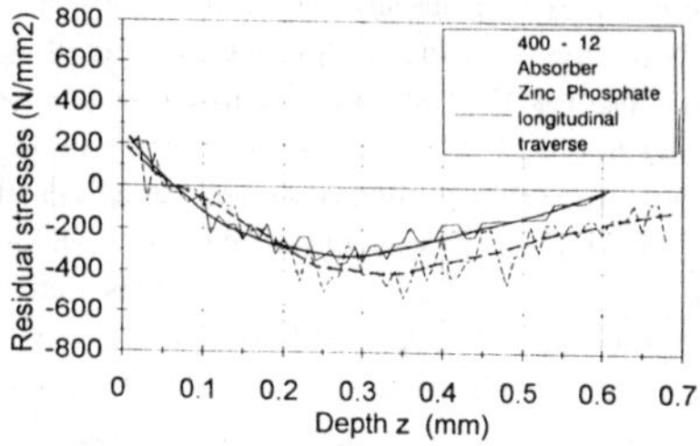

Fig. 5. Residual stresses in nodular iron 400-12 after remelting

In figure 4 we can see the variation of residual stresses as a function of the depth of the modified layer for gray iron Grade 200 and in figure 5 for nodular iron 400-12. Both figures present two measured curves, that is:

- the full line presents the measured residual stress for the specimen remelted with a zig-zag (longitudinal) traces lengthwise the specimen;
- the dashed line presents the measured residual stress for the specimen remelted with a zig-zag (traverse) traces across the specimen.
-

From the two graphs we can conclude the following:

- Residual stresses have a very similar profile in subsurface differing only in absolute values. In all cases and in remelting of all irons tensile residual stresses were found on the surface varying from 100 - 300 N/mm^2;
- The change from tensile into compressive residual stress takes place in the area between 50 μm to 100 μm. Maximal compressive residual stresses are found in the range between 200 μm to 300 μm and then very slightly to the depth of 550 μm or 650 μm;
- It is in the nodular iron 400-12 that compressive residual stresses are highest and amount even up to 500 N/mm^2 in the depth around 300 μm. In general, it can be stated that different nodular iron qualities reach the highest tensile stresses on the surface and also the highest compressive stresses below the surface depending of course on the quality of the nodular iron;
- Worth of attention are very high residual stresses occurring during specimen cooling, as the metallographical analysis of the remelted layer revealed longer or shorter cracks at random direction. Our assessment is that during the cooling process, due to high temperature differences, extremely high tensile stresses were generated, exceeding the yield point of the material in the remelted surface layer. Thus the material cracked in the direction of graphite flakes in the gray iron. Although the nodular iron was remelting at lower laser beam travelling speeds than the gray iron, it is our opinion that it is especially the shape of the graphite that is decisive for the occurrence of cracks during the cooling process;
- Gray iron retains less residual stresses after cooling especially because of its pearlite matrix and good solubility of graphite flakes in the austenite. These two ensure good homogenization of carbon in the remelted layer and heat affected layer and therefore also

lower residual stresses. The nodular irons of different qualities have a ferrite-pearlite or pearlite- ferrite matrix which in rapid heating and cooling does not grant homogenization either in the remelted layer or heat-affected layer. This results in big differences in residual stresses already during cooling as well as after cooling. Thus in our estimation the prevailing stresses are especially residual stresses between the particular crystal grains but there are also big differences in the magnitude of residual stresses on different places inside crystal grains on the microscopic level, which however our measurement did not reveal;

- Due to high roughness of the remelted surface layer it is in all cases necessary to apply fine-grinding. Fine-grinding can remove only a thin surface layer of some 10 μm into the depth of the specimen, which means that the tensile residual stress state is still maintained in the surface layer. Although the procedure is very interesting for surface hardening of different kinds of gray and nodular irons, the presence of tensile stresses in the remelted layer is a great disadvantage since the remelting components are subject to crack occurrence that may even lead to failure.

4. CONCLUSIONS

On the basis of the results of microstructure analysis and microhardness measurements on the studied irons, it can be concluded that laser surface remelting can be regarded as a highly successful method for increasing the hardness and wear resistance of gray and nodular irons. Great attention has to be given to the selection of optimal remelting conditions as different microstructure and the size and shape of graphite can substantially affect the thermal conduction of the material. Experimental results have confirmed that surface remelting can be successfully performed also with low power laser sources. They achieve a sufficient depth of the modified layer, desirable microstructure changes and good microhardness profiles of the modified layer.

After laser remelting of different types of gray and nodular irons the measured residual stresses show a similar variation as well as absolute values at different laser beam travelling speeds and at different kinds of guiding the laser beam across the surface. Residual stresses are in all the cases of tensile type on the surface and then slightly decrease to the depth of 100 μm or 200 μm when they transform into compressive stresses. The relatively great depths of transformation of tensile into compressive residual stresses confirm that even after fine-grinding it is not possible to achieve the desired stress state in the material with more or less high compressive residual stresses in the surface layer. The results of the research investigation confirm that especially gray iron components, as well as nodular iron components, have to be very carefully designed and carefully machined by grinding in order to avoid notch effects or ultimate failure.

5. REFERENCES

1. Freitas M, de Pereira M S, Michaud H, Pantelis D, Materials Science and Engineering, A167 (1993), 115
2. Denis S, Simon A, Beck G, Analysis of the Thermomechanical Behaviour of Steel During Martensitic Quenching and Calculation of Internal Stresses, Macherauch E, Hauk V, (Eds), Eigenspannungen: Entstehung - Messung - Bewertung, Band 1, Deutche Gesellschaft für Metallkunde E V 1983 211
3. Grevey D, Maiffredy L, Vannes A B, Journal of Mechanical Working Technology, 16, 1988, 65
4. Yang Y S, Na S J, Surface and Coating Technology 38 (1989) 311

5. Yang Y S, Na S J, Surface and Coatings Technology 42 (1990) 165
6. Domes J, Müller D, Bergmann H. W.: Evaluation of Residual Stresses after Laser Remelting of Cast Iron, ECLAT'88, DVS 163 1988 272
7. Grum J, Šturm R, Journal of Mechanical Engineering 41 (1995) 371
8. Grum J, Šturm R, Laser surface melt-hardening of gray and nodular iron Proceedings of the Conference "MAT-TEC 96" (Pariz) 1996 185
9. Grum J, Šturm R, Characteristics of laser surface melt-hardening and possibilities of optimizing the process; Proceedings of the conference "Quenching'96", Ohio, Cleveland, 1996, 193
10. Grum J, Šturm R, Surface and Coatings Technology 100-101 (1997) 455

KEYNOTE PAPER

MODELING OF WELD RESIDUAL STRESSES AND DISTORTIONS: COMPUTATIONAL PROCEDURES AND APPLICATIONS

Dr. Pingsha Dong
Center for Welded Structures Research
Battelle
505 King Avenue
Columbus, OH 43201-2693, USA

ABSTRACT

In this paper, the recent developments in advanced weld modeling procedures are highlighted. First, the multi-faceted process physics and mechanics associated with welding are briefly outlined based on a rapidly growing knowledge base resulting from some of the current research efforts. This includes the effects of fluid flow and heat transport in weld pool, high-temperature material behavior, residual stresses and distortions. And then, an engineering perspective for today's industrial applications is discussed in terms of both feasibility and practicality of the state of the art modeling techniques in the context of residual stress and distortion predictions. As the centerpiece of the advanced weld modeling procedures, a unified weld constitutive model for finite element simulation of welding processes is discussed in detail. Residual stress effects on structural integrity are also briefly discussed in light of recent advances in understanding weld residual stresses. Finally, attempt will also be made to outline future challenges in modeling weld residual stresses and distortions.

INTRODUCTION

Over the last decade, there has been an enormous progress in a better understanding of residual stresses and distortions in welded structures as discussed in Brust et al (1), Zhang et al (2), and Dong et al (3). This is mainly due to the rapid advances in computational techniques that can be used to take into account of some of the intrinsic process details associated with welding fabrications in complex structures. As a result, a mathematical framework has begun to emerge in fully integrated assessment of material's weldability, structure's fabricability, and structural integrity (4-6) that had been traditionally dealt with in separate engineering and manufacturing disciplines. The enormous benefits of using such a model-based approach have already been realized in various industries, particularly for developing today's high-performance structures.

In what follows, some of the important mechanisms contributing to final weld residual stresses are briefly highlighted. Some of the important modeling requirements are then discussed in view of both theoretical and practical concerns. Instead of providing comprehensive theoretical treatments on various subject areas in weld residual stress modeling, simple numerical examples will be used to demonstrate the contributions of various factors to the final residual stress states. A few real world examples with some level of complexity in terms of modeling techniques required are then used to illustrate the importance of a better understanding of the weld residual stresses in improving product performance. Finally, discussions are given on the importance of understanding the underlying physics and mechanics associated with weld residual stresses, even with today's increasingly advanced numerical techniques and faster computer speed.

COMPUTATIONAL PROCEDURES

The thermal and themomechanical processes associated with weld residual stress evolution during welding can be extremely complex, as shown in Fig. 1. As far as residual stresses are concerned, localized temperature distribution ranging from room temperature to above melting and structural restraint are of primary importance in determining the final residual stress state in a weldment.

Heat Flow Solution Procedures

As illustrated in Fig. 1, a base material (BM) can be subjected to a super-heated temperature above melting (depending welding processes) in the molten pool with a highly localized temperature distribution in a structure being welded. The resulting weld fusion characteristics can be directly related to the welding arc characteristics and molten pool dynamics. As shown in Fig. 2, the modeling of droplet impact for MIG weld pool (13) is essential for adequate prediction of the weld pool penetration. Although such modeling efforts are important in a better understanding of the welding process physics, both practical considerations and recent results have demonstrated that the heat flow solution procedures for residual stress and distortion predictions can be drastically simplified by considering the fusion profile as a known quantity. In this approach, typical weld fusion profile as shown in Fig. 3a can be used a parameter for defining an equivalent head source in heat conduction based analysis (Dong and Zhang, 14). (The material behavior within the molten pool was properly taken into account in the weld material model.) The validation results are summarized in Fig. 3b. When dealing complex structures, It is highly desirable that the heat flow solutions are independent of finite element models for residual stress and distortion predictions. An effective approach along this line is to employ analytically based heat flow solution methods to achieve a drastically improved thermal solution speed. Such a solution procedure was based on the 'Rosenthal type' methods as discussed in Cao et al (15). Additional capabilities have been added to account for radiation and convection losses, weld torch start/stop effects, and transient effects, among others.

Weld Constitutive Model

Within a weld pool, a material point typically undergoes rapidly heating, solidification, and rapid cooling. To establish what are the important material behaviors to be modeled, it is informative to examine a simple 1D problem as shown in Fig. 4, where the analytical (graphic) solution is also shown. By considering linear temperature with respect to time both on heating and cooling, the corresponding thermal strain history can be obtained. Assuming elastic perfectly-plastic material behavior and linear temperature dependence, as shown, the elastic strain or stress history can be readily calculated. Without losing generality, it can be assumed that as temperature increases, the material's yield strength decreases at θ_2, to zero at θ_l and melting occurs at θ_m. On cooling, the plastic strain can be calculated by simply subtracting the elastic strain from the total thermal strain, as shown in Fig. 4b. It can be seen that a completely different plastic strain history can be obtained if melting at θ_m is taken into account so that the material's virgin state is recovered. In almost all commercial finite element codes, this has been a major issue in simulating welding. Recently, in some codes, so called element "birth" and "death" operations with respect to a group of elements representing weld metal deposition may be used to eliminate some of the strain accumulation effects upon activation. However, re-melting such as those in multi-pass welds (see Fig. 1) still remains unresolved.

A fundamental approach to address some of the critical issues is to formulate a unified weld constitutive model using internal state variable approach, as in Brust et al (1). Along this line, the rate form of the strains may be written as follows:

$$\dot{\underset{\sim}{\varepsilon}}^{Tot} = \dot{\underset{\sim}{\varepsilon}}^{e} + \dot{\underset{\sim}{\varepsilon}}^{p} + \dot{\underset{\sim}{\varepsilon}}^{\theta} + \dot{\underset{\sim}{\varepsilon}}^{A} + \dot{\underset{\sim}{\varepsilon}}^{Tr} \tag{1}$$

where $\dot{\underset{\sim}{\varepsilon}}^{Tot}, \dot{\underset{\sim}{\varepsilon}}^{e}, \dot{\underset{\sim}{\varepsilon}}^{p}, \dot{\underset{\sim}{\varepsilon}}^{\theta}, \dot{\underset{\sim}{\varepsilon}}^{A}, \dot{\underset{\sim}{\varepsilon}}^{Tr}$ are the total, elastic, plastic, thermal, annealing, and phase transformation strain rate tensors, respectively. The elastic, plastic, and thermal strains are well understood in conventional thermoplasticity. We postulate the existence of an "annealing" strain, $\dot{\underset{\sim}{\varepsilon}}^{A}$ expressed as:

$$\dot{\underset{\sim}{\varepsilon}}^{A} = -\dot{\underset{\sim}{\varepsilon}}^{A}\left(\dot{\theta}, \theta, \underset{\sim}{\varepsilon}\right) \tag{2}$$

The "annealing strain component $\dot{\underset{\sim}{\varepsilon}}^A$ can be formulated for a given material by considering its detailed metallurgical behavior in terms of internal-state variables such as temperature, cooling rate, and the current accumulated strains (elastic and plastic). Recalling the simple 1D problem (Fig. 4), one can see that the definition of "annealing" strain can be used to "anneal" the strain history by setting reference temperature $\theta_A = \theta_2$. At the second reference temperature, e.g., $\theta_m = \theta_1$ in Fig. 4, all accumulated elastic and plastic strains $\underset{\sim}{\varepsilon}^e + \underset{\sim}{\varepsilon}^p$ can be eliminated and the material returns to the virgin state. For instance, the following functional forms of annealing strains can be used:

$$\dot{\underset{\sim}{\varepsilon}}^A = 0, \qquad \text{for} \quad \theta \langle \theta_A$$

$$\dot{\underset{\sim}{\varepsilon}}^A = \left(\frac{\dot{\theta}}{\theta_m - \theta} \right)^q \underset{\sim}{\varepsilon}\,. \qquad \text{for} \quad \theta_A \langle \theta \langle \theta_m \tag{3}$$

where 'q' is a parameter that characterizes the annealing strain behavior for a given material. Note that the definition of "annealing", although different from the one used in metal heat treatment operations, can be used to simulate annealing heat treatment with additional metallurgical parameters as state variables

With regard to the phase transformation strain ($\dot{\underset{\sim}{\varepsilon}}^{Tr}$), it can be decomposed into two parts:

$$\dot{\underset{\sim}{\varepsilon}}^{Tr} = \dot{\underset{\sim}{\varepsilon}}^{TrV} + \dot{\underset{\sim}{\varepsilon}}^{TrP} \tag{4}$$

where $\dot{\underset{\sim}{\varepsilon}}^{TrV}$ represents the strain rate due to the volume change associated with the transformation and $\dot{\underset{\sim}{\varepsilon}}^{TrP}$ is due to the phase transformation plasticity. The transformation volume change can be calculated based on the phase information during the transformation. The transformation plasticity is not only depended upon the phase information but also the stress states. The well-established Greenwood's relation can be used to calculate the strain rate due to transformation plasticity, which is expressed as:

$$\dot{\underset{\sim}{\varepsilon}}^{TrP} = \frac{3}{2} K \underset{\sim}{S} (2 - 2z - \dot{z}) \dot{z} \tag{5}$$

where K is a material constant and z is the fraction of transformed phase.

The finite element implementation of such a weld material constitutive law is illustrated in Fig. 5 in the form of a user-material model that can be readily interfaced with various commercial finite element codes. Note that in the present treatment, the annealing strain (primarily for modeling phase change involved melting/re-melting) and solid state phase transformation effects are separated in the formulation only for computational convenience.

FUNDAMENTAL MODELING ISSUES

In this section, a few selected numerical examples will be used to demonstrate some of the fundamental aspects of weld residual stresses and distortions and associated modeling techniques.

"Annealing" and Visco-Plasticity Effects

A rigid bar problem will be used to demonstrate some of the important modeling issues. As shown in Fig. 4 in the analytical solutions, solid mechanics based finite element codes without considering the melting effects typically provide an incorrect prediction of the plastic deformation behavior. Fig. 6 provides a detailed illustration of the finite element solution of this type, by assuming a more realistic temperature history imposed uniformly on the rigid bar under fully restrained conditions (Fig. 6a). The material is assumed to behavior elastic perfectly-plastic. The predicted plastic strain histories with and without the present weld material model are shown in Fig. 6d. The plastic strain behaviors share a similar trend with those in Fig. 4.

Visco-plasticity effects are also examined in this example, with representative properties from 304 stainless steel type. For comparison purposes, the evolutions of various strain components over the temperature cycle are summarized in Fig. 6c. It can be seen that creep strain is overall insignificant when compared with plastic strain, due to the short duration time within creep temperature range. Its effects on residual stress are minimal. In such applications, any strain-hardening effects will undoubtedly over-estimate the final residual stress state, if plastic strain development is correctly modeled.

The plastic strain accumulation effects should also be reflected in distortion prediction. Indeed, the distortion prediction and measurements in Fig. 7 for a side-welded aluminum plate demonstrate the importance of taking such effects into account. In this solution, a moving heat flow was used by considering both with "annealing strain" effects (present solution in Fig. 7) and without annealing (ABAQUS standard solution). The results in Fig. 7 show that at the beginning, the dial gage sensed positive displacement (upward movement) peaked at about 100 seconds when the arc was terminated. On cooling, the weld shrinkage effects generated a downward movement reaching its steady-state value at about 300 seconds. Note that the solution using ABAQUS significantly over-predicted the distortion whereas the present solution procedure provided accurate results for the distortion evolution throughout the entire welding process.

Phase Transformation Effects

An electro-slag weld cladding case is shown in Fig. 8, where phase transformation effects can be significant in the heat-affected zone (HAZ). As discussed in Dong, et al (3) using a 2D cross-section model, volumetric fractions of ferrite, pearlite, and martensite and their distributions in the clad weld were first estimated as internal state variables in Fig. 5 under specified welding and alloy conditions. The hardness estimation based on a simple mixture rule and measurements are shown in Fig. 8b, which also provides yield stress distributions in the residual stress model. By considering the detailed property distributions and volumetric changes associated with martensitic transformation on cooling, the final residual stress distributions are shown in Fig. 8c. In Fig. 8d, residual stress predictions with and without considering phase transformation effects are compared.

The results suggest: (a) the martensitic transformation effects are relatively confined within a small distance of the phase transformation region and impose local compression due to its volumetric dilation effects; (b) the overall distributions are similar between the two cases. From practical application point of view, such localized residual stress variations have been difficult to quantify experimentally due to its fine resolution requirements. In addition, in structural integrity assessment, upper bound residual stress distributions are typically used to provide conservative estimation of fracture driving force. For such purposes, it should be adequate to perform residual stress analysis without considering phase transformation effects, since such efforts often involves significantly increased complexity in numerical procedures and input data interpretation.

APPLICATIONS

In this section, a few selected examples will be used to demonstrate the applications of the modeling procedures discussed above for various engineering applications.

Residual Stresses in Pipe Girth Welds

In pressure and piping components, residual stresses are often needed for structural integrity assessment. A typical multi-pass girth weld and corresponding residual stress solutions are given in Fig. 9 (see Dong et al, 9). Good agreement between the finite element and experimental results can be seen. It should be noted that the finite element solutions in Fig. 9 were based on axisymmetric assumptions. As discussed in Dong et al (9), some periodic variations along the circumference exist, particularly for the axial stress component, as revealed by a 3D shell element model. Such variations should be taken into account in both axisymmetric model and experimental measurements if they are deemed significant. Note the through-thickness axial residual stress distributions take a form of "bending" type at the weld, i.e., compression at the outer surface and tension at inner surface. "Self-equilibrating" type residual stress distributions in girth welds were discussed Zhang et al (18) and Dong et al (19).

A repair weld analysis is performed for a similar multi-pass girth weld using a special shell element concept (Zhang et al, 2), as shown in Fig. 10. In this case, 3D effects must be considered to capture the structural restraint effects during repair welding. The shell element approach can be a very cost-effective for such purposes. As shown in Fig. 10d, the axial residual stresses are highly tensile within the repair area, and become compressive near the repair start and stop positions. Fracture mechanics based analysis incorporating the repair weld residual stress distributions can be found in Brust et al (7-8). One of the important parameters in controlling the final residual stress distributions is repair length, as discussed in Zhang et al (16).

Residual Stresses in Large Vessels

Residual stresses in Aluminum-Lithium cryogenic shuttle tanks were found to play an important role in both repair weldability and structural integrity (Dong et al, 10-11). Fig. 11 shows the predicted transverse residual stress distributions for a large welded panel. Detailed experimental validations can be found in Dong et al (10-11). For the original butt joint, the transverse residual stresses showed a significant variation along the weld direction. Such variations must be considered if one only uses a 2D model for residual stress analysis, as it often occurs in the open literature. It is worth noting that the transverse residual stresses for the repair weld (Fig. 11b) share almost identical features to those in the girth weld in Fig. 10d, even though both the geometry and material are significant different from each other. Due to typically high restraint conditions in repair, unlike initial welds, repair welds tend to show a similar distribution, regardless of detailed geometric configurations.

Prior Cold-Working Effects

In some applications, prior cold-working (strain hardening) can have significant effects on weld residual stresses and subsequent fatigue behavior. An informative example along this line is shown in Fig. 12a by an integrated simulation of hydroforming and welding operations for light-weight automotive frame constructions (Dong et al, 5). As shown in Fig. 12a, steel tubes undergoes a hydroforming (liquid-pressure forming) process to form a rectangular cross-section. Such a forming process typically induces severe cold working in contrast to traditional stamping. Consequently, the resulting in-situ yield strength can double the original yield strength of the base material and creates significant strength mis-match conditions across a welded joint. After simulating the hydroforming process, MIG welding assembly was simulated with the stress/strain histories from hydroforming as initial conditions. The resulting residual stress distributions are shown in Figs. 12b and 12c. The prior cold-working effects on weld residual stresses are evident, by comparing the residual stresses predicted without considering hydroforming. In particular, the longitudinal residual stresses (σ_{33}) become almost three times as high as the original yield strength (about 160MPa) of the tube both within and around the HAZ. This region is typically prone to fatigue failure in service.

Residual Stress Induced Tri-Axiality

It is often found, or commonly believed that "shake-down" effects under cylic loading or overloading under static conditions can significantly reduce the residual stress effects on fatigue and fracture behavior of a weldment. However, as more in-depth understanding of the weld residual stresses becomes available, such shake-down or overloading effects may not be as significant as commonly believed for some joint types where highly restrained conditions during welding tend to build up a high degree of the residual stress induced tri-axiality. A simple multi-pass wide panel weldment was recently studied in detail as a part of detailed investigation on fracture behavior of steel building moment frame connection (Zhang and Dong, 17). If nominal load and displacement curve is measured, the finite element results are shown in Fig. 13b for three cases, i.e., small coupon, with and without weld residual stresses. However, if any failure occurs in the weldment, local stress and strain development should provide a better indication. By considering a material point within the HAZ (under high bi-axial residual stress conditions), as marked in Fig. 13a, the effective plastic strain evolution as a measure of plastic deformation capability for a given load level is shown in Fig. 13c under the same three conditions. It can be seen that with the presence of high weld residual stresses, the gross yield is not only delayed, but the plastic strain magnitude becomes significantly lower than that without considering residual stresses. Without being able to develop adequate yielding in such cases, the over-loading induced stress relief effects will not be significant.

As a part of the same study, a more complex and highly restrained joint type is also analyzed as shown in Fig. 14. The resulting residual stress induced tri-axiality is examined in Fig. 14b as a function of remote loading. The initial stress tri-axiality at Position A reaches almost to unity before any loading is applied and can significantly delay plastic deformation in service. Fracture mechanics analysis shows that the fracture driving force is drastically increased as a result (Zhang and Dong, 19).

CONCLUDING REMARKS

As discussed throughout this paper, the recent rapid progresses in advanced modeling techniques provide researchers and engineers ever increasingly sophisticated tool sets to achieve a better understanding the complex nature of weld residual stress and distortions in welded structures. Some of the techniques have demonstrated its enormous potential in developing high-performance structures and advanced fabrication technologies in today's competitive environment. However, one should keep in mind that welding process modeling at present time requires a high degree of expertise in welding process physics, thermoplasticity, computational mechanics, etc, depending on specific objectives to be addressed. In order to obtain meaningful solutions, proper problem definition, assumptions, and simplifications are always a priori, at least for a foreseeable future. It is this intention that the this paper is laid out to not only clarify some of the fundamental issues regarding weld residual stress and distortion modeling, but also to demonstrate how engineering solutions can be derived with simplest possible modeling procedures required.

REFERENCES

1. Brust, F.W., P. Dong, J. Zhang, "A Constitutive Model for Welding Process Simulation using Finite Element Methods. Advances, *Computational Engineering Science*, ed. S. N. Atluri and G. Yagawa, 1997, pp. 51-56.
2. Zhang, J., Dong, P., and Brust, F.W., A 3-D Composite Shell Element Model for Residual Stress analysis of Multi-Pass Welds, Transactions of the 14th International Conference on Structural Mechanics in Reactor Technology (SMIRT 14), Lyon, France, August 17-22, 1997, pp.335-344.
3. Dong, P., Zhang, J., and Li, M.V., "Computational Modeling of Weld Residual Stresses and Distortions – An Integrated Framework and Industrial Applications, ASME Pressure Vessel and Piping Conference Proceedings, PVP-Vol. 373, *Fatigue, Fracture, and Residual Stresses*, pp. 311-335, 1998.
4. Dong, P., "Computational Modeling of Weldability, Fabricability, and Integrity of Welded Aluminum-Lithium Aerospace Structures," to appear in *Mathematical Modeling of Weld Phenomena V*, The Institute of Materials London, Eds. H. Cerjak, H.K.D.H. Badeshia, 2000.
5. Dong, P., Zhang, J., Yang, Y., and Cao, Z., "Computational Simulation from Hydroforming to Welding Assembly for Rapid Virtual Prototyping," SAE Paper #: 99IBECA-7, Proceedings of SAE IBEC International Conference, Detroit, October, 1999.
6. Dong, P., Sun, X., Lu, F., J. Zhang, "An Advanced Framework for Modeling Spot Welds in Finite Element Analysis of Auto-Body Structures," SAE Paper #: 99IBECA-14, Proceedings of SAE IBEC International Conference, Detroit, October, 1999.

7. Brust, F.W., Dong, P., and Zhang, J., "Influence of Residual Stresses and Weld Repairs on Pipe Fracture," ASME Pressure Vessel and Piping Conference Proceedings, PVP-Vol. 347, Approximate Methods in the Design and Analysis of Pressure Vessel and Piping Components, pp. 173-191, 1997.
8. Brust, F.W.; Zhang, J.; Dong, P. "Pipe and Pressure Vessel Cracking: The Role of Weld Induced Residual Stresses and Creep Damage during Repair", Transactions of the 14th International Conference on Structural Mechanics in Reactor Technology (SMiRT 14), Lyon, France, Vol. 1, 1997, pp. 297-306.
9. Dong, P., Ghadiali, and Brust, F.W., "Residual Stress Analysis of A Multi-Pass Girth Weld," ASME Pressure Vessel and Piping Conference Proceedings, PVP-Vol. 373, *Fatigue, Fracture, and Residual Stresses*, pp. 421-431, 1998.
10. Dong, P., Hong, J.K., and Rogers, P., "Analysis of Residual Stresses in Al-Li Repair Welds and Mitigation Techniques," *Welding Journal*, Vol. 77, No. 11, Nov., 1998, pp. 439s-445s.
11. Dong, P., Hong, J.K., Zhang, J., Rogers, P., Bynum, J., and Shah, S., "Effects of Repair Weld Residual Stresses on Wide-Panel Specimens Loaded in Tension, *ASME Journal of Pressure Vessel Technology* 120(2), 1998, 122-128.
12. Yang, Y.Y., Dong, P., J. Zhang, and Tian, X., "A Hot Cracking Mitigation Technique for TIG Welding of High Strength Aluminum Alloys," *Welding Journal*, Vol. 79, No. 1, 2000, pp. 9s-17s.
13. Cao, Z.N. and Dong, P., "Modeling of GMA Weld Pools with Consideration of Droplet Impact," ASME *Journal of Engineering Materials and Technology*, Vol. 120, October,1998.
14. Dong, Y and Zhang, J., "A New Heat Source Model for Arbitrary Weld Profile," to appear in *Mathematical Modeling of Weld Phenomena V*, The Institute of Materials London, Eds. H. Cerjak, H.K.D.H. Badeshia, 2000.
15. Cao et al, "A rapid thermal solution for welding process simulations," in preparation, 2000.
16. Zhang, J., Dong, P., Bouchard, "Repair length effects on weld residual stress distributions in a pipe," Proceedings of ASME PVP Conference, July, 2000.
17. Dong, P., and Zhang, J., "Residual Stresses in Strength-Mismatched Welds and Implications on Fracture Behavior," *Engineering Fracture Mechanics*, 64, 1999, pp. 485-505.
18. Zhang, J., Dong, P., Brust, F. W., William J. Shack, Michael E. Mayfield, Michael McNeil, "Modeling Weld Residual Stresses in Core Shroud Structures", *Nuclear Engineering and Design*, 195, 2000, pp. 171-187.
19. Zhang, J. and Dong, "Residual Stresses in Welded Moment Frames and Effects on Fracture," *ASCE Journal of Structural Engineering*, March, No. 3, 2000.

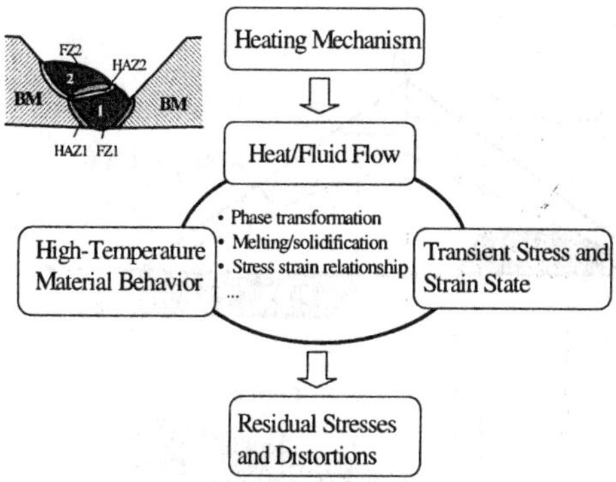

Fig. 1: Residual stress and distortion evolution in welded joints

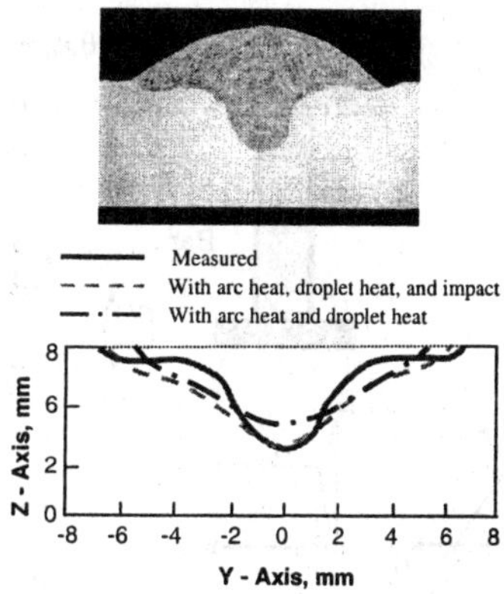

Fig. 2: Weld pool dynamics modeling - fusion profile prediction

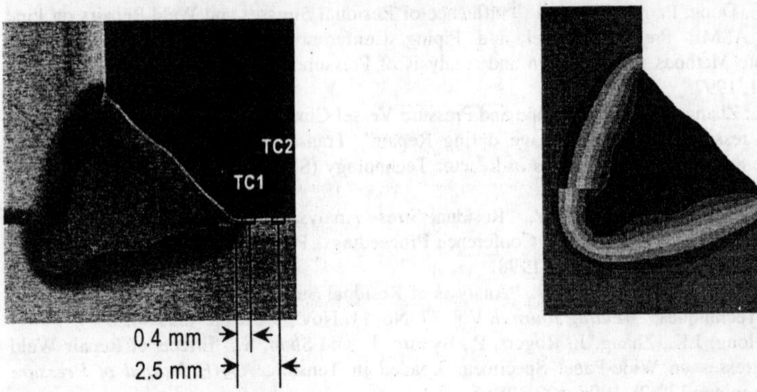

(a) Observed fusion profile and finite element model prediction

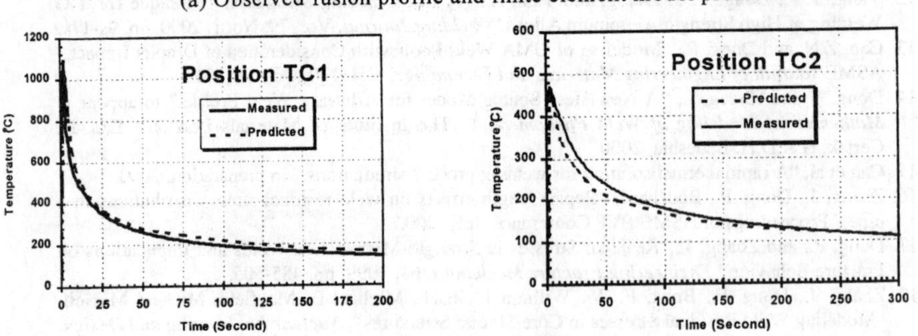

(b) Temperature histories at weld toe

Fig. 3: Welding-induced heat flow modeling using observed weld profile

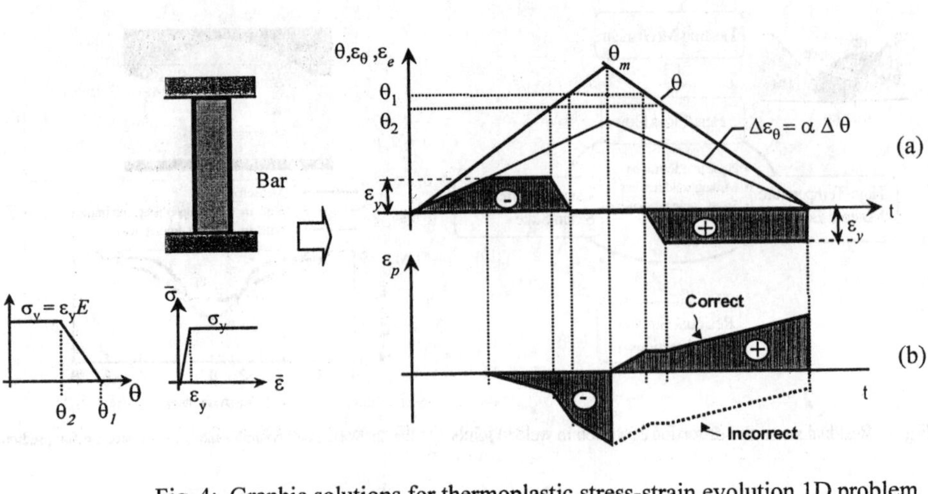

Fig. 4: Graphic solutions for thermoplastic stress-strain evolution 1D problem

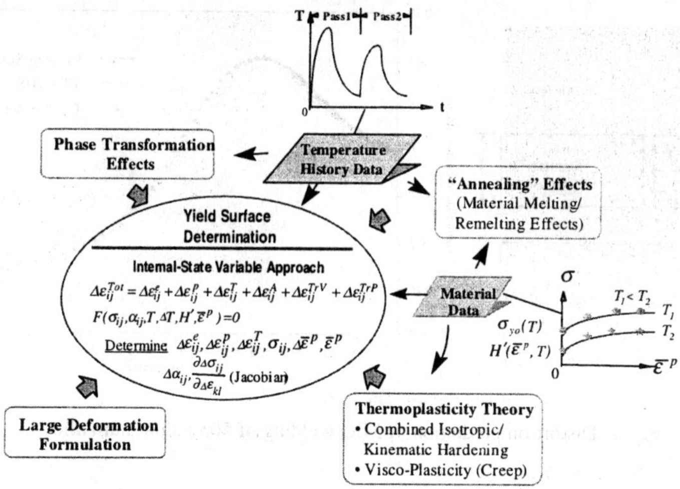

Fig. 5: Basic elements of unified weld constitutive model

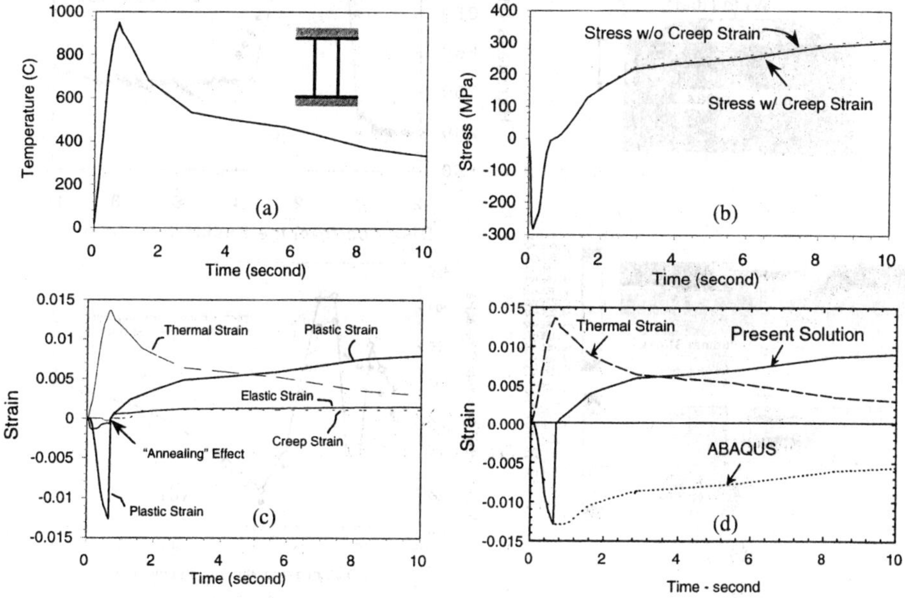

Fig. 6: Finite element solution with the unified constitutive law for a simple bar under rigid constraints: (a) Specific temperature history; (b) Predicted thermal stress evolution; (c) Strain components; (d) Comparison of plastic strain predictions.

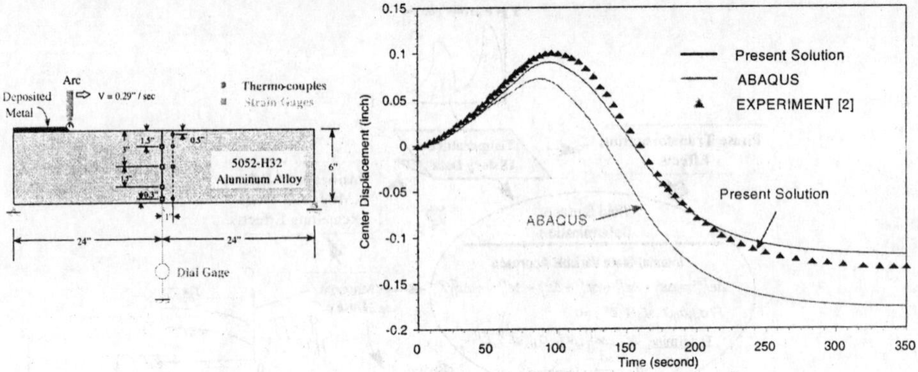

Fig. 7: Distortion prediction of MIG welding of 5052 aluminum alloy

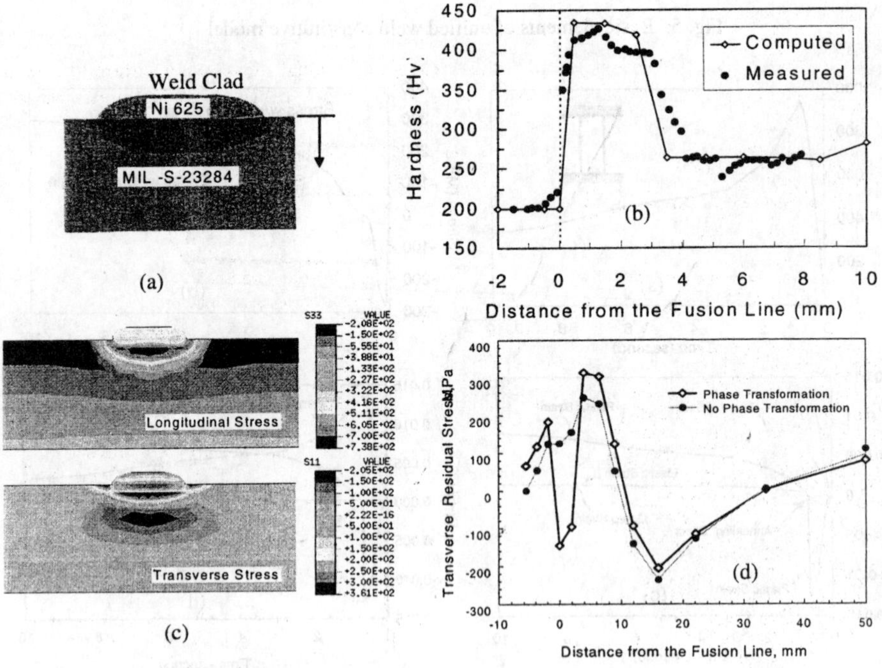

Fig. 8. Martensitic transformation effects on residual stresses - a clad weld: (a) clad weld mockup; (b) Hardness validation; (c) Predicted residual stress distributions with phase transformation effects; (d) Comparison of residual stress distributions with and without incorporating phase transformation.

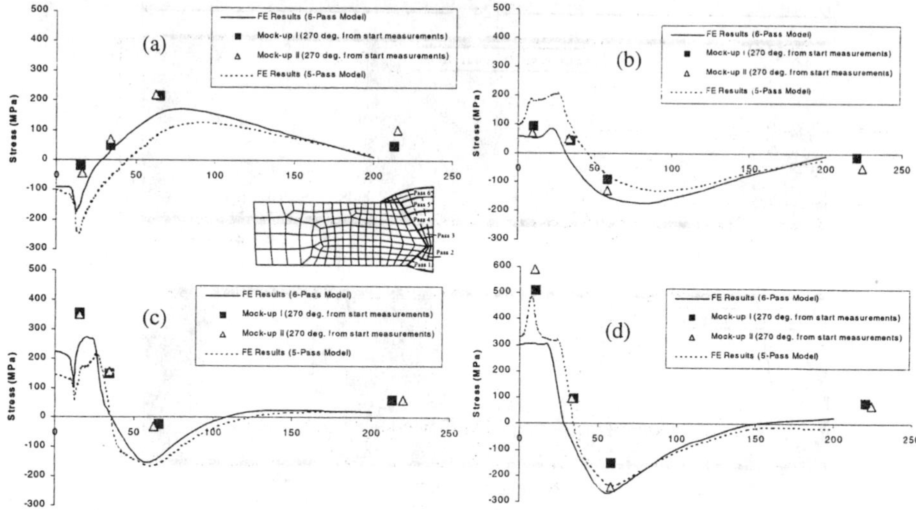

Fig. 9: Axisymmetric residual stress modeling results: (a) Axial residual stress - outer surface; (b) Axial residual stress - inner surface; (c) Hoop residual stress - outer surface; (d) Hoop residual stress - inner.

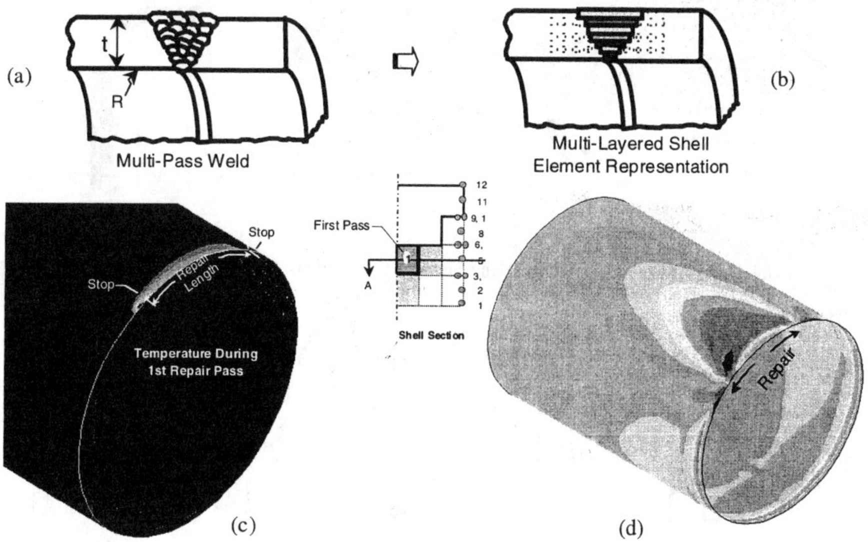

Fig. 10: Special shell element model for simulating multi-pass repair weld: (a) Typical multi-pass weld; (b) Shell element representation; (c) temperature solution for an intermediate pass for multi-pass repair weld; (d) Predicted transverse residual stress distribution on the outer surface

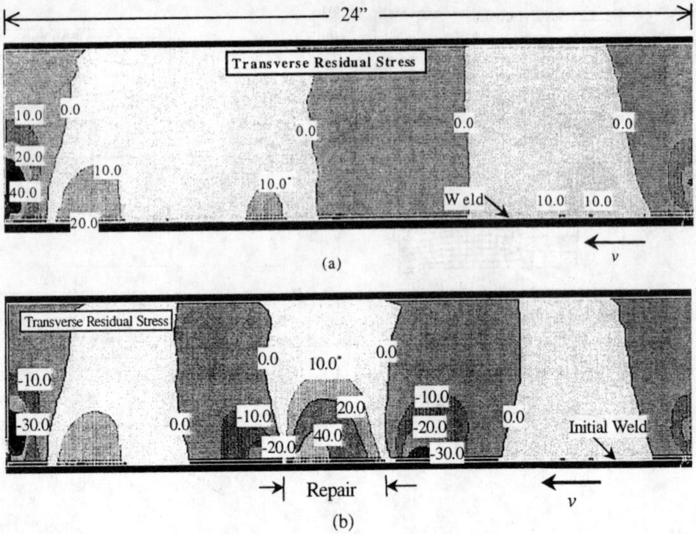

Fig. 11. Transverse residual stress distributions (units: ksi) in Al-Li specimen: (a) Original weld; (b) Repair weld

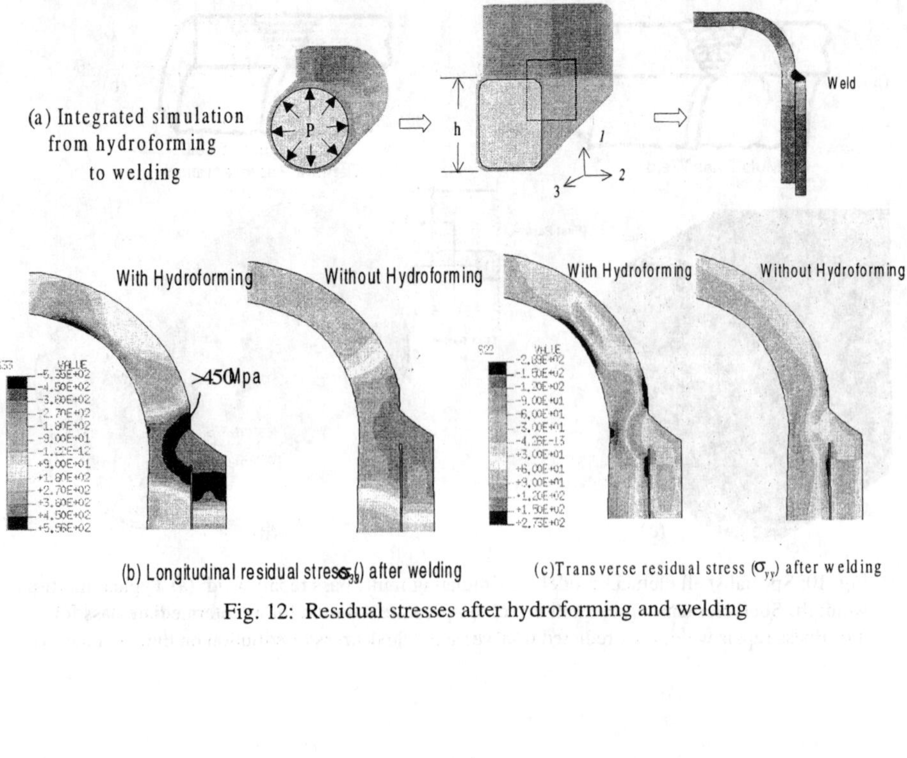

Fig. 12: Residual stresses after hydroforming and welding

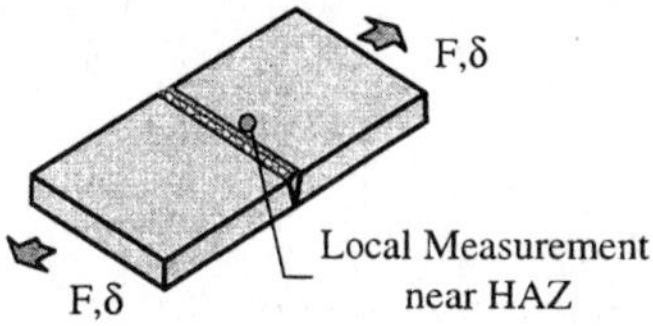

(a) A wide panel multi-pass butt joint

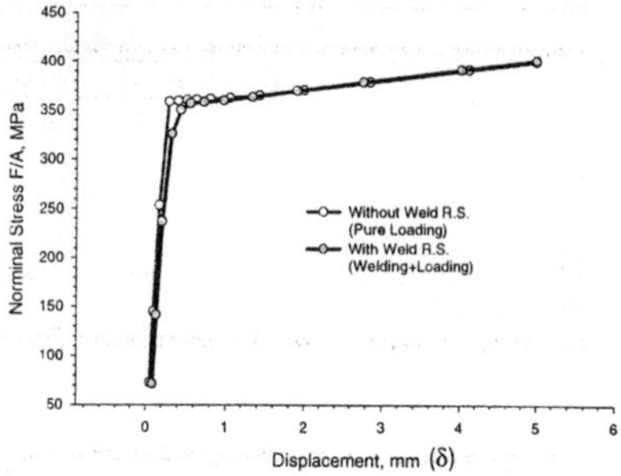

(b) Simulated global F-δ curves

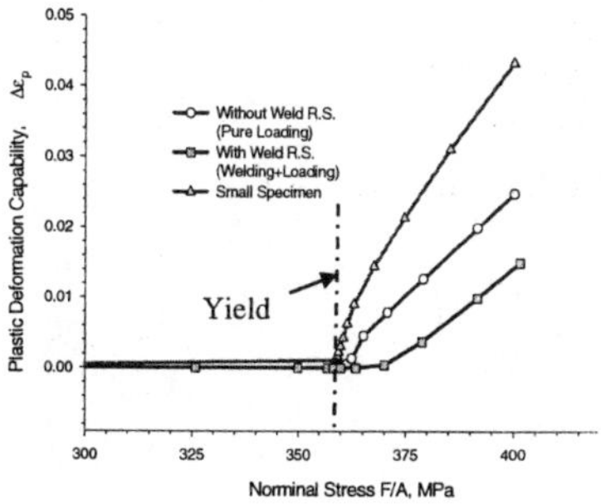

(c) Simulated local plastic strain development

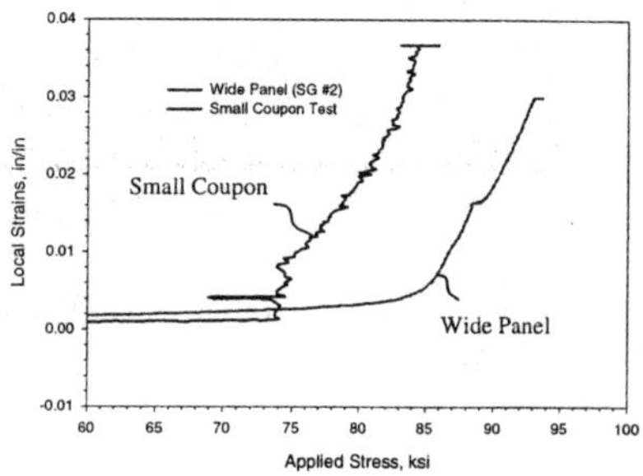

(d) Experimental results

Fig. 13: Residual stress effects on weld behavior

(a)

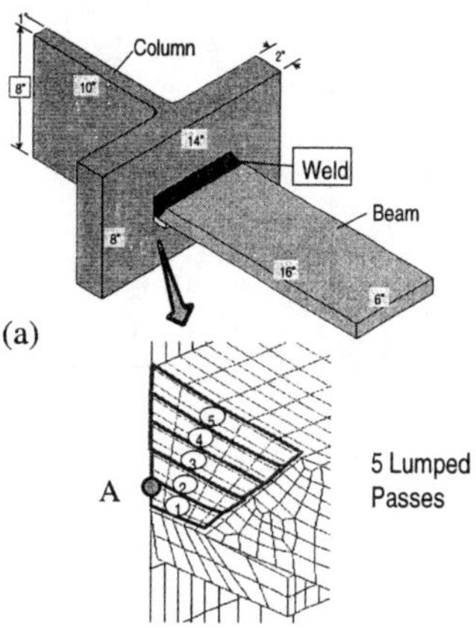

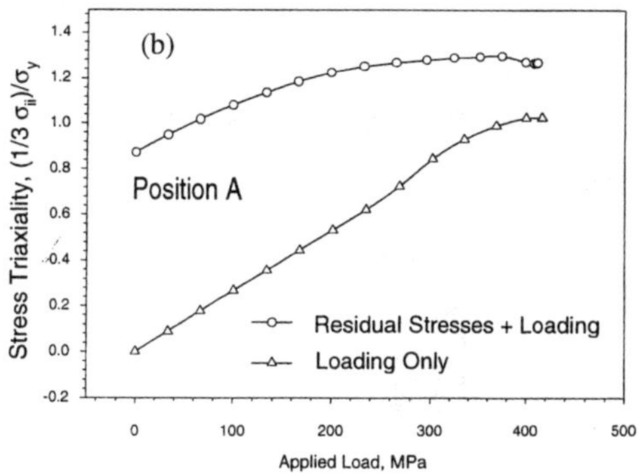

Fig. 14: Residual stresses and tri-axial stress state in a highly restrained joint: (a) Joint geometry and weld details; (b) Stress tri-axiality development under loading

SESSION 8A

NEUTRON TRANSMISSION SPECTROSCOPY: A SOLUTION TO THE d_0-PROBLEM?

A. Steuwer [1;2] , P.J. Withers [2] , J.R. Santisteban [3] , L. Edwards [3] ,
M. E. Fitzpatrick [3] , M.R. Daymond [4] , M.W. Johnson [4], G. Bruno [3]
[1] Department of Materials Science, University of Cambridge, UK
[2] Manchester Materials Science Centre, UMIST/University of Manchester, UK
[3] Department of Materials Engineering, The Open University, Milton Keynes, UK
[4] ISIS, Rutherford Appleton Laboratory, Chilton, Didcot, UK

ABSTRACT

Neutron diffraction has established itself as a powerful tool for the determination of stress fields in engineering components. In the time-of-flight method, two detectors are commonly placed at 90° to the incident beam to provide two perpendicular stress components and ensure rectangular gauge volumes. Neutron transmission, however, makes use of the fact that the highest resolution is achieved at large Bragg angles. The transmission spectrum of a polycrystalline material displays sudden, well-defined steps in the intensity whenever the incident wavelength ceases to fulfil the Bragg equation. The position and shape of these Bragg edges is used to extract information about the strain in the sample. Furthermore, by recording transmission spectra at different sample inclinations analogous to the $sin^2\psi$ technique it is possible to determine uniquely the unstrained lattice parameter. In this paper we present the basic analysis and preliminary results of a set of experiments, recorded with a 1D (10x1) detector at the ISIS neutron spallation source. The transmission data has been analysed with software specifically developed to allow single or Rietveld-type multiple-edge refinement. The results show excellent agreement with a conventional measurement of the unstrained lattice parameter.

INTRODUCTION

Neutron diffraction has proven to be a powerful tool for the determination of strains in materials and engineering components, Allen *et al.* (1). In essence the planes of atoms are used as internal strain gauges. The weak interaction of neutrons with solids has opened up the possibility of monitoring strains non-destructively far inside the bulk material, even under working/loading conditions. However, in any neutron diffraction experiment the problem of determining a stress-free lattice parameter (d_0), from which the elastic strains (and hence stresses) can be calculated remains an area of difficulty. In particular, in cases where there is a likelihood of compositional variation, this problem presents a tremendous challenge to the reliability of the technique. In this paper we propose a new solution to this problem based on neutron *transmission* measurements, to determine two-dimensional maps of the stress free lattice parameter across component slices at high rates of data acquisition.

This technique promises a major breakthrough for measurements where there may be a spatial variation in the stress free lattice parameter, e.g. for welds (easily the most popular type of problem currently tackled by neutron diffraction) where at the present time expensive component sectioning of the test-piece into small stress-free parts is required, Krawitz and Winholtz (2), Edwards *et al.* (3). The transmission geometry brings with it both advantages and constraints. For example, it opens up the possibility of using an array of detectors to produce a radiographic 'image' of the lattice parameter variation in the sample, however it also means that the measurement is an average over the complete transmission path through the sample. This makes the method useful for examining plates and other essentially two-dimensional objects. In addition because the path length is the same wherever the sample is placed along the beam path, unlike other diffraction methods the inferred lattice spacing is not sensitive to gauge location along the beam.

Conventionally, accurate measurement of lattice spacing has been done by measuring small shifts in the position of single diffraction peaks, using Gaussian, or more complex peak-profile fitting routines. Alternatively, in the case of the pulsed neutron technique Rietveld-type (3) fitting of many diffraction peaks simultaneously has been used to refine the lattice parameters. The Rietveld-type approach has the advantage that information from many peaks is used, which appears to increase the accuracy with which changes in lattice parameter (i.e. strain) can be determined. A similar approach has been taken in this project and special Rietveld-type refinement software for the analysis of transmission spectra has been developed.

THE TRANSMISSION BRAGG EDGE

At pulsed neutron sources, neutrons of all wavelengths emerge over a very short time pulse from the source. The small wavelength neutrons travel faster along the flight path from source to detector than the long wavelength neutrons. This means that the wavelength of a detected neutron can be deduced from its time of flight (TOF). If a detector is placed at a given angle the whole diffraction profile can be recorded as a function of time. In transmission geometries, if the neutron detector is placed behind a polycrystalline sample (such as a powder) the transmission spectrum exhibits step-like, so-called *Bragg,* edges (Fig. 1).

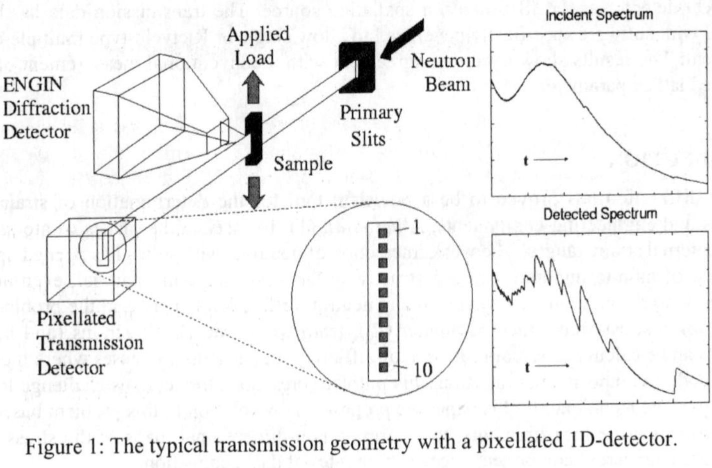

Figure 1: The typical transmission geometry with a pixellated 1D-detector.

Bragg edges occur because for a particular lattice spacing the diffraction angle increases as the wavelength increases according to the Bragg equation $\lambda = 2d \sin\theta$.At a certain wavelength (TOF) the diffraction angle reaches 90°, and the incident neutron is completely back-scattered towards the source. At longer wavelengths diffraction from that lattice spacing cannot occur. This is accompanied by a sudden increase in the transmitted intensity as neutrons can no longer be diffracted by that reflection. As a result, each Bragg edge corresponds to a particular lattice spacing for the crystal structure of the sample, see Fig. 2. A change in the position of a Bragg edge therefore corresponds to a change in the lattice spacing for planes normal to the beam and hence enables the determination of strain in that direction.

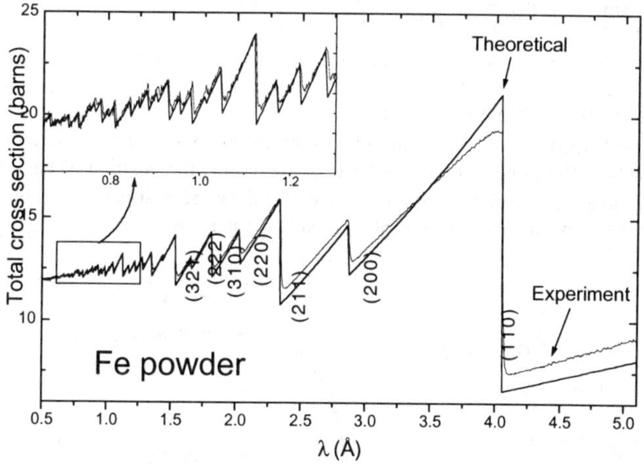

Figure 2: Normalised powder transmission spectrum, in this case for iron, displaying a large number of Bragg edges. Also shown for comparison is the calculated theoretical cross-section.

THE BASIC EQUATIONS

The fundamental equation of diffraction strain scanning is the Bragg equation:

$$\lambda = 2\, d \sin\theta \qquad (1)$$

Conventionally, the spectrum of diffraction peaks is obtained during a $\theta/2\theta$-scan using single, known incident wavelengths, where strains corresponds to a shift in the angular peak position, and can be calculated according to ε=-cot$\theta\, \Delta\theta$. In the TOF technique however, the scattering angle is kept constant and instead, the spectrum is recorded as a function of neutron wavelength $\lambda = h / p$, where h is Planck's constant, and p the neutron momentum. At spallation sources such as ISIS, in the thermal regime a range of wavelengths (typically 0.5Å to 4Å) received over a time scale equal to the pulse rate (50Hz) is produced. Since the flight path L on a TOF neutron beam-line is constant, and neutrons of all wavelengths emerge from the spallation event at the same time, fast neutrons arrive at the detector earlier than slow ones and the neutron wavelength can be expressed as function of time (hence the name). Explicitly, the relationship between neutron velocity v, wavelength λ and detection time t is given by $v = L / t = p / m = h / \lambda m$, where m denotes the neutron mass. For the transmission geometry the scattering angle equals θ = 90°, and inserting the above relation in the Bragg equation one obtains the linear relationship

Transmission: $$d = \frac{h}{2mL}t \qquad (2)$$

Straining of the lattice spacing corresponds to a shift of the position of the Bragg edges in the transmission spectra. Since, eqn.2 describes a simple linear relationship between lattice spacing and TOF, the equation for strain in transmission is the same as in conventional TOF-diffraction

Strain: $$\varepsilon_{hkl} = \frac{d_{hkl} - d_{hkl}^0}{d_{hkl}^0} = \left(\frac{\Delta d}{d}\right)_{hkl} = \left(\frac{\Delta t}{t}\right)_{hkl} \qquad (3)$$

REFINEMENT OF A BRAGG EDGE

For engineering purposes, it is important to know strains to an accuracy of the order of Δd /d = Δt / t = 0.01% = 100με or better. In order to achieve this, the position of each individual edge has to be determined very accurately, a task which can be best performed by fitting the data with the help of a least-squares algorithm on a computer.

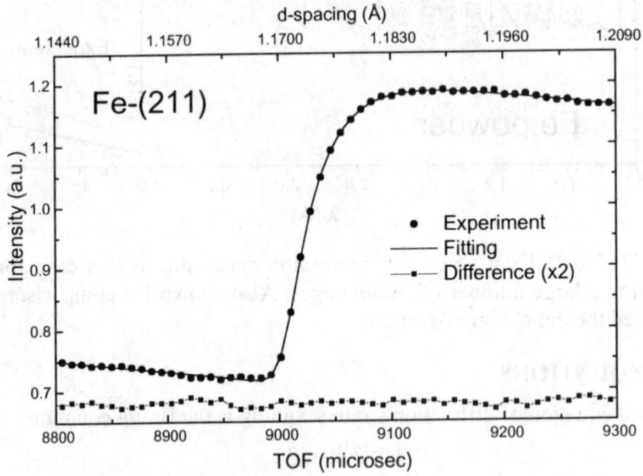

Figure 3: The refinement of the 211-edge of iron powder, displaying the characteristic asymmetry. The difference function at the bottom is enlarged by a factor of 2. The adopted model fits the data very well and is consistent with results of simultaneously recorded diffraction data.

As can be seen in Fig 3, the Bragg edge profile displays the characteristic asymmetry also observed in TOF diffraction experiments which is due to the particular way thermal neutrons at spallation sources are created. A proper mathematical description of the transmission edge profile is essential in order to achieve precise refinements and provide reliable values of the edge position. An analytical model of the Bragg edge profile has been developed, Steuwer *et al.* (5), based on a model proposed by Kropff *et al.* (6). Figure 3 shows the experimental data recorded for the (211) reflection of iron and the least-square fitting based on that model. The uncertainty in the position of the edge corresponds to ~35με.

A Rietveld-type software package has been developed that allows the refinement of Bragg edges singly and collectively to make use of the large amount of information displayed in the spectrum. Fitting several edges simultaneously not only improves the accuracy of the measurement and reduces the counting time but also provides information which is closer to the macrosocopic properties of the material as it has been already shown for diffraction, Daymond *et al.* (7).

THE DETERMINATION OF THE UNSTRAINED LATTICE PARAMETER

THE $\sin^2\psi$-TECHNIQUE

This technique is widely used in X-ray diffraction for measuring biaxial stress fields. It is rarely used in neutron scattering due to the long counting times required for carrying out the experiments involving different tilts of the sample and the fact that triaxiality of stress necessitates a d_0 measurement. However, measuring times can be significantly reduced in neutron transmission by recording strain images using pixellated detectors. A slight variation of this technique allows the estimation of the unstressed lattice spacing d_0.

Figure 4 shows the tilts required to infer d_0 using neutron transmission geometry and the $\sin^2\psi$ technique expressed in eqn.5, for a sample containing an in-plane biaxial stress field (σ_3=0). Taking the principal stress axes (σ_1 and σ_2) to be at some unknown angle ϕ to the sample axes, the basic equations linking the stresses to d_0 and the measured lattice spacing d are, Barret and Massalski (8),

$$\frac{d_\perp - d_0}{d_0} = s_1(\sigma_1 + \sigma_2) \qquad (5a)$$

$$\frac{d_{\phi\psi} - d_0}{d_0} = \frac{s_2}{2}\sigma_\phi \sin^2\psi + s_1(\sigma_1 + \sigma_2) \qquad (5b)$$

$$\frac{d_{\phi'\psi} - d_0}{d_0} = \frac{s_2}{2}\sigma_\phi \sin^2\psi + s_1(\sigma_1 + \sigma_2) \qquad (5c)$$

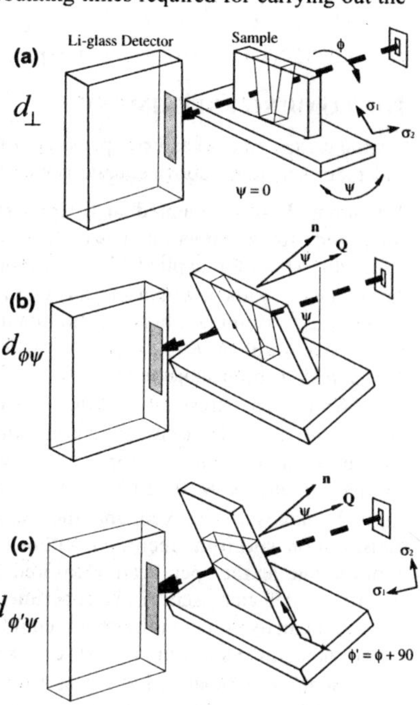

Figure 4: The $\sin^2\psi$ method (Eq.5) for the determination of d_0 by neutron transmission.

with $\sigma_\phi = \sigma_1 \cos^2\phi + \sigma_2 \sin^2\phi$, so the angle $\phi = 0$ corresponds to the direction of σ_1. Applying a little algebra and replacing the diffraction elastic constants by $s_1 = -\nu / E$ and $s_2 = 2(1 + \nu) / E = G$ the above equations can be solved for d_0. The equation defining d_0 is independent of the elastic modulus, but still depends on the Poisson's ratio, which is material dependent.

$$\textbf{(2D)} \qquad d_0 = \frac{\nu}{1+\nu}\,\frac{d_{\phi\psi} + d_{\phi'\psi} - 2d_\perp}{\sin^2\psi} + d_\perp \qquad (6)$$

For the case of a one-dimensional stress of known direction, such as the uniaxial loading experiment used here to prove the technique, the sample need only be tilted in one angular direction.

$$\textbf{(1D)} \qquad d_0 = \frac{\nu}{1+\nu}\frac{d_\psi - d_\perp}{\sin^2\psi} + d_\perp \tag{7}$$

In addition, there is an angle ψ^* at which d_ψ is equal to d_o, Eigenmann (9),

$$\sin^2\Psi^* = \frac{\nu}{1+\nu} = c^* \tag{8}$$

Finally, since eqns.5a-c are linear equations in $\sin^2\psi$, the slope m of the d v. $\sin^2\psi$ plot is proportional to the stress, hence

$$\sigma_1 = \frac{E}{1+\nu}\frac{m}{d_0} = \frac{s_2}{2}\frac{m}{d_0} \tag{9}$$

THE LOADING EXPERIMENT

A simple experiment has been performed to compare the unstrained lattice spacing derived under stress from the above equations with the lattice spacing measured under no stress.

A 6x6mm^2 Fe-rod mounted in a stress rig was subjected to a constant uniaxial strain of ε~1850με where the applied load was monitored during the experiment with a strain gauge fixed to the sample. Assuming a bulk elastic modulus for ferritic steel of about $E = 210$GPa , Brandes (10), the sample has been subjected to a stress of $\sigma = E\,\varepsilon = 388$MPa. The stress rig was then placed into the beam in this configuration, and the transmission spectrum recorded for various inclination angles ψ=0, ±15, ±30°. Then the applied load was removed and the unstrained transmission spectrum recorded without inclining the sample. Afterwards, the rig was removed and an the open beam measured for normalisation purposes. For the 10mm^2 glass-scintillator detector used in the experiment the typical exposure time was four hours and subsequent analysis has shown that it could be reduced without a significant loss of accuracy. Unfortunately, the spectrum at –30° could not be used as it was corrupted. The results of the experiment are summarized in Fig.6, where the d *vs* $\sin^2\psi$-plots coming from single (a) and multiple (b) edge fittings are presented. Also included in the graphs are the measured unstrained lattice spacing and the calculated values using eqn. 7 and ν_{211}=0.277 and ν=0.29, Hauk (11), for the respective Poisson's ratios. As shown in the pictures, the average calculated values of d_0 coincide with the directly measured ones within the experimental error, and the results provided by both analyses differed only by 45$\mu\varepsilon$(well within the accuracy of a d_o measurement typically required for strain scanning). It is also worth to point out that for the (211) single edge results, the stress (383MPa) calculated using eqn 9 and the corresponding X-ray elastic constant coincided with the value evaluated from the strain gauge. In contrast, the value given by the multiple edge refinement and the macroscopic elastic constants is lower (330Mpa), presumably due to a misfit between the true and the adopted elastic constants. As a final remark, the experimental values of c^*, indicating the

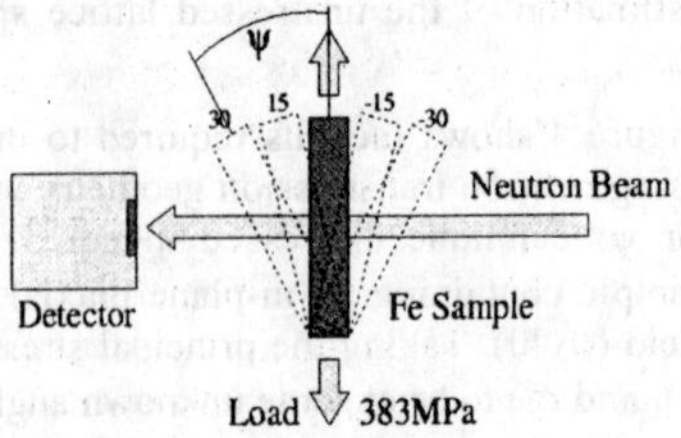

Figure 5: Schematic setup used in the uniaxial loading experiment.

angles ψ* for which the unstrained lattice parameter can be measured directly, are shown in the plots. The experimental values are close to the theoretical values (0.217 and 0.225) predicted by eqn 8.

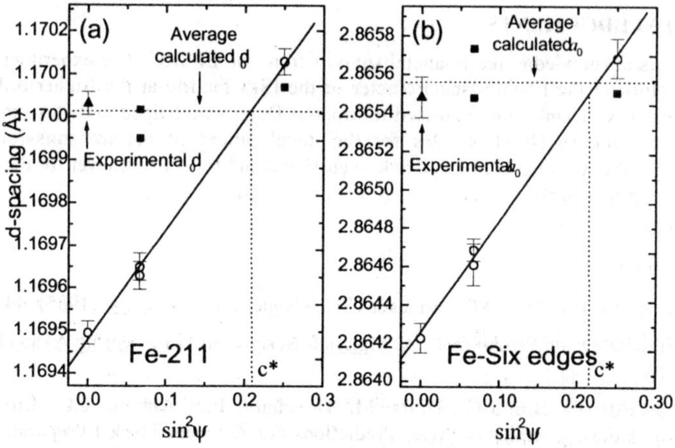

Figure 6: (a) Measured lattice spacing and calculated d_0 from the fitting of the Fe-211 Bragg edge (b) Same as before but performing a multiple-edge fitting of the six lowest edges.

CONCLUSIONS AND OUTLOOK

Neutron transmission experiments at pulsed neutron sources is a new tool for the accurate determination of unstrained lattice parameter profiles, providing important information for residual stress studies. The proposed technique is especially suitable for welds, where a big change in the chemical composition of the material is expected from point to point in the sample. If a thin slice is cut from the weld, the d_0 profile can, in principle, be defined by measuring the transmission of the sample in three different orientations even when the principal stress directions are unknown. The simple uniaxial loading experiment performed in this work has proved the capabilities of the proposed technique, encouraging us to develop a new pixellated detector for exploiting the unique advantages of the transmission geometry. As a first step towards the final 2D-pixellated detector a 1D-pixellated detector consisting of a row of 10 1mm^2 glass-scintillators has been built and its performance tested by recording the transmission of a plastically deformed EN8 steel bar. The average strains coming from a multiple edge analysis presented the expected behavior and are displayed in Fig. 7. The current work also involves the improvement of different aspects of the data analysis, in order to reduce the counting time and to expand the possibilities of the technique. As an example, the application of the method to strongly textured samples is under study and recent

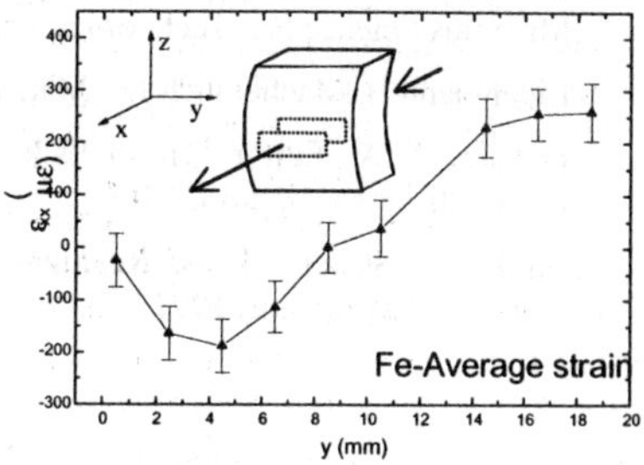

Fig 7: Pixellated detector showing strains in a bent bar.

experiments indicate that the use of the $\sin^2\psi$ technique is still valid in multiple edge analysis, even when the individual single edge fittings fail to provide linear *d vs.* $\sin^2\psi$ plots.

ACKNOWLEDGEMENTS

The authors acknowledge the financial support from the EPSRC. The experimental results were obtained at the ENGIN spectrometer of the ISIS facility at the Rutherford-Appleton Laboratory, UK. Thanks are expressed to Monojit Dutta who helped undertake many of the experiments and to Nigel Rhodes for the development of the transmission detector technology. We would also like to thank Sven Vogel and Hans Priesmeyer for their help and advice during this work.

REFERENCES

1. Allen W, Hutchings MT, Windsor CG, Advances in Physics 34 (1985), 445-473
2. Krawitz, D and Winholtz, R. A, Materials Science and Engineering A185 (1994) 123-130
3. Edwards, L., Bruno G., Dutta, M., Bouchard, P.J., Abbott, K.L., Lin Peng, R., Validation Of Residual Stress Predictions For A 19mm Thick J Preparation Manual Metal Arc Stainless Steel Pipe Girth Weld Using Neutron Diffraction, These proceedings.
4. Rietveld, H. M., Journal Applied Crystallography 2, (1969) 65-71
5. Steuwer A, Santisteban J. R., Edwards, Withers P. J, in preparation
6. Kropff F, Granada JR, Mayer RE, Nuclear Instruments and Methods 198 (1982) 515-521
7. Daymond, M. R., Bourke, M. A., Von Dreele, R,.B., Clausen, B and Lorentzen, T, Journal Applied Physics 82 (1997) 1554-1562
8. Barret C. and Massalski, T. B., 'Structure of metals'', International Series on Materials Science and Technology vol 35, Pergamon Press (Oxford) 1980
9. Eigenmann B, Macherauch E, , Mat.-wiss und Werkstofftech. 26 (1995) 148-160
10. Brandes, E. A., Editor, 'Smithells Metal Reference Book' 6th edition, Butterworth & Co. Publishers (London), 1983
11. Hauk V., 'Structural and Residual Stress Analysis by Nondestructive Methods', Elsevier (Amsterdam) 1997

CRYSTALLOGRAPHIC ORIENTATION-DEPENDENT RESIDUAL STRESS IN COLD-ROLLED STAINLESS STEEL

YD Wang[1], R Lin Peng[1,2], M Odén[2] and R McGreevy[1]
[1] Studsvik Neutron Research Laboratory (NFL)
Uppsala University
S-61182 Nyköping, Sweden
[2] Department of Mechanical Engineering
Linköping University
S-58183 Linköping, Sweden

ABSTRACT

The strain distributions in both austenite and martensite of a cold rolled stainless steel were measured by neutron diffraction, in a sample-fixed coordinate system and for a number of hkl-planes. It is evident that there is a large crystallographic orientation-dependent stress heterogeneity in both phases. The anisotropy of residual stress is determined from the experimental strain distributions by a spherical harmonics approach, via the determination of the stress orientation distribution function.

1. INTRODUCTION

Investigations on crystallographic orientation-dependent stress (CODS) heterogeneity in many engineering materials, such as metals, alloys and composites, have received a great deal of attention in the past five years (1-4) because of the significance for reliable evaluation of residual stress and for quality inspection. Actually, studies of this heterogeneity can also reveal some of the intrinsic nature of the influence of strain or stress anisotropy on transformation and recrystallisation texture evolution. The origin of anisotropic CODS is generally attributed to strain incompatibility between grains having different crystallographic orientations during various thermo-mechanical processes and is related to the elastic and/or plastic anisotropy of single crystallites.

The stress-orientation distribution function (SODF), which is defined as the mean stress field of grains with an identical direction as a function of crystallographic orientation, was developed as a statistical description of the CODS heterogeneity (5, 6). The SODF could be constructed by the following three methods.

1. The strain and stress states of each grain are simulated by some model, which considers the elastic and/or plastic anisotropy of single crystallites and the grain-to-grain interactions, then the simulated strains are transformed into various lattice strains which are compared to experimental values.
2. The strain and stress state of each grain is directly measured by synchrotron micro-beam diffraction and the SODF is constructed from the measured stress states.
3. Strain distributions in a sample-fixed coordinate frame, for some hkl-planes, are measured by neutron or x-ray diffraction and the SODF is constructed by solving a limited number of lower order terms of the series coefficients from those strain distributions, i.e. the spherical harmonic approach (SHA).

A detailed description of the SHA, including the definition and symmetry of SODF and its determination from strain distributions, has already been given in (5-7).

In this paper strain distributions in sample-fixed directions, for a number of hkl-planes, were measured in both austenite and martensite of a cold rolled stainless steel by neutron diffraction. The anisotropy of residual stresses in both phases has been quantitatively analyzed by the SHA from the experimental strain distributions.

2. EXPERIMENTAL

An austenitic (γ) stainless steel, equivalent to AISI 301 and with a nominal chemical composition of 17 wt-% Cr and 7 wt-% Ni (remainder Fe), was used in this study. It was received as 0.8 mm thick sheets, which were manufactured from 1.538 mm thick sheets by three-pass cold rolling. The yield and ultimate tensile strength are 1408 and 1500 MPa, respectively. Neutron diffraction measurement reveals a substantial amount of deformation-induced martensite (α) due to cold rolling. The volume fraction of the α phase, estimated by analyzing the peak intensities of $(111)_\gamma$, $(200)_\gamma$, $(220)_\gamma$, $(311)_\gamma$, $(200)_\alpha$ and $(211)_\alpha$, is about 38%. To avoid the influence of specimen geometry on absorption during strain measurements, three cylindrical specimens of 12 mm by Φ8 mm were used for mapping strain distributions in the RT, NT and NR planes (see below for definition). These were produced by spark erosion cutting from stacks of the cold roll sheets with the cylinder axis parallel to the normal direction (ND), the rolling direction (RD) and the transverse direction (TD) of the sheet, respectively.

The neutron diffraction measurements were carried out using the high resolution diffractometer, REST, at the Studsvik Neutron Research Laboratory in Sweden with a wavelength 1.76 Å. Lattice strains were measured on $(111)_\gamma$, $(200)_\gamma$, $(220)_\gamma$, $(311)_\gamma$, $(200)_\alpha$ and $(211)_\alpha$ planes. Strain distributions were mapped at 10° intervals in the γ phase and 5° in the α phase, for the above mentioned three planes, i.e. RT (from RD to TD), NT (from ND to TD) and NR (from ND to RD). A detailed description of strain and texture measurements by neutron diffraction has already been given in (4). In this paper the lattice constant of the standard stress-free γ phase has been obtained by averaging over all the measured {hkl} planes and sample directions. The standard lattice constant of the α phase has been derived by considering a proper stress balance between γ and α.

3. RESULTS AND DISCUSSION

3.1 Textures in austenite and martensite phases

Fig. 1 shows the constant φ cross-sections of the ODF of the γ phase in cold rolled stainless steel. It is shown that the texture components in the γ phase consist mainly of {110}<211> (Brass), {110}<001> (Gauss), {123}<634> (S) and {112}<111> (Copper), which are typical textures found in fcc metals or alloys. The φ=45° cross-sections of the ODF of the α phase are shown in Fig. 2a. Comparisons between the experimental ODF with the principle ideal bcc orientations located in or near the φ=45° cross-sections (Fig. 2b) show that the texture in the α phase consists of {332}<113>, {112}<131> and a component running from {211}<011> to {100}<011> (i.e. <011>//RD fiber). The observed components in the α phase are in good agreement with the characterization of transformation textures from γ to α (8). It is generally admitted that the observed transformation textures reveal the presence of considerably fewer variants than are predicted by the well-known Kurdjumov-Sachs relationship. Thus, variant selection takes place during phase transformation. Actually, the transformation textures can be readily reproduced with aid of some selection criteria, of which residual stress-based growth is an important one (8).

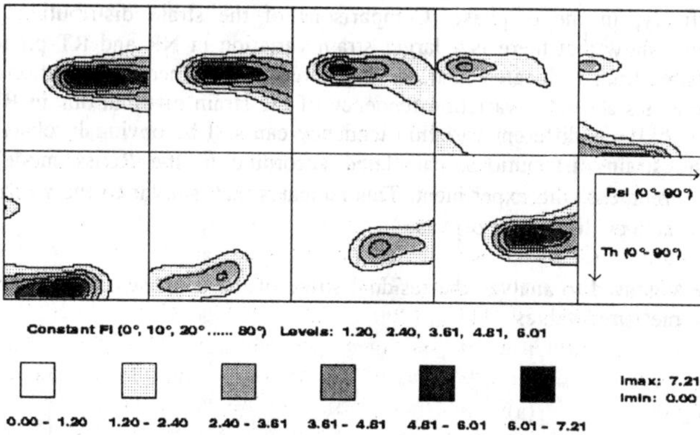

Fig. 1 ODF cross-sections of the γ phase in stainless steel with φ constant

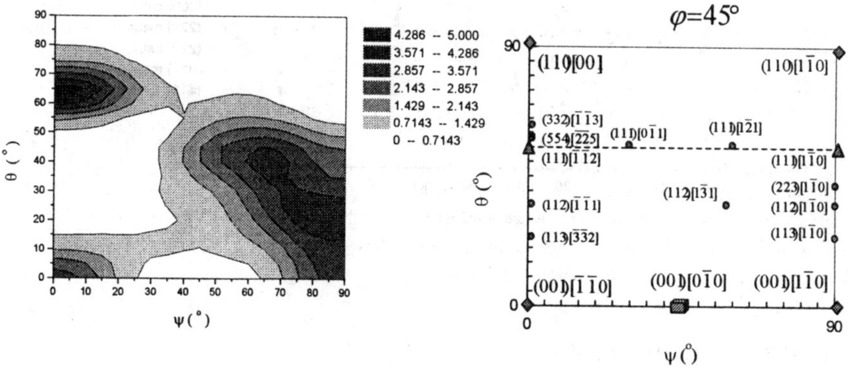

(a) (b)

Fig. 2 (a) ODF cross-sections of the α phase in stainless steel with φ=45°. (b) Key identifying the principle bcc ideal orientations located in or near the φ=45° cross-section of the ODF.

3.2 Strain distributions in austenite and martensite phase

The strain distributions, determined for each of $\{111\}_\gamma$, $\{200\}_\gamma$, $\{220\}_\gamma$ and $\{311\}_\gamma$, of the γ phase have already been reported in detailed (4). It was shown that the tendency of strain variations is obviously different for various {hkl} planes, which indicates the existence of crystallographic orientation dependent residual stress in the γ phase of the cold rolled stainless steel we have investigated. Further investigations show that traditional residual stress analysis, based on the Reuss, Voigt and Hill models, yields strain distributions that deviate significantly from the experimental values (4). In this paper, we use the SHA to investigate the crystallographic orientation-dependent anisotropy of residual stress. It is shown in Fig. 3 that the calculated strains using the SHA for all {hkl} planes are in good agreement with those measured values.

Figures 4 and 5 show the measured strain distributions for $\{211\}_\alpha$ and $\{200\}_\alpha$ diffraction peaks, respectively, in the α phase. Comparisons of the strain distributions for these diffraction peaks show that there is a larger strain variation in NR and RT planes and the maximum tensile strain is located near the RD direction. Further investigations find that although there exists a similar variation tendency of the strain distributions in RT and NR planes for two {hkl}s, a different variation tendency can still be obviously observed in the NT plane. The strain distributions, calculated according to the Reuss model, are not completely in agreement with experiment. This indicates that, similar to the γ phase, CODS heterogeneity is also evident in the α phase.

When the SHA is used to analyze the residual stress of the α phase, the calculated strains are close to the measured values.

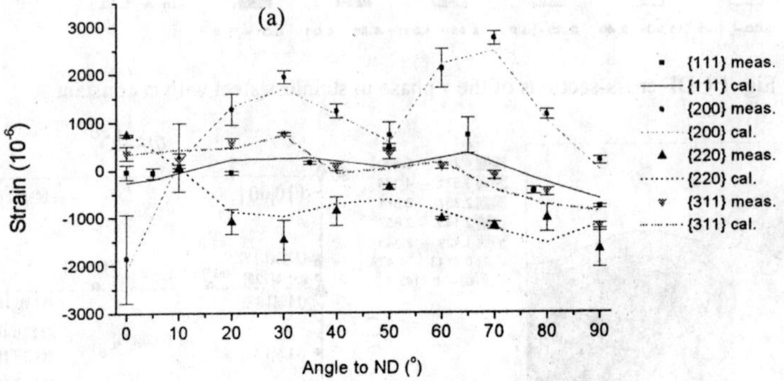

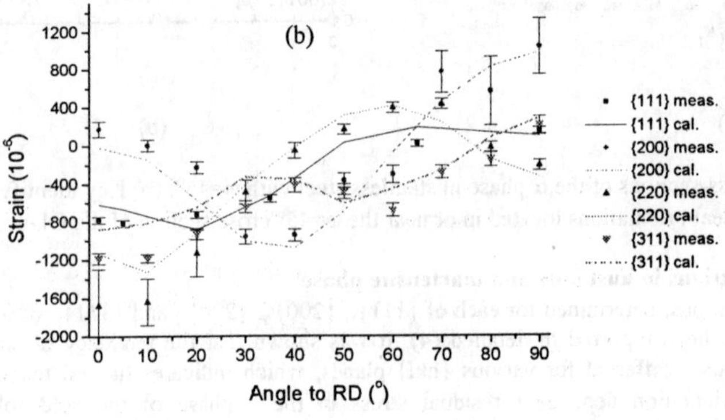

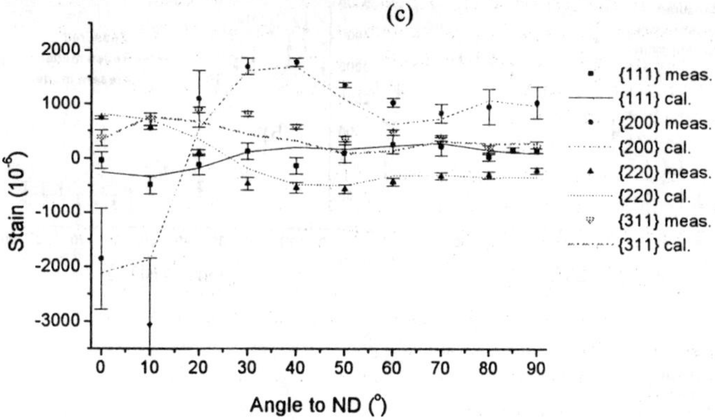

Fig. 3 The strain variation of the γ phase for {111}, {200}, {220} and {311} diffraction peaks (a) in the plane of ND and RD, (b) in the plane of RD and TD, (c) in the plane of ND and TD.

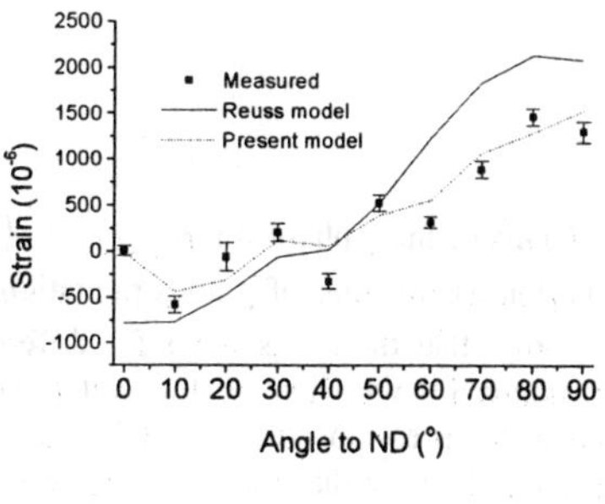

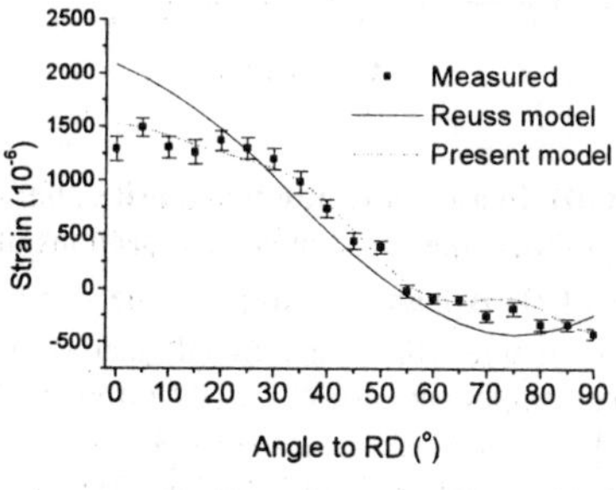

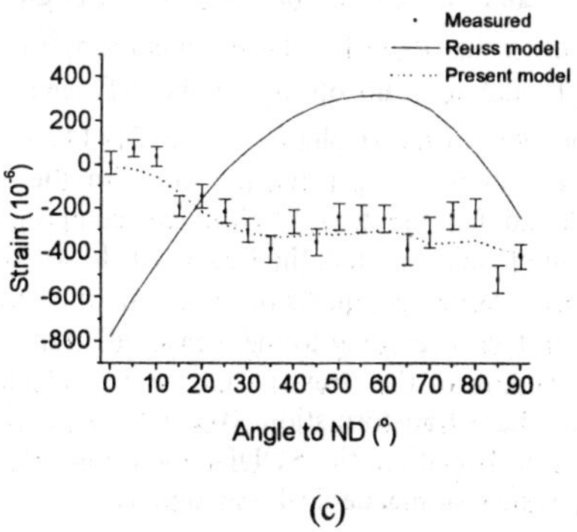

Fig. 4 The strain variation of the α phase for {211} diffraction peaks (a) in the plane of ND and RD, (b) in the plane of RD and TD, (c) in the plane of ND and TD.

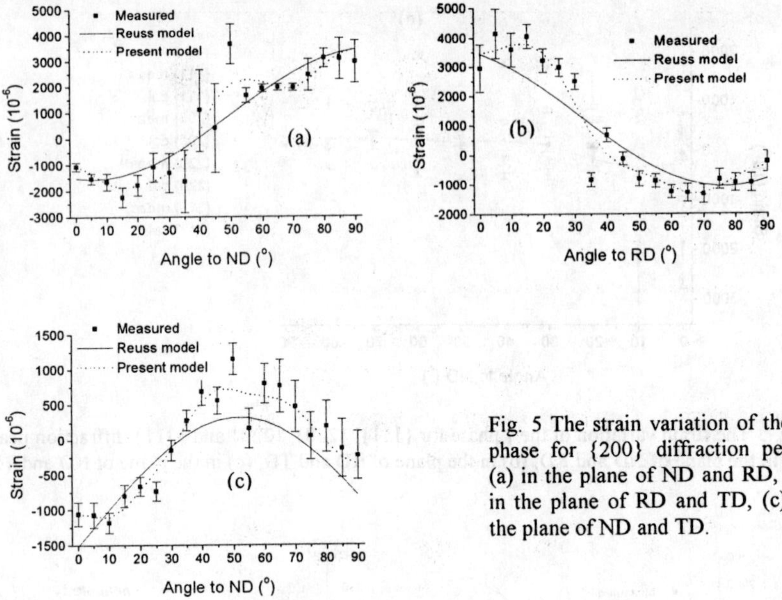

Fig. 5 The strain variation of the α phase for {200} diffraction peaks (a) in the plane of ND and RD, (b) in the plane of RD and TD, (c) in the plane of ND and TD.

3.3 SODF in austenite and martensite phases

Fig. 6 shows the constant φ cross-sections of the SODFs of the γ phase for $\sigma_{11}(\vec{g})$, $\sigma_{22}(\vec{g})$ and $\sigma_{33}(\vec{g})$. A high anisotropy of the stress distribution as function of grain orientation is seen in all three directions. SODF analysis further shows that the stress states for different texture components are obviously different. For example, for the Brass texture component ({110}<211>), there is a tensile stress in ND and a compression stress in RD and TD. Comparisons between the ODF and SODFs in the γ phase show that there is a correlation between the crystal anisotropy and residual stress anisotropy.

The SODFs of the α phase for $\sigma_{11}(\vec{g})$, $\sigma_{22}(\vec{g})$ and $\sigma_{33}(\vec{g})$ can be observed through the φ=45° cross-sections (shown in Fig. 7). It is shown that there is a larger anisotropy of the stress distribution in the RD direction ($\sigma_{11}(\vec{g})$) and less anisotropy in the ND and TD directions. For the two important texture components in the α phase, i.e. {332}<113> and {112}<131>, the crystals in those components sustain a larger tensile stress in the RD direction and relatively small stresses in the ND and TD directions. As the two components are usually referred as the transformed Brass components from fcc, the larger tensile stress of the α phase in the RD direction corresponds to a larger compression stress of the Brass component of the γ phase in the same direction. In fact, according to the measured strain and stress anisotropy, we may have a better understanding of the stress-based variant selection model to predict the transformed textures during phase transformation. Beyond the possible mechanisms of variant selections during phase transformation, the SODFs could also reveal the intrinsic nature of some other stress-related physical or mechanical phenomena.

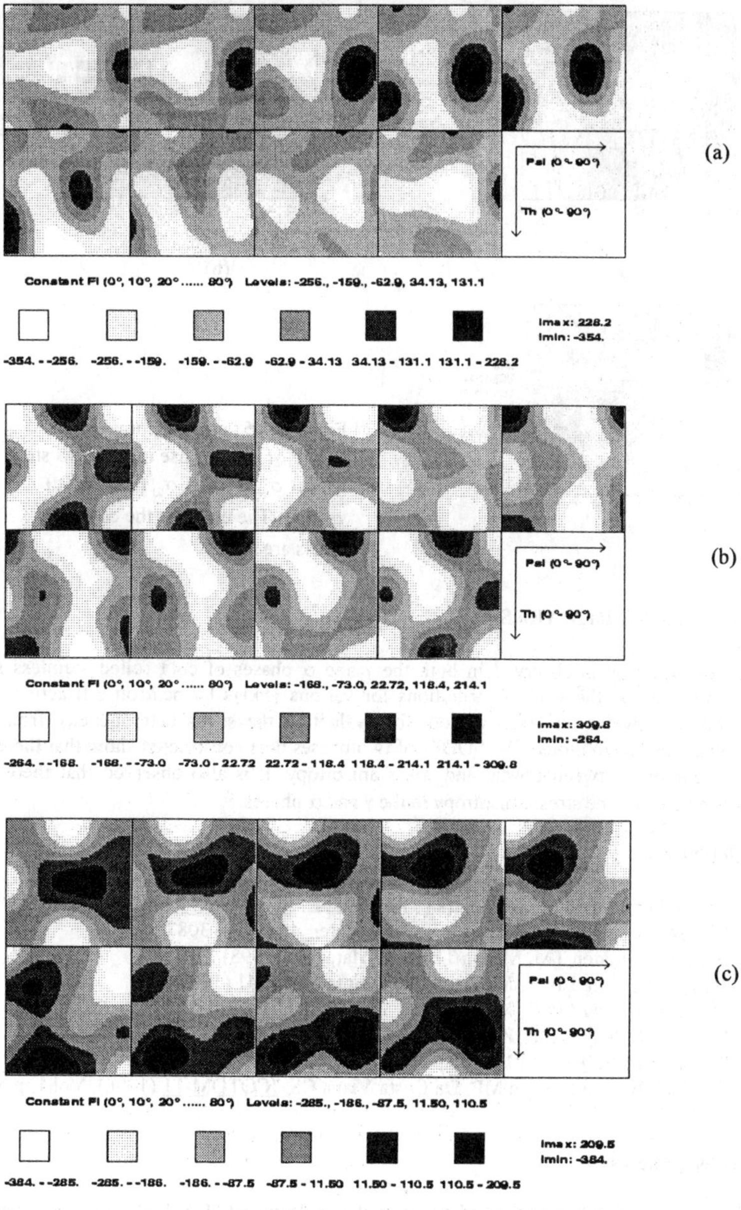

Fig. 6 SODF of the austenite phase in stainless steel for (a) $\sigma_{11}(\vec{g})$, (b) $\sigma_{22}(\vec{g})$ and (c) $\sigma_{33}(\vec{g})$. The units for the contour levels are MPa.

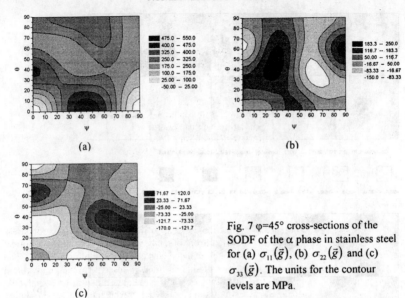

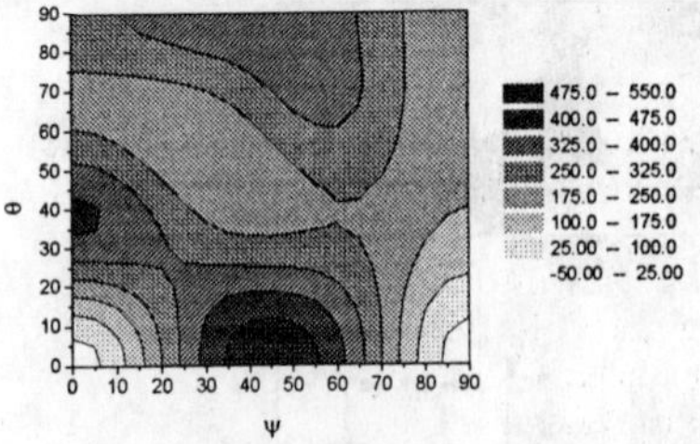

(a)

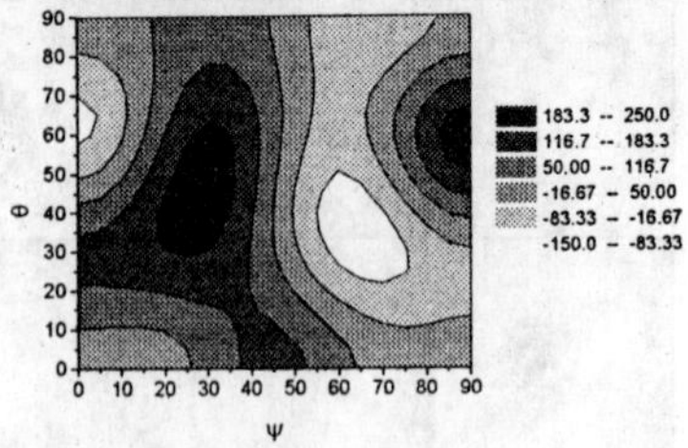

(b)

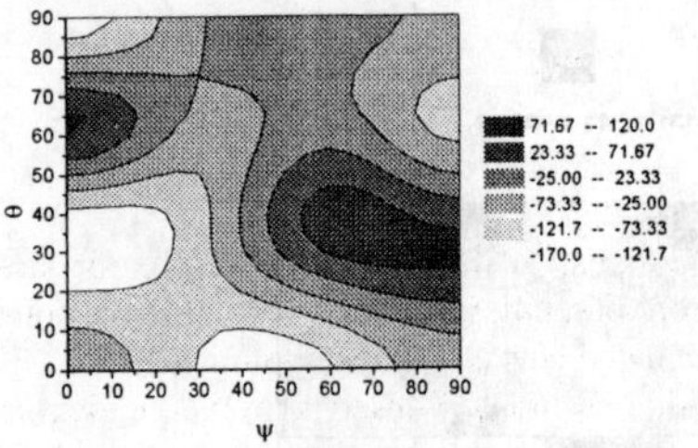

(c)

Fig. 7 φ=45° cross-sections of the SODF of the α phase in stainless steel for (a) $\sigma_{11}(\vec{g})$, (b) $\sigma_{22}(\vec{g})$ and (c) $\sigma_{33}(\vec{g})$. The units for the contour levels are MPa.

5. CONCLUDING REMARKS

CODS heterogeneity is observed in both the γ and α phases of cold rolled stainless steel through mapping of the strain distributions for various {hkl}s by neutron diffraction. The SHA method provides an effective tool for evaluating the stress heterogeneity from the measured strain distributions. The SODFs of two phases thus constructed show that there are some correlations between crystal and stress anisotropy. It is also observed that there is a correlation between the stress anisotropy in the γ and α phases.

REFERENCES

1. van Acker K, Root J, van Houtte P, Aernoudt E, Acta Mater. 44 (1996) 4039
2. Clausen B, Lorentzen T, Leffers T, Acta Mater. 46 (1998) 3087
3. Pang JW, Holden TM, Mason TE, Acta Mater. 46 (1998) 1503
4. Wang YD, Peng Lin R, McGreevy R, Scripta Mater. 41 (1999) 995
5. Wang YD, Peng Lin R, McGreevy R, ICOTOM-12 (1999), Vol. 1, p. 553.
6. Wang YD, Peng Lin R, Zeng XH, McGreevy R, ECRS-5 (1999), in press.
7. Behnken H, ECRS-5 (1999), in press.
8. Jonas JJ, Butron-Guillen MP, Da Costa Viana CS, ICOTOM-11 (1996), Vol.1, p.575.

Acknowledgements

One of the authors (Y.D. Wang) thanks Prof. dr. ir. P. van Houtte with Ktholieke Universiteit Leuven for his encouragement and promotion on this work. The authors are also grateful to Mr B. Trostell at Uppsala University for technical assistance with the neutron diffraction measurements.

Precise Determination of Sample Position with a Radial Collimator and/or Slit(s) for Stress Measurements via Neutron Diffraction

D.-Q Wang[a], X.-L. Wang[b] and C. R. Hubbard[a]
[a]High Temperature Materials Lab
[b]Spallation Neutron Source
Oak Ridge National Lab
Oak Ridge, TN 37831-6064, USA

ABSTRACT

Precise determination of the specimen position relative to the sampling volume for stress measurements by neutron diffraction is difficult or sometimes impossible using only optical devices due to large sample dimensions or complicated shape of the sampling volume. The sampling volume is usually defined by slits or radial collimators inserted in the incident and diffracted beam paths. In order to understand the effect of a radial collimator, both analytical modeling and Monte Carlo numerical simulation tools were developed. These simulation tools allow for accurate prediction of the transmission function in the sampling volume and the effective size of the scattered neutron beam. Comparison of data taken from the simulation with a radial collimator versus a conventional slit in the diffracted beam shows that the sampling volume is better-defined using a radial collimator. Accurate knowledge of the shape and size of the sampling volume allowed development of a general mathematical model of the intensity variation with a sampling volume moving from outside to inside of a specimen for both transmission and reflection geometric set-ups. The attenuation by the sample also has been taken into account in this model. Experimental results agree well with the model calculations.

1. INTRODUCTION

In a typical neutron diffraction experiment, the sampling volume is defined by slits inserted in the incident and diffracted beam paths near the specimen. In studies where the stresses change rapidly as a function of position, a small sampling volume and high position precision are required to reach the spatial resolution needed to resolve the stress gradients. It is difficult or sometimes impossible to precisely determine specimen surface position using only theodolites and telescopes, due to large sample dimensions or complicated diffractometer layouts. The location of the sample surface with respect to the beam centerline can be obtained by observing the increase in intensity as the sampling volume enters the sample. This method has been used by a number of researchers for years (1-3). It involves making a relatively quick scan, moving the sampling volume from a point off the surface to a point inside the sample. One then obtains a set of points of the integrated intensity versus position. A mathematical model then is fitted to the data to locate the sample surface position. The fitting models for the sampling volume with a rhombic prism and a rectangular section have been developed (2-3). However, a more generic section shape of the sampling volume is a parallelogram, which is considered in this paper for both transmission and reflection set-ups. The model calculations were validated with experiment results.

2. COMPARISON OF THE SAMPLING AREA DEFINED BY A RADIAL COLLIMATOR AND A SLIT

The sampling volume in stress and texture measurements is defined using either a radial collimator or a slit. An ideal sampling volume is such that the diffracted neutrons from the volume can be uniformly "seen" by detectors and nothing can be detected outside of the volume. In reality, a transmission function, which describes the spatial distribution of neutron scattering from an irradiated volume, can characterize the sampling volume.

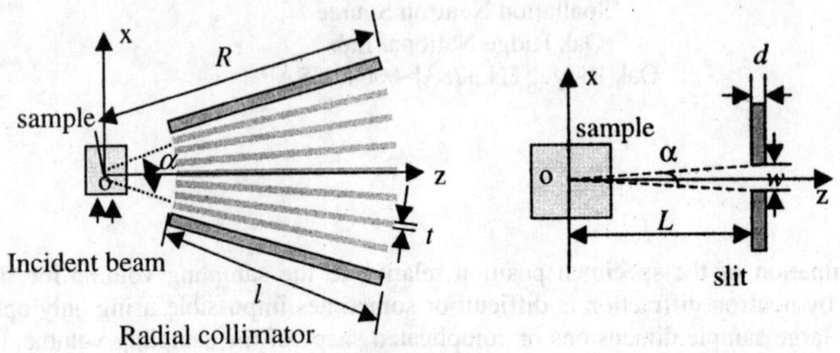

Fig.1 Schematic drawing of a radial collimator (left) and a slit (right) used in a diffracted beam.

To compare the transmission function defined by a radial collimator and a slit, the following assumptions have been made:

- Only two-dimensional modeling in the scattering plane was considered.
- The slit width was selected to be equal to the full-width-at-half-maximum (FWHM) of the transmission function of the radial collimator, e.g. 1.4 mm.
- A uniform and parallel incident beam is assumed.

The detailed computer model can be found in reference (4-5). A schematic drawing of a radial collimator and a slit is shown in Fig.1. The parameters used for the simulation are listed in Table 1. The comparison of the transmission functions defined by the slit and the radial collimator is shown in Fig. 2.

Table 1. Parameters of the radial collimator and slit used in the simulation.

Radial collimator	Radius R (mm)	Length l (mm)	Number of channels N	Acceptance angle α (degree)	Blade thickness t (mm)
	750	600	40	17.5	0.16
Slit	Width, w (mm)		Thickness, d (mm)	Distance from sample, L (mm)	
	1.4		1	20	

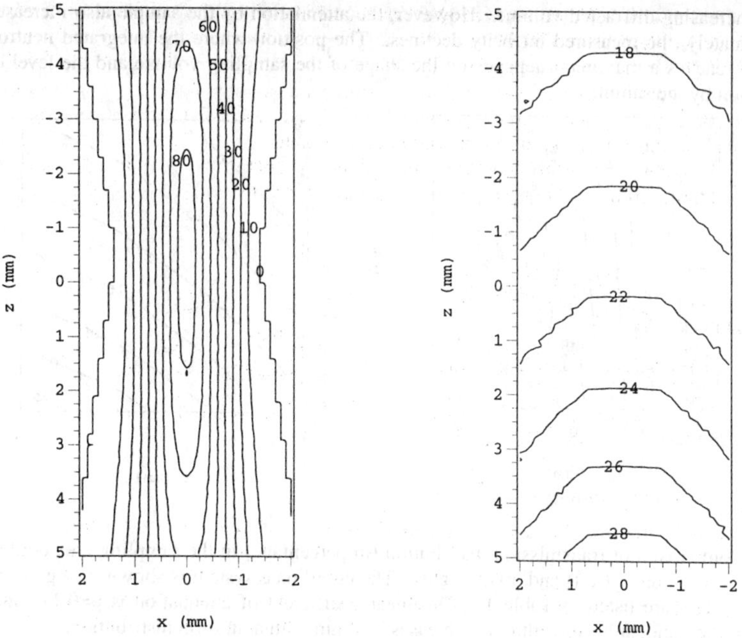

Fig. 2 Comparison of the transmission distribution (in percentage) in the sampling area which is defined by a radial collimator (left) and a slit (right). The coordinate system can be found in Fig. 1 and the parameters for the simulation are listed in Table 1.

It can be seen from Fig. 2 that transmission through the slit is much lower than that through the radial collimator due to the fact that the acceptance angle of the slit for detection is much smaller. To have the same acceptance angle as the radial collimator (17.5°), the slit has to be placed at 4.5 mm from the center of sampling area, which usually is at the rotation center of the positioner. Using a radial collimator, the sampling area is also better defined (Fig. 2). If the linear coefficient of attenuation for iron, $\mu=0.11\ mm^{-1}$ were assumed, the simulation shows that the center of gravity shifts towards the radial collimator or slit, as shown in Fig. 3. However, the shift of the center of gravity towards the neutron source in the z-direction is much smaller when using a radial collimator due to tighter constraints.

3. MODEL FOR CALCULATION OF INTENSITY VARIATION

The integrated neutron intensity during surface scanning is governed by two principal factors, absorption and scattering, though other phenomenon, such as multiple scattering, primary extinction, micro-absorption and texture (6) can also be involved in some circumstances. The integrated neutron intensity initially increases as the sampling volume enters the sample due to increasing diffracted volume. However, the attenuation by the sample also increases and ultimately, the measured intensity declines. The position where the integrated neutron intensity reaches a maximum depends on the shape of the sampling volume and the level of attenuation by the sample.

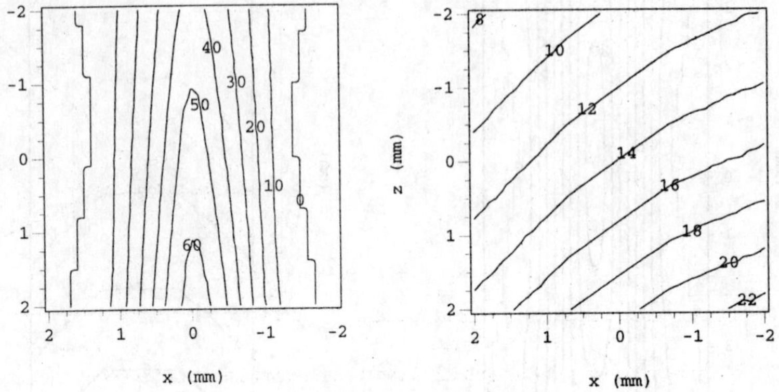

Fig. 3 Comparison of transmission distribution (in percentage) in the sampling area defined by a radial collimator (left) and a slit (right). The coordinate system is shown in Fig. 1 and the parameters are listed in Table 1. The linear coefficient of attenuation is μ=0.11 mm^{-1}. Note that the incident beam width in both cases is 4 mm with a uniform distribution.

If the diffracted volume and the attenuation are taken into account, the diffracted integrated intensity is given by (2):

$$I(L) = \int_{V_s} I_0(x, y, z)\exp(-\sigma l(x, y, z))dV \tag{1}$$

where x, y, z are the coordinates of the sample volume; I_0 is the incident neutron intensity; σ is the total attenuation coefficient; and l, the path length in the sample, is a function of the sampling volume size and position. The integration is performed over the diffracted volume, V_s.

Two typical geometric setups, reflection and transmission, in stress measurement will be discussed below. Both cases are simplified by considering two-dimensional scans in the horizontal scattering plane and that the moving direction of the specimen is perpendicular to the sample surface.

3.1 Reflection Set-up

This setup is for measurements of the strain component perpendicular to the sample surface, as shown in Fig. 4. Generally, the sampling volume enters the specimen from one side and exits from the other side. The calculation of the integrated intensity is divided into nine regions. From Fig. 4, one can obtain $p = \dfrac{h+f}{4\cos\theta}, q = \dfrac{h-f}{4\cos\theta}, h \geq f\ (x \leq x_0 - p)$, where h is the width of the diffracted beam; f is the width of the incident beam; 2θ is the diffraction angle; and x_0 is the position of the center of the sampling volume.

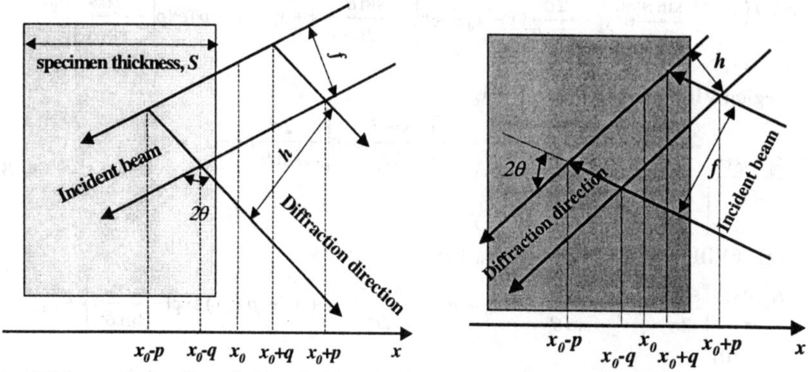

Fig. 4 Schematic drawing of the reflection (left) and transmission (right) geometric set-ups.

In region I, where the sampling volume is outside of the sample, only the background, I_b, is detected.

$$I = I_b \quad (2)$$

In region II, $x_0 - p \le x \le x_0 - q$

$$I = \frac{I_0 \cos\theta}{\sigma}(x - x_0 + p) - \frac{I_0 \cos\theta \sin\theta}{2\sigma^2}\left\{1 - \exp\left[-\frac{2\sigma}{\sin\theta}(x - x_0 + p)\right]\right\} + I_b \quad (3)$$

For region III, $x_0 - q \le x \le x_0 + q\ (h \ge f)$

$$I = \frac{I_0 \cos\theta}{\sigma}\left\{\frac{\sin\theta}{2\sigma}\exp\left[-\frac{2\sigma}{\sin\theta}(x - x_0 + p)\right] - \frac{\sin\theta}{2\sigma}\exp\left[-\frac{2\sigma}{\sin\theta}(x - x_0 + q)\right] + p - q\right\} + I_b$$

(4)

In region IV $x_0 + q \le x \le x_0 + p$

$$I = \frac{I_0 \cos\theta}{\sigma}\left\{\begin{array}{l}\frac{\sin\theta}{2\sigma}\exp\left[-\frac{2\sigma}{\sin\theta}(x - x_0 + p)\right] - \frac{\sin\theta}{2\sigma}\exp\left[-\frac{2\sigma}{\sin\theta}(x - x_0 + q)\right] \\ -\frac{\sin\theta}{2\sigma}\exp\left[-\frac{2\sigma}{\sin\theta}(x - x_0 - q)\right] + x_0 + p - x + \frac{\sin\theta}{2\sigma}\end{array}\right\} + I_b \quad (5)$$

In region V, $x_0 + p \le x \le S + x_0 - p$

$$I = \frac{I_0 \sin\theta\cos\theta}{2\sigma^2}\left\{\begin{array}{l}\exp\left[-\frac{2\sigma}{\sin\theta}(x - x_0 + p)\right] - \exp\left[-\frac{2\sigma}{\sin\theta}(x - x_0 + q)\right] \\ +\exp\left[-\frac{2\sigma}{\sin\theta}(x - x_0 - p)\right] - \exp\left[-\frac{2\sigma}{\sin\theta}(x - x_0 - q)\right]\end{array}\right\} + I_b \quad (6)$$

In region VI, $S - p + x_0 \le x \le S + x_0 - q$

$$I=\frac{I_0\cos\theta}{\sigma}\left\{\begin{array}{l}\frac{\sin\theta}{2\sigma}\exp\left[-\frac{2\sigma}{\sin\theta}(x-x_0-p)\right]-\frac{\sin\theta}{2\sigma}\exp\left[-\frac{2\sigma}{\sin\theta}(x-x_0+q)\right]\\-\frac{\sin\theta}{2\sigma}\exp\left[-\frac{2\sigma}{\sin\theta}(x-x_0-q)\right]+(\frac{\sin\theta}{2\sigma}+s+x_0-x-p)\exp\left[-\frac{2\sigma S}{\sin\theta}\right]\end{array}\right\}+I_b$$

(7)

For region VII, $S+x_0-q\le x\le S+x_0+q$

$$I=\frac{I_0\cos\theta}{\sigma}\left\{\begin{array}{l}\frac{\sin\theta}{2\sigma}\exp\left[-\frac{2\sigma}{\sin\theta}(x-x_0-p)\right]-\frac{\sin\theta}{2\sigma}\exp\left[-\frac{2\sigma}{\sin\theta}(x-x_0-q)\right]\\-(p-q)\exp(-\frac{2\sigma S}{\sin\theta})\end{array}\right\}+I_b \quad (8)$$

In region VIII, $S+x_0+q\le x\le S+x_0+p$

$$I=\frac{I_0\cos\theta}{\sigma}\left\{\frac{\sin\theta}{2\sigma}\exp\left[-\frac{2\sigma}{\sin\theta}(x-x_0-p)\right]-(\frac{\sin\theta}{2\sigma}+s+x_0+p-x)\exp(-\frac{2\sigma S}{\sin\theta})\right\}+I_b$$

(10)

In region IX, $S+x_0+p\le x$, where the sampling volume moves outside of the back surface of the sample, again only the background is detected.

$$I=I_b \quad (11)$$

3.2 Transmission Set-up

This set-up is particularly used for in-plane strain measurements, as shown in Fig. 4. The change of the diffraction intensity only comes from variation of the diffracted volume since the path length, l, in the sample is always the same when the sampling volume moves through the sample surface along the direction perpendicular to the sample surface. Five regions are considered in the calculation.

From Fig. 4, one can obtain $p=\frac{h+f}{4\sin\theta}, q=\frac{h-f}{4\sin\theta}, h\ge f$

In region I, $x\le x_0-p$,

$$I=I_b \quad (12)$$

In region II, $x_0-p\le x\le x_0-q$,

$$I=I_0 tg\theta[x-(x_0-p)]^2+I_b \quad (13)$$

In region III, $x_0-q\le x\le x_0+q$,

$$I=I_0\left[(p-q)^2 tg\theta+\frac{f}{\cos\theta}(x-x_0+q)\right]+I_b \quad (14)$$

In region IV, $x_0+q\le x\le x_0+p$,

$$I=I_0\left\{tg\theta\left[2(p-q)^2-(x_0+p-x)^2\right]+\frac{2fq}{\cos\theta}\right\}+I_b \quad (15)$$

In region V, $x_0+p\le x$

$$I=I_0[2tg\theta(p-q)^2+\frac{2fq}{\cos\theta}]+I_b \quad (16)$$

4. VALIDATION OF THE CALCULATION MODELS

4.1 Comparison with more limited models

The previous models for the sampling volume with a rhombic prism and a rectangular section (2-3) can be derived from this calculation. If h = f, the section of the sampling volume possesses a rhombic prism shape, $p = \frac{h}{2\cos\theta}, q = 0$. Equations (2-12) become the equations in reference (2) except that the scan for the backside surface of the specimen in the reflection geometry was ignored. If θ = 45°, the section of the sampling volume is a rectangle, $p = \frac{h+f}{2\sqrt{2}}, q = \frac{h-f}{2\sqrt{2}}, h \geq f$. Equations (2-12) are simplified to the cases in reference (3).

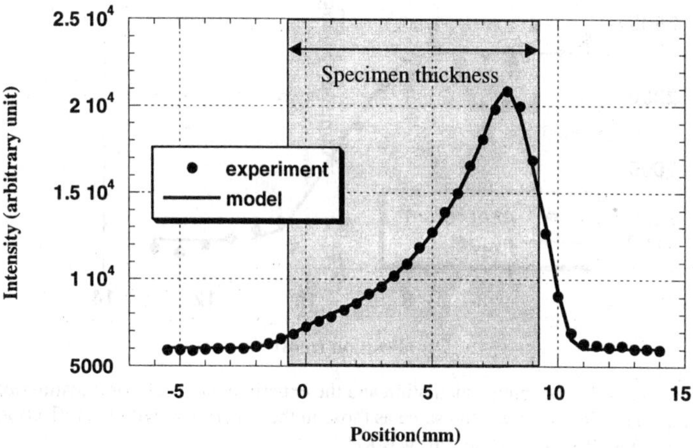

Fig. 5 Comparison of the model calculation and the experimental result. The incident slit size was 1 mm wide and 4 mm high. The width of the receiving slit was 2.5 mm. The diffraction angle (2θ) was 105°. The measurement errors of the intensity are smaller than the black spot symbols.

4.2 Comparison with experimental results

Experiments were carried out at HB2 of HFIR, Oak Ridge National Lab. A detector array consisting of seven ORDELA position-sensitive detectors distributed along a vertical arc at equal distance to the same position was used for data acquisition. The angular acceptance in the scattering plane for each detector is approximately six degrees in 2θ. The detectors are separated vertically by seven degrees with the central detector situated in the horizontal scattering plane. The integrated intensity used was the sum of the intensities from the seven detectors. A rectangular stainless steel plate (10x50x50 mm^3) was used for the validation. The incident slit size was 1 mm wide and 4 mm high, located 50 mm from the rotation center of the positioner. In order to test the model, large differences of the widths between the incident and receiving slit had to be made. Thus the receiving slit was 2.5 mm wide, placed at 40 mm away from the rotation center of the positioner. The wavelength of the incident neutron beam was 1.65 Å. For the reflection geometric setup, the (222) reflection of stainless steel was used at 105° (2θ). The results of the measurement are shown in Fig. 5. The fitting method was a standard least-square fitting routine (7). As can be seen, the experiment data are fitted well with the model. The measurement errors for the intensity were small, as a relatively long time was used for every point (1.6 minutes per step). The measured thickness of the stainless steel plate determined by the fitting method, *S*, was 9.93 mm, which is 0.07 mm smaller than the thickness measured by a caliper.

For the transmission setup, the (220) reflection was used and the diffraction angle (2θ) is at 81°. Fig. 6 shows the comparison of the experimental data with the model calculation. A good agreement was also observed, though the measurement errors were larger than those in Fig. 5 due to faster scan (0.2 minutes per step).

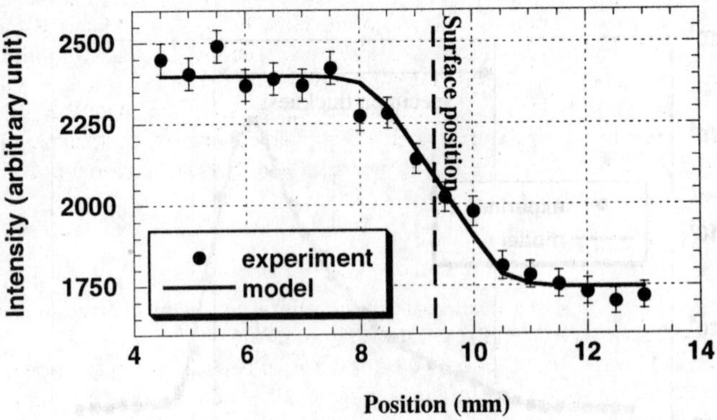

Fig. 6 Comparison of the modeling calculation and the experimental result for transmission geometric setup. The slit sizes were the same as those in the experiment with the reflection geometry setup. The diffraction angle (2θ) was 81°.

An assumption was made in the model that the spatial distribution of the intensity of both the incident and diffracted beams are "square pulses", e.g. the intensity is distributed constantly within the sampling volume and zero outside if the attenuation is ignored. This is not quite correct in reality because of the beam divergence. The incident beam divergence is largely determined by the characteristics of the monochromator/moderator and optical devices in the incident beam path (8-10) whilst the optical devices in the diffracted beam path and attenuation by the sample influence the diffracted beam divergence (4). The non-square-pulse distribution of beam intensity was replaced by the effective beam width, the full-width-at-half-maximum (FWHM) of the intensity (3) in our calculation. The size of the effective beam width relies on both the beam divergence and the distance between the center of the sampling volume and the slit. For this reason the incident and receiving slit width were taken as variables and the fitted widths are 1.3 and 3.0 mm, respectively, for both the reflection and transmission setup.

5. Conclusions

The transmission function of the sampling area defined by a radial collimator was compared with that defined by a slit using Monte Carlo simulation. It shows that using a radial collimator defines the sampling volume better and also has a larger acceptance angle for detection. A generic model calculation of the intensity variation with a sampling volume moving from off to inside a sample surface for both reflection and transmission setups was developed for use in stress measurement with neutron diffraction. Experiments for scans performed on a stainless steel plate at two different scattering angles show that the model calculation agrees well with the experiment result. The position of a sample surface was precisely determined using this model.

Acknowledgement

Research sponsored by the Assistant Secretary for Energy Efficiency and Renewable Energy, Office of Transportation Technologies, as part of the High Temperature Materials Laboratory User Program, Oak Ridge National Laboratory, managed by Lockheed Martin Energy Research Corp. for the U.S. Department of Energy under contract number DE-AC05-96OR22464. We also thank Dr Ru Lin Peng to provide the specimen. DQW was supported in part by an appointment to the Oak Ridge National Laboratory Postdoctoral Research Associates Program administrated jointly by the Oak Ridge National Laboratory and the Oak Ridge Institute for Science and Education.

Reference

1 Ezeilo A.N., "Residual stress determinations by neutron and X-ray diffraction methods", *Ph.D. thesis*, Imperial College, University of London, 1992

2 Brand P.C. and Prask H.J., “New methods for the alignment of instrumentation for residual-stress measurements by means of neutron diffraction”, *J. Appl. Cryst.* 27(1994)164

3 Wang D. Q., and Edwards L., “Precise determination of specimen surface position during sub-surface strain scanning by neutron diffraction”, Proc. of Fourth European Conference on Residual Stresses, p135-143, France 1996

4 Wang, D.-Q, Wang, X.-L., Robertson, J.L. and Hubbard, C.R., "Modelling radial collimator for use in stress and texture measurements with neutron diffraction", accepted by *J. Appl. Cryst*

5 Wang, D.-Q, Wang X.-L, Robertson, J. L, Hubbard, C. R, "RADFOCUS: a program for defining the size of diffracted beam with a radial collimator in stress and texture measurements by neutron diffraction", ORNL, TM1999/249

6 Bacon G .E., *Neutron Diffraction* (Clarendon Press, Oxford, 1962), Chap. 2 & 3

7 Press W.H., Teukolsky S.A, Vetterling W.T. and Flannery B.P., (Cambridge University Press, 1992), *Numerical Recipes in C*, Chapter 15

8 Copley, J. R. D., "Transmission properties of short curved neutron guides: Part I. Acceptance diagram analysis and calculations", Nuclear Instruments & Methods in Phyiscs Research A 355(1995)469-477

9 Wang, D.-Q, R. L. Robertson, Wang, X.-L, Crow L., Lee W.-T. and C. R. Hubbard, "Comparison of converging, straight and diverging neutron guides using Monte Carlo Simulation", to be published.

10 Popovici, M. and Yelon, W. B., "A high performance focusing silicon monochromator", *J. Neutron Research*, Vol. 5, pp227-239

IMPROVED MONOCHROMATOR DESIGN FOR NEUTRON RESIDUAL STRESS MAPPING

A. D. Stoica*, M. Popovici,
Missouri University Research Reactor, Columbia, MO 65211, USA

S. Spooner and C. R. Hubbard
Oak Ridge National Laboratory, Oak Ridge, TN 37831-6064, USA

***On leave from National Institute for Materials Physics, Bucharest, Romania**

ABSTRACT

Bent perfect crystals have proven to be excellent monochromators for neutron stress mapping. A single reflection, bulk silicon unit with (331) asymmetric reflection in beam condensation setting is currently the basic strain mapping option at the HFIR HB-2 beamport. This monochromator allows focusing in both the horizontal and vertical planes and gives good resolution in a large range of detector angles around 90°. Recently, by using a multi-wafer silicon monochromator unit made of a packet of 14 commercial (100) thin wafers, neutron flux at the sample was increased by a factor of 3.

The multi-dimensional Gaussian approximation in conjunction with phase space diagram simulation was used to compute the resolution and intensity for potential HB-2 monochromators in diffraction arrangements. To compare monochromator configurations a figure-of-merit related to the accuracy in the peak position measurement was defined. Using this concept the optimal focusing monochromators for residual stress mapping at HB-2 beamport after upgrades were found. The adjustment of the horizontal curvature for various sample *d*-spacings leads to a gain in the figure of merit by 2 to 10 relative to the existing Si (331) configuration in a large range of sample *d*-spacings (0.090 – 0.165 nm).

1. INTRODUCTION

During the last decade the focusing effects in real and reciprocal space have been understood and special monochromator focusing devices have been built: vertically focusing mosaic monochromators [1], doubly focusing mosaic monochromators [2], and doubly bent perfect monochromators [3-6]. Doubly bent perfect crystal monochromators, with predictable performances, seem to be the most promising for a large number of applications.

With replacement of the Be reflector at High Flux Isotope Reactor (HFIR) and with changes in the beam tube configuration at the HB-2 beamport during year 2000, we have initiated a program to upgrade the neutron residual stress facility at HFIR. Upgrades include new goniometers, a detector array, and new monochromators. The system goals are to improve sample positioning accuracy, to tighten spatial resolution, to improve accuracy of strain measurements, and to decrease measurement time per point. This presentation will focus on the selection of monochromators for strain mapping at the new HB-2 of HFIR.

2. DOUBLY BENT MONOCHROMATORS FOR DIFFRACTION

Doubly bent perfect crystal monochromators in arrangements with small sampling volumes and position sensitive detectors (PSD) allow spatial focusing (incident beam converging vertically to sample) and focusing in scattering (diffracted beam converging horizontally to the PSD).

The vertical convergence gives increased intensity from the large angular divergence defined by the total height of the monochromator. The optimal vertical radius depends on the monochromator take-off angle, but its adjustment is not critical because the vertical convergence usually is not strong enough to eliminate the need of a slit for defining the height of incident beam.

The optimal horizontal radius satisfies the condition of focusing in scattering [4]:

$$L_{MS}/f_H^* = (2-1/a) \quad (1)$$

where L_{MS} is the distance from monochromator to sample, f_H^* is the monochromator second focal length $f_H^* = (R_H/2)\ \sin(\theta_M-\chi_M)$, R_H is the crystal radius of curvature in the plane of reflection (horizontal), θ_M is the Bragg angle of the monochromator (the take-off angle is $2\theta_M$), χ_M is the cutting angle, a is the dispersion parameter $a=-\tan\theta_S/\tan\theta_M$ with θ_S the scattering angle (the detector angle is $2\theta_S$). When the horizontal radius is optimal the instrumental linewidth is at minimum. If the radius is not optimal for the selected peak the line broadens. The larger the horizontal beam divergence, the more marked the broadening is.

The numerical values of the resolution and intensity are determined by the monochromator thickness, the elastic constants of the crystal material, and the type of bending. Relation (1) gives a neutron equivalent of the focusing at the detector in X-ray powder diffraction (the Bragg-Brentano parafocusing). Characteristic monochromatic X-rays come from a point source, are diffracted by an extended plate sample, and go to a single point of detection. Neutrons, with no point sources and no strictly monochromatic beams, come from an extended focusing crystal, go to a point sample and – under focusing conditions – go to a single point of detection.

A way to achieve good resolution in a broad range of detector angles is to reduce the horizontal beam divergence through beam condensation (Fankuchen cut, χ_M close to θ_M). This solution has become standard in focusing high-resolution neutron powder diffraction [7]. It is not mandatory, though, in strain measurements when only a small range of the diffraction pattern is covered. In this situation one can gain intensity by relaxing the horizontal divergence and still have good resolution by fulfilling the focusing condition (1) for the measured diffraction peak. Condition (1) can be met by choosing the reflecting plane, thus the neutron wavelength, and by adjusting the radius of horizontal curvature.

Silicon has high transparency for neutrons and is commercially available in big sizes. Early focusing monochromators were bent pneumatically (quasi-spherically) [8] or mechanically (cylindrically) [9]. The latest focusing monochromators of high performance have a more complex design that will be described in the following.

2.1 Bulk silicon crystal unit

One unit developed at the Missouri University Research Reactor (MURR) [5,6] is made of 9 vertically stacked Si blades, mechanically bent in the horizontal (diffraction) plane and quasi-bent by segmentation in the vertical plane. All blades originate from the same plate, which automatically ensures their correct relative orientation. The plate is cut obliquely from an 8" diameter [100] ingot with a suitable cutting angle and, usually, with the <011> zone axis vertical.

The horizontal radius R_H is given by a 4-point elastic bending device and is adjustable with a fine screw. A stepping motor can be mounted to remotely drive the adjusting screw. The vertical radius of curvature R_V is set by the profile of the bending posts (barrel shaped on the front, concave on the back) and is fixed. A difference from the usual 4-point bending method is that the mobile posts revolve around axes that are close to the center of the device.

This eliminates the non-uniformity of the horizontal curvature over the height of the stack due to the varying thickness of the posts.

The usable monochromator area is 16.5 mm wide and 15.2 mm high. The blade thickness is usually between 5 and 6 mm. The horizontal curvature is limited by the breaking limit (safe when $R_H > 10$ m) of the silicon blades. Because the second focal length f_H^* must be comparable to the distance between monochromator and sample, which usually is short (1-2 m), the asymmetric reflection with beam condensation (Fankuchen range) is used. The cutting angle is close to the Bragg angle so that the radius of curvature is considerably larger than the second focal distance, thus avoiding breakage.

2.2 Multi-wafer silicon unit

Breakage restricts the range of applications of bent bulk silicon monochromators. A way to overcome the restriction is to use monochromators made of packets of thin silicon wafers [10]. Such monochromators allow for a smaller bending radius, hence for a stronger spatial focusing, and give more flexibility in the design of focusing arrangements.

A prototype was made at MURR of a packet of 14 commercial wafers, each of 20 cm diameter and 0.7 mm thickness, originating from the same Si [100] ingot (see Fig.4 of [10]). The bending device was basically the same as for bulk silicon crystals. The overall crystal thickness was about 10 mm, but designs having thickness between 3 mm and 15 mm can be fabricated. The vertical curvature is obtained by fine segmentation (5 mm). The unit has an adjustable horizontal curvature with a minimum radius of about 1 m (the breaking limit for commercial wafers). In the vertical plane the radius is fixed by the profile of bending posts.

3. EXPERIMENTAL TEST

A bulk crystal unit with fixed vertical and horizontal radii of curvature is now the basic option for the strain mapping diffraction arrangement at the HB-2 beamport. A new multi-wafer unit prototype with manually adjustable horizontal curvature was tested with the aim to compare the performances of these two options and to investigate the double reflection monochromator configurations.

The neutron source of 9 cm diameter was seen from the monochromator at a distance of 7 m under a 0.7° acceptance angle. The beam cross section was 63.5×63.5 mm, limited by the beamport shutter at 4 m before the monochromator. The doubly bent monochromator units used in this study were: a) bulk crystal unit: Si (331) reflection, 0.56 cm thickness, χ_M=28.5°, R_H=10.7 m, R_V=1.55 m (by segmentation, height of a segment 1.5 cm); b) multi-wafer unit: Si (400) reflection, 1 cm overall thickness, χ_M= 0°, R_H=4.8 m, R_V=1.38 m (height of a segment 0.5 cm).

The distance between the monochromator and sample was L_{MS}=177 cm. A tapered collimator 62.5 cm long with an opening cross section of 19×48 mm at entrance and 8×27.5 mm at exit was placed after the monochromator. In the case of the bulk crystal unit with narrow beam due to Fankuchen condensation, this collimator delivered the beam to sample without losses. When the bulk crystal unit was replaced with the multi-wafer unit, to accept the larger angular divergence of the beam (~2°) the tapered collimator was replaced with a larger (44.5×63.4 mm) coarse collimator. The slit before sample had the standard dimensions of 2 mm wide × 10 mm tall. A slit after sample was optionally used. The distance from the goniometer center to PSD was 80 cm. The bulk crystal unit had only the (331) reflection available. The multi-wafer unit was made from commercial silicon wafers of [100] orientation with the <011> zone axis vertical. A number of Bragg reflections were thus available by simply rotating the unit around the vertical axis. With the Si (400) reflection from the multi-wafer unit ($2\theta_M$=84^0, λ=1.81 Å) the flux at sample was about 3 times higher than with the bulk crystal unit ($2\theta_M$=84^0, λ=1.76 Å). The increase was basically due to the larger horizontal divergence of the beam. A lower peak reflectivity and a lower neutron flux at the longer wavelength canceled the gain from a larger crystal thickness. Comparative results in diffraction are shown in Fig. 1.

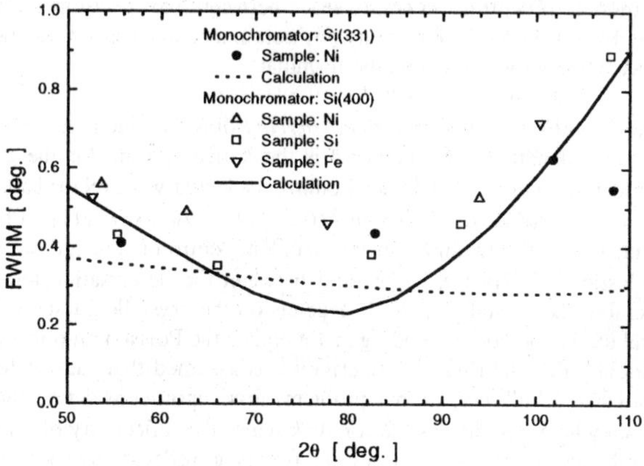

Fig. 1. Diffraction lines FWHM measured with bulk Si (331) and multi-wafer Si (400) monochromator. Angular dependence computed using phase-space acceptance diagram.

4. SIMULATION FOR THE NEW HB-2 CONFIGURATION

The neutron reflectivity of bent perfect crystals is well described by the lamellar approximation [11]. The local value of the reciprocal lattice vector is defined for every point of the crystal by taking into account the variation, due to elastic deformation, of the orientation and spacing of lattice planes. It is assumed that all neutrons along a given path are reflected with a constant probability when the Bragg condition is fulfilled.

On neglecting the intrinsic dynamic diffraction range (Darwin width, of a few seconds of arc) the diffraction by an elastically bent perfect crystal becomes deterministic. The point within the crystal where the reflection occurs is determined uniquely by the direction and the wave vector of the incoming neutron. The path of the reflected neutron is also determined uniquely. The crystal dimensions will thus fully define the domain in real and phase space where the Bragg reflection is possible.

A matrix method similar to that used in Gaussian lens optics has been worked out for neutron optics [8, 12]. The neutron state before reflection is specified by the spatial coordinates across the beam (y_i, z_i), the angular deviations (γ_i, δ_i) from the beam axis and the relative deviation of the wavevector $(\Delta k/k)$. The neutron state is actually defined in the five dimensions by the phase space vector $(y_i, k\gamma_i, \Delta k, z_i, k\delta_i)$. The neutron state after reflection is specified in the same way by changing the subscript $(i \rightarrow f)$. In the paraxial approximation of linear relations describing the Bragg reflection the neutron coordinates in the horizontal (diffraction) plane are not correlated with those in the vertical plane and the wave vector deviation has no influence on the vertical motion. One can thus consider separately the vectors $\boldsymbol{v}_i=(y_i, \gamma_i, \Delta k/k)$ and $\boldsymbol{v}_f=(y_f, \gamma_f, \Delta k/k)$ of the neutron state in the horizontal plane and the vectors $\boldsymbol{u}_i = (z_i, \delta_i)$ and $\boldsymbol{u}_f = (z_f, \delta_f)$ in the vertical plane.

The vectors $\boldsymbol{v}_i$ and $\boldsymbol{v}_f$ are related by the Bragg reflection matrix $\boldsymbol{S}_H$ and two restrictions mark the limits of phase space acceptance diagram (see [13], relations 2.6-2.7). In vertical plane the vectors $\boldsymbol{u}_i$ and $\boldsymbol{u}_f$ are related by the matrix $\boldsymbol{S}_V$ and a single restriction holds (see [13], relation 2.9 and following). These relations, together with the translation matrices describing the motion of neutrons in empty space between two spectrometer elements, allow the phase space diagram computation at any position in a neutron spectrometric arrangement.

The peak reflectivity is given by the formula:

$$P = 1 - exp(-Q|R_H/G|) \qquad (2)$$

where $Q = (\Delta k_o/D)tan\,\theta_M/k = (\Delta k_o/D)(d/\pi)(sin^2\theta_M/cos\,\theta_M)$ is the kinematic reflectivity per unit incident neutron pathlength in the crystal, d is the lattice spacing for the given reflection, $\Delta k_o/D$ is the reflectivity constant of Maier-Leibnitz (selected wavevector band per unit path) [14] and $G = (cos\chi_M/cos\theta_M)[1-(1+\kappa)sin(\theta_M+\chi_M)sin(\theta_M-\chi_M)]$ [11]. Physically G/R_H represents the change in Bragg angle per unit incident neutron pathlength in the crystal [11]. The material elasticity constant κ is the ratio between the deformation tensor components along and normal to the crystal surface. It depends on the crystallographic orientation of the crystal plate and on the method of bending and it equals the Poisson ratio in a particular case.

On modeling the multi-wafer reflectivity it is assumed that each wafer in the packet reflects neutrons like a bulk crystal, but problems arise upon considering the reflectivity of the packet of as a whole. On the θ scale (or $\Delta k/k$ scale) the reflectivity of a packet of wafers is generally comb-shaped. The width of a tooth (the band reflected by each wafer) is defined by the value of the elastic stress, but the distance between successive teeth is given by the geometry of bending only. The filling ratio is thus of concern. The reflectivity curve is approximated by a rectangle having the same overall width and a height equal to the average reflectivity over the many teeth. The filling ratio must be considered not solely on the θ or $\Delta k/k$ scales, but in the three-dimensional phase space. If the reflection is asymmetric, the overall phase space volumes before and after reflection will differ, leading to different phase space filling ratios. When the teeth superimpose, corrections must be introduced in the effective peak reflectivity to account for possible losses due to multiple reflections.

The elements of the Bragg reflection matrix $\boldsymbol{S}_H$ are different from those corresponding to the bulk crystal and the determinant of $\boldsymbol{S}_H$ is $cos(\theta_M-\chi_M)/cos(\theta_M+\chi_M)$, different from unity if the reflection is asymmetric. The overall volumes in the phase space may thus be different before and after reflection. This is an apparent violation of the Liouville theorem introduced by the approximation used in modeling. We know that no violation occurs in reality as each individual wafer does obey the Liouville theorem. To correct for this situation, a factor is introduced in the average peak reflectivity, which comes to depend on whether the phase space volume considered on its averaging is before or after reflection. Approximate formulae for peak reflectivity accounting for these considerations have been given [13].

The numerical technique to calculate the borders of the phase space diagram is similar to that described earlier [15]. For a fixed position at sample the borders of acceptance diagram in the $(\gamma_S, \Delta k/k)$ plane are calculated by using polar coordinates and by considering all limitations imposed by slits and crystals on vector modulus defined in this plane. Knowing the borders of the phase space diagram the neutron flux at sample can be estimated by numerical integration, peak reflectivity of the crystals accounted for. The diffraction line widths were computed in Gaussian approximation using the variances of the phase space diagram and the contribution of angular collimation after sample.

To search for an optimal monochromator one needs to define an appropriate parameter of the quality. A monochromator can be described by the phase space volume selected from the neutron source and the neutron transport efficiency from source to sample, but the shape of the selected phase space volume is also important. Since the goal in strain measurements is to determine *d*-spacing changes very precisely, a monochromator figure of merit must be related to the accuracy in the peak position measurement. The figure of merit will be in inverse proportion to the data collection time needed to reach a certain level of accuracy. Considering the instrumental contribution to the diffraction line standard deviation σ_R and the microstrain contribution σ_{ms} the figure of merit can be defined as [13]:

$$FM = \tan\theta_S \Phi_S \left(\sigma_{ms}^2 + \frac{\cot^2\theta_S}{4}\sigma_R^2 \right)^{-1} \quad (3)$$

where Φ_S is the neutron flux at sample. This expression will be used in the following to compare the monochromator performances at different wavelengths.

5. OPTIMAL CONFIGURATIONS AND CONCLUSIONS

The beam dedicated to stress mapping measurements is to be deflected 2° from the HB-2 beam line axis. At higher deflection angles the neutron beam would hit structural parts of the reactor wall. The monochromator will be located 768-788 cm from the end of the neutron beam pipe near the reactor core. A natural beam divergence of about 1° in the horizontal and vertical plane results from this geometry.

The beam diffracted from the monochromator will penetrate the shielding through an experiment shutter. The minimum distance between the monochromator and the goniometer center is 212 cm. The current experiment shutter design prescribes an opening of 7.6 cm wide and 12.7 cm high.

Many options for single reflection monochromators have been compared, including arrangements with transmission geometry and with strong asymmetric reflection geometry in beam condensation (Fankuchen range) or beam extension (inverse Fankuchen). The best solution for multiple choice of wavelengths was found to be a multi-wafer unit with commercial Si [100] orientation and with the <011> zone axis vertical. This unit provides the Si (400) symmetric reflection and the asymmetric reflections Si (311) and Si (511). At fixed take-off angle the wavelength is changed by simply rotating the monochromator to set another reflection. On changing the wavelength the horizontal curvature is adjusted by remote control. The vertical curvature may be fixed at a value representing a compromise for all wavelengths.

Varying the take-off angle was considered with the aim to adjust to 90° the detector angle for given reflections from various samples. It was found that such a variation would give only a marginal gain in the figure of merit while greatly complicating the beam extraction and dramatically increasing the cost to implement the solution. The take-off angle was therefore fixed at 88°.

The optimal radii of curvature and the corresponding performances of the monochromator are given in Table 1. At strong asymmetries with beam condensation (Fankuchen setting) bulk monochromators are better than multi-wafer monochromators. For symmetric or nearly symmetric reflection a multi-wafer monochromator has a larger angular acceptance ($\Delta\gamma$) and, in spite of the lower peak reflectivity (P_a), higher neutron flux at the sample position.

Table 1

Type	χ [deg.]	R_H [m]	R_V [m]	Δγ [°]	Δδ [°]	P_a	Flux relative to bulk (331)	FWHM at $2\theta_s$=90° [deg.]
(311)bulk	25.3	11.4	1.6	0.9	3.6	0.98	0.6	0.21
(311)multi	25.3	11	1.4-1.8	0.9	3.6	0.40	0.6	0.27
(400)multi	0	5.2-5.5	1.5-2.0	2.0	3.6	0.64	2.7	0.24
(331)bulk*	28.5	10.7	1.55	0.6	2.5	0.69	1	0.30
(331)bulk	28.5	13.4-13.8	1.3-1.7	0.7	3.6	0.86	1	0.21
(511)multi	15.8	7.7-7.8	1.5-2.0	1.4	3.6	0.35	2.1	0.26

* Existing Si (331) monochromator in the present HB-2 design.

To optimize the figure of merit of multi-wafer monochromators we looked for wafer orientations away from the [100], [111] and [110] directions. For the reflections (400), (511) and (311) the best choice of orientation is a moderate offset (10°-15°) of the normal to the surface from the [100] direction toward the [011] direction. The best choice for (331) reflection is just the [110] wafer orientation. The optimal total thickness was also considered. The best average figure of merit is obtained at a total crystal thickness of about 1.25 cm (18 wafers). An average increase of 50% in figure of merit is obtained in comparison with the configurations considered in Table 1 for the (400), (311) and (511) reflections and more than 100% increase for (331).

In Table 1 the horizontal curvature was set to at the value corresponding to minimal linewidths at $2\theta_S$ = 90°. By making the curvature variable to optimize the resolution at every scattering angle one can further improve the figure of merit. The figures of merit at variable radius are plotted in fig. 2 for three values of sample microstrain (0, 0.002, 0.004), the primary factor in the sample contribution to line broadening. The figure of merit of the present Si (331) bulk crystal unit on measuring the (211) line of α-iron without microstrain was taken as reference (figure of merit = 1). The *d*-spacing scale is independent of the choice of the wavelength. Different monochromators can thus be compared directly. The *d*-spacings frequently used in stress measurements on various materials are indicated.

Figures of merit increase at high detector angle (small d_S) because the optimal radii decrease there. Consequently, not only the linewidth improves on going to the optimal radius, but also the intensity. By adjusting the horizontal curvature and by choosing the reflection that gives the largest detector angle (below $2\theta_S$ =110°) for each material, figure of merit gains from 2 to 10 can be reached at sample *d*-spacings from 0.09 to 0.165 nm.

A possible substitute for Si in multi-wafer units is Ge. Germanium has better kinematic reflectivity but stronger absorption for neutrons. Consequently the peak reflectivity formulae must be corrected for absorption. As the lattice parameters for Ge and Si are close, it is possible to compare directly the corresponding monochromator performance by an "intensity ratio" for the same reflection. At 1 cm total thickness the intensity ratio (Ge/Si) is 0.85 for strong reflections like (400) and (311), 1.24 for (331), and 1.57 for (511). The gains in the case of weak reflections correspond to the same monochromator dimensions. Available

Ge wafers have smaller diameters (5") than Si (8" to 12"). Use of Ge instead of Si thus makes sense for incident beams of small size that cannot take advantage of large silicon monochromators.

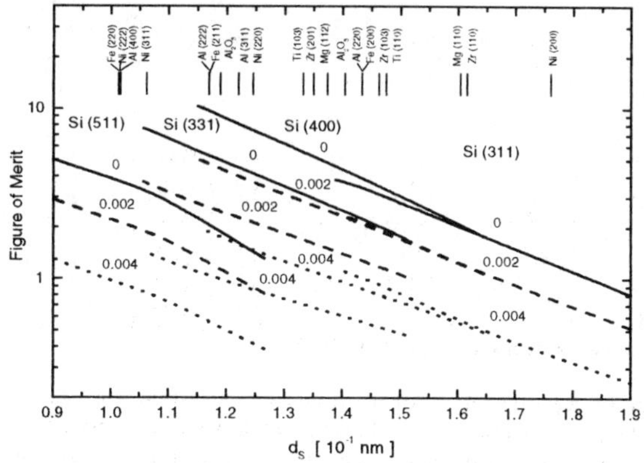

Fig. 2. Figure of Merit relative to existing Si (331) monochromator at d_S[Fe(211)] = 0.118 nm for different microstrain spreads ($\Delta d/d$ = 0, 0.002, 0.004), $2\theta_S$ = 70° – 110°. Horizontal curvature radius variable selected to minimize FWHM at $2\theta_S$ corresponding to each d_S.

REFERENCES

1. Axe, J. D., *et al.* (1994). *J. Neutron Research*, **2(3)**, 85-94.
2. Lechner, R. E., *et al.* (1994). *Nucl. Instrum. Meth.*, **A338**, 65-70.
3. Wagner, V., Mikula, P. & Lukas, P. (1994). *Nucl. Instrum. Meth.*, **A338**, 53-59.
4. Popovici, M., *et al.* (1994). *Nucl. Instr. Meth.*, **A 338**, 99-110.
5. Popovici, M. & Yelon, W. B. (1995). *J. Neutron Research*, **3**, 1-25.
6. Popovici, M. & Yelon, W. B. (1997). *J. Neutron Research*, **5**, 227-239.
7. Yelon, W. B., Berliner R. & Popovici, M. (1998). *Physica **B***, **241-243**, 237-239.
8. Popovici, M., Stoica, A. D. & Ionita, I. (1987). *J. Appl. Cryst.*, **20**, 90-101.
9. Mikula, P., *et al.* (1986). *J. Appl. Cryst.*, **19**, 324-330.
10. Stoica, A. D., *et al.* (2000). *J. Appl. Cryst.*, **33**, 147-155.
11. Stoica, A. D. & Popovici, M. (1989). *J. Appl. Cryst.*, **22**, 448-454.
12. Popovici, M. & Stoica, A. D. (1983). *J. Phys. E: Sci. Instr.*, **16**, 662-665.
13. Stoica, A. D., Popovici, M., Hubbard, C. R. & Spooner, S. (1999). *Report ORNL* **277**.
14. Maier-Leibnitz, H. (1972). Proc. Symp. *Neutron Inelastic Scattering*, Grenoble, 1972, Vienna: IAEA, p. 681-696.
15. Stoica, A. D., Popovici, M. & Yelon, W. B. (2000). *J. Appl. Cryst.*, **33**, 137-146.

Research sponsored by the Assistant Secretary for Energy Efficiency and Renewable Energy, Office of Transportation Technologies, as part of the High Temperature Materials Laboratory User Program, Oak Ridge National Laboratory, managed by Lockheed Martin Energy Research Corp. for the U.S. Department of Energy under contract number DE-AC05-96OR22464. The U.S. Department of Energy supported one of the authors (MP) in part also through grant DE-FG02-96ER45599.

SESSION 8B

INFLUENCE OF RAPID HEAT TREATMENTS ON RESIDUAL STRESSES AND CORROSION RESISTANCE OF A HIGH NITROGEN STEEL

C.Bohne*, A.Pyzalla*, M.Heitkemper**, A.Fischer**
* Hahn-Meitner-Institut, Glienicker Straße 100, D - 14109 Berlin, Germany
** Werkstofftechnik, Universität Essen, D - 45117 Essen, Germany

ABSTRACT

By rapid heat treatments surface layers with properties that are distinctly different from those of the initial microstructure can be generated. In case of high nitrogen steels the rapid heat treatment aims at generating a hard surface with compressive residual stresses and high corrosion resistance. Here, the microstructure, the residual stresses and their influence on the corrosion behaviour of the rapid heat treated high nitrogen steel X30CrMoN15 1 and the reference steel X39CrMo17 1 are presented in dependence of the maximum heat treatment temperature and the heating rate.

1. INTRODUCTION

Martensitic high nitrogen steels (1,2,3) due to their high corrosion resistance are used e.g. for bearings and thread gears in aerospace applications. With respect to the fatigue and wear resistance of these steels a laser hardening of the surface is supposed to be advantageous (4).
In order to maintain the corrosion resistance of the high nitrogen steels while achieving a martensitic hardening and compressive residual stresses at the surface the process parameters of the laser heat treatment have to be optimised. Therefore, the influence of the maximum laser heat treatment temperature as well as the heating ratio on the microstructure (5,6), the corrosion resistance and the residual stress state of the high nitrogen steels are studied systematically.

2. EXPERIMENTAL DETAILS

2.1 MATERIAL AND INITIAL HEAT TREATMENT

The chemical composition of the high nitrogen steel X30CrMoN15 1 and the reference steel X39CrMo17 1 are shown in table 1. The composition of both steels is in agreement with the specifications of the manufacturers (7).

Table 1: Chemical composition X30CrMoN15 1 , X39CrMo17 1

	C	Si	Mn	Cr	Mo	Ni	V	Al	Ti	Cu	N
X30CrMoN15 1	0,30	0,64	0,49	15,56	1,02	0,16	0,42	0,003	0,003	0,03	0,42
X39CrMo17 1	0,43	0,39	0,38	16,21	1,10	0,43					

Initially, the high nitrogen steel X30CrMoN15 1 and the reference steel X39CrMo17 were hardened at 1200°C/30min./oil and 1050°C/30min./oil, respectively. Afterwards the X30CrMoN15 1 was deep-cooled in liquid nitrogen in order to reduce the amount of retained austenite. Then the X30CrMoN15 1 was tempered three times at 620°C/2h/air while the X39CrMo17 1 was tempered once at 700 °C/2h/air.

2.2 LASER HEAT TREATMENT

The laser hardening of the samples was performed at the Fraunhofer Institut für Lasertechnik, Aachen, Germany. For the laser treatments a 3kW Nd:YAG – Laser was employed using a beam cross section of 1.8mm x 14mm. In order to increase the hardening depth a gas atmosphere with a mix of 15 l/min. N_2 and 0.13 l/min. O_2 was used.

2.3 MICROSTRUCTURAL INVESTIGATION

For microstructural investigations by microhardness testing, metallography and optical as well as scanning electron microscopy at the University Essen and for scanning and transmission electron microscopy at the HMI Berlin slices were retained from the centre of the samples. The retained austenite content (8) of the samples as well as the splitting up of the 200 reflection into its h00/0h0/00h parts in case of martensite and the dislocation densities (9,10) were determined by X – ray diffraction at the HMI Berlin.

2.4 RESIDUAL STRESS ANALYSES

Residual stress analysis was carried through on an X-ray diffractometer in ψ - configuration at the HMI Berlin. The residual stresses were evaluated in longitudinal and transversal direction to the laser track using the $\sin^2\psi$ – method (11). Measurements were performed across the laser track, the heat affected zone and in the parent material. In order to determine the in-depth distribution of the longitudinal and transversal residual stresses in the near surface zone, a layer with a thickness of several μm was removed by electropolishing and subsequent residual stress analysis was performed.

2.5 CORROSIONS TESTS

The corrosion tests in form of potentiodynamic tests were performed in a corrosion cell at the HMI Berlin according to ASTM G5-87 (12). The temperature was ambient temperature and a scanning rate of 720 mV/h was chosen.

In case of the pitting corrosion tests the medium was artificial sea water (3% NaCl solution, pH = 7). The scanning range started from –100 mV vs. open circuit potential.

3. RESULTS

3.1 MICROSTRUCTURE

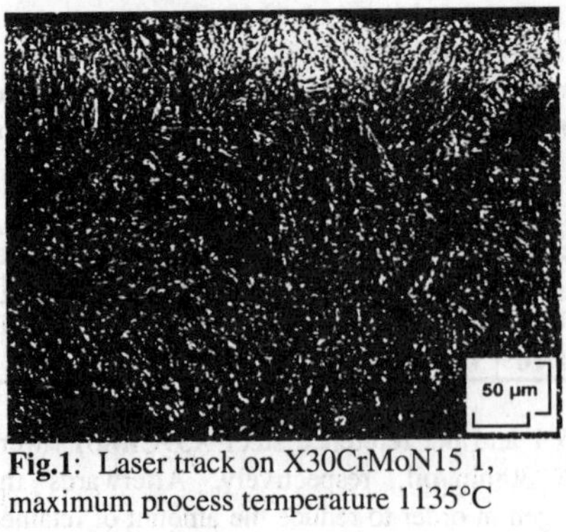

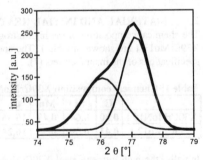

Fig.1: Laser track on X30CrMoN15 1, maximum process temperature 1135°C

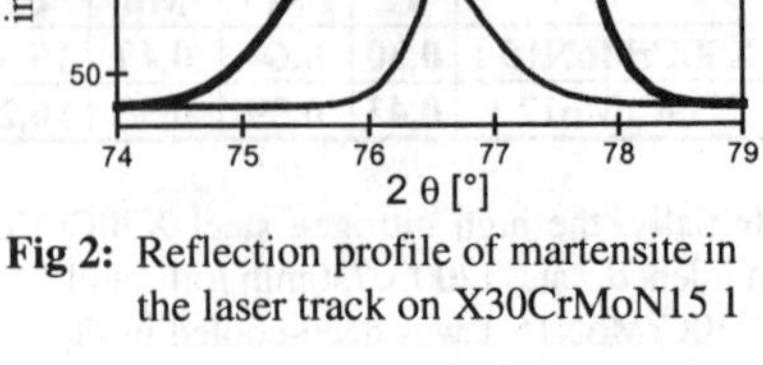

Fig 2: Reflection profile of martensite in the laser track on X30CrMoN15 1

Optical microscopy, microhardness tests and X-ray profile analysis (Fig. 1-4) reveal that initially, the microstructure of both the high nitrogen steel X30CrMoN15 1 and the reference steel X39CrMo17 1 is tempered cubic martensite ($c_m/a_m = 1$) with hardness values of 325 HV10 and 400 HV10, respectively.

Profile analysis on samples heated with a maximum temperature less than A_{c1b} shows recovery and the dislocation density decreases while the domain size increases. If the maximum temperature during the rapid hardening reaches A_{c1b} in the three-phase zone the phase transformation to austenite is initiated. During cooling the austenite partially transforms into martensite. Due to the fact that nitrogen and carbon atoms are dissolved above the equilibrium level newly generated martensite is no longer cubic but tetragonal distorted ($c_m/a_m > 1$), which is clearly visible in the X-ray line profile of the h00/00h – reflection (Fig.2). Due to the high nitrogen content soluted as interstitial atoms in the martensite the c/a ratio in case of the high nitrogen steel X30CrMoN15 1 is significantly higher than the c/a ratio of the martensite of the conventional cold work tool steel X39CrMo17 1.

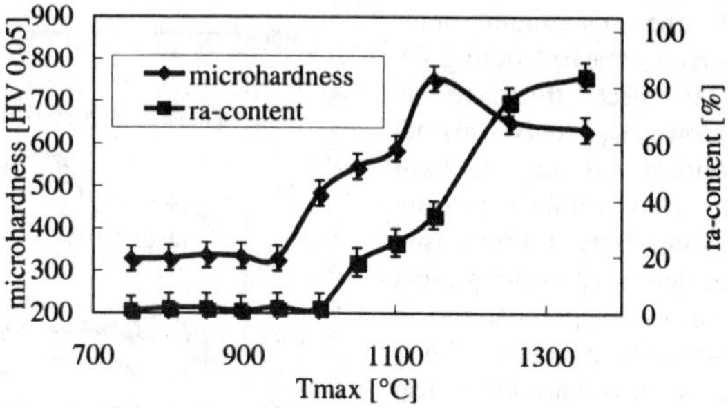

Fig.3: Microhardness and retained austenite content in laser track of X39CrMo17 1 versus maximum temperature of the laser heat treatment, heating rate (1010 K/s ÷ 1850 K/s)

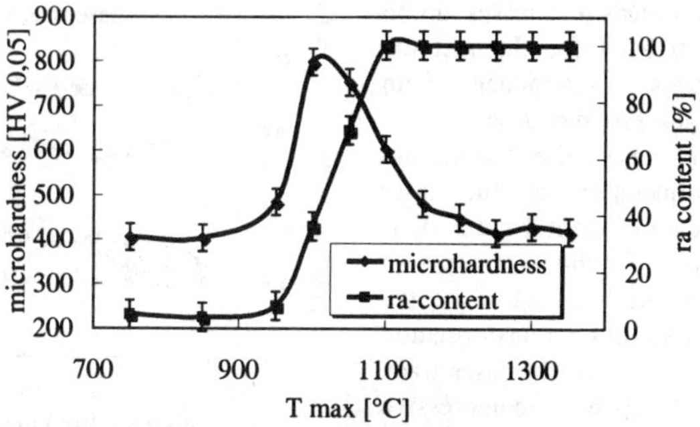

Fig.4: Microhardness and retained austenite content in laser track of X30CrMoN15 1 versus maximum temperature of the laser heat treatment, heating rate (1010 K/s ÷ 1850 K/s)

An increase of the maximum temperatures above A_{c1b} brings about an extending content of dissolved nitrogen and carbon and results in a higher distortion c_m/a_m of the martensite as well as an increasing content of retained austenite (Fig.2). If the maximum heat treatment temperature encounters Ac_{1e} the quenching effect of the surrounding material may not be sufficient for a martensitic transformation during cooling and in case of X30CrMoN15 1 a completely austenitic microstructure is stable even at room temperature. The value of Ac_{1e} and Ac_{1b} are lower in the system Fe-Cr-C than in the system Fe-Cr-N. Therefore, the maximum hardness and a comparable amount of retained austenite are reached at higher temperatures for the high nitrogen steel X30CrMoN15 1 than the conventional tool steel X39CrMo17 1.

3.2 Residual Stresses

The results of the residual stress analyses show that the residual stress distribution in the laser track and the heat affected zone essentially depends on the fact if the temperature of the heat treatment is below of above A_{c1b}.

If the maximum temperature reached during the laser heat treatment is below A_{c1b} only thermal residual stresses are built up. Thus, within the centre of the laser track tensile residual stresses are present both in longitudinal and in transverse direction in case of a maximum laser heat treatment temperature of the X39CrMo17 1 (Fig.5) which is below 950°C. The residual stress values obtained are comparatively high tensile stresses up to 750 MPa for the residual stress component in transverse direction.

In case the maximum temperature of the laser heat treatment exceeds A_{c1b}, due to the increase in volume caused by the martensitic transformation of the steel, the laser track is under compressive longitudinal and transverse residual stresses. The level of the compressive residual stresses increases with increasing maximum heat treatment temperature as a consequence of the rise in the amount of new martensite. The level of compressive residual stresses decreases again at high maximum temperatures since the amount of retained austenite in the microstructure increases. The heat affected zone contains tensile residual stresses which equilibrate the compressive residual stresses in the laser track. The maximum of these tensile residual stresses for the component in transverse as well as the component in longitudinal direction is located near the boundary of the laser track.

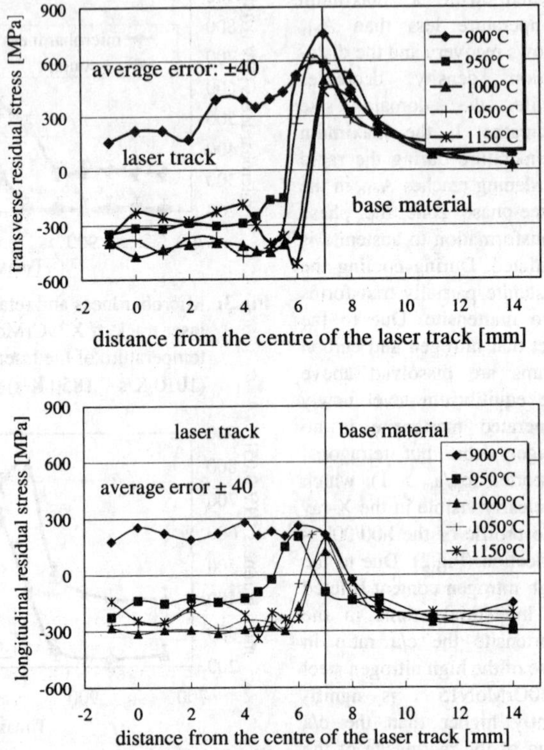

Fig. 5: Phase specific residual stresses in the martensite of the lasertrack on the base material X39CrMo17 1, dependence on the maximum heat treatment temperature, heating rate (1220 K/s ÷ 1570 K/s)

The compressive residual stresses in the laser track as well as the tensile residual stresses in the heat affected zone are higher in transversal direction than in longitudinal direction, which similar to welding residual stresses can be attributed to the stronger temperature gradient in transverse direction.

The residual stress state determined on the laser hardened high nitrogen steel X30CrMoN15 1 (Fig.6) after heat treatments with different maximum temperatures is similar to the residual distribution obtained in transverse and longitudinal direction for the conventional cold work tool steel X39CrMo17 1. Due to the higher Ac1e and Ac1b of the high nitrogen steel the transition from a residual stress state determined by pure quenching residual stresses to the residual stress state typical for martensitic hardening is shifted towards higher temperatures due to the higher Ac1e value of the high nitrogen steel. Further on the residual stress values at the surface of the laser hardened high nitrogen steel are higher than in case of the conventional tool steel.

The in-depth distribution of the residual stresses is characterised by a decrease of the compressive residual stresses in the laser track and also a decrease of the tensile residual stresses in the heat affected zone (Fig.8). In a depth larger than 100μm from the surface of the sample under the laser track even tensile residual stresses are present, the maximum tensile residual stresses in the laser track were determined in a depth of 200 μm beneath

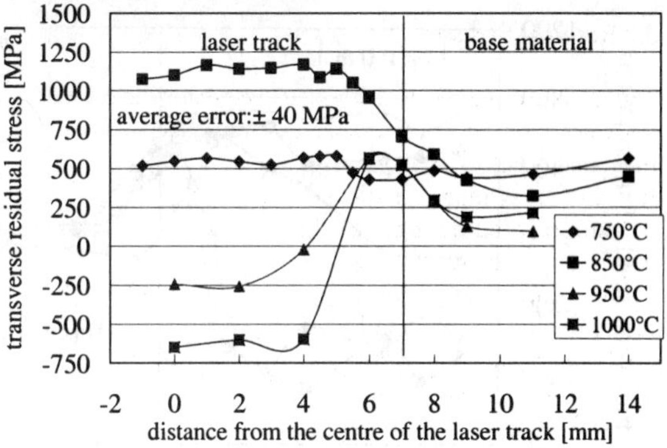

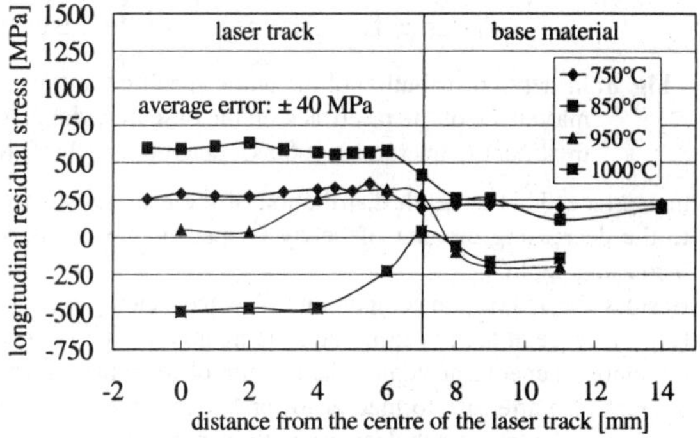

Fig. 6: Phase specific residual stresses in the martensite of the lasertrack on the base material X30CrMoN15 1, dependence on the maximum heat treatment temperature heating rate (1010 K/s ÷ 1360 K/s)

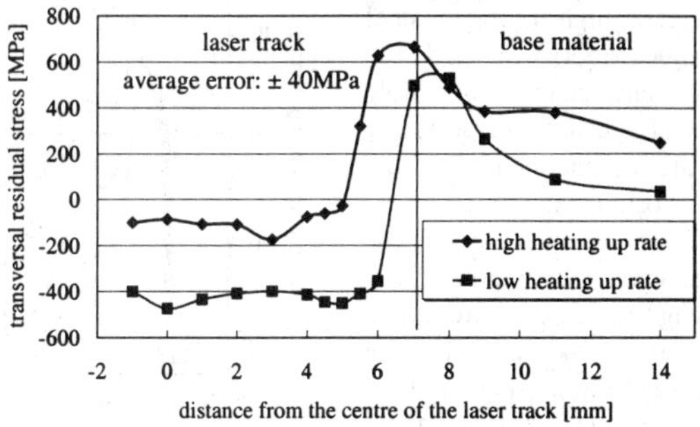

Fig.7: Phase specific residual stresses in the martensite of the lasertrack on the base material X30CrMoN15 1, dependence on the heating rate, maximum heat treatment temperature 1000°C

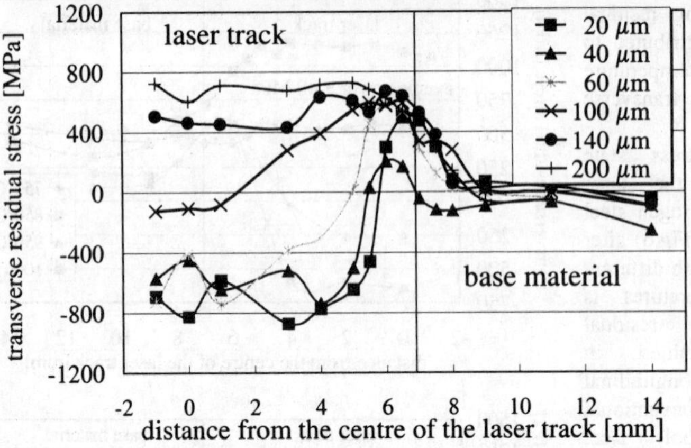

Fig. 8: In-depth distribution of the phase specific transverse residual stresses in the martensite of the lasertrack on the base material X30CrMoN15 1, maximum heat treatment temperature: 1000°C, heating rate: 1360 K/s

the surface. This in-depth distribution of the residual stresses in the laser track can be linked to the decreasing amount of newly formed martensite during the laser heat treatment with increasing depth.

Besides the maximum temperature also the heating rate influences the residual stress state (Fig.7). Since at high heating rates the microstructure is only for a short time in the regime of the inhomogeneous austenite, the amount of martensite formed during cooling is less than the amount of martensite formed at lower heating rates. Consequently, the compressive residual stresses in the laser track decrease with increasing heating rate.

3.3 RESIDUAL STRESSES AND CORROSION

The residual stresses and their influence on the corrosion of the rapid heat treated high nitrogen steel X30CrMoN15 1 and the reference steel is not visible in the usual characteristic values obtained by the corrosion test.

However, in case of the general corrosion test (Fig.9) in acid environment, local maxima of the current-density-potential-curve are visible at a potential of 700 mV approximately in those samples rapid heat treated with maximum heat treatment temperatures

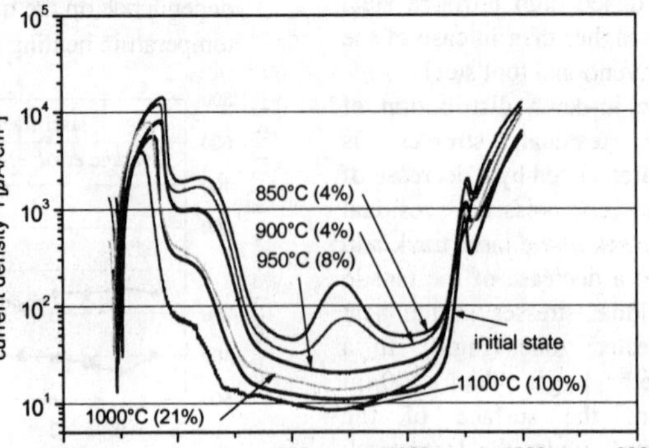

Fig.9: Current-density-potential-curves obtained in 3% H_2SO_4 in the the laser track on X30CrMoN15 1, dependence of the maximum heat treatment temperature, heating up rate (1150 K/s ÷ 1500 K/s)

beneath A_{c1b}, which consequently contain tensile residual stresses in the laser heat treated area. After the corrosion test the samples were annealed for 2h at 200°C in order to relax the residual stresses (Fig. 10). A second corrosion test in the laser track yielded a similar current-density-potential-curve compared to the original one despite the local maximum observed previously. Thus the tensile residual stresses originate stress corrosion which is visible in a local maximum of the current-density-potential-curve obtained in an acid environment. The mechanism resulting in this stress corrosion effect still has to be investigated.

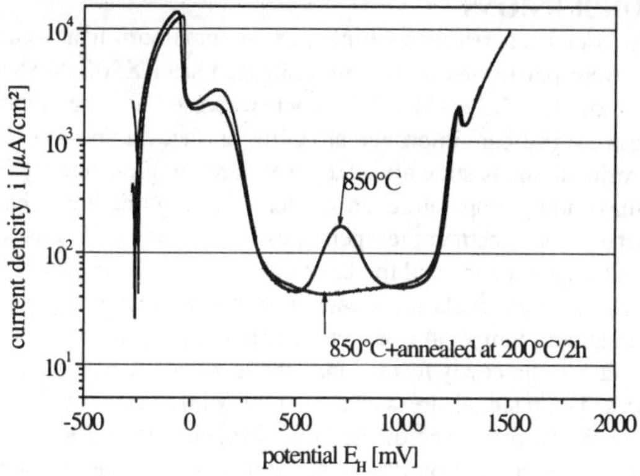

Fig.10: Change of the current-density-potential-curve obtained on X30CrMoN15 1 maximum heat treatment temperature 850°C, heating up rate (1150 K/s) in 3% H_2SO_4 due to annealing

In case of pitting corrosion an effect of the residual stresses on the current-density–potential-curve has not been detected. But, again those samples, which were heat treated with maximum heat treatment temperatures beneath A_{c1b} and thus contain tensile residual stresses show stress corrosion effects (13). They appear in scanning electron micrographs where both the high nitrogen steel X30CrMoN15 1 (Fig. 11-13) and the reference steel X39CrMo17 1 exhibit angular pits with cracks at the edges.

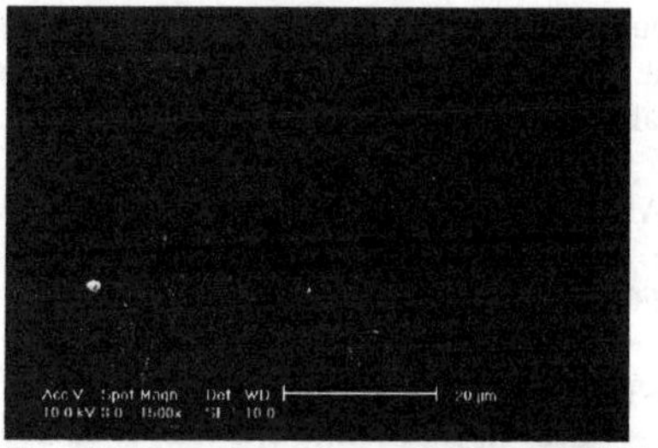

Fig.11: Pit on the surface of X30CrMoN15 1, cracks due to tensile residual stresses in cubic martensite, maximum laser heat 750°C, heating rate 1010 K/s

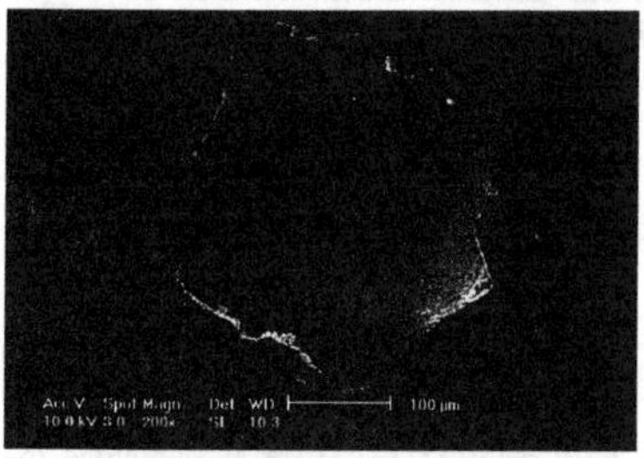

Fig.12: Pit on the surface of X30CrMoN15 1, cracks due to tensile residual stresses in cubic martensite, maximum laser heat 1000°C, heating rate 1360 K/s

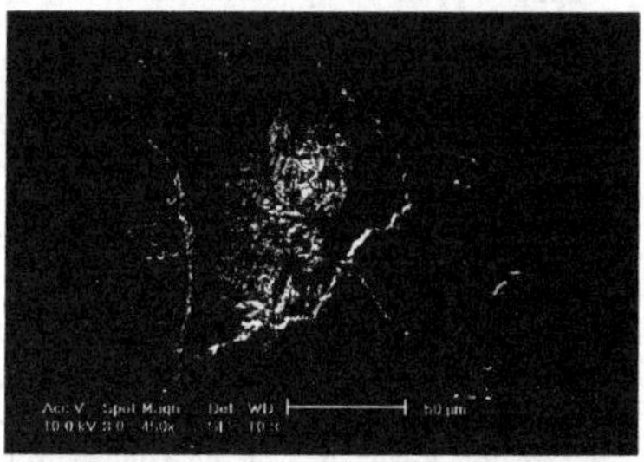

Fig.13: Pit on the surface of X30CrMoN15 1, cracks due to tensile residual stresses in austenite, maximum laser heat 1150°C, heating rate 1570 K/s

4. CONCLUSIONS

Rapid laser heat treatments with various maximum heat treatment temperatures and heating ratios were performed on the high nitrogen steel X30CrMoN15 1 and the conventional cold-work tool steel X39CrMo17 1 which was used as a reference steel. By the laser hardening process a significant improvement of the surface hardness could be achieved.
The residual stress state after the laser hardening essentially is given by the relation between the maximum temperature encountered during the laser hardening and Ac1b. In case of maximum heat treatment temperatures lower than Ac1b tensile residual stresses are present in the heat affected zone and the laser track. Due to the comparatively high value of Ac1b in case of high nitrogen steels these tensile residual stresses are particularly high. If the maximum heat treatment temperature exceeds Ac1e compressive residual stresses are present in the laser track, due to the newly formed martensite while the heat affected zone is under tensile residual stresses. The residual stress also is strongly influenced by the heating rate.
The corrosion resistance of the high nitrogen steel X30CrMoN15 1 can be essentially linked to the matrix content on dissoluted atoms. Thus, heat treatments with high heating rates and heat treatments with maximum temperatures below A_{c1b} are especially unfavourable with respect to the corrosion resistance. Further on in case of heat treatments where Ac1b is not reached the high tensile residual stresses have an effect on the shape of the current-density-potential curve obtained in general corrosion tests, which means that a stress corrosion mechanism is activated. The result of stress corrosion also is visible after pitting corrosion tests where a particular shape of the pits was found. The pits were not globular but rather angular formed and they show microcracks developing from their edges.
The experiments performed reveal that a laser hardening of high nitrogen steels enables a small process window.

5. ACKNOWLEDGEMENTS

We gratefully acknowledge financial support by the Deutsche Forschungsgemeinschaft (DFG), reference no. Fi 451/4 respectively Re 688/29.

6. REFERENCES

(1) Lueg J., Stickstofflegierte Werkzeugstähle, VDI-Fortschrittsberichte, Reihe 5, Nr. 188 (1990)
(2) Krafft F., Druckaufgestickte warmfeste Chromstähle, VDI-Fortschrittsberichte, Reihe 5, Nr. 222 (1991)
(3) Berns H., Wang G., Stainless High Nitrogen Steels. (Proc.Conf.) Bando, Y., Kosuge, K. (Hrsg.): 1993 Powder Metallurgy World Congress, Kyoto, Japan, (1993)
(4) Bohne C., Heitkemper M., Pyzalla A., Fischer A., Properties of Rapid Heat Treated High Nitrogen Steel. (Proc.Conf.) Euromat 99 – Surface Treatment, München, 1999
(5) Papaphilippou C., Spot laser hardening, Journal of Materials Science Letters 15 (1996)
(6) Müller K., Körner C., Bergmann H.W., Numerische Simulation der Eigenspannungen und Deformationen beim Laserstrahlrandschichthärten HTM 51 (1996)
(7) Datenblatt VSG, Werkstoffkenndaten (1997)
(8) Willbrand J, Hillnhagen E, HTM 24 (1966), 159
(9) Faninger G., Hartmann U., HTM 27 (1972), 233
(10) Klimanek P., Röntgendiffraktometrische Subgefügeanalyse an realen Vielkristalle, Habilitationsschrift, Freiberg (1990)
(11) Macherauch E., Müller P., Z. angew. Physik 13 (1961)
(12) ASTM G5-87: 1991 Annual Book of ASTM-Standards, Vol. 03.02, (1991)
(13) Pyzalla A., Bohne C., Heitkemper M., Fischer A., Influence of a Laser Heat Treatment on the Corrosion Resistance of the High Nitrogen Steel X30CrMoN15 1 + 0,3% N, submitted to Material and Corrosion

THERMOVISCOELASTIC ANALYSIS OF THE EFFECTS OF CURING PRESSURE ON RESIDUAL CURING STRESSES IN AUTOCLAVE-CURED LAMINATES.

Kheir Eddine TARSHA KURDI & Philippe OLIVIER
Laboratoire de Génie Mécanique de Toulouse
133, Avenue de Rangueil
31077 Toulouse cedex 04
France

ABSTRACT

It has been known for many years that the room temperature out–of–plane deflections that unsymmetrical composite laminates exhibit after curing can be related to the level of internal residual curing stresses. The residual curing stresses level is influenced by several factors such a curing dwell temperature, polymeric matrix degree of cure, glass transition temperature... So we decided to perform first an experimental study of the influence of autoclave pressure on residual curing stresses. To this end, unsymmetrical laminate were cured in autoclave according to the same temperature conditions, but either under a *0.1* MPa or under a *0.6* Mpa pressure. Three different cooling rates were tested : *0.5;3* and *5* °C/min. The purpose was to examine effectively, in that case, the thermoviscoelastic effects which take place while the laminates are cooled-down under the autoclave pressure. In order to set up a modelling of these combined effects, the classical laminated plate theory has to be modified. The material behaviour is temperature and time dependent and transverse shear stresses and deformations are introduced : $\sigma_{xz(t,T)}$, $\sigma_{yz(t,T)}$, $\varepsilon_{xz(t,T)}$ and $\varepsilon_{yz(t,T)}$ with *Z* axis perpendicular to the laminates mid-plane.
This means that Q_{44}, Q_{45} and Q_{55} terms have been introduced in the laminates stiffness matrix and that at the end of the curing dwell the laminates are both thermally and mechanically loaded. Taking into consideration such loading enable to get theoretical results which fit better experimental curvature values.

1. INTRODUCTION

Autoclave curing is, for more than 30 years, a widely used process in the manufacturing of aerospace composite structures. Numerous studies have been undertaken on residual curing stresses in composite laminates. The earliest work in the area of residual curing stresses can be traced to the understanding of their development and to modelling their prediction. Concerning the prediction of residual curing stresses, the calculations are usually made on the basis of classical laminated plate theory (CPLT) [1], [2]. It is always implicitly assumed that at cure temperature (Tc), the laminates are stress-free. In fact, from a manufacturing point of view, for autoclave-cured laminates a constant pressure (of about 0.1 – 1 MPa) is applied – with the aim of prepreg plies compaction – during all the cure cycle length, Fig 1. This means that even if the applied pressure is not very high, it should be taken into consideration in residual curing stresses prediction, since this pressure induces stresses in the laminate once it is consolidated. Effectively, the applied pressure may enhance residual stress relaxation processes of 90° plies of cross-ply laminates.

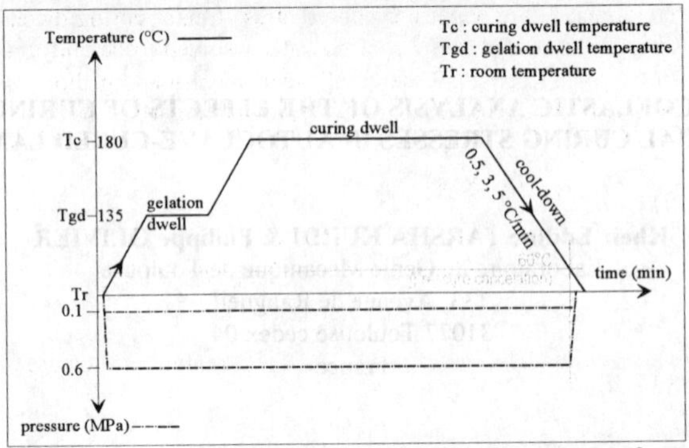

Fig. 1 Autoclave cure cycle recommended by prepreg manufacturer

This is why we will examine this latter point through the analysis of the room temperature shape of unsymmetric [$0°_2/90°_2$] laminated strips. The viscoelastic relaxation of 914 epoxy resin will also be examined by monitoring changes in the dimensionless curvature when the cool-down rate was changed.

Numerous authors have amply dealt with the effects of autoclave pressure and consolidation of laminated parts during cure [3]. It has been shown that during the first stages of a cure cycle, autoclave pressure generates an internal pressure gradient in resin (still fluid) trough the laminate thickness (because that there is a resin flow) and a flexural stress in the reinforcement fibres network [4]. It is important to mention that the autoclave pressure path applied on prepreg plies during the first stages of curing has a great influence on laminates properties [5]. Effectively, as we have shown in a previous study [6], the laminates void content and fibre volume fraction are highly dependent on the pressure path, while the mechanical characteristics of carbon/epoxy laminates undergo important changes because of voids.

Since the studied step of the cure cycle is here the cooling step, the polymeric matrix is far from being fluid and has an infinite viscosity. The laminate is then consolidated and behave as a solid. However, the classical two-dimensional relationships developed [7] for composite laminates must be modified in order to taken into consideration the effects of transverse (*z* axis) shear strains. In fact it is assumed here that autoclave pressure applied on the laminate generates two transverse shear effects Q_x and Q_y respectively, at the boundary surface. The effects of transverse shear deformation shown through the inclusion of the: σ_{xz} as a function of ε_{xz} and σ_{yz} as a function to ε_{yz}.

2. CONSTITUTIVE MODELS

Classical laminated plate theory (CLPT) was used to predict the laminates mid-plane curvatures k_{ox}, k_{oy} and k_{oxy}. Two distinct computations of curvature values were made. In the first one, the material behaviour is considered thermoelastic and all the thermomechanical characteristics are assumed to remain constant from curing dwell temperature to room temperature. A thermoviscoelastic behaviour is taken into consideration in the second one and two values of transverse coefficient of thermal expansion α_y^l for temperature below epoxy matrix *Tg* and α_y^h for temperatures laying between Tc and Tg are used.

In both cases, the laminates are never considered stress-free at curing dwell temperature and the temperature change associated to the cool-down is assumed to be uniform. Effectively, the autoclave pressure is considered as an external mechanical loading. For a *n* plies laminates equivalent thermal forces $\{N^T\}$and moments $\{M^T\}$are given by (eq 1 & 2) :

$$\{N^T\} = \Delta T \cdot \sum_{k=1}^{n} \left[\bar{Q}\right]^k \cdot \{\alpha\}^k \cdot h_k \tag{1}$$

$$\{M^T\} = \frac{\Delta T}{2} \cdot \sum_{k=1}^{n} \left[\bar{Q}\right]^k \cdot \{\alpha\}^k \cdot \left(z_k^2 - z_{k-1}^2\right) \tag{2}$$

To determine the transverse shear resultants Q_x and Q_y (resultant of the cure pressure), defined in equation (3), we have:

$$\begin{Bmatrix} Q_x \\ Q_y \end{Bmatrix} = \begin{bmatrix} L_{44} & L_{45} \\ L_{54} & L_{55} \end{bmatrix} \cdot \begin{Bmatrix} \varepsilon_{xz} \\ \varepsilon_{yz} \end{Bmatrix} \tag{3}$$

Where:

$$L_{ij} = \frac{5}{4} \cdot \sum_{k=1}^{n} [\bar{Q}]^k \cdot [Z_k - Z_{k-1} - \frac{4}{3} \cdot (Z_k^3 - Z_{k-1}^3) \cdot \frac{1}{h^2}] \qquad ;i, j = 4, 5$$

With: ΔT = Tr – Tc ; $\bar{Q}_{ij}$ the dimensionless stiffness matrix ; h_k ply thickness ; $\{\alpha\}^k$ coefficients of thermal expansion of *k* layer and z_k distance of considered layer from laminate mid-plane. Combining equations (1), (2) and (3) gives the mid-plane strain $\{\varepsilon_0\}$and laminate curvature $\{k_0\}$:

$$\{\varepsilon_0\} = \Delta T \cdot \left\{ [A^*] \cdot \sum_{k=1}^{n} \left[\bar{Q}\right]^k \cdot \{\alpha\}^k \cdot h_k + [B^*] \cdot \left(\frac{1}{2} \cdot \sum_{k=1}^{n} \left[\bar{Q}\right]^k \cdot \{\alpha\}^k \cdot \left(z_k^2 - z_{k-1}^2\right) \right) \right\} \tag{4}$$

$$\{k_0\} = \Delta T \cdot \left\{ [B^*] \cdot \sum_{k=1}^{n} \left[\bar{Q}\right]^k \cdot \{\alpha\}^k \cdot h_k + [D^*] \cdot \left(\frac{1}{2} \cdot \sum_{k=1}^{n} \left[\bar{Q}\right]^k \cdot \{\alpha\}^k \cdot \left(z_k^2 - z_{k-1}^2\right) \right) \right\} \tag{5}$$

$$\begin{Bmatrix} \varepsilon_{0xz} \\ \varepsilon_{0yz} \end{Bmatrix} = [L^*] \cdot \begin{Bmatrix} Q_x \\ Q_y \end{Bmatrix} \tag{6}$$

Where [A*], [B*], [D*] and [L*] are compliance.

In thermoelastic analysis, the equations (4), (5) and (6) are directly used to compute mid-plane strains and curvatures of $[0°_2/90°_2]$ laminate strips after curing. This means that the curvature values will be expressed as functions of fibre volume fraction *Vf(%)* (cf 3.1) and temperature difference ΔT. Concerning the laminate behaviour the following assumptions are made in consideration that $G_{xz} = G_{yz} = G_{xy}$ and $\nu_{13} = \nu_{23} = \nu_{12}$.

In thermoviscoelastic analysis, the transverse tensile E_y and the shear G_{xy}, G_{xz} and G_{yz} modules are depending on time and temperature. The transverse coefficient of thermal expansion α_y is expressed as a function of temperature *T*. It was assumed that the material is thermorheologically simple and the time-temperature principle was applied. According to this principle, the effect of a constant temperature change on all time-dependent response functions, such as modulus, is equivalent to a uniform shift in logarithmic time scale.

For example the modulus $E_{(t,T)}$ at time *t* and temperature *T* is equal to the modulus *E* at time $t / a_{T[T_{(t)}]}$ at a reference temperature T_0 :

$$E_{(t,T)} = E_{[t/a_{T(T(t))},T_0]} \tag{7}$$

Consequently, a time-temperature-dependent stiffness matrix $\left[\overline{Q}(\xi)\right]$ is introduced in equations (1), (2) and (3). This is done by the use of reduced times ξ(t) and ξ'(t) determined from the shift factor as :

$$\xi = \xi_{(t)} = \int_0^t \frac{dt}{a_{T[T_{(t)}]}} \quad \text{and} \quad \xi' = \xi'_{(t)} = \int_0^\tau \frac{dt}{a_{T[T_{(t)}]}} \tag{8}$$

Where $a_{T[T_{(t)}]}$ is the shift function obtained the master curves for the stiffness of the unidirectional layer (DMTA results are not presented in this paper).
This procedure gives for eq. (1), (2) and (3) :

$$\left[N^T(t)\right] = \sum_{k=1}^{n} h_k \cdot \int_0^t \left\{ \left[Q(\xi-\xi)'\right]^k \cdot \frac{\partial}{\partial\tau} \int_{T(0)}^{T(\tau)} \left[\alpha(T)\right]^k \cdot dT \right\} \cdot d\tau \tag{9}$$

$$\left[M^T(t)\right] = \sum_{k=1}^{n} h_k \cdot z_k \cdot \int_0^t \left\{ \left[Q(\xi-\xi')\right]^k \cdot \frac{\partial}{\partial\tau} \int_{T(0)}^{T(\tau)} \left[\alpha(T)\right]^k \cdot dT \right\} \cdot d\tau \tag{10}$$

$$\begin{Bmatrix} Q_x(t) \\ Q_y(t) \end{Bmatrix} = \begin{bmatrix} L_{44}(\xi-\xi') & L_{45}(\xi-\xi') \\ L_{54}(\xi-\xi') & L_{55}(\xi-\xi') \end{bmatrix} \cdot \begin{Bmatrix} \varepsilon_{xz}(t) \\ \varepsilon_{yz}(t) \end{Bmatrix} \tag{11}$$

And for equations (4), (5) and (6) when introducing time-dependent compliance [A*(ξ)], [B*(ξ)], [D*(ξ)] and [L*(ξ)] :

$$\{\varepsilon_0(t)\} = \int_0^t \left\{ \left[A^*(\xi-\xi')\right] \cdot \frac{\partial}{\partial\tau}\left[N^T(\tau)\right] \cdot d\tau \right\} + \int_0^t \left\{ \left[B^*(\xi-\xi')\right] \cdot \frac{\partial}{\partial\tau}\left[M^T(\tau)\right] \cdot d\tau \right\} \tag{12}$$

$$\{k_0(t)\} = \int_0^t \left\{ \left[B^*(\xi-\xi')\right] \cdot \frac{\partial}{\partial\tau}\left[N^T(\tau)\right] \cdot d\tau \right\} + \int_0^t \left\{ \left[D^*(\xi-\xi')\right] \cdot \frac{\partial}{\partial\tau}\left[M^T(\tau)\right] \cdot d\tau \right\} \tag{13}$$

$$\begin{Bmatrix} \varepsilon_{0xz}(t) \\ \varepsilon_{0yz}(t) \end{Bmatrix} = \int_0^t [L^*(\xi-\xi')] \cdot \frac{\partial}{\partial\tau} \begin{Bmatrix} Q_x(t) \\ Q_y(t) \end{Bmatrix} \cdot d\tau \tag{14}$$

An incremental numerical procedure was used to predict the thermoviscoelastic response of the laminates during cool-down. The cool-down is considered as a step by step cooling with small time increments. This procedure [8] enables the principal mid-plane curvature k_{ox} of $[0°_2/90°_2]$ laminated strips to be predicted (see Fig. 4).

3. EXPERIMENTAL STUDY

The material used in this study is the T300/914 prepreg manufactured by Hexcel-Composites. The prepreg initial average fibre volume fraction is Vf = 60%. Two kinds of manufacturing conditions were used. It is important to mention that in any cases the same bagging system is used.

Firstly, with the aim to study curing pressure effects, sets of $[0°_8]$, $[0°_4]$ and $[0°_2/90°_2]$ laminates were manufactured according to Fig 1 temperature conditions. All manufactured samples were autoclave-cured cooled down at 3°C/min. Some laminates were cured under 0.1

MPa pressure while some other were cured under a 0.6 MPa pressure (according Fig 1 cure cycle).

Secondly, to study the effects of the cooling rate on residual curing stresses, set of [$0°_8$], [$0°_4$] and [$0°_2/90°_2$] laminates were autoclave-cured (under a 0.6 MPa pressure) and cooled-down at 0.5 or 5°C/min. In that case the cure cycle is Fig 1 cure cycle in which only the cool-dawn rate is modified.

In order to avoid any effects of voids on experimental results, all the manufactured laminates were submitted to a 30 minutes ply by ply precompaction procedure under vacuum before being cured. This procedure enables to get void-free laminates. The fibre volume fraction was experimentally determined for each manufactured laminate by resin dissolution. As expected, the effects of pressure on fibre volume fraction *Vf(%)* are far from being negligible and must be taken into consideration for residual stresses prediction.

3.1 Static mechanical and physical characteristics

Mechanical tensile characteristics of [$0°_8$] laminates were determined according to appropriate European standards on a 8561 Instron. Where are also reported the longitudinal α_x and transverse α_y coefficients of thermal expansion which were measured using a Perkin-Elmer TMA7 (thermomechanical analyser) on coupons cut out from [$0°_8$] laminates. Note that α_y^l values are determined at temperatures below epoxy matrix *Tg*. From a physical point of view, the epoxy matrix degree of cure α and glass transition temperature *Tg* were determined by DSC. As we have already reported in a previous study [14] the effects of pressure and the changes that they induce in fibre volume fraction do not seem to have any influence of α and *Tg*. For [$0°_2/90°_2$] autoclave-cured samples the fibre volume fraction is $Vf = 61\%$ for 0.1 MPa pressure versus 65% for 0.6 MPa pressure cured. Table I values are directly input into the model for computation. The obtained results are plotted in Fig 4 where two Vf(%) values have been used: 61.5% and 66%. The obtained results are shown in Table I.

The effects of the cooling rate, on mechanical characteristics of [$0°_8$] laminates are extremely low. A maximum 2% difference in is recorded between 0.5°C/min and 5°C/min cooled samples. DSC results do not show any influence of the cooling rate on epoxy matrix *Tg* and α. As expected and as it can be seen in Table I, the curing mode and the induced changes in fibre volume fraction affect laminates mechanical characteristics. The main parameters usually strongly affected by the curing mode would certainly be the mechanical strength (transverse tensile strength, interlaminar shear strength), but they do not enter in the computation of thermal residual curing stresses. This the reason why results concerning those characteristics are not presented in this study.

Autoclave pressure (Mpa)	Vf (%)	E_x (MPa)	E_y (MPa)	G_{xy} (MPa)	α_x(°C^{-1}) x 10^{-6}	α_y^1(°C^{-1}) x 10^{-5}	α (%)	Tg (°C)
0.1	61.5	143800	8980	4590	-0.037	+2.93	98.5	155
0.6	66	145000	9390	4720	-0.041	+2.46	98.2	154

Table I: Mechanical and physical characteristics of [$0°_8$] laminates as a function of the curing pressure.

3.2 Viscoelastic characterisation

In order to take into account the effects of the cooling rate and the stress relaxation capabilities of the epoxy matrix during cool-down step a thermoviscoelastic characterisation of the composite material has been performed using a Polymer Lab MK2 DMTA (Dynamic ThermoMechanical Analyser). Effectively, it is common to assume that with viscoelastic materials, thermal residual curing stresses will be quickly relaxed as shown by [10]. The longitudinal tensile modulus E_x is considered to be time independent [11]. The Poisson's ratios have a little effect on the development of E_y and G_{xy} moduli [12] and therefore on residual curing stresses. Thus, it is assumed that ν_{xy}, ν_{xz}, and ν_{yz} are constant. Only the E_y, G_{xy}, G_{xz} and G_{yz} moduli are considered time and temperature dependent and for temperatures above Tg: $\alpha_y^h = 7.5.10^{-5}$ °C^{-1} and for temperatures lower than Tg α_y^l is taken in Table I data just like α_x which depends on *Vf(%)* only. DMTA results do not show any influence of pressure and cooling rate upon the composite whole thermoviscoelastic behaviour. In fact, the changes in [0_4] samples *Vf(%)* that the curing pressure (0.1 or 0.6 MPa) induces are not large enough to be detected by the experimental device during this thermoviscoelastic characterisation procedure.

3. 3. [0°$_2$/90°$_2$] laminated strips curvatures after curing

The room temperature shapes of laminated strips were measured immediately after curing using a profile projector. Several sets of [0°$_2$/90°$_2$] strips were manufactured according the curing procedures previously described: autoclave-cured with 0.1 or 0.6 MPa pressure cooled at 0.5 , 3 or 5°C/min. Their initial in-plane dimensions was : 100 x 10 mm. Given their in-plane dimensions, once cured the unsymmetrical laminated strips exhibit a principal curvature k_{ox} (mm^{-1}) which is determined from the purely geometrical following relation:

$$k_{ox} = \frac{1}{R_{ox}} \quad \text{with: } R_{ox} = \frac{L^2}{8 \cdot w_o(x)_{max}} + \frac{w_o(x)_{max}}{2} \qquad (15)$$

Equation (15) parameters are described in Fig 2. The profile projector enables to verify that [0°$_2$/90°$_2$] laminated strips have a cylindrical shape. The whole experimental procedure results in an accuracy on the principal curvature measurement of 6.5%. In spite of a large length to width ratio (length = 10 x width), small manifestations of the k_{oy} curvature can be detected.

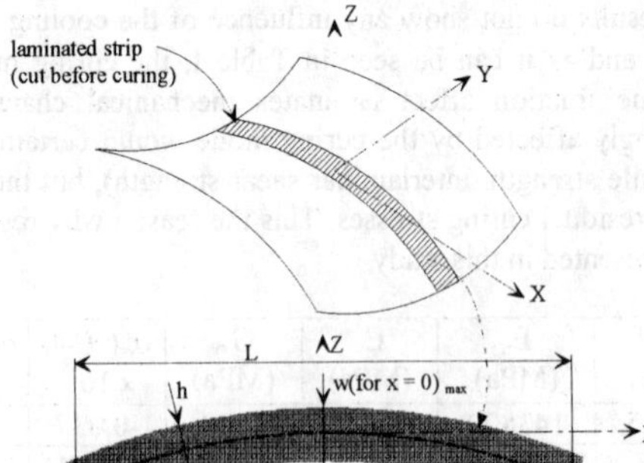

Fig. 2 Geometric shape of a [0°$_2$/90°$_2$] laminated strip at room temperature after curing. The curing mode (0.1 or 0.6 MPa pressure) also induces variations in laminates thickness *h*. For this reason it is more convenient to use dimensionless curvatures (k_{ox} x h).

4. DISCUSSION

Fig 3 shows that the dimensionless curvatures of 100 x 10 mm [$0°_2/90°_2$] laminated strips autoclave-cured under a 0.1 or 0.6 MPa pressure and cooled-down at 3°C/min. The obtained results show that the curvatures seem to be influenced by pressure. Effectively, dimensionless curvature of samples cured under a 0.1 Mpa pressure are about 9% higher than those of samples cured a 0.6 MPa pressure. Nevertheless, it is important to remind that the curvature values are determined with a 6.5% accuracy.

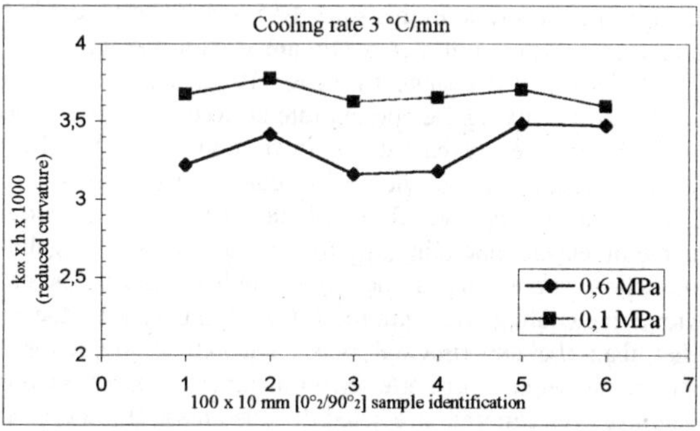

Fig. 3 Effects of pressure: dimensionless curvatures of oven and autoclave cured samples.

In fact, an important fraction of these differences in curvature values is certainly due to the changes in laminates thickness (denoted by h) and as a result, in fibre volume fraction *Vf(%)*. Changes in *h* and *Vf(%)* are induced by the value of the curing pressure

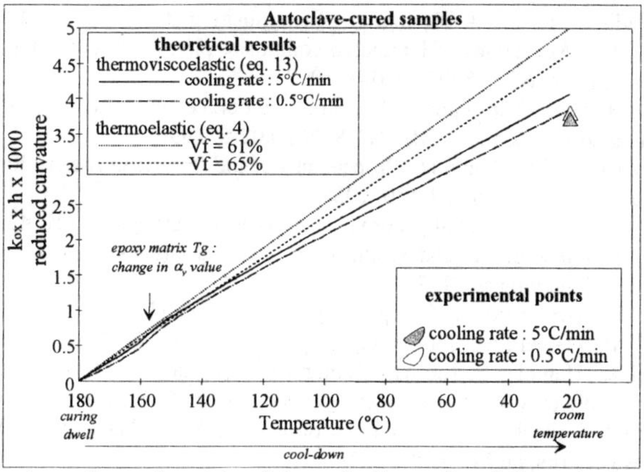

Fig. 4 Comparison of experimental and theoretically predicted dimensionless curvatures.

. Performing a quick simulation using CLPT with a thermoelastic behaviour enables to show that an increase by 4% in *Vf(%)* results in a 8% change in k_{ox} x h values (see Fig 4 thermoelastic predictions).So, theoretically, the difference in k_{ox} x h between the tow mode of curing should be of about 8%. This confirms the origin of the 9% difference in experimental dimensionless curvature between specimen cured under 0.1 and 0.6 MPa.

The changes in *Vf(%)* are the main contributing factor to the experimental changes in dimensionless curvatures of [$0°_2/90°_2$] laminated strips. Lay-up orientation defects can also be evoked and should not be ruled out. Effectively, during the manual lay-up of prepreg plies the angular accuracy can be estimated at ± 2°. The factors which cause the largest changes in unsymmetric laminated strips curvature are the laminate thickness and the transverse coefficient of thermal expansion [15]. The transverse coefficient of thermal expansion angular dependence is not sufficient for a 2° error induces any changes in curvature.

The two extreme cooling rates used in this study (0.5 and 5°C/min) are in fact corresponding to our industrial autoclave minimum and maximum capabilities in terms of cooling. Fig 4 experimental results show that a change by factor 10 in the cooling rate results in a 8% difference in k_{ox} x h. So, modifying the cooling rate between industrially acceptable limits do not induce sufficiently changes in curvatures to be considered (in the case of industrial autoclave curing) as a reduction way of thermal residual curing stresses.

From a theoretical point of view, two fibre volume fractions have been used for curvature prediction by the thermoelastic modelling (eq. 5): $Vf = 61$ and 65%. As shown in Fig. (4), the thermoelastic prediction overestimates the dimensionless curvatures of larger specimen. Effectively, whatever the cooling rate, with the 100 x 10 mm samples the predicted values are about 20% higher than the experimental ones. Theoretical predictions provided by the thermoviscoelastic model seem to fit better experimental points. Effectively, despite the fact chemical shrinkage has been ignored, predicted dimensionless curvatures are only 3% higher them experimentally ones and this whatever the cooling rate.

REFERENCES

[1] Jeronimidis G., Parkyn A. T., Journal of composite materials, V. 22, 401-415, 5-1988.

[2] Reddy J. N., "Mechanics of laminated composite plates – Theory and analysis", CRC Press, Inc., ISBN N°. 0-8493-3101-3, 1997.

[3] Ciriscioli P. R. and Springer G. S., "smart autoclave cure of composites", Technomic publishing company, Inc., ISBN N°. 87762-802-5, 1990.

[4] Gutowski T. G., Cai Z. and all, Proceedings of the American society for composites 1st technical conference, pp 154-170, 1988.

[5] Tang J. M., Lee W. I. and al., Journal of composite materials, V. 21, 421-439, 5-1987.

[6] Olivier P., Ioualalen K. and Cottu J. P., 23émes Journées d'Etudes des Polymères, France,17-22 septembre 1995.

[7] JAIN L. K., MAI Y.-W., J. Composite materials, Vol. 31, No. 7, pp 672-719, 1997.

[8] Wang T.M., Daniel I.M., Journal of composite materials, V. 26, n°6, pp883-899, 1992.

[9] White S. R., Hahn H. T., Journal of composite materials, V. 26, N° 16, 2402-53, 1992.

[10] Kim Y.K., White S.R., Journal of Reinforced Plastics Composites, V. 16, 2-12, 1996.

[11] Amijima S., Adachi T., Proceedings of ICCM IV, T. Hayashi, K. Kawata and S. Umekawa editors, pp 811-820, 1982.

[12] Bogetti T., Gillespie J.W. Jr, Journal of composite materials, V. 26, pp 626-660, 1992.

[13] Olivier P., Cavarero M. and Cottu J. P.,ICRS-5, Vol. 2, pp 898-903, 1997.

[14] Olivier P., Ferret B., Cottu J.P., Composites, Vol. 26, pp 509-515, 1995.

[15] Peeters L.J.B. and al., Journal of composite materials, Vol. 30, pp 603-626, 1992.

[16] Pen L. S. and al., Journal of composite materials, Vol. 23, pp 570-586, June 1989.

EFFECTS OF RESIDUAL STRESSES ON THERMAL EXPANSION OF CONTINUOUS ALUMINA FIBER-REINFORCED ALUMINUM

Yasukazu IKEUCHI*, Tatsuya MATSUE* and Takao HANABUSA**

* Niihama National College of Technology,
7-1, Yagumo-cho, Niihama 792-8580, JAPAN
** Faculty of Engineering, Tokushima University,
2-1 Minamijosanjima-cho, Tokushima 770-8506, JAPAN

ABSTRACT

The thermal expansion behavior along the fiber direction of a unidirectionally reinforced aluminum composite was studied in a temperature range of 300-800K. A strain hysteresis loop attributable to the presence of thermally induced residual stresses in the composite was observed. During cooling the composite from 800K to 300K, the matrix was plastically deformed in tension. With subsequent heating of the composite, the tensile matrix stress elastically decreased to zero stress level at about 330K and then the matrix was plastically deformed in compression. Time-dependent strain during isothermal holding of the composite at elevated temperatures was revealed. The change in strain of the composite under isothermal conditions was influenced by the sign of residual stresses. The relaxation behavior of the matrix stress during isothermal holding of the composite could be well described in a form of the power law for steady-state creep of pure aluminum. The activation energy for the relaxation process of the matrix stress was evaluated to be nearly equal to the activation energy for self diffusion of pure aluminum.

INTRODUCTION

Fiber-reinforced metal matrix composites are expected to be promising materials for structural components because of their high performances at elevated temperature as well as their high specific strength and modulus. In most composites, a large difference exists in the coefficient of thermal expansion between the matrix and fibers. When such a composite undergoes a change in temperature, residual stresses are induced in the composite because of the thermal expansion mismatch between fibers and matrix (1-4). These residual stresses are known to cause potentially undesirable outcomes for the composite such as dimensional instability or strain hysteresis (5,6).

Several groups have studied the thermally induced strain hysteresis in composites. Most theoretical studies on the strain hysteresis of the composites are based on the assumption of an elasto-plastic matrix combined with an elastic reinforcement. Garmong (7) used a one-dimensional model that included a thermally activated creep-type constitutive law for the matrix. This model was shown to agree well with experimental thermal expansion of eutectic composites (8). By using Garmong's analysis, Tyson (9) suggested that the creep strains during thermal cycling were very small, and that the thermal expansion behavior observed by Garmong could be explained without consideration of the matrix creep. On the other hand, Dutta et al. (10) demonstrated that matrix creep deformation played an important role in the thermal cycling response of continuous graphite fiber-reinforced aluminum composites. Zhang et al. (11) also studied hysteresis in the thermal expansion of continuous fiber-reinforced composites. They ignored creep but compared a one-dimensional model with their axisymmetric model. By considering the systematic variations between the two models, they have shown that the one-dimensional model can be used in a limited but quantitative manner.

Although a great deal of effort has been expended in understanding the thermal strain and stress response of the composite, little work has been done on the actual role of thermal stresses on the strain response of continuous fiber-reinforced composites, especially from a standpoint of the matrix creep. The purpose of this paper is to experimentally clarify the matrix creep and to reveal the relationship between residual stresses and thermal expansion along the fiber direction of a unidirectionally reinforced aluminum composite.

EXPERIMENTAL

The composite material studied was pure aluminum (99.95 wt%) unidirectionally reinforced with continuous alumina fibers (12). The composite with 50 vol% fibers was fabricated by a squeeze casting method, which was supplied by Sumitomo Chemical Co., Ltd. The alumina (85wt%Al_2O_3-15wt%SiO_2) fiber was circular in cross section with a 17-μm average diameter and consisted of very fine crystals with a γ-alumina type of structure. An average fiber spacing in the composite was found to be about 30μm. The specimens were shaped into dimensions of 3mm x 4mm x 20mm, the longitudinal axis being parallel to the fibers. The edges were polished up to a 1-μm diamond finish. Finally, they were annealed at 800K for 6hr and then cooled in the furnace.

Thermal expansion of the composite was measured along the fiber axis in a quartz tube type commercial dilatometer. The dilatometer was calibrated between 300 and 800K with pure aluminum of the same size as that of the composite specimen. All measurements of the thermal expansion were made in air at a heating and cooling rate of 6K/min. A fluctuation of room temperature was less than ± 1.0K. The thermal expansion of the composite was measured between 300 and 800K. After the measurement of the annealed composite, it was cooled down to liquid nitrogen temperature and heated back to room temperature (hereafter referred to as N treatment).

RESULTS

Axial thermal expansion curves of the N-treated composite during two times of thermal cycling between 300 and 800K are shown in Fig. 1 where the measurement was started at N. It is seen that the N-treated composite expands monotonously with increase in temperature along the curve NCD followed by rapid contraction with the cooling curve DA. A large hysteresis NDA as well as a compressive residual plastic strain of N to A at the end of the first cycle is apparent. On the second cycle, a closed hysteresis loop of AD is observed. This loop was found to be the same as that measured on the as-annealed composite within the limits of experimental uncertainty. In addition, the loop AD was found to be stable for repeating, at least 100 times, thermal cycling between 300 and 800k of the composite. No significant change in length of the cycled composite at 300K was also observed. For the composite system, it seems that excellent interfacial bonding had been achieved between the matrix and fibers, and that interphase sliding (or thermal ratcheting) such as observed on tungsten fiber-reinforced copper composites (5) can be neglected in this experiment.

As it will be explained in detail later, the dot-dash-line in Fig. 1 shows the middle curve between the curves ND and DA.

The composite was held at constant high temperatures during thermal cycling between 300 and 800K. For such that case, the axial thermal expansion behavior is shown in Fig. 2,

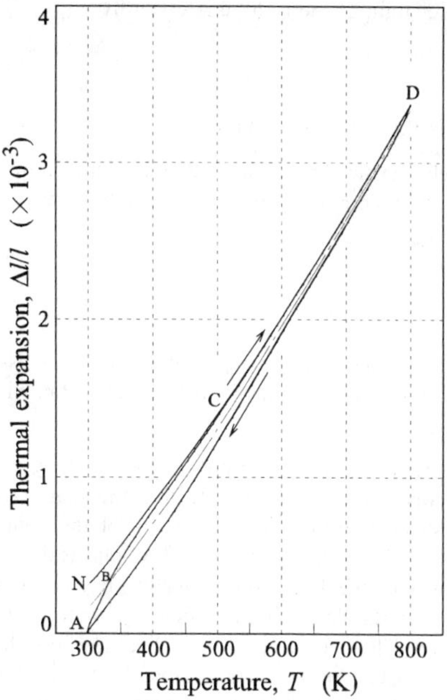

Fig. 1 Thermal expansion curves during thermal cycling of the composite.

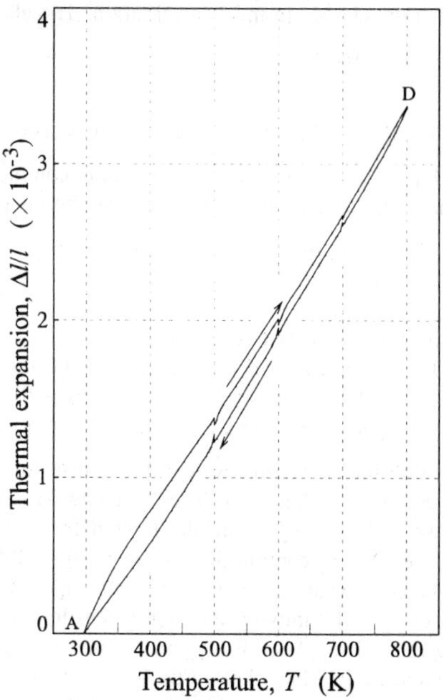

Fig. 2 Thermal expansion with holding the composite at given temperatures.

where the composite was held for 6hr at 500, 600, 700 and 800K, respectively. It can be seen that isothermal hold during heating process leads to contraction of the composite, whereas during cooling process, isothermal hold leads to expansion of the composite. It is apparent that thermal expansion of the composite depends upon its heating and cooling rates, while the rate used was just a rate of 6K/min on the measurements.

DISCUSSION

Let us consider a matrix material unidirectionally reinforced with continuous fibers. We make the assumptions that perfect bonds exist between the fibers and matrix, and that deformations remain essentially one-dimensional as Garmong's model (7). Furthermore, the stresses and strains are taken to be uniform within each phase.

Under the above assumptions and in the absence of any externally applied stress, we have the familiar rule of mixtures for stress equilibrium

$$\Delta\sigma_f V_f + \Delta\sigma_m V_m = 0 \qquad (1)$$

where $\Delta\sigma$ is the change in stress, V is volume fraction, and the subscripts f and m represent fiber and matrix, respectively. In order to ensure strain continuity across the interface, the length of the fiber and matrix must remain the same at a temperature change ΔT,

$$\Delta\varepsilon_\nu = \alpha_f\,\Delta T + \Delta\varepsilon_f = \alpha_m\,\Delta T + \Delta\varepsilon_m \qquad (2)$$

where $\Delta\varepsilon_\nu$ is the change in composite strain, α is the coefficient of thermal expansion and

$\Delta\varepsilon$ is the change in mechanical strain. The elastic strain of the i phase is given by

$$\Delta\varepsilon_i = \frac{\Delta\sigma_i}{E_i} \tag{3}$$

where i represents either fiber or matrix, and E is the Young's modulus.

By assuming that the fiber remains completely elastic throughout the entire temperature range, the change in matrix stress can be obtained by combining Eqs. (1) through (3) as

$$\Delta\sigma_m = \frac{V_f E_f}{V_m}(\alpha_f \Delta T - \Delta\varepsilon_v). \tag{4}$$

Thermally induced residual stress

Following Eq. (4), we can predict the matrix thermal stress $\Delta\sigma_m$ from the thermal expansion of a composite $\Delta\varepsilon_v$, if the stress-free thermal expansion of fibers $\alpha_f\Delta T$ is known. In this study, we estimate the $\alpha_f\Delta T$, as following.

With the composite system, the matrix flow stress is about 0.03 times as low as the yield stress of the fiber (12). Therefore, hysteresis curves in Fig. 1 indicate that the matrix is flowing plastically while the fiber deforms elastically during thermal cycling of the composite. During cooling the composite from 800K to 77K, the matrix will flow plastically in tension because the matrix contracts faster than does the fiber. When heating begins after reaching 77K, initially the matrix tensile stress reduces elastically, and then the matrix will begin to flow plastically again but in compression. Thus, at N of 300K in Fig. 1 where the composite had been heated up from 77K, the matrix can be in a compressive state (with the fiber in a tensile state). To the contrary, however, the matrix can be in a tensile state (with the fiber in a compressive state) at A where the composite was cooled down from the elevated temperature of 800K. Therefore, with both the fibers and the matrix, the stress-free state should be located at somewhere between A and N. In the previous study (3), which involved an X-ray *in-situ* measurement of the matrix stresses during thermal cycling between 300 and 600K of the same composite material as that used in this study, it was found for the matrix of the N-treated composite that absolute values of compressive flow stresses on heating were almost the same in magnitude as those of tensile flow stresses on cooling at temperatures ranging from 300K to near 500K. Now, on the assumption that the magnitude of the matrix flow stress is identically the same in tension and in compression, the middle curve between the two curves of ND with heating and AD with cooling (except near D) is to correspond to the thermal expansion $\alpha_f\Delta T$ of stress-free fibers in Eq.4, and is shown as the dot-dash-line in Fig. 1. From the difference in thermal strain between the composite and the stress-free fiber, both shown in Fig. 1, the matrix thermal stress can be determined by using Eq. (4) with E_f = 210 GPa, and is plotted in Fig. 3 as a function of temperature.

The changing manner of the matrix thermal stress in Fig. 3 would seem to reveal the *in-situ* behavior of an elasto-plastic deformation of the matrix in the composite being subjected to thermal cycling. When both the matrix and fibers are elastically deformed by a uniform temperature change ΔT to accommodate the thermal expansion mismatch between the two phases, a change in the matrix stress $\Delta\sigma_m$ occurs in the fiber direction. By combining the right hand side equality in Eq. (2) with Eqs. (1) and (3), the $\Delta\sigma_m$ is given by

$$\Delta\sigma_m = \frac{(\alpha_f - \alpha_m)V_f E_f E_m}{E_v} \times \Delta T \tag{5}$$

where E_v represents the Young's modulus of the composite ($E_v = V_f E_f + V_m E_m$) obtained

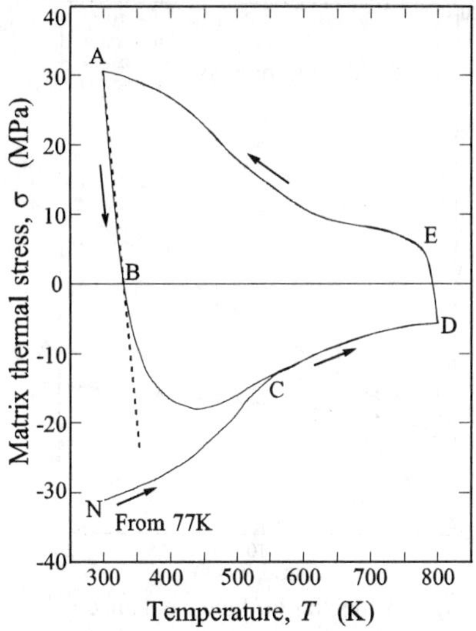

Fig. 3 Matrix thermal stress *vs*. temperature.

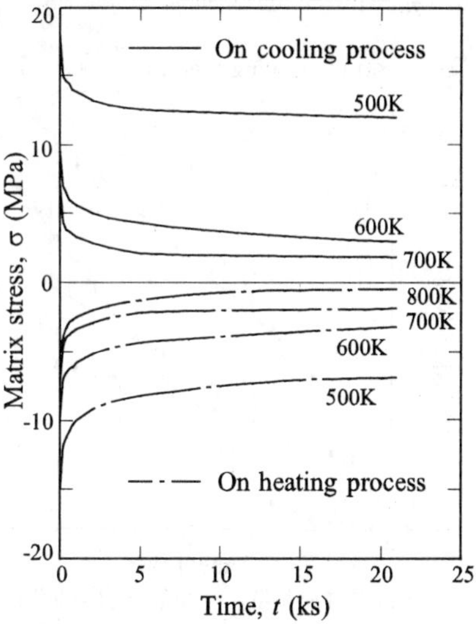

Fig. 4 Relaxation of matrix stress.

from the rule of mixtures. Since $V_f = V_m = 0.50$ in this composite system, by using the values around room temperature for aluminum and the fiber of $\alpha_m = 23.9 \times 10^{-6}$ /K, $E_m = 71.1$ GPa, $\alpha_f = 5.5 \times 10^{-6}$ /K, and $E_f = 210$ GPa, we can obtain Eq. (6):

$$\Delta\sigma_m = -\ 0.98 \times \Delta T. \tag{6}$$

The dashed line in Fig. 3 shows the prediction by Eq. (6) in the case of heating the composite from A. On this heating process, the matrix stress falls linearly along the dashed line from A to near B. Further heating of the composite causes compressive plastic deformation of the matrix because the stress follows curve BCD. Thus the aluminum matrix exhibits a Bauschinger effect in the composite upon a stress reversal. Upon cooling from the maximum temperature of 800 K at D, the matrix stress rises elastically to near point E, and then the matrix is deformed along curve EA in a tensile-plastic manner. Further cooling from A to 77 K by the N treatment results in further tensile-plastic deformation of the matrix. Upon re-heating the composite from 77 K, the matrix stress reaches N after reversing the stress state from tension to compression. During the subsequent heating process, the matrix is plastically deformed in compression from N to D by way of C. In region C to D at elevated temperatures, the flow stress of the matrix shows the same magnitude as that of the matrix heated from A. The reproducibility of the matrix stress changes along paths ABCD and NCD during repeated thermal cycling is thought to show that the matrix dislocation structures at elevated temperatures, C to D, are unaffected by the previous dislocation structures at A or N, and are thermally stable. The matrix thermal stresses measured in this study (Fig. 3) agreed well with those measured in the previous X-ray study (3) at the temperature range 300K to near 400 K. At above 400 K, however, the matrix thermal stresses measured by the X-ray method were observed to be reasonably small as compared with those measured in this study. This can be attributed to relaxation of the matrix stress during isothermal holding of the composite before (and for) the X-ray measurements.

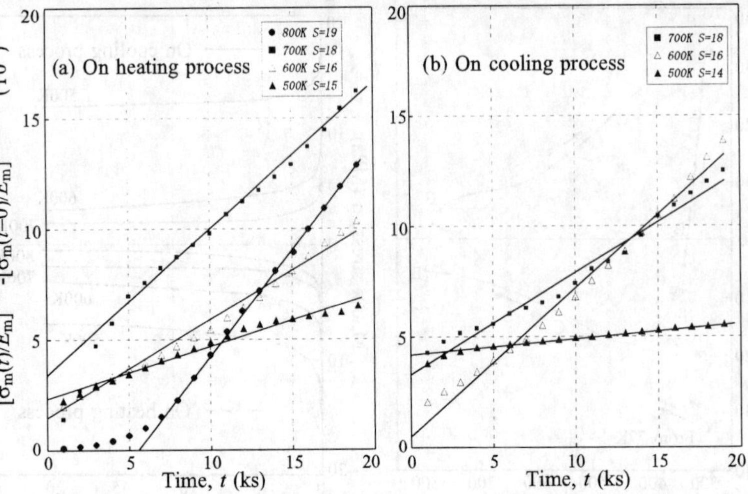

Fig. 5 The value of left hand side in Eq. (8) as a function of time t obtained from relaxation curves in Fig. 4. In the figure, s shows the s-th power of 10.

Relaxation of residual stress

When the stress level is high and the temperature increases, the matrix stresses will be relaxed by time-dependent plastic deformation of the matrix. The matrix stress as a function of time is shown in Fig. 4 where the composite was held at the given temperature during each of thermal cycling between 300 and 800K. The matrix stress was determined by using Eq. (4). In Fig. 4, it can be observed that, although the initial rate of stress relaxation is considerably high, the relaxation rate gradually decreases with increasing time. The matrix stress being calculated from Eq. (4) corresponds to the stress due to elastic deformation of the matrix. And, by changing a part of the elastic strain into a plastic strain, the stress relaxation may occur.

In the present study, the behavior of the stress relaxation was analyzed on the basis of Garmong's one-dimensional model (7) combined with Tyson's suggestion (9). In the model, at constant high temperatures, the matrix obeys creep law while the fiber deforms elastically. Here, the matrix creep is assumed to follow the power low for steady-state creep, stage II, of pure metals (13),

$$\dot{\varepsilon}_{mc} = A\left(\frac{\sigma_m}{E_m}\right)^n D_0 \exp\left(\frac{-Q_c}{RT}\right) \quad (7)$$

where ε is the steady-state creep rate, A is a structure dependent constant, n is the stress constant, D_0 is the pre-exponential constant, Q_c is the activation energy for creep, and R is the gas constant. The matrix stress $\sigma_m(t=0)$ at the start of a relaxation test will fall to $\sigma_m(t)$ after the period of t sec. On the assumption that a part of the matrix elastic strain changes into a plastic strain by the matrix creep governed by Eq. (7) during the stress relaxation test at constant high temperatures, the value of the matrix stress $\sigma_m(t)$ at time t is given as

$$\left[\frac{\sigma_m(t)}{E_m}\right]^{1-n} - \left[\frac{\sigma_m(t=0)}{E_m}\right]^{1-n} = \left\{\left[\frac{(n-1)V_f E_f}{E_v}\right] A D_0 \exp\left(\frac{-Q_c}{RT}\right)\right\} \times t$$
$$\equiv C(T) \times t \quad (8)$$

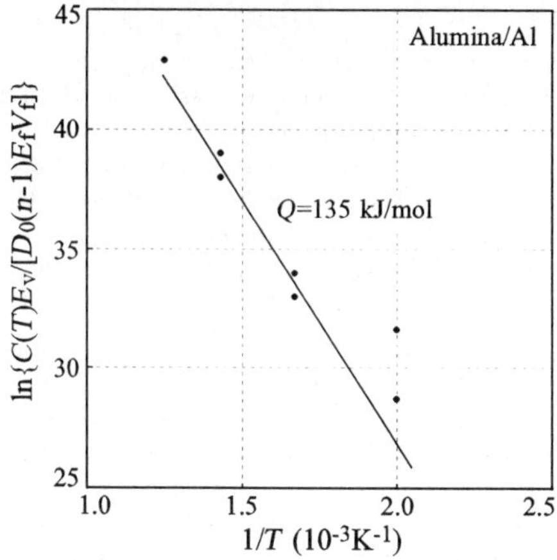

Fig. 6 The value of left hand side in Eq. (10) as a function of $1/T$.

where $C(T)$ is the temperature dependent constant. According to Eq. (8), the value of left hand side in Eq. (8) is proportional to the relaxation time t. This value can be obtained from a result of the relaxation tests such as shown in Fig. 4, if the stress exponent n is given. Here, we assume n = 5 for the high temperature creep of pure aluminum (12). In this study, while the value of E_f was taken to be constant of 210 GPa over the test temperature range, temperature dependence of the matrix Young's modulus E_m is taken into consideration as Eq. (9) where the E_ms were obtained from the reference (14).

$$E_m(T) = 75900 - 3.91\,T - 7.02 \times 10^{-2}\,T^2 + 4.14 \times 10^{-5}\,T^3 \quad \text{[MPa]} \tag{9}$$

The value of left hand side in Eq. (8) is plotted as a function of time in Fig. 5 where proportional relationship between the time and the value of left hand side in Eq. (8) is satisfied. The relaxation process of the matrix stress at constant high temperatures seems to be governed by Eq. (7).

By putting the slope of the straight line in Fig. 5 as $C(T)$, the following equation is derived from Eq. (8),

$$\ln\left[\frac{C(T)E_v}{D_0(n-1)V_f E_f}\right] = \ln A - \frac{Q_c}{RT} \tag{10}$$

For n = 5, the value of left hand side in Eq. (10) calculated from the slope of the straight line in Fig. 5 is plotted as a function of $1/T$ in Fig. 6. As shown in Fig. 6, at high temperatures, the activation energy Q for the relaxation process of the matrix stress is evaluated to be about 135 kJ/mol of which the value is nearly equal to the activation energy 142 kJ/mol for self diffusion of pure aluminum. Since the stress relaxation is derived from plastic deformation of the aluminum matrix during isothermal holds of the composite at high temperatures, it seems that a rate controlling process for the matrix stress relaxation is concerned with interplay of strain hardening and recovery of a dislocation substructure which has the same stress and temperature dependence as that being constructed during steady-state creep of pure aluminum.

CONCLUSIONS

The thermal expansion during thermal cycling of a continuous alumina fiber-reinforced aluminum composite was characterized by a strain hysteresis loop which could be attributed to time-dependent as well as time-independent plastic deformation of the matrix under thermally induced residual stresses. During cooling from an elevated temperature, the matrix was plastically deformed in tension. With subsequent heating after cooling the composite to room temperature, the tensile matrix stress elastically decreased to zero stress level and then the matrix was plastically deformed in compression. This means that the aluminum matrix exhibited a Bauschinger effect in the composite upon a stress reversal.

Time-dependent strain during isothermal holding of the composite at elevated temperatures in the absence of externally applied stress was revealed. The change in strain of the composite under isothermal conditions was influenced by the sign of the residual stress. Under compressive residual stress in the matrix, the composite contracted, whereas under tensile residual stress in the matrix, the composite expanded. The relaxation behavior of the matrix stress during isothermal holding of the composite could be well described in a form of the power law for steady-state creep of pure aluminum. The activation energy for the relaxation process of the matrix stress was evaluated to be nearly equal to the activation energy for self diffusion of pure aluminum.

REFERENCES

1. Chawla K. K, 'Composite Materials' 2nd ed., Springer-Verlag (New York) 1998
2. Ikeuchi Y, Fujiwara H, Residual Stresses in Science and Technology, ICRS-1, Macherauch E, Hauk V, eds., DGM Informationsgesellschaft, Oberursel (1987) 523
3. Ikeuchi Y, Hanabusa T, Fujiwara H, Residual Stresses-3, ICRS-3, Fujiwara H, Abe T, Tanaka K, eds., Elsevier, London (1992) 52
4. Ikeuchi Y, Matsue T, Hanabusa T, The Fifth International Conference on Residual Stresses, ICRS-5, Ericsson T, Odén M, Andersson A, eds., Linköping university, Linköping (1998) 958
5. Yoda S, Kurihara N, Wakashima K, Umekawa S, Metall. Trans., 9A (1978) 1229
6. Wakashima K, Otsuka M, Umekawa S, J. Compos. Mater., 8 (1974) 391
7. Garmong G, Metall. Trans., 5 (1974) 2183
8. Garmong G, Metall. Trans., 5 (1974) 2191
9. Tyson W.R, Metall. Trans., 6A (1975) 1674
10. Dutta I, Mitra S, Wiest A. D, Residual Stresses in Composites, eds., Barrera E.V, Dutta I, TMS (Warrendale) (1993) 273
11. Zhang H, Anderson P. M, Daehn G. S, Metall. Trans., 25A (1994) 415
12. Abe Y, Nakatani M, Yamatsuta K, Horikiri, S, Proc. First European Conf. on Composite Materials (1985) 604
13. Sherby O. D, Burke P. M, Prog. in Mater. Sci. 13, Pergamon, Oxford (1966) 323
14. Köster W, Z. Metallkd. 32-8 (1940) 282

RELIEF OF RESIDUAL STRESSES IN ALUMINIUM ALLOY 7010

DA Tanner[1], JS Robinson[2] and RL Cudd[3]
[1]Alcan International Ltd., Southam Road, Banbury, Oxon, OX16 7SP, UK
[2]Department of Materials Science and Technology, University of Limerick, Ireland
[3]HDA Forgings Ltd., Windsor Road, Redditch, Worcestershire, B97 6EF, UK

ABSTRACT

Large rectilinear open die forgings of aluminium alloy 7010 are generally cold compressed after solution heat treatment to relieve residual stresses that develop during the rapid quenching operation. The effect that natural ageing and cold compression direction (LT v L v ST) have on the final residual stress distribution is not generally known. Residual stress development during quenching is modelled using the finite element technique and the effect on the final residual stress magnitude of varying these process parameters is evaluated. The effect of stretching to relieve residual stresses and the effect on residual stress magnitudes of sectioning samples of the material is also analysed using the finite element technique. Residual stresses are measured using the X-ray diffraction technique to observe if natural ageing after solution heat treatment results in a reduction in residual stress magnitudes.

INTRODUCTION

The Al-Zn-Mg-Cu alloy 7010(1) obtains its high strength through solution heat treatment (475±5°C) followed by a rapid quench into water/organic quenchant and a subsequent artificial ageing treatment. The disadvantage of this heat treatment is that the quenching operation can lead to severe thermal gradients developing in the material that result in distortion or residual stress magnitudes that exceed the yield strength of the material. Parts machined from semi-finished products like open die forgings can distort due to the stress distribution becoming unbalanced and can also become susceptible to stress corrosion cracking (SCC) as underlying tensile stresses are exposed.

Established procedures exist to reduce residual stress by quenching into boiling water or organic quenchants at the expense of ageing response. Residual stresses can also be relieved after solution heat treatment by plastically deforming forgings in a controlled manner. This plastic deformation can take the form of a tensile loading (designated Tx51), compressive loading (Tx52) or a combination of the two (Tx54). While application of tensile deformation has been found to result in an almost complete removal of residual stress (2, 3) the technique is limited to parts that have a substantially uniform cross-section in the stretching direction (4) (e.g. sheet and plate products). Similarly, application of a combined compression-tension loading is limited by configuration shape and size (5).

Application of cold compression to closed die forgings is difficult in the finished dies given the large difference in thermal expansion coefficient between tool steels and aluminium. Combined with this, manufacture of special cold reduction dies for more complex forgings results in a large increase in cost. Open die forged products can be cold compressed relatively easily using standard platens with plastic deformation of 1-3% generally applied. Cold compression has traditionally been carried out in the ST direction. The effect on the residual stress distribution of applying cold compression in either the LT or L direction is unknown. A combination of deformation in two directions may also result in an increased stress reduction. Tensile plastic deformation is generally applied to sheet and plate material to relieve quenching residual stresses. Using the finite element method, the effect of applying a Tx51 temper as opposed to a Tx52 temper can be analysed for the same forging. Certain open die forgings are sectioned after solution heat treatment before they are used to machine smaller parts. The influence of sectioning of large forgings on the residual stress distribution can also be modelled using the finite element method.

This paper aims to model the development of residual stresses during quenching using the finite element method and to observe how the variable process parameters during cold compression affect the final stress distribution.

FINITE ELEMENT CALCULATION OF RESIDUAL STRESSES

The ABAQUS (6) finite element model used to predict the residual stress distribution after quenching large rectilinear 7010 forgings has been described in a previous paper (7). This isotropic model predicted compressive surface residual stress magnitudes of approximately 200MPa. This residual stress prediction was experimentally determined to be accurate (7) and similar to values published in the literature (3, 8, 9). The original model assumed that the material was strain rate dependent and that it followed perfectly plastic stress-strain behaviour at all temperatures observed during quenching. While this assumption was valid at high temperatures, it is not true at room temperature (<40°C). Therefore, in the cold compression models the input data has been modified to assume that the material work hardens and is strain rate independent at room temperature. All other mechanical and thermal properties remain the same. This change in material properties evoked a reduction in the final residual stress magnitudes predicted after quenching of between 7-25%.

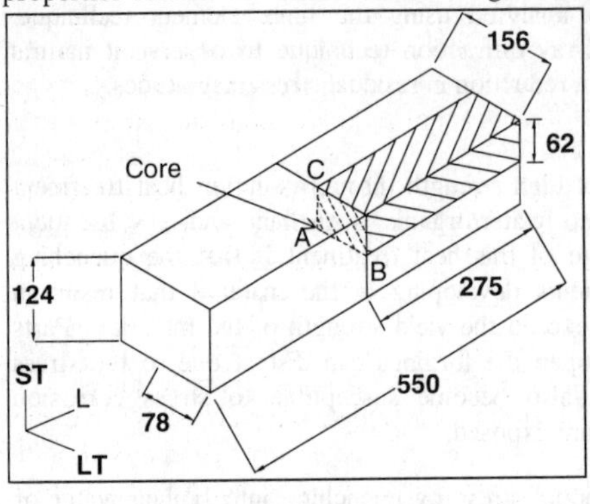

Figure 1 Diagram indicating section of block modelled for cold compression

An open die forging with dimensions of 124(ST)x156(LT)x550mm(L) was used for the computer model, Figure 1. The predicted residual stress distribution indicated surface compressive stresses (maximum of 212MPa) and tensile stresses in the core (maximum of 256MPa). To give an indication of the stress distribution after solution heat treatment, directional stresses (ST/LT/L) are plotted as a function of distance from the core of the block in both the LT and ST directions in Figure 2. The location of these stress distributions is indicated by the AB and AC lines in Figure 1.

Cold compression was modelled by moving a rigid surface towards one surface of the block at 6mm.s^{-1} while constraining the model in the opposing direction. It was generally possible to model one-eighth of the block due to symmetry. For all of the cold compression models a coefficient of friction of 0.06 was assumed to exist between the forged block and the steel platens (10). This value compared well with a value of 0.03 verified by HDA Forgings Limited, Redditch, UK using the ring test (11) with a light lubricating oil. When necessary, residual stresses were determined using the X-ray diffraction technique using procedures described in a previous publication (7).

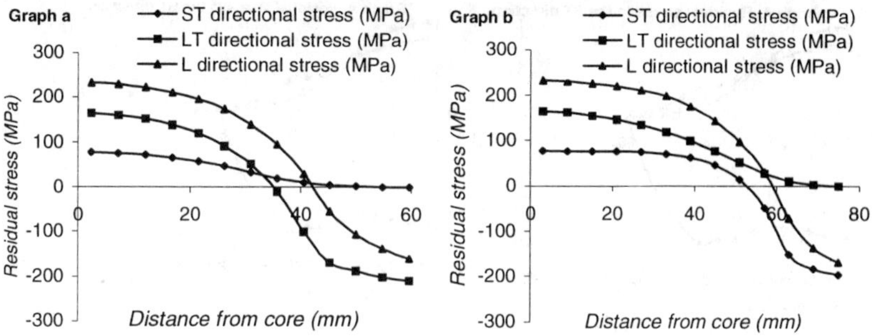

Figure 2 Graphs indicating residual stress distribution as a function of distance from the core of the block at a cross-section at its centre along AC (ST – Graph a) and AB (LT – Graph b) (see Figure 1) after solution heat treatment

RESULTS AND DISCUSSION

Influence of cold compression direction on residual stress magnitude

Previous work using the finite element model developed at the University of Limerick (12) has shown that 2% cold compression in the ST direction decreased the magnitude of the residual stress when compared with smaller amounts of deformation. Computer models were built to observe the effect on residual stress magnitudes of applying cold compression in the LT and L directions as opposed to the ST direction. The one-eighth model was modified so that the cold compression platen moved opposite the required surface for both cases. Cold compression of approximately 2% was applied in the LT direction resulting in a stress pattern similar to that obtained when deformation occurred in the ST direction. Figure 3 shows plots of directional stresses where the curves 'Compress LT 2%' and 'Compress L 2%' indicate the stress distribution after 2% cold compression in the LT and L directions respectively. Given that the model assumed isotropic mechanical properties, any differences observed should be related to the dimensions of the forging.

High tensile stresses (~120MPa) due to friction – similar to those observed with the ST cold compression – were again observed on the surface that was in contact with the platen. The main difference in the results was that while 2% cold compression in the ST direction resulted in compressive stresses remaining in the core of the sample, cold compression in the LT direction resulted in stresses of similar magnitudes (10 to 20MPa) but tensile. Another model with 3.2% cold compression showed that this trend continued with a slight decrease in stress magnitude (giving values of -2 to +5MPa). Cold compression in the LT direction as opposed to the ST direction can result in a difference of up to 40MPa in stress magnitude at certain locations for similar levels of deformation.

Tensile stresses are thought to remain after cold compression in the LT direction and not after cold compression in the ST direction due to one of two reasons:

- The dimensions of the block dictate the stress system introduced during quenching. This stress system may be such that stress relief in the ST direction (which has the shortest dimension) only results in core compressive stresses;
- The surface area in contact with the platens is largest for the case of cold compression in the ST direction and therefore results in lower core stresses.

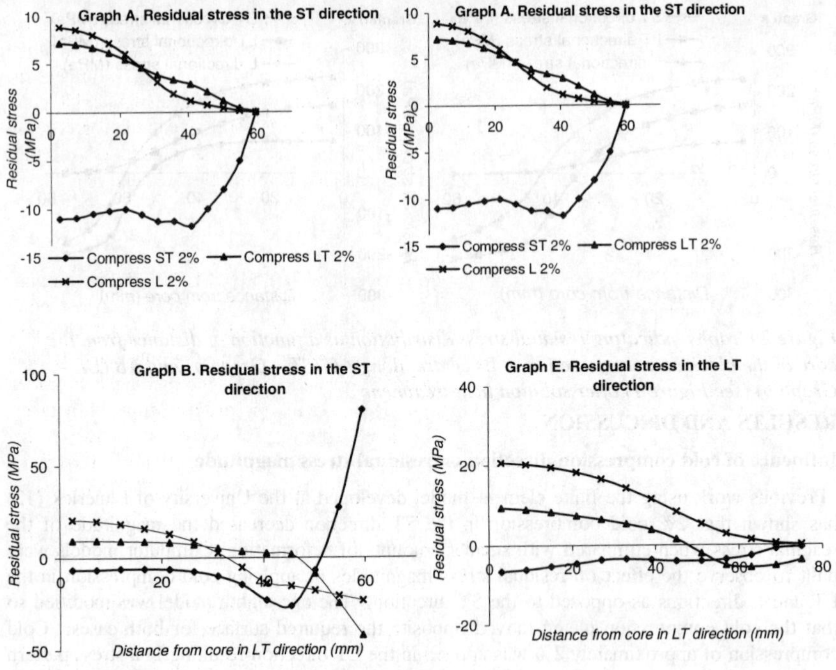

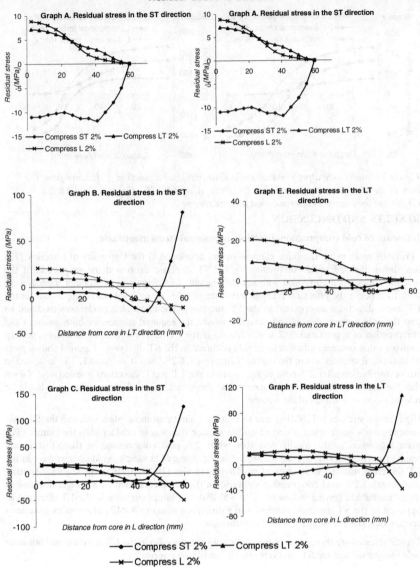

Figure 3 Graphs A, B & C represent residual stress acting in the ST direction versus distance from the core of block in the ST, LT and L directions respectively
Graphs D, E & F represent residual stress acting in the LT direction versus distance from the core of the block in the ST, LT and L directions respectively

The dimensions of the block dictate both of these possible answers. It can therefore be assumed that compressive stresses will be produced in the core of the material if cold compression is performed in the shortest direction. The validity of this statement is confirmed when the results for cold compression in the L direction are analysed. 2.4% cold compression in this direction resulted in tensile stresses of up 30MPa remaining in the core of the sample. The main advantage of applying cold compression in the L direction for this block is that the area in contact with the platens is small and therefore the area and magnitude of tensile stresses on the surface resulting from friction is reduced.

Effect of layer removal

A model of one quarter of the block (section measuring 124(ST)x78(LT)x275(L) mm was built to predict the residual stress distribution after 2% cold compression. After cold compression, a layer of material 4.77mm thick was removed from two opposing LT surfaces by deleting elements from these two surfaces. This resulted in maximum surface tensile stresses with magnitudes of up to approximately 60MPa remaining – comparing favourably with a magnitude of ~130MPa before removal. Removal of this material from both faces resulted in an overall deflection in the LT direction of the top of the block relative to the centre of ~0.0057mm. Removal of the first layer only resulted in a deflection of ~0.015mm which was then balanced by the removal of the opposing layer. It would therefore appear that the high tensile stresses that arise due to friction during cold compression can be machined away from the surface without resulting in large scale distortion as long as the machining is roughly symmetrical.

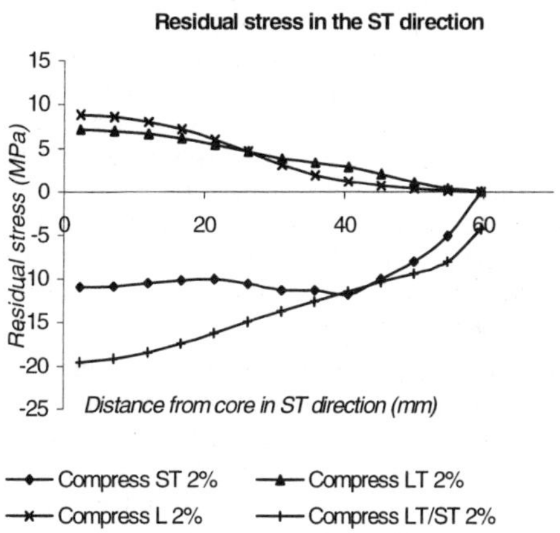

Figure 4 Effect of cold compression applied in two directions compared to ST and LT only.

Effect of applying cold compression in more than one direction

The advantages of applying cold compression in more than one direction would appear to be outweighed by the disadvantages. For example, cold compression in one direction results in high tensile stresses on the surfaces that are next to the platen. If cold compression were applied in two directions then four surfaces would be likely to contain high levels of tensile stress. However, cold compression first in the LT direction followed by the ST direction (or vice versa) may result in the complete removal of core stresses while the surface tensile stresses could be removed using a simple machining operation.

The computer model of cold compression was modified to allow deformation to take place first in the LT direction followed by the ST direction. The results of this analysis are plotted in Figure 4 as the curve 'Compress LT/ST 2%'. The results indicate that after cold compression in two directions the remaining residual stresses are generally higher than if the deformation is carried out in one direction. Therefore, no advantage is gained by deforming the forging in more than one direction.

Residual stress relief by stretching

Stretching (Tx51 temper) is often applied to plate as a stress relieving process as opposed to cold compression (Tx52 temper). It has been found that application of approximately 2% stretch results in almost complete relief of residual stresses while after even higher levels of cold compression (4-6%) significant stress magnitudes remain (2,3). It was therefore decided to model the application of a 2% stretch in the L direction to observe the effect on residual stress magnitude. Figure 5 displays the LT residual stress as a function of distance from the core in the LT direction.

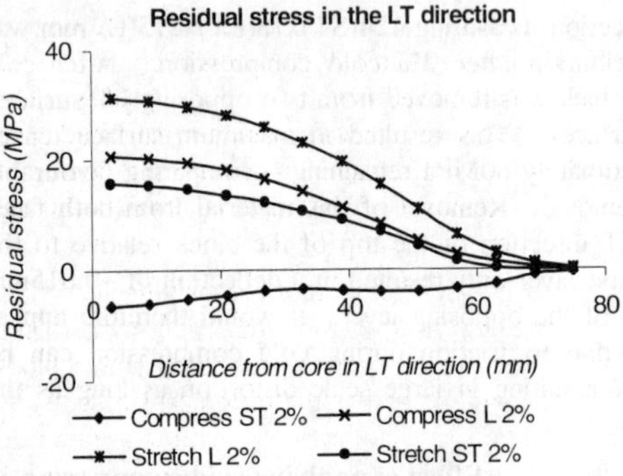

Figure 5 Comparison of the effect compression and stretching on LT residual stress.

A 2% stretch in the L direction resulted in a stress distribution where the maximum stress magnitude (compressive or tensile) did not exceed 60MPa in any of the three directions. This was an improvement on a similar percentage cold compression where surface stress magnitudes exceeded 130MPa due to the presence of friction between the platens and the forging. The remaining difference between the stress distributions was that the core stresses after the stretch remained tensile with magnitudes approaching 25MPa. The presence of tensile stresses in the core after stretching is similar to previous work carried out on stress relief of aluminium alloys. This work indicated that if tensile stresses existed before a Tx51 treatment then tensile stresses of smaller magnitudes remain (3,13), while if compressive stresses existed in the core of the sample before Tx51 treatment then compressive stresses of smaller magnitudes will remain (14). However, other investigators (15) found that stress relief by stretching resulted in tensile surface stresses (17MPa) while our computer model showed that these stresses remained compressive.

An obvious question arising from this work is that if cold compression in the ST direction results in compressive stress in the core of the material while deformation in the LT and L directions results in tensile stresses, would stretching in the ST direction result in compressive stresses also? A model applying a stretch of approximately 2% plastic deformation in the ST direction confirmed that tensile stresses also remained in the core of the material. This suggests that the tensile stresses that remain after cold compression may be due to the surface area in contact with the platens as opposed to the directions in which the stresses act prior to cold compression.

The effect of sectioning blocks containing residual stress

A finite element model of the forged block was transversely sectioned into six equal parts (measuring 124(ST)x156(LT)x41(L)mm) to observe how the residual stress magnitude varied as a result. Sectioning the block was achieved by removing elements from five locations in the modelled block. This model indicated that while there was considerable stress relief, surface compressive stress magnitudes acting in the LT direction of magnitudes up to 200MPa remained in the material. This indicates that even after a block has been sectioned, high stresses remain and that sectioning a block in one direction before a machining operation is unlikely to sufficiently relieve stresses to prevent distortion during machining. The main reason for this is that the stresses produced by quenching act in different directions depending on their location in the block. Therefore, sectioning the block in one direction will mostly result in the relief of residual stresses that are not parallel to that direction.

The influence of natural ageing on the efficacy of cold compression

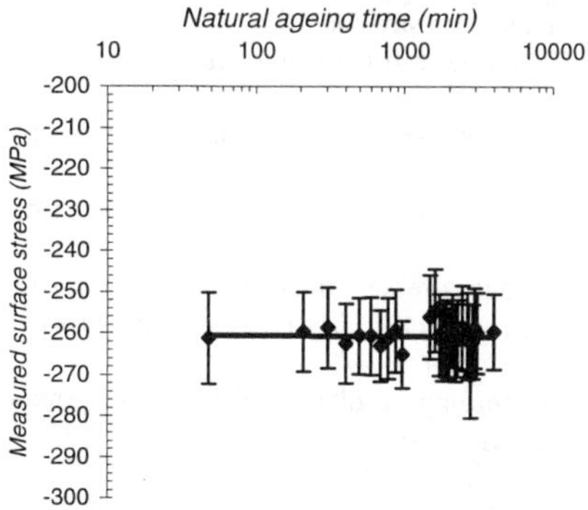

Figure 6 Surface residual stress magnitude versus natural ageing time

Residual stress measurements were taken immediately after solution heat treatment on a cubic block of 7010 with a side of length 52mm using the X-ray diffraction technique to determine if natural ageing resulted in any stress reduction. If the natural ageing process results in a reduction in residual stress magnitude then the deformation required to relieve the remaining internal stress distribution may be reduced.

X-ray diffraction measurements were taken in a diagonal direction at the centre of one surface on the 52mm cubic block. Figure 6 shows the measured surface stress plotted as a function of natural ageing time. These results indicated that the stress magnitudes at the centre of the face were relatively high (approximately -260MPa) but that was no stress reduction occurring due to the natural ageing process. This is similar to previous work (16) that has shown that ageing 7010 to a T6 type temper (24h at 120°C) results in no measurable reduction in residual stress magnitudes, while ageing at higher temperatures (e.g. T74, 8h at 110°C + 10h at 175°C) was found to result in significant stress reductions (~25%).

The finite element model was used to determine how natural ageing affected the residual stress distribution remaining after cold compression. The model of one-eighth of the block was modified so that the stress-strain curve originally input into the ABAQUS code at 20°C was input at 25°C and for 20°C the stress-strain curve measured after 2160 minutes natural ageing was input. The model was allowed to cool so that its temperature was approximately 20°C before cold compression. 2% cold compression was then modelled with the assumption that the material would deform as dictated by the data at 20°C. The change in mechanical data at room temperature did not affect the final residual stress prediction.

The finite element model indicated that tensile residual stresses of over 200MPa caused by friction between the block and the platen were created on the surface of the forging after cold compression. This residual stress magnitude exceeded that predicted using the stress-strain data measured directly after quenching ($R_{p0.2}$ = 133MPa). The results indicate that the stress magnitudes are generally higher after cold compression when the material has been allowed to naturally age. Tensile stresses in the core of the sample approach 30MPa where previously they were less than 20MPa. The main conclusions that can be drawn from these results are that allowing natural ageing to occur before cold compression results in higher residual stress magnitudes remaining due to the increased strength of the material. These higher stresses may lead to increased distortion in subsequent machining operations.

CONCLUSIONS

1. Residual stress magnitudes do not decrease with natural ageing time.
2. Allowing forgings to naturally age before cold compression results in higher residua; stress magnitudes than if they were compressed directly after quenching.
3. Cold compression in the LT and L direction results in a core stress distribution that is predominantly tensile, while cold compression in the ST direction results in compressive core stresses. For the geometry considered, compressing in one direction as opposed to another can result in a difference of up to 40MPa in core stresses.
4. Surface tensile stresses created by friction between the forging platen and the forging are higher where the surface area is larger.
5. Removal of the surface layers in contact with the cold compression platens (approximately 5mm) results in little distortion.
6. Applying cold compression in more than one direction results in an overall increase in residual stress magnitudes.
7. Sectioning of forged blocks containing residual stresses indicate that high stress magnitudes remain after the sectioning operation, especially in directions parallel to the sectioning direction.
8. Friction between the forging platens and the forging results in high tensile stresses developing on the surface in contact with the platens.

REFERENCES

1. Aerospace Material Specification, DTD5636, DTD5120B and DTD5130A, Materials Department, RAE, Farnborough, Procurement Executive, Ministry of Defence, UK, July 1981-1989.
2. Altschuler Y, Kaatz T, Cina B, 'Mechanical Relaxation of Residual Stresses', ASTM STP 993, Edited by L. Mordfin, 19-29 (1988)
3. Boyer JC, Boivin M, Materials Science and Technology, 1, 786-792 (1985)
4. Faulkner JF, 'ALCOA stress relieved forgings. Aluminium company of America - Sales division' (1963)
5. Bains T, Proceedings of the 1st International Non-Ferrous Processing and Technology Conference, 10-12 March 1997, St. Louis, Missouri, 221-231 (1997)
6. Hibitt, Karlsson & Sorensen Inc, 'ABAQUS user's manual, Version 5.7', Providence RI (1998)
7. Tanner DA, Robinson JS, Experimental Mechanics, 40, 75-82, (2000)
8. Jeanmart P, Bouvaist J, Materials Science and Technology, 1, 765-769 (1985)
9. Yoshihara N, Tsuyama S, Hino Y, Hirokami K, NKK technical review, 64, 21-27 (1992)
10. Schey JA, 'Metal Deformation Processes: Friction and Lubrication', Marcel Dekker Inc., New York (1970)
11. Male AT, Cockcroft MG, Journal of the Institute of Metals, 93, 38-47 (1964-1965)
12. Tanner DA, Robinson JS, Cudd RL, Fifth International Conference on Residual Stresses (ECRS5), September 28-30, 1999, Noordwijkerhout, The Netherlands
13. Myer RT, Kilpatrick SA, Backus WE, Metal Progress, March 1959, 112
14. Nickola WE, 'Residual stress Alterations via Cold Rolling and stretching of an Aluminium Alloy'. Mechanical Relaxation of Residual Stresses, ASTM STP 993 (1988), Edited by L. Mordfin, 7-18
15. Aerospace Technical Information Bulletin, 'Alcoa Stress Relieved Forgings,' Aluminium company of America, Series 68, Number 2, 1968
16. Tanner DA, Robinson JS, Whelan SD, Proceedings of the ASM Heat Treating Society Conference and Exposition, 12-15 October 1998, Rosemont, Illinois, 151-155, (1998)

SESSION 8C

SIMULATION OF STRESSES, RESIDUAL STRESSES AND DISTORTIONS DEVELOPING DURING GAS QUENCHING IN COMPLEX COMPONENTS

R. Kübler, C. Franz, N. Lippmann[1)], H. Müller, D. Löhe
Institute for Material Science and Engineering I, University of Karlsruhe (TH), P.O. Box 6980, D 76 128 Karlsruhe, Germany
[1)]Robert Bosch GmbH, 70233 Stuttgart, Germany

ABSTRACT

The residual stress distribution and the distortion of parts are influenced by the quenching process and the choice of the quenching media. The life-time of a part or a component depends on the sign of the residual stress state on the surface, whereas distortion influences the manufacturing costs, in particular the manufactoring time. When quenching huge numbers or only a few components manufacturers usually do not want to spend the time nor the money for preliminary experimental quench investigations or residual stress measurements.

On the other hand numerical simulation methods allow the investigation of temperature, microstructure and stress/deformation development in the whole part during the quenching process. For this purpose heat conduction, phase transformations, and mechanical behaviour of the steel as well as the couplings and the interactions between strains and phase transformations under consideration of transformation plasticity and the volume changes have to be modelled in the used FE-Program.

The choice of the quenchant has a large influence on the development of temperature, stress and deformation. Gas quenching - a modern, efficient and economical process - leads to a more homogeneous and reproducible cooling behaviour and generally to lower residual stresses compared to water and oil quenchants.

In this work, examples of simulations and experiments will be compared and discussed for cylinders. Cylinders with different dimensions were quenched in a single nozzle system using several gas media and pressures. Afterwards numerical and experimental results will be presented for a more complex two dimensional injection nozzle.

INTRODUCTION

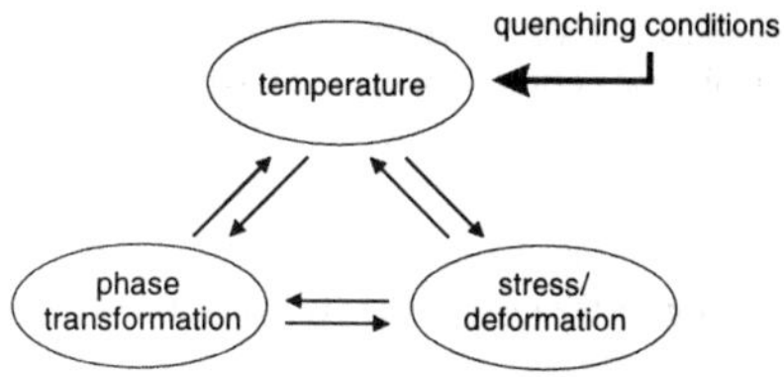

Fig. 1: Couplings between temperature, phase transformation and stress/deformation during the quenching process.

The geometry of steel parts as well as the material properties define the conditions during the quenching process. The measured residual stress distribution and distortions remaining after temperature equalization in the steel part are influenced by the used quenching process. The life-time of the part depends on the residual stress state on the surface, whereas distortions affect the production and processing costs significantly. At present, the numerical simulation of heat treatment processes like quenching, induction hardening, and laser hardening is more and more used in industrial applications in order to optimize the formation of the different phases and of course to optimize the mechanical behaviour and the residual stress distributions in the part. Using numerical methods it is possible to understand the formation of residual stresses and distortions in the part, because the development of temperature, microstructure, and deformations/stresses can be observed during the whole quenching process. Numerical simulations of such processes have to take into account complex interactions between the heat conduction, the phase transformations and the mechanical behaviour of the steel such as transformation plasticity (see Fig. 1 and [1, 2, 3]). In parallel, experimental investigations help to verify the numerical results. Not only the correct mathematical modelling of the physical phenomena between the temperature, the phase transformations, and the deformations/stresses has to be done but also the material properties, such as yield strength and modulus of elasticity, have to be known precisely. A lot of experimental investigations have to be carried out to obtain the temperature and microstructure dependent material input data.

MODELLING THE QUENCHING PROCESS

Modelling the temperature field

The transient temperature field in the quenched part has to be calculated by the general heat conduction equation. This universal three-dimensional nonsteady state equation is given by

$$\frac{\partial}{\partial x}\left(\lambda_x \frac{\partial T}{\partial x}\right)+\frac{\partial}{\partial y}\left(\lambda_y \frac{\partial T}{\partial y}\right)+\frac{\partial}{\partial z}\left(\lambda_z \frac{\partial T}{\partial z}\right)+\dot{Q}=\rho\, c_p \frac{\partial T}{\partial t}, \tag{1}$$

where T is the temperature field, λ is the thermal conductivity, $\dot{Q}$ is the heat source, c_p is the specific heat capacity, and ρ is the density of the steel. The relevant initial condition is

$$T_{t=0}=T(x,y,z)\,. \tag{2}$$

The first boundary condition at the surface of the part is given by the equation

$$T_{Surface}=T(x,y,z), \tag{3}$$

and the second boundary condition describes the heat flux perpendicular to the surface as follows:

$$q=-\left(\lambda_x \frac{\partial T}{\partial x} n_x+\lambda_y \frac{\partial T}{\partial y} n_y+\lambda_z \frac{\partial T}{\partial z} n_z\right)=h\,(T_{Surface}-T_{\infty}), \tag{4}$$

where h is the heat transfer coefficient, n_x, n_y, n_z are the components of the normal to the surface [3] and T_∞ is the quenchant temperature field in the unaffected region.

Modelling the phase transformation

The phase transformation kinetics of the diffusional and the martensitic transformation are very different from each other. The transformations have to be described by time-temperature-transformation diagrams [1,3]. The volume fraction of the diffusion controlled ferritic/pearlitic and bainitic transformation phase can be calculated by the following equation:

$$f(T,t)=1-\exp(-b\,t^{\,n})\,, \tag{5}$$

where t denotes time, and b and n are material dependent constants, which are determined by the isothermal-transformation (IT-) diagram. To compute phase transformations during cooling, first the incubation period of transformation has to be calculated with the Scheil method [4] which is given by

$$t=\sum_i \Delta t_i\,,\quad \sum_i \frac{\Delta t_i}{\tau_i}=1\,, \tag{6}$$

with τ_i being the incubation period of the isothermal transformation at temperature T_i. The volume fraction of the martensitically transformed phase can be calculated by the following equation:

$$f_{Martensite}=f_D\left[1-\left(\frac{T-M_f}{M_f-M_s}\right)^{\kappa}\right], \tag{7}$$

where $f_D = 1 - (f_{F/P} + f_B)$ denotes the volume fraction of austenite which can transform into martensite, M_s the martensite start temperature, M_f the martensite finish temperature and κ is a parameter which is set between 2...3. During the phase transformation the share in latent heat has to be considered in equation (1) and is determined by

$$\rho c_p^{*}=\rho c_p+\frac{\sum_k df_k\,\Delta H_k}{\Delta T}, \tag{8}$$

where ΔH_k is the latent heat of the kth-phase.

Modelling of strain and stress

The modelling of the mechanical behaviour of steel undergoing a phase transformation has to include the thermoelastic and plastic behaviour of the stable multiphase steel and the effect of the phase transformation. The total strain rate can be written as a sum of different contributions [2]:

$$\dot{\varepsilon}_{ij}^{t} = \dot{\varepsilon}_{ij}^{e} + \dot{\varepsilon}_{ij}^{pl} + \dot{\varepsilon}_{ij}^{th} + \dot{\varepsilon}_{ij}^{tp} + \dot{\varepsilon}_{ij}^{tr}, \quad (9)$$

where $\dot{\varepsilon}_{ij}^{e}$ is the elastic strain rate which is related to the stress rate by Hooke's law; $\dot{\varepsilon}_{ij}^{pl}$ is the plastic strain rate; $\dot{\varepsilon}_{ij}^{th}$ is the thermal strain rate that takes into account the different thermal expansion coefficients of each temperature dependent phase; $\dot{\varepsilon}_{ij}^{tp}$ is the transformation plasticity strain rate and $\dot{\varepsilon}_{ij}^{tr}$ is the strain rate due to the volume change caused by phase transformation. The mechanical behaviour of steels depends on temperature and the volume fraction of the different phases. For the investigation of steel hardening by gas or water quenching and case hardening a special FE/FD-program has been developed [1].

HEAT TRANSFER DUE TO GAS QUENCHING

The heat transfer between the surface of the part and the quenchant is one of the most important parameters. The surface temperature of the part is controlled by the heat transfer coefficient. The heat transfer is of the utmost significance for the temporal and spatial development of temperature, microstructure, deformations and stresses. Decisive for the level and the sign of the residual stress distribution in the part is the point in time at which the maximum temperature difference between the center and the surface and the point in time at which the beginning of the martensitic transformation takes place. Therefore several publications deal with modelling of heat transfer during the quenching process and its influence on the residual stress distribution [5,6,7].

During gas quenching the heat transfer is characterized only by convection. The heat flux can be calculated by the following equation

$$\dot{q} = h \cdot (T_{Surface} - T_{Gas}), \quad (10)$$

where h is the heat convection coefficient, $T_{Surface}$ the temperature at the surface of the part and T_{Gas} the temperature of the gas. Convection depends mainly on the flow velocity and pressure of the media, physical properties of the gas, properties of the boundary-layers, and on the difference between the temperatures of the surface and the fluid. The thin boundary-layers merge the different temperature and velocity conditions on the surface of the part and in the unaffected region. On the surface of the part the gas velocity is zero (no slip condition) and the gas temperature approaches the surface temperature.

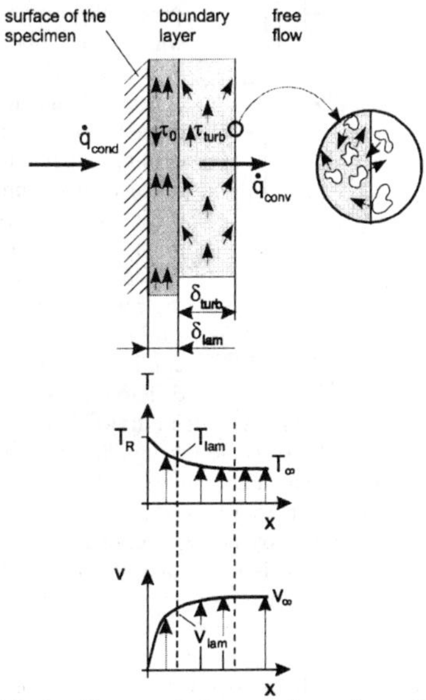

Fig. 2: Heat transfer between the surface and the quenchant for a turbulent velocity- and temperature- boundary-layer (Pr=1).

The velocity-boundary-layer thickness is usually defined in the literature as the distance from the surface where the gas velocity just reaches 0.99 of the velocity of the undisturbed region. In a similar way the temperature-boundary-layer is defined as shown in Fig. 2 for the Prandtl Number equal to 1.

In the boundary-layer the heat flux of the fluid can take place by laminar or turbulent fluid flow. In the laminar boundary-layer the heat flux perpendicular to the surface is transfered only by conduction.

The heat flux from the surface of the specimen into the quenchant is very low because of the absence of macroscopic particle movement perpendicular to the surface of the part. For industrial applications an improved heat transfer perpendicular to the surface of the specimen is needed. This can be achieved by turbulent flow. Conduction occurs in the laminar sublayer of the turbulent boundary-layer, whereas outside this sublayer convection and macroscopic particle movement take place (see Fig. 2, zoom-in). The increase of fluid velocity, the grade of turbulence, gas pressure and the use of lighter gases with higher heat conductivity improve the heat flux. No different stages are found during the gas quenching process, therefore a nearly constant heat transfer coefficient is assumed. Start-up effects at the beginning of the cooling process can be taken into account using temperature dependent values of *h*.

EXPERIMENTAL INVESTIGATIONS

Cylinder

Cylinders made of SAE 52100 (100Cr6) were chosen for the experimental investigations. The diameters of the cylinders are $D_{Cyl.}$ = 10, 20, 30 mm and the length is L = 3 $D_{Cyl.}$ (see Fig. 3). The roughness of the machined surfaces is $R_a \approx 5$ - 8 µm and all the edges are sharp. Drillings were made using spark-erosion in order to place thermocouples in the center of the cylinders. The cylinders were heated up to 860°C, then austenized from 20 min. under inert atmosphere and afterwards quenched in air, nitrogen, or helium at different gas pressures. The experimental set-up consists of a nozzle field, as shown in Fig. 4. The optimized position, and the right spacing and diameter of the nozzles were designed according to [8]. The temperature was measured and recorded during the heating, holding and quenching process using a thermocouple which was placed in the center of the cylinder. The experimental investigations were carried out in this experimental set-up, which guaranteed constant boundary conditions. Cylinders with different dimensions were quenched by air, nitrogen, or helium under various pressures. In Fig. 5, the cooling behaviour in the center of different cylinders quenched by helium under constant pressure is presented. The different cooling curves in Fig. 5 depict the spread of five experimental investigations under constant boundary conditions and quenching parameters. Increasing the volume-to-surface ratio shifts the cooling curves to later times. The difference between the cooling behaviour for $D_{Cyl.}$ = 10 mm and $D_{Cyl.}$ = 20 mm is very small, but for $D_{Cyl.}$ = 30 mm the cooling time increases strongly. Decreasing the rate of cooling, tantamount to increasing the surface-to-volume ratio, leads to different phase transformations. In case of $D_{Cyl.}$ = 10 and $D_{Cyl.}$ = 20 mm the beginning of the martensitic transformation is detected at 230 °C (cf. the discontinuity in the curve). Both cylinder sizes are through-hardened and only a low content of pearlite, bainite, and retained austenite is found. In the case of $D_{Cyl.}$ = 30 mm at about 40 seconds after starting the quench experiment the temperature of the cylinder increases. After temperature balance almost 100 Vol-% of pearlite were found by metallographic examination. Therefore the reason for the increasing center temperature can be found in the latent heat. Consequently the surface-to-volume ratio is a natural limit for the use of these quenchants. The cooling behaviour in the center of the specimen $D_{Cyl.}$ = 20 mm quenched with helium under different pressures is shown in Fig. 6. Again the cooling curves represent the spread of five experimental investigations under constant boundary conditions and quenching parameters. The temperature-time curves during the quenching with different pressures are very similar. Constant time differences between each cooling curve can be observed for constant temperatures. Increasing pressure increases the volume fraction of martensite in the center of the cylinder and decreases the cooling time.

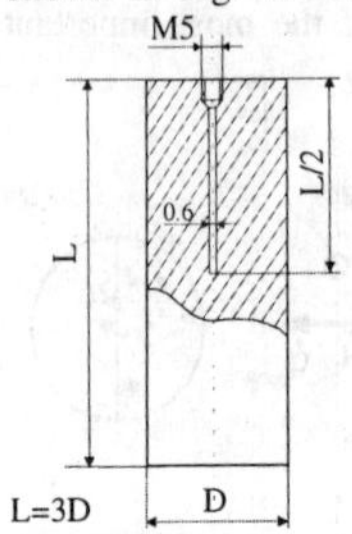

Fig. 3: Geometry of the cylindrical specimen.

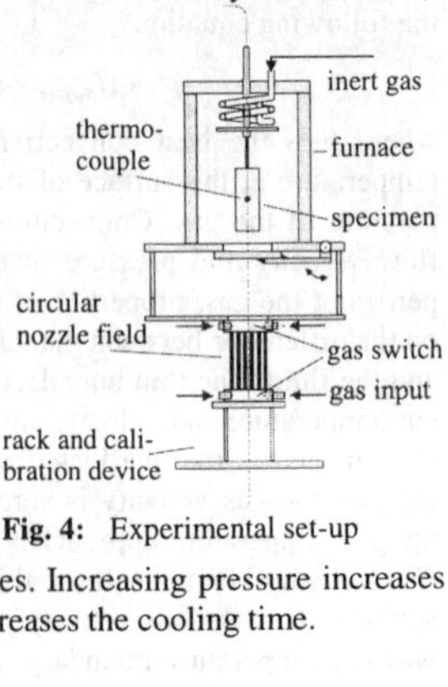

Fig. 4: Experimental set-up

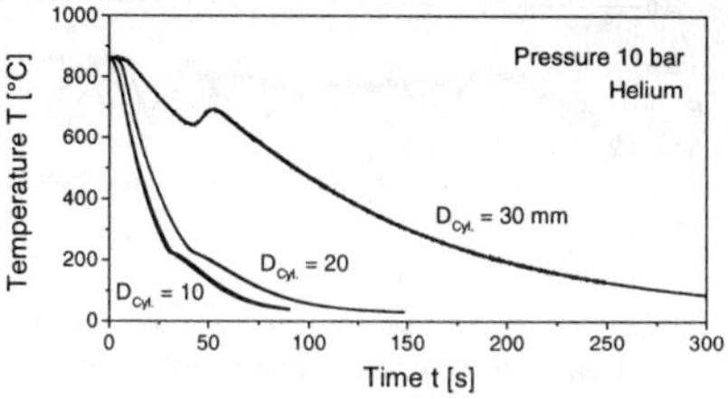

Fig. 5: Cooling behaviour in the center of different specimen sizes quenched with helium under 10 bar pressure.

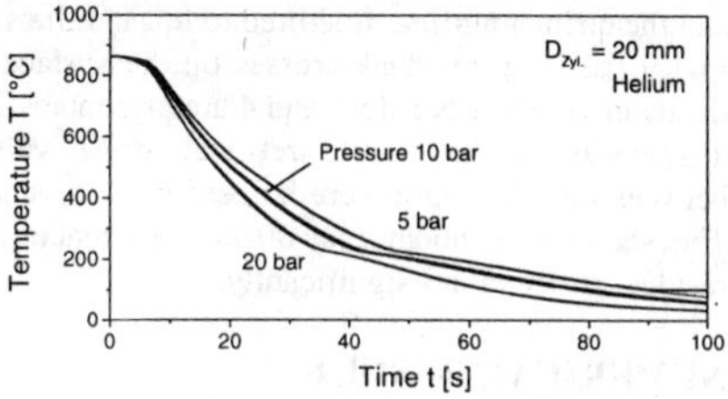

Fig. 6: Cooling behaviour in the center of the specimen $D_{Zyl.}$ = 20 mm quenched with helium under different pressures.

Tuyere holder

A tuyere holder of SAE 4140 (42CrMo4) representing a more complex geometry was used for experimental quenching investigations. The shape of the part is very complicated, hence not all dimensions are specified. The outer diameter (inner diameter) is approximately *28 mm (5 mm)* and the length is *96 mm* (see Fig. 7). In order to get informations about the temporal development of temperatures at different positions of the part several thermocouples were used. The drillings for the ∅ *1 mm* thermocouples were made using spark-erosion. The batch of parts was quenched from *860 °C* in a vacuum furnace after *20 min* of austenitization in nitrogen with *10 bar* pressure. A whole batch of parts was quenched to simulate an industrial quenching process, however only one tuyere holder was equipped with thermocouples. The temperature-time curves which characterize the cooling behaviour of the tuyere holder are presented in Fig. 8 for the different thermocouple gauging points. In Fig. 8 a) the temporal temperature development of thermocouples T1, T2, T3, and T4 is presented. For z = *5 mm* nearby the top end face of the part the temperature is decreasing rapidly. With increasing z-values the influence of the high heat transfer coefficient on the top end of the part is reduced and the increasing surface-to-volume ratio becomes dominant. Therefore the T,t-curves from the gauging points T3, T1, and T2 are shifted to later times. The differences in the cooling behaviour between T3 and T1, T2 are caused by the increasing surface-to-volume ratio and decreasing heat transfer coefficients with increasing z. The differences in theT,t-curves between the gauging points T1 and T2 are very small and the influence of the heat transfer on the inner diameter is low. The discontinuity in the T,t-curve for the gauging points T1, T2, and T3 insinuate a bainitic transformation. The surface-to-volume ratio for the gauging points z = *37*, z = *51*, and z = *59 mm* is equal. Therefore the lower cooling rate for the gauging points T5 and T6 compared to T1 is caused by increasing gas temperature and the reduced heat transfer with increasing z (see Fig. 8 b). Decreasing surface-to-volume ratio at z = *80 mm* increases the cooling rate

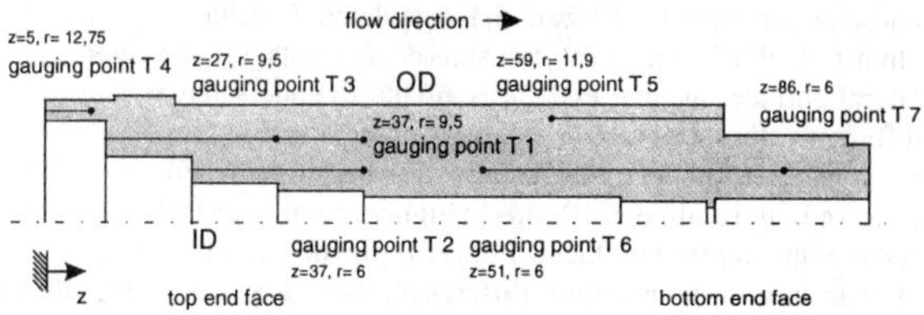

Fig. 7: Geometry of the tuyere holder.

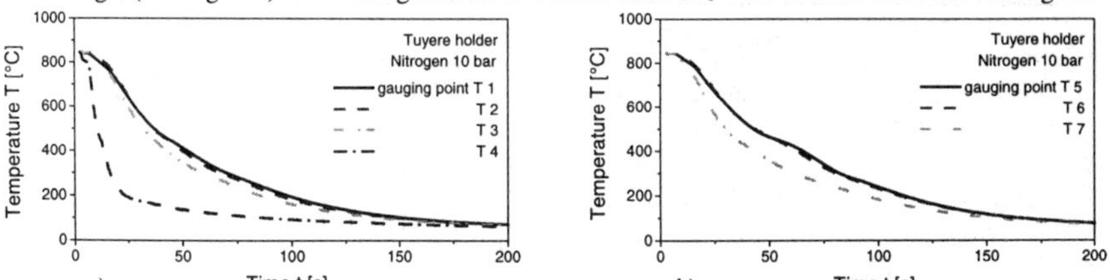

Fig. 8: Temporal development of temperatures for gauging points T 1, T 2, T3, and T 4 (a) and T 5, T 6, and T 7 (b) during the quenching process.

and the quenching-time is shifted to lower values. In Fig. 9 the hoop residual stresses on the surface of the tuyere holders No. 1, 2, and 4 are presented. The differences in the tensile residual stress values between the different tuyere holders are very small. The shoulder at about $z = 80\ mm$ influences the residual stress values significantly.

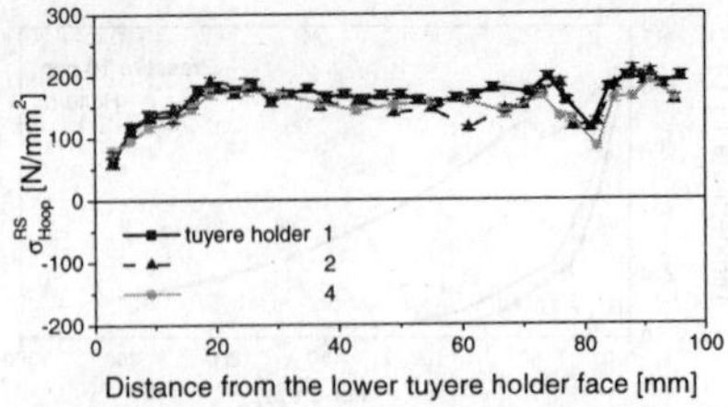

Fig. 9: Residual stress distribution on the surface of the different tuyere holders.

NUMERICAL RESULTS

Cylinders

For the numerical simulations the one-dimensional heat transfer coefficient *h* was calculated from experimental temperature-time curves from the center and close to the surface using a one dimensional FD-program [9]. In order to closely approximate the heat transfer for cylinders with different dimensions, for different gases and different pressures local and temperature dependent heat transfer coefficients *h* - as shown in Fig. 10 - were taken into account for each simulation. Using this method good accordance between numerically determined and experimental results is obtained. In Fig. 10 the differences in heat transfer coefficients for different types of gases are presented for constant cylinder dimensions $D_{Cyl.} = 20$ mm on the bar surface. At the beginning of the quenching process *h* increases strongly. After this start-up effect *h* is nearly constant.

Changing the quenchant from air to helium under constant pressure of 10 bar, the calculated *h* value is almost doubled. The heat transfer coefficients on the lateral surface and the end faces of the cylinders have different values, because on the bar surface an impinging flow and on the end faces only a parallel flow are observed. *h* is almost 10 times higher on the lateral surface than on the end faces. In Fig. 11 the development of temperature, temperature difference, axial stress and microstructure in the center and on the surface of the middle plane of the cylinders when using air and helium as quenchants under constant pressure of 10 bar is presented. In the following curves the point of the maximum temperature difference between the center and the surface of the specimen and several phase transformation intervals in the presented locations are marked. Comparing both types of gases, significant differences in the development of temperature, microstructure and stresses can be observed. As a result of the increasing *h*-values, the maximum temperature difference for the helium quenched specimen was shifted to later times and

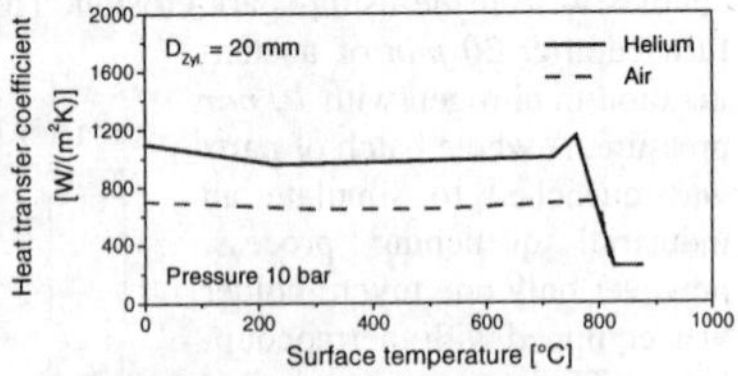

Fig. 10: Effect of gas type on heat transfer coefficient vs. surface temperature for helium and air quenched cylinder on the lateral surface.

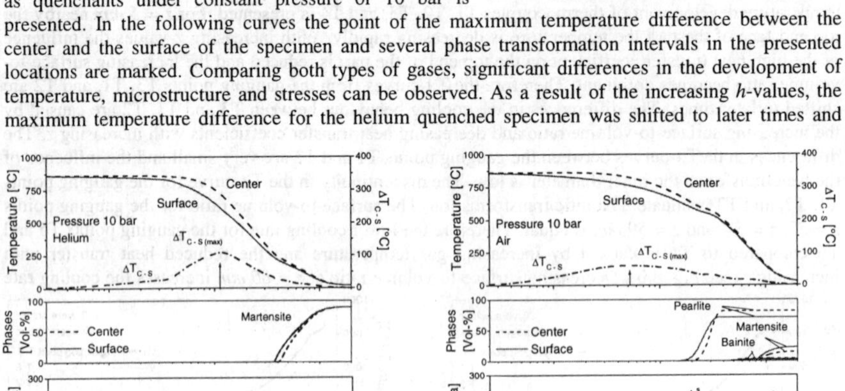

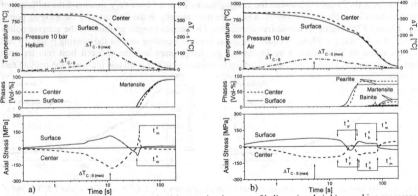

Fig. 11: Temperature, microstructure, and axial stress development of helium a) and air b) quenching processes.

higher values compared to air. After temperature balance the microstructure of the helium quenched specimen consists of martensite and retained austenite. During the air quenching process, at about 600 °C, the latent heat of the pearlite formation is set free. Using air as quenchant the reduced temperature difference between surface and center leads to lower axial stresses. The beginning of the pearlitic transformation decreases the axial stresses during the quenching process. At the end of the air quenching process the residual stress distribution differs from the one observed for through-hardened helium-quenched cylinders. Furthermore, reverse sign and higher amounts of axial residual stresses in the air quenched cylinders are a result of the pearlitic, bainitic and martensitic phase transformation. Especially the sign of the stress distribution before the start of the martensitic transformation plays a major role for the investigated quenching conditions and specimens. A comparison between the calculated and measured tangential residual stresses on the surface of the cylinders quenched by helium and air as quenchant is given in Fig. 12. Each different single symbol represents the average of five X-ray measurements on the surface of the cylinders. The calculated hoop residual stress data have the same tendency as those observed experimentally. The conformance between the calculated and measured hoop residual stresses is excellent for both gas quenchants. Quenching with helium leads to a residual stress distribution called "transformation type" with tensile residual stresses on the surface. On the other hand quenching with air results in the "quenching type" with compressive residual stresses on the surface.

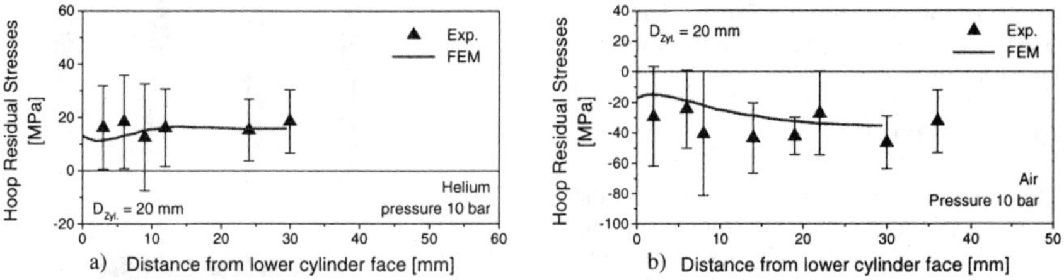

Fig. 12: Comparison of calculated and measured hoop residual stresses on the surface of the cylinder after quenching with helium a) and air b).

Tuyere holder

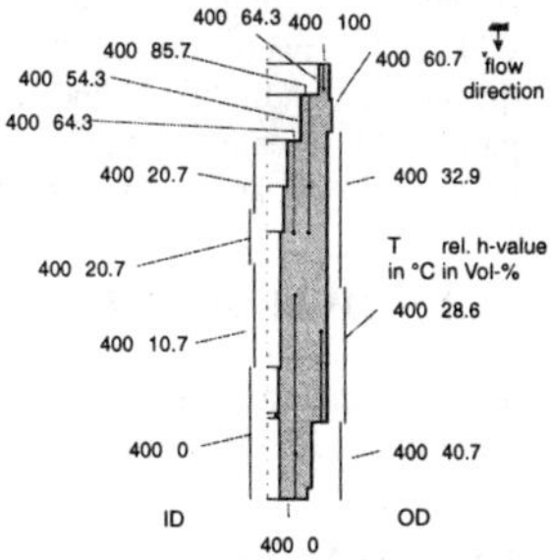

Fig. 13: Assumed heat transfer coefficient eq. at 400 °C.

Using a vacuum furnace for the gas quenching process the heat transfer from the surface of the tuyere holder is generally a function of the location, flow direction, and the temperature. The heat transfer is closely approximated for the quench process simulation using local and temperature dependent *h*-values, as shown in Fig. 13. *h* is very high on the top end of the part and decreases with increasing *z*-values. On the shoulder the higher turbulent flow increases *h*. The different cooling behaviour on ID leads to lower *h*. The heat transfer is only ≈ 40 to 70-% of the one OD. Using this method excellent agreement is observed between the num. and exp. T-t-curves. The temporal development of temperature, hoop stresses, and deformation (magnification *V=50*) during the quenching process is presented in Fig. 14. At the beginning of the quenching process the temperature distribution in the whole part is almost equal, only on the top and on OD lower values are found. At this time step tensile (compressive) stresses are found on OD (ID). The lower moment of resistence on the top of the tuyere holder leads to high deformations. The top of the part cools down very quickly and a high axial temperature gradient can be observed at *t=12.6 s*. The temperature in the bulk center portion is almost *850 °C*, but on the top the M_S-temperature is reached and the martensitic transformation starts. Therefore high compressive stresses and increasing deformations working against the shrinkage of the part can be observed. At *t=21 s* increasing axial and radial temperature gradients and a more and more complex hoop stress distribution can be observed. After the tuyere holder is transformed martensitically high hoop compressive stresses on OD and hoop tensile stresses on ID are calculated. After the quenching

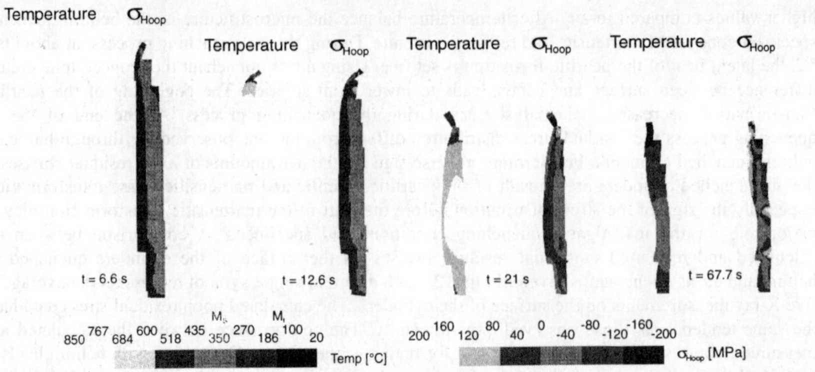

Fig. 14: Temporal development of temperature, hoop stresses, and deformations of the tuyere holder during the nitrogen quenching with 10 bar (magnification V=50).

process on OD (ID) tensile (compressive) residual hoop stresss are found as shown in Fig. 15. The location dependent *h*-values lead to axial gradients in the martensitic and bainitic microstructure.

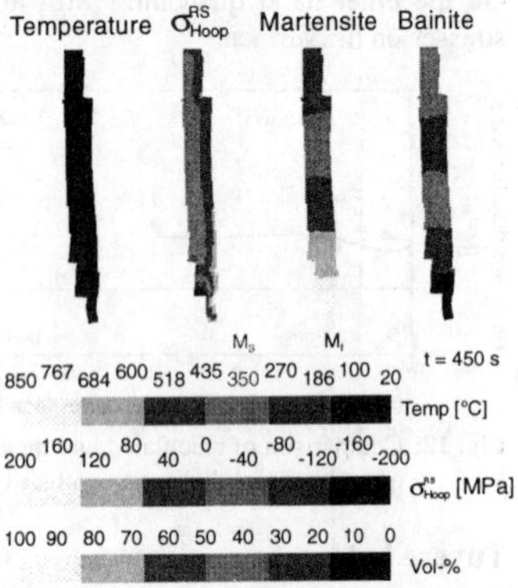

Fig. 15: Temperature, residual hoop stress, deformation and microstructure distribution after quenching.

CONCLUSIONS

The simulation of steel hardening requires the modelling of heat conduction, phase transformations and mechanical behaviour as well as the couplings between these parameters. Furthermore, temperature and phase dependent input data have to be determined, especially *h* is of primary importance. However the cooling behaviour of the surface of the part can not be measured directly. The conformance between the calculated and measured hoop residual stresses is excellent for the helium and air quenched cylindrical specimens. The complex flow field in a vaccum furnace and the interactions with and between the parts in the batch lead to difficult quenching conditions. Numerical simulation can be used as a tool for the simulation of complex 2D-parts. The agreement between the numerically and experimentally measured results for T-t-curves, microstructure, and residual stresses is good.

ACKNOWLEDGEMENT

The financial support of this research program by the DFG (Deutsche Forschungsgemeinschaft) is gratefully acknowledged.

REFERENCES

[1] H.-J. Yu, et al., *HTM*, Vol. **51**, p. 48 – 54, (1996).

[2] G. Besserdich, B. Scholtes, H. Müller, E. Macherauch, *Steel research 65*, No. 1, (1994).

[3] A. J. Fletscher, *Thermal Stress and Strain Generation in Heat Treatment*, Elsevier Sc. Publishers Ltd, Essex, (1989).

[4] E. Scheil, *Arch. Eisenhüttenwesen*, **8**, p. 565 –567, (1935).

[5] R. Kübler, H. Müller, D. Löhe, *Proceedings of the 3rd International Conference On Quenching and Control of Distortion*, Prag, Czech Republic, p. 333 – 339, (1999).

[6] R. Kübler, H. Müller, D.,Löhe, *DFG-Abschlußkolloquium*, Bonn-Bad Godesberg, (1999).

[7] *Proceedings of the 19th ASM Heat Treating Society Conference*, Cincinnati, Ohio, USA, (1999) (to be published)

[8] B. Gromoll, Dissertation Technische Universität Aachen, (1978).

[9] A. Majorek, Dissertation Universität Karlsruhe (TH), (1995).

THE VALIDATION OF MODELS FOR THE TIG WELDING OF NICKEL-BASE SUPERALLOYS BY NEUTRON DIFFRACTION

D. Dye, S. M. Roberts and R. C. Reed
University of Cambridge / Rolls-Royce University Technology Centre, Department of Materials Science and Metallurgy, Pembroke Street, Cambridge CB2 3QZ, UK

ABSTRACT

The post-welding residual stresses in four welded nickel-base superalloy plates have been measured and compared to the results predicted by a finite element model. The welds were manufactured under nominally identical conditions in 2 mm thick plates of rolled sheet IN718 & C263 and spray cast IN718 & RS5. The strain measurements were performed using the {111} composite reflection at the ILL, France and were converted to stress using diffraction elastic constants calculated by the Eshelby-Kröner-Kneer approach. The models for each weld use the same values of the fitting parameters for heat source width and thermal efficiency, the significance of which is discussed. The agreement between the measured residual stresses and the model results is generally good. It is recommended that the heat source used in such models be fitted to the results from welding test coupons where possible in order to eliminate the differences between model and experiment which were found. The longitudinal stress in the heat affected zone (HAZ) adjacent to each weld is of the order of the yield stress of each material.

1 INTRODUCTION

The drive to increase the thermodynamic efficiency and to reduce the cost and weight of aero-engines demands the use of improved grades of nickel-base superalloy in the combustor liner and casing. Furthermore, experience has shown that the production of welds in such high integrity structures often generates costly rework and scrap. Weldability can be defined as "the capacity of a material to be welded... and to perform satisfactorily in the intended service" [1]. Therefore weldability concerns an element of fitness for purpose, including the deformation and residual stress induced by the welding process. Excessive deformation in particular is a major cause of rework, and the presence of residual stress fields must be taken into account when estimates are made of the useful working life of the structure manufactured. Finally, in-service failure of the combustor, which is a safety-critical structure, is potentially a high consequence event. There is a need to be able to reliably model and understand the development of stress and distortion in shell structures of alloys used in this application.

In this paper, detailed characterisations of the residual strain state around welds in 2 mm thick plates of rolled sheet IN718 & C263 and spray cast IN718 & RS5 are reported and compared to the results from a mechanical 3D finite element model for welding.

Neutron Diffraction Strain Measurement The determination of residual stresses using neutron diffraction involves the measurement of interplanar spacings and thus the use of lattice planes as internal strain gauges [2]. If d_0 is the stress-free interplanar spacing of interest, typically one might measure the corresponding spacings d_i $(i = 1, 3)$ along three mutually orthogonal directions i, and then estimate the lattice strains ε_i according to

$$\varepsilon_i = \frac{(d_i - d_0)}{d_0} \qquad (1)$$

The problem is thus reduced to one requiring the determination of the residual stress state from the lattice strains ε_i. However, it is not sufficient to simply use the bulk mechanical properties for this purpose [3]. Consider the loading of a initially strain-free untextured polycrystalline material in the elastic regime; the applied load is partitioned between the crystallites because of their different orientations with respect to the coordinates of the stress tensor and their inherent elastic anisotropy, and hence the apparent plane-specific Young's modulus, E_{hkl}, and Poisson's ratio, ν_{hkl}, differ from those of the bulk. If the orthogonal directions i are chosen appropriately, it is often sufficiently accurate to assume that these correspond to the principal axes, so that the stresses may be determined from linear elastic theory to be

$$\sigma_i = \frac{E_{hkl}}{(1+\nu_{hkl})}\varepsilon_i + \frac{\nu_{hkl}E_{hkl}}{(1+\nu_{hkl})(1-2\nu_{hkl})}\sum_{j=1}^{3}\varepsilon_j \tag{2}$$

where σ_i is the stress in the direction i.

The elastic constants can be measured experimentally or calculated by a number of approaches, for example using the Voigt assumption (equal strain), the Reuss assumption (equal stress) or Eshelby's approach of a particle within a homogeneous matrix. The Eshelby model was developed by Kröner [4], Kneer [5] and Behnken [6] for the elastic deformation of crystallites in a polycrystalline aggregate. Application of this algorithm to single-phase materials, after scaling the single-crystal elastic constants by the bulk properties of the material, allows a prediction of the diffraction elastic constants (DEC's) to within the uncertainty in the experimental data [7], which is typically around 8%.

The onset of localised plasticity is known to introduce further complexity, since additional load then partitions only to unslipped grains. In Ni-base superalloys, there is now considerable evidence to suggest that the {111}, {311} and Reitveld-refined lattice parameters are insensitive to plastic deformation [8]. Nonetheless, the possibility of further complications due to the presence of grain texture should not be discounted.

Mechanical Modelling of Welding A possible alternative to measuring the strain around a weld is to use a validated mechanical model, such as those developed in recent years by Goldak, Karlsson or Oddy [9, 10, 11, 12, 13]. Such an approach may be preferable, since the sensitivity of the stress and distortion to welding conditions and material properties can be examined without the need for a prohibitively expensive series of welding trials and subsequent strain measurements. These models rely on an *a priori* knowledge of the weld pool shape and approximate knowledge of the welding thermal efficiency. They involve a conduction-based thermal model, typically using a distributed heat source, to model the welding thermal cycle, which is sequentially coupled to a thermal expansion-based elastic-plastic mechanical model in the Lagrangian (laboratory) frame of reference.

The thermal model used here is a development of the Rosenthal [14] approach in that the problem is modelled as one of heat diffusion from a defined source. It is acknowledged that the majority of the finite element timesteps used in the analysis where the steady state is valid are wasted compared to an Eulerian solution [10], however it is preferred because it is easier to couple a Lagrangian mechanical model [15] and permits the modelling of complex component geometries and weld paths.

In the finite element approach the thermal problem is treated as one of diffusion away from the fusion zone boundary. The molten region cannot support stresses and temperatures within it are therefore irrelevant to the subsequent mechanical model, so this approach is reasonable. In order to model the melt zone an appropriate distributed heat source is selected by the user and the parameters of this heat source fitted to the observed fusion zone shape [16]. The resulting temperature field can be checked against thermocouple or thermal imaging results from welding test coupons. For welding in atmosphere or on a jig it is necessary to incorporate heat sink terms to obtain an adequate fit to experiment.

Welding of thin sheet materials involves significant plastic strain in the weld and heat affected zone, and significant deformations (of order mm), and therefore the element s-tiffness matrices must be updated between iterations and loading steps, requiring a large strain approach to the problem [17]. The element formulation also requires some thought. The loading produced by the thermal analysis must be compatible with the mechanical element type, or else the problem will be overconstrained [12]. In practice this means that the mechanical problem should be solved using elements with a displacement field description one order higher than the thermal strain field imposed by the thermal model, or alternatively an interface routine should be used which conserves thermal energy such that the two are compatible, as adopted in ABAQUS [15].

The mechanical element selected must be able to reproduce all the deformation modes observed in the real problem, without introducing any spurious low or zero-energy modes. In this study the linear hexahedral element with enhanced bending behaviour is used in order to avoid such problems [17]. To achieve a solution at an acceptable computational cost, the degrees of freedom in the problem should be minimised by using as few elements and as few timesteps as possible. However, this is constrained by the need to capture the heat source in the thermal problem and to adequately model any through-thickness effects near the weld due to the thermal gradient. Therefore derefinement of the mesh away from the weld region is required, for example by the use non-orthogonal elements [16], the approach adopted here.

Nickel-Base Alloy Metallurgy The alloys used in this study, C263, IN718 and RS5 have the compositions shown in Table I. IN718 consists of four main phases, the FCC γ phase, a nickel-based solid solution, the cubic P γ' phase based upon $Ni_3(Al,Ti)$ which forms a coherent interface with γ, the cubic P γ'' phase based on Ni_3Nb and the FCC MC carbide. However, all four of these phases have a very similar lattice parameter and the extra peaks from the γ' and γ'' are extremely weak. Therefore when performing measurements upon these alloys the composite {111} peak has been used [8].

RS5 is a development of IN718 that removes the Fe but preserves the phase composition while C263 is a traditional γ/γ' polycrystalline nickel-base superalloy. In this study, the alloys are used both in their wrought forms (IN718 and C263) and the spray cast form (IN718 and RS5) which results in a smaller grain size and correspondingly higher yield strength.

Alloy	Ni	Cr	Co	Fe	Mo	Nb	Ti	Al	Ta	W	Zr	C
IN718	bal.	18.2		18.5	2.96	5.10	1.06	0.52	0.01			0.055
C263	bal.	19.7	19.7		5.77		1.93	0.44				0.060
RS5	bal.	16.0	10.2		5.00	4.66	2.66	0.98	1.32	1.99	0.03	0.060

Table I: Measured compositions of the three alloys used, in wt%.

2 METHOD

Weld Fabrication Autogenous bead-on-plate welds of length 80 mm were manufactured using square wave d.c. tungsten inert gas (TIG) welding in solution heat treated $100 \times 50 \times 2$ mm sheets of each material. The welds were placed centrally on each plate under the welding conditions shown in Table II. The workpiece was insulated from the welding jig using graphite plates and was unconstrained, allowing large, easily measurable distortions to develop. This also meant the effect of constraint did not have to be modelled.

velocity	1.59 $mm\,s^{-1}$
peak current	80 A
base current	40 A
frequency	2 Hz
% cycle at peak current	60
torch-work potential	9 V

Table II: Conditions under which square-wave d.c. TIG welding was performed.

Neutron Diffraction Strain Measurement Neutron diffraction measurements of the lattice strain in the longitudinal, transverse and through-thickness directions with respect to each weld were made at the mid-length of each plate using the {111} reflection at the D1A diffractometer of the Institut Laue Langevin (ILL), France. A wavelength of 2.994 Å was used. In the longitudinal direction incident slits 1 mm high and 1 mm wide were employed with 1 mm collimator slits on the diffracted beam. For the transverse orientation 10 mm high and 1 mm wide incident slits were used.

For the purposes of calibration, d_0 measurements were made from strain-free $2 \times 2 \times 50$ mm sticks electro-discharge-machined from nominally identical welds which were taken from both the heat affected zone (HAZ) of each weld and from the plate edge, Table III. The measurements were made in the transverse orientation with respect to the welding direction. The HAZ to far field variation in lattice parameter was up to a factor 3.4×10^{-4}, and a linear correction was used to the corresponding lattice strain measurements. The longitudinal measurements were also corrected for a factor 4.1×10^{-4} change in the measured strain free lattice parameter of all the samples to account for the translation of the slits in the incident beam in this configuration. This figure was arrived at post-experiment in order to obtain a stress balance over all of the samples.

The measured lattice strains were converted to stress using calculated diffraction elastic constants, Table III. These were calculated with Hauk's algorithm [3] using the single crystal properties of the γ and γ' phases, scaled to give the correct bulk elastic properties. This approach has been shown to have an uncertainty of around 8% [7].

material	form	E_{bulk} (GPa)	ν (-)	E_{111} (GPa)	ν_{111} (-)	d_0 (Å)	σ_y (MPa)
IN718	wrought	204	0.299	246	0.258	3.6082	300
C263	wrought	223	0.288	261	0.251	3.5877	400
IN718	spray cast	204	0.299	246	0.258	3.6043	650
RS5	spray cast	210	0.3	253	0.258	3.6068	700

Table III: The room temperature bulk elastic properties E_{bulk} & ν, calculated diffraction elastic constants E_{111} & ν_{111}, measured strain-free lattice parameter d_0 and room temperature yield strength σ_y of the materials considered.

Finite Element Model Description The finite element model used in this study was a 3D model constructed using elements of dimensions $1 \times 1 \times 0.5$ mm in the weld region and $4 \times 4 \times 1$ mm in the far field. Derefinement between the two regions was achieved with non-orthogonal elements after Goldak [16]. A circular constant flux heat source 4 mm in radius and a welding thermal efficiency of 0.55 were used, which were produced by fitting to the fusion boundary width and thermocouple results of a weld in a larger wrought IN718 sheet produced under the same welding conditions. This heat source was applied to all four models, assuming that the model heat source is a function of the welding conditions and not the alloy. Convective cooling was also applied to the surfaces of each plate.

ABAQUS [15] was used with linear elements to solve the thermal problem, dividing the welding path into 160 equal steps plus the subsequent cooling. The temperatures derived were then used in a mechanical model with an identical mesh. The mesh used had 3744 elements and 5289 nodes and typically required one hour for the thermal analysis and five hours for the mechanical on an SGI Origin 2000 computer with an R10000 processor.

The bulk room-temperature Young's modulus, yield strength and Poisson's ratio used are given in Table III for each alloy. Temperature-dependent values were used in the models, which were derived from test data. These were extrapolated to the melting temperatures of each alloy and then extended to model a compliant, thermally conducting solid above melting.

3 RESULTS AND DISCUSSION

Measurement of lattice strain The strain measurements made and the associated uncertainties are shown in Figure 1. The strain scans were made on both sides of each weld, to check that the positioning away from the weld line was correct. Measurements from the fusion zone showed almost no intensity because of the strong <100> texture in the weld direction, and measurements where the gauge volume is considered to have been partially immersed in the weld have been excluded. This is because the resultant shift in the centre of gravity of the gauge volume changes the 2θ angle measured and therefore the apparent strain. The longitudinal strains show a consistent pattern of a tensile region in the heat affected zone of magnitude between 1500×10^{-6} in the wrought IN718, to 2300×10^{-6} in the spray cast materials.

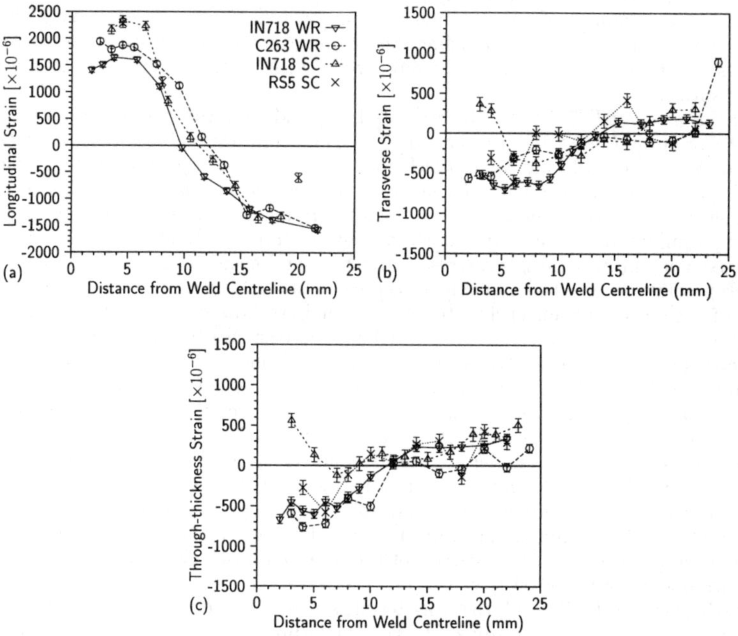

Figure 1: Measured {111} longitudinal (a), transverse (b) and through-thickness (c) lattice strains within the welded plates of spray cast (SC) and wrought (WR) forms of the alloys C263, IN718 and RS5. The symbol labelling is consistent in all three diagrams.

The longitudinal strain remains constant in the near-HAZ to a distance of approximately 6 mm in all the welds. The longitudinal strain then decreases rapidly to zero over 4 mm in the wrought IN718. In contrast, the decrease occurs over 7 mm in C263, which has the highest Young's modulus of the alloys in the study. The longitudinal strain continues to decrease to around -1500×10^{-6} a distance 15 mm from the weld centre in all the welds except in RS5. The strain then remains nearly constant to the edge of the plate.

The measured transverse and through-thickness strains range, with one exception, between -900 and 600×10^{-6}. With the exception of the spray cast IN718 all the welds display through-thickness and transverse strains of approximately -700×10^{-6} adjacent to the weld. At a distance of 4 to 8 mm from the weld the strains increase towards an approximately constant strain of 0 to 300×10^{-6} in the far field. The width of the compressive region varies widely for the transverse strain, and is smallest for the C263 and greatest for the wrought IN718 plate. The increase in strain is again shallowest for the stiffest material, C263. However, this pattern is not repeated for the through-thickness strain for which all three alloys show a very similar distribution.

The spray cast IN718 plate shows a rise into tension immediately adjacent to the weld 7 mm from the weld centre from a transverse strain of -300×10^{-6}. The pattern is repeated for the through-thickness measurements, with a rise into tension from approximately zero strain.

Comparison of measured stress with the finite element (FE) model The measured and predicted residual stresses in each plate are shown in Figure 2. The computed stresses which are quoted have been determined from the FE model by averaging over a volume equivalent in shape and magnitude to the gauge volume. This is in order to avoid any error introduced by the different volume represented by the finite element and the neutron diffraction gauge volume. As an example of why this must be important, consider the strain which would be measured in a beam in pure bending: the strain average through-thickness that would be measured by neutron diffraction is zero, whereas the actual strain is zero only at the neutral surface.

For the wrought IN718 weld, the measured longitudinal residual stress has a plateau in the HAZ of around 390 MPa at a position 3 to 6 mm from the weld centre. The measured stress decreases towards the weld, which may be because the yield strength of the weld is lower than in the parent plate, owing to a larger grain size and strong <100> texture. The longitudinal stress then decreases, passing through zero at approximately 9 mm and reaching a minimum of -400 MPa a distance 18 mm from the weld centre. The measured transverse and through-thickness stresses are small and negative, around -50 MPa.

The predictions are in reasonable agreement with the measurements, except that the width of the tensile region of longitudinal residual stress is overestimated by 2 mm and the minimum is underpredicted at -280 MPa. The decrease towards the weld is not reproduced, possibly because microstructural changes which arise during welding are not accounted for in the finite element model. However, it is felt that the observed residual stresses are reproduced reasonably well, especially since the fitting parameters of the thermal model have not been explicitly fitted to this weld.

Even for welds produced under laboratory conditions, significant weld-to-weld variation in the weld width and measured residual stress field are observed. This is due to many factors; the secondary welding process variables may be quite variable, *e.g.* the shielding gas flow rate and atmospheric moisture levels both of which can affect the arc. Also the composition and mechanical properties of the material may exhibit considerable scatter, even within a single parent sheet.

For the wrought C263 weld, the peak tensile stress is correctly predicted, but the width of the tensile region of longitudinal stress is underpredicted by around 2 mm and again the minimum in the far field is underpredicted. Additionally the change from nearly zero transverse and through-thickness stress in the HAZ to around -170 MPa in the far field is not reproduced. From a comparison to the measured strains, this appears to be caused by underprediction of the longitudinal strain because the predicted stress pattern is similar

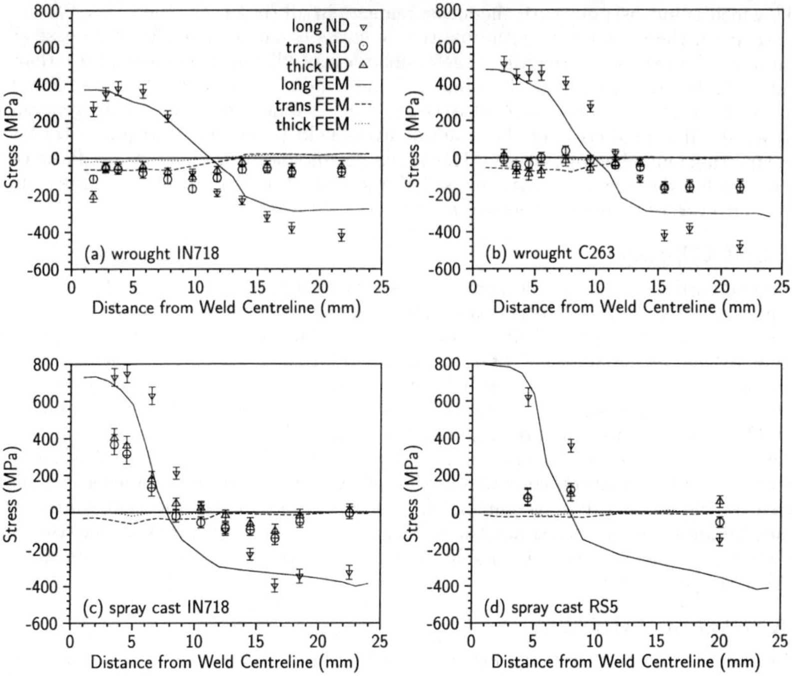

Figure 2: Longitudinal (long), transverse (trans) and through-thickness (thick) stresses at the mid-length for the welded plates measured by neutron diffraction (ND) and predicted by the finite element model (FEM).

to that for the wrought IN718 weld, as is the measured strain.

For the wrought C263 and spray cast IN718 & RS5 welds the fusion boundary profiles in particular are not well predicted, with the weld width overpredicted in the C263 and IN718, and underpredicted in the RS5 by up to 1 mm on widths of around 7 mm. This implies that the amount of heat has been over- or under-estimated respectively. One would expect this to be reflected in the widths of the tensile regions of longitudinal stress.

In the spray cast IN718, the most noticeable difference is the tensile transverse and through-thickness stresses observed close to the weld, a feature not predicted by the finite element model. It is not clear why this is observed, but it has been reported in other welding situations such as the electron beam welding of Waspaloy [18]. The peak longitudinal stresses are again just greater than the nominal yield stress. The width of the tensile region is underpredicted by the finite element model by 2.5 mm. Again the peak distortion is overpredicted by the finite element model, but by a lesser amount. However, the magnitude of the compressive minimum in the far field, −390 MPa, is correctly predicted.

For RS5, where very few residual stress points are shown due to the lack of longitudinal strain measurements, the tensile region of transverse and through-thickness stress observed in the spray cast IN718 is not observed. Similarly the width of the tensile region of longitudinal stress is underpredicted, by around 2 − 3 mm. However, the far field longitudinal residual stress measured is much higher than predicted by the model. It is possible that the gauge volume was not fully immersed when the longitudinal strain measurement was made, which is inconsistent with the measurements in all the other alloys.

In general, the region of longitudinal tensile stress is narrower in the spray cast alloys which have greater yield strengths. The fusion zone profiles in particular imply that the use of a single heat source for the same welding condition in different alloys cannot be justified. However, the agreement observed in the residual stress fields is in general felt to be good. If a prediction of the residual stress field is all that is required then such approximations may be appropriate. This is significant since it means that predictions can be made with some confidence for proposed alloys without having to make welding coupons for the purposes of fitting the thermal model.

4 CONCLUSIONS

Residual stresses in tungsten inert gas (TIG) welded sheets of wrought IN718 & C263 and spray cast IN718 & RS5 nickel-base superalloys have been characterised using neutron diffraction and compared with a finite element model. The measured near-weld longitudinal residual stresses are, in all cases, of order the material yield stress. They then decrease to a minimum of -400 MPa in the far field away from the weld. The measured transverse and through-thickness stresses are small except in the spray cast IN718 plate adjacent to the weld, where they rise to approximately 280 MPa.

The model results for residual stress compare well, given that the models have not been fitted to the thermocouple results or the weld fusion boundaries. However, significant differences remain and it is recommended that where practicable the heat sources used for such models are calibrated against welding test coupons. It is noted that they may nevertheless be able to give reasonable predictions of residual stress for proposed alloy modification programmes.

ACKNOWLEDGMENTS

The authors acknowledge funding from the Engineering & Physical Sciences Research Council (EPSRC), Rolls-Royce plc. and the Defense Evaluation & Research Agency (DERA). The assistance of Paul Andrews and Colin Small of Rolls-Royce, Dr. Mike Henderson of DERA and Prof. Philip Withers is acknowledged. Beamtime was provided by the ILL (experiment 5-26-83). The assistance of Alex Madgwick, Robin Preston and Howard Stone in performing the experiment is gratefully acknowledged.

REFERENCES

[1] 'Metals Handbook Vol 6: Welding, Brazing and Soldering', ASM (OH USA), 9th ed., 1983 609–646
[2] Smith D J, Leggatt R H, MacGillivary H J, Webster P J, Mills G. J Strain Analysis (1988) 23:201–211
[3] Hauk V, 'Structural and Residual Stress Analysis by Nondestructive Methods', Elsevier (UK), 1997
[4] Kröner E, Z Physik (1958) 151:504–518
[5] Kneer G, Phys Stat Sol (1963) 3:K331–K335
[6] Behnken H, Hauk V, Z Metallkunde (1986) 77(9):621–626
[7] Holden T M, Clarke A P, Holt R A, Met Mat Trans A (1997) 28A:2565–2576
[8] Stone H J, Holden T M, Reed R C, Acta mater (1999) 47(17):4435–4448
[9] Goldak J A, Bibby M, In Giamei A F, Abbaschian G J, eds,'Proc. Modelling of Casting and Welding Processes IV,' TMS (PA USA), 1988 153–166
[10] Goldak J A, Breiguine V, Dai N, In Smart H B, Johnson J A, David S A, eds,'Trends in Welding Research - Proceedings of the 4th International Conference,' ASM (OH USA), 1995 5–11
[11] Karlsson R I, Josefson B L, J Pressure Vessel Tech (1990) 112:76–84
[12] Oddy A S, McDill J M J, Goldak J A, J Pressure Vessel Tech (1990) 112:309–311
[13] Lindgren L-E, Häggblad H A, McDill J M J, Oddy A S, Comp Method Appl Mech and Eng (1997) 147:401–409
[14] Rosenthal D, Trans ASME (1946) 849–866
[15] 'ABAQUS/Standard User's Manual', HKS (RI USA), 1999
[16] Goldak J, Chakravarti A, Bibby M, Metall Trans B (1984) 15B:299–305
[17] Zienkiewicz O C, Taylor R L, 'The Finite Element Method Vol 2: Solid and Fluid Mechanics, Dynamics and Non-linearity', McGraw-Hill (Maidenhead UK), 4th ed. 1994
[18] Stone H J, 'The Characterisation and Modelling of Electron Beam Welding', PhD. thesis, Cambridge University (Cambridge UK) 1999

NUMERICAL SIMULATION OF THE PRIMARY RESIDUAL STRESSES IN PLASMA SPRAYED THERMAL BARRIER COATINGS

MK Kiriakopoulos and AG Youtsos
European Commission, Joint Research Centre, Institute for Advanced Materials,
P.O. Box 2 – 1755 ZG Petten, The Netherlands

ABSTRACT

In the course of the last two decades thermal barrier coatings (TBCs) have been used effectively in aircraft engine technology to reduce the thermal load of the underlying load bearing metallic material. Despite of the strain tolerant characteristics that TBCs exhibit, premature failure is sometimes observed. The large number of parameters involved during processing, the composition of the sprayed particles as well as the subsequent phase transformations and the combination of mechanical, thermal and environmental loading conditions give rise to a number of possible failure scenarios. Additionally, accelerated laboratory testing often imposes a number of unjustified assumptions with respect to simulating service conditions, which consequently complicate further the failure identification. In this paper, the induced residual stresses in PS coatings are addressed as a first step towards better understanding of their behavior. Processing parameters and the substrate temperature have a profound effect on the formation of porosity in PS coatings, which is intimately related to the development of residual stresses, strain tolerant behavior and thermal conductivity. In this paper the deformation characteristics, the solidification process and the induced quenching stresses of a representative set of plasma spray droplets are numerically studied based on given sets of initial conditions for the droplets. The results of this work demonstrate that the primary induced stresses and subsequent cracking are the link between the selected PS processing parameters and the resulted microstructure that is called to sustain the applied thermo-mechanical load. This link has been vastly ignored from previous research efforts. This work is part of the JRC research effort directed at improving our understanding of the behavior of PS TBCs, at failure identification and at life prediction modeling.

1. INTRODUCTION

Demands for efficient, environmentally superior and cost competitive aircraft engines and stationary gas turbines for power generation have led to the development of new materials and new processing techniques. TBCs allow the surface temperature of components to increase without compromising the structural properties of the alloy. The majority of TBCs currently used on turbine components is based on the yttria stabilized zirconia (YSZ) system. TBCs are applied by plasma spraying (PS) or electron beam - physical vapor deposition (EB-PVD). The two distinctly different processes reflect to completely different observed failure patterns.

One of the aims of the JRC research on TBCs is to better understand the plasma spray forming process, estimate the porosity of PS YSZ and evaluate the quenching and cooldown residual stresses based on numerical calculations and correlation with experimental evidence obtained from X-ray (Morreto (1)) and neutron diffraction experiments (Youtsos (2)) as well as thermal conductivity measurements. Residual stresses are often included in studies aimed at predicting the structural response of TBCs to thermo-mechanical loads, but unfortunately calculation is often based on unrealistic assumptions. The porous and lamellar nature of PS-TBCs is disregarded and no mechanism is included to account for its strain tolerant nature. The processing parameters and deposition temperature effects have profound effects on the morphology of the coating. Optimized processing balances the strain tolerant nature of the produced coating towards a favorable more compliant system but unavoidable reduces its life expectancy. Additionally, the evolution of the PS morphology cannot be disregarded, since high degree of strain tolerance increases the growth of the oxide layer and possible sintering increases the thermal conductivity of the PS coating. Both mechanisms act against long life PS systems. The above phenomenological arguments are mostly completely absent in published residual stress calculations since homogeneous, isotropic elastic material properties are often assigned to the PS coatings. Such finite element calculations show that the thermal expansion misfit during a thermal cycle gives rise to tensile stresses of the order of 0.1 to 0.5 GPa in the ceramic coating, whereas its failure in tension lies between 20 and 100 MPa! The outcome of such numerical modeling, in the authors' opinion, adds very little to the advancement and further understanding of the PS technology.

During the plasma-spray coating process, individual sprayed particles are subject to the *primary* cooling process. In modeling of PS this primary cooling stage was seldom taken into account before the 90's (Takeuchi (3), Kuroda (4)). The reason is that it is both experimentally and numerically difficult to be evaluated quantitatively. The last decade, three research groups, (i.e. SUNY, MIT and NIST) contributed significantly to better understanding of the spraying parameters on the final properties. A schematic drawing of the plasma spray process is shown in figure 1. At the end of the process and depending upon the processing parameters selected, the TBCs have a microstructure of lamellae, pores and cracks. Porosity of the order of 5 to 15 % is usually obtained.

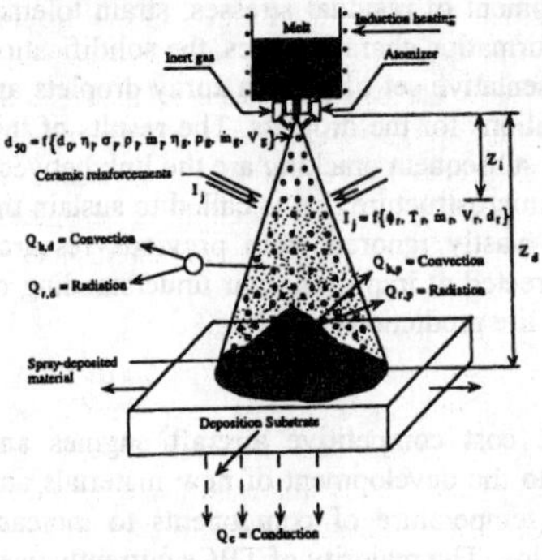

Fig. 1 Schematic of the PS atomization and deposition (after E.J. Lavernia, Wiley, 1996)

The post-fabrication cooldown induced residual stresses are often called *secondary*. They strongly depend upon the volume fraction and orientation of the pores and cracks. Although they have been investigated by several research groups, measurements and calculations have revealed a wide spectrum of values in the top coating both in magnitude and in sign. The main reason is that the tens of parameters that play a major role during spraying are not reflected adequately in the macroscopic characterization of their thermomechanical properties. Initial porosity and crack saturation lengths within TBCs have never been previously introduced in published calculation of secondary cooling stresses. Instead, homogeneous isotropic layers of YSZ are used in the calculations. The results expected from such calculations vary with respect to the introduced material data not only in magnitude but also in sign. It is therefore evident that rigid conclusions cannot be drawn. Research efforts excluded from the above description are summarized hereafter. Bengtsson and Persson (5) presented calculations from primary and secondary cooling as well as measurements obtained by the modified layer removal method. Gill (6), (7) suggested a finite difference scheme to account for the thermal field and strain energy balance. A review work on the residual stresses in thermal spray coatings (Clyne et al (8)) pays particular attention on the measurement methods and the effect of residual stresses on adhesion.

2. FORMULATION

In this section the procedure we follow to simulate the deposition process of metallic and ceramic systems is described. Our objective is to use appropriate constitutive equations for metallic and ceramic systems that incorporate particular flow rules, shear modulus and yield strength dependence on temperature, pressure, strain and strain rate. The resulted configuration is used as an initial state for the solidification process in order to obtain the quenching stresses. The substrate temperature effect on the splatting event is also investigated.

Spray deposition is an integrated process which consists of three consecutive steps, namely atomization of liquid metal or ceramic into droplets, travel of the droplets in the atomization gas and deposition of the droplets into a three dimensional preform. In general, deposition, heat transfer and solidification process can be coupled or uncoupled. The droplet diameter, temperature, viscosity and its velocity roughly determine if the two processes are coupled or not. In this case study, the diameter of the droplet is 100 μm and impinges the substrate with velocity ranging from 50 to 200m/s. Spreading time is calculated to be a few microseconds whereas the solidification lasts several tens of microseconds. Therefore, the two phenomena are treated as uncoupled hereafter.

The input needed from the first two steps is velocity and temperature distribution of the droplets just before impinging upon the substrate. Many experimental campaigns have been launched over the last ten years towards this end. Pyrometers or infrared detectors are used to measure the temperature distribution. Streak cameras or laser Doppler interferometers monitor its velocity. We assume four cases with respect to the temperature distribution that cover a wide spectrum and reflect realistic situations, namely three cases with uniform temperature throughout the droplet of 0.3, 0.6 and 0.9 the melting temperature as well as one case of partially molten droplet as suggested by Lavernia (9).

On the problems surrounding primary cooling, i.e. fluid flow, heat transfer and solidification of molten droplets impinging upon solid substrates, Trapaga and Szekely (10) have developed a mathematical model and presented results for the spreading of droplets impacting onto a solid substrate. Westhoff (11) studied the interactions between plasma jet exiting a non-transferred arc plasma torch and injected solid particles. In the present work no attempt was made to solve for the velocity and temperature fluid field as it results from the heat and mass transfer from the particles and plasma. The initial conditions of a single molten or partially molten droplet with known velocity and temperature distribution at the instant before impinging the substrate were assumed. Trapaga et al (12) pursued a comparison study between large and small droplets. Cai and Lavernia (13) studied numerically the porosity during spay forming. Most research groups have treated the problem using an Eulerian frame of reference and have imposed material interfaces using the volume-of-fluid (VOF) method. Typical codes used from the groups of

Trapaga, Szekely and Lavernia to solve the Navier-Stokes equations are FLOW-3D (14) and RIPPLE (Kothe et al (15)). Alternatively, explicit finite element codes based on Langrangian coordinate system can tackle the problem. Rezoning capabilities are often needed when the mesh is distorted beyond acceptable limits. In such cases the Courant time step attains very small values and the analysis can become prohibitive. We have used the explicit finite element code LS-DYNA2D (Hallquist (16)). No additional effort is needed to track material interfaces in such an approach. In addition, we are currently pursuing a comparative study based on the RIPPLE code. The results of this study will be published in an upcoming communication.

The solution of the equations of motion requires a set of constitutive equations to be supplied. The selected constitutive equations should describe the material behavior under the given loading conditions. The ceramic droplet is in a semisolid state and undergoes moderate strain rates. Under these conditions the selected constitutive equation should include yield and shear modulus dependence upon pressure and temperature and furthermore to account for appropriate damage and fracture criteria. The significance of the constitutive equations is increased with decreasing temperature upon solidification where strength effects are more pronounced. The most complete constitutive model capable to describe such behavior applicable to high strain rates has been developed by Steinberg, Cochran and Guinan (17) in Lawrence Livermore National Laboratories (LLNL). Steinberg (18, 19) has made available to us comprehensive data for many metals and ceramics and in the past we have successfully modeled impact dynamics phenomena using these equations (Kiriakopoulos (20)). In brief, the model is valid for high deformation rates, and accounts for pressure and temperature dependence of the yield strength Y and shear modulus G, work hardening, pressure-dependent melting, Bauschinger and strain rate effects and internal decohesion. The yield strength is decomposed in a thermally activated Y_T and an athermal part Y_A which are added and then multiplied by the ratio of the shear modulus at the given pressure P and temperature T, G(P,T) to the shear modulus at reference state G_0:

$$Y = [Y_T(\dot{\varepsilon},T) + Y_A f(\varepsilon_p)]\left[\frac{G(P,T)}{G_o}\right] \qquad [1]$$

where $\dot{\varepsilon}, \varepsilon_p$ are the strain rate and plastic strain respectively. The rate-independent model was historically derived first and ignores the first strain rate and thermally activated part of the yield strength. The thermally activated part is an implicit function of the plastic strain rate given by:

$$\dot{\varepsilon}_p = \left[\frac{1}{C_1} e^{\left(\frac{2U_k}{kT}\left(1-\frac{Y_T}{Y_P}\right)^2\right)} + \frac{C_2}{Y_T}\right]^{-1} \qquad [2]$$

where C_1 and C_2 are material coefficients, U_k the activation energy and k the Boltzman's constant. The thermally activated part of the yield strength is limited by the Peierls stress Y_P, while the athermal part:

$$Y_A f(\varepsilon_p) = Y_A[1 + \beta(\varepsilon_p + \varepsilon_i)]^n \le Y_{max} \qquad [3]$$

is limited by the maximum yield strength at room temperature. In the above equation, β and η are the work-hardening parameters and ε_i is the initial plastic strain. The weight of the two parts of the yield strength cannot be generally estimated a priori. This holds true especially in our case, where the droplet is at a temperature very close to the melting point. In general, increasing temperatures, decrease the rate-dependent effects. In liquids in particular, rate-dependent effects decrease exponentially with temperature. The shear modulus is given as a function of the cubic root of the compression (η=initial specific volume divided by the specific volume) and temperature:

$$G(P,T) = G_o\left[1 + \frac{AP}{\eta^{1/3}} - B(T-300)\right] \qquad [4]$$

where A and B are the pressure and temperature dependence coefficients of the shear modulus G. Up to now, we have described the deviatoric part of the stress tensor and the yield strength. The dilatational part is described by a Mie-Grüneisen or linear polynomial equation of state (EOS). In general Y and G increase with increasing pressure and decrease with increasing temperature. A major problem lies now in the selection of the ceramic droplet constitutive equation. Steinberg (16) has published a work on the dynamic strength of ceramics based on the work of Grady (21). The latter has developed a model for fracture stress versus strain rate for brittle materials in tension that appear to hold experimentally for the yield strength in compression as well. The brittle fracture stress is given as: $\sigma_c = D\dot{\varepsilon}^n$ with $D = (3\rho_0 C_0 K_{IC})^n$. C_0 is the sonic velocity of the medium and K_{IC} is the critical stress intensity factor. The shear modulus is described in the same way as in metals, whereas the yield strength of the ceramic is also decomposed in a strain rate - but not temperature - activated part and an athermal part. As in the case of metals, the strain rate activated part of the yield strength is limited by the difference between the yield at Hougoniot elastic limit (HEL) and the athermal part Y_A. The above constitutive equation valid for ceramics has been implemented in the LS-DYNA2D finite element code based on appropriate modifications of the constitutive equation valid for metals. The implicit relationship between the strain rate and the strain activated part of the yield strength, which is maximum limited, is solved iteratively. The new constitutive equation performs well and is currently under more extensive testing against experimental data.

3. RESULTS AND DISCUSSION

The conservation of momentum, the constitutive equations as well as the equations of state described above define a well-posed system. In this study we examine three temperature distributions, namely at 30%, 60% and 90% of the melting temperature T_m as well as one at partially solidified state of YSZ impinging upon NiCrAlY. The droplets are impinged at an initial velocity 50m/s. Furthermore, parametric studies were pursued with respect to the temperature of the substrate that is maintained during deposition. The deposition process lasts for a few microseconds. Figures 2a, 2b, and 2c, show the final deformed states that represent a YSZ droplet at 30%, 60% and 90% its melting point. At 30% T_m the deformation of the ceramic droplet is not significant and the droplet bounces back. At 60% and 90% T_m, a bell shaped splat (figure 2b) and a cone shaped flat splat (figure 2c) are obtained respectively. The axial stresses during the impact process are superimposed to the deformed shapes. One can observe in all three cases the compressive stress wave that propagates inside the NiCrAlY. Accurate experimental results to describe decohesion of YSZ at different temperature levels are currently missing. Therefore, in this case study the breakup of the droplet cannot be adequately simulated. The numerical results obtained from the attempt to describe the temperature effects were not satisfactory, partly due to lack of decohesion data. Jiang et al (22) have presented experimental results of the deposition temperature effects on the splat formation, microstructure development and properties of PS coatings. As shown in figure 3, the fragmented morphology of zirconia droplet at 75 °C is compared against a more contiguous shape at 300 °C. Current efforts are aimed at reproducing such experimental observations. This completes the first step of the analysis.

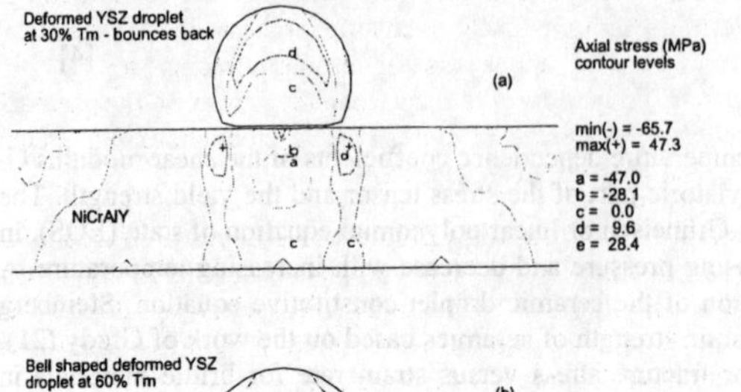

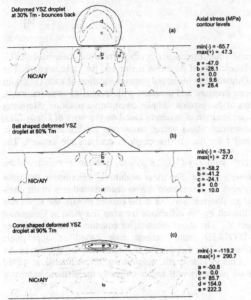

Fig. 2 Deformed PS-YSZ droplet at 30% (a), 60% (b) and 90% (c) the melting temperature

A deformed configuration of the partially solidified droplet was then used as an initial state to the solidification process. As the PSZ flattened splat cools down, from approximately 2500 °C, phase transformation will induce a volume increase. In the case of unstabilized pure zirconia, due to tetragonal to monoclinic transformations, this increase is significant and is found to be around 8%. In the case of YSZ such volume increase is relatively small and can be neglected. When the developed quenching stresses reach the tension limit, the droplet breaks apart. Thermal contact resistance is used to model this behavior. The magnitude of these stresses exceeds the failure of YSZ in tension. After breakage, tension cannot be further sustained.

Further increase in tensile thermal stresses will cause subsequent cracking of the YSZ splat in smaller pieces. A parametric study with respect to the flattening ratio was also performed. The shape of the deformed splat, used as initial state for the solidification process, as shown in figure 4 has flattening ratio 2.4. Such a splat, breaks in many pieces close to the roots of the cone. On the contrary, a more uniform breakage is obtained when the splat is almost flat with a large flattening ratio. It is conceivable that this predicted cracking pattern gives rise to reduced strength. Despite annealing, a large number of microcracks remains. It remains to be seen experimentally if optimization of the processing parameters towards flattening ratios from 2 to 3, gives enough strain tolerant characteristics without compromising the strength of the final plasma sprayed coating.

The next step is to perform calculations to model a multiple droplet deposition in order to account for the interstitial porosity. The deformed state is shown in figure 5. A large gap is created between the two splats which leads to thermal and load transfer only in the center of the double cone shaped structure. The volume of such interstitial porosity can be easily estimated. It is indeed the percentage of the melting temperature of the incident droplet that determines interstitial porosity. The current effort to model residual stresses differentiates from previous attempts in the sense that porosity is taken into account as well as strain relaxation due to microcracking. Previous efforts to model the deposition process were based on the assumption of rectangular layers with perfect bonding. Although PS is a chaotic process and a statistical distribution of three dimensional modeling of thousands of droplets seems to be still computationally prohibitive, the results of this study give a qualitative picture of the primary induced residual stresses as well as of the amount of porosity and microcracking. Better numerical data will enhance the accuracy of the present analysis.

Fig. 3 Deposition temperature effects on the splat formation (after X. Jiang et al)

An experimental campaign from the JRC research group is underway to characterize the thermophysical properties of TBCs. Porosity and thermal conductivity measurements along with microstructural analysis of as-received specimens will give estimates of the degree of microcracking.

The time delay in the thermal diffusivity measurements is translated to thermal contact resistance between splats. Inverse finite element modeling has already been performed in order to estimate the intersplat TCR by matching numerical and published experimental results from the laser flash technique (Kiriakopoulos (23)).

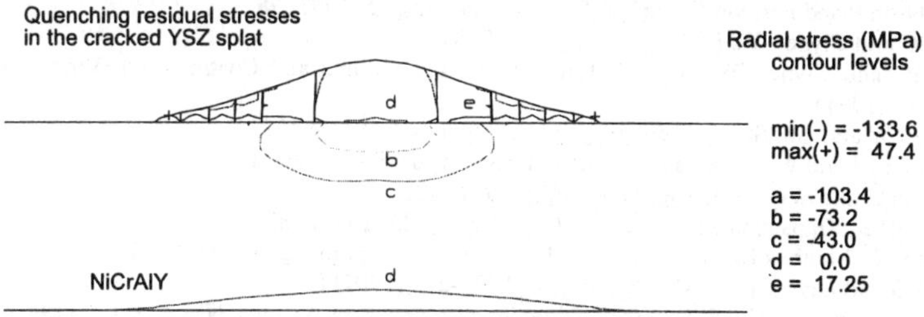

Fig 4. Primary residual radial stress distribution in a cracked PS-YSZ splat upon NiCrAlY

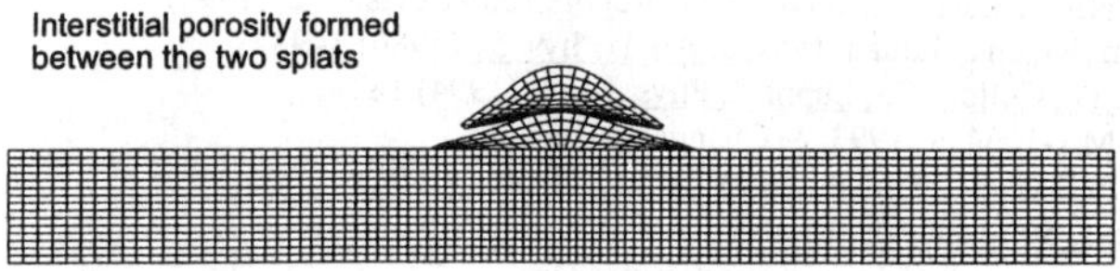

Fig. 5 Deformed finite element mesh of the double droplet deposition

4. CONCLUSION

It is one of the main aims of the JRC research group to better understand the plasma spray forming, estimate the porosity of PS YSZ and evaluate the quenching and cooldown residual stresses based on numerical calculations and correlation with experimental evidence obtained from X-ray and neutron diffraction facilities as well as thermal conductivity measurements.

The use of appropriate constitutive equations for metallic and ceramic systems that incorporate particular flow rules, shear modulus and yield strength dependence on temperature, pressure, strain and strain rate has been investigated. The deformed splat configuration is used as an initial state for the solidification process in order to obtain the quenching stresses and microcracking. Interstitial porosity that results from the successive deposition has also been investigated numericaly.

ACKNOWLEDGEMENTS

This work has been performed under the European Commission Research and Development Program. The authors would like to acknowledge the valuable discussions with the following colleagues: V. Stamos, V. Tzimas, H. Müllejans, B. Baufeld, S. Peteves and J. Bressers.

REFERENCES

1. Moretto P, Internal report, JRC-IAM, Petten (1999)
2. Youtsos AG and Ohms C, Internal report, JRC-HFR-IAM, Petten (1999)
3. Takeuchi S, Ito M and Takeda K, Surface & Coating Technology 43/44 (1990) 426
4. Kuroda S and Clyne TW, Thin Solid Films 200 (1991) 49
5. Bengtsson P and Persson C, Surf. & Coat. Technology 92 (1997) 78
6. Gill SC and Clyne TW, Met. Trans. B21 (1990) 377
7. Gill SC and Clyne TW, High Performance Ceramic Films and Coatings, ed. Vincenzini, Elsevier (1991)
8. Clyne TW and Gill SC, J. Thermal Spray Technology 5 (1996) 401
9. Lavernia EJ and Wu Y, Spray Atomization and Deposition, Wiley, 1996.
10. Trapaga G and Szekely J, Met. Trans. B22 (1991) 901
11. Westhoff R, Trapaga G and Szekely J, Met. Trans. B23 (1992) 683
12. Trapaga G, Matthys EF, Valencia JJ and Szekely J, Mat. Trans. B23 (1992) 701
13. Cai WD and Lavernia EJ, Mat. Sc. & Eng. A226-228 (1997) 8
14. FLOW-3D, Report No. FSI-88-00-1, Flow Science, Inc., Los Alamos, NM, vol. 1-4, (1988)
15. Kothe DB, Mjolsness RC and Torrey MD, RIPPLE, LANL (1994)
16. Hallquist JO., LS-DYNA2D User's manual, LSTC Report 1004 Revision 2, (1994)
17. Steinberg DJ, Cochran SG, and Guinan MW, J. Appl. Phys. 51 (1980) 1498
18. Steinberg DJ, J. Phys. IV, Colloq. C8, Suppl. J. Phys. III, 4, (1994) 183
19. Steinberg DJ, UCRL-MA-106439, 1993, & Change 1, 1996.
20. Kiriakopoulos M.K., PhD Thesis, University of Patras - Greece (1996)
21. Grady D, J. Mech. Phys. Solids 36 (1988) 353
22. Jiang X, et al. http://dol1.eng.sunysb.edu/tsl/ctsr/nuggets/nugget24/
23. Kiriakopoulos MK, Internal report, JRC-IAM, Petten, 1999.

CHARACTERISATION OF THE RESIDUAL STRESS STATE IN A DOUBLE 'V' STAINLESS STEEL CYLINDRICAL WELDMENT USING NEUTRON DIFFRACTION AND FINITE ELEMENT SIMULATION

PJ Bouchard[1], MT Hutchings[2*] and PJ Withers[3]
[1] British Energy, Barnett Way, Barnwood, Gloucester, GL4 3RS, UK
[2] National NDT Centre, AEA Technology Energy, E1 Culham Science Centre, Abingdon, OX14 3ED,UK
[3] Manchester Materials Science Centre, Grosvenor St., Manchester, M1 7HS, UK

ABSTRACT

Extensive numerical and measurement studies have been carried out to characterise and understand the residual stress state in a high heat input, double 'V' preparation, stainless steel cylindrical weld of inner diameter 781 mm and thickness 15.9 mm. This paper reports the programme of neutron diffraction strain measurements on a mock-up of the weldment. It includes experiments to quantify the stress-free lattice parameter, elastic constants, pseudo-strains and absorption effects to give confidence in the derived stresses. The measured results are compared with the residual stress field predicted by a finite element simulation of the welding process. A good agreement of stresses in the axial and hoop directions is found in the heat affected zone, and base material up to 50 mm from the weld centre-line.

INTRODUCTION

Coleman et al. (1) have reported many incidents of delayed reheat cracking in austenitic AISI Type 316 stainless steel power plant components operating at high temperature (>450°C). Metallurgical examinations have characterised the failure mode as creep ductility exhaustion, believed to arise from accumulated creep strains mainly associated with the relaxation of weld residual stresses. There is evidence that both the magnitude and three dimensional nature of the weld residual stress field influences not only the relaxation of the residual stresses and accumulation of creep strains, but also the local creep ductility. An understanding and characterisation of the stress field in such weldments is therefore of considerable importance.

A finite element (ABAQUS, 2) based weld residual stress simulation approach has been developed and refined by British Energy and the results used in a new creep damage assessment model (Bradford et al., 3). Extensive measurement studies have been carried out to validate the simulated residual stress field in a high heat input, double 'V' preparation, stainless steel cylindrical weld of inner diameter 781 mm and thickness 15.9 mm (see Figures 1 and 2). Transient temperatures were recorded during welding and compared with two and three-dimensional thermal modelling results. Displacements and hardness measurements have been correlated with the predicted distortion and plastic strain. Also diverse residual stress measurement techniques have been applied including ring opening measurements, near-surface hole-drilling and destructive sectioning techniques. Here, surface and through-thickness residual stresses derived from a programme of neutron diffraction strain measurements are reported and compared with the finite element weld simulation.

* Present address: Department of Materials Engineering, The Open University, Oxford Research Unit, Boars Hill, Oxford OX1 5HR

Neutron diffraction is the only measurement technique with the potential for quantifying three-dimensional strain and stress fields deep within engineering materials. (Allen et al. 4). However the task of interpreting neutron measurements on welds raises a number of issues such as:- the possible influence of compositional variations, the effect of plastically-induced intergranular stresses, texture (particularly in the weld metal itself) and the general problem of how to establish stress-free lattice parameters. The measured strains have to be converted to macro-stresses using appropriate elastic constants, and pragmatic assumptions about principal stress directions often have to be made since full stress tensor measurements are prohibitively expensive.

THE MOCK-UP WELDMENT

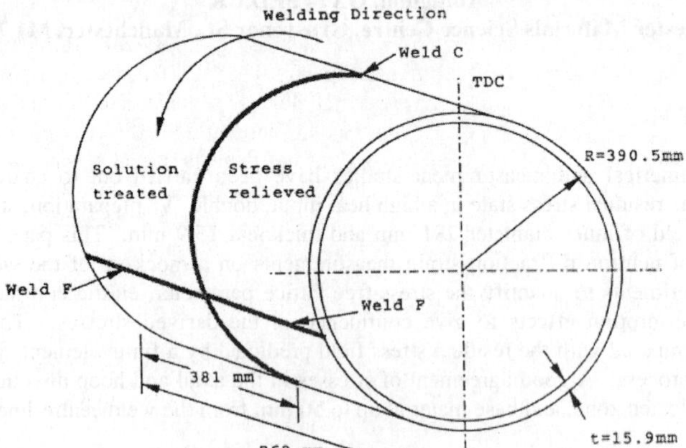

Figure 1. Geometry of mock-up weldment.

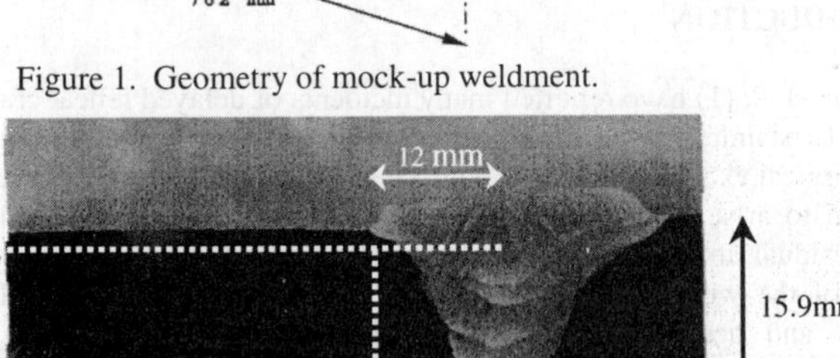

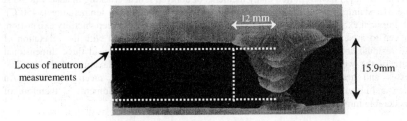

Figure 2: Macrograph of weld showing measurement positions

A mock-up weldment (Figure 1) was fabricated in the following manner. Two cylinders of internal diameter ~781 mm were fabricated from AISI Type 316L stainless steel plate (~16 mm thick) by rolling into cylindrical form and longitudinally welding. Each cylinder was given a different heat treatment: one for 'stress relief' at 590-620ºC for 1 hour with a furnace cool; and the other 'solution treated' at 1045 ±15ºC for 1 hour with an air quench to completely remove fabrication stresses. After machining a double 'V' geometry weld preparation, the cylinders were tack welded together on the outside and then three layers of manual metal arc (MMA) weld metal deposited in the inner 'V' preparation. After back-gouging, four layers of submerged metal arc (SAW) weld metal were deposited filling the outer weld preparation (see Figure 2). A high heat input was used for the final SAW passes as indicated by the welding parameters summarised in Table 1.

Weld Pass	1	2	3	4	5	6	7
Type	MMA	MMA	MMA	SAW	SAW	SAW	SAW
Heat Input (KJ/mm)	0.56	1.06	1.39	1.32	2.13	2.13	2.22

Table1: Mock-up weld heat input data

NEUTRON DIFFRACTION MEASUREMENTS

Principal strain measurements

Neutron diffraction strain measurements were made using the TAS 8 diffractometer at the DR3 reactor, Riso National Laboratory, Denmark. The ~240kg weldment was partially supported from an overhead crane, and a special stage was constructed to allow its manual rotation about the vertical instrument sample axis. Vertical adjustments were made using a jack. The weldment could be oriented to enable the three principal strain directions to be aligned along the scattering vector. To facilitate the hoop strain measurements with the cylinder's axis vertical, a window hole 56mm wide and 75mm long was cut to allow the incident beam to enter the region of measurement without absorption.

Preliminary measurements were made using a neutron wavelength of 2.638 Å and the high intensity (002) fcc steel Bragg reflection at a scattering angle of 94°. The detailed measurements, reported here, were then made using the (111) Bragg reflection with a neutron wavelength of 3.04 Å and scattering angle of 94.5°. It was assumed that the axial, hoop and radial directions were coincident with the local stress principal directions, thus reducing the number of orientations to be measured to three. Predicted stress field results from the ABAQUS weld simulation implied that this assumption was reasonable, and measurements made by rotation of the sample about two points confirmed this. The sampling volume depended on the strain component being measured; 1x1x20 mm^3 for axial and radial strains with the long dimension being in the hoop direction, and 2x2x2 mm^3 for hoop strains. The (111) plane lattice strains were measured in the three assumed principal directions at a number of locations in the 'solution treated cylinder' away from the weld near both the inner and outer surfaces (Figure 2). Through wall thickness measurements were made at 12mm from the weld centre-line. At some positions, measurements were not made in all three strain directions; angles for those not measured were interpolated from adjacent positions. In all cases, the diffracted peak profile was fitted by a Gaussian function to determine the scattering angle, using a least squares fitting routine. Small corrections were made for the change in absorption by the sample as the peak scattering angle was scanned.

Stress-free reference measurements

Stress-free reference values of lattice spacing were measured using a stack of 12 electro-discharge machined 3x3x3mm^3 cubes, which had been removed from a ring cut from the end of the 'solution treated' cylinder. The stacked column of cubes was rotated about the sample axis at intervals of 45 or 90° and an average of scattering angles from the fitted peak profiles evaluated. This 'zero' stress reference angle was determined separately after the hoop strain measurements, and after the radial and axial strain measurements as the beam set-up differed slightly in the two geometries. The corresponding value was used to determine each set of strains.

Calibration of elastic constants

In order to calibrate the lattice plane specific elastic constants, a series of measurements were made on tensile specimens using the Riso National Laboratory stress rig. This rig enables uni-axial loads to be applied to the specimen, while the corresponding strain parallel and perpendicular to the load direction are measured. The results are shown in Figure 3, where they are compared with the bulk behaviour and the results of theoretical estimates. The neutron elastic constants for (002) and (111) plane reflections were measured as a function of load up to the 0.2% yield strength of the material over several loading cycles. The mean values of the measured lattice plane Young's modulus E, and Poisson's ratio ν, were:-

(002) $E_{002} = 144 \pm 4$ GPa $\nu_{002} = 0.32 \pm 0.05$

(111) $E_{111} = 240 \pm 10$ GPa $\nu_{111} = 0.33 \pm 0.11$

The uncertainty band for the 'Poisson's ratio' reflects the very large scatter observed in perpendicular measurements. Because of this measurement uncertainty and the large effect ν has on the conversion of strain to stress, the measured (111) lattice strain was converted into stress using theoretical neutron diffraction elastic constants, E_{111} = 238 GPa and ν_{111} = 0.249 rather than the measured values. These theoretical neutron elastic constants were derived from single crystal data for Type 316 austenitic stainless steel using the Kroner model (5) as implemented by Dolle (6). This model is known to account well for measurements of elastic constants made in a number of metals.

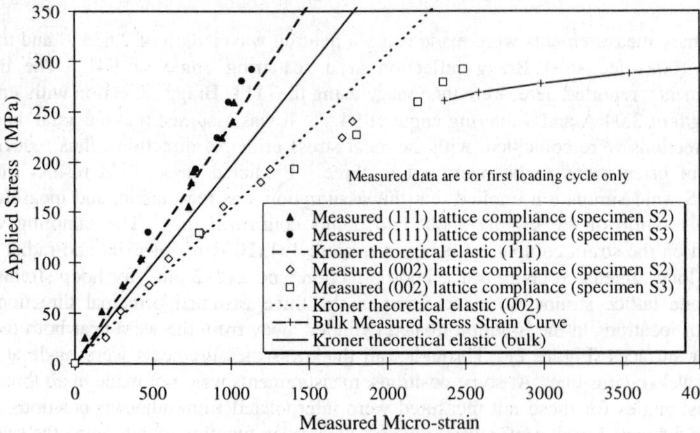

Figure 3: Comparison of measured applied tensile stress - lattice strain for the first cycle.

Non-linear stress-lattice strain behaviour

The tensile specimen tests were also used to investigate the magnitude of 'pseudo strains' which might arise from grain interaction stresses during plastic deformation. The lattice strain measurements for (002) planes in the loading direction revealed non-linear behaviour on the first loading cycle for stresses above about 200MPa. On unloading this resulted in a zero load strain shift implying that a grain to grain residual micro-stress field had been induced. The magnitude of this 'plastic pseudo strain' depends on the load and grain to grain interaction mechanisms. In contrast, the corresponding stress-lattice strain behaviour for the (111) planes was found to be linear up to 300MPa, the maximum stress tested. However, both sets of planes gave rise to similar sized residual pseudo strains perpendicular to the loading direction. Similar results have been found from previous studies (see 7).

Absorption effects

It is important that the neutron wavelength used does not lie close to a Bragg edge which can cause anomalous absorption (Hsu et al 8). Although the wavelengths were chosen carefully to avoid this, the absorption constant was checked by measuring the intensity versus depth of the gauge volume through the wall thickness of the weldment, and found to be as expected. Measurements using TAS 8 were also made of both (002) and (111) lattice strains in the section of the weldment cut from the cylinder in forming the beam aperture. The strains were found to be much smaller than in the parent weldment, indicating relaxation of the stresses by removal of the section. Measurements of strain at a position accessed by different paths in the material agreed within the uncertainty.

Match-stick experiment to check pseudo strain effects

The presence of pseudo lattice strains can have a significant effect on the accuracy of stresses derived from neutron diffraction strain measurements. Pseudo strains can develop from plastic anisotropy, or changes in stress free lattice parameters arising from chemistry variations - such as carbon content in the HAZ of welds. The stress rig measurements described above imply that (002) plane plastic pseudo strains are important for Type 316 stainless steel.

A further experiment was performed to investigate these effects using the ENGIN neutron diffraction instrument at the ISIS neutron spallation source at the Rutherford Appleton Laboratory. The ENGIN diffractometer uses an incident time-pulsed 'white' beam of thermal neutrons, and measures the time of flight of neutrons scattered into two banks of detectors. Bragg reflections from many crystallographic planes are recorded simultaneously as a spectrum of intensity versus wavelength. These data can be analysed using a Rietveld (9) procedure, which assumes a perfect crystal lattice, to yield a cell-average lattice parameter. The Rietveld approach averages out residual anisotropic elastic and plastic strain effects for practical engineering measurement purposes, and the average lattice parameter strain can be related to stress by the macroscopic elastic constants (Daymond et al 7). For strong reflections, where the neutron counts are sufficient, individual diffraction peaks can also be analysed.

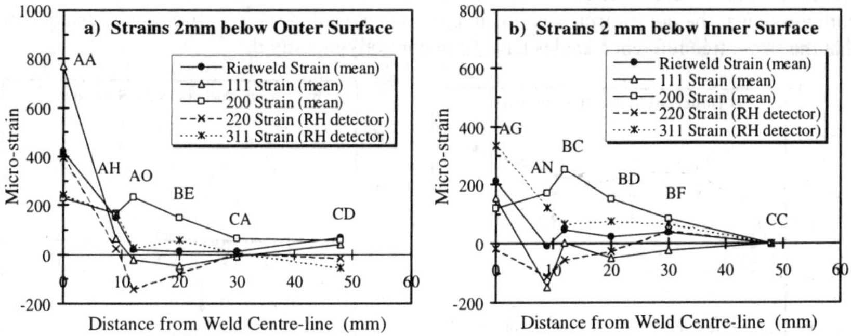

Figure 4. Strains measured in 'matchstick' samples taken along lines 2 mm below the inner and outer surfaces at positions away from weld.

Small 'match-stick' samples (2x2x16mm) of parent HAZ and weld material were cut from the mock-up weldment (see Figure 2) by a 'stress-free' electro-discharge machine technique.

These samples corresponded to the exact measurement positions used for the TAS 8 neutron diffraction measurements described above, and included additional samples from the weld metal itself. Lattice parameter variations in planes oriented at 45° to the cylinder radial-axial directions were measured for each match-stick. Both a full Rietveld analysis using all the diffraction peaks, and four individual (111, 200, 022 and 311) diffraction peaks analyses, were carried out for each specimen. Residual micro-strains were calculated from the measurements by assuming a zero strain reference point to be at 48mm from the weld centre-line; that is strains at this location were assumed to be unaffected by local compositional variations and plastic strain-induced residual micro-stresses. The results of a hardness survey confirmed that no significant plastic strain had been induced this far from the weld.

The measured near-surface distributions of micro-strains are shown in Figures 4a-b. The 'mean' plots are averaged results from the two detector banks. It is evident that the 'Rietweld' cell average lattice parameter micro-strains are negligible apart from in the weld metal (locations AA and AG). The (200) plane results reveal positive residual micro-strains in the parent material, which are comparable to those measured in the TAS cyclic tensile rig tests. The (111) strains generally show a compressive tendency, also observed in the cyclic tensile tests, and appear to be much less sensitive to plastic strain effects. At 12 mm from the weld centre-line, and beyond, the (111) strains are less than -25×10^{-6} implying compressive residual pseudo-stresses no greater than -6 MPa. However at 9 mm from the weld centre-line (i.e. close to the weld fusion boundary) the (111) strains are somewhat larger and imply stress errors of up to about –36 MPa. These 'match-stick' sample results confirm that neither composition induced lattice spacing variations, nor inter-grain micro-stresses arising from plastic anisotropy significantly affected the accuracy of the (111) reflection stress measurements for parent material locations 12mm or greater from the weld centre-line.

Measured stresses in the weldment

The stress variations deduced from the TAS 8 neutron diffraction measurements on the weldment mock-up are presented in Figures 5 and 6. The uncertainties show one standard deviation, 68% probability. Through-wall stress results at 12 mm from the weld are presented in Figures 5a-b. The hoop stress component is dominant, and increases with depth from the outer surface. The axial stress component varies from tension at the inner surface to compression at the outer surface, and is in approximate balance. This stress balance confirms that the stress free reference angles have been correctly measured.

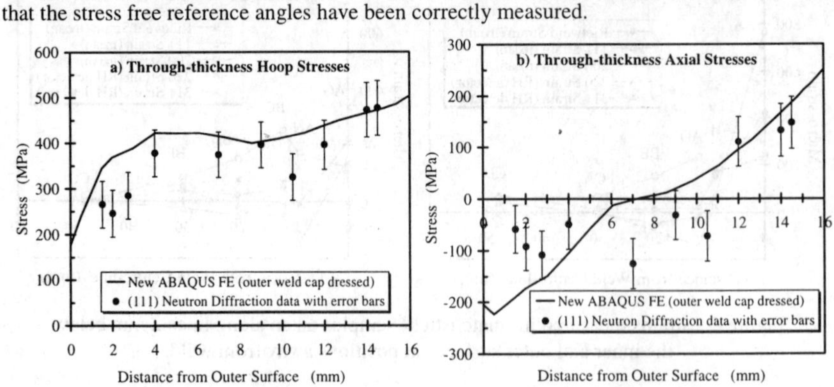

Figure 5. Stresses from (111) neutron diffraction measurements in the HAZ at 12mm from weld centre-line compared with ABAQUS weld simulation results.

The near-surface residual stress measurements are shown in Figures 6a-d. The radial stress components were found to be close to zero within the measurement error.

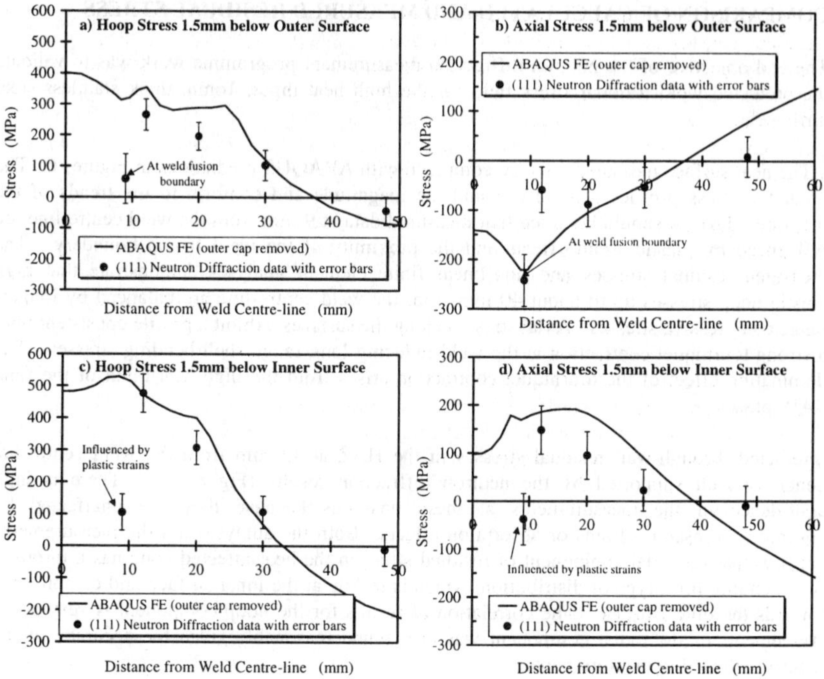

Figure 6. Near-surface stresses from (111) neutron diffraction measurements compared with ABAQUS weld simulation results

FINITE ELEMENT SIMULATIONS

Several separate finite element based simulations of the weldment residual stresses have been carried out including:-

a) An axi-symmetric analysis using Battelle's TEMPER/WELDS software.
b) A 3-D shell analysis for the last pass weld using ABAQUS.
c) An axi-symmetric analysis using British Energy's ABAQUS modelling approach.

Results from the TEMPER/WELDS analysis a) have been favourably compared with near-surface hole-drilling residual stress measurements in (10). This paper also describes the 3-D ABAQUS shell analysis b) which showed no significant circumferential variations in residual stress for this large diameter weld geometry, except near the arc start/stop position of the SAW pass modelled. The final analysis c) is judged to provide the best available prediction of the detailed residual stress field in the mock-up. It includes weld metal properties, an isotropic strain hardening model to account for increases in yield strength of the heat affected zone, and introduction of strain free weld filler metal. In addition, this analysis incorporates measured thermal properties and tensile data specific to the mock-up material. The predicted residual stresses are shown in Figures 5 and 6.

COMPARISON OF CALCULATED AND MEASURED RESIDUAL STRESS

The end objective of the neutron diffraction measurement programme work was to validate the predicted weld residual stress field for the high heat input, 16mm thick stainless steel girth weld.

The near surface measurements are compared with ABAQUS predictions in Figures 6. The predicted stress profiles generally bound the magnitude and conform to the trends of the measured data. It should be noted that measured data at 9 mm from the weld centre-line are influenced by plastic strain effects and the proximity of the weld fusion boundary. The measured residual stresses and non-linear finite element analyses demonstrate that high tensile hoop stresses up to about 40 mm from the weld centre-line are balanced by longer-range compressive stresses. Axial stresses along the surfaces exhibit a profile consistent with a strong tourniquet contraction at the weld inducing long range shell bending stresses. The dominating effect of the tourniquet contraction arises from the high heat-input of the final SAW passes.

Predicted through-wall residual stresses in the HAZ at 12 mm from the weld centre are generally well supported by the neutron diffraction results (Figures 5). There is high confidence in the measurements at these positions because they are unaffected by composition, pseudo-strains or absorption effects. Both the analysis and the measurements confirm that the axial component of residual stress in the heat affected zone has a through-wall bending form type of distribution, which is tensile at the inner surface and compressive towards the outer surface. The correlation of results for the hoop component is very good. Agreement for the radial component was also found reasonable given the accuracy of the neutron diffraction measurements.

Acknowledgement
This work is published with permission of British Energy Generation Ltd. The authors are grateful to Dr Torben Lorentzen for extensive advice and assistance during the course of the measurements using TAS 8 and John Wright for help on ENGIN.

REFERENCES

1. ABAQUS Version 5.6, Hibbitt, Karlsson and Sorensen Inc
2. Coleman M C, Miller D A, Stevens R A, Proc. Int. Conf. Integrity of High Temperature Welds. PEP Ltd., London, (1998) 169
3. Bradford R, I Mech E Conf. Trans. Assuring It's Safe, PEP Ltd., London, (1998) 287
4. Allen A J, Hutchings M T, Windsor C G and Andreani C, Adv. Phys. 34 (1985) 445
5. Kroner E, J. Mech. Phys. Solids 15 (1967) 319
6. Dolle H, J. Appl. Cryst. 12 (1979) 489
7. Daymond M R, Bourke M A M, Von Dreele R B, Clausen B and Lorentzen T, J Appl. Phys. 82 (1997) 1554
8. Hsu T C, Marsiglio F, Root J H and Holden T M, J Neutron Research 3 (1995) 27
9. Rietveld H M, J Appl. Crystallogr. 2 (1969) 65
10. Dong P, Ghadiali N and Brust F W, ASME PVP-Vol.373 (1998), 421

SESSION 9A

Determination of Residual Stresses in Nitrided layers generated by Gas Nitriding

J.M. Sprauel*, L. Barrallier*, A. Lodini **, A. Pyzalla*, W. Reimers*****

* **Laboratoire MécaSurf, ENSAM, Aix en Provence (France)**
** **Laboratoire Léon Brillouin , Saclay (France)**
*** **Hahn Meitner Institut, Berlin, (Germany)**

ABSTRACT

This paper is dedicated to the evaluation by neutron diffraction of near surface stress profiles obtained in a steel specimen after nitriding. Such measurements are particularly difficult due to parasitic peak shifts of the diffraction peaks, which are obtained when the neutron gauge is not entirely immersed in the studied sample. To correct this effect, a complete numerical simulation of the two-axis neutron spectrometer has been developed. This program allows also to optimise the experimental conditions and to define precisely the true volume of the neutron gauge. The depth affected by the stresses remains low in comparison to the size of the neutron beam (about 1mm). It is therefore necessary to localise very precisely the true position of the neutron gauge inside the sample. This is obtained through strain scanning across the studied surface. The true position of the neutron gauge volume is then derived from the evolution of the diffracted intensity versus the scanned depth. The reliability of this method is better than 0.1 mm. Such measurements were carried out for nine different ψ incidences (in ω mode). The experiments were conducted on the {310} diffracting planes of the α iron with a wavelength of 0.137 nm ($2\theta = 98°$). The reliability of the stress evaluations is thus of about 30 MPa. The values defined by neutron diffraction have been compared finally to results obtained by X-rays. Both results are in very good agreement.

INTRODUCTION

As it has been demonstrated by different round robin tests (like the experiments carried out in the VAMAS program), neutron stress evaluation is reliable in normal condition where the neutron probe is entirely immersed in the sample. However, near surface measurements and experiments carried out at the interface between two different materials are difficult to analyse. This is due to great parasitic peak shifts which are obtained in such condition (Webster et al (1), Wang et al (2)). However near surface measurements are of great interest for the engineers, since cracks are often initiated from this zone. To correct these systematic errors, a numerical simulation of the whole two-axis neutron spectrometer has been developed (Pluyette et al (3)). The main aim of our study is then to validate these calculations. For that purpose, our correction procedure has been applied to the evaluation of near surface residual stresses induced by the nitriding of a steel specimen. For such treatment, in fact, the residual stresses can be defined accurately by X-ray diffraction. This allows us to check the reliability of our improved neutron stress scanning method . For that purpose, the in-depth stress profiles obtained by neutron diffraction will be compared to the data defined by X-rays.

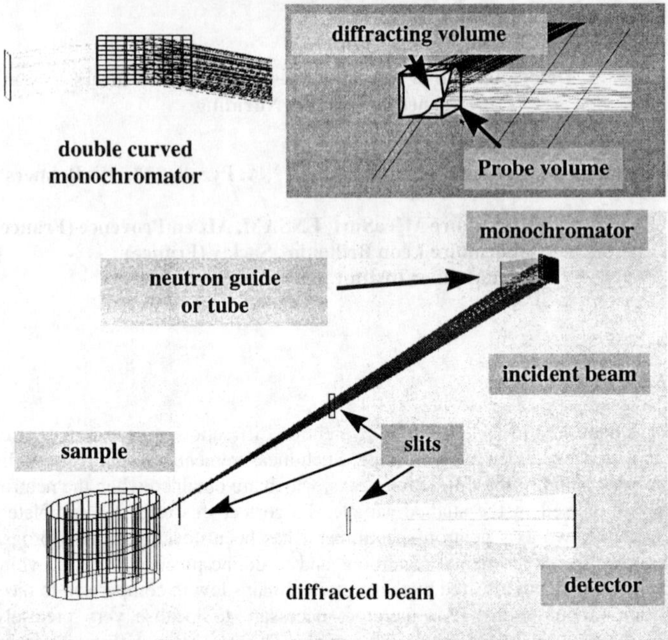

Fig. 1 Example of simulation of a two-axis neutron spectrometer

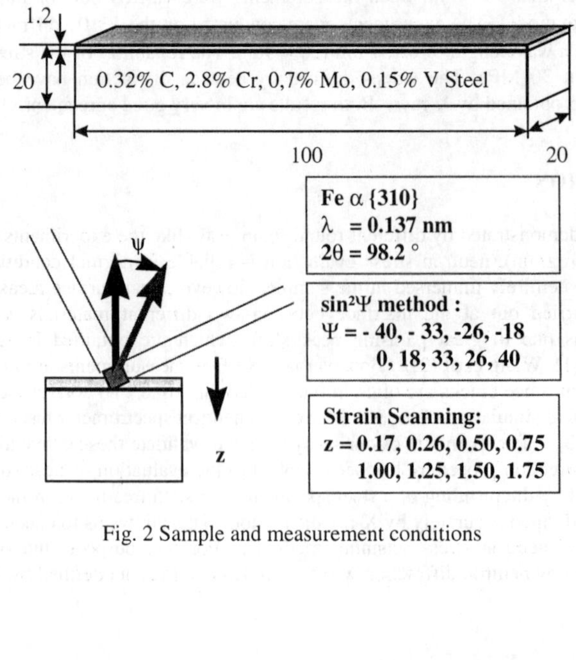

Fig. 2 Sample and measurement conditions

SIMULATION OF THE TWO-AXIS NEUTRON SPECTROMETER

As it has already been pointed out, parasitic shifts of the diffraction peaks arise when the neutron gauge volume is not entirely immersed in the studied material (Webster et al (1), Wang et al (2)). Such impediment is particularly important in the case of near surface measurements or during the crossing of the interface between two different materials. To correct the parasitic peak shifts, a numerical simulation of the whole two-axis neutron spectrometer has been developed (Pluyette et al (3), Fig. 1).

The simulation program accounts for all the major components of the neutron spectrometer: the characteristics of the neutron guide or tube, a double curved mosaic monochromator, up to hundred primary and secondary slits, a classical or position sensitive detector. The sample is defined by an integrated feature oriented CAD drawing module. This allows the description of very sophisticated specimens. The software accounts for the horizontal and vertical divergence of the incident and diffracted beams, for the local conditions of diffraction in the monochromator and the sample, and for the absorption by the monochromator and the sample.

The simulation program first computes the distribution of intensity and wavelength across the incident beam. The precise shape and size of the probe volume is then calculated. The intersection between this neutron probe and the sample is also computed, thus defining the diffracting volume. A theoretical diffraction peak is finally calculated through a Monte Carlo simulation method. The whole simulation program allows thus to optimise the experimental conditions and to predict all parasitic shifts of the diffraction peak.

This approach has already been tested on neutron experiments carried out on a double V weldment between a ferritic and an austenitic steel (Pluyette et al (4)). In order to check the limits on the method, in the case of near surface measurements, the same procedure will now be applied to the evaluation of the residual stresses induced by the nitriding of a flat steel specimen.

EXPERIMENTAL PROCEDURE

The studied material is a chromium–molybdenum-vanadium alloy steel (0.32% C, 2.8% Cr, 0,7% Mo, 0.15% V) generally used by the aircraft industry. The surface of the sample has been gas-nitrided for 120 hours at a temperature of 560 °C. The depth affected by this treatment is thus of about 1.2 mm (Fig. 2). The sample has been analysed by neutron diffraction on the E3 instrument of the Hahn-Meitner Institute of Berlin.

The {310} reflection of the α phase of iron has been analysed for that purpose with a wavelength of about 0.137 nm (diffraction angle $2\theta = 98°$). The neutron gauge was set to $1 \times 1 \times 10$ mm^3. The $\sin^2\psi$ method has been used to evaluate the stresses in the transverse direction of the sample. These measurements were carried out in ω mode with nine independent ψ incidences. For each Ψ direction strain scanning has been performed for depths up to 1.75 mm. To define the lattice parameter of the unstressed material, small particles were filed off each depth of the nitrided layer and analysed by X-ray powder diffraction. The elastic constants required to compute the stresses from the measured lattice strains depend on the selected crystal reflection. These values have been computed from the iron single crystal compliance's, using Kröner's self consistent model (Kröner (5)).

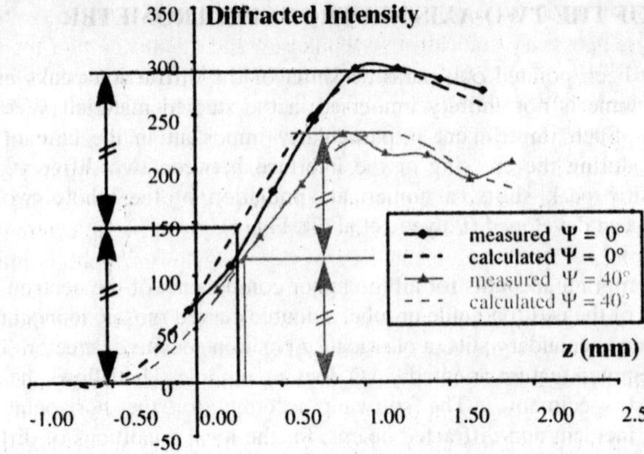

Fig. 3 Distribution of the diffracted intensity versus the scanned depth

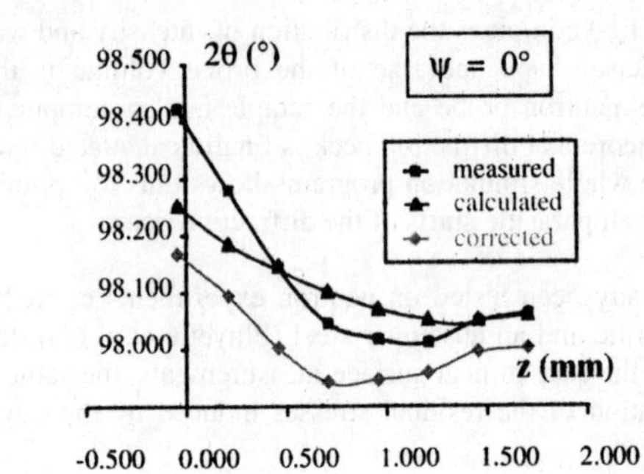

Fig 4 Distribution of the diffraction peak position versus the scanned depth

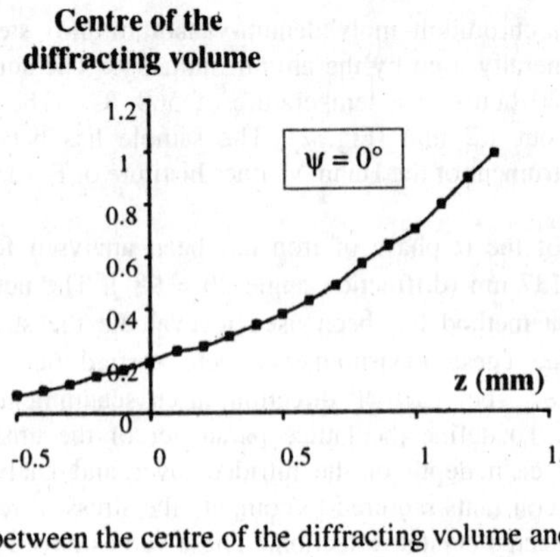

Fig. 5 Relation between the centre of the diffracting volume and the scanned depth

The depth affected by the stresses is of the same order of magnitude as the size of the neutron beam. It is therefore necessary to localise very precisely the true position of the neutron gauge inside the sample. This is obtained by a fine analysis of the evolution of the diffracted intensity versus the scanned depth z. Such a curve can be defined experimentally or theoretically through the Monte Carlo simulation program. The results obtained for $\Psi=0°$ and $\Psi=40°$ are presented in figure 3. The intensity increases when the neutron probe enters into the sample and finally decreases due to the absorption of the neutrons by the material. For these curves, the depth z of each scan is defined by the position of the centre of the neutron probe. The position z = 0 is thus obtained when half the neutron probe is immersed in the sample. The intensity obtained at this point is then usually assumed to be half the maximum intensity. This is questioned by our numerical simulations. In fact, the theoretical results show that half the maximum intensity is obtained for a depth of about 0.3 mm. This depth slightly varies with Ψ. For that reason, the true position of the neutron probe has been defined for each Ψ direction by an adjustment of these theoretical curves to the experimental results. This allows to define the position of the neutron probe with an accuracy of about 50 μm.

The in-depth stress profiles of the nitrided layer are derived from the diffraction-peak positions obtained for the different ψ incidences. Figure 4 shows the distribution of the peak position versus the scanned depth obtained for $\psi=0°$. The calculated values correspond to the parasitic peak shifts which are obtained with an unstressed specimen when the neutron probe is not entirely immersed in the sample. The measured values are the results obtained experimentally on the true treated surface layer. These curves show clearly that a great part of the peak shifts observed experimentally is due to the geometrical errors and has to be corrected.

This has been done for the stress evaluation. Moreover, the true depth analysed by the neutrons has to be computed. It corresponds to the centre of the diffracting volume (the intersection between the neutron probe and the sample). For each ψ inclination, the relation between this last distance and the scanned depth (which is defined by the centre of the neutron probe) has been defined by the Monte Carlo simulation program (Fig. 5). These curves account for the absorption of the neutrons by the material and for the local conditions of diffraction.

STRESS RESULT – COMPARISON TO X-RAY MEASUREMENTS

The in-depth stress profile of the nitrided layer has been evaluated finally using the classical $\sin^2\psi$ law. The results are presented in Figure 6. The error bars of the neutron stress evaluations is about 30 MPa, which is of the same order of magnitude than those obtained in classical X-ray measurements. As expected, the stresses are mainly compressive. The depth affected by these compressions is about 1.2 mm

To check the reliability of our improved experimental procedure, the results defined by neutron diffraction have been compared to values obtained by X-rays. Measurements have been conducted, for that purpose with the chromium $K\alpha$ radiation and the {211} reflection of the ferritic phase (2θ = 156°). The in-depth stress profile was determined stepwise by successive removal of thin layers using electro-etching. The thickness of the specimen is great enough to neglect the redistribution of the internal forces due to this surface removal.

The stress profiles obtained by neutron diffraction and X-rays are very close. This demonstrates the efficiency of our procedure used to correct the parasitic peak shifts obtained in near surface neutron strain scanning.

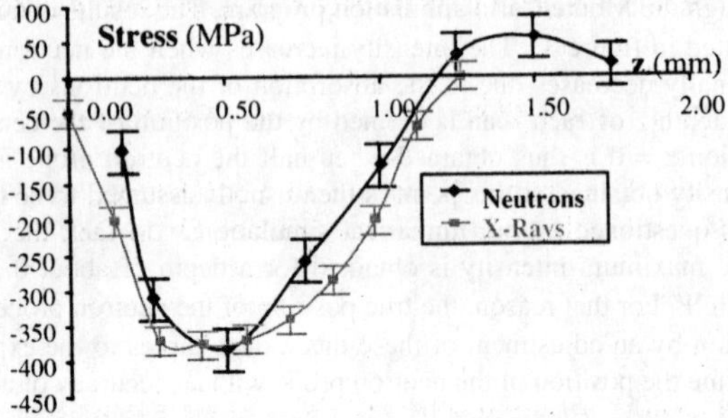

Fig. 6 In-depth distribution of the residual stresses induced by the nitriding

CONCLUSION

In our study, residual stresses have been evaluated by neutron diffraction in a nitrided steel layer. To allow such near surface measurements, a complete modelling of two-axis spectrometers has been developed to correct all parasitic peak shifts which arise when the neutron probe is not entirely immersed in the studied phase. This program allows the correction of all systematic errors and to define precisely the true depth analysed by the neutrons. The position of the neutron gauge volume has been derived from the evolution of the diffracted intensity versus the scanned depth. The resolution of this method is about 50µm. The in-depth stress profile of the nitrided layer has thus been evaluated accurately. These values have been compared to results obtained by X-rays. Both results are in very good agreement.

ACKNOLEDGMENTS

These experiments at BENSC in Berlin were supported by the European Commission through the TMR/LSF Access Programme (Contract: ERB FMGE CT 950060). Sincere thanks are due to the staff of HMI Berlin without whose help the measurements would not have been possible.

REFERENCES

1. Webster P.J, Mills G, Wang X.D, Kang W.P, Holden T.M, Journal of Neutron Research, Vol.3, 1996, 90-98.
2. Wang D.Q, Edwards L, Harris I.B, Withers P.J, ECRS4, 1996, 69-77.
3. Pluyette E, Sprauel J.M, Lodini A, Perrin M, Todeschini P, ECRS4, 1996, 153-163.
4. Pluyette E, Sprauel J.M, Cerretti M, Todeschini P, Lodini A, ICRS5, 1997, 604-609.
5. Kröner, E., J. Mech. Phys. Solids, Vol.15, 1967, 319-329.

INTERPRETATION OF EXPERIMENTS AND MODELING OF INTERNAL STRAINS IN BERYLLIUM USING A POLYCRYSTAL MODEL

C N Tomé [1], M R Daymond [2] and M A M Bourke [1]

[1] MST Division, Los Alamos National Lab, Los Alamos, NM 87545, USA
[2] ISIS, Rutherford Appleton Lab, Chilton, Didcot, Oxon OX11 0QX, England

ABSTRACT
The elastic and plastic anisotropy of Be have been examined during a uniaxial compression test, by in-situ monitoring in a pulsed neutron beam. Comparisons between the measured hkil strains and the predictions from an elasto-plastic self-consistent (EPSC) model are made. Agreement is qualitatively correct for most planes in the elasto-plastic regime. Possible mechanisms responsible for the quantitative discrepancies between model and experiment are discussed.

INTRODUCTION
The use of neutron and x-ray diffraction to measure the spacing of atomic lattice planes and interpretation of their variation in terms of strains has been well established [1, 2, 3]. It has also been recognized that the elastic anisotropy of the single crystal results in different directional stiffness depending on the individual diffraction peak which is being monitored. However once plasticity occurs, the ease of slip upon certain planes preferentially unloads certain lattice planes, and hence the response of individual hkil reflections upon a simple uniaxial load is non-linear.

The modeling of polycrystalline plasticity in metals has been aided in the last few years by comparing neutron diffraction measurements of the response of different hkil reflections during uniaxial loading with model predictions. Validation using *in situ* data is inherently more demanding on the model than simply examining the end residual strains produced by deformation, since not only the latter, but also the path dependence has to be reproduced. Previous work has addressed fcc structures such as steel, aluminum or copper [4], and hexagonal zirconium alloys [5-7]. Here we address industrially pure beryllium with aim of identifying the respective contributions of different crystallographic mechanisms to the hkil anisotropies.

EXPERIMENT
The *in situ* loading measurements were carried out at the Lujan Center, Los Alamos National Lab., using a pulsed neutron source. A description of the technique can be found elsewhere [8]. We performed a series of measurements under uniaxial compressive loading, simultaneously recording the stress-strain response of the sample, and the elastic response of individual reflections. The load frame is

designed for use in the neutron beam [9]. The loading axis is horizontal and at 45° to the incident beam, allowing simultaneous measurements of lattice plane spacing parallel and perpendicular to the load in opposing 90° detector banks. The load was applied in 18 steps to a maximum of 380 MPa and about 1.1% deformation. At each measurement the sample was held at constant load for 30 minutes to provide time to collect sufficient neutrons for good statistics on the single peak fits. During the stress hold some room temperature relaxation was observed, although it was only significant above 300 MPa. Single peak fits were carried out on the 0002 & 0004, $10\bar{1}0$ & $20\bar{2}0$, $10\bar{1}1$ & $20\bar{2}2$, $10\bar{1}2$, $10\bar{1}3$, $10\bar{1}4$, $11\bar{2}0$, $20\bar{2}1$ and $11\bar{2}2$ peaks. A 'zero' point of –5 MPa was chosen to hold the sample in the grips, and all strains of individual hkil reflections are reported relative to the lattice spacings measured at –5MPa, rather than to a 'stress-free' universal lattice parameter. This *modus operandi* ignores the presence of pre-existing residual strains induced by prior thermal or mechanical treatments.

The source of the Be used for the specimen was a hot isostatically pressed plate which was cut by electrical discharge into a cylindrical sample 24mm long with 10mm diameter. The grain size of the Be was ~45µm, and micrographs showed the material was well consolidated and with an uniform grain size distribution. The diffraction measurements indicate a close-to-random texture.

POLYCRYSTAL MODEL

The elasto-plastic self-consistent (EPSC) model used in this paper is described in detail elsewhere [5,7]. Briefly, a population of grains is chosen with orientations and weights appropriate for the texture which is to be modeled. In this case the random texture was represented by 1000 orientations. Each grain is modeled as a spherical elasto-plastic inclusion embedded in a Homogenous Effective Medium (HEM). The elasto-plastic properties of the HEM correspond to the average of all the grains and they must be solved iteratively. Each grain is defined with appropriate elastic and thermal single crystal constants. The active slip and twinning systems are defined through their Critical Resolved Shear Stress (CRSS) and some hardening behavior. In this work we assumed that all systems have an initial CRSS τ_0^s and that they harden linearly according to a law

$$\Delta\tau^s = \theta_0^s \sum_{s'} \Delta\gamma^{s'} \tag{1}$$

Where θ_0^s is a hardening coefficient and $\Delta\gamma^{s'}$ is the plastic shear increment in system s'. In the model the load was applied in strain control in 110 steps, to a total strain of 1.1% consistent with the experiment, while zero lateral stresses were enforced in the compression sample.

For comparison with the diffraction measurements subsets of grains are chosen whose hkil plane normals are oriented as the measured ones. The average of the strain over all the grains in each subset for the diffracting plane can then be calculated. In practice grains with normals within an angular range (±5°) of the exact diffraction requirement are used; this compares with the angular range of the detectors, which is ±5.5°.

RESULTS AND DISCUSSION

In what follows we compare both the macroscopic stress-strain response and the evolution of crystallographic strains predicted by the EPSC model, with the corresponding experimental values. The purpose is to gain a better understanding of the deformation systems. The single crystal elastic constants used in the calculation are: C_{11}=292.3, C_{33}=336.4, C_{12}=26.7, C_{13}=14.0 and C_{44}=162.5 GPa [10]. The directional Young's moduli are 335.6 and 289.3 GPa in the directions parallel and perpendicular to the c-axis, respectively, and indicate that the elastic properties of Be are not markedly anisotropic. However, Be exhibits an unusually low Poisson modulus (ν=0.038 in the basal plane). The thermal expansion coefficients of Be are: α_{11}=10.4 and α_{33}=13.9 10^{-6} K^{-1}. Their difference is large enough to expect a build-up of non-negligible internal strains when cooling the material from typical fabrication conditions to room temperature.

While the thermo-elastic properties of the individual grain are reasonably well known, the plastic mechanisms are much less clear. Be has an hcp structure, and undergoes slip readily on the basal (0002) plane, and with a higher critical resolved shear stress (CRSS) on the type 1 prism $(10\bar{1}0)$ plane [10]. The observed fracture stress is relatively low on the basal plane, although fracture is also observed on the type 2 prism $(11\bar{2}0)$ plane, and twinning fracture on the pyramidal $(10\bar{1}2)$ plane [10]. Basal slip can only accommodate shear in the basal plane and, as a consequence, prismatic slip, and/or pyramidal slip, and/or twinning is required in order to give general deformation. Hence, we explored simulations using different combinations of plastic modes with different yield strengths. Here we choose to report four cases that illustrate the effect of assuming different combinations of deformation systems. The systems and their associated CRSS's and hardening coefficients are reported in Table I. We regard case 1 as our best fit to the experimental data, and the results of cases 2 to 4 will be discussed using case 1 as a reference.

The results corresponding to case 1 are reported in Fig.1 and will be described here in some detail, in order to illustrate the connection between plastic activity and crystallographic strain evolution. Figure 1a depicts the predicted and measured macroscopic stress-strain response, together with relative activity of the deformation modes used in the simulation. Basal slip is activated first, followed by prism slip and, only after a deformation of about 1.5×10^{-3}, by pyramidal slip (tensile twins were not activated). In case 1 the model captures the initial elastic response, the elasto-plastic transition, and the final hardening slope. During unloading, though, the experimental curve exhibits a marked plastic relaxation, which for the predicted unloading is very small.

The measured (elastic) strains determined from the diffraction peaks are compared with model predictions parallel (Fig.1b) and transverse (Fig.1c) to the load. Here we only report results for the $(10\bar{1}0)$ prism planes, the $(10\bar{1}1)$ pyramidal and (0002) basal planes during loading. The other planes are not plotted in order not to clutter the graphs. Full symbols represent model predictions and open symbols represent experimental measurements. The latter are affected by an uncertainty of $\pm 50\times10^{-6}$.

Table I: Sets of critical stresses τ_0 [MPa] and hardening parameters Θ_0 [MPa] used in the simulations discussed in this work.

	case 1		case 2		case 3		case 4	
Basal slip $\langle 11\bar{2}0\rangle(0002)$	60	800	60	800	60	800	60	800
Prism slip $\langle 11\bar{2}0\rangle(10\bar{1}0)$	120	800	120	800	120	800	120	800
Pyram slip $\langle 11\bar{2}3\rangle(11\bar{2}2)$	170	2000	300	2000	300	2000	170	2000
Tensile twin $\langle 10\bar{1}\bar{1}\rangle(10\bar{1}2)$	230	2000	160	2000	-		230	2000
Compr twin $\langle 10\bar{1}\bar{2}\rangle(10\bar{1}1)$	-		-		160	2000	-	
ΔT	0		0		0		-300 K	

The simulated initial response of the various diffraction planes is linear, which indicates macroscopic elastic loading, until at an applied load of around 100 MPa some deviations from linearity become apparent. These features are not particularly clear in the experimental results, given the experimental uncertainty. As plastic shear starts to occur in certain slip systems, some planes are less able to bear increments in load and show, as a consequence, a smaller increase in elastic strain per increment of applied stress than in the elastic region. Stress equilibrium requires other planes to take up this increased load and, as a consequence, to increase their elastic strain. This is particularly clear in Fig.1c above 250 MPa, where the $(10\bar{1}1)$ and the (0002) planes bear relatively less and more load, respectively, than in the elastic regime.

Case 1 captures most of the experimental features, such as the relative position of each reflection and the signs of the residual strains after unloading. However, it fails to reproduce particular details of the strain evolution. In the first place, the initial slopes of the longitudinal experimental strains (Fig.1b) are smaller than the minimum Young modulus of the single crystal. This may be signaling the presence of plastic relaxation from the beginning of the experiment. Also, since the first point is taken as a reference for the subsequent measurements, an inaccuracy associated with the first measurements could be responsible for the shift observed between experiment and model at small stresses. Such shift would also affect the prediction of residual strains upon unloading. As for the transverse strains (Fig.1c), the initial elastic slope is very steep due to the nearly zero Poisson modulus of Be, and the model captures this effect correctly. It also captures the split of the three peaks above a stress of 100 MPa, when basal becomes active, as well as the dramatic changes in slope when pyramidal slip relaxation begins at about 250 MPa. All the above features are present in the experimental measurements, and the sign of the residual strains upon unloading is also correctly reproduced. However, the experiment indicates that the basal and the pyramidal planes eventually carry around twice as much load as the model predicts. We find that changing the parameters of the deformation modes to increase these strains adversely affects the prediction of the longitudinal ones.

The fits represented in Fig.1 are predicated on the activation of pyramidal slip, a deformation mode not reported for Be. As was mentioned above, single crystal Be is known to undergo both fracture of the basal plane and pyramidal twinning, which are not included in the calculation of case 1. Any of these mechanisms would induce strain relaxation in selected crystallographic planes, although including twinning or fracture effects in a polycrystal model is not straightforward. If twinning were active, one effect would be to alter the diffraction peak intensity, increasing certain peak heights, and decreasing others. No experimental evidence for this was found, but this may only be due to the fact that the twinning volume is less than about 5%, below the resolution of the NPD instrument.

To assess the possible twinning implications in the strain evolution, in case 2 we activate tensile twinning of the type $(10\bar{1}2)\langle 10\bar{1}1\rangle$, by lowering the initial CRSS of twinning and increasing that of pyramidal slip (see Fig. 2 and Table I). In our model twinning is treated as a directional plastic shear mechanism which can be activated in only one direction, but no other relaxation effects are accounted for. Although the macroscopic response is still reasonably reproduced (Fig.2a), grains oriented with the c-axis along the compression direction cannot deform by twinning and, as a consequence, they accumulate large elastic strains across the (0002) basal planes until pyramidal slip is enabled and relaxation takes place. Such response is evident in Fig. 2b, where the predicted basal strain grossly exceeds the observed evolution of the (0002) strains. As for the transverse strains (Fig.2c), the twinning activity induces relaxation in grains with the c-axis perpendicular to the compression axis, and forces other orientations to carry more load. As a consequence the predicted evolution of the transverse (0002) and $(10\bar{1}0)$ strains exhibits a larger deviation from the experiment than in case 1. The results of case 2 are puzzling given reported deformation modes, since they may indicate that tensile twinning is not an active mode under the present experimental conditions.

The fact that a directional mechanism may be responsible for the observed evolution of internal strains is illustrated in case 3, where we consider the presence of compressive twinning of the type $(10\bar{1}1)\langle 10\bar{1}2\rangle$. We achieve this by switching the CRSS's of pyramidal slip and twinning (see Table I). The macroscopic response is still reasonably reproduced (Fig.3a) and the twinning activity in grains with the c-axis parallel to the compressive direction does not change the response of the longitudinal strains with respect to case 1 (Fig.3b). A change in the correct direction is observed, however, for the transverse strains (Fig.3c): the share of load in the basal planes increases without the benefit of relaxation from the hard pyramidal slip and, as a consequence the load in the prismatic $(10\bar{1}0)$ planes decreases, giving an evolution more compatible with the one observed experimentally, although achieved by assuming a deformation mode uncharacteristic of Be.

Finally, in case 4 we analyze the effect that initial thermal residual strains may have on the subsequent mechanical response. Using the same plastic parameters as case 1 (Table I), the calculation is preceded by a build up of thermal strains associated with cooling a stress-free aggregate at 325°C down to 25°C. Given the thermal expansion coefficients of Be, the net effect is to induce tensile strains across the basal (0002) planes and compressive strains across the prismatic planes. During subsequent compression, these pre-existing thermal stresses lower the macroscopic yield stress (Fig.4a) and affect the evolution of internal strains. In particular, the initial tensile stress along the c-axis allows those grains with the c-axis parallel to the compression axis to accumulate more compressive load in the basal planes before pyramidal slip kicks in (Fig.4b). Concurrently, the contribution from these same grains to the $(10\bar{1}0)$ peak in the transverse direction shows that they increase their share of tensile strain, thus relieving the grains with the c-axis perpendicular to the compression axis (i.e. transverse basal peaks, Fig.4c). As a consequence of this strain shift the agreement between model and measurements is worse for the case 4 than for the case 1.

CONCLUSIONS

In-situ measurements of the elastic strain response of different diffraction peaks have been carried out for Be under increasing compressive loads, to 1.1% plastic strain. These results are compared with predictions from an EPSC model. Our findings are puzzling in several respects: a) the experimental evidence seems to be compatible with pyramidal slip activity or, to a lesser extent, with compressive twinning, neither of which are reported in Be [10]; b) the inclusion of more obvious mechanisms, such as tensile twinning or thermal residual strains, predict trends which are contrary to the experimental evidence.

ACKNOWLEDGEMENTS

The Lujan Center, Los Alamos Neutron Science Center (LANSCE) at Los Alamos National Laboratory is a national user facility funded by the United States Department of Energy, Office of Basic Energy Science and Defense Programs. This work was supported in part by DOE contract W-7405-ENG-36.

REFERENCES

1. Cheskis HP, Heckel RW, in 'Metal Matrix Composites', ASTM STP 438, American Society for Testing and Materials **1** (1968) 76-91
2. Krawitz AD, Journal of Metals 32 (1980) 72-92
3. Noyan IC, Cohen JB, 'Residual Stress - Measurement by Diffraction and Interpretation' New York, Springer-Verlag (1987)
4. Clausen B, Lorentzen T, Bourke MAM, Daymond MR, Mats Sc and Engng A259 (1999) 17-24
5. Tomé CN, Christodoulou N, Turner PA, Miller M, Woo CH, Root JH, Holden TM, J Nucl Mater 227 (1996) 237-250
6. Pang JWL, Holden TM, Turner PA, Mason TE, Acta Mater 47 (1999) 373-383
7. Turner PA, Christodoulou N, Tomé CN, Int J Plasticity 11 (1995) 251-265
8. Bourke MAM, Goldstone JA, Holden TM, in 'Measurement of Residual and Applied Stress Using Neutron Diffraction' Hutchings MT and Krawitz AD, Eds., Kluwer Academic Publishers. NATO ASI Series E No 216 (1992) 369-382
9. Bourke MAM, Goldstone JA, Shi N, Allison JE, Stout MG, Lawson AC, Scripta Mater 29 (1993) 771-776
10. Webster D, London GJ, Ed. 'Beryllium Science and Technology, Vol. 1'. New York, Plenum Press (1979)

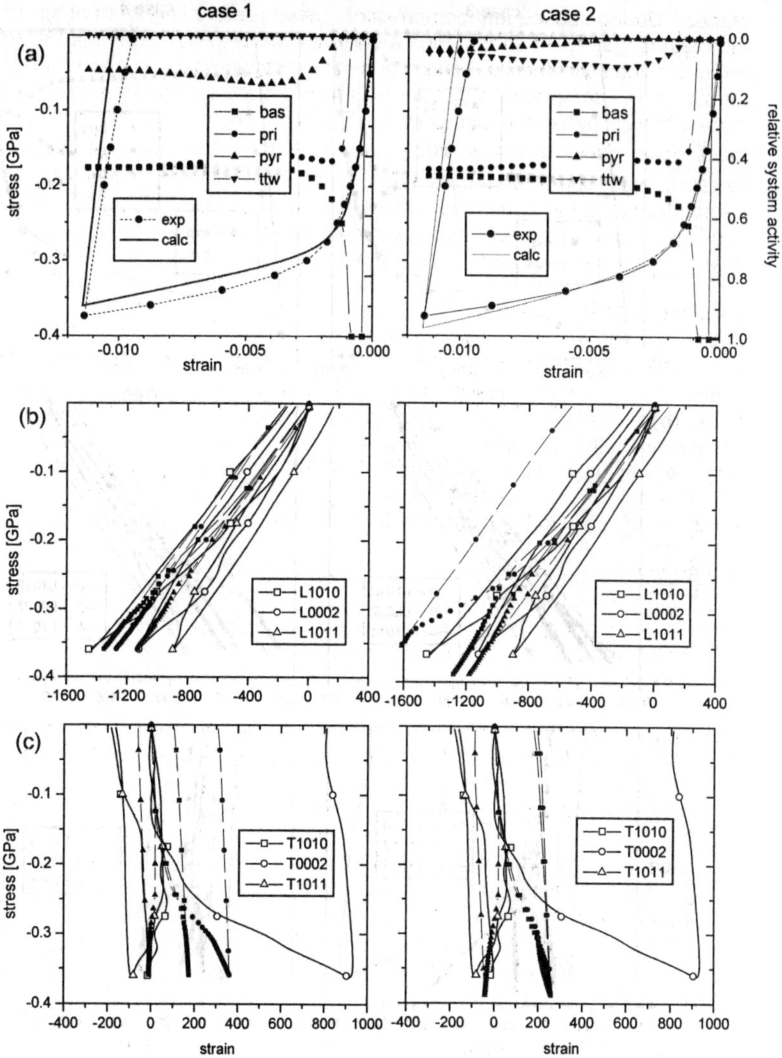

Figures 1 and 2: (a) Measured and predicted stress-strain response during compression of the Be sample. Also shown are the relative contributions of each deformation mode to deformation. (b) Experimental (open symbols) and predicted (full symbols) evolution of strain in longitudinal crystallographic planes. (c) Same as (b) for transverse planes.

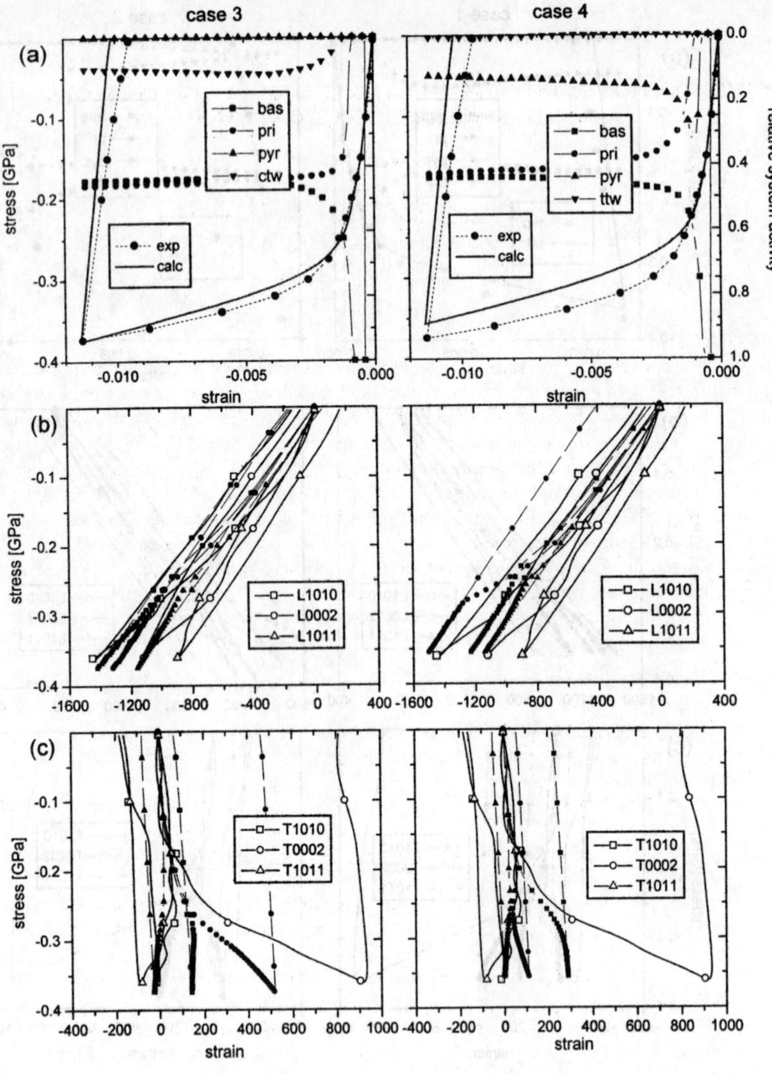

Figures 3 and 4: (a) Measured and predicted stress-strain response during compression of the Be sample. Also shown are the relative contributions of each deformation mode to deformation. (b) Experimental (open symbols) and predicted (full symbols) evolution of strain in longitudinal crystallographic planes. (c) Same as (b) for transverse planes.

DETERMINATION OF INTERGRANULAR ANISOTROPY STRAIN FROM ANALYSIS OF SINGLE DIFFRACTION PEAKS

M.R. Daymond
ISIS Facility, Rutherford Appleton Lab.,
Chilton, Didcot, OX11 0QX, UK

ABSTRACT

The stress-strain response of various individual lattice reflections measured during diffraction exhibit different gradients in the elastic region, and non-linear behaviour once plasticity occurs. This can be explained via the elastic and plastic anisotropy of the individual crystallites within a metal polycrystal. A single parameter elastic approximation to the differing responses of the peaks has been shown to allow semi-quantitative evaluation of the macroscopic plastic strain, Daymond et al. (1, 2); Korsunsky et al. (3), within the context of a Rietveld refinement on data obtained from a time-of-flight 'white' neutron source. It is demonstrated that the analysis of strains obtained from a small number of individual peaks, as might be collected at a monochromatic source, allows a determination of an anisotropy strain in good agreement with that obtained from time-of-flight data. An identical analysis procedure is carried out on predictions from a self-consistent model, which supports the use of anisotropy strain as a direct evaluation of macroscopic plastic strain.

INTRODUCTION

Neutron diffraction allows the bulk mapping of three dimensional (type I) strain fields within engineering components, using sampling volumes of a few cubic millimetres. When a variation of macrostrain occurs within a sample, the individual lattice reflections in a polycrystal typically follow this global trend with however, differences in response i.e. intergranular strains, caused by the elastic and plastic anisotropy of the individual crystallites. Self-consistent modelling techniques have proved extremely successful in the prediction of the response of individual reflections for f.c.c. materials, e.g. Clausen et al. (4), highlighting the effect of intergranular interactions in the understanding of polycrystalline plasticity.

Macrostrain determinations using the lattice parameter obtained from Rietveld refinement analysis of diffraction data, provide results comparable with the 'best' single peak analysis, Daymond et al. (1, 2). In addition, accounting for the elastic strain anisotropy within the Rietveld refinement has been shown to provide a quantitative, though empirical, evaluation of macroscopic plastic strain, Daymond et al. (1, 2); Korsunsky et al. (3). One of the major attractions of using Rietveld refinement on pulsed neutron data is the potential to include such descriptions of the physics describing the overall deformation of the polycrystal directly within the refinement.

However, due to the scarcity of time-of-flight (TOF) neutron sources at present, the majority of residual stress measurements by neutron diffraction are carried out at reactor sources, using monochromatic radiation. In such measurements, as in the majority of standard x-ray or synchrotron determinations of stress, only a small number or even a single diffraction peak is measured. By avoidance of peaks which are susceptible to large intergranular effects, accurate determinations of macrostrain profiles relevant to engineering continuum calculations are possible, Daymond et al. (1). Nonetheless, the potential to determine considerably more about the internal state of the material, through a determination of the anisotropy strain from a combined analysis of individual peaks still exists. While it would be possible to combine multiple intensity-2θ scans of individual peaks into a single spectra suitable for analysis within a standard Rietveld package, an alternative approach is taken here. Strains determined from single peak fits are combined with appropriate weightings. While this procedure is highly simplistic, it utilises only the information which would be available after the analysis of a typical monochromatic measurement. Using this procedure the influence of the number of diffraction peaks included within the strain determination is evaluated. This information is also of considerable interest in light of the new generation of TOF engineering diffractometers presently under construction at the ISIS and Los Alamos pulsed neutron sources. These instruments will have variable wavelength 'windows' on the diffraction spectra, and thus offer the opportunity to balance the competition between larger wavelength ranges (and hence more diffraction peaks) and the corresponding reduction in neutron flux.

The analysis procedure used has the advantage that since only the output from single peak fits are required, it is possible to analyse also the predicted single peak positions obtained from modelling techniques. In particular we show the predicted anisotropic strain obtained from a self-consistent model, Clausen et al. (4). Finally this paper will consider the influence of these results in terms of residual stress measurements.

RIETVELD REFINEMENT

At a TOF source, pulses of neutrons, each with a continuous range of velocities and therefore wavelengths, are directed at a specimen. Measurement of the flight times of the detected (diffracted) neutrons allows calculation of wavelength. Since the incident spectra are polychromatic, all possible lattice planes in an orientation defined by the fixed detector angle are recorded in each measurement. The scattering vectors for all reflections recorded in one detector lie in the same direction, and thus measure the strain in the same direction. Each reflection is thus produced from a different family of grains, oriented such that the given *hkl* plane diffracts to the detector.

In addition to fitting the individual lattice reflections from such spectra it is possible to perform a Rietveld refinement on the data, Von Dreele et al. (5). In the Rietveld method a crystal structure is proposed, from which a predicted diffraction spectrum is compared with a measured spectrum. The idealised structure is then optimised to maximise the agreement between prediction and measurement. By making a least squares fit between the observed and predicted profiles, the atomic positions and, more importantly in our context, the lattice parameters can thus be determined. However a complication arises when a solid polycrystalline material is deformed since the displacements of the lattice reflections (relative to an unstrained reference) depend on the elasto-plastic history of the polycrystal.

Accordingly the peak positions of the distorted polycrystal include deviations from the 'mean' response that are not easily described. Even in the presence of substantial anisotropy, in almost all cases even a Rietveld refinement that does *not* incorporate a description of the anisotropic strains will converge to a solution; the explanation for this is twofold. Firstly, for data collected in a single detector bank (i.e. for which the scattering vector lies in the same direction with respect to the sample) the majority of lattice reflections move in the same direction. Secondly, the elastic strains are usually small (rarely exceeding 2×10^{-3}) while the anisotropic spread typically is a modest percentage of this maximum. Thus the deviation from the nominal powder crystal structure is usually insufficient to preclude a convergent fit. Obviously the predicted individual peak strains are over or underestimates depending on the behaviour of the specific peak relative to the mean Rietveld strain response. The magnitude of the disparities will depend on the level of deformation and on the degree of anisotropy for the material in question.

UNIAXIAL TENSILE TEST ON STAINLESS STEEL

The sample set of experimental data used in this analysis is that described in Daymond et al. (1), the results of which are reviewed in the following section. A series of measurements were performed under uniaxial tensile loading, on a fully austenitic stainless steel sample *in-situ* on the Neutron Powder Diffractometer (NPD) at the Manuel Lujan Jr. Neutron Scattering Center at Los Alamos National Laboratory. This allowed adjustment of the applied load and, using an extensometer, observation of the onset of macroscopic plasticity, whilst simultaneously the elastic response of individual reflections was recorded. The sample has an approximately random texture.

In Figure 1 the response of the first five lattice reflections are plotted against the applied stress. Table 1 indicates the uncertainty obtained from the least squares fit to the first 15 individual peaks - all that it was possible to do reliable single peak fits for. Three of these peaks are second order, as indicated by the italics in Table 1. For clarity not all peak strains are shown in the figure. Note that the 200 and 111 lattice planes represent the extremes of elastic stiffness in a cubic material with the 311 lying approximately halfway between.

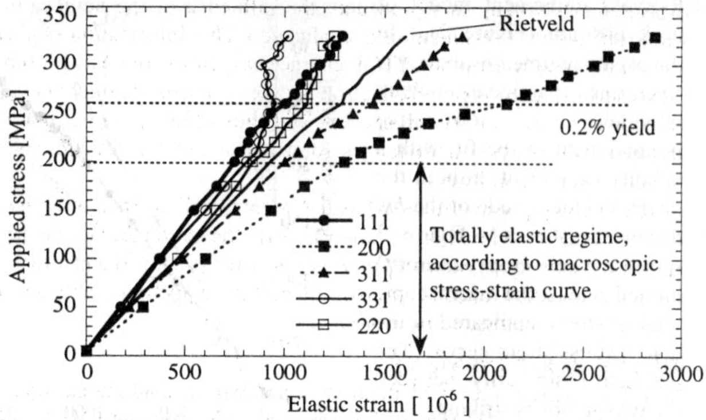

Figure 1. The change in elastic strain of five lattice planes during a uniaxial tensile test on stainless steel, as shown in Daymond et al. (1). The Rietveld isotropic strain is also shown. Lattice plane normals are parallel to the loading direction.

Peak	Mean uncertainty [10^{-6}]
111	19
200	20
220	25
311	16
222	*26*
400	*39*
331	29
420	33
422	32
511	32
531	50
442	*55*
620	91
533	90
622	*103*

Table 1) Mean uncertainty in strain obtained from least squares fits to single diffraction peaks.

ANISOTROPY IN THE RIETVELD REFINEMENT

In its simplest implementation the Rietveld description does not account for the elastic or plastic anisotropies present in polycrystalline materials under load though, as explained, in this form it does provide a good empirical bulk average, Daymond et al. (1, 2). Inclusion of the elastic divergence of the various planes from the Rietveld mean lattice parameter is a first step in describing polycrystalline deformation within the refinement. For a cubic crystal the single crystal plane specific modulus, E_{hkl} can be expressed as, Nye (6):

$$1/E_{hkl} = S_{11} - 2(S_{11} - S_{12} - {}^1/_2\, S_{44})A_{hkl} \quad (1)$$

where S_{ij} is the single crystal compliance tensor in collapsed matrix notation and

$$A_{hkl} = (h^2k^2+h^2l^2+k^2l^2)\,/\,(h^2+k^2+l^2)^2 \quad (1b)$$

and thus has limiting values of $A_{h00} = 0$ and $A_{hhh} = {}^1/_3$.

Daymond et al. (1) describe how, in order to take this into account, a fitting parameter, γ, in the Rietveld refinement was used, shifting the position of each peak *hkl* from a perfect cubic structure by a quantity proportional to γA_{hkl}. Accordingly, the refinement is modified so that the lattice parameter now tracks a nominal *h00* direction, and the other reflections are anisotropically strained according to

$$\varepsilon_{hkl} = \varepsilon_{h00} - \gamma A_{hkl} \quad (2)$$

where ε_{hkl} is the strain of a particular reflection.

In the elastic regime the parameter γ correlates solely with the elastic anisotropy and therefore, from Equation 1, we expect it will be proportional to the applied stress if we can make a Reuss (7) assumption. The Reuss assumption, of equal stress in all elements (grains) of the system, is expected to be incorrect in a normal polycrystal. However in a sufficiently large population of grains, it appears that the approximation that each *family* of grains on average experiences the applied (mean) stress is sufficient, at least in the case of ductile materials, Howard et al. (8). Excellent agreement is thus obtained in the elastic regime between actual single peak fits and the

Rietveld refinement model of peak position (Figure 2). In the plastic regime however, γ is a fitting parameter which provides a qualitative improvement to the fit, with a validity dependent on both the range and magnitude of the *hkl* dependent strains. Figure 3 shows the anisotropy strain (γ) plotted against the macroscopic applied stress, compared to the macro stress-strain curve. The qualitative similarity between the two graphs is striking.

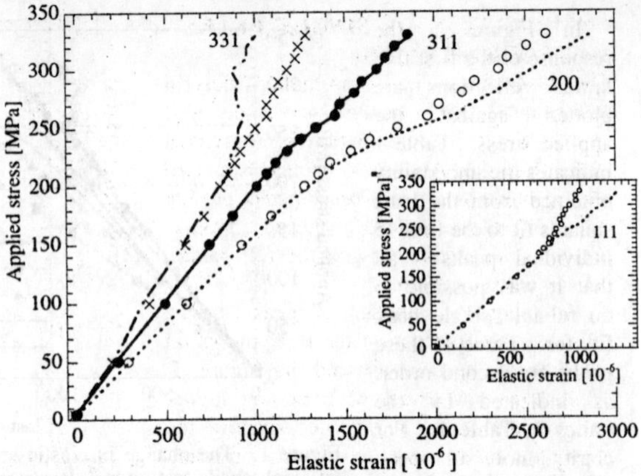

Figure 2) The strain response in the axial direction of the 200, 311, 331 and 111 planes 1) as determined by single peak fits (lines), and 2) as calculated from the Rietveld fit using the anisotropy factor γ (points), as shown in Daymond et al. (1). For clarity, the 111 planes are shown in the insert.

In Daymond et al. (1) we postulated that γ can be separated into two contributions; namely elastic (γ^{el}) and plastic (γ^{pl}) components, where $\gamma = \gamma^{el} + \gamma^{pl}$. This assumption was successfully used to provide an empirical prediction of macroscopic plastic strain. A similar approach has also been used elsewhere, Korsunsky et al. (3), though in this case the material under study was aluminium which has a negligible elastic anisotropy, somewhat simplifying the analysis.

Weighting of contributions to the Rietveld lattice parameter

If we wish to recreate a lattice parameter comparable to that obtained from a Rietveld refinement from a direct combination of measurements of single peak positions, the first step must be to find the appropriate weightings used in the refinement itself. The derivation of the appropriate weightings is given in Appendix 1. Two different weightings must be determined, for the two situations we wish to examine. Firstly, the weighting of experimentally measured (single) peak positions, with a known statistical uncertainty obtained from the least squares fit, and secondly the weighting for peak positions predicted by the self consistent model. Fortunately, relatively little information is required beyond which peak is being observed, in order to determine the required weighting. This makes this approach practical for real measurements.

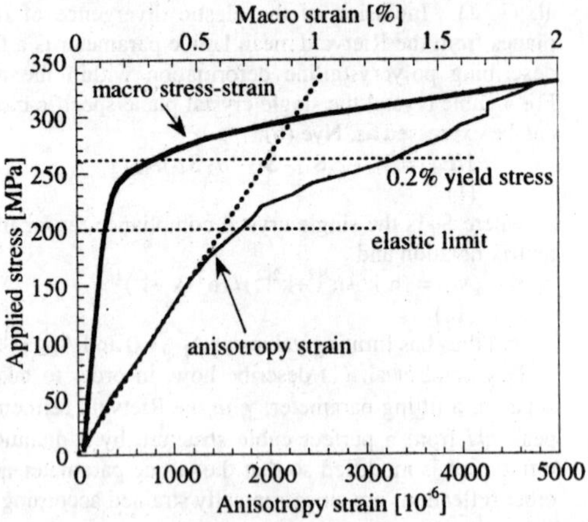

Figure 3) The variation of anisotropy factor with applied stress, superimposed with the stress-strain relationship, as shown in Daymond et al. 1.

COMBINATION OF SINGLE PEAKS - ISOTROPIC STRAINS.

The isotropic, i.e. 'normal' Rietveld refinement strain is matched extremely well by the weighted combination of individual peaks (Fig. 4). Almost no change is caused by use of only the first order peaks present within the range, instead of the all 15 peaks present, and agreement with the full pattern refinement is excellent.

Reducing the number of peaks has a relatively small effect on the isotropic strain determined, as demonstrated in Figure 5. This shows the effect of removing higher order peaks consecutively i.e. keeping the maximum d-spacing observed constant. Provided at least 5 peaks are included in the analysis, differences between the various responses are less than the experimental uncertainty, in agreement with the trend of results shown by Daymond et al. (1).

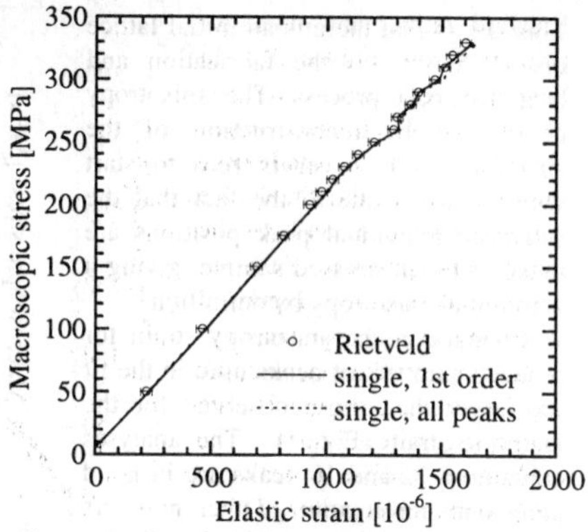

Figure 4) Comparison between single peak least squares analysis and Rietveld refinement (points) predictions of lattice parameter. The broken line represents analysis of all 15 measured single peaks (first and second order), the continuous line just the 12 first order peaks.

We can imagine making a similar trend of peak removal, concentrating on peaks at smaller d-spacings. Provided the instrumental resolution is sufficient to allow individual peaks to still be resolved a given wavelength window will view a larger number of peaks at the smaller wavelength. Though space restrictions preclude inclusion of such a figure, initial removal of the 200 and 111 peaks from the analysis each produces relatively large fluctuations in the Rietveld mean, at least in the plastic region. This might be expected due to the large shifts relative to the mean, and large weightings, of these peaks. Further removal of peaks has less effect, with an approximately stable isotropic strain, slightly different from that observed with the full pattern analysis until 6 peaks or less are included in the analysis. Of course for these peaks, uncertainties in peak position are relatively poor.

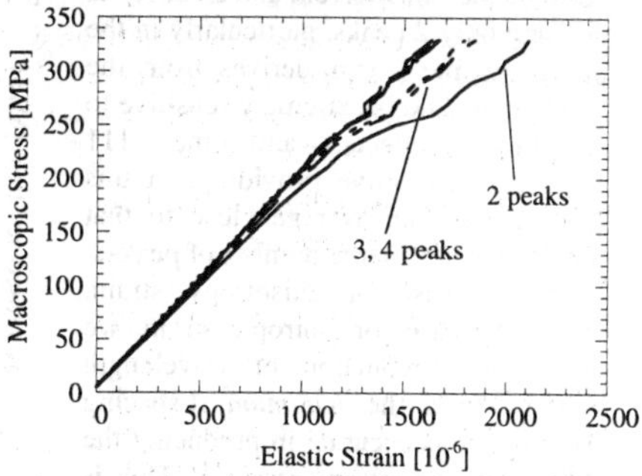

Figure 5) Effect of reducing the number of peaks within the single peak least squares analysis, using only 1st order peaks. Shown are results for 12, 10, 8, 6, 5, 4, 3, and 2 peaks.

Discrepancies between the Rietveld and single peak combination approaches can be explained in at least two ways. Firstly the true peaks at a time-of-flight source are asymmetric, and the weightings used may be slightly incorrect as the level of asymmetry changes. For instance the sharp rise at the forward edge of the peak tends to aid determination of peak position (from the gradient term in Appendix 1). Secondly, during plastic straining, there will be an increase in peak width, and if this is not uniform across the peaks, again we may expect discrepancies due to the constraints on width imposed within the Rietveld refinement.

COMBINATION OF SINGLE PEAKS - ANISOTROPIC STRAINS

In Figure 6 we show the strains ε_{h00} and γ from Equation 2 as determined by a direct Rietveld refinement and by single peak reconstruction; good agreement is obtained. Again this agreement is relatively insensitive to use of first order peaks alone. In passing we should note however that the Rietveld anisotropy strain is not zero when the sample has no macroscopically applied stress.

This shows that there is an initial lattice distortion, due to the fabrication and heat treatment process. The anisotropy determined by reconstruction of the single peaks however *is* zero to start with. This is due to the fact that the reference individual peak positions are those of the unstressed sample, giving a zero initial anisotropy by definition.

Changes in the anisotropy strain for reduced numbers of peaks used in the fit are larger than those observed for the isotropic strain (Fig. 7). The analyses containing 12 and 10 peaks are in good agreement throughout. Other numbers of peaks do differ, with the largest deviation obtained for around 5 peaks, though even here qualitative agreement is reasonable. It is perhaps surprising that good agreement is in fact obtained between the full Rietveld and an analysis utilising only 2 peaks, particularly in the plastic regime. This derives from the fact that the 200 is extremely sensitive to anisotropic effects, and the 111 relatively insensitive providing, in this case at least, an average close to that obtained using a large number of peaks.

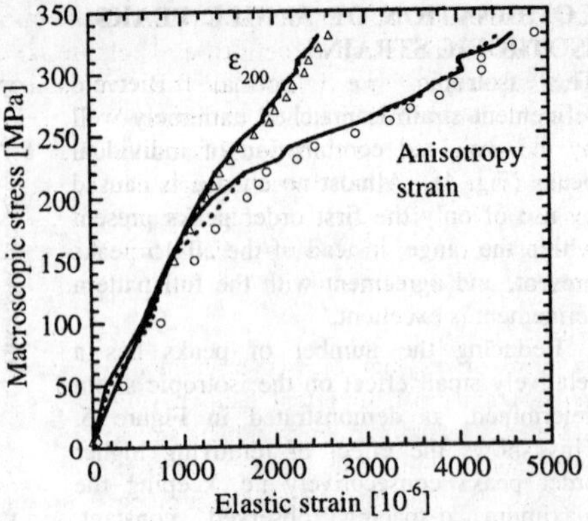

Figure 6) Comparison between 1st order (continuous) and all (broken) single peak least squares analysis and Rietveld refinement predictions (points) of lattice parameter, showing the 200 nominal strain and the anisotropic strain parameter γ

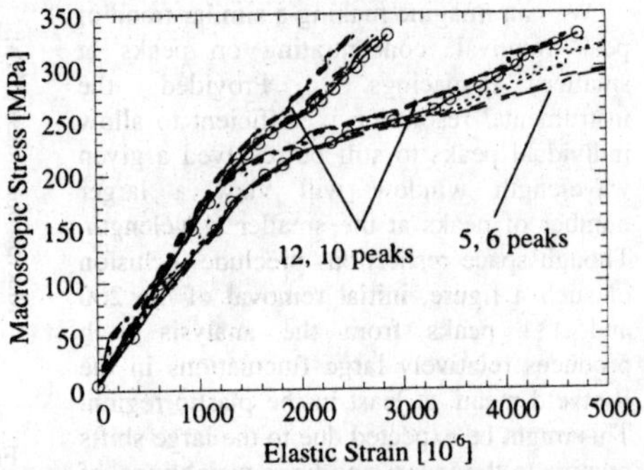

Figure 7) Effect of reducing the number of peaks within the single peak least squares analysis, using only 1st order peaks. Shown are results for 12, 10, 8, 6, 5, 4, 3 and 2 peaks. The 12 peak data is shown in thick lines, the 2 peak data also shows the points, as circles.

In the case of anisotropy strain, unlike the case for isotropic strain, we note that a reduction of wavelength window with the *minimum* d-spacing fixed is not as accurate in producing the full pattern anisotropy strain . This is partly due to the fact that the first peak removed from the analysis, the 200, is one of the primary contributors to, and strongest exhibitors of anisotropy strain. In the case where 10 or more peaks are used in the analysis, a reasonable agreement (better than 10%) with the full pattern analysis is nonetheless achieved. The fact that more peaks are required than the case for the isotropic strain, we might attribute to the fact that two fitting parameters must be determined, and that once the peaks exhibiting primary effects of anisotropy (e.g. 200) are removed, the diffraction pattern is less sensitive to the anisotropy effects.

SINGLE PEAK STRAIN PREDICTIONS FROM THE SELF-CONSISTENT MODEL

Given a method for treating the combination of individual peak fits, we can also conduct an analysis of the self-consistent model's predictions of anisotropy strain. Here we have no weighting from a known intensity spectra (i.e. the uncertainty obtained from least square peak fits), thus we assume a constant incident flux in Equation 5 to produce the appropriate weightings, as described in the Appendix. Whilst reasonable agreement is obtained between model and experiment for the single peak strains, as would be expected given the agreement in peak strains demonstrated, Clausen et al. (4), examination of the anisotropy strain elucidates one point of further interest. The anisotropy strain from the model shows a distinct tri-linear behaviour (Fig. 8). These regions can be defined as 1) elastic, 2) elasto-plastic transition (where new groups of grains are undergoing yield for the first time) and 3) plastic zone, where the same grains continue to yield, but with increasing hardnesses.

In contrast the experimental results exhibit a bi-linear behaviour, though the uncertainty in the experimental determination of anisotropy does not preclude a tri-linear result.

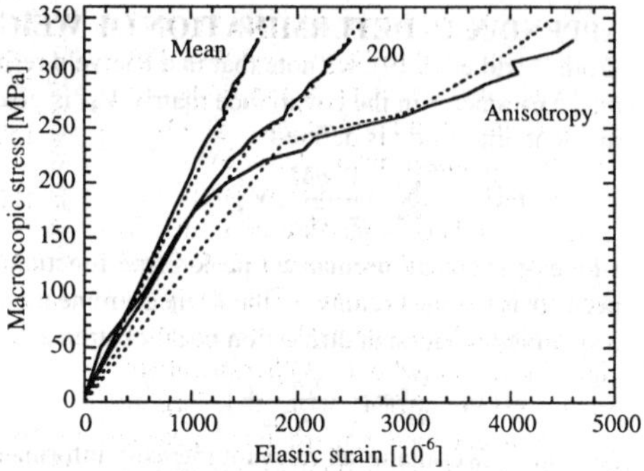

Figure 8) Comparison between model (broken) and experiment (continuous) for isotropic strain, and the ε_{h00} and anisotropy strains from Equation 2.

DISCUSSION

In terms of residual stress measurement, perhaps the most important factor is for the new generation of residual stress instruments built at pulsed neutron sources. We note that running at a given frequency of source a long flight path (i.e. high resolution) diffraction instrument will have a relatively small window of available d-spacings. This analysis seems to suggest that in terms of isotropic strain, around 5 peaks are sufficient for an accurate determination, which is a relatively small wavelength window. Determination of the anisotropy strain using just 5 peaks however is poor, with the strain determined using just the 111 and 200 peaks actually in better agreement with that obtained from a full diffraction pattern analysis. This fact allows useful comparisons between the anisotropy generated at 'white beam' sources, whether neutron or synchrotron, and similar measurements at monochromatic sources e.g. Korsunsky et al. (3), where typically a relatively small number of peaks is measured.

CONCLUSIONS

These results show that by use of suitable weightings on results from single peak analysis, good agreement can be obtained with strain determined from whole pattern Rietveld analysis. This is true for the isotropic strain, and for anisotropic strain calculations as well, though with somewhat poorer accuracy. The strains determined are fairly insensitive to the number of diffraction peaks included in the analysis. This bodes well for the determination of anisotropy strains from reactor or synchrotron measurements, where fewer peaks would typically be measured.

Analysis of single peak positions predicted by the self-consistent model demonstrate that the anisotropy strain is a good measure of global macro strain, at least in the small plasticity range, though at higher strains damage effects may reduce this validity.

ACKNOWLEDGEMENTS

The author would like to thank Prof. Bill David and Dr. Mike Johnson for useful discussions of this work. The ISIS facility is funded by the UK EPSRC.

REFERENCES

[1] Daymond, M.R., Bourke, M.A.M. et al. J. Appl. Phys. (1997) **82**(4): 1554.
[2] Daymond, M.R., Bourke, M.A.M. et al. J. Appl. Phys. (1999) **85**(2): 739.
[3] Korsunsky, A.M., Daymond, M. R. et al. *at* ECRS-5, Noordwijk, Holland. 1999. *in press*
[4] Clausen, B., Lorentzen, T., Daymond, M.R. et al. Mat. Sci. Eng. (1999) **259**(1): 17.
[5] Von Dreele, R.B., Jorgensen, J.D. et al. J. Appl. Cryst. (1982) **15**: 581.
[6] Nye, J.F. "Physical Properties of Crystals", OUP. 1992.
[7] Reuss, A. Z. angew. Math. Mech. (1929) **9**: 49.
[8] Howard, C.J. and Kisi, E.H. J. Appl. Cryst. (1999) **32**(4): 624.
[9] David, W.I.F., Ibberson, R.M. et al. Proc. Roy. Soc. A (1993) **442**(1914): 129.
[10] Buras, B. and Gerward, L. Acta Crystallogr. (1975) **A31**: 372.

[11] David, W.I.F. and Jorgensen, J.D. *in* The Rietveld Method. R.A. Young ed. OUP. (1993): 197
[12] Larson, A.C. and Von Dreele, R.B. (1994). GSAS, LAUR86-748, Los Alamos National Lab.
[13] Sivia, D.S. "Data Analysis - A Bayesian Tutorial", OUP. 1996.
[14] Edwards, L., Fitzpatrick, M.E., Daymond, M.R. et al. *this volume,* ICRS VI, Oxford. 2000.

APPENDIX 1 - DETERMINATION OF WEIGHTING FACTORS

From David et al. (9), we note that in a Rietveld refinement, the impact dV_{jk} of the ith data point on the jth parameter in the covariance matrix V_{jk}, is given by $-\alpha t_j t_j$, where α is the fractional increase in count time, and t is defined

$$t_j(i) = \sum_{k=1}^{No.pars} \frac{1}{\sigma_i} \frac{\partial M_i}{\partial p_k} V_{jk} \qquad (3)$$

where M is the un-normalised peak shape function, p are the fitting parameters to the diffraction peak, σ_i is the uncertainty on the ith measurement and V is the covariance matrix. We will assume a symmetric Gaussian diffraction peak, centred at d_{hkl} with width ω, i.e.

$$M(x_i) = \frac{M_0}{\omega} \exp\left(-\frac{x_i - d_{hkl}}{\sqrt{2}\omega}\right)^2 \qquad (4)$$

Note that M_0 contains all relevant intensity information for the peak, such that, Buras et al. (10):

$$\int M_i dx_i \propto d_{hkl}^4 \varepsilon(\lambda) I_0(\lambda) m_{hkl} \qquad (5)$$

where I_0 is the incident neutron flux, ε represents the detection efficiency and m_{hkl} is the multiplicity of the *hkl* reflection, and we have used the fact that for a given detector at a time-of-flight source, $d_{hkl} \propto \lambda$. Note that we are neglecting the effects of texture here. The influence of a given data point on the position d_{hkl} is then $(1/\sigma_i)(\partial M_i/\partial d_{hkl})$, which is proportional to $M_i/(\sigma_i \omega^2)$. However, we are concerned with the effect of the observed data on the lattice parameter a, hence our interest, for cubic materials, lies instead with

$$\frac{\partial M_i}{\partial a} = \frac{\partial M_i}{\partial d_{hkl}} \frac{d_{hkl}}{a} \qquad (6)$$

To a good approximation the number of data points contributing to a diffraction peak measured at a pulsed source is independent of wavelength, and hence *hkl*, due to the use of logarithmic time binning, David et al. (11). We will make one further approximation in this analysis, namely that the predominant contributions to the peak width are i) instrumental and ii) isotropic strain broadening, in which case we can assume $\omega^2 \propto d_{hkl}^2$, Larson et al. (12).

Combining these parameters and assuming Poisson counting statistics, we obtain the weighting for the contribution of an individual diffraction peak to a determination of the lattice parameter as

$$w_{hkl} \propto \frac{M_0}{\omega^4} d_{hkl}^2 \qquad (7)$$

Thus the weighting contribution from an individual experimentally determined peak to the Rietveld determined lattice parameter will be

$$w_{hkl} \propto \frac{M_0}{d_{hkl}^2} \qquad (8)$$

From this we can obtain the weighting to use for combining model predictions of the lattice spacing; substituting for M_0, and assuming a uniform incident flux:

$$w_{hkl} \propto d_{hkl}^2 m_{hkl} \qquad (9)$$

In passing, we note that from statistical arguments, e.g. Chapter 2 of Sivia (13), the weighting for a combination of data is just $1/\sigma^2$, where σ is the uncertainty on the individual measurement (here the individual peak position). If we equate this with the weighting from Equation 8, remembering that M_0 is proportional to the integrated intensity in the peak, we obtain once more the ubiquitous

$$\frac{1}{\sigma^2} \propto \frac{I}{\omega^2} \qquad (10)$$

which appears elsewhere in this volume, Edwards et al. (14), and in Chapter 7 of Sivia (13).

Measurement of Residual Stress Distributions in T-plate Joints

P. S. May, N. P. O'Dowd and G. A. Webster

Department of Mechanical Engineering
Imperial College
London, SW7 2BX, UK

ABSTRACT

The residual stress distributions in a 25 mm fillet welded T-plate joint and a beam with a mechanically induced stress field are presented. The distributions have been measured using the neutron diffraction technique, a method which uses the diffraction pattern of a neutron beam after collision with a crystalline material to determine the lattice spacing of the material. The elastic strains in the material may then be measured at an atomic level and stresses calculated at the macro level using the measured strains and Hooke's law.

Duplicate measurements were carried out using a monochromatic neutron source (ILL, Grenoble, Fr.) and a spallation source (ISIS, Didcot, UK). At ILL a single atomic plane (the (211) plane in this investigation) is used to obtain the lattice spacing of the material whereas ISIS uses a Rietveld refinement method which averages over a number of planes. ISIS data have also been analysed using only the (211) reflection.

Measurements in a mechanically overloaded beam have been made to establish the measurement accuracy. From these measurements it was found that both methods give satisfactory results. The differences obtained may be due to inaccuracies in the positioning of the sample.

The tensile residual stress at the toe of the weld was found to be of yield strength magnitude (approximately 350 MPa), but with a steep stress gradient leading to compressive stresses at distances greater than 7 mm from the weld toe.

INTRODUCTION

Welding is known to generate tensile residual stresses in structures. These stresses can contribute significantly to failure mechanisms such as creep, fatigue and stress corrosion cracking. Allowance must therefore be made for the presence of residual stresses in the design of structures. To do this accurately, residual stress distributions in welded structures must be known. However, little information on welded T-plate joints is available in the literature [1]. This paper presents the residual stress distributions measured in a ferritic steel fillet T-plate weld and also on a bent bar for calibration purposes.

Residual stresses have been measured by the neutron diffraction method using a pulsed neutron spallation source (ISIS, Didcot, UK) and a monochromatic reactor neutron source (ILL, Grenoble, Fr.). The neutron diffraction method was preferred over destructive methods such as sectioning and deep hole drilling because it allows subsequent fracture

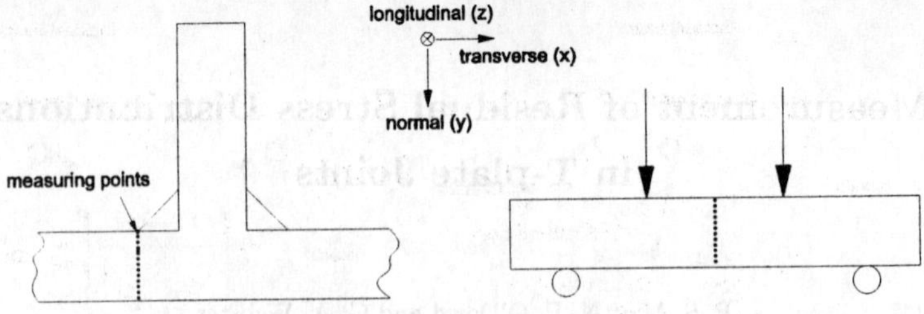

Figure 1: (a) T-plate weld sample (b) Bent bar

toughness tests to be carried out on the samples. Residual stresses have been measured along a line down the toe of the weld as indicated in Figure 1 (a). and also across the middle of a plastically bent bar, Fig. 1 (b), for comparison with finite element predictions to verify the measurement accuracy.

THE NEUTRON DIFFRACTION METHOD

Neutrons can penetrate deeply into crystalline materials compared to other particles such as X-rays. This makes them useful for measuring the internal stress state in a body non-destructively. The neutron diffraction method uses the interatomic distance in crystalline materials as a microscopic strain gauge. A beam of neutrons that penetrates a crystalline material will, after collision with the atoms in the sample, scatter in a preferred direction as described by the Bragg equation:

$$n\lambda = 2d_{hkl} sin\theta \tag{1}$$

where λ is the wavelength of the neutron beam, n is an integer, d_{hkl} is the distance between the lattice planes in the direction hkl and θ is the scattering angle as indicated in Figure 2. Equation 1 indicates that for a monochromatic neutron beam the lattice spacing in the direction of the Q-vector can be determined from the scattering angle θ.

Spallation neutron sources however generate polychromatic neutron pulses. To obtain the lattice spacing d_{hkl} from a polychromatic beam the scattering angle is kept at a constant angle leaving the wavelength as the variable. The wavelength of a neutron is related to its velocity by de Broglie's relation:

$$\lambda = \frac{h}{mv} \tag{2}$$

where h is Planck's constant, m is the neutron mass and v is the neutron velocity. The velocity of the neutron can be determined from its time of flight (*tof*) and the distance between the moderator and the detector. For a constant scattering angle the lattice spacing d_{hkl} is thus related to the *tof* of the neutrons. Because the spallation source generates a polychromatic neutron beam a diffraction pattern over several different crystallographic planes can be obtained simultaneously. To obtain the lattice spacing in the direction Q a Rietveld analysis can be employed which uses a weighted average of the individual peak positions.

In general the lattice spacing of the material is desired to be measured over a well defined volume. To restrict the sampling volume over which the strain measurement is

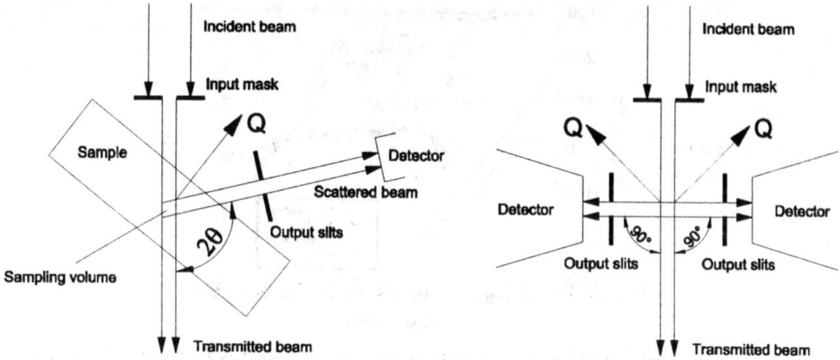

Figure 2: (a) Experimental setup at ILL and (b) ISIS

made the incident beam is masked to the desired height and width. The scattered beam is then masked at the detector to define the size of the sampling volume. This setup is shown in Fig. 2 (a) for the ILL. At ISIS a fixed angle $2\theta = 90°$ is used to produce a square cross-section sampling volume (Fig. 2 (b)).

The strain in the material in the direction of the Q vector can be calculated from the measured lattice spacing d and the stress free lattice parameter d_0 which can be measured in a stress free part of the sample. When strains are measured in three perpendicular directions and isotropic material behaviour is assumed, stresses can be calculated using the generalised Hooke's Law:

$$\sigma_{xx} = \frac{E}{(1+\nu)(1-2\nu)}[(1-\nu)\epsilon_{xx} + \nu(\epsilon_{yy} + \epsilon_{zz})] \tag{3a}$$

$$\sigma_{yy} = \frac{E}{(1+\nu)(1-2\nu)}[(1-\nu)\epsilon_{yy} + \nu(\epsilon_{xx} + \epsilon_{zz})] \tag{3b}$$

$$\sigma_{zz} = \frac{E}{(1+\nu)(1-2\nu)}[(1-\nu)\epsilon_{zz} + \nu(\epsilon_{xx} + \epsilon_{yy})] \tag{3c}$$

where E is the modulus of elasticity, σ_{xx}, σ_{yy}, σ_{zz}, ϵ_{xx}, ϵ_{yy} and ϵ_{zz} are the stress and strain tensors respectively, and ν is Poisson's ratio. In general the modulus of elasticity is taken to be dependent on the crystal plane used for the measurement when calculating stresses from an experiment using a single reflection. The elastic modulus E_{hkl} used in the analysis is calculated for the (211) crystal plane from [2]:

$$\frac{1}{E_{hkl}} = s_{11} + \frac{(2s_{12} - 2s_{11} + s_{44})(k^2l^2 + l^2h^2 + h^2k^2)}{(h^2+k^2+l^2)^2} \tag{4}$$

where s_{11}, s_{12} and s_{44} are the components of the compliance matrix for cubic materials. A Poisson's ratio of 0.3 was used. When a Rietveld analysis is employed to obtain strain the bulk modulus of elasticity is used.

EXPERIMENTAL PROCEDURE

The neutron diffraction technique has been employed to measure the residual stress distribution in a ferritic steel fillet T-plate weld and in a mechanically overloaded beam of

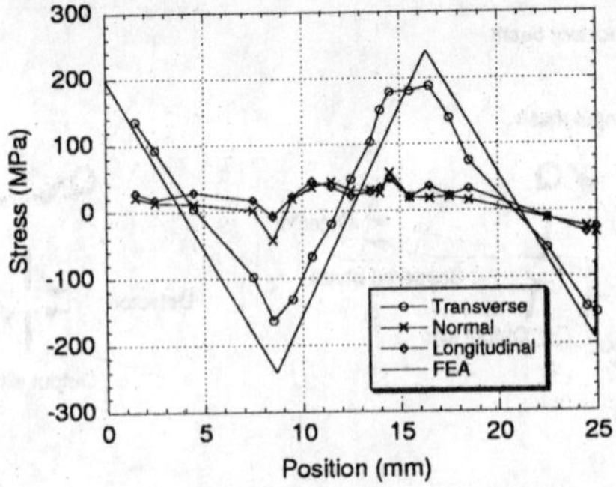

Figure 3: Residual stress distribution measured at ILL

the same material. Figures 1 (a) and (b) illustrate the weld sample and beam respectively with their measuring positions indicated. Note that the conventions to indicate directions are equivalent for the weld and the beam. Both samples are manufactured from 25 mm plate material and have a thickness of approximately 12 mm. The rolling direction of the plate is in the transverse direction as indicated. The material under examination is the offshore steel BS7191 Grade 355EMZ. This is a low carbon (0.15 %) ferritic steel which was supplied in the normalised condition to give a yield stress of approximately 400 MPa.

Duplicate measurements have been carried out at both ISIS and ILL. It was found that a sampling volume of approximately $2 \times 2 \times 2$ mm^3 was most efficient for all measurements made at both neutron sources. Ezeilo *et. al.* [3] have shown that the most suitable crystallographic plane for neutron diffraction measurements in ferritic steels are the (200) and the (211) planes, based on a minimal effect of intergranular stresses. For this reason the measurements carried out with a monochromatic neutron source were made on the (211) crystallographic plane. Reference measurements for the determination of d_0 have been made at locations where the material is assumed to be stress free. A $4 \times 4 \times 4$ mm^3 sampling volume was employed to obtain the stress free lattice parameter. Reference measurements have also been carried out on a sample of the weld material to determine the difference in d_0 between the weld and parent material. The difference in d_0 was found to be negligible and is therefore ignored in further analysis.

Residual stress measurements have also been made in three orthogonal directions at mid-thickness in a beam containing a mechanically induced stress field for verification of the measurement accuracy. This method was chosen because the residual stress field in the beam is easily obtained from finite element analysis (FEA) or analytical solutions, and only homogeneous material is involved which increases the reliability of the measurements [4]. The beam has been loaded to a surface strain of 0.7 % in a four point bend configuration. Upon unloading the locally yielded material causes incompatible strains in the material which result in a residual stress distribution [5].

Measurements in the T-plate weld sample have been carried out in three orthogonal directions at mid-thickness along a line down the weld toe. This location was chosen because this is where cracks usually initiate. The investigation focuses on the stresses in the transverse direction because these contribute most to the fracture behaviour of the joint.

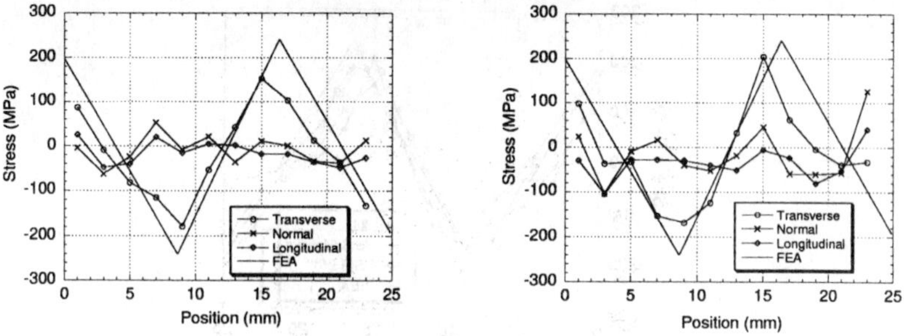

(a) (b)

Figure 4: (a) ISIS Rietveld refinement (b) (211) single peak analysis

MEASUREMENTS ON BEAM SAMPLE

Strain measurements in a mechanically overloaded beam have been made on the (211) crystal plane using the monochromatic neutron source at the ILL. The strains were converted into stresses using the generalised Hooke's law, Eqns. 3. The elastic modulus used in the analysis was 220.4 GPa as determined from Eq. 4. The Poisson's ratio was taken as the bulk value of 0.3.

Measurements have been made at 19 locations along the y-direction in the sample as indicated in Fig. 1. The stress distributions obtained from these measurements are shown in Fig. 3. It can be seen that the stress distribution in the transverse direction compares well with the FEA assuming plane stress conditions, but that non-zero stresses in the normal and longitudinal directions were measured. These stresses are, however, mainly within the uncertainty of the measurements of about ± 25 MPa so that plane stress conditions can be considered to have been met. Further detailed consideration of the transverse residual stress data reveals that the peak stresses are underestimated by about 50 MPa. Some rounding off is to be expected in a sampling volume size of $2 \times 2 \times 2$ mm^3 due to averaging of strain over this region. There would also appear to be an uncertainty in positioning of ± 1 mm in the experimental measurements.

Measurements were made on the same overloaded beam at 12 locations along the y-direction using the pulsed neutron beam at ISIS. Strains were calculated from the time of flight of the neutrons using both the Rietveld refinement procedure and a single peak analysis taken from the (211) reflection. Stresses were calculated from the strains as described earlier but the elastic modulus for the (211) crystallographic direction was replaced by the bulk modulus of 212 GPa for the Rietveld analysis. The results obtained from the Rietveld analysis and (211) reflection are shown in Figs. 4 (a) and (b) respectively.

It can be seen in Fig. 4 (a) that the normal and longitudinal stresses measured at ISIS are similar to those measured at ILL (Fig. 3). Both the Rietveld analysis and the (211) single peak analysis give reasonable agreement with the theoretical (FEA) result. It appears from Fig. 4 that there could be a similar positioning uncertainty to that noted at ILL. The comparison between both methods at ISIS and the ILL measurements is shown in Fig. 5. From this figure it appears that the stress distribution measured at ILL lies slightly nearer to the FEA results. However, given the experimental uncertainties in the measurements (calculated to be ±22 MPa for the ISIS data and ±25 MPa for the ILL

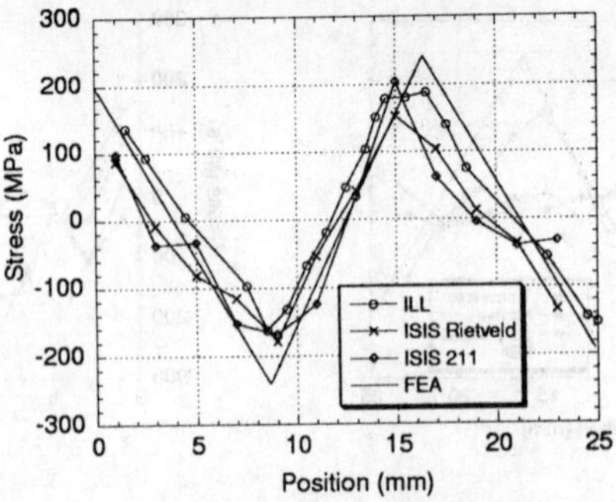

Figure 5: Comparison between the transverse stresses measured in the bar and FEA

data) the agreement is reasonable. Both methods are therefore regarded equally reliable.

MEASUREMENTS ON T-PLATE WELD SAMPLE

Results of the measurements which were carried out on the T-plate weld sample at ILL and ISIS are shown in Figs. 6 and 7 respectively. Measurements at ILL were made at fifteen locations along a line down the toe of the weld as shown in Fig. 1 (a) and at thirteen locations along the same plane at ISIS. All the measurements indicate that the stress distributions in the three orthogonal directions are very similar. In general the ISIS measurements show that lower stresses in the region of the weld toe are obtained when the Rietveld refinement procedure is adopted than when the single peak (211) data are used.

A comparison between the residual stress distributions measured at ISIS and ILL is shown in Fig. 8. Although similar trends are observed, lower stresses are obtained close to the weld for the measurements made at ISIS. The data obtained using the (211) reflection lies closer to the ILL result but shows stronger variability. From further investigations carried out it has been shown that the peak stress in the region below the weld toe ($y \leq 5$) is strongly dependent on the x and z positions close to the weld toe. It is

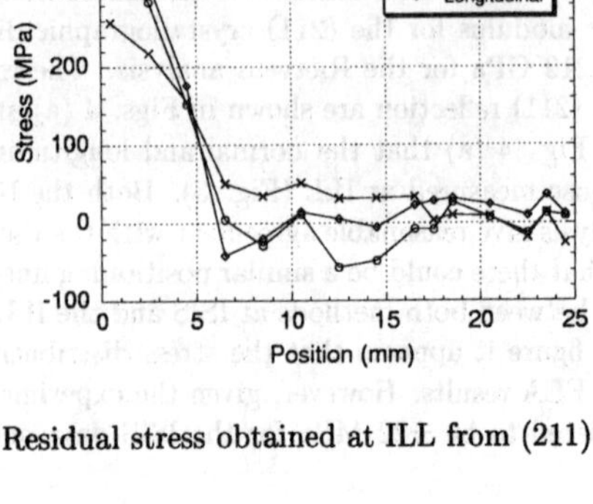

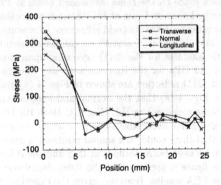

Figure 6: Residual stress obtained at ILL from (211) reflection

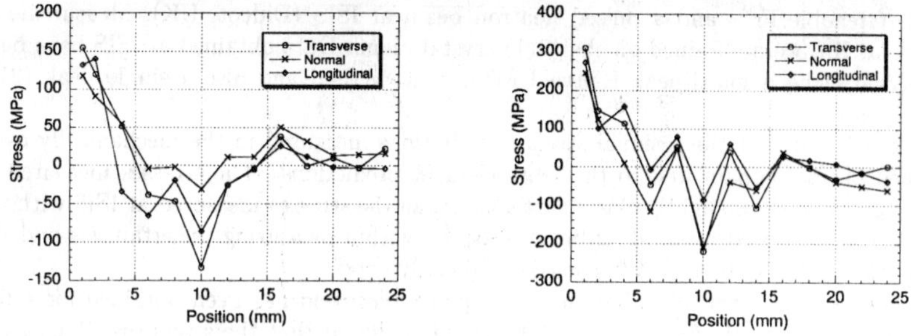

(a) (b)

Figure 7: ISIS Rietveld (a) and 211 Refinement (b)

therefore believed that the large differences in stress in this region can be attributed to the problem associated with achieving positioning repeatability adjacent to the weld. Based on these measurements and the findings of others [6] the maximum residual stress at the toe of the weld is believed to be about the yield strength of the plate material, which is approximately 350 MPa.

Analyses have been carried out on all measured stress distributions to establish whether equilibrium conditions in the transverse direction are satisfied. This is done by assuming the stress distribution does not vary over the thickness of the sample (longitudinal direction) and integrating the stresses with respect to distance in the y-direction. It has been found that although equilibrium is not totally obtained, axial equilibrium can be achieved by a shift in the lattice parameter d_0 corresponding to a stress of about 35 MPa ($\sim 10\%$ of the material yield stress).

CONCLUSIONS

Residual stress measurements using the neutron diffraction technique have been carried out on a T-plate weld sample and on a beam with a mechanically induced residual stress field. Measurements were carried out using a monochromatic neutron beam at

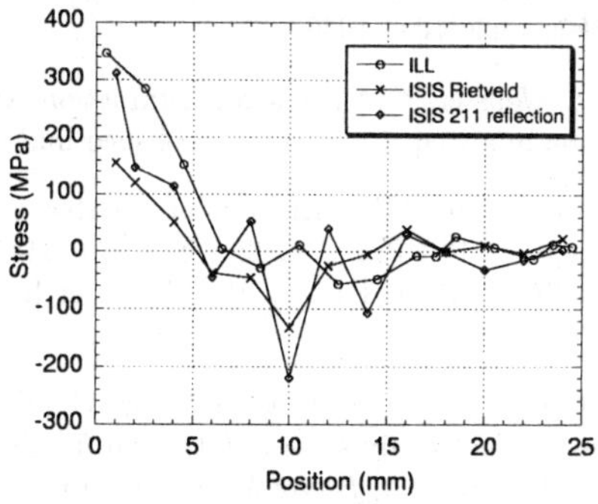

Figure 8: Comparison between transverse stresses obtained from ILL and ISIS

ILL (Grenoble Fr.) and a pulsed neutron beam at ISIS (Didcot, UK). Measurements made at ILL were obtained on the (211) crystal plane. Data obtained at ISIS have been analysed using a multi-peak Rietveld refinement method and also a single peak (211) procedure.

It is found that the residual stress distributions measured in the mechanically overloaded beam compare well to the finite element predictions. The stresses measured at ILL appear to show slightly closer agreement than the stresses measured at ISIS with the ISIS. The measured stress distributions are all within measuring uncertainties and the different methods are therefore considered equally good.

The residual stress distribution in a T-plate fillet weld has been obtained for a line through the plate thickness at the weld toe. It is found that the stress distributions in the three measured orthogonal directions are very similar. The residual stress profiles obtained from the different measurement and refinement methods show similar trends with the (211) measurement at ISIS showing most variability. The Rietveld refinement method shows the lowest stresses. It appears from these measurements that the maximum magnitude of the residual stress is approximately 350 MPa directly at the weld toe.

ACKNOWLEDGEMENTS

Funding for this research has been provided by EPSRC, IMC, HSE and DERA. ISIS and ILL are acknowledged for providing the beam time. The help with the experiments provided by M.R. Daymond, J.S. Wright, T. Pirling and A.N. Ezeilo is greatly acknowledged.

REFERENCES

[1] 'A review of residual stress distributions in welded joints for the defect assessment of offshore structures' prepared by MaTSY (Marine Technology Support Unit) for the Health and Safety Executive, 1996.

[2] Hosford, W.F., The mechanics of crystals and textured polycrystals, 1993, Oxford University Press, Oxford

[3] Ezeilo, A.N., Webster, G.A., Webster, P.J. and Wang, X., 'Characterisation of elastic and plastic deformation in a nickel superalloy using pulsed neutrons', *Physica B*, **180 & 181**, 1992, 1044-1046.

[4] Ezeilo, A.N. and Webster, G.A.,'Neutron Diffraction Analysis of the Residual Stress Distribution in a Bent Bar', To be published in:*Journal of strain analysis.*

[5] Webster, G.A. and Ezeilo, A.N.,'Principles of the Measurement of residual stress by neutron diffraction', PSI Proc. 96002, ISSN 1019-6447, New Instruments and Science around SINQ (Ed. A. Furrer), Paul Scherrer Institut, Switzerland, 217-234, Nov 1996.

[6] Holden, T.M., Root, J.H., Holt, R.A. and Roy, G., 'Neutron diffraction measurements of the residual strain state of a tubular T-joint', *Proceeding of the 7th International Conference on Offshore Mechanics And Arctic Engineering*, p127-131, February 1988.

THROUGH-THICKNESS DISTRIBUTIONS OF WELDING RESIDUAL STRESSES IN AUSTENITIC STAINLESS STEEL CYLINDRICAL BUTT WELDS

R Bradford
British Energy
Barnett Way
Barnwood
Gloucester GL4 3RS

ABSTRACT

The purpose of this paper is to present a general prescription for as-welded residual stress distributions in austenitic stainless steel butt welds of arbitrary diameter and thickness. This has been obtained by interpolation of finite element model results. The derived residual stress distributions are compared with recommended 'bounding' distributions from other sources. The distributions derived here are rather more detailed than previously available bounding distributions. In typical cases the weld material overmatches the parent in terms of tensile properties. This is shown to lead to residual stresses in the heat affected zone which can exceed the parent 1% proof stress substantially. It is intended that the general prescription for the residual stress distributions derived here should be of use to the engineer in performing structural assessments.

INTRODUCTION

British Energy's Advanced Gas Cooled Reactors make extensive use of austenitic stainless steels. These materials commonly entered service without post-weld heat treatment, and hence contain yield magnitude residual welding stresses. A detailed knowledge of these residual stress distributions is of central importance to structural integrity assessments, and hence to nuclear safety cases. In recent years British Energy has used finite element techniques to model residual stresses in a range of plant geometries. The results, in the geometrically simple case of cylindrical butt welds, show a consistent trend against welding heat input per unit thickness (q). This permits a general prescription for as-welded residual stress distributions in austenitic butt welds to be devised using 'q' as the controlling parameter.

DEFINITION OF HEAT INPUT PARAMETER, q

Following Scaramangas et al (1), 'q' is defined as the heat input per unit length of one weld bead, divided by the section thickness. No allowance for welding efficiency is included in the definition of 'q' (although the finite element models do make allowance for efficiency). Hence, $q = VA/St$, where V is the closed circuit welding voltage, A is the welding current (amps), S is the arc speed (mm/sec) and t is the section thickness (mm), giving q in units of J/mm^2.

THE MODELS ANALYSED

Eight cases were analysed using ABAQUS. The geometries, welding procedures and heat input parameters are summarised below.

Weld	R^{mean} mm	T Mm	R/t	q J/mm^2	Weld Type
S5	184	64	2.9	21	MMA
S6	203	26.2	7.75	56	MMA
Spine	261	19	13.7	56	MMA
R4C3	161	18	9.0	65	MMA
Weld C[(1)]	398	15.9	25.0	65	SA
Weld 7.03	152	21.5	7.06	89	TIG
SW1	159	12.7	12.5	89	MMA
Weld C	398	15.9	25.0	167	SA

[(1)] This is a sensitivity study for Weld C which considered a reduced heat input.

All these welds were made from a single-sided weld prep (outer-V) with the exception of Weld C which comprises internal MMA runs together with external submerged arc welding, the latter being dominant as regards the resulting residual stresses.

The modelling procedure in all cases was to build the weld bead-by-bead, calculating the heat transfer during and after each weld bead deposition. For thick weldments, a 'lumped bead' approximation was employed (each modelled bead representing 2 or 3 actual beads). For each time step, the elastic-plastic stresses and strains were solved. The material in all cases was AISI Type 316H stainless steel. Modelling the different tensile data and hardening responses of the weld and parent materials was found to be important.

TENSILE DATA AND NORMALISATION OF RESIDUAL STRESSES

For 316H stainless steel, a reasonable approximation is to equate the weld 1% proof stress with the virgin parent 10% proof stress. This was adopted throughout, with perfect plasticity in the parent at strains greater than 10% and perfect plasticity in the weld at strains greater than 1%. This was found to lead to stresses which varied smoothly over the fusion boundary. All residual stresses presented below are normalised by the parent 10% (= weld 1%) proof stress.

GENERAL PRESCRIPTION FOR RESIDUAL STRESS DISTRIBUTIONS

Figures 1 and 2 show idealised distributions through the thickness for the axial and hoop residual stresses respectively. Comparison of the individual curves in Figures 1 and 2 shows how the residual stresses vary with the heat input parameter (q). Distributions for intermediate values of 'q' may be derived as follows;

Axial Stress Distributions: Define a dimensionless position parameter, x, such that x = +1 on the outside surface, x = 0 at the middle of the section, and x = -1 on the inside surface. Define a function f(x) by,

For $-2x_o < x < +2x_o$, $f(x) = \sin[\pi(x/x_o - \phi)/2]$
For $x > +2x_o$, $f(x) = \pi(2 - x/x_o)/2$
For $x < -2x_o$, $f(x) = -\pi(2 + x/x_o)/2$

The normalised axial residual stress is then given by,

$$\sigma_{axial}/\sigma_{10\%(parent)} = A\,[\,f(x) + \xi\,] \quad \textbf{(1)}$$

In the above formulation, x_o, ϕ and ξ are fitted parameters. The values of these parameters for the five different modelled values of 'q' are as follows;

Heat Input q, J/mm^2	x_o	ϕ	ξ	$\tilde{\sigma}$	A
21	0.72	0.28	0.43	-	0.65
56	0.50	0.46	0	-	0.82
65	0.38	0	0	1	0.72
89	0.35	0	0	1.35	0.49
167	0.1	0	4	12.6	0.030

For any value of 'q' between 21 J/mm^2 and 167 J/mm^2, the x_o, ϕ, ξ parameters may be found by linear interpolation. The amplitude factor, A, can be found from the bounding line for the peak axial residual stress, see Figure 3. Thus the value for A is chosen so that the maximum of Eqn.(1) agrees with Figure 3. This is achieved as follows;

For $x_o > 0.38$, A = graph maximum / $(1 + \xi)$
For $x_o < 0.38$, A = graph maximum / $(\tilde{\sigma} + \xi)$
where, $\tilde{\sigma} = \pi(1/x_o - 2)/2$

Hoop Stress Distributions: The residual hoop stress distributions can be described reasonably well by a tri-linear distribution through the thickness (see Figure 4). The parameters x_1, x_2, σ_1 and σ_2, defined in Figure 4, have been chosen as follows;

Analysis	Material	q, J/mm^2	x_1	x_2	σ_1	σ_2
S5	Weld+HAZ	21	0.58	-1.0	1.13	-0.48
S6,Spine	Weld+HAZ	56	0.24	-0.34	1.11	0.1
Weld C* and R4C3	HAZ	65	0.56	-0.25	1.0	0.5
Weld C* and R4C3	Weld	65	0.25	-0.5	1.17	0.6
Weld 7.03 and SW1	HAZ	89	0.1	-0.2	0.98	0.37
Weld 7.03 and SW1	Weld	89	-	-	1.0	1.0
Weld C	Weld+HAZ	167	-	-	0.9	0.9

*reduced heat input.

For values of 'q' between 21 J/mm^2 and 167 J/mm^2 the appropriate values for x_1, x_2, σ_1 and σ_2 may be found by linear interpolation.

FINITE ELEMENT RESULTS: COMPARISON WITH GENERAL PRESCRIPTION

The normalised stress distributions resulting from the finite element models are shown in comparison with the above general prescription in Figures 5 to 16. For each model two sections have been illustrated; one through the weld centre line, and one through heat affected zone (HAZ) material. The general prescription provides a good representation of the FE data. It is generally bounding, especially for HAZ.

COMPARISON WITH SINTAP COMPENDIUM

A Compendium of Residual Stress Profiles has been compiled recently by Barthelemy (1). For pipe butt welds, the residual profiles have been parameterised against section thickness, t. Consequently, a rigorous comparison with the general prescription given here is problematical due to the latter being based on the heat input parameter, q, rather than thickness, t. However, Figures 17 to 20 compare the profiles from the two procedures as applied to two actual geometries (with q=65 J/mm^2, t=18mm and q=56 J/mm^2, t=26mm, R/t=7.75). Whilst not entirely dissimilar, the profiles show significant differences. In addition, it should be noted that the two sets of profiles are based on different stress normalisations. The present procedure normalises the stresses using the parent 10% (=weld 1%) proof stress, whereas Barthelemy (2) uses the weld 0.2% proof stress for the hoop stress and the parent 0.2% proof stress for the axial stress.

VALIDATION AGAINST MEASUREMENTS

Although beyond the scope of this paper, we note that many of the above FE models have been directly validated against sub-surface residual stress measurements on mock-ups or ex-service plant. This has covered the full thickness range, from relatively thin (16mm and 19mm), see Bouchard et al (3) and Bruno et al (4), through intermediate (35mm) and thick (≥65mm), see Smith et al (5) and Bate et al (6). Good agreement has been reported in all cases. The measured axial peak stress generally exceeds the 0.2% proof stress.

CONCLUSION

A general prescription for welding residual stresses in single-sided, austenitic butt welds in cylinders has been presented. It is rather more detailed than existing prescriptions, eg. (2), with more complex through-thickness profiles and larger peak axial stresses.

REFERENCES

1. Scaramangas A, Porter Goff, RFD, 17th Annual OTC, Houston, Texas, May 6-9, 1985
2. Barthelemy JY, 'Compendium of Residual Stress Profiles', Brite-Euram SINTAP report BRPR-CT95-0024, May 1999
3. Bouchard PJ, Hutchings MT, Withers PJ, ICRS-6 *(these proceedings)*
4. Bruno G, Edwards L, Dutta M, Bouchard PJ, Abbott KR, Lin Peng R, ICRS-6 *(these proceedings)*
5. Smith DJ, George D, Bouchard PJ, Watson C, I.Mech.E Seminar 'Recent Advances in Welding Simulation', 26 Nov 1999.
6. Bate SK, et al, ICRS-6 *(these proceedings)*

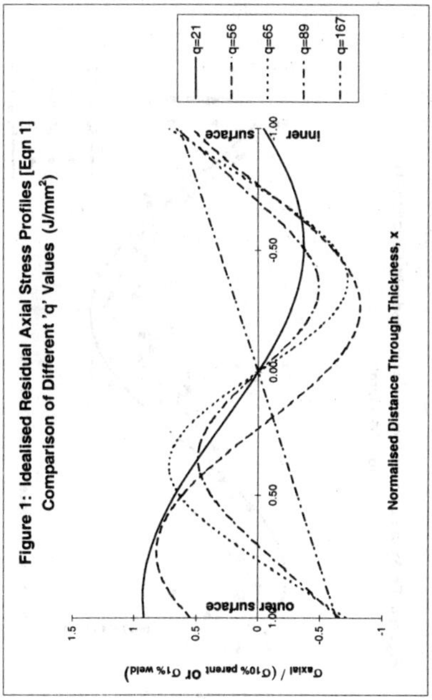

Figure 1: Idealised Residual Axial Stress Profiles [Eqn 1] Comparison of Different 'q' Values (J/mm²)

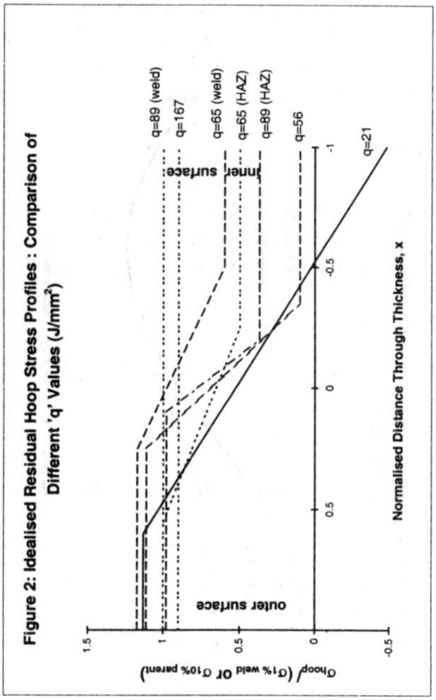

Figure 2: Idealised Residual Hoop Stress Profiles : Comparison of Different 'q' Values (J/mm²)

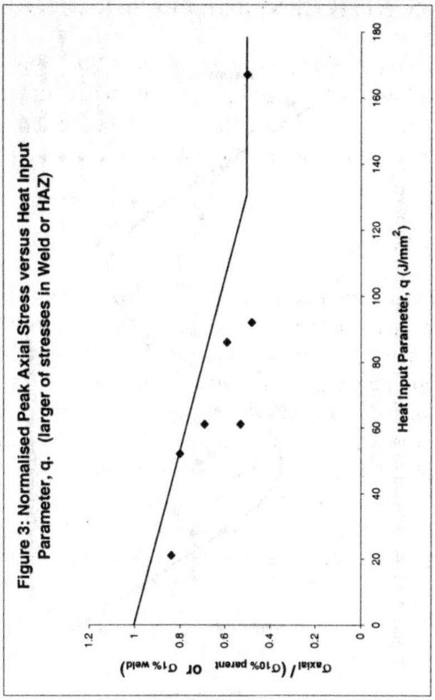

Figure 3: Normalised Peak Axial Stress versus Heat Input Parameter, q. (larger of stresses in Weld or HAZ)

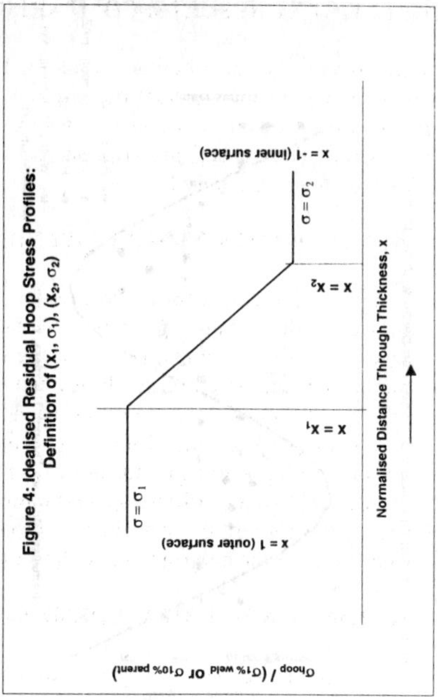

Figure 4: Idealised Residual Hoop Stress Profiles: Definition of (x_1, σ_1), (x_2, σ_2)

Figure 5: FE Axial Residual Stresses compared with Equation (1) (q = 21 J/mm²)

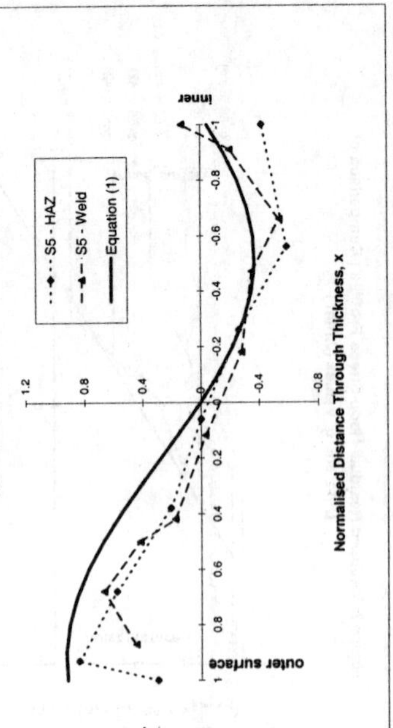

Figure 6: FE Axial Residual Stresses compared with Equation (1) (q = 56 J/mm²)

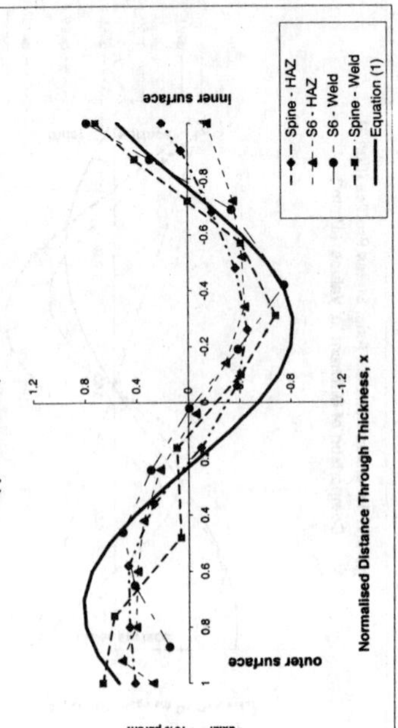

Figure 7: FE Axial Residual Stresses compared with Equation (1) (q = 65 J/mm²)

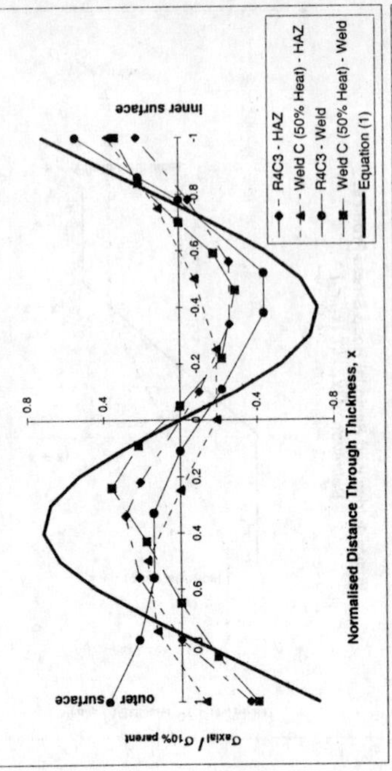

Figure 8: FE Axial Residual Stresses compared with Equation (1) (q = 89 J/mm²)

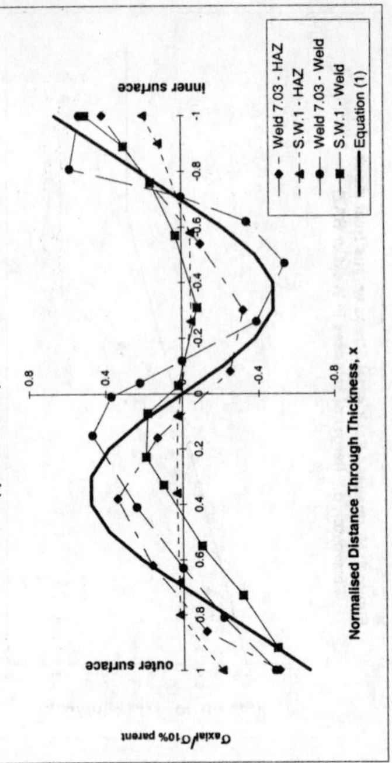

Figure 9: FE Axial Residual Stresses compared with Equation (1) (q = 167J/mm²)

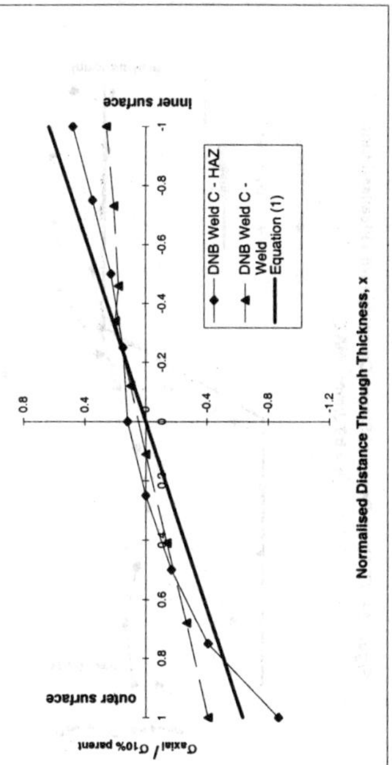

Figure 10 : FE Hoop Residual Stress compared with Idealised Line (q = 21 J/mm²)

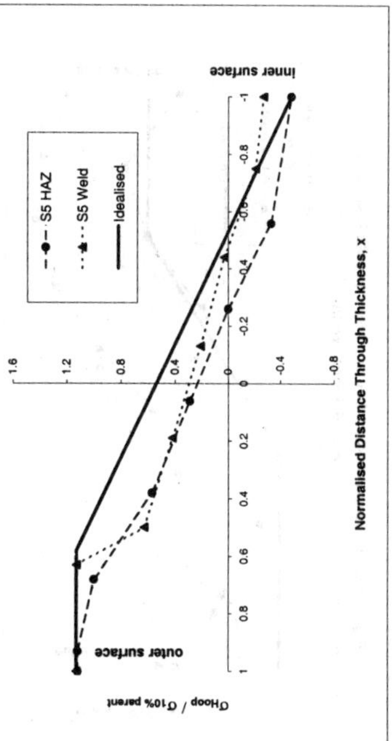

Figure 11 : FE Hoop Residual Stress compared with Idealised Line (q = 56 J/mm²)

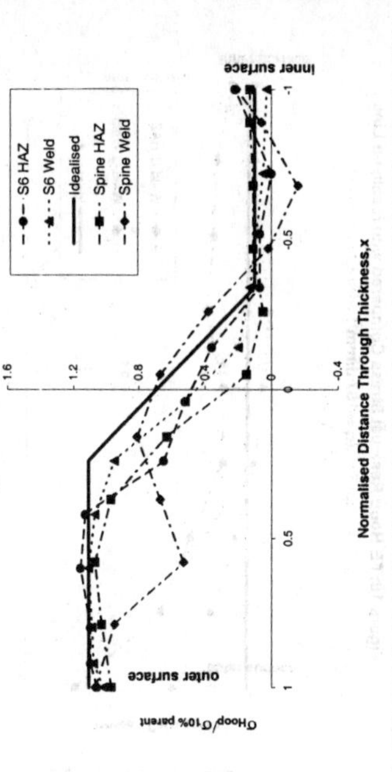

Figure 12 : FE Hoop Residual Stress compared with Idealised (q = 65 J/mm², HAZ)

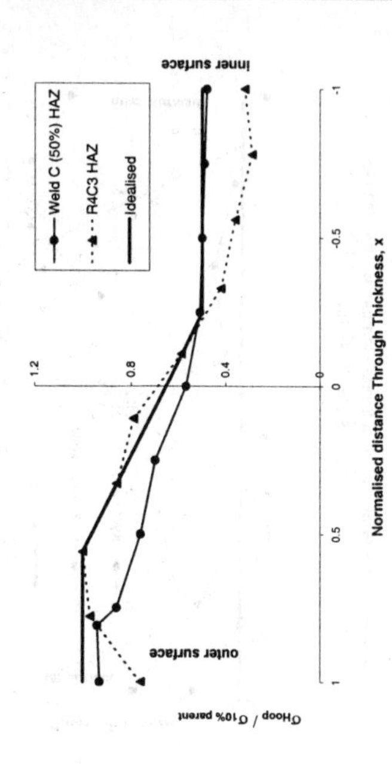

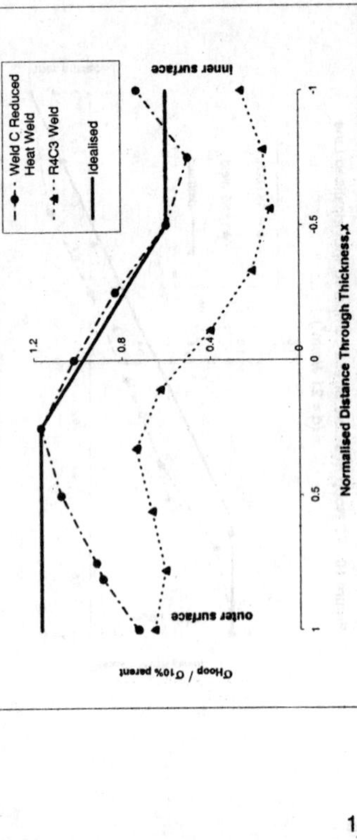

Figure 13: FE Hoop Residual Stress compared with Idealised Line (q = 65 J/mm^2, Weld)

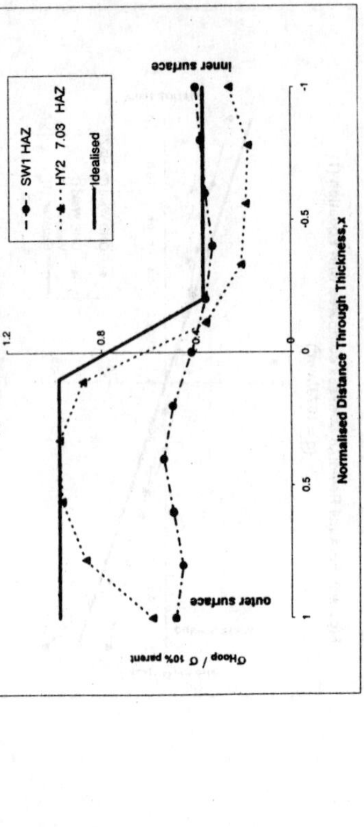

Figure 14: FE Hoop Residual Stress Compared with Idealised Line (q = 89 J/mm^2, HAZ)

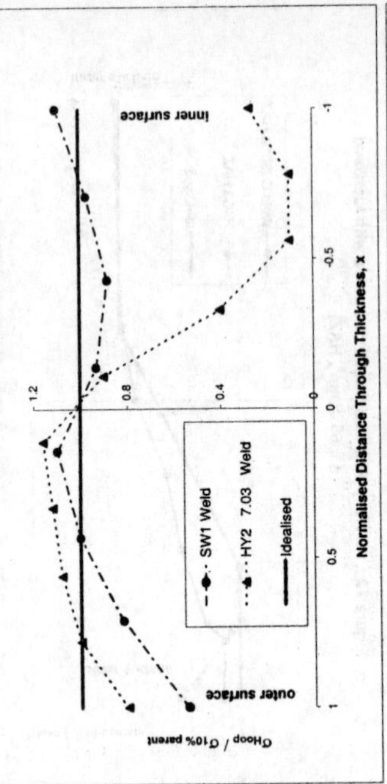

Figure 15 : FE Hoop Residual Stress Compared with Idealised Line (q = 89 J/mm^2, Weld)

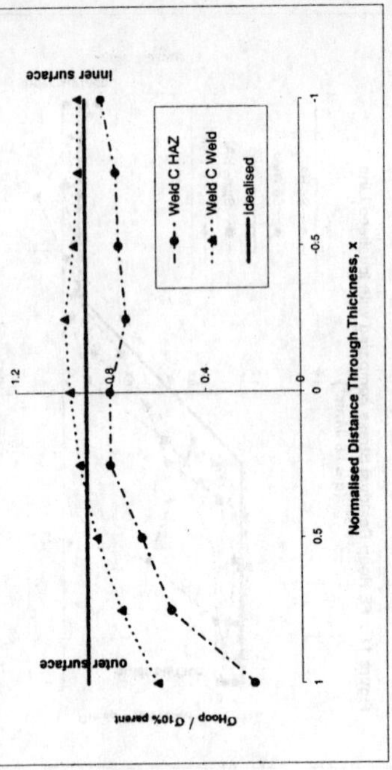

Figure 16: FE Hoop Residual Stress Compared with Idealised Line (q = 167 J/mm^2)

Figure 17: Eqn (1) for Axial Stress with q = 65 J/mm^2 compared with SINTAP for t = 18mm.

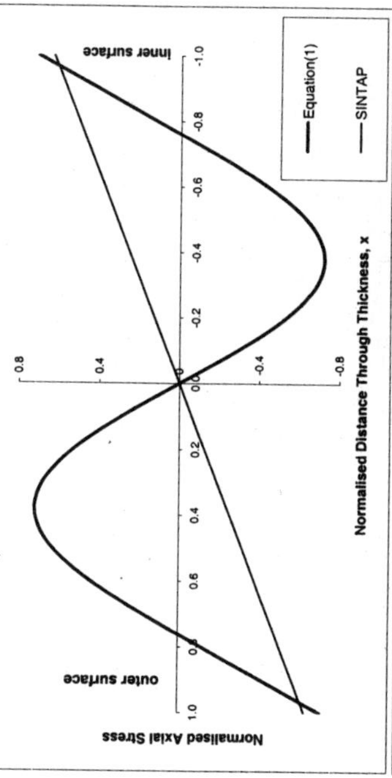

Figure 18: Eqn (1) for Axial Stress with q = 56 J/mm^2 compared with SINTAP for t = 26mm and R/t = 7.75

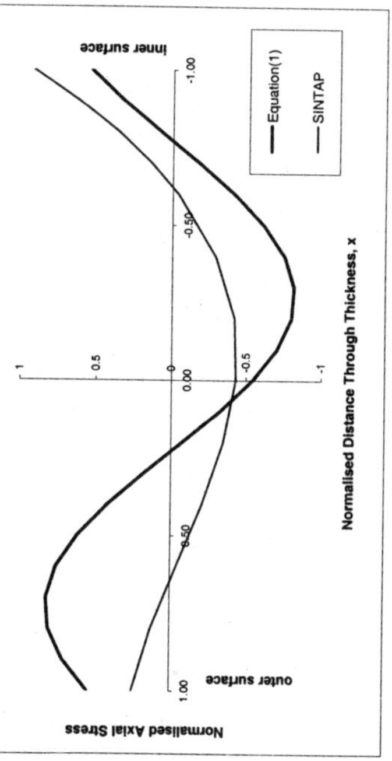

Figure 19: Idealised Residual Hoop Stress for q = 65 J/mm^2 compared with SINTAP for t = 18mm

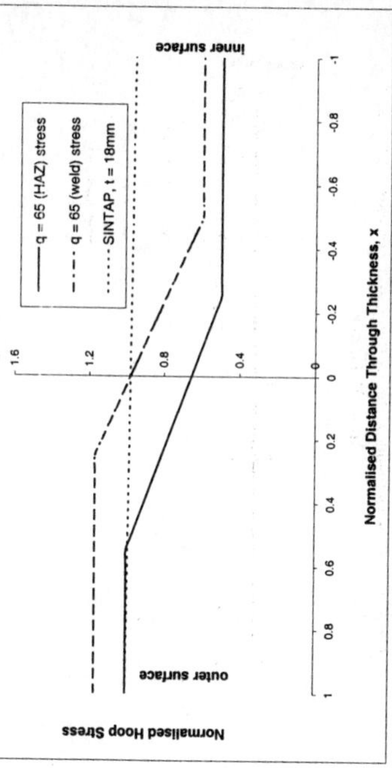

Figure 20: Idealised Residual Hoop Stress for q = 56 J/mm^2 compared with SINTAP for t = 26mm

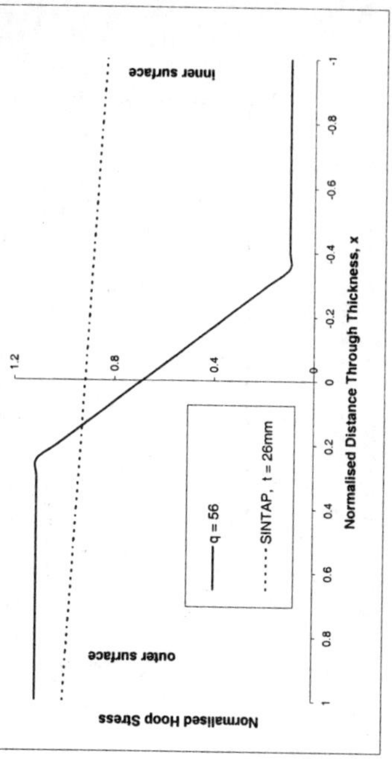

SESSION 9B

RESIDUAL STRESSES ARISING FROM LINEAR FRICTION WELDING OF A NICKEL BASE SUPERALLOY

NW Bonner* and AN Ezeilo**
*** Rolls-Royce plc, PO Box 31, Derby, DE24 8BJ, United Kingdom**
**** MSX International, Endeavour Drive, Pipps Hill Business Park, Basildon, Essex, SS14 3WF, United Kingdom**

ABSTRACT

Linear friction welding is a novel joining technique that is potentially of great interest to the aeroengine industry. It is important, however, that an accurate quantification of the residual stresses associated with such welds is obtained. In this example, two nickel base superalloy blocks were linear friction welded using parameters representative of commercial practice. No post-weld heat treatment was performed. Neutron diffraction and X-ray diffraction were used to measure the residual stress distributions at the mid-thickness position and at the surface respectively. The neutron results display large tensile values in the weld and in a narrow region on either side. At greater distances, the stresses become compressive before approaching zero. The X-ray results agree well with the neutron results for the longitudinal direction, although their magnitudes are lower in the tensile region by a factor of around one third. Stress analysis is used to explain the differences between the mid-thickness and surface distributions. There is evidence to suggest that the uncertainties for the X-ray data are dominated by grain size effects, whereas those for the neutron data are dominated by instrument accuracy.

INTRODUCTION

Linear friction welding (see for example Nicholas et al (1)) is a novel joining technique in which the surfaces to be joined are rubbed together using a rapid reciprocating motion and a normally applied force. The resultant friction at the surfaces causes localised plastic flow of the material, producing a significant flash (material extruded from the sides of the interface) and upset value (loss in specimen length normal to the surfaces). When the rubbing is ceased, the two component parts have fused.

A straightforward joining method of this type is potentially of great interest to the aeroengine industry, since it may be used to simplify the process of attaching compressor or turbine blades to discs. In particular, a significant reduction in weight may result, leading to a greater overall efficiency and lower operating costs. It is of course important, however, that an accurate quantification of the associated residual stresses is achieved, for use in assessments of structural integrity, fatigue life, etc. In this example, two nickel base superalloy blocks, representing aeroengine blade and disc material respectively, were linear friction welded using parameters representative of those employed in industry. The resultant as-welded specimen was then reduced in cross-section by the spark erosion method, so as to shorten the neutron beam pathlength of subsequent investigations. No post-weld heat treatment was performed.

SPECIMEN AND MATERIAL

A rectangular nickel base (Waspaloy) linear friction weldment of approximate dimensions 96mm length × 36mm width × 15mm thickness was produced for this investigation (see Figure 1). The specimen was manufactured by pressing two blocks of the alloy together, through the application of a force parallel to their length with simultaneous sliding parallel to their thickness, thereby producing a steady friction. The resultant weld was located at the mid-length and the two halves of parent material had been chosen such that their microstructures represented aeroengine blade and disc material respectively. In particular, measurements of the average uniform grain size carried out by Rolls-Royce plc provided values of around 64 and 12μm (ASTM 5 and 10 respectively) for the two respective materials.

The spark erosion method was used to cut the above specimen into three separate parts (see Figure 1). This resulted in samples with a reduced cross-section, for which the neutron diffraction counting times were adequately short, but which ought to retain similar (although modified) levels of residual stress to the original specimen. Sample B was selected for this investigation, with approximate dimensions 96mm length × 25mm width × 4mm thickness. The newly cut 96 × 25mm face was mechanically polished to identify the position of the weld.

The chemical composition of Waspaloy is shown in Table I below. Waspaloy exhibits almost exclusively a face centred cubic crystal structure, the majority of which is gamma phase and the remainder gamma prime phase. For diffraction purposes, it should be noted that the lattice parameters of these phases are very similar and so the detected diffraction peaks will include a contribution from both.

Table I. Chemical Composition of Waspaloy.

Element	Ni	C	Cr	Co	Al	Mo	Ti	Zr	B
Mean Composition (weight %)	Balance	0.08	19.5	13.5	1.3	4.3	3.0	0.06	0.006

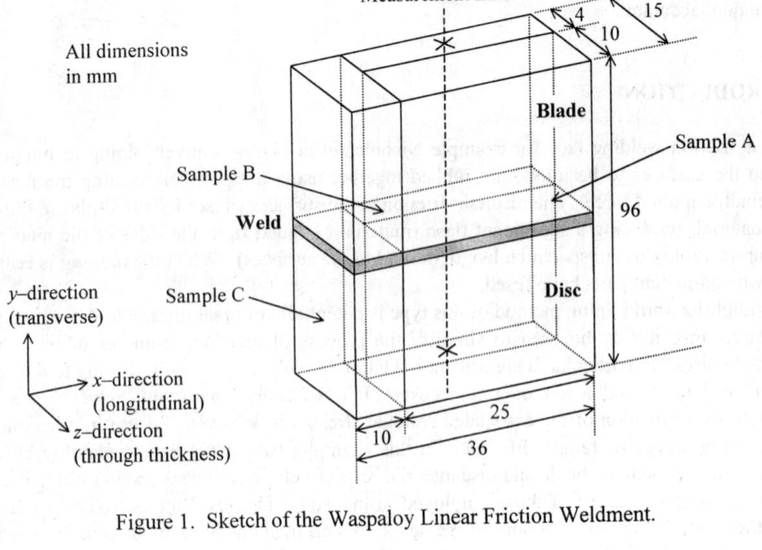

Figure 1. Sketch of the Waspaloy Linear Friction Weldment.

EXPERIMENTAL METHODS

The residual stress measurements were conducted using two diffraction based techniques, namely neutron diffraction (Allen et al (2)) and X-ray diffraction (Cullity (3)) or XRD. Both rely upon the changes in the lattice spacing of a crystalline material that occur as a result of the existence of residual stresses. The former examines material within the body of the sample under test, averaging the lattice behaviour over a clearly defined 'gauge volume', whilst the latter considers only the specimen surface region and employs a 'gauge area'. Additionally, neutron diffraction measures strain in the direction of interest directly, whereas the X-ray technique considers only strains at various angles to this direction (see below).

Neutron Diffraction Measurements

These were performed using ENGIN instrument at ISIS, Rutherford Appleton Laboratory, UK. ENGIN employs a polychromatic neutron beam and the time-of-flight measurement method as described in Johnson (4). In particular, it features two detectors directed orthogonally to the incident beam, designated LHD (left hand detector) and RHD (right hand detector), which allow diffraction data to be obtained in two directions simultaneously. Radial sollers are positioned in front of both detectors, that precisely define a 1.4mm gauge width (full width half maximum) along the line of the incident beam. The other gauge volume dimensions are produced by placing an input slit in the path of the incident beam. Before the experiments were begun, the equipment was calibrated using a standard in-house procedure detailed in Ezeilo (5). In all cases, it was assumed that the principal stress directions were oriented along the *xyz*-coordinates of the specimen. For measurement of the *x*- and *z*-direction strains (longitudinal and through thickness respectively), the specimen was mounted with its weld horizontal and its sides at 45° to the incident beam; the input slit was 1mm high along the *y*-direction (transverse) by 3mm wide. Data was then obtained along a single *y*-direction line scan located at the mid-width and mid-thickness position. The locations of the data points were $y = 0, \pm1, \pm2, \pm3, \pm5, \pm10$ and ±20mm relative to the weld centre, being concentrated in the weld and the heat affected zones where the stress gradient was expected to be steepest. In addition, 'strain free' reference values were obtained near to the four corners of the specimen. Equivalent *y*- and *z*-direction strain measurements were made with the specimen mounted with its weld vertical and its sides at 45° to the incident beam; in this case, the input slit was 10mm high by 1mm wide.

X-Ray Diffraction Measurements

Complementary XRD measurements were carried out by Rolls-Royce plc. TEC 1610-2b X-Ray Stress Analysis System was used with an iron X-ray source and a manganese filter to examine the (311) nickel lattice planes. Previous work on Waspaloy by Stone et al (6) has concluded that this reflection is preferred if only one Bragg diffraction peak is to be considered. The incident beam wavelength and lattice spacing were around 1.94 and 1.08Å respectively, resulting in a peak at around $2\theta = 128°$. The standard $\sin^2\psi$ technique described by Cullity (3) was employed with $\psi = 0, 15, 24, 35$ and 45°. The gauge areas were defined by placing a collimator in the path of the incident beam, providing 2mm diameter for measurements in the *x*-direction and 5mm along *x* by 1mm along *y* for measurements in the *y*-direction. These were made only on the polished face at the mid-width position at the same thirteen *y* values relative to the weld centre as were the earlier neutron diffraction measurements. As expected, a compressively stressed surface layer had been introduced by the mechanical polishing process. This was therefore removed to a depth of around 100μm by electro-chemical polishing prior to these measurements. No allowance has been made for the (small) redistribution of stress that will have occurred as a result of this material removal.

ANALYSIS AND RESULTS

Since the ENGIN neutron beam is polychromatic, diffraction occurs from all the Waspaloy (*hkl*) reflections and the data obtained can be analysed individually (as single peaks) or collectively (by Pawley refinement). The fitting of individual (*hkl*) peaks is not considered here. Instead, the refinement of the lattice parameter a using the Cambridge Crystallography Routines (CCR) is described. Other work for which ENGIN has been used to examine the residual stresses in Waspaloy specimens (by Ezeilo et al (7)) has indicated that this is a reliable approach. The analysis required involves the calculation of an a value that is based upon the positions of the diffraction peaks resulting from a distorted lattice. The refined a value obtained in this manner represents an average over all (*hkl*) reflections in the lattice. It was apparent that there were systematic differences in the a values measured by the two detectors. This was taken into account in the analyses by employing four different strain free reference values a_0, namely for the LHD and RHD measured in both blade and disc material. In the fusion zone, it was assumed that these values varied only in a stepwise manner at the weld centre line, where the mean was adopted. The residual strains ε in the *x*- *y*- and *z*-directions were then determined from the fractional changes in the lattice parameter, thus:

$$\varepsilon_{x,y,z} = \left(a_{x,y,z} - a_0\right)/a_0 \tag{1}$$

ensuring that the appropriate a_0 value was employed in each case. As two independent sets of data had been measured in the *z*-direction, the average strains $\varepsilon_z = \left(\varepsilon_{z1} + \varepsilon_{z2}\right)/2$ were calculated. Typical uncertainties in strain were around ±70 microstrain. It has been observed by Ezeilo (8) that the elastic constants Young's modulus E and Poisson's ratio ν obtained by averaging the response of all the reflections closely match the macroscopic values. On this basis, the residual stresses σ were obtained from the following standard expression using macroscopic values for E = 220GPa and ν = 0.285 as measured by Ezeilo (9):

$$\sigma_{x,y,z} = \frac{E}{(1+\nu)(1-2\nu)}\left[(1-\nu)\varepsilon_{x,y,z} + \nu\left(\varepsilon_{y,z,x} + \varepsilon_{z,x,y}\right)\right] \tag{2}$$

The neutron results are displayed in Figure 2, normalised with respect to the tensile yield stress of Waspaloy at room temperature. Typical scatter in stress was around ±25MPa, although the normalised error bars are shown in the figure.

The analysis of the XRD data is more straightforward. The location of the diffraction peaks 2θ were converted to lattice spacing d using Bragg's law. It has been shown by Cullity (3) that the (horizontally oriented) surface residual stresses σ_S obey this equation:

$$\frac{d_\psi - d_n}{d_n} = \frac{\sigma_S}{E}(1+\nu)\sin^2\psi \tag{3}$$

where d_ψ is inclined at angle ψ to the surface normal (in a vertical plane containing σ_S) and d_n is parallel to the surface normal and E and ν are the diffraction elastic constants (DECs) of the lattice planes under consideration. A linear regression of d_ψ versus $\sin^2\psi$ therefore provides the best estimate of the gradient $\sigma_S d_n(1+\nu)/E$ and a knowledge of the appropriate DECs infers σ_S. In this case, the (311) nickel planes were examined, for which the DECs 226GPa and 0.258 respectively were employed. The consequent XRD results are given in Figure 3 for both the *x*- and *y*-directions, again normalised to the tensile yield stress. Typical uncertainties in stress were around ±120 and ±35MPa for blade and disc material respectively (the normalised error bars are again shown in the figure).

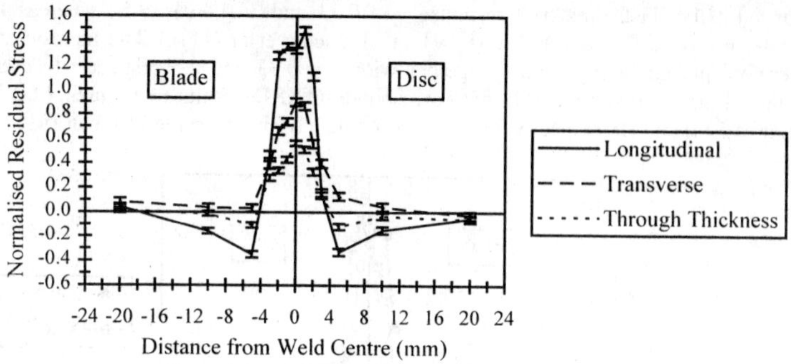

Figure 2. Mid-thickness Residual Stress Distributions Determined by Neutron Diffraction.

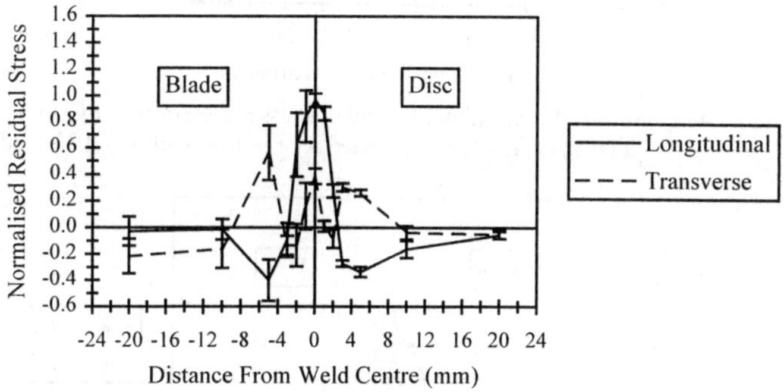

Figure 3. Surface Residual Stress Distributions Determined by X-Ray Diffraction.

Since the neutron diffraction and XRD measurements were made at the mid-thickness position and at the surface respectively, a disparity in the residual stress distributions would be expected. This is attributable (at least in part) to the behaviour of the *z*-direction stress, which was significant at the mid-depth (see Figure 2), but which must decay to zero at the surface. In order to produce a more realistic comparison between the two sets of results, the neutron data were used to predict values at the surface. In the interior and at the surface, the direct stresses in the *x*-, *y*- and *z*-directions are denoted by σ_{xI}, σ_{yI} and σ_{zI} and σ_{xS}, σ_{yS} and σ_{zS} respectively. The direct strains are denoted by ε accordingly and the relationship between the two is given by Equation 2 above. It is clear that $\sigma_{zS} = 0$ and therefore Equation 2 provides:

$$\varepsilon_{zS} = -\left(\frac{\nu}{1-\nu}\right)\left(\varepsilon_{xS} + \varepsilon_{yS}\right) \tag{4}$$

Strain compatibility also requires that $\varepsilon_{xI} = \varepsilon_{xS}$ and $\varepsilon_{yI} = \varepsilon_{yS}$ (Timoshenko et al (10)). It can therefore be shown that:

$$\sigma_{xS,yS} = \sigma_{xI,yI} - \left(\frac{\nu}{1-\nu}\right)\sigma_{zI} \tag{5}$$

For a totally elastic material response $\nu = 0.33$ and $\nu/(1-\nu) = 0.5$, whereas for a totally plastic response $\nu = 0.5$ and $\nu/(1-\nu) = 1$ (Francois et al (11)). The neutron stresses were therefore placed in Equation 5 together with $\nu = 0.33$ and 0.5 respectively and the results obtained are plotted alongside the corresponding XRD results in Figures 4.(a) and (b) and Figures 5.(a) and (b) respectively. The error bars have been omitted for clarity.

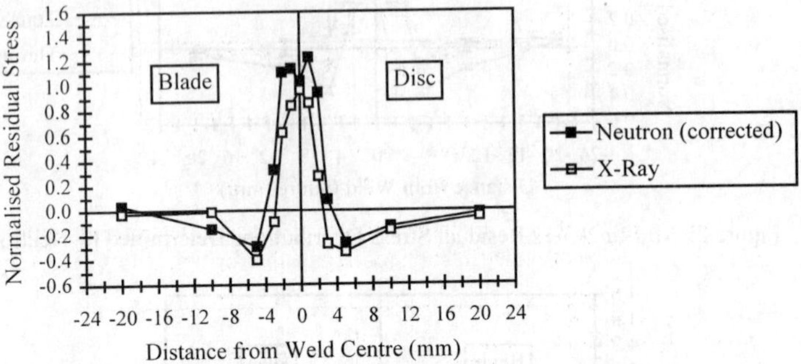

Figure 4.(a). Surface Longitudinal Residual Stresses Determined by Both Neutron Diffraction (corrected for position with $\nu = 0.33$) and XRD.

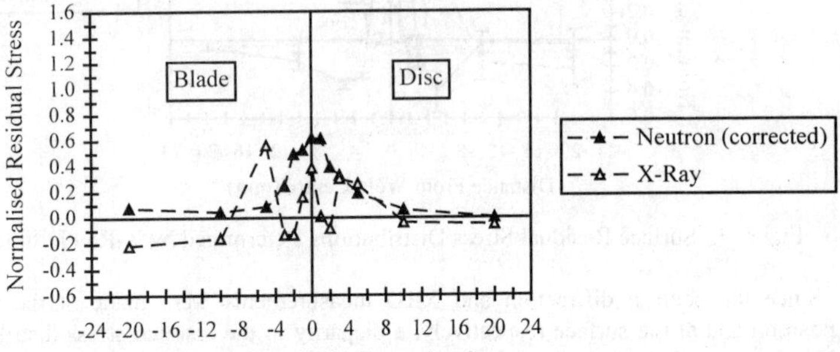

Figure 4.(b). Corresponding Transverse Residual Stresses.

DISCUSSION

It is clear that the neutron results at the mid-thickness position (see Figure 2) show high tensile residual stresses in the weld and in a region around 1 to 2mm on either side. The longitudinal stresses are greatest in magnitude, exceeding the parent material yield stress in this region, followed by the transverse and then the through thickness stresses. Such large longitudinal stresses are unexpected, although it should be noted that the von Mises stress (Francois et al (11)) does not reach 90% of the yield stress. Additionally, the localised plastic flow of the parent material will cause significant work hardening (thereby increasing the yield stress) and may change the a_0 value (an increase acting to reduce the tensile stress results). At greater distances from the weld, the stresses become predominantly compressive before approaching zero at around 20mm from the weld centre line. In these regions, the longitudinal, transverse and through thickness stresses generally maintain the same order in terms of relative magnitude. There is a high degree of symmetry in the results about the weld

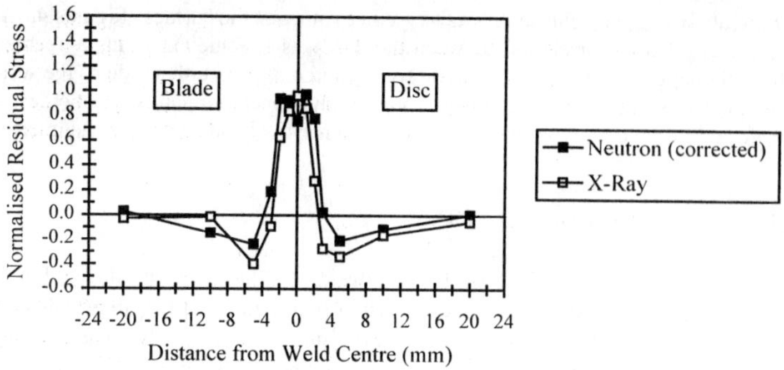

Figure 5.(a). Surface Longitudinal Residual Stresses Determined by Both Neutron Diffraction (corrected for position with $\nu = 0.5$) and XRD.

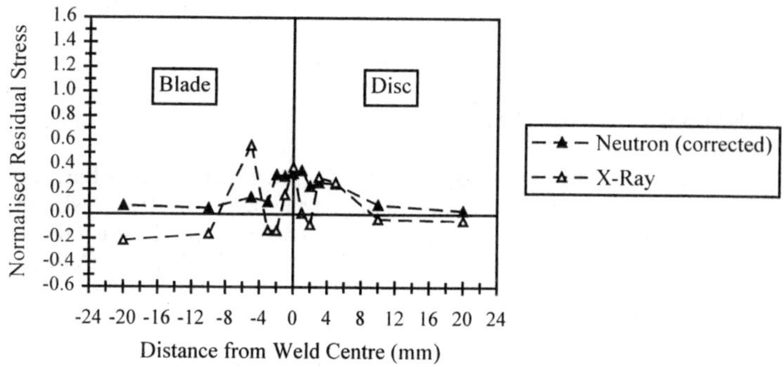

Figure 5.(b). Corresponding Transverse Residual Stresses.

centre, with little difference between those measured in blade and disc material. The error bars are generally small and do not appear to vary between the two materials.

The corresponding XRD results at the surface (see Figure 3) also show large tensile stresses in the weld region and adjacent material for the longitudinal direction. These stresses again become compressive and then approach zero with increasing distance from the weld, exhibiting a largely symmetrical distribution. The transverse stresses are quite different, however, displaying an oscillatory pattern. Nevertheless, the distribution is fairly symmetrical and efforts to remeasure the data yielded very similar results. The error bars are generally larger than for the neutron results and there is a significant difference between the sizes determined for the two materials, with the ratio for blade to disc generally being around 3 or 4 to 1. This can be explained using the results for the average uniform grain size (see above) which indicated a ratio in excess of 5 to 1 for blade to disc material. Moreover, this would suggest that the error bars for the XRD measurements, which averaged the lattice behaviour over a gauge area, were dominated by grain size effects. For the neutron measurements, however, which represent a volume average, thereby sampling a much larger number of grains, the error bars seem to be dominated by instrument accuracy.

In comparing the as-measured results (Figures 2 and 3), although there is good agreement between the longitudinal stresses obtained by neutron diffraction and XRD, the magnitudes of the latter are lower in the tensile region by a factor of around one third. This supports the argument that there is a through thickness variation in the magnitude of these stresses.

On re-analysing the neutron results to predict values at the surface (Figures 4.(a) to 5.(b)), it is clear that a better correlation between the data sets is achieved. This agreement is closer in the weld region for $\nu = 0.5$ (plastic response) and closer on either side of the weld for $\nu = 0.33$ (elastic response). This is again consistent with expectation, since plastic deformation of the blade and disc parent material occurs only in a narrow band centred at the interface.

SUMMARY AND CONCLUSIONS

A nickel base superalloy linear friction weldment has been produced for residual stress measurements. These were carried out using both neutron diffraction and X-ray diffraction, examining the mid-thickness position and the surface respectively. The neutron results show large tensile values in the weld and in a narrow region on either side. At greater distances, the stresses become compressive before approaching zero. The X-ray results agree well for the longitudinal direction, although their magnitudes are lower in the tensile region by a factor of around one third. Stress analysis has been used to explain the differences between these results.

ACKNOWLEDGEMENTS

The authors would like to express their thanks to DG XII, Central European Commission, Belgium that has contributed to the funding of this work via RESTAND (EC Contract No. SMT4-CT97-2200), ISIS, Rutherford Appleton Laboratory, UK for the provision of neutron beam time and Prof. G.A Webster and Dr. R.C. Wimpory, Imperial College, UK who have assisted in the interpretation of the results.

REFERENCES

1. Nicholas D., Dawes C., Thomas W., 'Friction Processes', Technical Document, TWI, Abington, UK, 1993.
2. Allen A.J., Hutchings M.T. Windsor C.J., Andreani C., Advances in Physics 34 (1985) 445-473.
3. Cullity B.D., 'Elements of X-Ray Diffraction', 2nd Edition, Addison-Wesley, 1978.
4. Johnson, M.W., PREMIS Final Technical Report, BriteEuram II Project No. 5129, Technical Report RAL-TR-96-068, Rutherford Appleton Laboratory, Didcot, UK, 1996.
5. Ezeilo A.N., 'An Investigation of the Residual Stresses Produced by Linear Friction Welding', Experimental Report, Imperial College, London, UK, 1998.
6. Stone H.J., Holden T.M., Reed, R.C., Scripta Materiala 40 (1999) 353-358.
7. Ezeilo A.N., Webster G.A., 'Neutron Diffraction Analysis of the Residual Stress Distribution in a Bent Bar', accepted for publication in Journal of Strain Analysis (1999).
8. Ezeilo A.N., 'Residual Stress Determination by Neutron and X-Ray Diffraction Methods', Ph. D. Thesis, University of London, UK, 1992.
9. Ezeilo A.N., 'Uniaxial Stress versus Strain Behaviour of Waspaloy', Experimental Report, Imperial College, London, UK, 1998.
10. Timoshenko S.P., Goodier J.N., 'Theory of Elasticity', 2nd Edition, Mc-Graw Hill, 1951.
11. Francois D., Pineau A., Zaoui A., 'Mecahnical Behaviour of Materials: Volume 1. Elasticity and Plasticity', Kluwer Academic Publishers, 1993.

The Correlation of Fracture Mechanism and Behavior of Residual Stress in Ceramic/Metal Joints

Naoto SHIRAKI, Yoshihiro SUGIYAMA, and Kimihisa MINO
Faculty of Engineering, Musashi Institute of Technology,
1-28-1 Tamazutsumi, Setagaya, Tokyo 158-8557, Japan

1. ABSTRACT

The fracture initiation was at the interface between ceramic and brazing filler on the ceramic side in ceramic/metal joints. The crack propagated at the interface stably, and finally kinked into the ceramic in fracture. Authors suggested that the interface crack could be treated as a parameter of fracture mechanics. There are many papers about the correlation of the strength and bonding residual stress. But, most of them are investigated the residual stress without applied stress.

As specimen material for ceramic, a sintered silicon nitride (Si_3N_4) was used, and for metal stainless steel (SUS304) was used. Both materials were joined by the active brazing method. The purpose to clarify the correlation of the fracture mechanism and behavior of the residual stress in ceramic/metal joint. So, the residual stress was measured by X-ray diffraction method during applied bending stress. The measured stress by X-ray diffraction method and the stress analysis by finite-element method (FEM) were compared. The results obtained were as follows: (1) as the applied stress was larger, the measured stress was larger. (2) the singularity at the interface, which is the each material, agreed the measured stress by X-ray diffraction method with the analytical results based on FEM. (3) by observing K and λ which changes as the applied stress was lager, the fracture mechanism of various joint might be made clear.

2. INTRODUCTION

Ceramics are expected to be widely used as materials for machine application in the future due to their heat and corrosion resistant properties. There are already many applications for ceramic. Because they are brittle materials, ceramics and metal joining is considered the best method to use ceramics as materials for machine applications (1). The active brazing method seems to attract the most attention because of its reliable strength and economical characteristics. So, it is used as part of car components (2). However, as this method requires a high bonding temperature, bonding residual stress is produced from the difference between the thermal expansion coefficient in both materials. The strength of the joint is depending on bonding residual stress (3).

3. THE FRACTURE MECHANISM OF CERAMIC/METAL JOINT

Authors carried out the 4-point bending test on ceramic/metal joints bonded by the active brazing method at various temperatures, and investigated the characteristics of bending strength. Then, as a result of the fractography after bending test, the fracture initiation of joint was at the interface between brazing filler in ceramic side and ceramics, as shown in Fig.1. The crack propagated at the interface stably, and finally kinked into ceramic in fracture. Then, it was clarified that the interface crack length could be treated as the parameter of fracture (4). However, stress and fracture criterion of interface crack was not clear.

On the other hand, though the results of residual stress measurement in ceramic/metal joints are reported in great numbers (5), the residual stress after bonding of which the correlation of

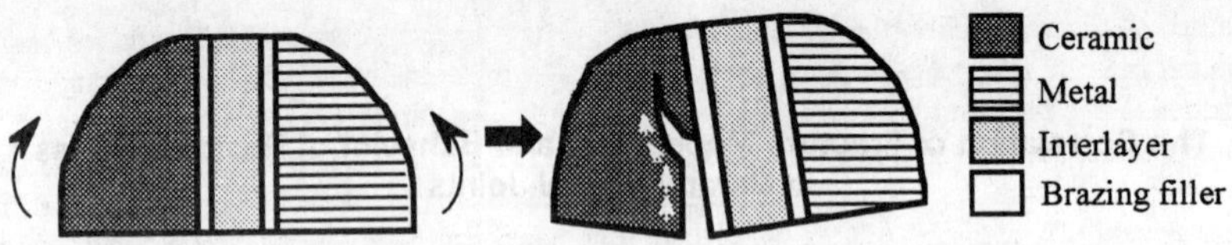

Fig.1 Schematic illustration of fracture mechanism

fracture strength and these was described in paper (6). However, the experimental research of which change of bonding residual stress with the load and singularity of interface were not almost described. The authors used for metal an austenitic stainless steel (SUS304) and carbon steel (S45C), for ceramics Si_3N_4. They carried out four-point bending test at room temperature. Then, the AE sensor was put on Si_3N_4. The high elastic wave that differs from the process of the loading near about 80% of breaking load was detected, and that it was regarded as the formation of the interface crack. Then, they reported that there was correlation between stress of interface crack initiation and bonding residual stress in the no-load (7). From the above result, the interface crack propagated in loading and the result that bonding residual stress of the unloaded condition becomes the strength controlling factor. The change of the bonding residual stress in loading of the load clarifies the stress level of interface crack initiation. To clarify the interface crack initiation may establish the design criterion of different material joint and standardization of the non-destructive inspection.

In this study, ceramic/metal joints of which various thickness of interlayer and specimen size were produced and measured bonding residual stress in loading by the X-ray diffraction method. Then, change of bonding residual stress and the singularity at interface was investigated from the results of bonding residual stress measurement by the X-ray diffraction method and analysis by the finite element method (FEM)

4. EXPERIMENTAL MATERIALS

As specimen material for ceramic a sintered silicon nitride (β-Si_3N_4 : TSN03 Toshiba Co. Ltd.) was used, and for metal, stainless steel (SUS304) was used. In addition, for the relaxation of bonding residual stress, plastic deformation of oxygen free copper, which was inserted as interlayer between Si_3N_4 and SUS304 was used. Thickness of interlayer (T_i) was 0.2, 0.3, 0.5, 1.0mm. Mechanical property of elements for preparation of the joint was shown as Table I.

Table I Mechanical properties of the elements for preparation of the joint

Material	Young's modulus (GPa)	Thermal expansion coefficient (10^{-6}/K)	Tensile strength (MPa)	Elongation (%)	Vickers hardness (HV)
Si_3N_4	304	3.7	>870	——	1460
Cu	130	17.6	237	>35	117
SUS304	196	18.7	>520	>40	180

5. JOINING METHOD AND CONDITION

Shape and dimension was of specimen was shown as Fig.2. Si_3N_4 and SUS304 were joined against each other in center of specimen. Both materials were jointed by the active brazing method. As brazing filler, Ag-Cu-Ti alloy (TKC-710 t=50 μm) between Si_3N_4 and interlayer, another brazing filler, Ag-Cu alloy (BAg-8(8) t=50 μm) between SUS304 and interlayer was inserted. Specimen was jointed in three kinds of sectional area, 3×10mm, 5×10mm, 10×10mm. Specimen was joined in vacuum (1×10^{-5} Torr). Bonding temperature was 1113K and duration time was 25 min. Then, heating and cooling rate were 10K/min and 5K/min respectively. In joining, 1.2kPa was loaded at sectional area of specimen. And bonded specimen was finished the shape and dimension as shown in Fig.2 by grinding.

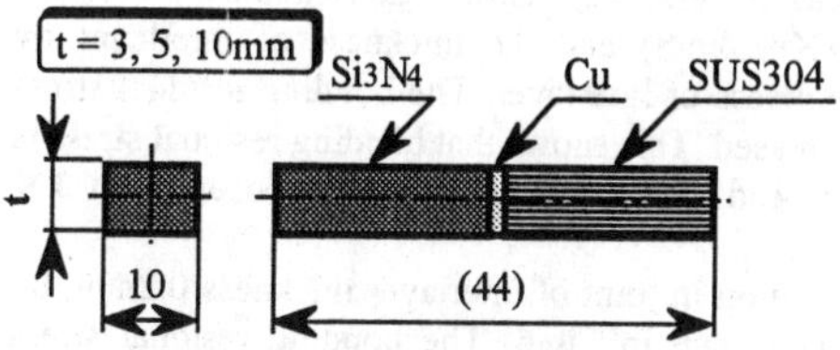

Fig.2 Shape and dimension of specimen

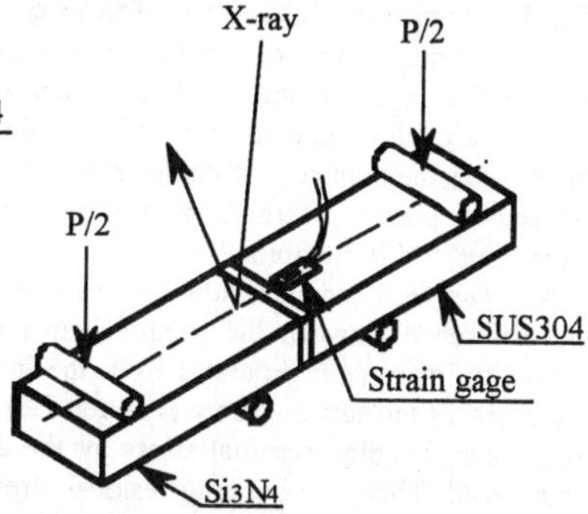

Fig.3 Schematic illustration of jig construction

6. EXPERIMENTAL METHODS

In order to apply load in Si_3N_4 /SUS304 joint, the jig of the mechanism equal to the jig for X-ray stress constant measurement was used. Schematic illustration of jig was shown as in Fig.3. The strain gage was put on SUS304 in tension side. And the specimen was applied six kinds of stress (0~100 MPa) in room temperature. Loading condition was four-point bending, and outside and inside span were 30mm and 10mm respectively.

Residual stress was measured by X-ray diffraction method used under condition shown in Table II. Fig.4 shows the measuring position of residual stress It was on the surface of Si_3N_4, 0.5~1.0mm away from the interface on center line of 10mm wide specimen. Also measured stress direction was residual stress of X-direction which was considered most influential on its fracture strength.

Table II Condition for measuring residual stress

Method	Parallel beam method
Characteristic X-ray	Cu-kα
Diffraction plane	3 2 3
Filter	Ni
Tube voltage (kV)	40
Tube current (mA)	200
Irradiated area (mm)	0.5×2
Scan speed (deg/min)	2.0
Diffraction angle (deg)	141.7
ψ_0 angle (deg)	0, 12, 18, 22, 26, 30, 33, 36, 39, 42, 45
Stress constant (MPa/deg)	-806.9

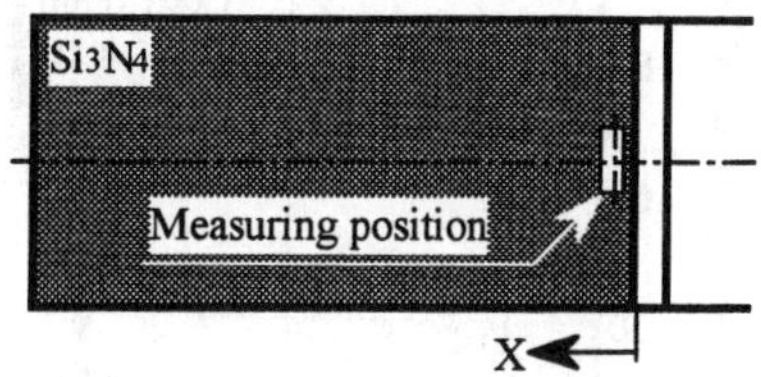

X=0.5, 1.0, 1.5, 2.0, 2.5, 3.0 mm

Fig.4 Measuring position of residual stress

7.EXPERIMENTAL RESULT AND CONSIDERATION

7.1 Bending strength and fracture mechanism

As a result of four-point bending test in the room temperature, fracture mechanism of all joints were shown in Fig.1 In all specimens, bending strength become maximum strength at certain thickness of interlayer. When the thickness increases, the strength lowers. Compared to the strength at the equal thickness of interlayer, as the sectional area increases, the bending strength decreases. In the next passage, bonding residual stress before the bending stress of each specimen was compared.

7.2 The residual stress in no-loading

As example of bonding residual stress measurement, Fig.5 shows the relationship between the bonding residual stress of the point (X=1.0mm) and the thickness of interlayer by difference of the sectional area. In either thickness of interlayer, The bonding residual stress lowered, as the thickness of the interlayer increased. This shows that bonding residual stress is relaxed by plastic deformation in interlayer. And, such tendency was also observed in 3×9mm joint, 5×10mm joint.

As example, bonding residual stress distribution in joint of interlayer thickness 0.2mm, by the difference between the sectional area is shown in Fig.6. The bonding residual stress tended to lower as it separates from the interface of Si_3N_4.The bonding residual stress also increases, as the sectional area is larger. However, in 10mm the distance from the interface of Si_3N_4 side, bonding residual stress by the difference of the interlayer thickness hardly was recognized. Then, the bonding residual stress in 3×9mm joint and 5×10mm joint, there is not large difference, and bonding residual stress in 10×10mm joint was larger than other two kinds of joints.

7.3 The effect of applied stress on the residual stress distribution

As example, Fig.7 (a), (b) shows result of measurement stress distribution on the Si_3N_4 surface in applied each stress of joint in which the thickness of interlayer 0.2mm and 1.0mm in 3×10mm joint respectively. The bonding residual stress lowers, as it fades away from the bonded interface, when it is unloaded. Then, as the applied stress increases, the measured stress by the X-ray increases. The applied stress in about 60MPa, the measurement stress became almost constant near the interface. And, though there were some differences on this tendency, it was observed in the specimen of either sectional area. When two materials were joined together, the stress singularity observed near the bonded interface arises by the difference between mechanical property of both materials. It is possible to show the vertical

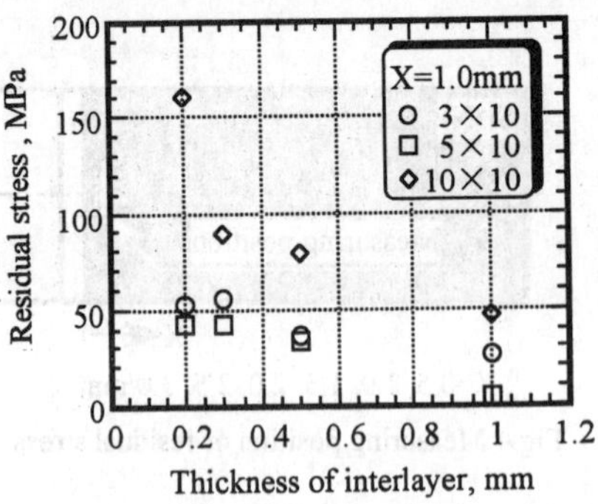

Fig.5 Relationship between residual stress at X=1.0mm and thickness of interlayer

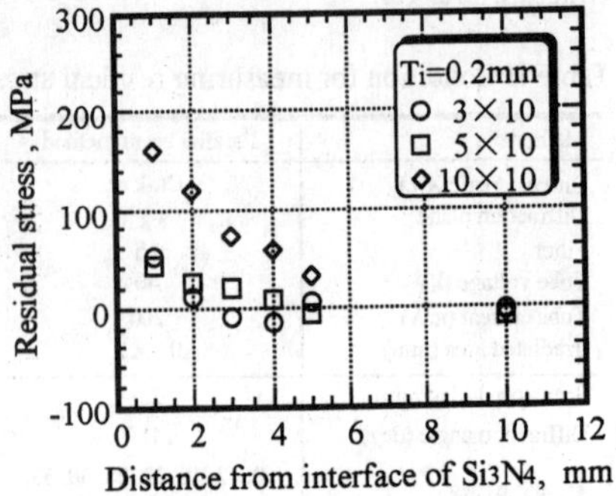

Fig.6 Relationship between residual inTi=0.2mm joint stress and distance from interface of Si3N4

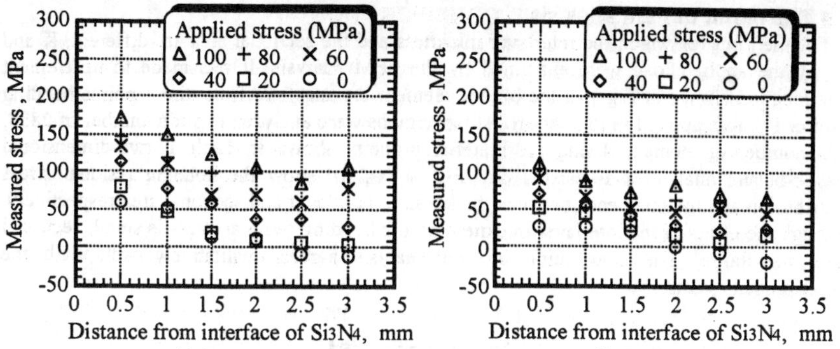

(a) Ti=0.2mm (b) Ti=1.0mm

Fig.7 Relationship between measured stress and distance from interface of Si_3N_4 in 3×10mm joint

stress against bonding interface by the following equation (9).

$$\sigma = KX^{-\lambda} \qquad (1)$$

σ is the stress which is vertical against the interface. X is the distance from the interface edge, K is the stress intensity factor, and λ is the exponent which shows the intensity of the specificity. K and λ are obtained from logarithmic plots of stress and distance from the bonded interface by the least squares method linearly. Then, the residual stress at 0.5~2mm was approximated by least squares method, and K and λ were calculated. The result of calculating the value of K and λ from these results is shown in Fig.8 (a), (b) respectively far different thickness of interlayer. When the load increases, K increases, λ was decreased, and λ tended to settle it in 0 in the high applied stress. Then, λ was no change in the certain applied stress. Specimen in which the sectional area is smaller, stress singularity of bonded interface become difficult to have disappeared, when the load increases. Specimen in which the sectional area is smaller, λ approaches 0, when the applied stress is small. When the equal stress was applied, the bonding residual stress is lager, λ is lager. Then, λ became constant that the load was taken to some extent.

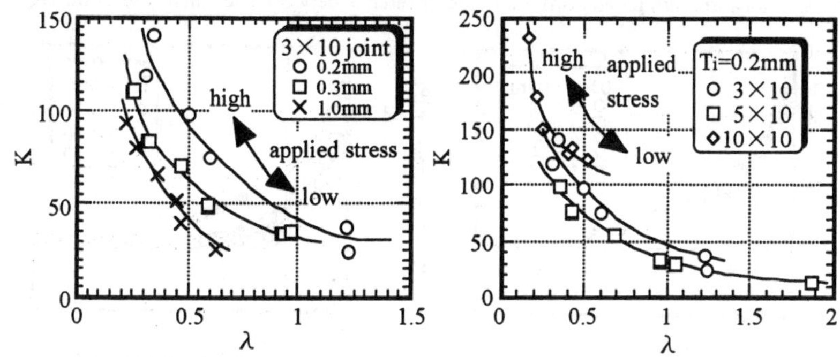

(a) Difference of interlayer thickness in 3×10 joint

(b) Difference of sectional area in Ti=0.2mm joint

Fig.8 Relationship between K and λ

7.4 The result of FEM analysis

For the joint for which the interlayer thickness and the sectional area are different, K and λ by the applied load were examined by the FEM analysis. It was made to be element fractionation shown in Fig.9 in the 8 node element the analysis. Then, the 4 points bending load of P/2 was applied in this model. All specimens were analyzed in node number of 2833, 896 number of element. Using the material property shown in Table I, two-dimensional elastic-plastic analysis was carried out. Fig.10 (a), (b) show the bonding residual stress distribution and the difference between thickness of interlayer and sectional area respectively. Though the effect of the interlayer thickness on the bonding residual stress is small, sectional area was large. The distribution by the analysis agrees qualitatively well with the experimental results.

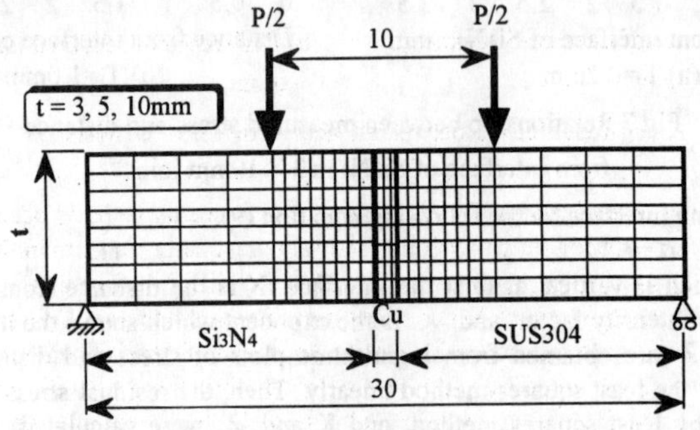

Fig. 9 Element division

It is shown in Fig.11 (a), (b) that it obtained the value of K and λ by the FEM analysis on the difference between thickness of interlayer and sectional area respectively. Though large change could not be observed for the value of K and λ in the specimen of which the interlayer thickness differs, the effect of the difference between the specimen size was remarkable. And, compared to experimental result and analytical result, K and λ exactly do not agree, they agree qualitatively well.

The bending strength of joint can not be simply guessed from bonding residual stress of the bonded interface as it was described in the introduction. As it is considered from the result that the bending strength greatly differs by the difference between specimen configuration, the

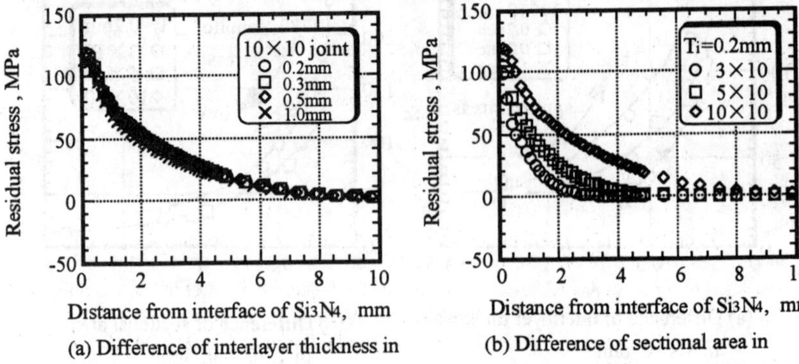

(a) Difference of interlayer thickness in 10×10 joint

(b) Difference of sectional area in Ti=0.2mm joint

Fig.10 Relationship between residual stress and distance from interface of Si_3N_4 by FEM analysis

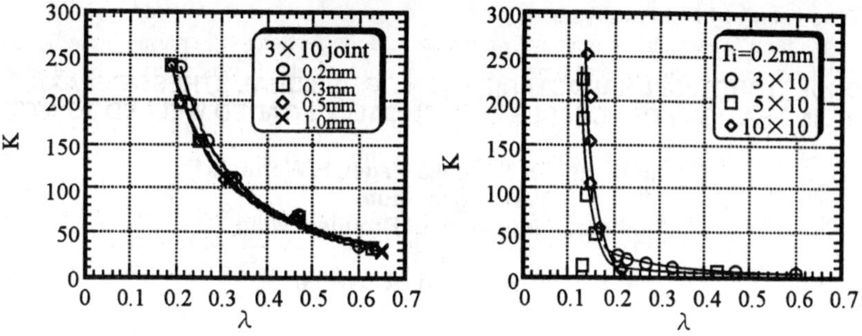

(a) Difference of interlayer thickness in 3×10 joint

(b) Difference of sectional area Ti=0.2mm joint

Fig.11 Relationship between K and λ by FEM analysis

interface crack is low-loaded (the high λ region), and it seems to have been formed. This stress is also about 50~60MPa on either joint, and it is drastically lower than the result of AE by authors. On the reason for showing the result of greatly differing like this, it seems to base it on threshold of the AE sensor and X-ray stress measurement accuracy. When the specimen configuration is different, the difference in the bonding residual stress behavior is remarkably observed for unloading and loading. It is well-known that there are correlation between bending strength and bonding residual stress, and it seems to be the correlation between it and stress of the interface crack initiation, too. There was a difference on K and λ by the difference between the specimen configuration in the low loading (high λ region). From considering the problem of crack, the interface crack is initiated in the high λ region (low-stress region) from correlation between bonding residual stress and bonding strength. Then, λ which shows the intensity of the stress singularity greatly change for loading, bonding residual stress was lager, behavior of residual stress is more remarkable.

8. CONCLUSION

Bonding material used were austenitic stainless steel (SUS304) as metal, sintered silicon nitride (β-Si_3N_4) as ceramic, and the oxygen-free copper as interlayer.

(1) When the interlayer thickens and the sectional area decreases, the bonding residual stress decreases.

(2) With the increase of the applied stress, the stress measured by the X-ray increases.

(3) The value of measured value and K of analytic value and λ agreed qualitatively well.

(4) By observing the change of K and λ with stress loading of joints, the fracture mechanism of joint may be clarified.

REFERENCES

1. M.G.Nicholas, "Joining of Ceramics", (1990).
2. T.Shimizu, K.Tanaka, et al. SAE Paper, No.900656 (1990), 163.
3. K.Asami, N.Shiraki, et al. Transaction of the JSME, A, 60-578 (1994), 2280.
4. N.Shiraki, H.Morita et al. Transaction of the JSME, A, 62-598 (1996), 1513.
5. S.Tanaka et al. Proceeding of Annual Meeting of the Japan Institute of Metals, (1989), 153.
6. K.Asami, N.Shiraki, Transaction of the JSME A, 59-561 (1993), 1202.
7. N.Shiraki, Y.Sugiyama et al. Proceeding of the Annual Meeting of JSME/MMD, No.95-2, vol.B (1995), 241.
8. JIS Z 3261 "Silver Brazing Filler Metal" (1985).

NONDESTRUCTIVE CHARACTERIZATION OF RESIDUAL STRESS RELAXATION AND FATIGUE PROCESSES IN CYCLICALLY LOADED WELDED JOINTS

C Lachmann, Th Nitschke-Pagel, H Wohlfahrt
Welding Institute
Technical University of Braunschweig
Germany
E-mail: c.lachmann@tu-bs.de

ABSTRACT

The fatigue behaviour of welded joints is dependent on the weld geometry, its microstructure, the cyclic material properties of the different weld zones and the magnitude and relaxation behaviour of residual stresses. In this work, the nondestructive micromagnetic testing method is applied for the characterization of fatigue-related processes such as residual stress relaxation, cyclic hardening or softening and the corresponding microstructural changes. The results are compared to measurements by means of X-rays, X-ray line profile analysis and strain measurements. Under fatigue loading, an advancing residual stress relaxation in the weld is accompanied by a characteristic change in the micromagnetic parameters. The results also indicate that a characteristic change of the nondestructive parameters shortly before failure of the welded joint can be used as an indicator of severe fatigue damage and a prediction of the location of failure within the weld. The presented results illustrate the potential of the micromagnetic testing system for the assessment on fatigue processes and the implementation in an adaptive life prediction for cyclically loaded weldments.

1 INTRODUCTION

The behaviour of components during cyclic loading is influenced by the material properties based on the microstructure and in many cases by the magnitude and distribution of residual stresses (1). Welded joints consist of different zones with different material properties, e. g. yield strength, ductility, hardness, grain structure, chemical composition etc., and residual stresses (2). In general, the zones of a weld can be divided into the formerly molten weld bead, the heat affected zone (HAZ) which was not molten and the unaffected base material. Besides the material properties, the fatigue life of a weld is influenced by the size and sharpness of notches, especially at the weld toe where certain welding processes produce undercutting or high reinforcement angles. Additionally, so-called metallurgical notches at the intersections of two microstructures with significantly different material properties can lead to local stress concentrations reducing the fatigue life, too. To assess the fatigue behaviour of the whole welded joint it is essential to characterize the microstructural processes and the residual stress relaxation in each zone of the weld during cyclic loading. Changes in microstructure and residual stresses can be observed both in the period before crack initiation and during the micro- and macrocrack growth period (3). Therefore, an observed change in the residual stresses could be used to characterize the actual stage of fatigue of a loaded weldment. This information can be used as an indicator of severe fatigue damage and thus can serve as a correcting factor for the fatigue life prediction of the actual welded joint.

Residual stresses in the weld during cyclic loading are commonly measured by X-ray diffraction. But since this laboratory technique is rather costly and time consuming, there is a need for fast and mobile methods which are also suited for inspections on large welded parts or steel constructions. The micromagnetic Barkhausen noise method fits these requirements in an ideal way. Additionally, this technique provides measuring quantities that are sensitive to residual stresses and microstructural changes. Parallel to X-ray diffraction measurements, using suitable calibration procedures (4), the micromagnetic method can be applied for the measurement of residual stresses and the assessment of fatigue-related processes in welds.

2 EXPERIMENTAL SETUP AND EVALUATION PROCEDURE

The investigations were carried out using flat specimens (thickness 10 mm) of the structural steel S355J2G3 in a normalised state (according to Eurocode 10 027-1) having a nominal yield strength of 380 MPa and an ultimate tensile strength of 574 MPa. A three layer DV butt weld was welded transverse to the loading direction using the gas-metal-arc (GMA) welding process (Fig. 1). To illustrate the internal structure of the weld, Fig. 2 shows a micrograph of a transverse section of the weld bead and the adjacent zones HAZ and base material. The test welds were cyclically loaded with pure pulsating tension using a 400 kN servohydraulic material testing system. After each decade of loading, the nondestructive parameters from X-ray residual stress determination and the micromagnetic testing method were measured at distinctive locations on a line transverse to the weld.

To investigate the stress and microstrucural behaviour of the micromagnetic quantities in detail, specimens were prepared using the welding simulation technique. These specimens consisted of the same base material as the welding specimens (S355J2G3) and were conductively heated to different peak temperatures. The cooling in a nitrogen gas stream was computer-controlled and established cooling conditions similar to those in a real HAZ during GMA welding. The simulated specimens were loaded in the testing machine while simultaneously the micromagnetic measurements were performed dependent on load stress and plastic strain.

The macro-residual stress components longitudinal and transverse to the weld were determined in a thin surface layer of the weld area with a usual X-ray stress and texture diffractometer in a ψ-arrangement using Cr-Kα-radiation. The evaluation was performed on the diffraction lines of the {211}-lattice planes of the ferrite according to the $\sin^2\psi$-method (5).

Parallel to the determination of the macro-residual stresses the inhomogeneous micro-

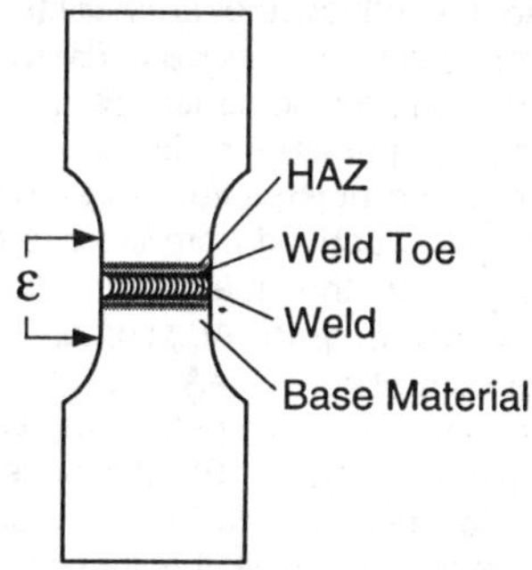

Fig. 1 Weld specimen geometry and gauge length for strain measurements

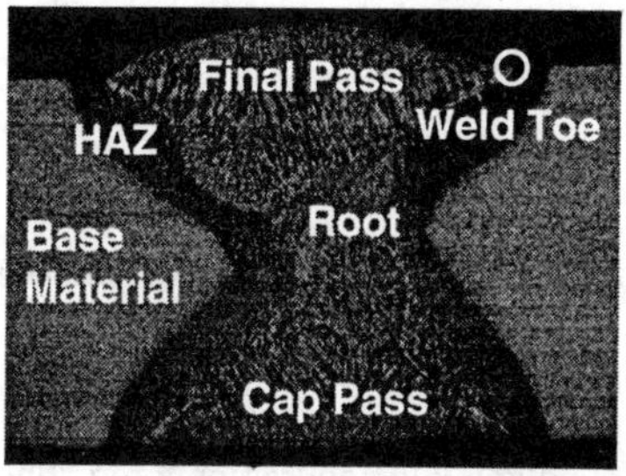

Fig. 2 Micrograph of a transverse section of a 3-layer GMA-DV-weld in the steel S355

residual stresses were determined by the means of X-ray line profile analysis using the single-line Voigt method (6). Before the calculation of the microstructural parameters, the diffraction lines of the {211} lattice planes were corrected from the angle-dependent Lorentz- and polarisation factors. To remove the $K\alpha_2$–component, the Rachinger correction was applied. Using a special evaluation software a Voigt-function was fitted to the corrected line profiles to determine the line profile parameters. From these parameters the X-ray microstructural parameters average domain size $<D>$, average lattice strain $<e^2>^{1/2}$ and dislocation density ρ could be determined (6). The dislocation density was derived according to Mikkola (7) from

$$\rho = \frac{k_2}{b} \frac{<e^2>^{1/2}}{<D>}.$$

b represents the magnitude of the burgers vector and the constant k_2 was set to $k_2 = 2/\sqrt{3}$.

The relaxation of residual stresses and microstructural changes during loading were also studied by the use of the micromagnetic testing method (8, 9). In general, the parameters measured by this method are dependent on microstructure, hardness and residual stress state of the investigated ferromagnetic material since these characteristics interact with its magnetic domain structure.

Under the influence of an oscillating magnetic field (Fig. 2), irreversible movements of the magnetic domain walls (Bloch-walls) induce small electrical pulses in the coil of the micromagnetic sensor resulting in the so-called "Barkhausen Noise". The corresponding parameter is the maximum Barkhausen noise level M_{max} and the coercivity H_{cm} derived from the coercive field strength at the maximum Barkhausen noise level (Fig. 2). Additionally, the computer-controlled 3MA (micromagnetic multi-parameter microstructure and residual stress analysis (9)) testing system is able to measure further micromagnetic parameters such as the incremental permeability $\mu_{\Delta max}$, the corresponding tangential field strength $H_{c\mu}$ and also quantities resulting from the analysis of the upper harmonics of the tangential field strength time signal (8).

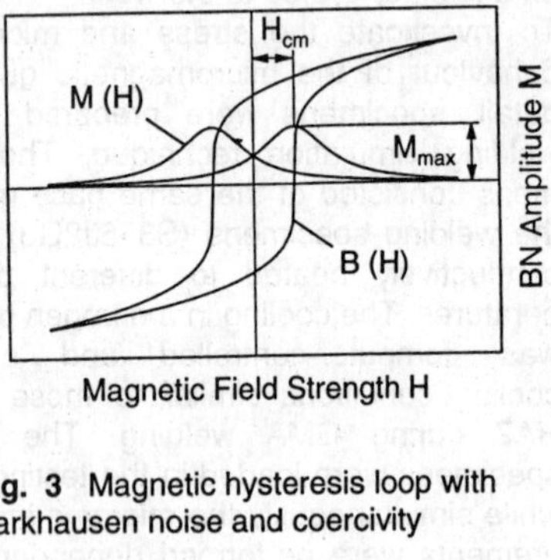

Fig. 3 Magnetic hysteresis loop with Barkhausen noise and coercivity

3 DEPENDENCE OF MICROMAGNETIC PARAMETERS ON STRESS AND MICROSTRUCTURE

Most micromagnetic parameters are dependent on stress and hardness or microstructure, respectively. In welds both characteristics vary across the joint, therefore quantitative measurements requiring a separation of both effects need a special calibration and thus are difficult and time consuming. In this paper, the focus is mainly on the qualitative changes of micromagnetic quantities.

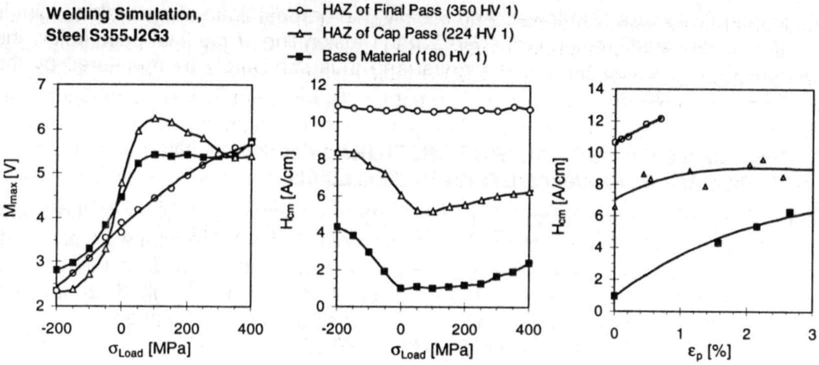

Fig. 4 Micromagnetic parameters for two different microstructures of weld simulation specimens of steel S355 dependent on the load stress and plastic strain

To illustrate the characteristic behaviour of the different micromagnetic parameters with respect to different microstructures, load stresses and plastic strains, simulation specimens with three different microstructures were loaded in a testing machine. Under load and after certain degrees of plastic strain without outer loads, the micromagnetic measurements were conducted. In Fig. 4 the Barkhausen noise M_{max} and the coercivity H_{cm} are plotted against the load stress. According to (8) the Barkhausen noise shows a stronger stress sensitivity whereas the coercivity is more dependent on the microstructure. Especially for the hardest microstructure (HAZ of final pass with 350 HV1) M_{max} is nearly linear dependent on the load stress and H_{cm} changes only gradually with stress. For the softer HAZ of the cap pass (224 HV 1) and especially for the base material (180 HV 1), M_{max} shows a strong dependency for load stresses between –100 and +100 MPa. But above or below these limits, a slight or nearly no change can be observed. H_{cm} on the other side increases significantly with compressive load stresses but grows only gradually with increasing tensile stresses. Thus, especially for softer microstructures of the steel S355, a calibration of the micromagnetic method for stress can reveal problems. The right hand side of Fig. 4 shows the coercivity H_{cm} plotted against the plastic strain after loading. Similar to the stress-strain curves of the respective microstructures, H_{cm} increases with growing plastic strain. This clear dependency proves that H_{cm} is not only sensitive to the initial hardness of different microstructures but also to work hardening mechanisms due to plastic deformation.

As an example for the correlation of H_{cm} and hardness, Fig. 5 shows H_{cm} and the micro-hardness HV1 across the final pass of a GMA weld. The coercivity increases with increasing hardness from the soft base material to the weld metal. Since the hardness of the final pass is lower than that of the simulation specimen, the values

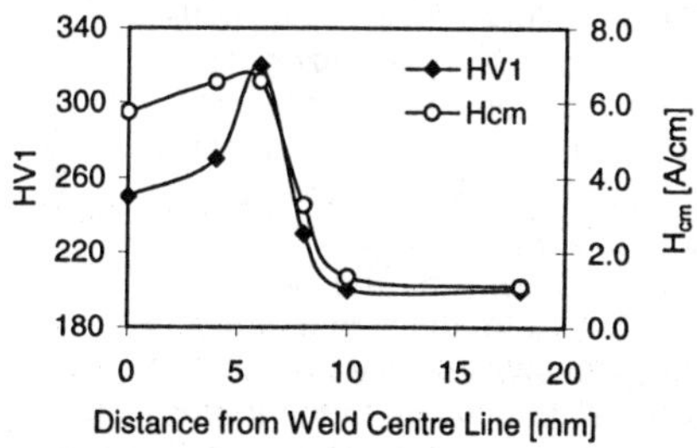

Fig. 5 Vickers hardness and coercivity H_{cm} across GMA-weld

of the coercivities are also lower. Additionally, the hardest zone of the welded joint is found in a very small region of the HAZ at the fusion line of the final pass below the surface where the cooling rate is highest and thus can hardly be measured by the micromagnetic system.

4 RESIDUAL STRESSES, MICROSTRUCTURAL CHANGES AND MICROMAGNETIC PARAMETERS UNDER LOAD

The upper part of Fig. 6 shows the quasi-static relaxation behaviour of the transverse and longitudinal residual stresses in the weld centre of the final weld pass. After the first load cycle, the residual stresses in the weld seam relax dependent on the load stress and their orientation to the weld centre line. For the longitudinal direction parallel to the weld seam, the magnitude of this residual stress relaxation

$$\Delta\sigma^{RS} = \sigma^{RS}{}_{N} - \sigma^{RS}{}_{N=0}$$

and the change of the Barkhausen noise amplitude

$$\Delta M_{max} = M_{max,N} - M_{max,N=0}$$

increase nearly linear with growing load stress due to increasing plastic deformations. However, since the residual stresses in the initial state have a magnitude of only ≈100 MPa, not a pure relaxation behaviour but a steady build-up of compressive residual stresses can be observed. At low load amplitudes, the combination of residual and load stress begins to exceed the local yield strength and leads to local plastications followed by a relaxation of residual stresses. At higher loads, the whole specimen begins to plasticize and thus, compressive residual stresses begin to build up due to local differences of the inelastic material behaviour across the entire welded joint. The softer base material plasticizes to a greater extent than the harder weld and this difference in lateral contraction leads to compressive deformation stresses in the weld. This also explains the phenomenon that the magnitude of residual stress relaxation parallel to the weld but transverse to the loading direction often is much greater than in loading direction transverse to the weld. In that direc-

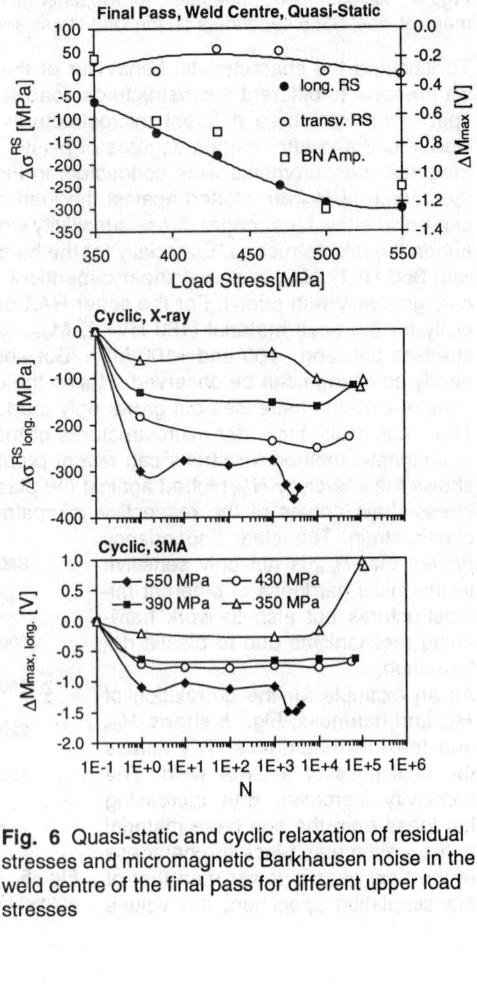

Fig. 6 Quasi-static and cyclic relaxation of residual stresses and micromagnetic Barkhausen noise in the weld centre of the final pass for different upper load stresses

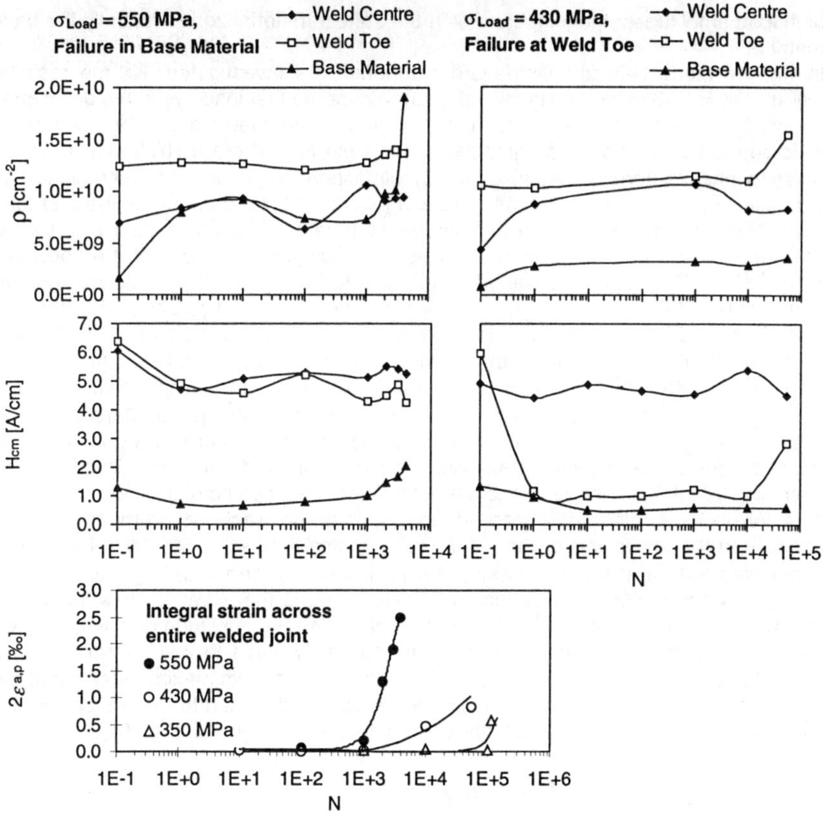

Fig. 7 Upper part: dislocation density determined by X-ray line profile analysis and micromagnetic coercivity measured at weld centre, weld toe and base material during cyclic loading at two different upper load stresses. Lower part: plastic strain at different upper load stresses measured across whole welded joint

tion, only a small change of the transverse residual stresses can be observed (see Fig. 6).

During cyclic loading until approx. 1000 load cycles, the longitudinal residual stresses and Barkhausen noise amplitude remain relatively constant (see Fig. 6). After this period, both σ^{RS} and M_{max} begin to change. Especially at the highest upper load stress of 550 MPa, the correlation between the X-ray and micromagnetic parameters is strong. Both characteristics decrease and shortly before fracture they increase to a small extent. This characteristic behaviour of σ^{RS} and M_{max} was also observed in the weld centre of cyclically loaded GTA-welds (4).

To investigate the microstructural processes under cyclic loading more in detail, in Fig. 7 the dislocation density determined by X-ray line profile analysis and the micromagnetic parameter coercivity are plotted versus the number of load cycles at three different locations of the welded joint and two load amplitudes. In general, welded joints usually fail at the weld toe where the notch stress is highest. But at very high load amplitudes, the joint can fail in the softest material zone – usually the base material.

In Fig. 7 these two different failure categories are investigated. As the residual stresses in Fig. 6 exhibit a significant change after the first load cycle, the dislocation density increases after the first load step, mainly in the base material but also in the weld seam, but to a lower magnitude. At the weld toe, where a HAZ-microstructure leads to a high hardness (see also Fig. 5), almost no change in ρ can be detected. In opposite to the dislocation density, the magnitude of H_{cm} drops after the first load cycle. Since the coercivity as a micromagnetic parameter is also sensitive to stress, the great change of the residual stresses influence the behaviour of the coercivity (see Fig. 4). But during the period shortly before fracture, both non-destructive parameters begin to increase at that location at which failure takes place. For the high load stress of 550 MPa, the base material is subjected to strong plastications leading to failure which is accompanied by a remarkable increase of ρ and H_{cm}. At the lower load stress of 430 MPa, the welded joint cracks at the weld toe also indicated by the increase of ρ and H_{cm}. In the weld centre or base material both parameters exhibit no relevant change. At those locations where cyclic plastications are strongest and lead to crack formation and failure, a significant increase of the dislocation density and the coercivity, which is sensitive to microstructural changes, can be observed.

This correlation is also underlined by the results of the plastic strain measurements depicted in the lower part of Fig. 7. At the high load stress of 550 MPa the plastic strain amplitude and the non-destructive parameters ρ and H_{cm} begin to increase extensively from 1000 load cycles. Since the strain is measured across the whole joint with a gauge length of 40 mm, this high plastic strain amplitude is mainly caused by cyclic plastication of the base material and finally leads to crack formation and failure here. At lower load stresses, the increase in $\varepsilon_{a,p}$ and its maximum amplitude is much less since the failure mechanisms are limited to the weld toe - a much smaller region of the weld having also a higher hardness and strength (cf. Fig. 5).

5 CONCLUSIONS AND OUTLOOK

The present investigations show that characteristic changes of welding residual stresses, the dislocation density determined by X-ray line profile analysis and micromagnetic parameters under quasi-static and cyclic loading are interdependent with respect to each other and can also be used for an assessment of ongoing fatigue processes.

Under quasi-static loading, the residual stresses within a weld relax dependent on the load stress and the amount of local plastic deformation in the respective weld zone. In the weld seam of the investigated steel, the magnitude of quasistatic residual stress relaxation followed by a build-up of compressive residual stresses with increasing load stress is much greater in the direction transverse to loading (parallel to weld) than in loading direction (transverse to weld). This build-up of compressive residual stresses can be explained by the difference in plastic lateral contraction of weld, HAZ and base material. For a complete understanding of this phenomenon, plastic FEM-calculations using a 3-D weld model are part of ongoing investigations. This nearly linear increase of compressive longitudinal residual stresses with growing load stress leads also to a corresponding decrease of the Barkhausen noise amplitude that is especially sensitive to residual stresses. Thus, the Barkhausen noise amplitude M_{max} can be used for a qualitative characterization of residual stress changes in welds.

For the case of cyclic loading the correlation is not as good as in the quasi-static load step since the microstructural processes of cyclic hardening, softening and crack formation also affect the Barkhausen noise. But relevant changes in the residual stresses and M_{max} indicate damage processes such as the formation of (micro-) cracks and an approaching failure of the weld. By the characteristic behaviour of the microstructural parameters dislocation density and coercivity also a statement about the location of failure in the welded joint can be made. Both parameters show a remarkable increase especially at that position, for the case of the base material accompanied by a strong increase of the plastic strain amplitude. As a conclusion, cyclic plastications leading to crack formation and failure can be detected by these nondestructive methods. Especially the micromagnetic technique has a potential for a fast and mobile inspection of loaded steel structures enhancing the possibilities for an adaptive and safer lifetime prediction.

The authors would like to thank the German Research Foundation (DFG) for the financial support of the investigations which are part of an ongoing research project within the collaborative research center SFB 477 "Life cycle assessment of strucures via innovative monitoring" (see also `www.sfb477.tu-bs.de`*).*

REFERENCES

1. Nitschke-Pagel T, "Eigenspannungen und Schwingfestigkeitsverhalten geschweißter Feinkornbaustähle", Diss. TU Braunschweig, 1994
2. Nitschke-Pagel T, Wohlfahrt H, "The Generation of Residual Stresses due to Joining Processes", in: Residual Stresses - Measurement, Calculation, Evaluation, DGM Informationsgesellschaft, 1991, 121-134
3. Munz D, Schwalbe K, Mayr P, "Dauerschwingverhalten metallischer Werkstoffe", Vieweg, 1971
4. Lachmann, C, Nitschke-Pagel, T, Wohlfahrt, H, Nondestructive Characterization of Fatigue Processes in Cyclically Loaded Welded Joints by the Barkhausen Noise Method, "Structural Health Monitoring 2000", Proceedings of the 2nd International Workshop on Structural Health Monitoring, 8.-10.09.1999, Stanford University, Stanford, CA, Technomic Publ. Co., S. 327-337
5. Hauk V, Macherauch E, "Die zweckmäßige Durchführung röntgenographischer Spannungsermittlungen" (RSE), in: HTM-Beiheft, Eigenspannungen und Lastspannungen, hrsg. v. V. Hauk und E. Macherauch, Hanser, 1982, 1-19
6. Delhez R et al, "Determination of Crystallite Size and Lattice Distortions through X-Ray Diffraction Line Profile Analysis", Fresenius Z. Anal. Chemie, 312 (1982), 1-16
7. Mikkola, D.E.: Examples of Applications of Line Broadening, Met. Soc. Sonf., 1965
8. Theiner W A, "Physical Basis of Micromagnetic Methods and Sensor Systems and their Application Areas", Proceedings of the 1st International Conference on Barkhausen noise and Micromagnetic Testing, Hannover, 1998, 197-218
9. Theiner W A, Brinksmeier E, Stücker E, "Stress Measurements on Components with Nondestructive Ferromagnetic Methods", in: "Residual Stresses in Science and Technology", Bd. 2, DGM Informationsgesellschaft, 1987, 167-174

NEUTRON DIFFRACTION STUDY OF RESIDUAL STRESSES IN FRICTION STIR WELDS

X.-L. Wang*, Z. Feng**[(1)], S. A. David*, S. Spooner*, and C. R. Hubbard*
* Oak Ridge National Laboratory, Oak Ridge, TN 37831-6430, USA
** Edison Welding Institute, 1250 Arthur Adams Drive, Columbus, OH 43221-3585,USA

ABSTRACT

We report a neutron diffraction study of residual stresses in 6061-T6 aluminum friction stir welds. The specimens were 6 mm thick plates friction stir welded in the butt joint configuration at two welding speeds, 279 and 787 mm/min, respectively. The experimentally determined residual stresses show a symmetric double-peak profile across the weld center line, with the peaks located in the middle of the heat-affected zone. The maximum tensile stress, which is in the longitudinal direction, is 130 and 200 MPa, respectively. It is shown that the difference in the residual stress is due to a change in the microstructure and stress relaxation that occurred as a result of the longer heating time associated with the low welding speed. The impact of these residual stresses on the mechanical properties of friction stir welds is discussed.

INTRODUCTION

Friction stir welding is an emerging solid-state joining technique [1]. The process is illustrated in Figure 1, where a weld is formed by plunging a rotating non-consumable tool into the workpiece materials and driving the tool from beginning to finish. In the region of contact, the welding tool generates frictional heat and induces extensive plastic deformation within the workpiece materials. As the tool moves forward, the deformed materials are driven to the rear of the tool and mixed together, creating a dense, porosity-free weld zone. Because they are made by solid-state joining methods, friction stir welds are inherently immune from the cracking problems associated with solidification of liquid weld deposits. Welding related distortion is also smaller due to the low heat input and the use of fixtures during friction stir welding. In addition, high integrity welds with good mechanical properties have been made using friction stir welding for several classes of alloys which were previously deemed unweldable.

Despite the considerable progress made in recent years, the fundamental aspects of thermal-mechanical deformation in friction stir welds have not been well understood. In particular, little information is available about the magnitudes of the residual stress in friction stir welds, much less about the impact of these stresses on the mechanical properties. The low heat input and the forging force imposed by the tool in friction stir welding could lead to a very different residual stress profile than that generated by conventional fusion welding. Furthermore, the rotating tool adds a shear force in the stirred or weld zone. It is unclear how

---

[(1)] Currently at Engineering Mechanics Corporation of Columbus (Emc^2), 3518 Riverside Dr., Suite 202, Columbus, OH 43221-1735, USA this shear force would modify the resultant residual stress profile. Issues like these have limited the broad use of this technology in many industrial applications.

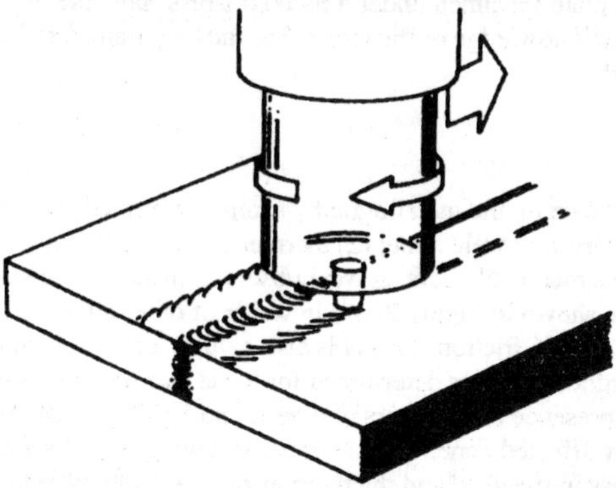

Fig. 1 Schematic illustration of the friction stir welding process.

In this paper, we report a neutron diffraction study of residual stresses in 6061-T6 aluminum (Al-6061-T6) friction stir welds made at two welding speeds (279 and 787 mm/min, respectively). Al-6061-T6 is a heat treatable wrought aluminum alloy. It has excellent acceptance of coatings and is typically used in fittings, brake pistons, computer parts, couplings, and valves. Due to hot cracking problems, fusion welding of Al-6061 alloys generally requires the use of a filler metal, whose presence modifies the properties of the welded region. However, using the friction stir welding method, high integrity Al-6061 welds have been obtained in the absence of a filler metal.

EXPERIMENTAL

The specimens were made by friction stir welding of two large (~150×300 mm^2), 6 mm thick Al-6061-T6 plates in the butt joint configuration. Two specimens were prepared with a welding speed of 279 and 787 mm/min, respectively, in order to investigate the influence of welding speed on the magnitudes of the residual stress gnereated. Coupons of 200×200×6 mm^3 were cut from each welded piece for residual stress measurements. Additional coupons were cut out of the remaining weld pieces for metallographic observations and hardness measurements.

Samples for microstructure analysis were mounted, and polished using standard metallographic procedures. The specimens were etched with Kellers reagent. Hardness profile was taken at mid-depth at an interval of 0.25 mm across the samples using LECO hardness tester with a diamond pyramid indenter and a load of 100 grams. The residual stress measurements were conducted at the High Flux Isotope Reactor of Oak Ridge National Laboratory using a modified triple-axis spectrometer. Details of the instrument have been given previously [2]. In the present experiment, a (3 3 1) reflection off an elastically bent Si crystal was used as the monochromator. The take-off angle for the monochromator was 84° and the incident neutron wavelength was 1.513 Å. A sampling volume of 2×2×2 mm^3 was used in the neutron diffraction experiment and the measurements were made on a mid cross-section normal to the weld center line. The aluminum (3 1 1) reflection was used for determination of strains. The residual stresses were derived assuming the bi-axial stress condition. For a thin plate specimen under a bi-axial stress state, the in-plane stresses can be determined without the knowledge of the stress-free lattice parameter, d_0, which in this case varies across the weld.

RESULTS

Optical micrographs taken on the metallography samples revealed four regions with distinct microstructures: (1) stirred or weld zone; (2) thermal-mechanically affected zone (3) heat-affected zone; (4) base metal. No defects were observed in any of the samples examined. The hardness data are shown in Figure 2. As in welds of other aluminum alloys in the fully aged condition, Al-6061-T6 friction stir welds also exhibit a rather complex hardness profile. Qualitatively, the hardness profiles determined for these two specimens look similar and are characterized by the presence of two pairs of a peak and a valley located on each side of the thermal-mechanically affected zone. Considerable softening was observed in the weld zone. However, the hardness in the weld and the thermal-mechanically affected zones is higher than that in the heat-affected zone. This difference is attributable to the dynamic recrystallization that took place within the weld zone as a result of the friction heat and mechanical work [3]. In the heat-affected zone, the hardness increases with increasing distance from the weld center and approaches that of the base metal (110 VHN) at 12-15 mm from the weld center.

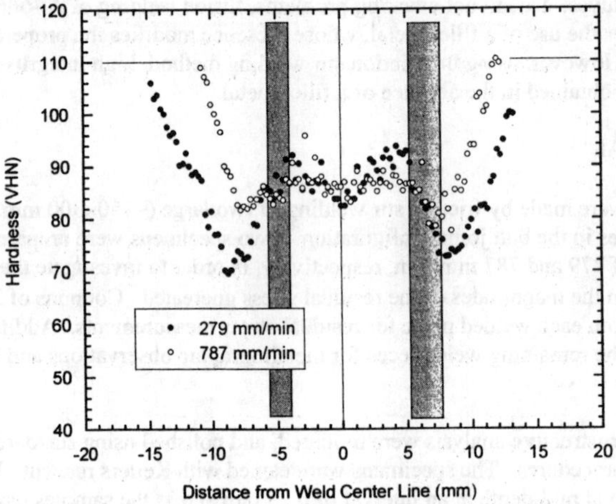

Fig. 2 Hardness profile in the vicinity of the weld zone. The base metal has a hardness of 110 VHN, as indicated by the horizontal bars. The shaded areas are thermal-mechanically affected zones and between them is the weld zone.

The residual stress in Al-6061-T6 friction stir welds exhibits a double-peak profile across the weld center line that is much similar to that in fusion aluminum welds [4-5]. The peaks are located in the middle of the heat-affected zone. For both specimens, the stress data obtained at three depths (0, and ±2 mm from mid-depth) revealed no evidence of through-thickness dependence. In addition, no apparent asymmetry was observed with respect to the weld center line, indicating that the effect of asymmetric material flow induced by the rotating tool is not evident for the two specimens under investigation. Figures 3(a) and 3(b) shows the

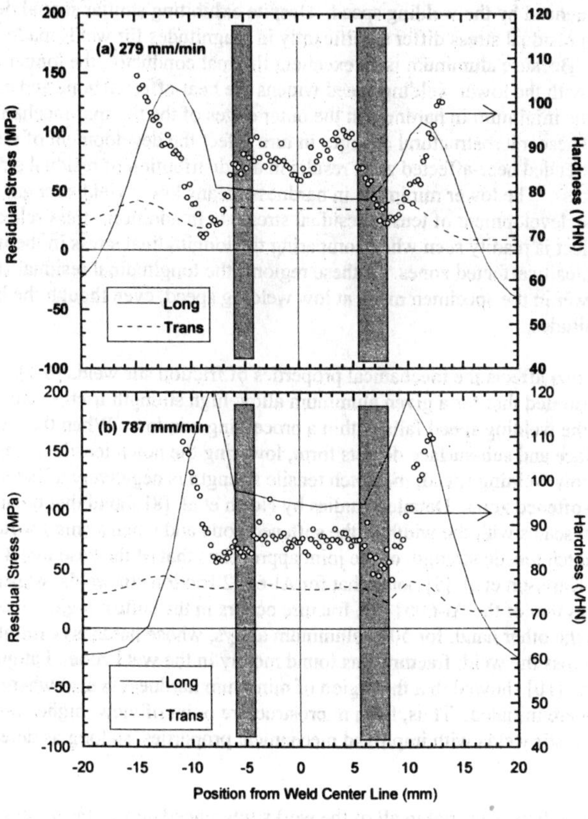

Fig. 3 Residual stress in Al-6061-T6 friction stir welds for specimens made at (a) 279 mm/min; (b) 787 mm/min. The estimated standard deviation is approximately 15 MPa.

longitudinal and transverse stress data for each specimen. The maximum tensile stress, which is in the longitudinal direction, is 130 and 200 MPa, respectively, for the 279 and 787 mm/min specimens. These stress values amount to 53% and 73% of the yield strength of Al-6061-T6 alloy, which is 276 MPa at room temperature. To facilitate discussions, the hardness data are also plotted in the figures. For both specimens, the transverse stress is small at all locations.

DISCUSSION

As can be seen from Figures 2-3, the microstructure and residual stress in friction stir welds are strongly influenced by the welding speed. Despite exhibiting similar spatial dependence, the hardness and residual stress differ significantly in magnitudes for welds made at different welding speeds. Because aluminum is an excellent thermal conductor, the longer heating time associated with the lower welding speed widens the heat-affected zone and continued heating lowers the minimum in hardness at the outer edges of the thermal-mechanically affected zone. These microstructural changes in turn affect the development of residual stresses. The extended heat-affected zone results in a redistribution of residual stresses, with reduced peak stress. The lower minimum in hardness means lower yield strength, which further limits the development of tensile residual stresses. In addition, stress relaxation occurs. This effect is readily seen when comparing the longitudinal stress in the weld and thermal-mechanically affected zones. In these regions, the longitudinal residual stress is considerably lower in the specimen made at low welding speed, even though the hardness is of similar magnitudes.

Welding speed also affects the mechanical properties of friction stir welds [6-7]. Hashimoto et al. [6] demonstrated that for a given aluminum alloy, high strength friction stir welds are obtained when the welding speed falls within a processing window. When the welding speed is too high, surface and sub-surface defects form, lowering the notch tensile strength in the weld zone. At low welding speed, the notch tensile strength is negatively affected by the formation of a softened zone. Detailed studies by North et al. [8] found that the notch tensile strength, in fact, scales with the width of the softened zone and when a small softened zone is produced, the notch tensile strength of the joint approaches that of the base metal. In a separate study, Karlsson et al. [9] noted that for Al-6082 friction stir welds, whose hardness profile resembles that of the Al-6061-T6, fracture occurs in the softest region outside the weld zone. On the other hand, for 5083 aluminum alloys, whose hardness exhibits hardly any variation across the weld, fracture was found mostly in the weld zone. Fatigue tests by Bussu and Irving [10] showed that the region of minimum hardness is also where most of the fatigue cracks were initiated. Thus, from microstructure point of view, higher welding speed produces friction stir welds with improved mechanical properties, so long as defects are not formed.

It should be noted, however, that in all of the works referenced above, the specimens were quite small in which much of the residual stresses are relaxed due to specimen preparation. In real components, where significant residual stresses are present, the influence of the residual stress cannot be ignored. The present experiment has shown that higher welding speed also leads to a higher tensile residual stress. This apparently will negate the effect produced by the less softened microstructure. To quantify the influence of the residual stress, mechanical testing results on large welded pieces are needed. Once the influence of the residual stress is established, it should be possible to optimize the welding speed, or in general welding parameters for that matter, based on a compromise between the microstructure and residual stress to produce friction stir welds with desirable mechanical properties.

CONCLUDING REMARKS

Residual stresses in Al-6061-T6 friction stir welds were determined with neutron diffraction and the influence of welding speed was investigated. The experimental data show that residual stresses in Al-6061-T6 friction stir welds exhibit a double-peak profile across the weld center line, with the peaks located in the middle of the heat-affected zone. Welding speed has significant influence on the magnitude and spatial distribution of the resulting residual stresses. The specimen made at low welding speed exhibits lower residual stress, due to a change in the microstructure and stress relaxation that occurred as a result of the longer heating time associated with the low welding speed. Further development of friction stir welding techniques requires quantitative assessment of the influence of the residual stress on the mechanical properties of welded components.

ACKNOWLEDGEMENT

This research was supported in part by the U. S. Department of Energy, Assistant Secretary for Energy Efficiency and Renewable Energy, Office of Transportation Technologies as part of the High Temperature Materials Laboratory User Program. Neutron diffraction measurements were made at the High Flux Isotope Reactor, operated with the support from U.S. Department of Energy, Office of Basic Energy Sciences. Oak Ridge National Laboratory is managed by Lockheed Martin Energy Research Corporation for the U.S. Department of Energy under contract number DE-AC05-96OR22464.

References

1. W. M. Thomas, *International Patent Application*, No. PCT/GB92/02203, June 10, 1993.
2. X.-L. Wang, C. R. Hubbard, S. Spooner, S. A. David, B. H. Rabin, and R. L. Williamson, "Mapping of the residual stress distribution within a brazed zirconia-iron joint," *Mat. Sci. Eng.* **A211**, 45-53 (1996).
3. L. E. Murr, G. Liu, and J. C. McClure, "A TEM Study of Precipitation and Related Microstructures in Friction Stir Welded 6061 Aluminum," *J. Mat. Sci.*, **33**, 1243-1251 (1998)
4. K. Masubuchi, *Analysis of Welded Structures*, Pergamon Press, United Kingdom, Chapter 6 (1980).
5. X.-L. Wang, S. Spooner, C. R. Hubbard, Z. Feng, B. Taljat, "Characterization of Welding Residual Stresses with Neutron Diffraction," pp. 491-494 in *Proceedings of the 1998 SEM Spring Conference on Experimental and Applied Mechanics*, Society for Experimental Mechanics, Bethel, Connecticut (1998).
6. T. Hashimoto, S. Jyogan, K. Nakata, Y. G. Kim, and M. Ushio, "FSW joints of high strength aluminum alloy," Paper # 9-3 in *Proceedings of the 1st International Symposium on Friction Stir Welding* (June 14-16, 1999, Thousand Oaks, California, USA), The Welding Institute, Cambridge, United Kingdom (CD-ROM).

7. G. Biallas, R. Braun, C. D. Donne, G. Staniek, and W. A. Kaysser, "Mechanical properties and corrosion behavior of friction stir welds," Paper # 3-3 in *Proceedings of the 1st International Symposium on Friction Stir Welding* (June 14-16, 1999, Thousand Oaks, California, USA), The Welding Institute, Cambridge, United Kingdom (CD-ROM).
8. T. North, G. Bendzsak, C. Maldonado, and Y. Zhai, "New advances in friction welding," pp.533-540 in *Trends in Welding Research*, Edited by J. M. Vitek et al., ASM International, Materials Park, Ohio, USA (1999).
9. L. Karlsson, L.-E. Svensson, and H. Larsson, "Characteristics of friction stir welded aluminum alloys," pp. 574-579, *Trends in Welding Research*, Edited by J. M. Vitek et al., ASM International, Materials Park, Ohio, USA (1999).
10. G. Bussu and P. E. Irving, "Fatigue performance of friction stir welded 2024-T351 aluminum joints," Paper # 3-1 in *Proceedings of the 1st International Symposium on Friction Stir Welding* (June 14-16, 1999, Thousand Oaks, California, USA), The Welding Institute, Cambridge, United Kingdom (CD-ROM).

THE DEVELOPMENT OF RESIDUAL STRESSES IN INERTIA FRICTION WELDING OF NI SUPERALLOYS

JWL Pang, M Preuss and PJ Withers
Manchester Materials Science Centre
Grosvenor Street, Manchester, M1 7HS, United Kingdom
GJ Baxter
Rolls Royce plc, Derby DE24 8BJ, England

ABSTRACT

Residual stresses in Ni superalloy inertia welds, one with post weld heat treatment and one without, have been measured at depth by neutron diffraction. It was found that the residual stresses generated by the welding process are large, especially in the region close to the inner surface of the welded ring. The experimental results have shown that post weld heat treatment can reduce the magnitudes of residual stresses by almost 50%.

INTRODUCTION

Inertia welding is a joining method based on friction. The technique involves the rotation of one piece attached to a flywheel while the other piece is pushed towards the surface of the rotating piece under hydraulic pressure. The energy source for the weld formation without liquidation is the heat generated by friction at the surfaces of contact. The whole process takes place under ambient conditions. The major advantage of this welding technique is its potential to join dissimilar tubular structures made from alloys that are conventionally difficult to weld.

The next generation of nickel-base (Ni) superalloys have excellent mechanical and creep properties at high temperature and are candidates for the manufacture of aeroengine components but are difficult to weld. Inertia welding offers a viable solution to the formation of Ni superalloy welds. Before these inertia welds can be put into commercial use, the residual stresses in the welds have to be known to facilitate component lifing. A common practice to reduce the residual stresses in welds is by post weld heat treatment (PWHT).

Most of the measurements performed to date are restricted to surface measurements as reported in Priesmeyer et al (1), Abdel Moniem et al (2) and *Rolls Royce* (3). Measurements at depth were mostly limited to the axial direction and no residual stresses could be calculated. However, the tubular geometry of the weld and the welding process suggests the residual stress will be largest at the inner surface in the hoop (tangential) direction of the tube. In this paper, experiments to study the effect of PWHT on the distribution of residual stresses in Ni superalloy inertia welds by neutron diffraction are reported.

SPECIMENS

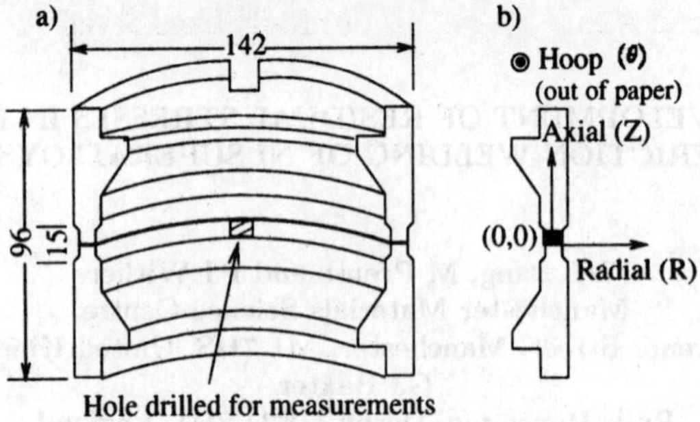

Fig. 1: a) Dimensions of $Weld_A$ and $Weld_B$. They have identical dimensions and the widths of the welds are 8 mm wide in the radial direction. All dimensions are in millimetres; b) the coordinate system of the measured cross section. The shaded region highlights the area measurements were made.

Two nickel superalloy inertia welds were provided by *Rolls Royce plc.* The room temperature yield strength, σ_y, and ultimate tensile strength, σ_{UTS}, are 1080 and 1600 MPa. Both specimens are of tubular structure and were welded under same weld conditions. The only difference is that one has not been post weld heat treated whereas the other one has. The two welds, without and with PWHT, are denoted as $Weld_A$ and $Weld_B$ respectively. The dimensions of $Weld_A$ and $Weld_B$ are identical and are shown schematically in Fig. 1.

Due to the relativey large neutron absorption coefficient of Ni, a neutron path length of 10 mm in Ni will reduce the diffracted beam intensity by $\sim$ 80%. In order to minimise the path length, a small hole of 9 mm in height and 7 mm in width has been cut from the weld region of each specimen to facilitate the measurements, particularly the determination of the hoop components as shown in Fig. 2.

The core cut away from $Weld_A$, denoted as Ref_A, was used to determine the stress-free lattice parameter for $Weld_A$. Unfortunately, the core from $Weld_B$ was not available during the experiment, and the stress-free lattice parameter for $Weld_B$ was obtained from far-field measurements on the part.

NEUTRON DIFFRACTION RESIDUAL STRAIN MEASUREMENTS

All the measurements in this experiment were made with the spectrometer ENGIN at the ISIS spallation neutron source in the United Kingdom.

The orientation of the specimens with respect to the neutron beam is shown in Fig. 2. The direction of the measurement is parallel to the scattering vector **Q** — the bisector of the incident and diffracted neutrons. The presence of two detector banks 180° apart means that strains along two perpendicular sample directions can be measured simultaneously. The gauge volume is defined by the intersection of the incident and diffracted beams. The lattice parameter, a, of the lattice planes with normal vector parallel to **Q**, averaged over the grains within the gauge volume, is determined by refinement of the spectrum collected based on Rietveld analysis as described in Young (4). Strain is then calculated with

$$\epsilon = \frac{a - a_0}{a_0}, \qquad (1)$$

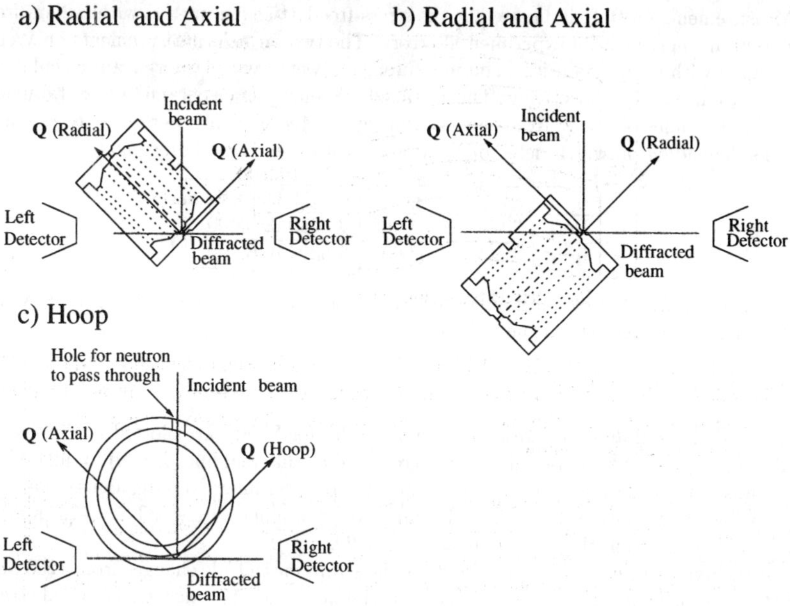

Fig. 2: Orientations of the specimen with respect to the neutron beams for the a) radial and axial components from the mid-wall thickness towards the inner diameter, b) radial and axial components from the mid-wall thickness towards the outer diameter and c) hoop components. The axial measurements obtained from the setup shown in c) were discarded because of poor statistics due to long path length.

where a_0 is the stress-free lattice parameter.

Measurements were made on a cross section of each weld, concentrated in the area from the weld line to 5 mm above the weld line. A previous experiment at Risø (5) indicated that the residual stresses in a similar weld were essentially symmetric about the weld line. This had led to a decision to make measurements only on one side of the weld instead of both below and above the weld line in this experiment. The sample coordinate system defined for the experiment is shown in Fig. 1. Strains along the three sample directions: radial, axial and hoop, were measured.

The stress-free lattice parameter for Weld_A was determined by making measurements on the core Ref_A at 1 and 2 mm below the surface which was originally at the weld line. For Weld_B, radial and axial measurements at 40 mm above the weld line and 1 mm from the outer diameter of two 180° apart tubular cross-sections were averaged to determine the stress-free lattice parameter.

RESULTS

Stress-free reference lattice parameter

Measurements on Ref_A indicate that the stress-free lattice parameters within 2mm from the weld line agree within experimental errors. The two far field measurements on $Weld_B$ also agree within uncertainties. The measurements were averaged for strain calculations of $Weld_A$ and $Weld_B$ respectively. The averaged reference lattice parameters are tabulated in Table I. Values obtained from the left and right detector banks were used to calculate strains depending on which detector bank was used for each measurement.

	Left Detector	Right Detector
Ref_A	3.6044 ± 0.0003	3.6049 ± 0.0001
Ref_B	3.6021 ± 0.0002	3.6024 ± 0.0002

Table I Stress-free lattice parameters used for strain calculations for $Weld_A$ and $Weld_B$. All lattice parameters are in the units of Å.

Residual strain profiles

The radial, axial and hoop residual strain profiles for $Weld_A$ are plotted in Fig. 3a.
The largest compressive radial strains were found at the weld line ($Z = 0$) for all depths. The radial strain decreases as the depth moves from the inner to outer diameters. The peak value changes from -2800 $\mu\epsilon$ at 1.5 mm from the inner diameter (R = -2.5 mm) to 60 $\mu\epsilon$ at 1.5 mm from the outer diameter (R = 2.5 mm).
For the axial strains, it was observed that the strain magnitude changes from 1200 $\mu\epsilon$ to -4000 $\mu\epsilon$ from the inner to outer diameters at the weld line. The variation of axial strains over the range of $Z = 0$ to $Z = 6$ for all depths R is much smaller than the variation with respect to R. Such a strain variation is indicative of a bending moment.
Hoop strains were found to be largest at the weld line and decrease as distance from the weld line increases for all depths. Maximum hoop strains of 5500 $\mu\epsilon$ were measured at both 1.5 mm from the inner diameter and the mid-wall thickness (R = 0 mm). At 1.5 mm from the outer diameter, the peak decreases slightly to a value of 4200 $\mu\epsilon$.
The residual strain profiles for $Weld_B$, a weld with PWHT, are plotted in Fig. 3b. The variations of strains are very similar between the two welds for all three directions, except the strain magnitudes of $Weld_B$ are smaller than those of $Weld_A$, particularly in the hoop direction.
The axial strain changes from 600 $\mu\epsilon$ to -2400 $\mu\epsilon$ from the inner to outer diameters at the weld line (Z = 0 mm). As with $Weld_A$, the hoop strains of $Weld_B$ were found to be maximum at the weld line, however with a magnitude of only ~ 3000 $\mu\epsilon$.

Residual stress profiles

The residual stress fields of $Weld_A$ and $Weld_B$ were calculated based on the assumption that the radial, axial and hoop directions are the principal axes of the stress field. The equation for calculation of stresses is

$$\sigma_{\text{radial}} = \frac{E}{(1+\nu)(1-2\nu)}[(1-\nu)\epsilon_{\text{radial}} + \nu(\epsilon_{\text{hoop}} + \epsilon_{\text{axial}})], \text{ etc.} \quad (2)$$

E, the bulk Young's modulus, and ν, the Poisson's ratio are 224 GPa and 0.37. The residual stress profiles were obtained by interpolating the strain measurements. The average error for the calculated residual stress is 60 MPa. The radial, axial and hoop residual stresses of $Weld_A$ and $Weld_B$ are shown in Fig. 4.

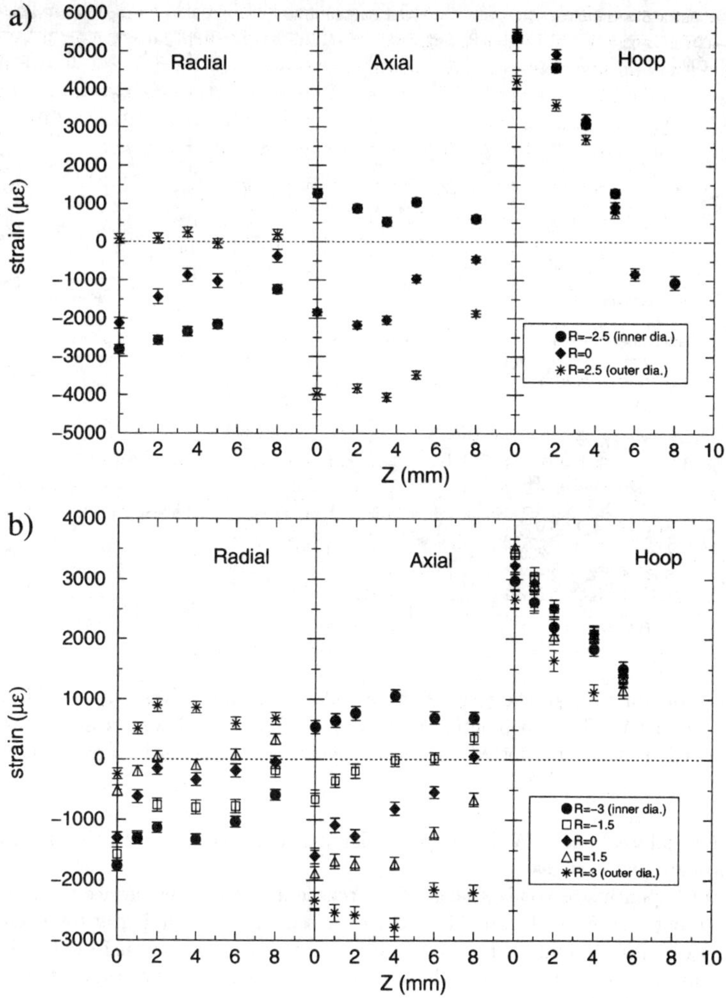

Fig. 3: Residual strain profiles of the tube cross section as a function of axial distance from the joint for a) $Weld_A$ (without PWHT) and b) $Weld_B$ (with PWHT). The distances, R, are from the mid-wall thickness in the radial direction, and Z, are from the weld line in the axial direction.

DISCUSSION

Large tensile stresses were found in all three directions in the region close to the inner

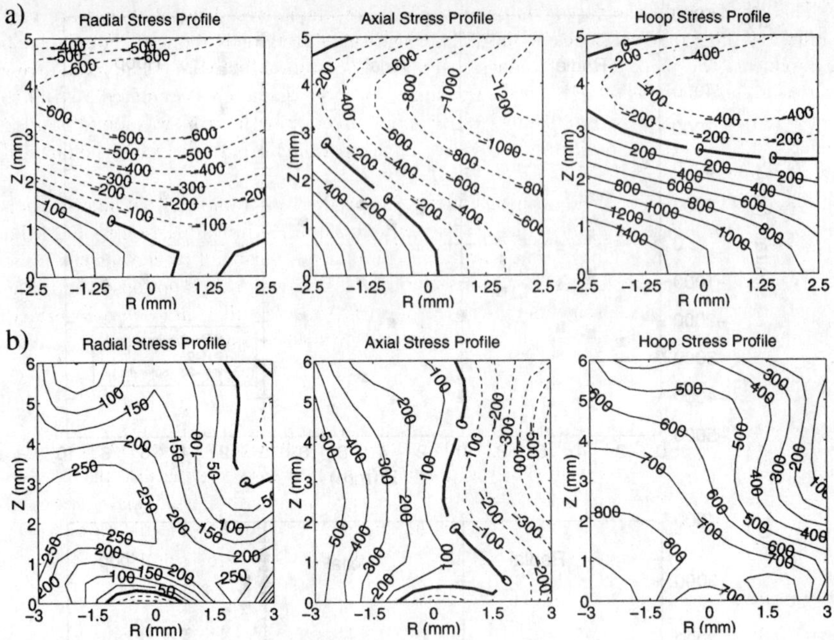

Fig. 4: Contour plots of the residual stress field of a) $Weld_A$ (without PWHT) and b) $Weld_B$ (with PWHT) as a function of R and Z. Tensile and compressive stresses are represented by solid and dotted lines respectively. All stress values are in the units of MPa.

diameter and weld line of $Weld_A$, in particular the hoop component which is approaching the ultimate tensile stress.

Axial components of $Weld_A$ changes from tensile near the inner surface to compressive near the outer surface. This is likely to be caused by the clamping of the ends of the workpieces during welding. The bending forces introduced by clamping would relax once the clamps were removed, however the joint of the two pieces prevents complete relaxation leading to the development of axial residual stresses.

In principle, one would expect stress balance for the axial component across the thickness of the weld at all Z levels. According to the experimental data of $Weld_A$, stress balance is fulfilled within experimental errors for $|Z| < 2$ mm. However, the sum of axial stresses at other Z levels yields a compressive value. This indicates that the stress-free lattice parameter used for $Weld_A$ may be too large for positions further than 2 mm from the weld line. This is not surprising as the stress-free lattice parameter was determined from measurements on the core at locations close to the weld line originally. In order to achieve stress balance, the stress-free lattice parameter would need to be decreased by 0.04% ($\sim$ -450 $\mu\epsilon$) for $|Z| > 2$ mm. The corresponding increase in radial and hoop stresses would be about 400 MPa.

The variations in the three components of the residual stress field of $Weld_B$ are very similar to those of $Weld_A$, except the stress magnitudes are largely reduced. For the hoop component, the peak stress is reduced to 900 MPa, from 1400 MPa. The axial stress varies from 500 to −500 MPa from the inner to outer diameters, compared to 700 to −1200 MPa in $Weld_A$. Stress balance in the axial direction with errors was found at all Z levels, and justifies the use of the stress-free lattice parameter obtained from the far-field measurements.

The radial stresses of $Weld_B$ are within experimental errors from the weld line to 5 mm away from it. The maximum radial stress is about 250 MPa in comparison to 400 MPa in $Weld_A$. It is worth noting that the radial components must fall to zero at the inner and outer surfaces according to boundary conditions. However, this is not observed in the experiment. Since measurements closest to the surfaces were still 1 mm beneath surface, the surface effects probably could not be captured by such measurements.

CONCLUSION

The experimental results show that residual stresses introduced during welding are large. The hoop stresses are very close to the ultimate tensile stress. Tooling also plays a key role in the development of residual stresses as observed from the large axial stresses in the welds. The significant decrease in stress magnitudes validates the application of post weld heat treatment as an appropriate technique for reduction of residual stresses.

ACKNOWLEDGEMENTS

The authors would like to thank Dr. M.R. Daymond and J. Wright (ISIS) for experimental assistance. This experiment is performed under the EPSRC project GR/M68704 and is financially supported by EPSRC and Rolls Royce.

REFERENCES

(1) Priesmeyer HG, Schröder J, 'Residual Stresses - III: science and technology, 1992, edited by Fujiwara H, Abe T and Tanaka K', Elsevier Applied Science (London), 253

(2) Abdel Moniem MEs, Serag SM, Nasses AA, Moustafa AA, Wear, (1980) 227

(3) Private communication (*Rolls Royce plc)*

(4) Young RA, 'The Rietveld method', Oxford University Press (Oxford), 1993

(5) Pang JWL, Baxter GJ, Withers PJW, Rauchs G, Preuss M, 'Effects of tooling on the residual stress distribution in an inertia weld' to be submitted to Mat. Sci. & Eng. A.

SESSION 9C

MEASUREMENT OF THERMAL STRESSES IN A PLASMA SPRAYED NiCoCrAlY COATING DURING THERMAL CYCLING

RO Howells[1], RI Todd[1], J Wigren[2] and P Bengtsson[2]
[1]University of Oxford, Department of Materials,
Parks Road, Oxford, OX1 3PH, UK.
[2]Volvo Aero Corporation, SE-461 81 Trollhättan, Sweden.

ABSTRACT

Residual stresses in NiCoCrAlY bond coatings deposited on Hastelloy X substrates have been measured during the first thermal cycle to 1000°C using Stoney's method, where the stress is deduced from the curvature of the coated substrate. Quenching stresses in the as-sprayed coatings were measured by preferentially dissolving the bond coat and the average value was 94MPa ± 37. Peak tensile stresses of the order of 125MPa were recorded at around 200°C during the heating phase (at 350°C/hr). From 400°C onwards a stress relieving mechanism operated to reduce the stress in the coating until it reached zero at around 600°C. Compressive stresses of ~ –150MPa were present in the coating at the end of the cycle. The thermomechanical properties of the coating and substrate were also measured to provide data for an elastic prediction of the stress and to aid explanation of the stress variations. The stresses in the coating could be explained largely in terms of elastic accommodation of the CTE mismatch with the substrate at temperatures below 400°C during heating and 500°C during cooling. Above these temperatures creep caused relaxation of the coating stress.

INTRODUCTION

Thermal barrier coatings (TBCs) are used to protect components in gas turbine engines from the high temperatures and corrosive nature of their operating environments. This allows higher engine operating temperatures, which aids both efficiency and performance. While current TBC technology has approached maximum development in terms of the temperatures at which they can be used, significant effort is being channelled into understanding how TBC lifetimes may be prolonged. Several workers have pointed to the role of residual stresses as being key to understanding TBC failure. In particular, recent work has indicated that residual stresses and creep in the bond coatings of TBC systems may play an important part in determining TBC lifetimes (1, 2).

Tensile quenching stresses in excess of 100MPa are known to exist in many thermally sprayed coatings after deposition (3,4,5). It has also been shown (6) that positive stress changes in excess of 100MPa can occur during the heating phase of thermal cycles of heat treated NiCoCrAlY bond coatings. It might be expected, therefore, that during the first heating of a coating after deposition, stresses sufficient to cause cracking of the coating might arise, unless other mechanisms operate to reduce the thermal stress (6). The current work addresses this question by measuring the residual stresses in NiCoCrAlY bond coatings during the first few thermal cycles after deposition. The work is part of a broader project to quantify the effects of mechanical properties and microstructure on the residual stress changes during thermal cycling of these coatings. The residual stress measurements were made by curvature measurement, using the Stoney principle (7). The long-term aim is to develop a 'cradle to grave' understanding of the variations of residual stress in thermally sprayed coatings through measurement and modelling. Data for modelling has been acquired from a programme of thermomechanical testing that included 4-point bend tests, tensile tests, and dilatometer measurements.

EXPERIMENTAL METHODS AND MATERIALS

All materials were kindly provided by Volvo Aero Corporation. The bond coat composition was Ni-23Co-16Cr-12.5Al-0.45Y (wt%) and all coatings were air plasma sprayed onto 1.5mm thick grit blasted Hastelloy X substrates (100mm x 20mm). The coating thickness was 150µm. In addition ~1mm thick coatings were deposited onto thicker mild steel substrates which were subsequently dissolved selectively to leave freestanding bond coat material. Bond coats were also preferentially dissolved to leave grit blasted Hastelloy X samples.

The curvature (*k*) was measured by reflecting a laser from the uncoated side of the substrate. The laser was mounted on a travelling stage that allowed accurate measurement of the vertical position (*l*) of the laser. The sample was clamped upright in a furnace with a window. The laser was scanned along the length of the sample and the position of the reflected beam, (*h*), recorded for each laser position on a screen positioned parallel to the sample plane at a distance, (*d*), from the sample. The gradient (*m*) of the straight line plot of *h* vs. *l* was used to deduce the curvature of the sample from the following equation:

$$k = \frac{(m+1)}{2d} \tag{1}$$

Residual stresses were calculated via the Stoney equation from the measured curvatures of the samples:

$$\sigma_c = \frac{E_s t_s^2}{6(1-\nu_s)t_c} k \tag{2}$$

Where σ, E, t, ν denote stress, elastic modulus, thickness and Poisson's ratio, respectively and the subscripts *c* and *s* refer to the coating and the substrate. Grit blasting stresses quoted are based on an assumed thickness of 200µm for the plastically deformed layer (4). Curvature measurements were made on coated substrates and substrates from which the coating had been dissolved. Values for the quenching stress were calculated by comparing the measured surface forces associated with coated samples before and after dissolution of the bond coat. Stress vs. temperature data were calculated by subtracting the surface force vs. temperature data of grit blasted substrates (after dissolution of the coating) from the force vs. temperature data for coated substrates. The stresses were measured during thermal cycling to various temperatures in an Argon atmosphere with a heating rate of 350°C/hr. The cooling rate was nominally 350°C/hr, but was limited by the furnace cooling rate at low temperatures. Curvature measurements were taken at intervals of 50°C. The furnace control thermocouple was placed adjacent to the sample to ensure accurate curvature/temperature data. Control experiments on plain substrates were carried out to ensure that the effects of furnace expansion were negligible.

An alumina assembly was used to carry out 4-point bend tests up to 1000°C. Three LVDT's were used to measure the deflection of the sample in the region of constant bending moment. Bend tests were carried out on freestanding bond coats, coated substrates and uncoated substrates to measure elastic modulus. The elastic modulus of the coatings *in situ* was deduced by comparing the results obtained for coated and uncoated substrates. A nickel based superalloy assembly was used for tensile testing specimens of gauge length 20mm at temperatures up to 1000°C. A crosshead velocity of 0.5mm/min was used. A dilatometer was used to measure the thermal expansion coefficient of freestanding coatings and uncoated substrates during three consecutive thermal cycles to 1000°C with the same heating and cooling rate as for the curvature measurements. X-ray diffraction, optical microscopy and SEM were used to characterise the microstructure. Samples were examined in the following conditions; as-sprayed, thermally cycled and heat treated in air for 1hr at intervals of 100°C at temperatures up to 1000°C.

RESULTS AND DISCUSSION

Characterisation of NiCoCrAlY bond coat microstructure and thermomechanical properties

The as-sprayed microstructure of the coating was typical of thermally sprayed metallic coatings (fig. 1a). It has a lamellar structure built up of splats and contains significant porosity. The splats do not exhibit any resolvable internal microstructural features in the as-sprayed condition but a fine-grained microduplex structure is evident after heat treatment for 1 hour at 1000°C (fig. 1b). X-ray diffraction showed the main phases present to be β, based on BCC Ni (Co, Al) and γ, based on FCC Ni solid solution.

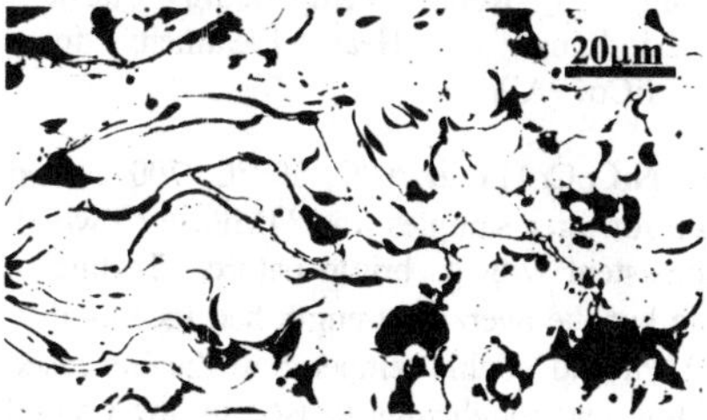

Fig 1a. As-sprayed NiCoCrAlY

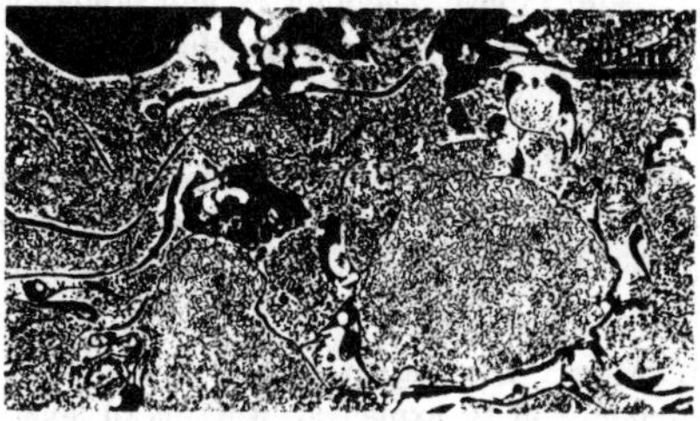

Fig 1b. NiCoCrAlY after 1st thermal cycle

Figure 2 shows how the elastic modulus of the substrate and the coating *in situ* vary with temperature. The substrate stiffness decreased with temperature, as is the case for most metals. The data for the bond coat, however, show that the elastic modulus increased by a factor of two as the temperature was increased to 800°C. Figure 3 shows the room temperature elastic modulus of the coating as a function of prior heat treatment temperature. It is evident that heat treatment at 1000°C also increases the room temperature modulus, by a factor of between four and six. The stiffness increases are presumably a consequence of the microstructural changes that occurred during the first thermal cycle. This could have happened on two levels. First the structure of each splat changed significantly from the metastable rapidly quenched as-sprayed structure to a fine grained microduplex structure. In addition, the splats that make up the coating may have sintered or welded together. The latter contribution is thought to be the stronger, as the modulus increases are too great to be explained by the former.

Figure 4 compares the dilatometer traces of the coating with those of the substrate for three cycles to 1000°C. The average coating CTE is low ($\sim 10 \times 10^{-6}$ °C^{-1}) below 200°C, but increases significantly between 200°C and 500°C so that there is negligible difference between the CTE's of the coating and the substrate. This increase is attributed to changes in the microstructure. From ~500°C, the CTE of the coating is reduced and the strength measurements described below suggest that this is due to sintering/splat welding. The coating exhibits a characteristic discontinuity in expansion behaviour in the 800-1000°C range during the first cycle. Comparison with the x-ray diffraction results showed that this is probably due to attainment of the equilibrium phase structure, and is not evident in the traces obtained for the second and third cycles.

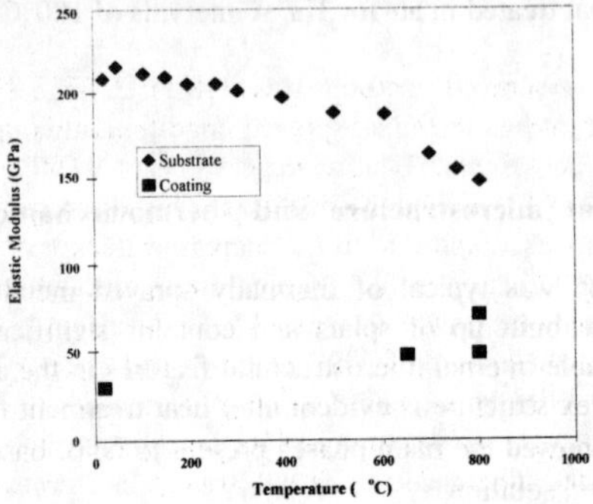

Fig. 2 Elastic Modulus vs. temperature for Hastelloy X substrate and NiCoCrAlY coating

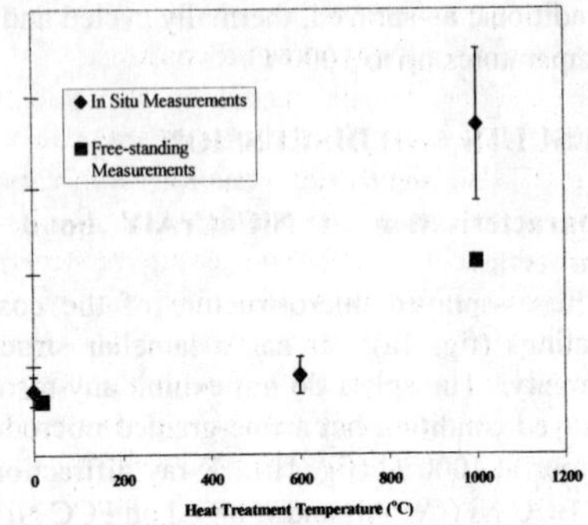

Fig. 3 Room Temperature Elastic Modulus vs. Heat Treatment for NiCoCrAlY

Figure 5 shows tensile test data for freestanding NiCoCrAlY at 20°C, 600°C, 700°C, and 1000°C. At room temperature the average strength for three samples was 84MPa ± 15 which shows the coating to be of variable strength, consistent with its brittle nature. Testing at 200°C showed that the strength remained variable but the average strength had increased to 120MPa ± 28. The strength at 600°C was 120MPa and at this temperature the increased strength can be explained in terms of splat welding and toughening caused by the limited plastic flow observed. The strength was reduced to ~50MPa at 700°C and more extensive plastic deformation was evident. At 1000°C there was extensive plastic yielding and a lower flow stress of ~20MPa. The constant stress maintained in the material after yielding is indicative of creep.

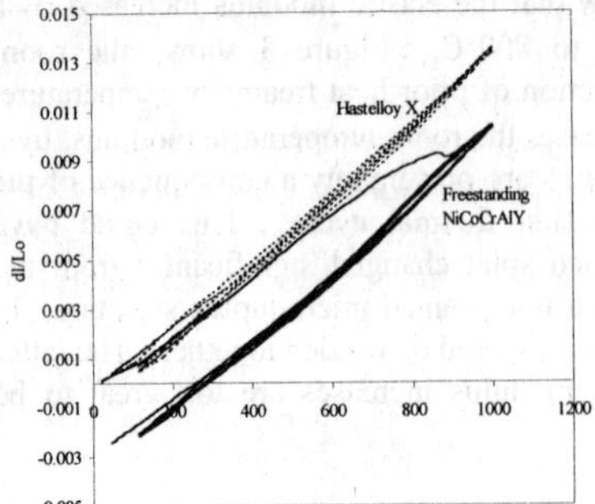

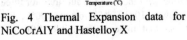

Fig. 4 Thermal Expansion data for NiCoCrAlY and Hastelloy X

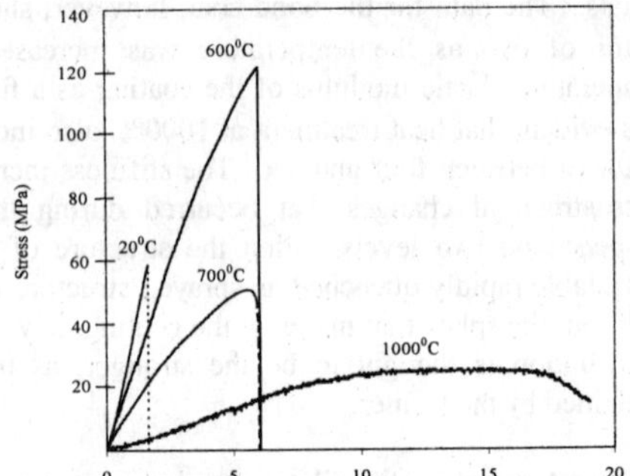

Fig. 5 Tensile Testing Data for NiCoCrAlY at 20°C, 600°C, 700°C and 1000°C

Grit blasting stresses after dissolution of the coating

The average grit blasting stress measured after dissolution of the bond coat was –170MPa ± 42. Figure 6 shows the thermal cycling behaviour of two nominally identical grit blasted substrates after deposition and subsequent dissolution of the bond coat. There is a small amount of stress relaxation during the cycle in both cases. It is also evident that there is a significant sample to sample variation in stress level, which is greater than can be explained by the experimental uncertainty.

Stresses in as-sprayed bond coatings

The average tensile quenching stress in the as-sprayed coatings was 94MPa ± 37. The results show a significant tensile stress in the coatings in the as-sprayed condition, although there is also significant variation from sample to sample. The average value of 94MPa is lower than values reported in other works, (4,5) by around 20-50MPa. This discrepancy arises due to the different measurement methods used and due to the increased thickness of the coatings in this work. The Stoney method measures the average stress through the thickness of the coating, whereas the measurements made in refs. 4 and 5 (using layer removal) were made midway through the thickness of the coating and near the coating/substrate interface, where the stresses could be expected to be more tensile, (4,5). The quenching stresses are produced when the molten bond coat splat hits the substrate and is rapidly cooled but contraction is hindered by its adherence to the substrate. In thermally sprayed coatings the quenching stress is usually significantly lower than the maximum theoretical stress [$\sim E_c\alpha_c (T_{mc} - T_s)$], (3) (where c, s, and m denote coating, substrate and melting respectively and the other symbols have their usual meanings). The theoretical quenching stress is at least 500MPa (dependent on assumptions made about the coating modulus). The most likely reason that the actual stress is lower is that inter-splat sliding, plastic yield or creep occur during deposition.

Stresses during thermal cycling

Figure 7 shows the average bond coat response (3 specimens) during a thermal cycle to 1000°C. The error bar indicates the approximate range of stress in the individual specimens at any position on the curve. As the temperature was increased from room temperature to 200°C the measured stress reached a maximum value of ~125MPa. This was followed by a gradual reduction, until above 600°C the stress in the coating was essentially completely relaxed. The stress remained close to zero between 600°C and 1000°C, both during heating and subsequent cooling. During cooling below 600°C, significant compressive stresses accrued in the coating. At the end of the cycle a compressive residual stress of the order of –150MPa existed in the coating.

Figure 8 shows how the residual stress in the bond coat varied during two thermal cycles to 500°C. Although the initial stress level was significantly higher than in the specimens cycled to 1000°C, the sample displayed the same characteristic tensile stress peak at ~200°C as the samples that were cycled to 1000°C. The stress did not follow a reversible path, indicating that inelastic processes were operating. The second cycle to 500°C was predominantly elastic. Figure 8 also includes the result of a thermal cycle to 300°C. The response of the bond coat to thermal cycling below 300°C is primarily elastic, although a small amount of stress relaxation is observed over the duration of the cycle, which shows that inelastic mechanisms begin to operate from around 300°C.

Comparison of measured and predicted stresses during thermal cycling

Figure 9 compares the elastic prediction of the stress changes during the first thermal cycle with the measured result. The prediction was calculated from the dilatometer results and stiffness measurements, assuming a biaxial stress in the coating. The absolute stress level was predicted by addition of the stress change prediction to the start point of the measured result for the heating phase, and to the end point for the cooling phase. It should be noted that the predicted results are directly dependent on accurate measurement of the CTE mismatch between the coating and the substrate. The dilatometer results presented in figure 4 illustrate the difficulty of obtaining accurate data for the mismatch, as it represents the difference between two similar values.

Up to 200°C the elastic prediction accurately reflects the measured result showing that the elastic accommodation of the CTE mismatch between the coating and substrate is dominant. Between 200°C and 400°C the predicted and measured curves diverge slightly, indicating the onset of inelastic behaviour. Above 400°C, large tensile stresses are predicted, far in excess of the measured results. One possible explanation for this discrepancy concerns the CTE data used in the prediction, which were measured from freestanding material. It is possible that this does not accurately reflect the *in situ* behaviour. The tensile stress applied during thermal cycling could prevent the sintering/shrinkage of the splats that occurs in the freestanding material, so that the *in situ* CTE mismatch above 400°C would be reduced or even reversed, compared to the prediction of the dilatometer measurements. This hypothesis is not the sole reason for the discrepancy, however. The thermal cycling experiment to 500°C shows irreversible deformation of the coating, which cannot be explained in this way. This shows that an inelastic mechanism such as fracture or creep of the coating must operate above 400°C to relax the tensile stress that has accrued.

A detailed consideration of the results shows that fracture is unlikely. The peak stress is similar to the macroscopic strength of the freestanding bond coat at 200°C. Multiple fractures would be necessary to reduce the average stress in the coating, however, and this would all require a stress higher than the tensile strength, in which failure occurs from the single largest flaw in the sample. Furthermore, microscopy showed no evidence of cracking. Finally, experiments not described here did not detect any acoustic emission during thermal cycling. This leaves creep as the most likely stress relaxation mechanism operating during the thermal cycling experiments. Creep at 400°C was not evident in the tensile test results but this may have been because the strain rate was approximately one thousand times higher than the value the coating sees during thermal cycling (due to the limitations of the testing equipment). However, the result at 600°C does indicate that creep is occurring. A low strain rate and small particle size in combination could lead to creep at temperatures as low as 400°C that would relax most of the tensile stress. Above 600°C, creep clearly explains the low stresses measured in the coating given the low strain rate that the coating sees during thermal cycling.

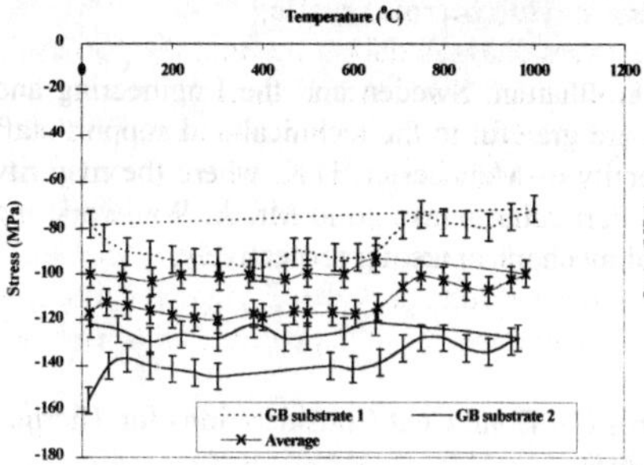

Fig. 6 Thermal Cycling Response of Grit Blasted Substrates

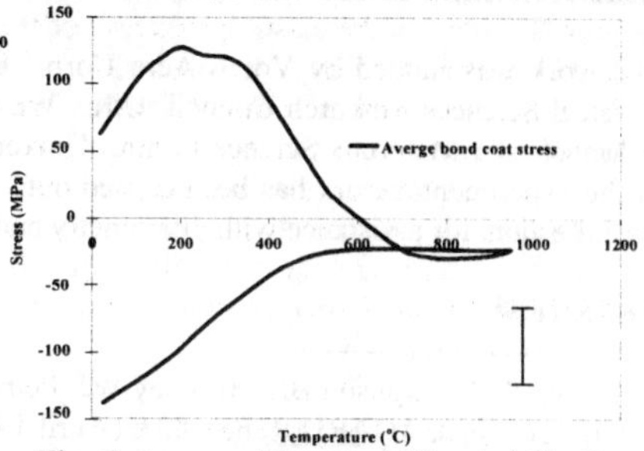

Fig. 7 Average Measured Thermal Cycling Response of NiCoCrAlY Bond Coat

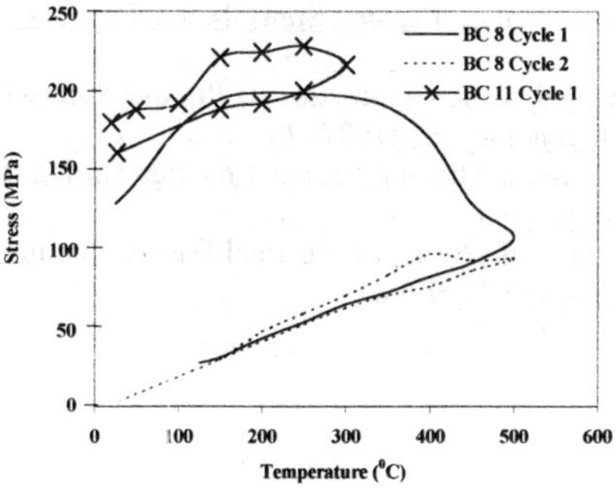

Fig. 8 Thermal Cycling Response of Coating During Cycles to 300°C and 500°C

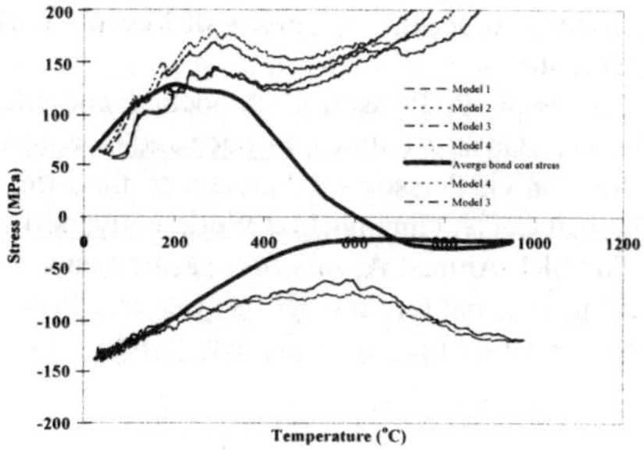

Fig. 9 Measured and Predicted Thermal Cycling Response of Coating

CONCLUSIONS

The curvature measurement technique has been used to determine the residual stress variations in NiCoCrAlY bond coatings during the first thermal cycle to 1000°C after deposition. During heating, the initial tensile stress of 50-100MPa increased to a peak of ~125MPa at 200°C, after which the stress reduced and was almost completely relaxed by 600°C. After cooling, a residual compressive stress of the order of –150MPa was left. Comparison of the measured stress results for the first thermal cycle with an elastic prediction based on thermoelastic property measurements showed that the coating behaved inelastically above 400°C in the heating phase and above 500°C in the cooling phase. Cycling experiments to 300°C and 500°C have confirmed experimentally that the onset of inelastic behaviour occurs at about 300°C. All the inelastic deformation observed was attributed to creep. Characterisation of the coating showed that significant changes in microstructure, CTE, and elastic modulus occur during the first thermal cycle, all of which may affect the residual stress and its relaxation.

ACKNOWLEDGEMENTS

The work was funded by Volvo Aero Corp., Trollhättan, Sweden and the Engineering and Physical Sciences Research Council, U.K. We are grateful to the technical and support staff at Manchester Materials Science Centre, University of Manchester, U.K, where the majority of the experimental work has been carried out. Particular thanks go to Mr. A. Wallwork and Mr I. Easdon, for assistance with dilatometry and mechanical testing respectively.

REFERENCES

1 Freborg AM, Ferguson BL, Brindley WJ, Petrus GJ, Bond Coat Considerations for Thermal Barrier Coatings, AGARD Report 823, (April 1998)
2 Freborg AM, Ferguson BL, Brindley WJ, Petrus GJ, Modelling Oxidation Induced Stresses in Thermal Barrier Coatings, Mat. Sci. and Eng. A245, (1998) 182
3 Clyne TW, Gill SC, Residual Stresses in Thermally Sprayed Coatings and Their Effect on Interfacial Adhesion: A Review of Recent Work, Journal of Thermal Spray Technology 5(4), (1996) 401
4 Bengtsson P, Persson C, Modelled and Measured Residual Stresses in Plasma Sprayed Thermal Barrier Coatings, Surface and Coatings Technology 92, (1997) 78
5 Jonsson G, Persson C, Analysis of the Stress State in Thermal Barrier Coatings During a Thermal Cycle, Unpublished Work, University of Lund
6 Todd RI, Ahmed A, *In situ* Measurements of Residual Stress in a Thermal Barrier Coating During Thermal Cycling, British Ceramic Proceedings 59 (1999) 83
7 Stoney GG, Proc. Royal Society London A82, (1909) 172

EFFECT OF LAST PASS HEAT SINK WELDING AND SERVICE TRANSIENTS ON RESIDUAL STRESSES

E. Keim, E. Weiß, S. Fricke, J. Schmidt
Siemens AG
Erlangen Germany

ABSTRACT

Residual stresses play an important role for crack initiation during operation of pipes in nuclear power plants. Formation, magnitude and distribution of the residual stresses make a significant contribution to the integrity of components, particularly if corrosion mechanisms are of importance. The origin of the residual stresses is at first the heat, which causes the melting pool, in the following the cooling down, which causes local deformations in the welding region.

The aim of this paper is to demonstrate the effect of "Last Pass Heat Sink Welding" (LPHSW) on the residual stresses of an austenitic pipe. During LPHSW (welding of a last pass on the outer surface during simultaneous cooling of the inner surface with water) the high tensile residual stresses in the heat affected zones (HAZ) near the weld are redistributed and result in compression stresses. With the aid of numerical simulations (3D finite element calculations) and experimental methods (ring core, X-Ray) the distributions of the residual stresses in and near the weld can be calculated and measured.

After the welding process the pipes undergo the normal operation of the plants. Because there was no evidence up to now how the residual stresses behave during service transients, a test pipe was welded with LPHSW and loaded by combined thermal/mechanical cycles. The residual stresses were calculated and measured before and after the test. Because of the small diameter of the pipe (100 mm), the residual stress distribution is not constant along the pipe circumference, therefore only 3D finite element calculations will lead to reasonable results. In addition to the calculations the residual stresses have been measured.

It could be shown that the residual stresses will be influenced by the operational load, but the compression stresses in the HAZ still remain; this means the protection against any corrosion attack is maintained.

INTRODUCTION

Intergranular corrosion attack of SS piping in BWR plants is concentrated in an area immediately adjacent to the fusion line of the weld root. A remarkable feature is the synergistic occurrence of such defects in association with contraction folds.

Residual stresses are thought to trigger IGSCC. Many different measurement methods have therefore been used to determine residual stresses both in representative new welds and in weldments (circumferential pipe welds) which are already in service. However, a disadvantage common to all of these measurement methods to a greater or lesser degree, is that they integrate the results over a specific measurement length and therefore yield only an approximation of the actual value measured in the component only a short distance away from the fusion line.

Tolerances, whether dimensional (root dimensions) or those associated with welding parameters, which unavoidably affect the component during fabrication, and tolerances inherent to the measurement technique tend to produce results with wide-ranging tolerance limits. Numerous measurements must be performed to express these limits in a tangible and acceptable form, and this, in turn, demands complex and costly experimental procedures. This latter consideration is an important starting point for applying numerical simulation to obtain quasi-neutral results with defined boundary conditions while also allowing parameters to be varied without the need for expensive experimental work.

EXPERIMENTS

The experimental part of the work consisted mainly of two steps:

- welding of an austenitic pipe by manual arc weld (TIG process) with an additional last pass heat sink weld (LPHSW = welding of a last pass on the outer surface during simultaneous cooling of the inner surface with water) to improve the stresses at the inner surface, Figure 1
- after welding loading of pipe by pressure and temperature cycles, Figure 2.

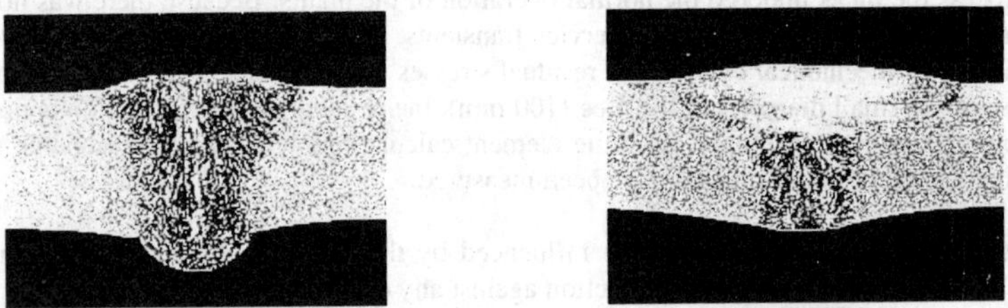

without LPHSW   with LPHSW

Figure 1: Cross section of the manual TIG weld

The according residual stresses were measured after the normal welding, the LPHSW and after operational load.

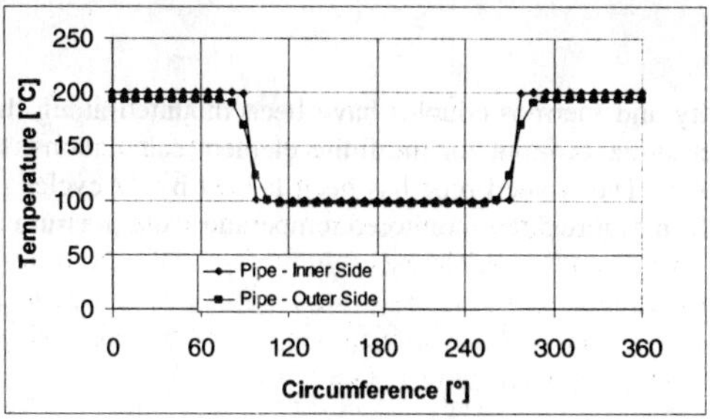

Figure 2:Temperature during cold / warm water injection

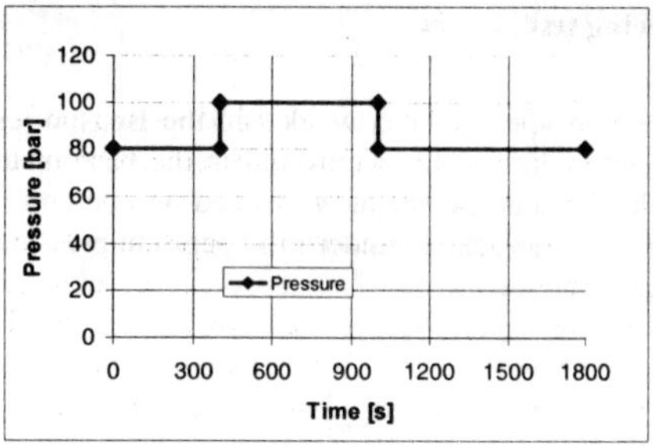

Pressure distribution during ageing cycle

Welding of the pipe

The austenitic pipe with the following geometry

outer diameter: 114.3 mm

wall thickness: 6.3 mm

pipe length 700 mm

has been welded together by two 6 pass weldments in 2G - welding position (horizontal pipe axis), one weld with an additional LPHSW. Passes 1 to 6 are welded in two steps, whereas the LPHSW has been performed in one step. During welding the temperatures were recorded at different positions at the inner and outer surface of the pipe, see Figure 3, for comparison with the numerical data. All other necessary input data for the numerical investigations have also been recorded and fixed in the welding procedures (number and sequence of passes, heat input for each pass, velocity).

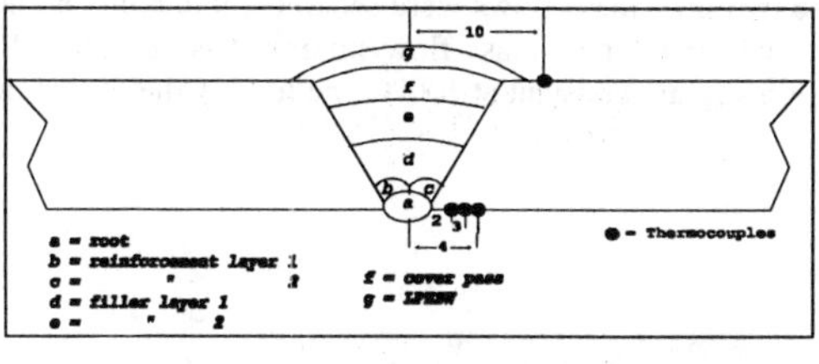

Figure 3: Position of thermo- couples during welding

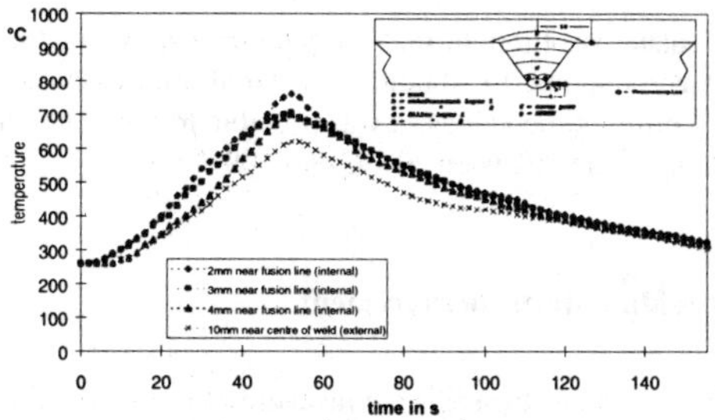

Figure 4: Measured temperatures during welding of the 2nd reinforcement layer

In Figure 4 the results of the temperature measurement with the thermo-couples is shown during welding of the 2nd reinforcement layer as an example.

Ageing test

The test pipe has been welded in the Benson test facility and thermo- couples have been mounted along the circumference of the welds and in the base metal to get an exact input for the finite element calculations. In addition an extensometer was fixed on one end of the pipe. The welded pipe has been loaded by 77 cycles of thermal stratification under full operation pressure cycles. In Figure 5 the monitored temperature and pressure is shown for one cycle.

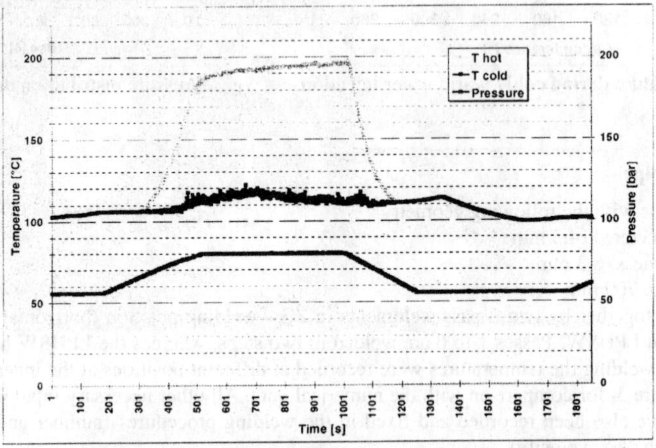

Figure 5: Monitored temperature and pressure during one aging cycle

A plate was brought into the pipe in such a way that the two inlet mass flows were separated into cold and hot water regions, to obtain the desired stratification. A small amount of mass flow mixing was accepted. By controlling the valves, it was possible to hold one inlet temperature constant at 100°C and to vary the other inlet temperature between 200°C and 100°C.

Residual stress measurement

The residual stresses were measured through the thickness by applying the ring-core-method. It is a well known procedure for residual stress measurement and is a purely mechanical technique which always integrates residual stresses over a certain area. In Figure 6 the mock up of the device is shown.

On the inner surface of the pipe in the heat affected zone (HAZ) of the weld a three-directional strain gage rosette is attached to the surface. Then a circular annulus with a diameter of 5 mm is eroded step by step around the rosette. The remaining cylindrical core becomes more and more free from the surrounding stress field. The resulting relaxation strains are measured with the aid of the attached strain gauges. From these data, the residual stresses can be calculated. With increasing depth of the eroded annulus, the reaction of the strain gauge decreases for constant stress in the material. This must be taken under consideration by an experimental declining function.

In the actual case, strain gauge rosettes with an active length of the strain gauges of about 1,6 mm were used. The strain gauge rosettes were attached in the HAZ of the welds in a distance of 1mm from the fusion line (=middle of the active length).

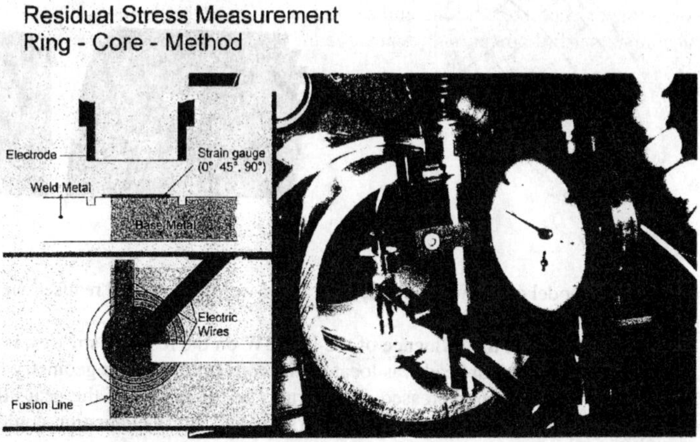

Figure 6: Mock up of residual stress measurement

Using this rosette the maximum penetration depth is 2 mm. After reaching this depth, the remaining cylindrical core is removed completely by electric erosion and a new strain gauge rosette is attached at the ground of the cylindrical bore. Then again a circular annulus is eroded step by step until a penetration depth of 4 mm is reached. At this depth, the remaining cylindrical core is removed again and the whole procedure is repeated. The three measurements (0-2 mm, 2-4 mm and 4-6 mm) are afterwards mathematically connected (by using calibration curves).

NUMERICAL SIMULATION

The aim of the numerical analyses is to assist the welding processes. The process of welding has therefore been simulated under the most realistic conditions possible using the three dimensional finite element method. For appropriate calculation with the FE-code ABAQUS, Hibbitt [1], three dimensional 8 node bricks are used with reduced integration order.

The problem is treated as an uncoupled thermal and mechanical problem, first the temperature field is evaluated and from these results stresses and displacements are calculated. An elastic-plastic mixed hardening material behavior is supposed for austenitic material. All material data are introduced in the model with their temperature dependency.

The model size could best be described by the number of nodes and elements:

Number of nodes:	8370 nodes	full geometry pipe
Number of elements:	6570	

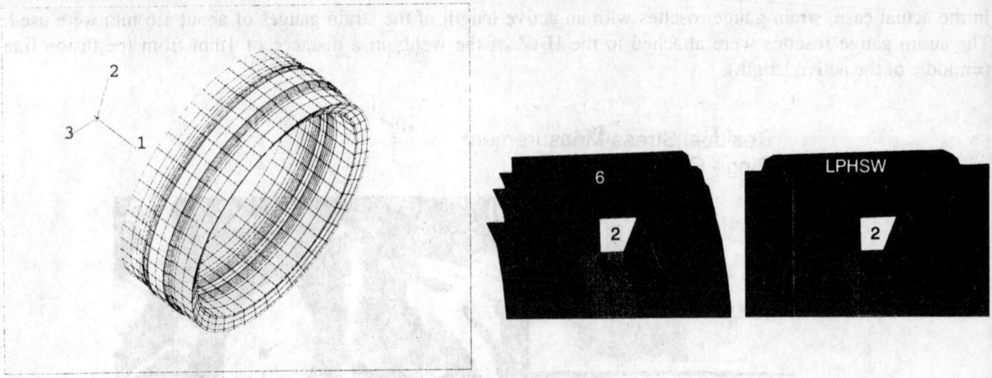

Figure 7: Finite Element model of the welded pipe (extract of weld)   and realised welding sequence

To get valuable information about the influence of the LPHSW on the residual stresses, it was impossible to use a symmetrical model. Each individual bead was located in a conventional weld geometry using realistic welding parameters. The element density was increased considerably in the region of the heat-affected zone (elements width approx. 0.1 to 0.2 mm), so that a realistic temperature and stress evaluation could be performed. Mesh details including the last pass are shown in Figure 7.

The welding process was simulated as a freely moving heat source controlled by corresponding time functions of the elements. Transition from liquid to solid phase was allowed for on the basis of latent heat; parameters for surface radiation and convection were also defined. The preheat and inter pass temperatures specified in the welding plans were observed for each bead. According to available information from numerous numerical parameter calculations, these parameters significantly affects the formation of the 3 D temperature and stress fields and thus, ultimately, post-weld deformation. The LPHSW was performed after the last bead of the joint weld has been welded. During welding of the LPHSW the pipe has been cooled at the inner surface with cold water.

The aging cycles after welding were performed as a restart run of the weld simulation. This means, the residual stress and deformation field after last pass heat sink welding was the basis for this analysis. The aging cycles were again performed as an uncoupled thermal and mechanical problem. After 10 cycles the analysis was interrupted, because no further effect on the stress and strain field could be observed.

RESULTS

The results of the simulation are mainly presented as residual stress fields during the welding process, after welding all passes, after LPHSW and finally after the operation cycles. A comparison is made between numerical and experimental results.

The axial stresses are the most relevant stress components, because possible flaws are supposed to originate in the HAZ of this circumferential weld in circumferential direction. Therefore the Figures are focused on the axial stresses.

The sketch in Figure 8 shows the welding sequence and the according positions with respect to the pipe axis.

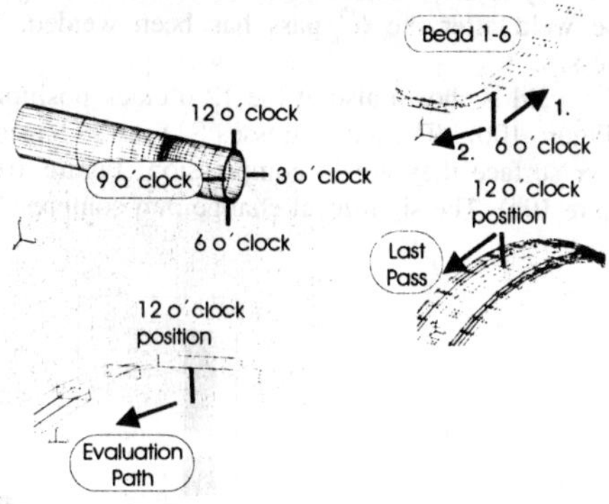

Figure 8: Welding sequence of the single passes

In Figure 9 the axial stresses are shown during the welding process for each welded pass at the inner and outer surface of the pipe (I1 and O1 in the legend means first pass, I6 and O6 means 6th pass) and the LPHSW, which is denoted as IL and OL, depending on which surface is regarded. The stresses are plotted along the axis of the pipe, where the middle of the weld is located at a distance of 500 mm, this means the stresses are given over a distance of 100 mm (50 mm left and right to the weld). The condition is that each single pass is welded and cooled down to interpass or room temperature. The circumferential position is 12 o'clock which is opposite to the starting point of the weld, see Figure 8.

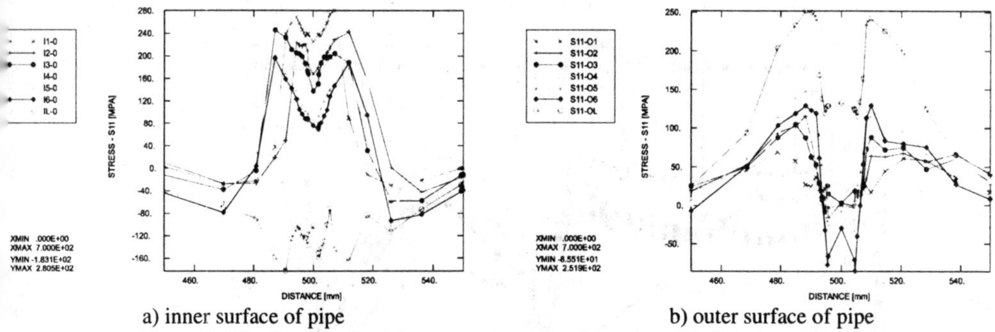

a) inner surface of pipe b) outer surface of pipe

Figure 9: Distribution of axial stresses along the pipe axis at 12 o'clock position

In Figure 9a it can be seen that the axial stresses at the inner surface of the pipe become smaller during the progress of the welding process. The maximum stresses are obtained after welding of the root pass. In the weld middle a local minimum forms and the stresses are highest in the HAZ. The LPHSW is applied to improve the stresses at the inner surface for prevention of the IGSCC attack. It can be clearly seen that this measure yields the desired effect. The tensile stresses after the 6th pass change to compression stresses over the whole weld region and also for all positions along the circumference at the inner surface, which can be seen later. Because the compression axial stresses need to be balanced across thickness, the stress distribution at the outer surface of this thin pipe, Figure 9b, looks contrary to the inner surface. The stresses being set up during welding of each pass show compression over the weld after the 6th pass has been welded. The LPHSW turns back the compression stresses to tensile stresses.

In Figure 10 a cross section of the weld is shown also at the 12 o'clock position of the circumference before (Figure 10a) and after LPHSW (Figure 10b). The axial stresses S11 are in tension over a long distance across wall thickness, only near the outer surface they are in compression (Figure 10a). As mentioned before this situation turns after LPHSW (Figure 10b). The significant change into compression stresses in the HAZ of the ID is obvious.

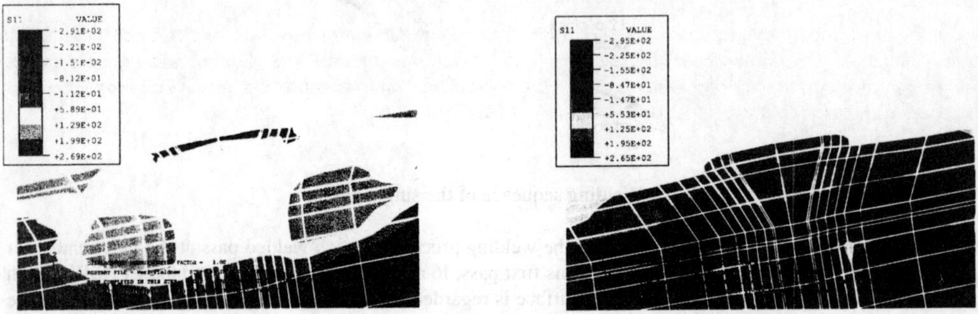

10a) passes 1-6 10b) LPHSW

Figure 10: Distribution of axial stresses through the thickness in the vicinity of the weld at 12 o'clock position after welding

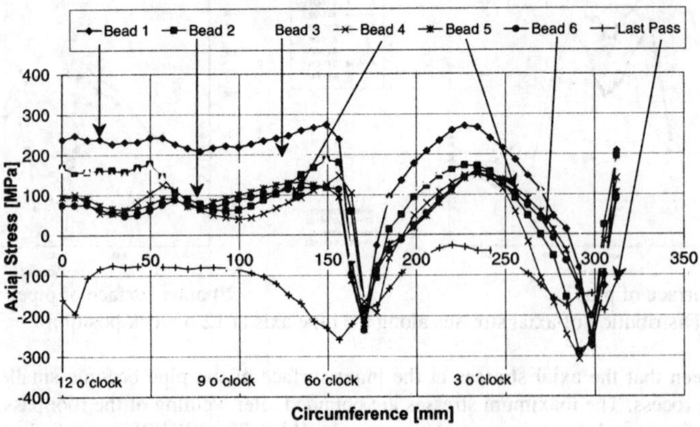

Figure 11: Axial stresses at the inner surface (0.2 mm pos. direction from fusion line) - after cooling down to interpass temperature (1-6 pass) or room temperature (last pass)

From the 3D analysis not only information about the stress distribution in thickness direction is available, but also along the circumference of the pipe. The welding sequence of the single passes is important for the development of the residual stresses. The distribution of the axial stresses along the inner circumference is shown in Figure 11 for the most interesting region, the HAZ, being relevant for an IGSCC attack. As mentioned before, the distribution is quite irregular along the circumference. Because passes 1 to 6 are welded in two steps, a minimum is obtained in 6 o'clock (begin of welding) and 12 o'clock position (stop of first half of welding). After LPHSW all axial stresses at the inner surface are in compression mode not only in the position 0.2 mm from fusion line, but up to an axial distance of 5 mm from weld middle.

One of the most important question is whether this improved compression stresses in the HAZ will alter during normal operation. For this purpose the test pipe was subjected to thermal stratification and pressure cycles measured in plants by monitoring systems and described before. Simultaneously the numerical simulation was also continued, based on the residual stress state after LPHSW.

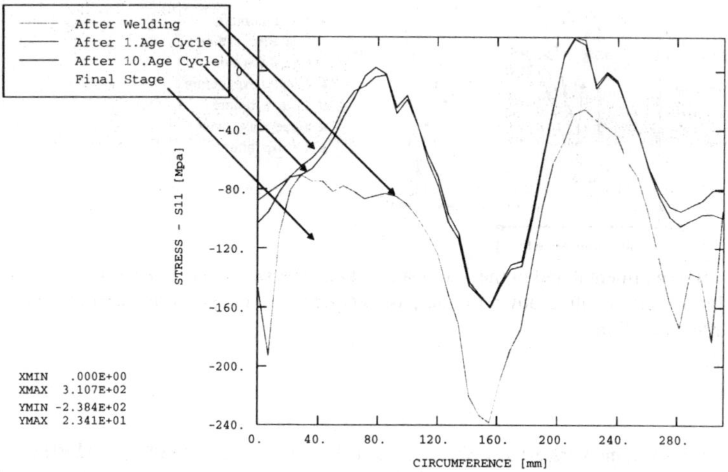

Figure 12: Axial stress (inner surface - 0.2 mm from fusion line) after welding sequence and ageing 1st and 10th cycle

77 pressure and temperature cycles have been conducted in the experiment. In the analysis the effects seemed to vanish after 10 cycles, therefore it has been interrupted after this time. The influence of operation cycles can be seen in Figure 12 where again the results of the calculated axial stresses are given along the inner circumference in the HAZ starting at 12 o'clock position. The condition after welding represents the residual stresses after LPHSW and cooled down to room temperature. Following the pipe has been loaded by internal pressure and operation temperature and afterwards loaded by cycles. It is important to note that during operation cycles (condition 1st and 10th age cycle) the compression residual stresses reduce, but still remain in the compression stage. At the final stage, which means cooled down to room temperature, a certain relaxation took place compared to the stage after welding, but all stresses are still in compression. This means the beneficial effect of LPHSW has not been compensated by loading cycles.

After the experiment has been conducted, the residual stresses have been measured by ring core method. In Figure 13 the numerical and experimental (gained on 4 different welds) results are compared at four different stages (measured at room temperature):

- pass 6 (without LPHSW) before and after operation cycles
- LPHSW before and after operation cycles.

The agreement between measurement and calculation is quite good, but the difficulties are also obvious. Because the stress distribution is not homogeneous around the circumference, it is very important to measure at a location where the stresses are not influenced by start or end point of the welding.

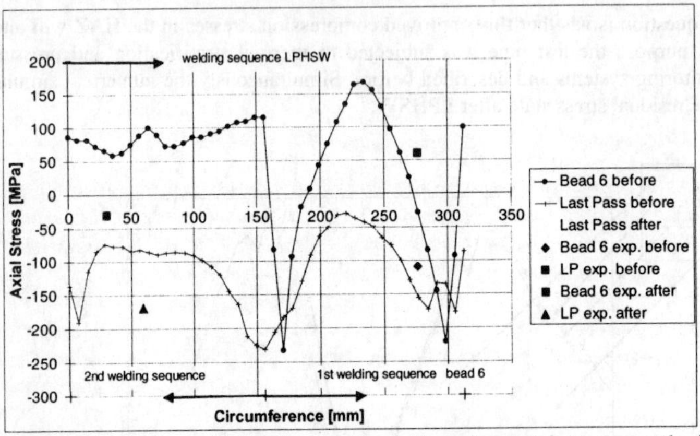

Figure 13: Comparison of experimental and numerical results: Axial stresses at the inner surface (0.2 mm neg. direction from Fusion line) - after cooling down to interpass temperature (1-6 pass) or room temperature (last pass), each before and after operation

SUMMARY

The aim of this paper was to demonstrate the effect of "Last Pass Heat Sink Welding" (LPHSW) on the residual stresses of an austenitic pipe by means of three dimensional finite element calculations and experimental measurements. In addition it should be demonstrated whether the beneficial effect of the LPHSW remains during operation cycles. For this purpose a test pipe has been welded and after welding it has been tested in a special test facility by measured operation temperature and pressure cycles.

It could be shown that

- the residual axial stresses are not homogeneous around the circumference, this means only a 3D simulation is adequate for an according stress simulation
- the LPHSW alters the stresses in the HAZ from tensile to compression
- the residual stresses will be influenced by the operational load, but the compression stresses in the HAZ still remain; this means the protection against any corrosion attack is maintained.
-

REFERENCES

1. HIBBITT, KARLSSON & SORENSEN, Inc.: ABAQUS USERS MANUAL, Version 5.8, 1998

VARIATION OF THE RESIDUAL STRESSES IN BRASS SUBJECTED TO THE AGEING PROCESS

ZL Kowalewski, L Dietrich, G Socha
Institute of Fundamental Technological Research P.A.S., 00-049 Warsaw, ul. Świętokrzyska 21, Poland

ABSTRACT

The paper presents an experimental evaluation of the residual stresses in the brass in the as-received state and after annealing and ageing processes. An analysis was carried out using the concept of yield surface determined in the two-dimensional stress space (σ, τ). It is shown that the brass in the as-received state exhibited an initial anisotropy coming from the manufacturing processes applied to produce rods used subsequently as the blanks for specimens. An annealing process was applied to remove the initial anisotropy. In order to assess an evolution of the residual stresses in the aged brass the subsequent yield surfaces were determined after different time periods measured with respect to the end of annealing process.

INTRODUCTION

Manufacturing processes commonly used to produce semifinished products in form of rods, sheets, tubes, etc. induce residual stresses which may change considerably material strength in particular directions. Such effect may have a strong influence on the lifetime limitations of the responsible elements of many constructions. To avoid these circumstances the annealing processes are used to remove the residual stresses.

By annealing we understand the thermal process commonly used to rebuild the structure of a material to that which would be more homogeneous on the one hand, and to remove the residual stresses coming from manufacturing processes on the other.

The ageing phenomenon is mainly observed during storage of certain materials. Since both these processes may change considerably the mechanical properties of many engineering materials, it is desirable to evaluate a character and type of effects induced, and to assess whether they are beneficial or detrimental from engineering point of view.

EXPERIMENTAL DETAILS

Tests have been carried out with the use of specimens manufactured from brass. Chemical composition of the material is presented in Table I. The MO58 brass is susceptible to hot plastic forming. It may be applied mainly for those elements of constructions where the machining processes require a good cutting ability.

Tubular thin-walled specimens were machined from rods produced with the use of the rolling process. An engineering drawing of the specimen used to investigate brass is presented in Fig.1.

Table I. Chemical composition of the MO58 brass (CuZn40Pb2)

Cu [%]	Zn [%]	Pb [%]
56-60	39-42.5	1.0-3.5

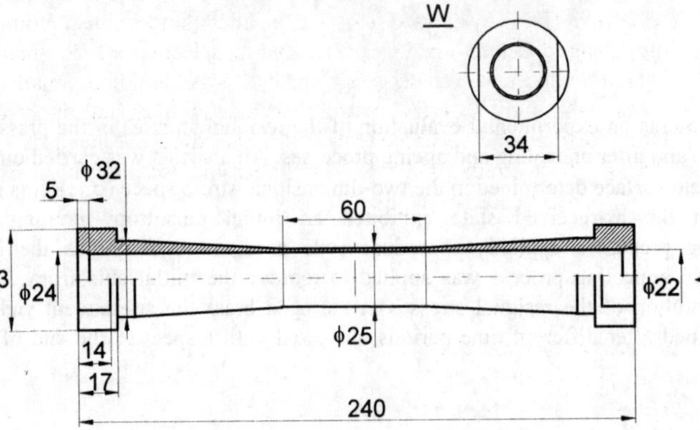

Fig. 1 Geometry of the specimen

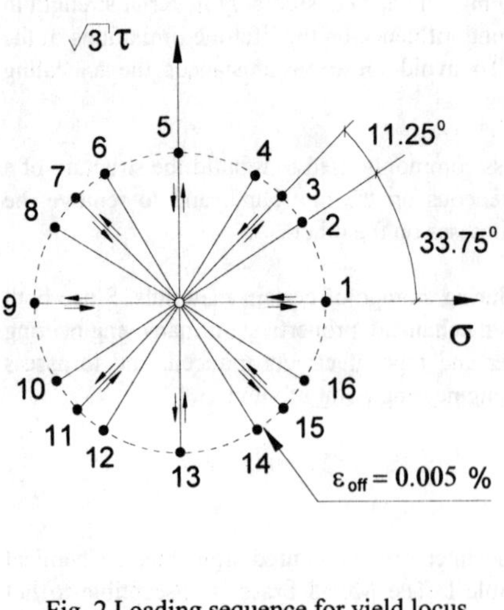

Fig. 2 Loading sequence for yield locus determination

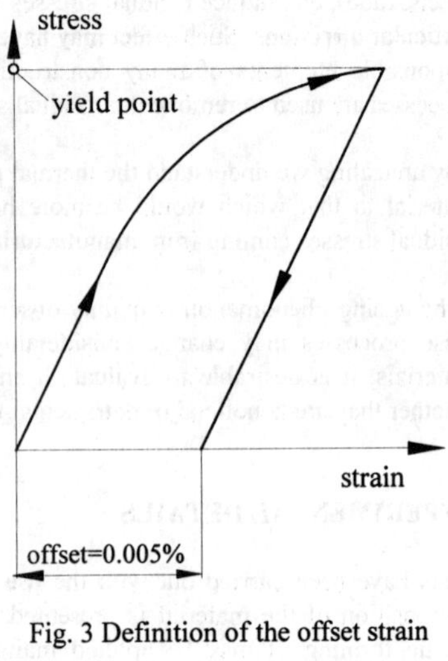

Fig. 3 Definition of the offset strain

The specimens were tested on multiaxial testing machine enabling combined loading in tension - compression - torsion - reverse torsion. The strains were measured with the use of strain gauges bonded to the outer surface of the gauge length of each specimen, Kowalewski & Śliwowski (1). The experimental programme comprised three parts. In the first part an initial yield surface was determined for the material in the as-received state. In the next two parts of the experimental programme the processes of yield locus determination were carried out after annealing of specimens or after different periods measured with respect to the end of annealing. During these periods the mechanical properties of the material were changed due to ageing at the room temperature. The initial yield surface was determined using a number of specimens loaded along different paths in the two-dimensional stress space. The rest of the yield surfaces presented in the paper were determined using a single specimen technique, Kowalewski & Dietrich (2), Kowalewski (3), Fig.2. Such a technique required both a sequential loading along different loading paths, and a selection of as small value of permanent plastic strain induced at each successive path as possible, Fig.3. Small value of the offset strain is necessary to limit an effect of strain accumulation during the probing at the subsequent directions of the yield locus determination procedure, Hecker (4). The loading paths and the plastic offset strain (0.005%) were the same for the entire experimental programme.

RESULTS

Results for the brass in the as-received state

An initial yield surface has been determined in order to check initial mechanical properties of the tested material. The brass in the as-received state exhibited certain form of an anisotropy which can be clearly observed by comparison of the experimental data with the predictions obtained using the isotropic Huber-Mises yield condition. The effect manifests itself by the shift of yield locus in the compression direction, Fig.4.

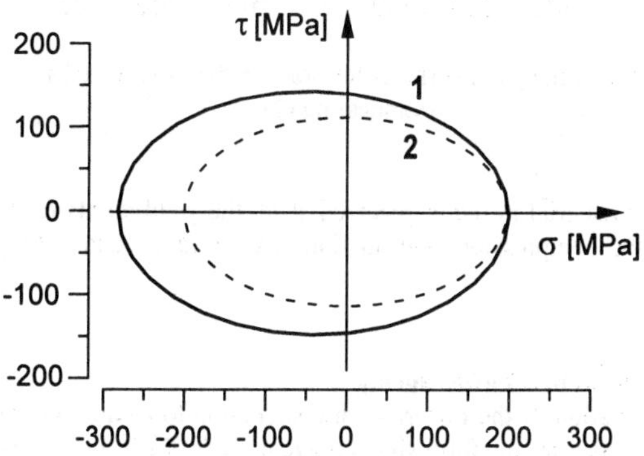

Fig. 4 Comparison of the initial yield locus (1) with the yield locus predicted using the isotropic Huber-Mises yield condition (2)

Results for the annealed material
The main task of the annealing process is to reconstruct the crystallographic structure of the material. The problem, which arises in such a case, deals with the assessment of an anisotropy induced during manufacturing processes and a choice of the appropriate annealing temperature.

The tests were carried out at one annealing temperature equal to 923K to be contained in the range of temperature where the recrystallization process takes place. The duration of the annealing was equal to two hours, and then the specimens were cooled down to the room temperature together with the furnace. The subsequent yield surface has been determined directly after the thermal treatment of the material. This surface is presented in Fig. 5 where it is compared with the yield locus of the brass in the as-received state. The material after annealing gained the isotropic properties reflected by almost perfect coincidence of the experimental yield surface with that predicted using the isotropic Huber-Mises yield condition, and moreover, the residual stresses induced in brass due to manufacturing processes were completely removed, Fig.5. So, the origin of the yield locus for the annealed brass is located exactly in the origin of the co-ordinate system.

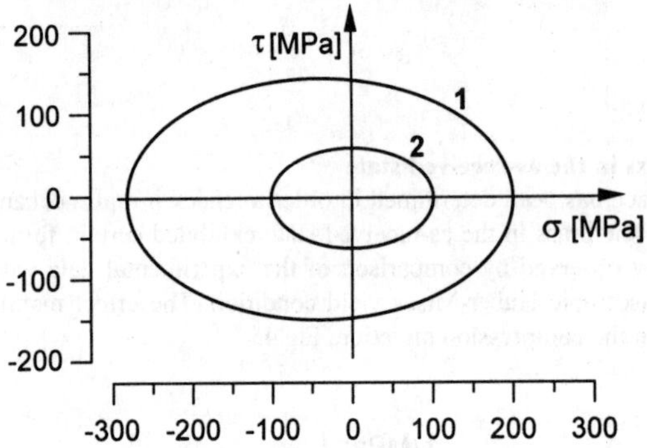

Fig. 5 Comparison of the yield surfaces for brass in the as-received state (1) and after annealing (2)

In comparison to the material in the as-received state, the yield points for the annealed brass tested under tension, compression and torsion decreased around 49%, 68% and 59%, respectively.

Results for the annealed brass after ageing
In order to assess variation of the material parameters due to ageing the yield surfaces were determined for the brass after the following storage periods: 22.0, 143.5, 166.5, 286.5, 335.0, 337.0, and 550.5 hours. Time of these periods was counted from the moment when the yield locus determination procedure was completed for the directly annealed brass. In all diagrams of Fig.6 the yield surfaces for aged brass are presented. As it is clearly shown in Fig.6, the subsequent yield surfaces increase their sizes, and moreover, a significant shift of the yield

surfaces origins can be observed in comparison to the yield locus for the directly annealed brass.

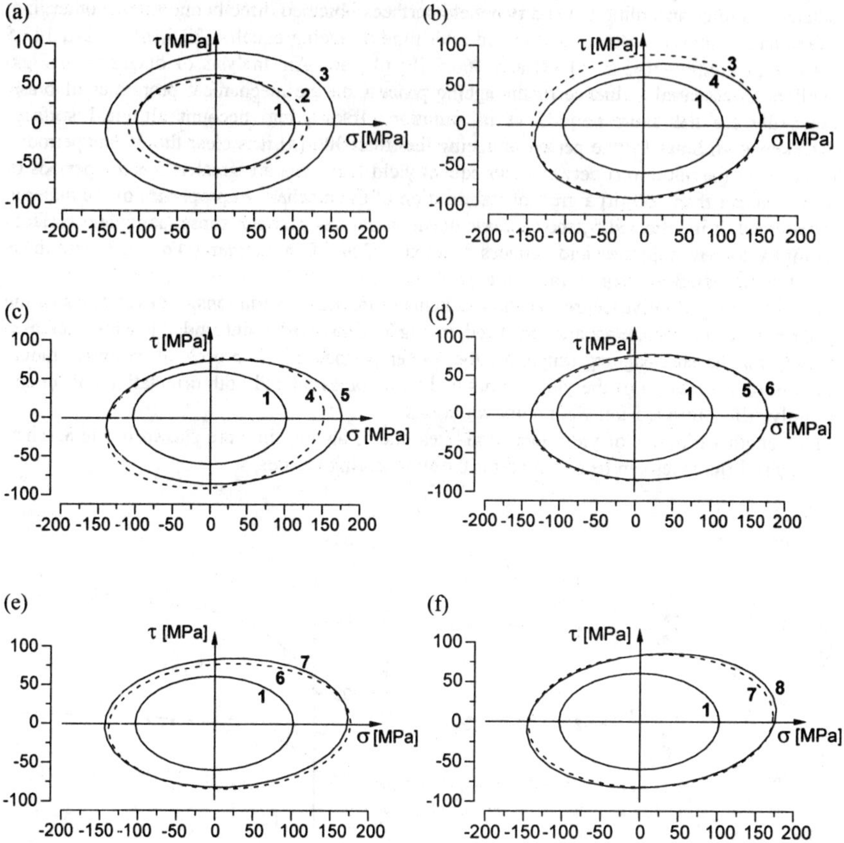

Fig. 6 Evolution of the yield surface for the annealed brass due to the ageing process (1 - yield surface determined directly after annealing; 2, 3, 4, 5, 6, 7, 8 - yield surfaces for the brass after period of ageing equal to 22.0, 143.5, 166.5, 286.5, 335.0, 337.0 and 550.5 hours, respectively)

The ageing effect can be already observed for the brass after the period of time equal to 22.0 hours. It is shown in Fig.6a, where the yield locus of the annealed material (1) is compared with the yield locus determined after ageing for 22.0 hours (2). The effect increases with the increase of a duration of the ageing process, and it is expressed by the significant increase of the yield locus sizes. In order to identify an evolution of the yield locus of the annealed brass due to the ageing process the yield locus after the period of ageing equal to 143.5 [h] is also presented in Fig.6a. Entire evolution of the mechanical properties of brass is summarised in diagrams (a), (b), (c), (d), (e), (f) of Fig.6. Each diagram contains the yield locus determined directly after annealing (denoted as 1) which is compared with the yield loci of the brass subjected to the process of ageing. Each diagram shows three surfaces: the yield locus determined after annealing (1) and two yield surfaces obtained directly one after another, i. e. in Fig.6a are shown surfaces determined after time of ageing equal to 22.0 [h] (2) and 143.5 [h] (3), in Fig.6b - 143.5 [h] (3) and 166.5 [h] (4), etc. An analysis of diagrams in Fig.6 exhibits an essential influence of the ageing process on the mechanical properties of brass, especially for the short periods of its duration. Taking into account all yield surfaces determined on brass for the period of ageing less than 300 [h] it is clear that if this period is longer then the variations between subsequent yield loci sizes are greater. For the periods of ageing longer than 300 [h] a gradual stabilisation of the mechanical properties of the material is observed. It is reflected by the decrease of the variations between subsequent yield surfaces (compare for example the yield surfaces denoted as 7 and 8 in diagram (f) of Fig.6 with those denoted as 2 and 3 in diagram (a) of Fig.6).

To obtain a qualitative degree of the mechanical properties variations the evolutions of the yield points due to ageing are presented in Fig.7. The yield point under tension increases rapidly for the short ageing times, for the longer periods of the process it exhibits gradual stabilisation. Changes of the yield points under compression and both orientations of torsion slightly differ from tension yield point variations.

The length variations of yield loci semi-axes due to ageing time are shown in Fig.8. Their strongest differences can be observed for the short ageing periods.

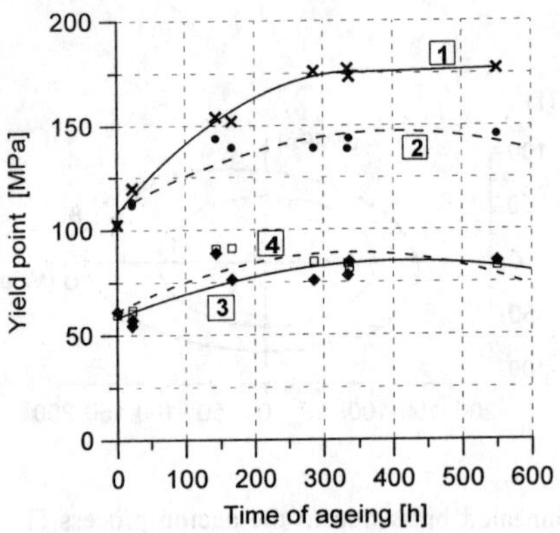

Fig. 7 Variations of yield points under tension (1), compression (2), torsion (3), and reverse torsion (4) versus time of ageing

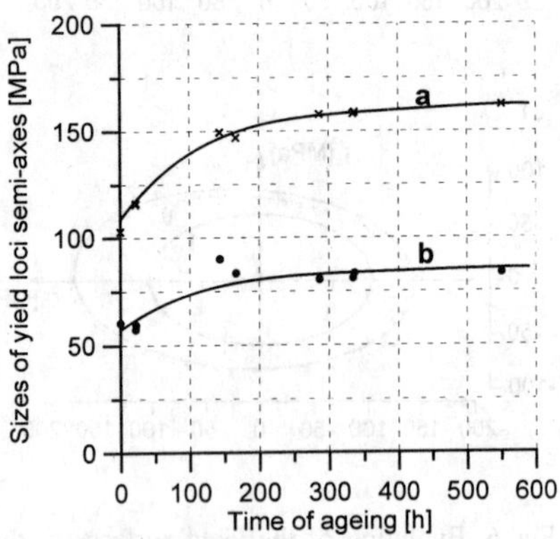

Fig. 8 Variations of yield surface semi-axes due to ageing (a - major semi-axis, b - minor semi-axis)

The character of the yield points variations for different loading paths tells us that the yield locus origin changes its initial position due to the increase of the ageing period. Graphical presentation of the origin co-ordinates variations is shown in Fig.9. The locations of experimental points prove that a shift of the yield locus along the vertical direction (torsion-reverse torsion) is practically independent on the time of ageing. A different character exhibits movement along the tension-compression direction. In this case a shift of the yield surface depends on the ageing time. As it is shown in Fig.9, the yield surface of the annealed brass gradually drifts in the direction of tension stress with the increase of ageing time. For longer ageing periods the rate of this increase decreases, and as a consequence, the shift tends to the certain asymptotic value.

For the directly annealed material a little rotation of yield locus can be observed after ageing. However, it is difficult to reflect a clear variation character of this parameter with respect to the time of ageing, Fig.10.

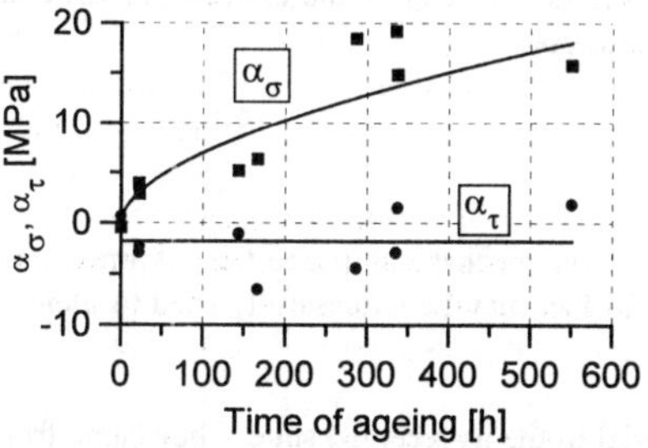

Fig. 9 Evolution of the yield surface centre due to ageing (α_σ - shift in the tension-compression direction, α_τ - shift in the torsion-reverse torsion direction)

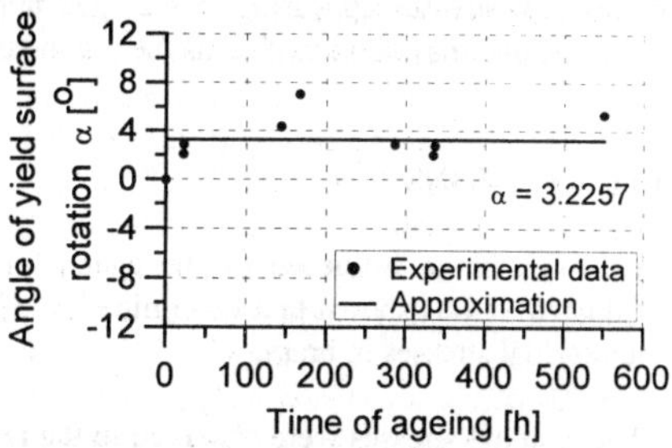

Fig. 10 Rotation of yield surface due to ageing

An important effect can be observed by comparison of the initial yield locus for the brass in the as-received state with the yield loci determined directly after annealing and after ageing for 550.5 [h], Fig.11. Namely, the shift of the yield surface for the as-received material which vanished after annealing appeared again after ageing, and it has an opposite sense as that for the as-received brass observed.

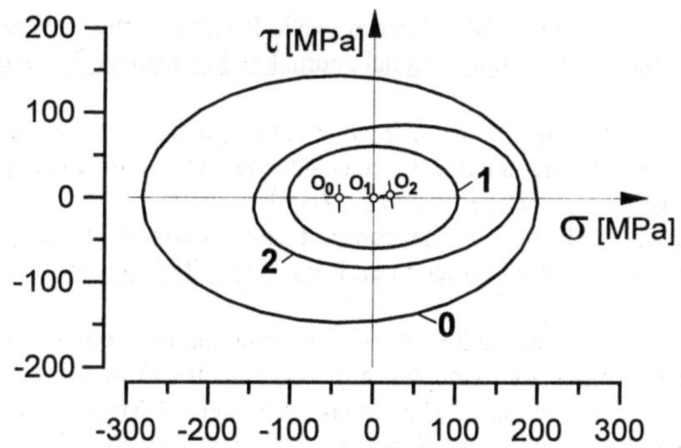

Fig. 11 Comparison of the yield locus of brass in the as-received state (0) with the yield locus after annealing (1) and ageing process carried out for the period of 550.5 hours (2), (O_0, O_1, O_2 denote origins of the respective yield surfaces)

The co-ordinates of the yield locus origin are usually identified as the residual stresses. In the case of the as-received material they came from the manufacturing processes applied to produce rods used subsequently as the blanks for specimens. These stresses were removed from the brass using the annealing process. They appeared again in this material during the ageing process, however, in this case the reason of their creation was different than that for the as-received material suggested. The appearance of the residual stresses in the material after ageing may suggest that the type of annealing process applied did not rebuild sufficiently the material structure or that the grain growth process was partially developed and hence the structure of the brass was not homogeneous. It seems to be reasonable to conclude that a type of residual stresses appearing in the aged brass differs than that in the as-received material observed and may be identified as the second order stresses.

CONCLUSIONS

In this paper an influence of the ageing process on mechanical properties of brass was evaluated. It was shown that determination of yield loci may be successfully used to identify the residual stresses in brass.

The residual stresses were observed in the material in the as-received state. They came from manufacturing processes used to produce rods from which the specimens were machined.

The residual stresses removed from brass using the annealing process arose again in this material due to the ageing phenomenon which took place during the long-term storage at room temperature.

Acknowledgement
The authors gratefully acknowledge the support of the Polish State Committee for Scientific Research under grant 7T07 048 14.

References

1. Kowalewski ZL, Śliwowski M, Effect of cyclic loading on the yield surface evolution of 18G2A low-alloy steel, International Journal of Mechanical Sciences (1997), 39, 1, 51-68
2. Dietrich L, Kowalewski ZL, Experimental investigation of an anisotropy in copper subjected to predeformation due to constant and monotonic loadings, International Journal of Plasticity (1997), 13, No. 1/2, 87-109
3. Kowalewski ZL, Influence of the constant and monotonic loading on subsequent biaxial behaviour of 15HM boiler steel, Engineering Transactions (1996), 44, 2, 181-206
4. Hecker SS, Experimental studies of yield phenomena in biaxially loaded metals, in: Constitutive Equations in Viscoplasticity: Computational and Engineering Aspects, The Winter Annual Meeting of The American Society of Mechanical Engineers, New York City, NY, Ed. Stricklin and Saczalski, ASME, AMD, 20, 1-33, 1976

ELASTIC CONSTANTS OF SILICON NITRIDE FOR STRESS MEASUREMENTS BY DIFFRACTION METHODS

Keisuke TANAKA*, Kenji SUZUKI**, Yoshihisa SAKAIDA***
and Hirohisa KIMACHI*

*Department of Mechanical Engineering, Nagoya University, Nagoya 464-8603, Japan,
** Faculty of Education and Human Science, Niigata University, Niigata 950-2181, Japan
***Japan Fine Ceramic Center, Nagoya 456-8587, Japan

ABSTRACT

The X-ray elastic constants of two kinds of β silicon nitride, gas-pressure sintered (EC141) and pressureless sintered (SN1), were experimentally determined for ten different reflections by using Kα radiation of Cu, Co, Fe, Cr and V. The 323 diffraction by Cu-Kα_1 radiation, 251 and 232 diffractions by Fe-Kα radiation,and 411 diffraction by V-Kα radiation are recommended for the stress measurement with the $\sin^2\psi$ method. The X-ray compliances, $(1+\nu'_X)/E'_X$ and ν'_X/E'_X (E'_X= Young's modulus, ν'_X= Poisson's ratio), change as a second power function of $\cos^2\phi$ (ϕ = angle between the diffraction plane normal and the c-axis of hexagonal crystal) for both kinds of silicon nitride. On the basis of Kröner's model combined with the self-consistent analysis of the X-ray elastic constants of multi-phase materials, the elastic constants of single crystal of silicon nitride were determined by the simplex method.

1 INTRODUCTION

The X-ray and neutron diffraction methods are very powerful non-destructive techniques to measure the residual stress in crystalline materials. In both methods, the stress is determined from the measured lattice strains. Since the lattice strain is different from the strain measured by mechanical methods, the elastic constants for diffraction stress measurements are different from the mechanical values. They are called the diffraction elastic constants or the X-ray elastic constants, and are dependent on diffraction planes. The diffraction elastic constants for single-phase polycrystals can be derived from the single crystal elastic constants by using Kröner models (1). For multi-phase materials, the self-consistent model can be used to obtain the diffraction elastic constants (2). For silicon nitride, Hay et al. (3) recently reported the elastic constants of silicon nitride whiskers measured by the nanoindentation method under some assumptions of the characteristics of elastic constants of hexagonal crystals. In the present paper, the X-ray elastic constants were measured for ten different reflections, and used to determine the elastic constants of single crystals of silicon nitride.

2 DIFFRACTION ELASTIC CONSTANTS

2.1 Micromechanics for diffraction elastic constants of single-phase polycrystals

The diffraction elastic constants of single-phase polycrystals can be calculated from the elastic constants of single crystals. Among several models, Kröner's model (1) gives the best prediction of the experimental results. According to Kröner's model of hexagonal polycrystals with random orientation, the diffraction Young's modulus and Poisson's ratio, E_X and ν_X, are related to the mechanical Young's modulus and Poisson's ratio, E and ν, as follows (4, 5):

$$\frac{1+\nu_X}{E_X}=\frac{1+\nu}{E}+\frac{2t_{11}-t_{12}-t_{13}}{2}-\frac{5t_{11}-t_{12}-4t_{13}-t_{31}+t_{33}-3t_{44}}{2}w^2 + \frac{3(t_{11}-t_{13}-t_{31}+t_{33}-t_{44})}{2}w^4 \quad (1)$$

$$-\frac{\nu_X}{E_X}=-\frac{\nu}{E}+\frac{t_{12}+t_{13}}{2}+\frac{t_{11}-t_{12}-2t_{13}+t_{31}+t_{33}-t_{44}}{2}w^2 - \frac{t_{11}-t_{31}-t_{13}+t_{33}-t_{44}}{2}w^4 \tag{2}$$

where t_{ij} is the tensor corresponding to the constraint by neighboring grains and $w=\cos\phi$ (ϕ is the angle between the normal of the diffraction plane (*hkl*) and the *c*-axis). The mechanical elastic constants of polycrystals are also calculated from the single crystal elastic compliances by using the equation derived on the basis of Kröner's model by Kneer (6).

2.2 Micromechanics for diffraction elastic constants of multi-phase polycrystals

For the case of multi-phase materials, the mean stress of the diffracting phase is not equal to the macrostress. Secondary phases of sintered ceramics, such as glassy phase and pores, may influence the diffraction elastic constants. The diffraction elastic constants of multi-phase materials correlate the lattice strain of the diffracting phase to the macrostress. Among several models of elastic deformation of multi-phase materials, the self consistent model was found to give the best estimation of the diffraction elastic constants of sintered alumina (2). According to the self-consistent model, the diffraction values of Young's modulus and Poisson's ratio of multi-phase materials, E'_X and ν'_X, are related to those of single-phase polycrystals as

$$\frac{1+\nu'_X}{E'_X}=\frac{1+\nu_X}{E_X}B' \tag{3}$$

$$-\frac{\nu'_X}{E'_X}=\frac{1+\nu_X}{E_X}\frac{A'-B'}{3}-\frac{\nu_X}{E_X}A' \tag{4}$$

where

$$A'=\frac{3(1-\nu')E_0}{(1+\nu')E_0+2(1-2\nu_0)E'} \tag{5}$$

$$B'=\frac{15(1-\nu'^2)E_0}{2(4-5\nu')(1+\nu')E_0+(7-5\nu')(1+\nu_0)E'} \tag{6}$$

and E' and ν' are the mechanical Young's modulus and Poisson's ratio of multi-phase materials, and E_0 and ν_0 are those of the diffracting phase.

2.3 Experimental determination of diffraction elastic constants

In the experiment by the X-ray method, the diffraction elastic constants are determined from the changes of the slope and the intercept of the linear regression lines in the $2\theta_\psi$-$\sin^2\psi$ diagram taken under the different values of the uniaxial applied stress σ_A as follows (2):

$$\frac{1+\nu'_X}{E'_X}=-\frac{\cot\theta_0}{2}\frac{\partial}{\partial\sigma_A}\left(\frac{\partial 2\theta_\psi}{\partial\sin^2\psi}\right) \tag{7}$$

$$-\frac{\nu'_X}{E'_X}=-\frac{\cot\theta_0}{2}\frac{\partial(2\theta_{\psi=0})}{\partial\sigma_A} \tag{8}$$

where $2\theta_0$ is the diffraction angle of the stress-free materials.

For stress measurement by the $\sin^2\psi$ method, the slope of the $2\theta_\psi$-$\sin^2\psi$ diagram is multiplied by the stress constant, K, defined by

$$K=-\cot\theta_0\frac{E'_X}{2(1+\nu'_X)}\frac{\pi}{180} \tag{9}$$

Therefore, the value of $E'_X/(1+\nu'_X)$ is particularly significant for X-ray stress measurement.

3 EXPERIMENTAL PROCEDURE

The experimental materials are two kinds of silicon nitride: gas-pressure sintered (EC141) and pressureless sintered (SN1) silicon nitride (7). The mechanical Young's modulus and Poisson's ratio were 320GPa and 0.270 for EC141, and 294GPa and 0.281 for SN1. The specimen was 10 mm in width, 4 mm in thickness and 55 mm in length. The specimen surface for X-ray measurement was finished by lapping.

The diffraction elastic constants were experimentally determined by the $\sin^2\psi$ method for ten different lattice reflections by $K\alpha_1$ radiations of Cu, Co, Fe, Cr, and V characteristic X-rays. The conditions of X-ray measurement are summarized in Table 1. The X-ray equipment had a parallel beam optics and the iso-inclination mechanism (ω-diffractometer). The value of the $\sin^2\psi$ was changed from 0 to 0.6 with an interval of 0.1 to obtain the $2\theta_\psi$-$\sin^2\psi$ diagram. The diffraction angle was determined as the center of the half breadth at the 2/5 to 4/5 height of the peak position depending on the diffraction plane as shown in Table 1.

A four-point bending stress was applied to the specimen. The tension side of the bent specimen was irradiated by X-rays and the applied strain was monitored by a strain gage glued on the specimen surface. The $2\theta_\psi$-$\sin^2\psi$ diagram was obtained at five strains : 0, 400×10^{-6}, 800×10^{-6}, 1200×10^{-6}, 1600×10^{-6}. The applied stress was calculated by multiplying the strain by the mechanical Young's modulus.

4 EXPERIMENTAL RESULTS

The measured relations between $2\theta_\psi$ and $\sin^2\psi$ were all linear and did not show any systematic non-linearity. The slope and the intercept of the regression line in $2\theta_\psi$-$\sin^2\psi$ diagram changed linearly with the applied stress. The diffraction elastic constants determined by using Eqs. (7) and (8) are summarized in Table 2 for EC141 and Table 3 for SN1, where the confidence limit of 68.3% is also indicated in the table. For the stress measurement with high accuracy, the 323 diffraction by Cu-$K\alpha_1$ radiation, 251 and 232 diffractions by Fe-$K\alpha$ radiation, and 411 diffraction by V-$K\alpha$ radiation were recommended, because the confidence limit is narrow and the stress constant is small.

According to Kröner's model, the X-ray compliances, $(1+\nu'_X)/E'_X$ and ν'_X/E'_X (E'_X=Young's

Table 1. Measurement conditions.

Characteristic X-ray	Diffraction	Diffraction angle $2\theta_0$ (deg)	Scanning range (deg)	$\sin^2\psi$ (0.1 step)	Breadth method	w^2 ($\cos^2\phi$)
Cu-$K\alpha_1$	323	141.260	138~145	0~0.6	4/5	0.708
Co-$K\alpha_1$	203	148.091	145~152	0~0.6	4/5	0.920
Fe-$K\alpha$	251	155.332	152~158	0~0.6	2/5	0.116
	610	149.299	146~152	0~0.6	2/5	0
	142	142.553	139~145	0~0.6	1/2	0.494
	232	135.059	130.5~137.5	0~0.6	1/2	0.519
Cr-$K\alpha$	212	131.649	129~134	0~0.6	1/2	0.745
	330	129.479	127~131	0~0.6	1/2	0
	411	125.668	123~128	0~0.6	1/2	0.196
V-$K\alpha$	411	152.682	149~155	0~0.6	1/2	0.196

Table 2. X-ray elastic constants and stress constant for EC141.

Characteristic X-ray	Diffraction	X-ray compliances $(1+\nu'_X)/E'_X$ (10^{-3}/GPa)	ν'_X/E'_X (10^{-4}/GPa)	X-ray elastic constants $E'_X/(1+\nu'_X)$ (GPa)	E'_X (GPa)	ν'_X	Stress constant K (MPa/deg)
Mechanical	―	3.97	8.44	252	320	0.270	
Cu-Kα_1	323	3.78±0.09	8.39±0.49	264	339	0.285	-811
Co-Kα_1	203	3.69±0.15	7.87±0.32	271	344	0.271	-675
Fe-Kα	251	3.82±0.20	8.14±0.74	262	332	0.271	-499
	610	3.63±0.11	8.29±0.71	275	356	0.296	-659
	142	4.16±0.09	9.20±0.28	240	308	0.284	-711
	232	3.89±0.11	8.63±0.28	257	330	0.285	-927
Cr-Kα	212	3.77±0.37	9.64±1.54	265	357	0.344	-1040
	330	3.55±0.29	9.07±1.58	282	378	0.343	-1159
	411	3.34±0.19	9.45±0.79	300	418	0.395	-1342
V-Kα	411	3.59±0.22	7.74±1.53	279	355	0.274	-591

Table 3. X-ray elastic constants and stress constant for SN1.

Characteristic X-ray	Diffraction	X-ray compliances $(1+\nu'_X)/E'_X$ (10^{-3}/GPa)	ν'_X/E'_X (10^{-4}/GPa)	X-ray elastic constants $E'_X/(1+\nu'_X)$ (GPa)	E'_X (GPa)	ν'_X	Stress constant K (MPa/deg)
Mechanical	―	4.36	9.56	230	294	0.281	
Cu-Kα_1	323	4.29±0.15	9.68±0.63	233	301	0.292	-719
Co-Kα_1	203	3.73±0.32	8.18±0.76	268	343	0.281	-677
Fe-Kα	251	4.10±0.06	9.65±0.13	244	319	0.308	-470
	610	3.93±0.82	9.29±0.28	254	333	0.309	-612
	142	4.21±0.41	11.3±0.53	237	325	0.368	-706
	232	4.31±0.03	12.1±0.29	232	322	0.388	-841
Cr-Kα	212	4.06±0.10	7.98±2.37	246	306	0.244	-966
	330	3.84±0.41	11.7±0.74	261	375	0.438	-1079
	411	4.38±0.15	9.88±2.21	228	295	0.292	-1025
V-Kα	411	4.22±0.11	9.88±0.25	237	309	0.306	-507

modulus, ν'_X =Poisson's ratio), change as a second power function of $\cos^2\phi$ (ϕ = angle between the diffraction plane normal and the *c*-axis of hexagonal crystal) as shown Eqs. (1) and (2). The X-ray compliances are plotted against $w^2=\cos^2\phi$ in Fig. 1 for EC141 and Fig. 2 for SN1. The variations of the compliances are not large and close to the mechanical values drawn with the dot-dash line in the figures. The regression relations for $(1+\nu'_X)/E'_X$ (10^{-3}/GPa) and for ν'_X/E'_X (10^{-4}/ GPa) are by the second order polynomial of w^2 are

$$\frac{1+\nu'_X}{E'_X} = 3.53 + 1.20\,w^2 - 1.10\,w^4 \tag{10}$$

$$\frac{\nu'_X}{E'_X} = 8.41 + 2.24\,w^2 - 2.56\,w^4 \tag{11}$$

for EC141, and

$$\frac{1+\nu'_X}{E'_X} = 3.90 + 2.12\,w^2 - 2.50\,w^4 \tag{12}$$

$$\frac{\nu'_X}{E'_X} = 9.90 + 5.57\,w^2 - 8.42\,w^4 \tag{13}$$

for SN1.

5 ELASTIC CONSTANTS OF SINGLE CRYSTAL OF SILICON NITRIDE

From the experimental relations between the X-ray compliances and $\cos^2\phi$, the single crystal elastic constants of silicon nitride were determined by the simplex method. Figure 3 shows the flowchart for the determination of the single crystal elastic constants. The elastic constants of single crystals of alumina and the mechanical elastic constants were used as the initial values. The initial value of the elastic constants of polycrystals, E_0 and ν_0, were calculated by the Kneer's equation from single crystal elastic constants. From the initial values, *t*-matrix is calculated and then the X-ray elastic constants, E_X and ν_X, by using Eqs. (1) and (2). Then, the X-ray elastic constants of E'_X and ν'_X are calculated by Eqs. (3) and (4). The sum of the square of the difference between the calculated and experimental values of $(1+\nu'_X)/E'_X$ for all the measured diffractions is used as the error function. The simplex method is adopted to reduce the error function. New values of the single crystal elastic constants are obtained, and then new values of the elastic constants of polycrystals are obtained by the Kneer's equation. This calculation loop is repeated until to get the minimum value of the error function.

The results of single crystal elastic constants obtained by the simplex method are shown in Table 4, together with the data reported by Hay et al (3). The polycrystalline elastic constants calculated by Kneer's equation are also shown in the table. The c_{33} value is larger than the the c_{11} value. The amount of difference between c_{11} and c_{33} for the Hay data is larger than the X-ray value. The value of the other constants are nearly the same. The elastic constants of single crystals embedded in polycrystals may be different from the values for whiskers. No other data have been reported for the elastic constants of silicon nitride.

6 CONCLUSIONS

The X-ray elastic constants of two kinds of β silicon nitride, gas-pressure sintered (EC141) and pressureless sintered (SN1), were experimentally determined with the $\sin^2\psi$ method for ten different diffractions by using Kα radiation of Cu, Co, Fe, Cr and V.

(1) The 323 diffraction by Cu-Kα_1 radiation, 251 and 232 diffractions by Fe-Kα radiation, and 411 diffraction by V-Kα radiation are recommended for the X-ray stress

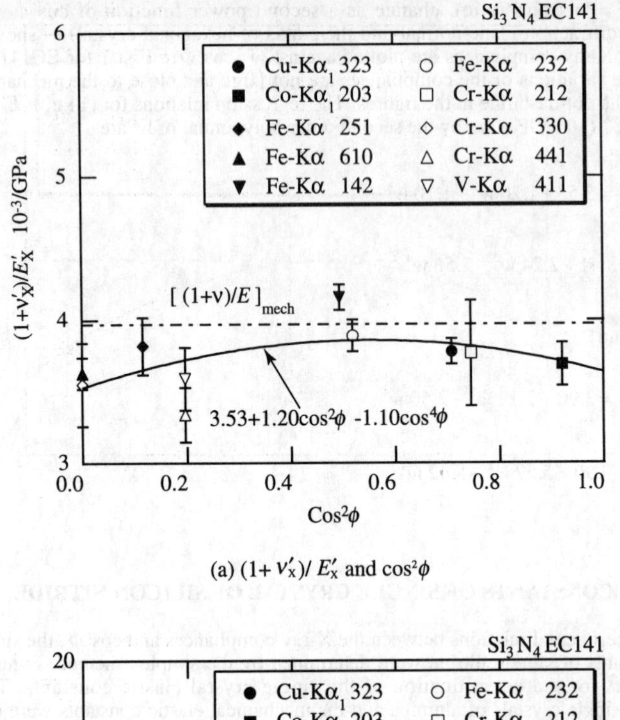

(a) $(1+\nu'_x)/E'_x$ and $\cos^2\phi$

(b) ν'_x/E'_x and $\cos^2\phi$

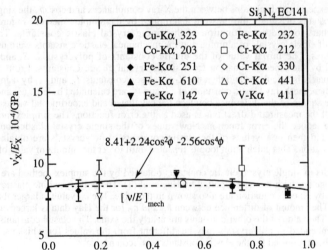

Fig. 1. Relation between X-ray compliances and $\cos^2\phi$ for EC141.

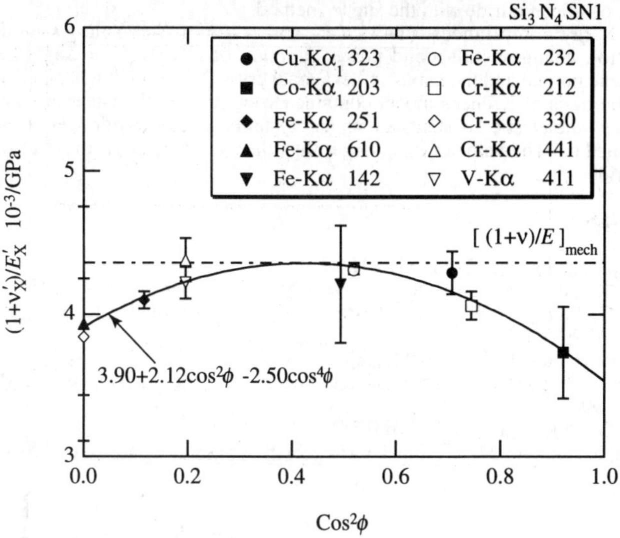

(a) $(1+\nu'_x)/E'_x$ and $\cos^2\phi$

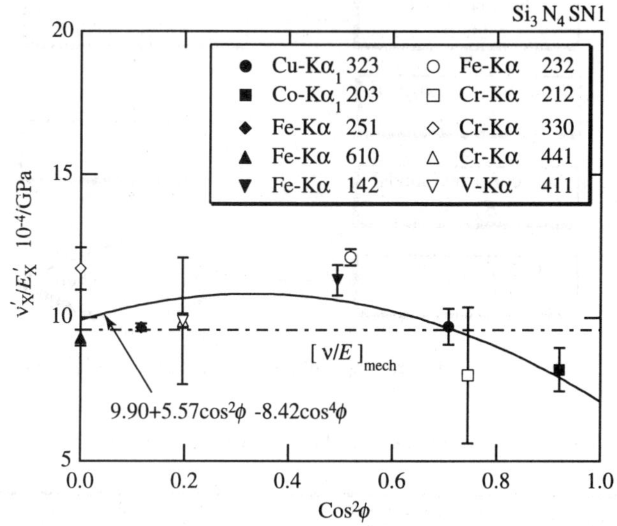

(b) ν'_x/E'_x and $\cos^2\phi$

Fig. 2. Relation between X-ray compliances and $\cos^2\phi$ for SN1.

measurement of silicon nitride with the $\sin^2\psi$ method.

(2) The X-ray compliances, $(1+\nu'_X)/E'_X$ and ν'_X/E'_X (E'_X= Young's modulus, ν'_X= Poisson's ratio), change as a second power function of $\cos^2\phi$ (ϕ = angle between the diffraction plane normal and the *c*-axis of hexagonal crystal) for both kinds of silicon nitride.

(3) On the basis of Kröner's model combined with the self-consistent analysis of multi-phase materials, the elastic constants of single crystal of silicon nitride were determined by the simplex method. The value of c_{33} is larger than the c_{11}, which show the elastic anisotropy of silicon nitride.

REFERENCES

1. Kröner, E., Z. Physik 151 (1958) 504.
2. Tanaka K., Akiniwa, Y. and Ito, T., J. Soci. Mat. Sci. Japan 48 (1999) 1352.
3. Hay, J. C., Sun, E. Y., Pharr, G. M., Becher, P. F., and Alexander, K. B., J. Am. Ceram. Soci. 81 (1998) 2661.
4. Behnken, H. and Hauk, V., Z. Metallkde 77 (1986) 620.
5. Tanaka, K., Yamashita, Y., Mine, N. and Suzuki, K., Proc. 32 Japan Cong. Mat. Res., (1989) 199.
6. Kneer, G., Phys. Stat. Sol. 3 (1963) 331.
7. Tanaka, K., Hattori, M. and Tanaka, H., J. Soci. Mat. Sci. Japan 44 (1995) 1110.

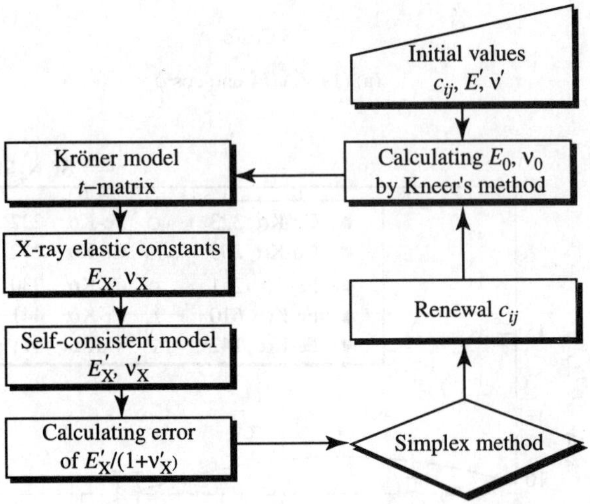

Fig. 3. Procedure for determining stiffness of single crystal silicon nitride.

Table 4. Elastic constants of silicon nitride determined by X-rays.

Material	Single crystal elastic constant (GPa)					Polycrystal	
	c_{11}	c_{12}	c_{13}	c_{33}	c_{44}	E_0 (GPa)	ν_0
EC141	438	115	138	466	117	353	0.252
SN1	410	126	145	503	106	329	0.270
Hay et al. (3)	343	136	120	600	124	317	0.259

SESSION 10A

X-RAY FRACTOGRAPHY OF FATIGUE FRACTURE UNDER MODE I AND III LOADING

Yoshiaki AKINIWA, Keisuke TANAKA and Tsuyoshi TSUMURA
Department of Mechanical Engineering, Nagoya University,
Furo-cho, Chikusa-ku, Nagoya 464-8603, Japan

ABSTRACT

The propagation behavior of a circumferential fatigue crack in cylindrical bars of a carbon steel (JIS SGV410) and a stainless steel (JIS SUS316NG) was studied under cyclic axial and torsional loadings. The J-integral range was used as a fracture mechanics parameter. The residual stresses in the radial direction, σ_r, and in the tangential direction, σ_θ, were measured for both mode I and mode III fatigue fracture surfaces. For mode I fracture surface, σ_r was tension, and was almost constant irrespective of the applied J-integral range. σ_θ was close to zero for both materials. On the other hand, for mode III, σ_r and σ_θ were compression. For SUS316NG steel, the compressive stress of σ_θ increased with the J-integral range. For SGV410 steel, the change of σ_θ with the J-integral range was small. The breadth of diffraction profiles increased with J-integral range for both mode I and III. The breadth was found to be a good parameter to evaluate the fracture mode and the J-integral range.

1. INTRODUCTION

Since the X-ray diffraction yields useful information to analyze the cause of fracture, X-ray fractographic analysis has been widely adopted. Many engineering components, such as turbine shafts and crankshafts, are subjected to reversed torsional loading. In that case, fatigue cracks propagate in a mode III manner [1, 2, 3]. In comparison with the case of mode I, not many studies have been conducted on X-ray fractographic analysis of mode III fracture.

In the present study, the propagation behavior of a circumferential fatigue crack in cylindrical bars of a carbon steel and a stainless steel was studied under cyclic axial and torsional loadings. The residual stress and the breadth of diffraction profiles were measured on mode I and III fatigue fracture surfaces as a function of the J -integral range.

2. EXPERIMENTAL PROCEDURE

2.1. Materials and specimens

The materials used in the present study were a carbon steel (JIS SGV410) and an austenitic stainless steel (JIS SUS316NG). The chemical compositions of the materials are presented in Table I. The SGV410 steel specimens were annealed at 630℃ for 4 h 36 min. The mechanical properties after the heat treatment are shown in Table II.

The shape and dimensions of the specimen are shown in Fig. 1. The specimen was cylindrical in shape with a diameter of 16 mm and a length of 220 mm. A circumferential

Table I Chemical compositions.

	C	Si	Mn	P	S	Cu	Cr	Ni	Mo	Nb
SUS316NG	0.01	0.61	1.49	0.019	0.002	—	17.36	11.91	2.48	—
SGV410	0.10	0.25	1.15	0.018	0.003	0.33	0.23	0.13	—	0.02

Table II Mechanical properties.

	Yield stress σ_Y (MPa)	Tensile strength σ_B (MPa)	Elongation δ (%)
SUS316NG	254	564	82
SGV410	343	461	37

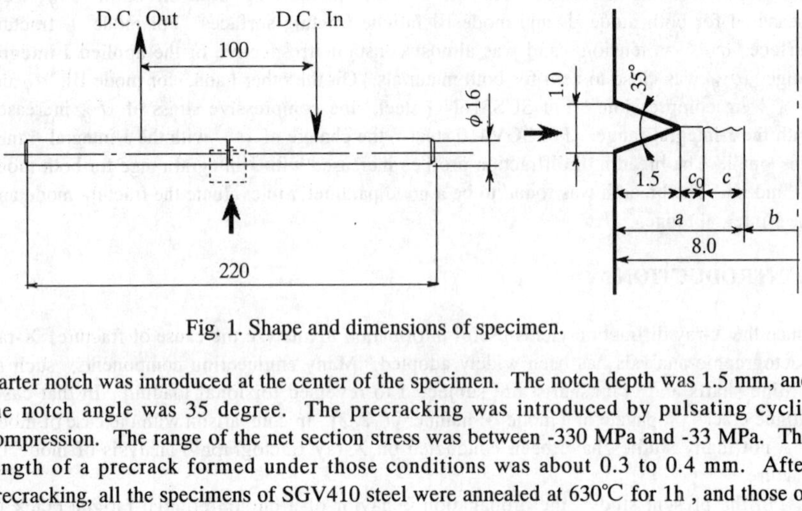

Fig. 1. Shape and dimensions of specimen.

starter notch was introduced at the center of the specimen. The notch depth was 1.5 mm, and the notch angle was 35 degree. The precracking was introduced by pulsating cyclic compression. The range of the net section stress was between -330 MPa and -33 MPa. The length of a precrack formed under those conditions was about 0.3 to 0.4 mm. After precracking, all the specimens of SGV410 steel were annealed at 630℃ for 1h , and those of SUS316NG steel at 900℃ for 30 min.

2.2. Crack length measurement

The total crack length which was the sum of notch depth, pre-crack length and crack length from the pre-crack was measured with the d.c. potential method [3]. A constant direct current adopted was 20 A for SGV410 steel, and 10 A for SUS316NG steel. Nickel wire of a diameter of 0.3 mm was welded onto the specimens as potential probes.

2.3. Fatigue testing

Fatigue tests were performed with a tension-torsion biaxial electro servo-hydraulic fatigue testing machine (Shimadzu EHF-EDIO/TQ-40L) in air at room temperature. The specimen

Table III X-ray conditions.

Characteristic X-Ray	Cr-Kα	Mn-Kα
Material	SVG410	SUS316NG
Diffraction	211	311
Diffraction angle (deg)	156.41	151.52
Tube voltage (kV)	30	30
Tube current (mA)	200	30
Scanning speed (deg/min)	1.00	0.25
Preset time (sec)	2	20
Stress constant (MPa/deg)	-318	-339

was clamped with a hydraulic wedge grip. The loading frequency was 1 Hz. For mode I fatigue testing, the tests were conducted in displacement controlled conditions. The displacement range of the gage length of 12.5 mm was controlled. The displacement range was adjusted manually to keep the J-integral range constant at appropriate interval. The J-integral range was controlled at two values: 2×10^3 and 1×10^4 N/m. The crack opening point was determined by the unloading elastic compliance method. The ratio of minimum to maximum displacement was -1. For mode III fatigue testing, the tests were conducted in angle of twist controlled conditions. The angle of twist range of the gage length of 45 mm was controlled. The J-integral range selected was 2×10^4 and 5×10^4 N/m. The ratio of minimum to maximum angle of twist was -1.

The hysteresis loops of the load vs. displacement and torque vs. angle of twist were recorded with the use of a computer. The J-integral range for modes I and III was evaluated from those hysteresis loops [3, 4].

2.4. X-ray measurement

The X-ray beam was irradiated on fatigue fractured surfaces. The X-ray diffractions from α-Fe 211 by Cr-Kα radiation for SGV410 steel and γ-Fe 311 by Mn-Kα radiation for SUS316NG steel were used for X-ray stress measurements. The X-ray conditions are shown in Table III. The parallel-beam slits were attached to the divergent and receiving sides of a goniometer. The X-ray irradiated area was 1.5×2 mm^2. The stress was evaluated by the 2θ-$\sin^2\psi$ method. The residual stresses in the radial direction, σ_r, and in the tangential direction, σ_θ, of the circular fracture surface were measured. The full width at half maximum, $B_{0.5}$, for SGV410 steel and full width at 40% maximum, $B_{0.4}$, for SUS316NG steel were measured from diffraction profile obtained at $\psi=0°$.

3. EXPERIMENTAL RESULTS AND DISCUSSION

3.1 Crack propagation behavior of mode I

Figure 2 (a) shows the hysteresis loop of load v.s. displacement obtained for SGV410 steel under mode I. The total crack length is 3.56 mm. The crack propagated under elastic-plastic conditions as seen in a fairly wide breadth of the hysteresis loop. Figure 2 (b) shows the relation after subtraction. The abscissa denotes u-αP, where α is the unloading elastic

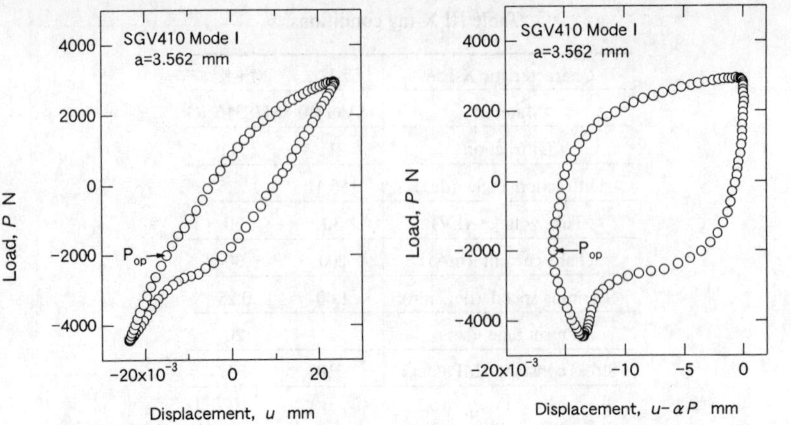

(a) P vs. u. (b) P vs. u- α P.

Fig. 2. Hysteresis loop of load vs. displacement for SGV410 under mode I.

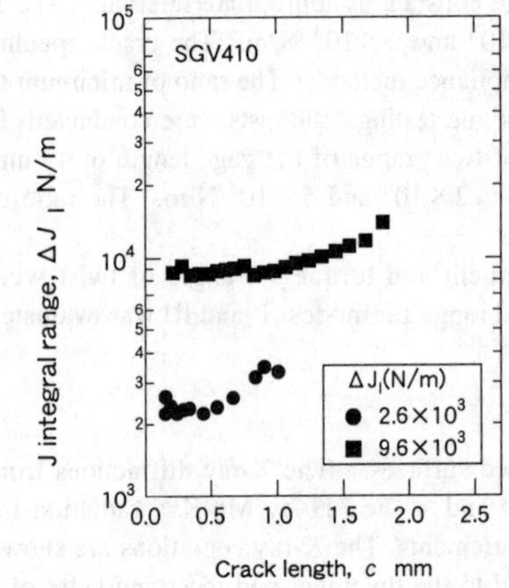

Fig. 3. Change of ΔJ_I with crack length under mode I.

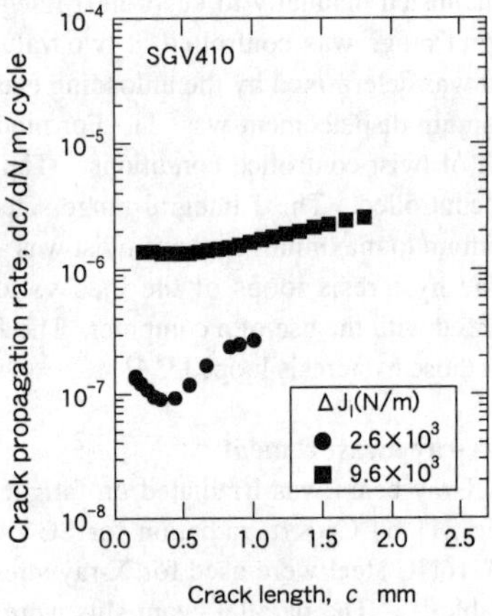

Fig. 4. Change of crack propagation rate with crack length under mode I.

compliance. The arrow mark in the figure indicates the crack opening point determined by the unloading elastic compliance method. The crack opening point is in compression side. The J-integral range, ΔJ_I, was evaluated from the data obtained between the crack opening point and the maximum point.

Figure 3 shows the change of the ΔJ_I with crack length from the pre-crack. The results obtained for two conditions were plotted. ΔJ_I slightly increases with crack length. The mean values of ΔJ_I are 2.6×10^3 and 9.6×10^3 N/m. Figure 4 shows the change of the crack propagation rate, da/dN, with crack length. da/dN slightly increases with crack length. The change of the crack propagation rate with crack extension corresponds to that of ΔJ_I

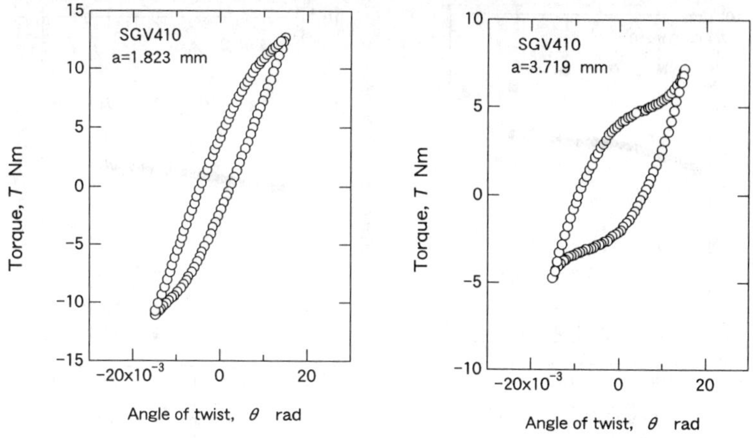

(a) a=1.823 mm. (b) a=3.719 mm.

Fig. 5. Hysteresis loop of torque vs. angle of twist for SGV410 under mode III.

as shown in Fig. 3.

For the case of SUS316NG steel, ΔJ_{I} and the crack propagation rate with crack extension were also constant. The mean values of ΔJ_{I} obtained for SUS316NG steel were 2.7×10^3 and 1.0×10^4 N/m.

3.2. Crack propagation behavior of mode III

Figures 5 show the hysteresis loops of torque v.s. angle of twist obtained for SGV410 steel under mode III. Figures 5 (a) and (b) show the results obtained for a=1.82 mm and a=3.72 mm, respectively. The crack also propagates under elastic-plastic condition. As the crack length becomes large, the hysteresis loop shows a sharp bend near the tip of the loop. This is caused by the sliding contact of the fracture surface under torsion. The J-integral range, ΔJ_{III}, was evaluated from whole range of the hysteresis loop. The effect of the sliding contact of the fracture surface was neglected to evaluate the J-integral range for mode III.

Figure 6 shows the change of ΔJ_{III} with crack length. ΔJ_{III} is approximately constant during fatigue test. The mean values of ΔJ_{III} are 1.7×10^4 and 4.4×10^4 N/m. Figure 7 shows the change of da/dN with crack length. The crack propagation rate obtained for $\Delta J_{\mathrm{III}} = 4.4\times10^4$ N/m is nearly constant irrespective of crack length. For the case of $\Delta J_{\mathrm{III}} = 1.7\times10^4$ N/m, da/dN slightly increases with crack extension. The change of da/dN corresponds to that of ΔJ_{III}.

The mean values of ΔJ_{III} obtained for SUS316NG steel were 2.8×10^4 and 5.0×10^4 N/m.

The relation between the crack propagation rate and the J-integral range was shown in Fig. 8. When compared at the same ΔJ, the crack propagation rate under mode III is smaller than that under mode I. In the figure, the solid lines and the broken lines indicate the results of SUS316NG steel and medium carbon steel (JIS 45C) obtained by Tanaka et al [4]. For the case of mode III, they determined the crack propagation rate as the value without contact shielding. When compared at the same ΔJ_{III} for SUS316NG steel, crack propagation rate obtained in this study are smaller than the thick solid line.

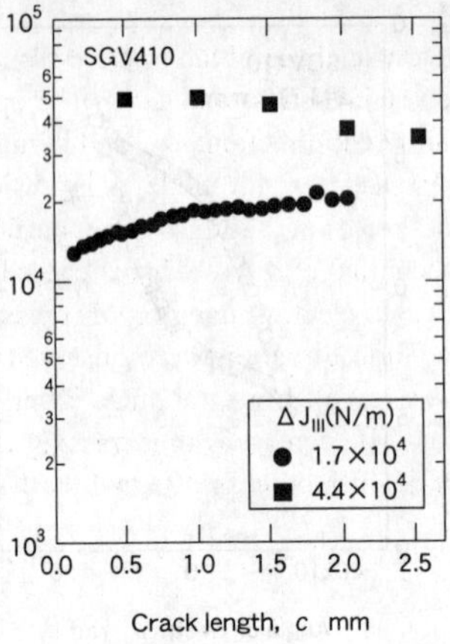

Fig. 6. Change of ΔJ_{III} with crack length under mode III.

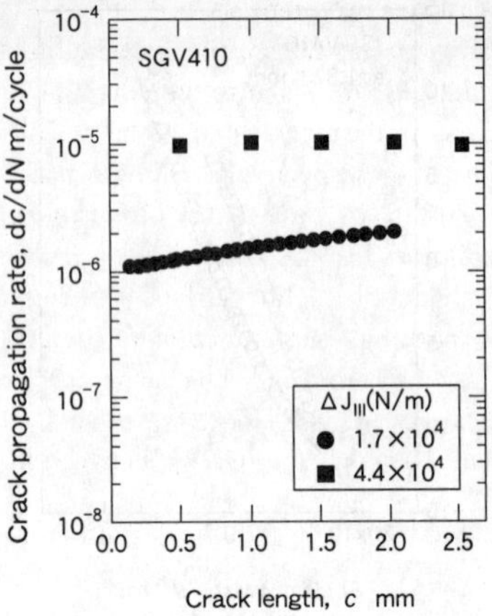

Fig. 7. Change of crack propagation rate with crack length under mode III.

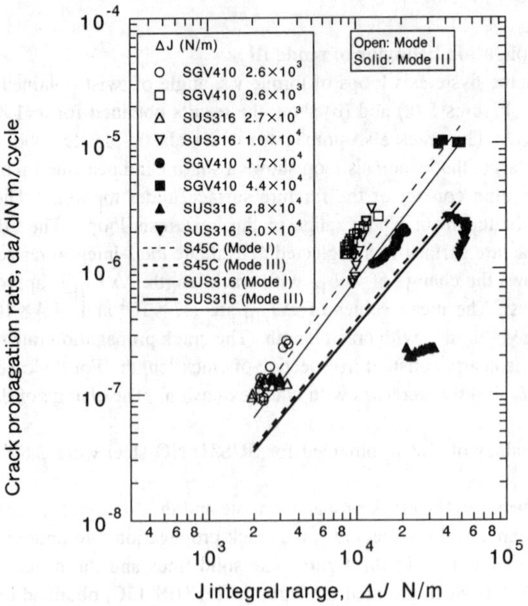

Fig. 8. Relation between crack propagation rate and J-integral range.

3.3. X-ray measurement

After fatigue tests, the specimens were broken and X-ray analysis of the fracture surface was conducted. Figure 9 shows the relation between the residual stress and ΔJ. The open and solid marks in the figure indicate the residual stress in radial direction, σ_r, and in tangential direction, σ_θ, respectively. For the case of SGV410 steel, σ_r for mode I is tension, and is larger than σ_θ which is close to zero. On the other hand, σ_r for mode III is compression. The absolute value of σ_r is smaller than that of σ_θ. This is caused by the sliding contact of fracture surface as mentioned above. In electron microscopic observation, parallel markings perpendicular to the crack propagation direction were observed on the fatigue fracture surface. The change of the residual stress with J-integral range is very small. For the case of SUS316NG steel, σ_r and σ_θ for mode III decrease with increasing ΔJ_{III}.

Figure 10 shows the relation between the breadth of diffraction profile and the J-integral

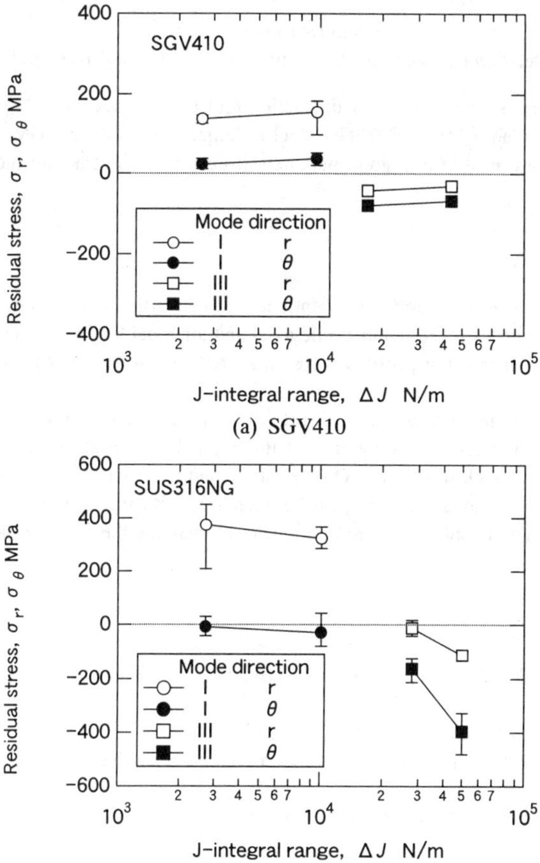

(a) SGV410

(b) SUS316NG

Fig. 9. Relation between residual stress and J-integral range.

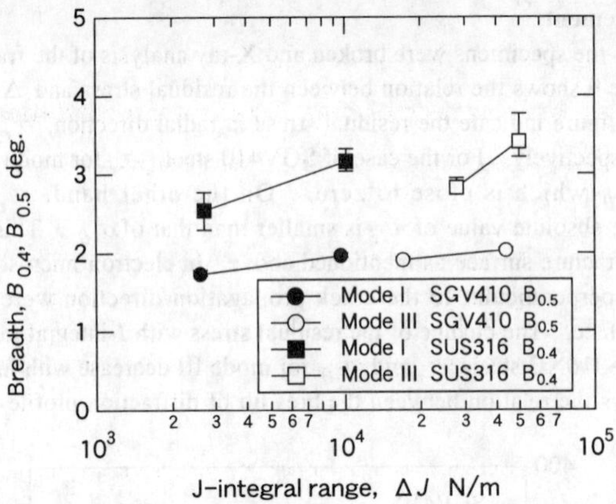

Fig. 10. Relation between breadth of diffraction profile and J-integral range.

range. In both modes, the breadth of diffraction profile increases with ΔJ. The rate of increasing of the breadth for SUS316NG steel is larger than that for SGV410 steel. The breadth of diffraction profile is a good parameter to estimate the fracture mode and the J-integral range.

4. CONCLUSIONS

Propagation behavior of a circumferential fatigue crack in cylindrical bars of a carbon steel and a stainless steel was studied under cyclic axial and torsional loadings. The residual stress and the breadth of diffraction profiles were measured for mode I and mode III fatigue fracture surfaces.

For mode I fracture surface, the residual stress in the radial direction, σ_r, is tension, and is approximately constant irrespective of the applied J-integral range. The tangential residual stress, σ_θ, is close to zero. On the other hand, σ_r and σ_θ are compressive for mode III. The breadth of diffraction profiles increases with the J-integral range for both mode I and III. The breadth is a good parameter to evaluate the fracture mode and the J-integral range.

REFERENCE

1. Ritchie R. O., McClintock F. A., Nayeb-Hashemi H. and Ritter M. A., *Met. Trans.*, **13A** (1982) 101.
2. Tschegg E. K., *Mater. Sci. Eng.*, **54**, (1982) 127.
3. Tanaka K. , Akiniwa Y. and Nakamura H., *Fatigue Fract. Engng Mater. Struct.*, **19** (1996) 571.
4. Tanaka K. , Akiniwa Y. and Yu H. C., *7th. Int. Fatigue. Conf., Fatigue '99*, **2** (1999) 929.

X-Ray Fractography Using Synchrotron Radiation

(Residual Stress Distribution in X-Ray Penetration Depth)

K. Akita*, Y. Yoshioka**, H. Suzuki*** and S. KODAMA
*Tokyo Metropolitan University, Japan, akita-koichi@c.metro-u.ac.jp
**Musashi Institute of Technology, Japan, yoshioka@me.ese.musashi-tech.ac.jp
***Graduate Student of Tokyo Metropolitan University, Japan

ABSTRACT

Residual stress distributions just beneath the fatigue fracture surface were measured using synchrotron radiation at three different wavelengths, i.e., three different penetration depths. The residual stress distributions were estimated from three kinds of diffraction data using the following process.
First, a temporary residual stress distribution in the depth direction is assumed. Theoretical 2θ-$\sin^2\psi$ diagrams for each wavelength, where each has a different penetration depth, are calculated using the $\cos\psi$ method developed by one of the authors. The sum total of the differences between the theoretical and experimental values of the diffraction angle in 2θ-$\sin^2\psi$ diagrams is calculated. Changing the assumed stress distribution by the quasi-Newton optimization method minimizes this total value. Finally, optimized 2θ-$\sin^2\psi$ diagrams for each penetration depth and detailed stress distribution are determined.
The residual stresses on the fracture surface became higher with increasing load ratio, R, when these were measured by the proposed method. On the basis of this, the stress intensity factor range, ΔK, can be estimated from the residual stress on the fatigue fracture surface.

INTRODUCTION

X-ray fractography is a powerful technique for failure analysis of machine components and structures. For example, the maximum stress intensity factor in linear elastic fracture mechanics, K_{max}, can be estimated from the monotonic plastic deformation depth. The stress intensity factor range, ΔK, which corresponds to the fatigue crack propagation rate, can be estimated from the residual stress on the fatigue fracture surface and K_{max}, estimated by the above method for high strength steel (1). However, an estimation method for ΔK has not been established for low strength steels where residual stress is not dependent on the load ratio, R.

Residual stresses of fatigue fracture surfaces are generally measured by the $\sin^2\psi$ method. However, sometimes 2θ-$\sin^2\psi$ diagrams with curvature are also observed indicating the existence of a steep stress gradient in the depth direction. It is important to evaluate the real residual stress distributions near the fatigue fracture surface for the estimation of ΔK.

In this study, the residual stress distributions just beneath the fatigue fracture surface were measured using synchrotron radiation at three different wavelengths, i.e., three different penetration depths. The residual stress distributions in X-ray penetration depth were estimated from three kinds of diffraction data using the method proposed in this study. The relationships between the residual stress on the fatigue fracture surface and the stress intensity factor are discussed.

EXPERIMENTAL PROCEDURE

Specimens and fatigue tests

A low carbon steel (JIS S15C, Tensile strength≒350MPa) was used in the annealed condition and a high strength steel (HT100, Tensile strength≒1000MPa) was used as received. Specimens used were compact tension type fatigue specimen (CT). Fatigue tests were performed at room temperature in laboratory air by an electro-hydraulic testing machine with sinusoidal wave loading. Constant amplitude tests were carried out at two load ratios, R (R=0.1 and 0.5 in S15C, R=0.1 and 0.6 in HT100).

Synchrotron radiation source and the conditions of stress measurement

The synchrotron radiation (SR) system at the Photon Factory (PF) of the High Energy Accelerator Research Organization, KEK, in Tsukuba, Japan was used as the X-ray source. BL-3A beam line was used. The optical layout, shown in Fig.1 (2), consists of a double Si 111 crystal monochromator, collimating mirror and focusing mirror. X-rays between λ=0.25 nm and 0.12 nm are available with this optical system. The divergence angle of the beam source was 1.2 mrad in the vertical direction and 12 mrad in the horizontal direction. The minimum beam size on the specimen was 0.55 mm (vertical) by 1.5 mm (horizontal).

The use of SR enables measurements at a constant Bragg angle 2θ on many diffraction planes. We adopted a constant Bragg angle of 2θ=154deg for all diffraction planes (3). For

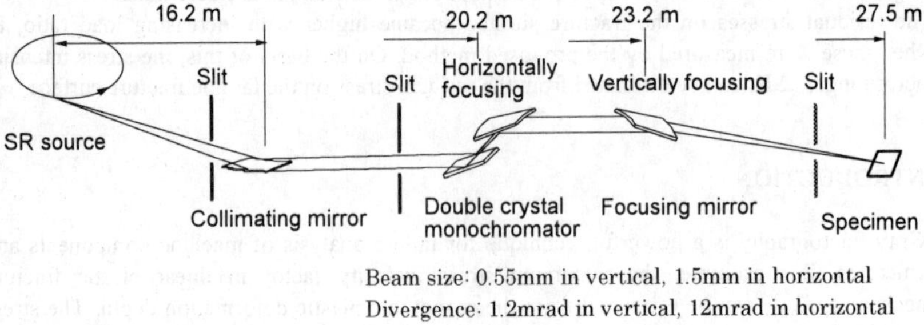

Fig.1 Schematic layout of beam line 3A at Photon Factory of KEK.

Table 1. Conditions of diffraction measurement.

Diffraction of α-Fe	Wave length (nm)	2θ (deg.)	Linear absorption coefficient (1/cm)	Penetration depth (μ m) (Intensity ratio=63%, ψ=0 deg.)
211	0.22804	154	857	5.9
220	0.19749	154	568	8.7
310	0.17664	154	413	12

example, stresses in the α-Fe211 planes were measured at the wavelength of 0.2280 nm. A goniometer was prepared for stress measurement as shown in Fig.2. The goniometer was configured with a position-sensitive proportional counter (PSPC) having an effective length of 110 mm, a specimen holder and a beam slit. The width of the beam slit was 2mm and its height was 5mm.

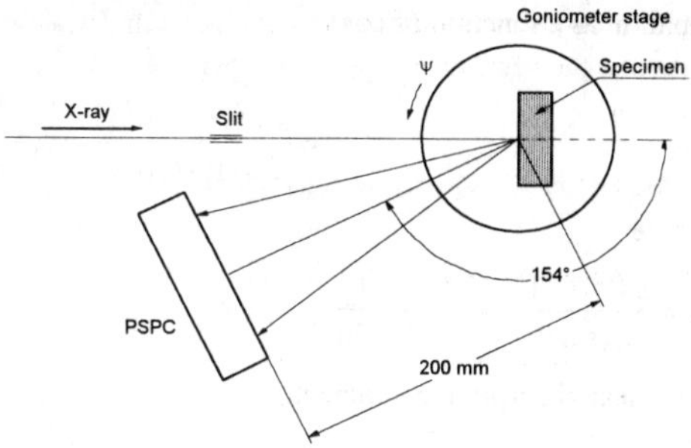

Fig.2 Layout of goniometer for stress measurement.

The measured diffraction peaks in α-Fe were 211, 220 and 310. Table 1 shows the combinations of diffraction peaks and wavelength used in this study. X-ray tilt angles, ψ, varied from 0 to 60 degrees. The irradiated position was at the center of the thickness of a specimen. The direction of the measured residual stress was in the crack growth direction.

RESIDUAL STRESS ANALYSIS

The cosψ method developed by one of the authors (4) was applied to obtain the residual stress distribution in the depth direction of fatigue fracture surfaces. The depth at which the intensity ratio of X-ray diffraction becomes 63% is defined as the X-ray penetration depth. X-ray penetration depth for 211, 220 and 310 diffraction is 6μm, 9μm and 12μm, respectively. The shape of the residual stress distribution in the depth direction was assumed to be linear (cosψ-Linear method) or quadratic (cosψ-Quadratic method). The biaxial plane stress condition was assumed to be the stress state in X-ray penetration depth. The X-ray stress constants at each diffraction were calculated using elastic compliance of single crystal of α-Fe and the Kröner model (5). The X-ray stress constant was calculated with –353 MPa/deg for 211 and 220 diffraction peaks, and with –291 MPa/deg for 310 diffraction peak.
The 2θ-$\sin^2\psi$ diagram assumed initially for the residual stress distribution in the depth direction is obtained as following process. The stress distributions in the depth direction were assumed for two cases. The case in which the stress distribution in the depth direction is assumed to be a straight line is called the cosψ-Linear method. In the other method, the stress distribution in the depth direction is assumed to be a quadratic curve; this is called the cosψ-Quadratic method. The stress distribution is assumed to be described by the following equation in the cosψ-Quadratic method.

$$\sigma_{ij}(z) = az^2 + 2bz + \sigma_{ij0} \qquad (1)$$

Where

$a = (\sigma_{ij0} - \sigma_{ijp}) / z_p^{\,2}, \quad b = -az_p,$

z : depth from fracture surface,
σ_{ij0} : the surface stress, σ_{ijp} : the peak stress in the X-ray penetration depth,
z_p :the depth at which the stress reaches a peak.

The X-ray penetration depth, T, in the iso-inclination method is given by the following equation as a function of $\cos\psi$.

$$T = \frac{\sin^2\theta - \sin^2\psi}{2\mu\sin\theta\cos\psi} = T_1\frac{1}{\cos\psi} + T_2\cos\psi \tag{2}$$

Where

$$T_1 = \frac{\sin^2\theta - 1}{2\mu\sin\theta},\quad T_2 = \frac{1}{2\mu\sin\theta},$$

μ = linear absorption coefficient.

The stress measurement value as the stress gradient exists in the X-ray penetration depth becomes the weighted mean stress, $<\sigma_{ij}>$, to depth z_1, and can be described by the following equation.

$$\langle\sigma_{ij}\rangle = \frac{\int_0^{z_1}\sigma_{ij}(z)I(z)dz}{\int_0^{z_1}I(z)dz}$$

$$= \sigma_{ij0} + 2T(aT+b) + \frac{z_1\exp(-z_1/T)\{az_1 + 2(aT+b)\}}{\exp(-z_1/T)-1} \tag{3}$$

Equation (3) becomes the following equation, when z_1 is equal to T.

$$\langle\sigma_{ij}\rangle = \sigma_{ij0} + 2T(aT+b) + \frac{T\exp(-1)(3aT+2b)}{\exp(-1)-1} \tag{4}$$

The mean strain up to a certain depth is calculated from $<\sigma_{ij}>$, and shown by the following equation.

$$\langle\varepsilon_{\phi\psi}\rangle = \frac{1+\nu}{E}\left[\langle\sigma_{11}\rangle\cos^2\phi + \langle\sigma_{22}\rangle\sin^2\phi\right]\sin^2\psi - \frac{\nu}{E}\left[\langle\sigma_{11}\rangle + \langle\sigma_{22}\rangle\right] \tag{5}$$

This equation is shown at diffraction angle as the following equation.

$$\langle 2\theta_{\phi\psi}\rangle = -2\tan\theta_0\langle\varepsilon_{\phi\psi}\rangle + 2\theta_0 \tag{6}$$

The 2θ-$\sin^2\psi$ diagram assumed initially for the residual stress distribution in the depth direction is obtained from this $2\theta_{\phi\psi}$ for various ψ angles.

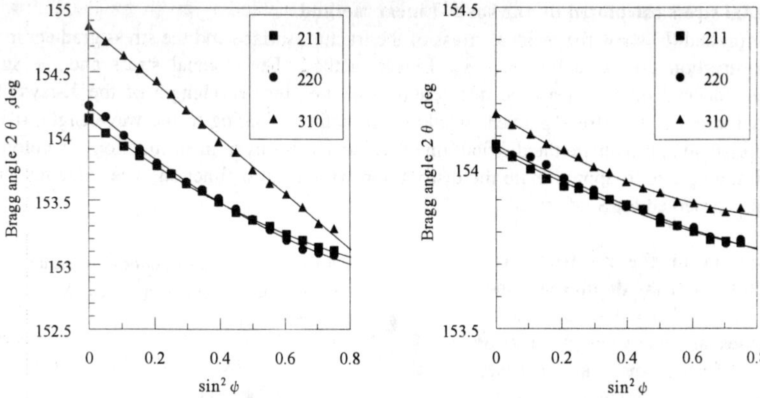

(a) HT100

(R = 0.1, K_{max} = 44 MPa√m)

(b) S15C

(R = 0.5, K_{max} = 37 MPa√m)

Fig.3 Examples of 2θ-$\sin^2\psi$ diagram measured on the fatigue fracture surface.

RESULTS AND DISCUSSIONS

2θ-$\sin^2\psi$ diagrams

Almost all of the 2θ-$\sin^2\psi$ diagrams obtained on fatigue fracture surfaces with curvature were observed in the high-ψ angle region. Fig.3 (a) and fig.3(b) show examples of 2θ-$\sin^2\psi$ diagrams on the fatigue fracture surfaces of HT100 steel and S15C steel. Possible reasons for curvature of the 2θ-$\sin^2\psi$ diagram include not only a steep stress gradient in the X-ray penetration depth but also the existence of texture in a material or a tri-axial shear stress state at X-ray penetration depth. However, there was no texture in materials used in this study and the ψ-split phenomenon, which occurs in the tri-axial shear stress state, was not observed. Therefore, it is understood that the reason for curvature of the 2θ-$\sin^2\psi$ diagrams in this study is the existence of a steep stress gradient at X-ray penetration depth.

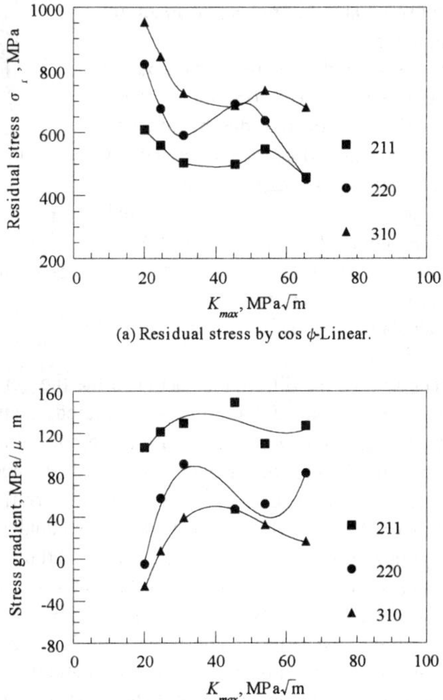

(a) Residual stress by cos ψ-Linear.

(b) Stress gradient by cos ψ-Linear.

Fig.4 Residual stress and stress gradient obtained by cos ψ-Linear method (HT100, R=0.6).

Residual stress calculated by the cosψ-Linear method

Figs. 4(a) and (b) show the residual stress of the fracture surface and the stress gradient in the depth direction estimated by the cosψ-Linear method. The residual stress and the stress gradient depend on the measured diffraction peak, i.e., the wavelength of the X-rays. The residual stress or the stress gradient would agree without relating to the wavelength, if it is appropriate to approximate the distribution of residual stress by a linear function. Therefore, it is not appropriate to approximate the distribution with a linear function. The same tendency was also observed for S15C steel.

Estimation of the residual stress distribution in the depth direction

Fig.5 shows that the stress gradient decreases as the X-ray penetration depth of the material inceases. Therefore, it is anticipated that the stress distribution under the fracture surface becomes convex on the top, as shown schematically in fig.6. This stress distribution can be approximated simply by a quadratic function.

In this study, a new method to determine the residual stress distribution in the depth direction was developed. First, a temporary residual stress distribution in the depth direction is assumed. Theoretical 2θ-$\sin^2\psi$ diagrams for each wavelength, where each has a different penetration depth, are calculated by the cosψ method.

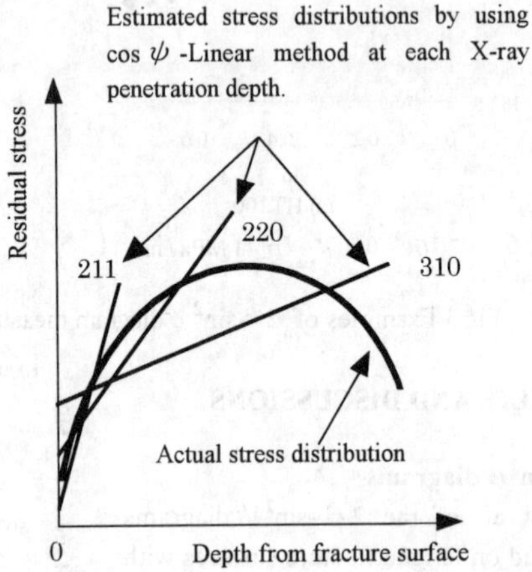

Fig. 5 Schematic illustration of the actual stress distribution and the linear stress distributions estimated by the cosψ-Linear method.

The sum of the differences between the theoretical and experimental values of the diffraction angle in 2θ-$\sin^2\psi$ diagrams is calculated. Changing the assumed residual stress distribution by the quasi-Newton optimization method minimizes this total value. Finally, optimized 2θ-$\sin^2\psi$ diagrams for each penetration depth and detailed stress distribution are determined. The true surface residual stress is obtained from this stress distribution in the depth direction.

Fig.7 (a) shows an example of the residual stress distribution in the depth direction that optimized by the above-mentioned method. Fig.7(b) shows the results comparing the calculated and the experimental diagrams of 2θ-$\sin^2\psi$ at each diffraction. The calculated and experimental values of 2θ agree well. Therefore, it seems appropriate to assume the quadratic distribution. The three straight lines in fig.7(a) are the residual stress distributions obtained using the cosψ-Linear method. The stress gradient decreases as the X-ray penetration depth increases when the cosψ-Linear method is used because the real distribution of residual stress is the convex. Fig.8 shows the result of similarly arranging with fig.7 in S15C steel. The calculated and experimental values of 2θ agree well. Therefore it is clear that a quadratic curve approximation of the stress distribution is appropriate.

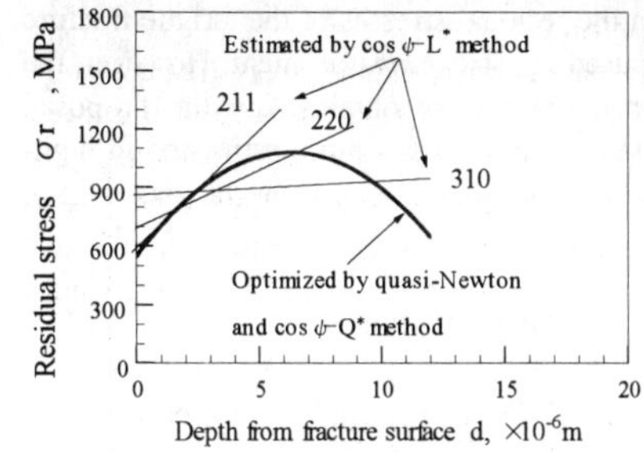

*L : Stress gradient is approximated by linear function.
*Q : Stress gradient is approximated by quadratic curve.

(a) Residual stress distribution.

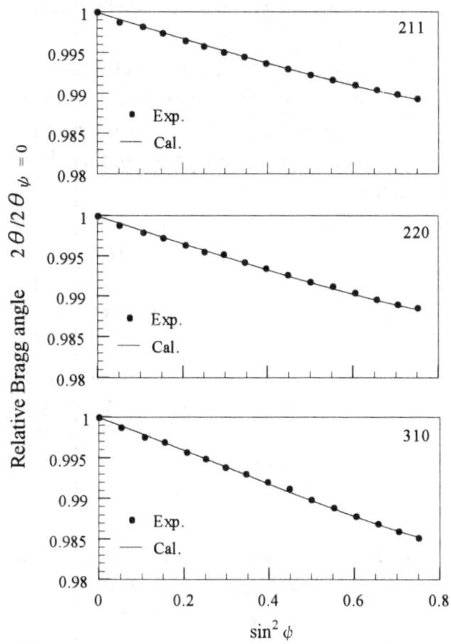

(b) Comparison of calculated and experimental values of 2θ-$\sin^2\psi$ diagram.

Fig.6 An example of optimized result of residual stress distribution just beneath the fracture surface of HT100 (R=0.6, K_{max}=25MPa$\sqrt{m}$).

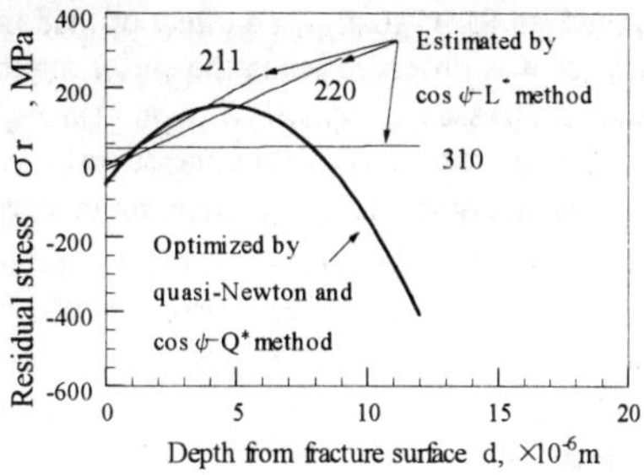

*L : Stress gradient is approximated by linear function.
*Q : Stress gradient is approximated by quadratic curve.

(a) Residual stress distribution.

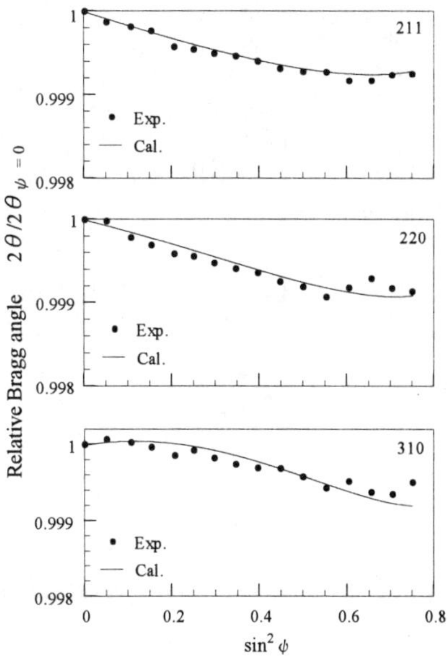

(b) Comparison of calculated and experimental values of 2θ-$\sin^2\psi$ diagram.

Fig.7 An example of optimized result of residual stress distribution just beneath the fracture surface of S15C (R=0.1, K_{max}=48MPa$\sqrt{m}$).

Residual stress of the fatigue fracture surface obtained by cosψ-Quadratic curve

Fig.9 (a) and (b) show the residual stress on the fatigue fracture surface obtained by the proposed method on HT100 and S15C steel, respectively. In HT100 steel, residual stresses are higher when the load ratio, R, is 0.5 than when R=0.1, without regard to the calculation method. In S15C steel, no effect of load ratio on the residual stresses of the fatigue fracture surfaces was observed when the $\sin^2\psi$ method is used for stress measurement. However, the residual stresses increased with increasing R when these were obtained by the proposed method. On the basis of this, the stress intensity factor range, ΔK, can be estimated in high- and low-strength steels if the maximum stress intensity factor is known from the plastic zone depth.

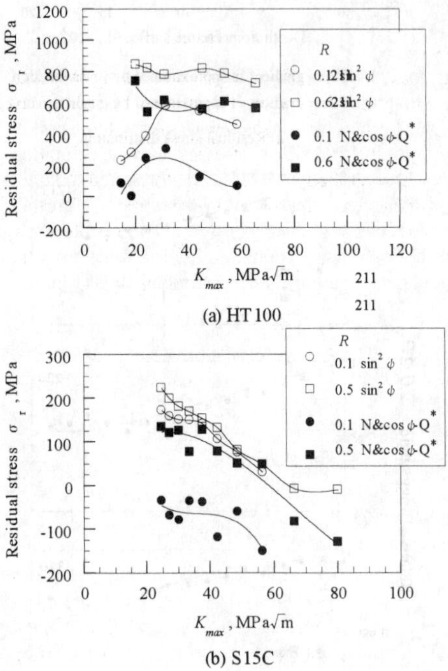

*: Optimized by quasi-Newton and cos φ-Quadratic method (the proposed method).

Fig.8 Residual stress distribution on the fatigue fracture surface obtained by the proposed method.

CONCLUSIONS

(1) The stress gradient decreases as the penetration depth increases when the stress distribution is approximated by a linear function. From this result, it is clear that the residual stress distribution under the fatigue fracture surface has a convex distribution.

(2) An optimization method was proposed to determine the residual stress distribution in the depth direction from diffraction data measured by three kinds of wavelengths.

(3) The residual stress on a fatigue fracture surface increases, as the load ratio increases for both high strength HT100 steel and a low strength S15C steel. Therefore the method for estimating ΔK from residual stress on a fracture surface that was developed for high strength steel can be applied for low strength steel.

This work has been performed under the approval of the Photon Factory Program Advisory Committee of the High-Energy Accelerator Research Organization, Japan (Proposal No. 98G265 and 99G037). This study was supported by the research grant from the Ministry of Education, Japan (1999, Commendatory Research (A) No.11750086).

REFERENCES

1. Akita, K., Kodama S. and Misawa, H., Proc. of ICRS4, 1024 (1994)
2. Kawasaki, K. et al: Rev. Sci. Instrum, 63, 1023 (1992)
3. Yoshioka, Y., Current Japanese Materials Research, 10,109 (1993)
4. Yoshioka, Y., Sasaki, T. and Kuramoto, M., Adv. X-Ray Anal. 28, 255 (1985).
5. E. Kröner, Z.Physik, 151, 504 (1958)

ANALYSIS OF THE EFFECT OF TENSILE RESIDUAL STRESS ON FATIGUE CRACK PROPAGATION

Y Prawoto[1] and RA Winholtz[1,2]
[1]*Department of Mechanical and Aerospace Engineering, University of Missouri*
[2]*Research Reactor Center, University of Missouri*

ABSTRACT
Fatigue crack propagation rates have been predicted for specimens containing residual stresses. Experiments using two different loading modes, constant applied stress intensity factor and constant applied load ranges, were performed for samples with and without initial tensile residual stresses. The samples with initial tensile residual stresses show acceleration of the crack propagation rates. Both the residual and applied stresses were converted to stress intensity factors independently and combined using the superposition principle. To further verify that superposition is valid, the plastic zone size was also measured. The results show that the weight function method, combined with the three-component model of crack growth, provides a good prediction of fatigue crack propagation rates in tensile residual stress fields.

1. INTRODUCTION
The existence of residual stresses in a material affects its fatigue performance. Previous studies (e.g., 1-5) have found that residual stresses can either increase or decrease fatigue resistance. However, quantitative studies are still limited.

1.1. *Crack Propagation Rate Modeling using LEFM*
Fig. 1 shows an illustration of a typical material's fatigue crack propagation rate dependence on the stress intensity factor range. In general, fatigue crack propagation rates can be divided into three major regions, Stages I, II, and III. During early development of modeling, only Stage II could be predicted. However, in later developments, several models were developed capable of modeling Stages I and III (6, 7). In general, all available models based on LEFM can be classified into three groups. The first group consists of the most primitive models represented by Paris model. This model does not consider the effect of load ratio, $R = K_{min}/K_{max}$. The second group considers the load ratio effect and it is represented by the Walker model (8). Walker introduced an effective stress, $\overline{\sigma} = \sigma_{max}^{1-m} \Delta\sigma^{m}$ where m is assumed a material constant. This constant m is later known better as γ, the Walker exponent. Using simple manipulation, the Paris equation can be rewritten as

$$\frac{da}{dN} = C\left[\frac{\Delta K}{(1-R)^{1-\gamma}}\right]^{n}. \tag{1}$$

This equation successfully models the load ratio dependence of crack propagation rates but only models Stage II growth.

The third group, the most recently published models, is represented by the three-component model of Saxena et al. (6). They were able to fit experimental data, which was taken from a 2219-T851 aluminum alloy and a Ni-steel at various load ratios, for all three stages of crack growth rate. Although it does not have a fundamental physical basis, the model is widely acceptable. The three-component model is

$$\frac{1}{(da/dN)} = \frac{A_1}{(\Delta K)^{n_1}} + A_2\left[\frac{1}{(\Delta K)^{n_2}} - C'\right]. \tag{2}$$

The constant C' in Eqn. 2 represents the load ratio term.

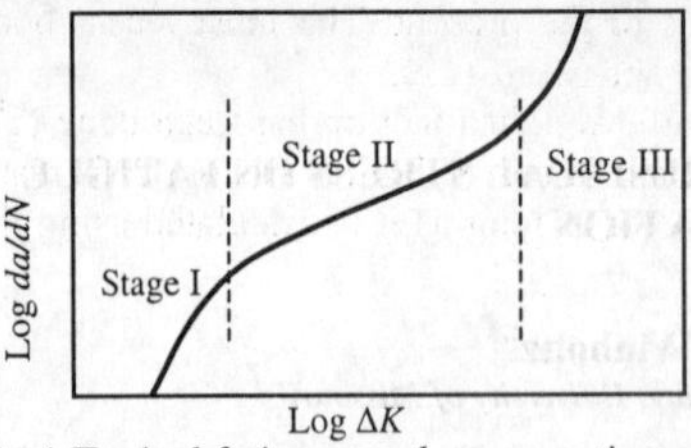

Fig.1 Typical fatigue crack propagation rate curve

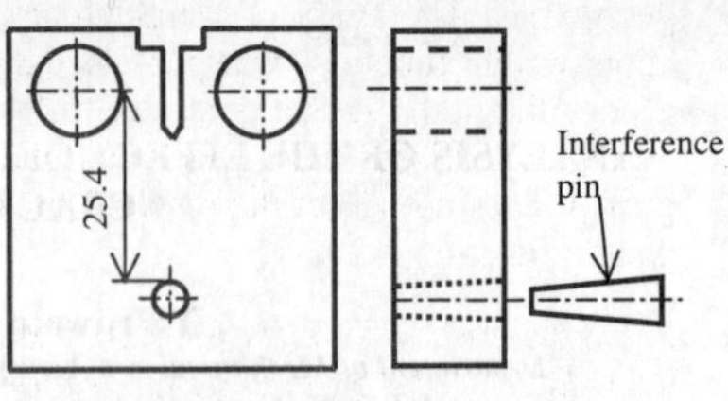

Fig. 2 CT specimen with interference pin

1.2. *Crack Propagation in Residual Stress Field*

Studies of crack propagation in residual stress fields began in the 1970s. In 1977 Underwood et al. (1) published research on fatigue crack propagation through a measured residual stress field in alloy steel. Using bend specimens of nickel-chromium-molybdenum steel, they tested two groups of specimens, stress free and residual stressed specimens. They used localized plastic deformation to generate residual stress. With strain gages applied to the sample before it was deformed, they verified the residual stress. They detected lower fatigue crack propagation rates in samples with compressive residual stress relative to the residual stress free samples. In a different publication, Underwood also found similar results in his next study (2). There he used notched bend specimens of ASTM A723 steel with three types of notch treatment and resulting residual stress: shot peening, hole swaging, and tensile overload. Using x-rays to measure the residual stresses, he found that the specimens with the highest compressive residual stresses lasted the longest. He again implies the concept of superposition of the applied and residual stress intensity factors.

Elber made a great contribution on the early development of the research on residual stress in relation to the fatigue crack propagation rate (3). In his study, using 2024-T3 aluminum alloy sheet, he showed that residual compressive stresses tend to close the crack tip over some distance. Subsequent cycling can cause crack growth only if the residual stresses are overcome to a degree that the crack tip is opened again.

In 1982, Nelson laid the concrete concept of the use of the superposition principle. He added the residual and applied stress intensity factors and named it the effective stress intensity factor (4). Using this, he analyzed crack propagation rates. The analysis gave similar predictions on the fatigue crack propagation to the other model he used, a simplified crack closure model. In the same year, Parker published his research (5). Similar to what Nelson did, Parker used effective stress intensity factors for components containing residual stress. The most important thing he found was that there is no reason to assume that the superposition principle is violated by 'stress fading' during fatigue crack growth in residual stress fields at stress levels which only produce localized (crack tip) yielding.

It is agreed that engineering practice often presents problems of cracks in complex stress fields, e.g. residual stress fields, which make it difficult to determine the stress intensity factors. Under such circumstances, the weight function method provides a powerful and simple means for calculating stress intensity factors from the residual stresses. This was also realized by Wu, who in 1984 published his work on approximate weight functions for center and edge cracks in finite bodies (9). In his paper, Wu calculated various weight functions to be used for calculating stress intensity factors. He claimed that his approximate weight functions were powerful, efficient, and simple to use in determining stress intensity factors with satisfactory accuracy for cracks in finite bodies under load or displacement control, particularly when the cracks were situated in complex stress fields, e.g. residual stress fields. Wu and Carlsson published a book on weight functions and stress intensity factor solutions (10). In this book, they show analytical results of weight functions for various sample geometries. The study of weight functions continues to the present. The most recent book about weight functions was published in 1997 by Fett and Munz (11).

Since the mid 1980s a great deal of research using the weight function has been done (12-19). Most of them have concluded that the residual stress redistribution arising from crack growth does not affect the residual stress intensity factor as long as it is calculated using the weight function.

2. EXPERIMENTAL PROCEDURES

2.1. *Material and Specimen Preparation*

The material used for this study was spheroidized 1080 steel. The material was obtained in the form of 12.7 mm hot rolled plate. The material was austenitized for 30 minutes at 800 °C followed by a water quench. The specimens were then tempered at 700 °C for 3 hours and air cooled. The average ferrite grain size and cementite particle sizes were 5.6 μm and 1 μm, respectively. The fine microstructure was chosen because a small particle size is needed to illuminate many grains in a small diffraction gage volume to get a proper powder diffraction average. After the heat treatment, the specimens had an oxidized and decarburized layer. Since this layer is not characteristic of the whole material, it was removed for accurate x-ray diffraction measurements because x-rays only sample a layer extending ~20 μm below the surface. Electro-polishing was used to remove 0.5 mm from the surfaces without introducing residual stresses.

The specimens were then machined into ASTM standard compact tension (CT) specimens (20). In some specimens, interference pins were inserted. The center of the pin was inserted at 28.6 mm from the centerline of the pin loading holes. Consequently, the edge of the interference pin is 25.4 mm from the center of the loading holes, see Fig. 2. The hole that was drilled for the tapered pin had a taper equal to that of the taper of the pin. In the other half of the specimens, no pin was inserted, and therefore, no hole was drilled. The pins were made of plain carbon steel that had been case hardened. The pins had a taper of approximately 20.8 mm/m. Tapered pins were chosen to facilitate the insertion of the pins to create residual stress. An interference level between the specimen and pin of approximately 0.125 mm was needed. The misfit was achieved by pressing the pin into the specimen.

2.2 *Initial Residual Stress Measurements*

The initial residual stresses were measured using x-ray diffraction at Northwestern University (21). A rotating anode source was used with chromium characteristic x-rays of wavelength 2.2897 Å. The x-rays were focused on the specimen using a tapered glass capillary tube. The capillary produced a spot size of 210 μm on the surface of the specimen. The stress component perpendicular to the direction of crack propagation and perpendicular to the crack faces was measured along the prospective crack line.

2.3. *Fatigue Crack Propagation Measurements*

Fatigue precracking was performed under software control (22). A precrack of approximately 8.6 mm was achieved before starting the fatigue tests. For both the precracking and cracking a sinusoidal wave-form of 4 Hz was used. The crack length was measured using the double-cantilever clip-in displacement gage mounted in the crack mouth using the compliance method suggested by ASTM standard (20). The crack length was also carefully monitored using a traveling microscope.

The experiments were started by investigating the basic characteristics of the material. This was done by using constant load range with various load ratios, *R*, giving the material's load ratio dependency. Next, specimens were cracked with six constant stress intensity factor ranges, ΔK, ranging from 17.5 to 25 MPa$\sqrt{m}$, for samples with residual stresses and without residual stress. These experiments give a direct comparison for the same series of ΔK. The *R* used was 0.1 for all of the tests. The loads used during constant ΔK tests were determined by the software program to keep a constant applied ΔK. Then specimens with and without residual stresses were cracked under constant load range modes. Here the R values used were 0.1 and 0.2.

2.4. *Plastic Zone Size Measurements*

The size of the plastic zone was measured using the diffraction line broadening from a small synchrotron x-ray beam. The method relies on the changing of the diffraction peak width with plastic deformation due to an increased dislocation density. By comparing the full width at half-maximum (FWHM) of the diffraction peaks from various positions within the material, one can determine the plastic zone sizes. To obtain the interior plastic zone size, the specimens were sectioned longitudinally. The surface of the samples was metallographically polished and etched. These processes remove the metallurgical damage that may occur during the sectioning. Since the material has quite fine grains (5.6 μm ferrite and 1 μm cementite) the beam size used was 50 x 50 μm.

Experiments were performed at the SRI CAT 1-BM beamline at the Advanced Photon Source, Argonne National Laboratory. The x-ray energy used was 10 keV and the Fe-411 peak was studied. The approximate 2θ was 132.7°. The experiment started with finding the position of the crack surface. This can be done by monitoring fluorescence produced by the beam and scanning from outside the sample into the sample. The position where the fluorescence from ferrite changes suddenly from almost zero to a maximum was the edge of the sample, in this case the crack surface. Once this surface is found, the line broadening scanning can be done for different positions. Near the crack face the peak was broader than areas remote from the crack face, since the area around the crack face had undergone plastic deformation as the crack grew. As the sample was moved, the boundary where the peaks become narrow indicates the plastic zone boundary.

3. RESULTS AND ANALYSIS

3.1. *Residual Stress Intensity Factor*

Fig. 3 shows the initial residual stresses along the prospective crack line, that is, the stress distribution on the specimen before fatigue cracking. Both the front and back faces of the specimen were measured. Near the pin interface there are some differences between the front and back faces due to the friction of inserting the pin. Finite element modeling of the insertion process gives comparable results for the faces and shows that the stress distribution in the interior is similar (23).

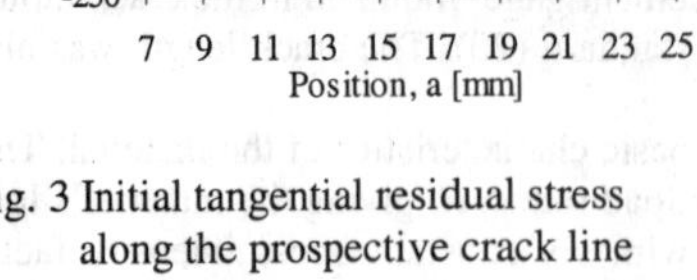

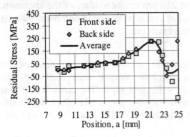

Fig. 3 Initial tangential residual stress along the prospective crack line

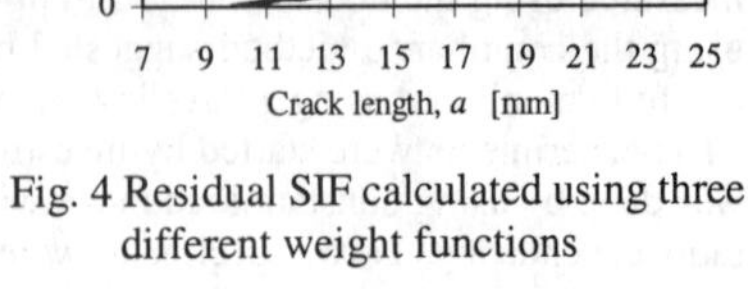

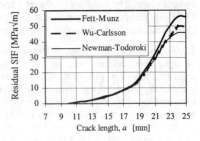

Fig. 4 Residual SIF calculated using three different weight functions

The residual stresses were converted to a residual stress intensity factor using the weight function for a CT specimen and the relation (11)

$$K_R = \int_0^a \sigma(x) \cdot m(a,x)dx. \qquad (3)$$

This gives the stress intensity factor of the system when the sample has a crack length a. Before the fatigue crack is introduced this residual stress intensity factor does not actually exist. Here the weight function $m(a,x)$ depends only on the geometry of the component and a is the crack length of interest. Fig. 4 shows the result of these calculations using three different solutions for the weight functions (10, 11, 18). The final analysis was done using the Fett-Munz solution because it was the most recent and best fit the experimental data.

3.2. *Fatigue Test*

Fatigue tests begin with basic fatigue crack propagation characterization of the base material. Table I shows the material constants obtained for the Paris, Walker, and TC models.

Table I. Fatigue characterization results.

Model	Equation	Constant	Note
Paris	$\dfrac{da}{dN} = C(\Delta K)^n$	C=2.6x10^{-10} n=4	The constants expressed in this table correlate *da/dN* and the stress intensity factor range when their units are in [mm/cycle] and [MPa√m], respectively.
Walker	$\dfrac{da}{dN} = C\left[\dfrac{\Delta K}{(1-R)^{(1-\gamma)}}\right]^n$	C=2.4x10^{-10} n=4 γ=0.8	
Three-Component	$\dfrac{1}{(da/dN)} = \dfrac{A_1(R)}{(\Delta K)^{n_1}} + A_2(R)\left[\dfrac{1}{(\Delta K)^{n_2}} - \dfrac{1}{(K_c(1-R))^{n_2}}\right]$ where $A_1(R) = C_1(1-R)^\alpha$ for $0.1 \le R \le 0.5$ $A_1(R) = C_2$ for $0.5 \le R \le 0.8$ $A_2(R) = C_3(1-R)^\beta$	C_1=1.6 x 10^{18} C_2=1.5 x 10^{12} C_3=4 x 10^9 α=20 β=0.5 n_1=10.5 n_2=4 K_c=83	

Fig. 5 shows one of six experimental results performed with constant applied ΔK on a specimen containing residual stresses. The figure relates the crack length a and the fatigue crack propagation (FCP) rate. In the figure, the prediction based on the three models is also plotted. The predictions based on the TC model fit best with the experiment results. The other results, which are not shown here, also show similar trends.

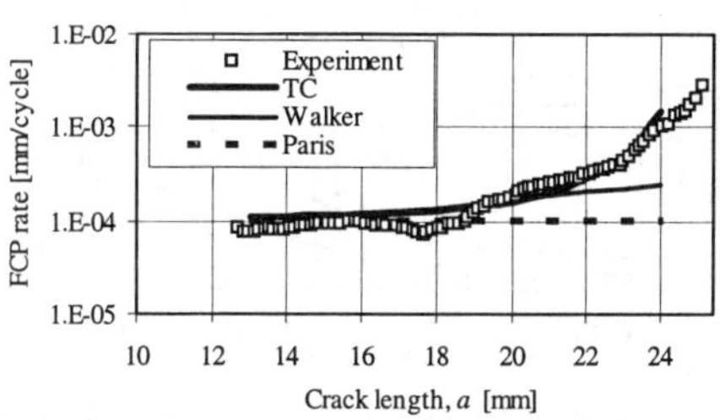

Fig. 5 Experiment with constant applied SIF range applied load ΔK=25 MPa√m

Fig. 6 shows the typical result for a residual stress specimen using a constant applied load range, ΔP. The other result performed with R=0.2, which is not shown in here, is similar. As with the constant applied ΔK mode, the predictions based on the TC model fit best with the experiment results.

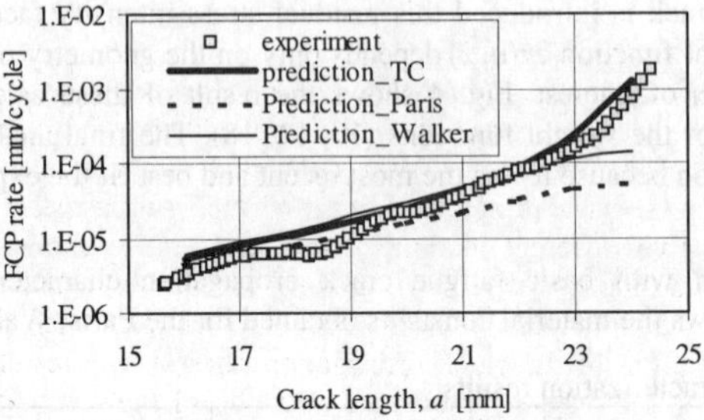

Fig. 6 Experiment with constant ΔP=3.36 kN with load ratio R= 0.1

The predictions were made as follows. Using the superposition principle the effective load ratio can be calculated

$$R' = \frac{K_{\min} + K_{\mathrm{R}}}{K_{\max} + K_{\mathrm{R}}}. \tag{4}$$

The effective load ratio R' changes from the original applied load ratio. Here, $K_{\min}$ and $K_{\max}$ are minimum and maximum applied stress intensity factors. K_{R} is the residual stress intensity factor shown in Fig. 4. Having calculated R' for every position, the predictions were then made using the constants obtained in material characterization shown in Table I.

3.3. *Plastic Zone Measurements*

Fig. 7 shows experimental results of plastic zone size along the crack length. Even though the sample experienced a constant maximum applied SIF throughout the experiment, the plastic zone size was found to vary. The results here are also compared with some analytical and experimental approximations available (24-28). The prediction lines in the figures were made by assuming that the total maximum SIF is the superposition of the maximum applied SIF and the residual SIF. The experimental result obtained here falls in between Rice's and Irwin's analytical solutions (26, 27).

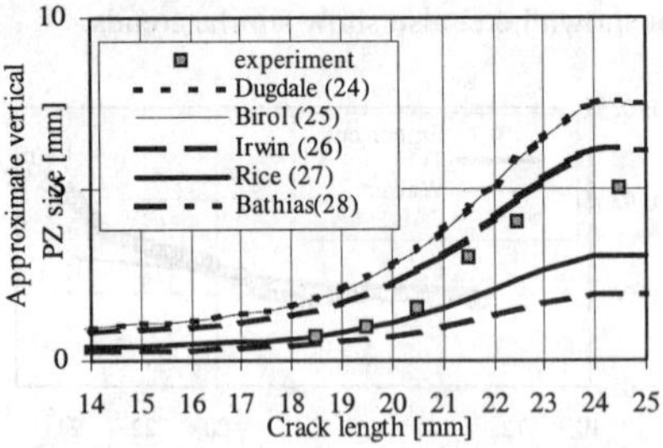

Fig. 7 Vertical plastic zone sizes in the interior of the sample

The experimental results are also laid in between the calculation based on constants experimentally obtained by Birol (25), which was based on an etching method, and Bathias (28), which was based on the microhardness method. It can be implied that the diffraction line broadening method has a sensitivity in revealing the plastic zone in between these two methods.

4. SUMMARY AND CONCLUSION

Simplifications of the interaction between residual stresses and applied stresses were performed. Both the residual stresses and the applied stresses were converted to stress intensity factors independently. Having been converted to stress intensity factors, they are combined easily using the basic principle of linear elastic fracture mechanics.

Experiments using two different loading modes, constant applied stress intensity factor range and constant load modes, were performed for samples with and without initial tensile residual stresses on their prospective crack lines. The samples with initial tensile residual stresses show acceleration of the crack propagation rates. These results are compared with predictions based on three different models. Evaluation of the results lead to the following conclusions:

1. The residual stresses in a specimen can be used, with the weight function, to compute a residual stress intensity factor that a crack will experience as it propagates through the residual stresses.

2. Combining the residual stress intensity factor and a crack propagation law, one can predict the fatigue crack growth rate of a crack growing into a tensile residual stress field. Superposition may not work satisfactorily if either the residual or applied stress intensity factors are compressive. If the net stress intensity factor is decreasing as the crack grows, the plastic zone size is decreasing which can cause the crack to behave differently than the growth model.

3. Tensile residual stresses accelerate a fatigue crack by increasing the load ratio. This has two effects. First, materials display a load ratio sensitivity, usually quantified by the Walker exponent γ, such that cracks grow faster at a higher load ratio. Secondly, at a higher load ratio cracks will transition into the more rapid Stage III growth regime at a lower stress intensity range. This effect can be seen in Figs. 5 and 6 as the point where the TC model deviates from the Walker model predicting higher crack growth rates better representing the experimental data.

4. The three-component model of Saxena gives a good prediction of fatigue crack propagation rates when used with the superposition of the applied and residual stress intensity factors. It captures both of the load ratio sensitivity and the transition to Stage III growth and hence makes a better prediction for the crack growth rate than the Walker or Paris models.

5. The size of the plastic zone can be measured with a small synchrotron x-ray beam along a fatigue crack by measuring the diffraction line broadening of the material perpendicular to the crack faces. The superposition of the residual stress intensity factor and the maximum applied stress intensity factor during fatigue crack growth correctly predicts the shape of the plastic zone size variation as a fatigue crack grows into a tensile residual stress field. The measured size of the plastic zone falls between the theoretical predictions of Rice and Irwin, which give upper and lower bounds, respectively.

ACKNOWLEDGEMENTS

The authors would like to acknowledge the University of Missouri Research Board for funding this research. They also express thanks to J.D. Almer for performing the initial residual stress measurement at Northwestern University. The assistance of D.R. Haeffner and P.L. Lee with the synchrotron x-ray measurements is gratefully acknowledged. The use of the Advanced Photon Source was supported by the U.S. Department of Energy, Basic Energy Sciences, Office of Science, under Contract No. W-31-109-Eng-38.

REFERENCES

1. Underwood J.H, Pook L. P, and Sharples J.K, ASTM STP 631 (1977) 402
2. Underwood J.H, Experimental Mechanics (March 1995) 61
3. Elber W, ASTM STP 486 (1971) 230
4. Nelson D. V, ASTM STP 776 (1982) 172
5. Parker A. P, ASTM STP 776 (1982) 13
6. Saxena A, Hudak S. J. Jr, and Jouris G. M, Engng Fracture Mechanics 12 (1979) 103
7. Miller M. S and Gallagher J. P, ASTM STP 738 (1981) 205
8. Walker K, ASTM STP 462 (1970) 1
9. Wu X. R, Engng Fracture Mechanics 20 (1984) 35
10. Wu X. R and Carlsson A. J, 'Weight functions and stress intensity factor solutions', Pergamon Press (Oxford-UK), 1991
11. Fett T and Munz D, 'Stress Intensity Factors and Weight Functions', Computational mechanics publications (Southampton-UK), 1997.
12. Stacey A and Webster G. A, ASTM STP 1004 (1988) 37
13. Nguyen N and Wahab M. A, Welding Journal 75 (1996) 55s
14. Itoh Y. Z, Engng Fracture Mechanics 33 (1989) 397
15. Okamoto A and Nakamura H, Journal of Pressure Vessel Technology 112 (1990) 199
16. Glinka G, ASTM STP 677 (1979) 198
17. Glinka G, Advances in Surface Treatments: Technology-Applications-Effects, Pergamon press, (1987) 413
18. Todoroki A and Kobayashi H, Trans of the Japan Society of Mechanical Engineers A-54 (1988) 30
19. Todoroki A and Kobayashi H, Proceeding of the LSME/JSME Joint Conference, Seoul, Korea, (1990) 367
20. ASTM Standards, ASTM Designation E 647-95a.
21. Almer J. D, Cohen J.B, and Winholtz R.A, Metall. and Matls. Trans 29A (1998) 2127
22. MTS Systems Corporation, '759.40 Testware fatigue crack growth test operator's guide', 1993, MTS System Corporation.
23. Almer J.D, Cohen J.B, McCallum K.R, and Winholtz R.A, Proceedings of the Fifth International Conference on Residual Stress, Soc. Exp. Mech., Bethel, CT (1997) 1072
24. Dugdale D.S, Journal of Mechanics and Physics of Solids 8 (1960) 100
25. Birol Y, Journal of Materials Science 23 (1988) 2079
26. Irwin G.R, Proceeding of Seventh Sagamore Ordnance Materials Conference, Syracuse University, (1960) IV.63
27. Rice J.R, Int. J. Solids Structures 8 (1972) 751
28. Bathias C and Pelloux R.M, Metallurgical Transactions 4 (1973) 1265

TRIAXIAL RESIDUAL STRESSES AFFECT DRIVING FORCE AND CONSTRAINT TO ALTER FRACTURE TOUGHNESS

Michael R. Hill and Theodore Yau
Mechanical and Aeronautical Engineering
University of California
One Shields Avenue, Davis, CA 95616, USA

ABSTRACT

This paper discusses the role of triaxial residual stresses in altering fracture behavior. Historically, residual stress effects in fracture have focused on the crack driving force, so that opening mode residual stresses are assumed solely to influence fracture. However, residual stresses can also impact constraint conditions at the crack-tip, thereby altering effective material toughness. This paper illustrates these two residual stress effects by discussing recent numerical and experimental results. The numerical aspects of the paper employ non-linear finite element analyses in which residual stresses are handled using eigenstrain. Micromechanical fracture prediction schemes, which depend directly on the crack-tip conditions rather than a global parameter, are used to predict fracture. Domain integral solutions for the crack driving force, derived from FEM results, allow comparison between the micromechanical and more traditional global parameter approaches. Experimental toughness measurements from notched bend bars containing triaxial residual stresses due to local compression complement the numerical work by demonstrating the accuracy of the micromechanical approach. Finally, discussions highlight the need to consider both the driving force and constraint effects caused by residual stresses when predicting structural failure.

1 INTRODUCTION

Recent research in micromechanical modeling has made progress toward the accurate prediction of fracture under various crack-tip constraint conditions. Historically, fracture prediction has focused on determining a global fracture parameter (e.g., the J-integral, J, or the Mode-I stress intensity factor, K_I) as a function of applied load, and finding the load at which the parameter exceeds a critical level for fracture. This approach rests on the assumption that the fracture parameter alone controls the crack-tip stress and strain. Unfortunately, in application, material non-linearity (i.e., yielding) at the crack-tip invalidates this assumption. Yielding is a function of the triaxial state of stress, and the crack-tip stress state has a range of variation in real structures. In fact, it is well known that differences in crack-tip triaxiality (or, more commonly "constraint") can exist in structures due to differences in geometry and applied loading (e.g., thick versus thin, or tension versus bending). Further, different crack-tip stresses lead to fracture at different levels of the global fracture parameter. An alternative method to parameter-based approaches, micromechanical methods directly examine the crack-tip stress and strain state to provide an estimate of fracture propensity. Implementation of the micromechanical approach therefore requires the prediction of crack-tip stress and strain, and its history with applied loading. In practice, finite element methods (FEM) are used to compute the crack-tip conditions, as a function of applied loading.

Application of the micromechanical approach to predict fracture in residual stress bearing structures provides some surprising results. The traditional approach to predict fracture of residual stress (RS) bearing, flawed components involves linear superposition. This approach assumes that only opening mode RS will impact the fracture process, when, in fact, residual stresses are often triaxial. Triaxial RS will influence non-linear material behavior at the crack-tip, a process not accounted for by superposition. Including RS in a micromechanical approach, however, does allow the residual stress field to affect the behavior of material at the crack-tip. Accordingly, the micromechanical approach offers a more complete accounting of RS effects in fracture, and gives insight to the fracture process when RS is present.

This paper explains the application of micromechanics when RS is present, and illustrates the significance of RS-induced constraint.

2 FRAMEWORK

This section describes a computational and analytical framework for predicting fracture in flawed, RS bearing structures using micromechanics. We first lay out the general finite element procedures employed. Next, we describe methods for introducing RS into the computation. The computational results provide the crack-tip stress and strain history as a function of applied load, which serve as input to a micromechanical fracture prediction model. Two such models for predicting fracture are presented: the RKR model for brittle fracture, and the SMCS model for ductile fracture. Finally, *J-Q* analysis is described, which helps to interpret the stress and strain history at the crack-tip, and to compare the results of micromechanics to those that would be obtained using a traditional global parameter approach.

2.1 General analysis techniques

Elastic-plastic finite element computation is used to simulate the response of a structure of interest to both applied and residual stresses simultaneously. The finite element solutions employ a non-linear, finite strain formulation. Plasticity is assumed to follow isotropic, incremental J_2 flow theory with a piece-wise linear Cauchy-stress logarithmic-strain curve obtained from tensile testing. Commercial codes can be used to perform these analyses. Mesh refinement in the crack-tip region is critical, and must assure that stress and strain are accurately captured in the near crack-tip region. Time-stepping in the analysis provides a means to capture the developing crack-tip state with increasing applied load.

2.2 Inclusion of residual stress

Residual stress is included in the finite element computation using eigenstrain. Eigenstrain is a combination of all the non-elastic, incompatible strains set up during processing of a material Mura (1). In welding, the eigenstrain is a combination of thermal, plastic, and transformation strains; in coining or autofrettage, the eigenstrain is due to plasticity. The eigenstrain field is defined with reference to elastic deformation of the structure, and reproduces the entire RS state when the material behavior is elastic. For a particular process the eigenstrain field is a tensor with spatial dependence, and can be found experimentally Hill (2) or by modeling Goldak (3).

The use of an eigenstrain distribution in modeling offers several advantages for further analysis. First, the residual stress present can be determined by imposing the eigenstrain distribution in a linear elastic finite element model of the geometry. (Note that residual stresses, by their nature, do not result in active yielding, and a valid eigenstrain field must impose stresses that satisfy the yield criterion). Although an eigenstrain analysis is complicated by the spatial variation of each component of the eigenstrain tensor, a general-purpose finite element program can be used to produce the RS field. Further, when the eigenstrain field is known, the entire, full-field, triaxial RS state is known at every point within the structure.

When the eigenstrain field is known for the unflawed structure, the analysis of a flawed structure can be performed. The addition of a crack introduces new surfaces, and the RS state in the flawed body depends on these surfaces. If the structure is linear elastic, the state is found simply by modeling the traction-free surfaces. In non-linear materials, crack-tip yielding must be allowed when introducing the flaw. To handle this situation, the eigenstı distribution is first imposed in the body with crack-face nodes restrained, and the equilibriuı. RS state found (this step is elastic). Then, the crack-face nodes are released in succession, so that the crack gradually extends from the free surface to simulate fatigue (this step can be elastic-plastic). The rate at which the crack is extended will have a bearing on the crack-tip fields, and one must ensure that the opening is gradual enough (e.g., so subsequent fracture analysis is not affected). When properly executed, this process redistributes the original RS field, allowing for crack-tip yielding, and resulting in a flawed RS bearing structure.

Once RS is introduced into the computation, applied loading is simulated. During this subsequent loading phase, the residual and applied stresses act together at the material level. Any new plastic deformation is the result of both stress types. Therefore, this analysis technique allows for the non-linear interaction of RS and applied loading, which is not accounted for when applying global approaches.

An alternative to using eigenstrain is to directly simulate the process causing the RS field. Results of this simulation can then be used as initial conditions for the simulation of applied loading. However, direct simulation can only be readily pursued for simple problems, with small amounts of plasticity or other non-linear strain.

2.3 Micromechanical fracture prediction

Since the analysis technique just described provides a complete description of the material state in the presence of residual and applied loading, the crack-tip material history can be used within a micromechanical scheme to predict fracture. The physical phenomena occurring in the fracture process vary, and it is generally useful to consider brittle and ductile fracture processes separately Shih (4). Here we briefly describe one model for predicting each type of fracture. In principle, other micromechanical models could be employed.

2.3.1 The RKR model for cleavage fracture initiation

Initiation of cleavage fracture in mild steels can be predicted using the RKR micromechanical model Ritchie (5). This simple model predicts fracture when the opening stress, σ_{yy}, ahead of the crack-tip exceeds a fracture stress, σ_f*, over a microstructurally relevant distance, l*. In applying this model, one monitors the progress of the opening stress ahead of the crack-tip due to residual and applied loading. Once the RKR criterion is satisfied, fracture is predicted. The parameters in the RKR model are typically found through laboratory testing for a given material and reported ranges for steels are 2 to 5 grain diameters for l*, and 2 to 4 times the yield strength for σ_f* Ritchie (5). When the micromechanics condition for fracture initiation is satisfied, the associated applied load and global fracture parameters (e.g., *J*-integral) can be found from the FEM results.

2.3.2 The SMCS model for ductile fracture initiation

Ductile fracture behavior is dependent upon both the stress and deformation state at the crack-tip. The micro-mechanisms of ductile fracture are void nucleation and growth, both of which precipitate from second-phase particles within the microstructure. Local plastic strain and hydrostatic stress drive the nucleation and growth process. Mackenzie, et al., proposed a model which predicts the initiation of ductile fracture when equivalent plastic strain near the crack-tip, $\varepsilon_p'(r,\theta)$, exceeds a critical amount, $\varepsilon_p^{crit}(r,\theta)$, over some distance ahead of the crack-tip, l_d* (where r and θ are crack-tip centered coordinates) MacKenzie (6). This critical level of plastic strain depends on the ratio of hydrostatic to von Mises stress at a given material point, $\bar{\sigma}/\sigma'$. The characteristic length, l_d*, is related to the spacing of second-phase particles. The critical level of plastic strain can be written for many materials as Rice (7)

$$\varepsilon_p^{crit}(r,\theta) = \alpha \exp\left(-\beta \frac{\bar{\sigma}(r,\theta)}{\sigma'(r,\theta)}\right) \qquad [1]$$

β are material parameters, fitted to data obtained from tests and analyses of e specimens MacKenzie (6). To predict fracture initiation, one can compute the

$$\mathrm{SMCS}(r,\theta) = \varepsilon_p'(r,\theta) - \varepsilon_p^{crit}(r,\theta) \qquad [2]$$

CS reflects the common name for this method: stress-modified critical strain (8). For a given loading condition, fracture is predicted when

$$\mathrm{SMCS}(r,\theta) \geq 0 \text{ for all points } r \leq l_d^*,\ \theta = \overline{\theta} \qquad [3]$$

In this expression it is recognized that ductile fracture will not necessarily initiate directly ahead of the crack-tip, but possibly at an oblique angle, $\theta = \overline{\theta}$. In application, $\overline{\theta}$ is found by maximizing SMCS with θ for $r = l_d^*$.

2.4 Characterization of crack-tip behavior

When the above procedures are used to predict fracture, none of the traditional global fracture parameters are used. Nevertheless, it is useful to compare the micromechanical predictions with those that might be made using a traditional approach. To perform this comparison, we utilize two parameters, one related to driving force and one to constraint. Specifically, we invoke *J-Q* theory, which was developed from simulation of crack-tip fields in finite and infinite size bodies O'Dowd (9), O'Dowd (10).

During the non-linear analysis, the *J*-integral is estimated at each increment of applied loading using the domain-integral technique. As such, the computed value of *J* includes the contribution of residual stress within the material. For a given level of *J*, the constraint conditions at the crack-tip are represented by the parameter Q. Q has been shown to characterize the magnitude of the hydrostatic stress over the forward sector ahead of the crack-tip to a good approximation. Q is formally defined as

$$Q = \frac{\sigma_{\theta\theta} - \sigma_{\theta\theta}^{ssy}}{\sigma_o} \text{ at } \theta = 0,\ r/(J/\sigma_o) = n \qquad [4]$$

where, σ_o is the material yield strength, and n is a constant, usually taken in the range 2 to 4 O'Dowd (9), O'Dowd (10). Q depends on the crack-tip stress state in the body of interest, $\sigma_{\theta\theta}$, and on the stress state in a plane-strain, Mode I loaded, small-scale yielding reference solution, $\sigma_{\theta\theta}^{ssy}$, where both are subject to the same applied J.

Because Q is a constraint parameter, it provides insight into the fracture process. Q near zero suggests that a body is in small-scale yielding. As deformation levels increase in finite specimens, the hydrostatic stresses at the crack-tip are relieved, producing a negative Q value, and signaling a loss in constraint. A negative value of Q indicates lower crack-tip stress compared to a body in small-scale yielding and, therefore, a reduced propensity for cleavage fracture at a given value of J. A positive Q-value indicates that high constraint exists for a particular crack-tip state.

Having the above framework at hand, we employ it in two examples, one purely computational, and one a hybrid of computation and experiment. These two examples illustrate the method and bring up some interesting results for discussion.

3 TRIAXIAL STRESS EFFECTS IN BRITTLE FRACTURE

This section summarizes a recent numerical study on the influence of RS on brittle fracture of a welded mild steel structure. The RKR micromechanical model is used to predict fracture. Details of the study can be found in Panontin (11).

3.1 Geometry and material

This section focuses on the prediction of brittle fracture of the axially loaded, girth-welded

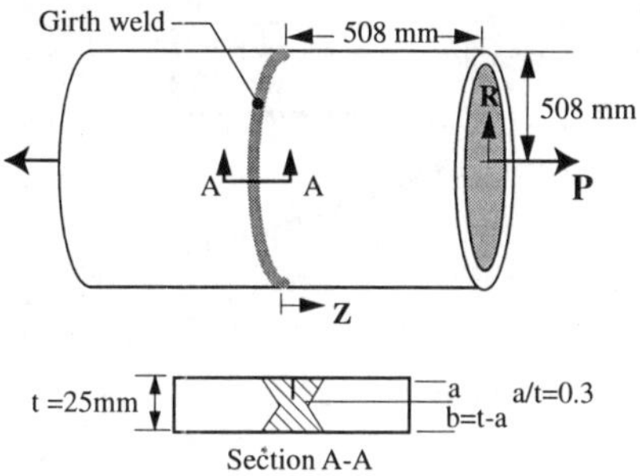

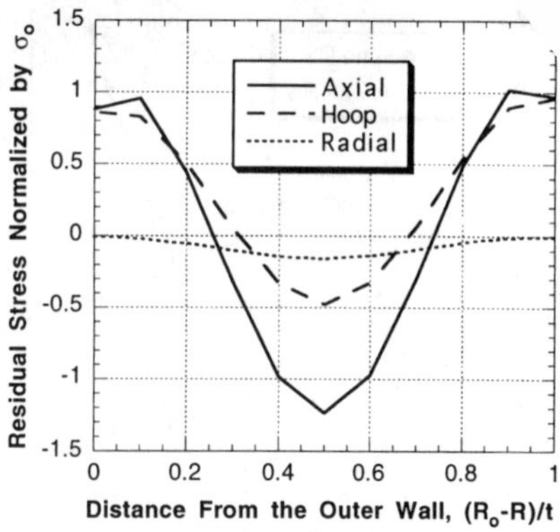

Figure 1 – (a) Girth-welded pressure shell, (b) RS in the unflawed condition

shell shown in Figure 1(a), initiating from a circumferential external flaw. The properties assumed are those of A516-70, a high hardening, ferritic, pressure vessel steel with uniaxial yield strength of 303 MPa. The RKR parameters for this material are assumed to be $\sigma_f^* = 3.5\sigma_o$ and $l^* = 0.15$ mm, or about 3 ferritic grain diameters.

3.2 Residual stresses

This analysis makes use of an assumed eigenstrain distribution. This distribution gives rise to residual stresses that are typical of a continuously welded, double-sided joint in mild steel plate Gunnert (12). The nature of continuous welding allows the assumption of an eigenstrain field that depends on the transverse and through-thickness welding directions, but is independent of position along the weld. Further, the eigenstrain field is assumed symmetric about both the centerline of the weld and the mid-wall of the shell. The residual stress field computed when the assumed eigenstrain field is imposed in the un-flawed geometry is shown in Figure 1(b), on the plane where the crack will be introduced. For the flaw orientation shown in Figure 1(a), axial stresses correspond to the opening mode, and over the length of defect considered (from 0 to 0.3 in Figure 1(b)), the axial RS is tensile. Accordingly, RS will tend to increase the crack-driving force and therefore decrease the fracture load.

3.3 Results

Fracture predictions using the RKR model show a strong constraint effect caused by RS. Fracture loads are predicted to be 21.3 MN and 9.83 MN without and with RS, respectively. Because RKR is satisfied at these loads, crack-tip opening stresses are nearly the same in each different geometry. However, this occurs at markedly different values of J, 36.7 kN/m without RS and 13.5 kN/m with RS. Recall that these values of J are computed using the domain integral, so they include the influence of RS on driving force. As shown in Figure 2(a), the significant change in J at fracture is due to high constraint imposed by the RS field. Figure 2(b) shows that this additional constraint suppresses plastic strain formation compared with the non-residual stress bearing case. These interesting results demonstrate that RS can cause a significant change in crack-tip constraint. Figure 2(a) shows clearly that the tension loaded shell has quite low constraint when RS is absent, but behaves like a body in small-scale yield when RS is present. If the RS bearing shell were assumed to have constraint similar to the RS-free shell, the superposition approach would lead to an erroneous and non-conservative fracture assessment. This observation gives credence to codified assumptions of high constraint, as RS can combine with applied loads to produce highly constrained crack-

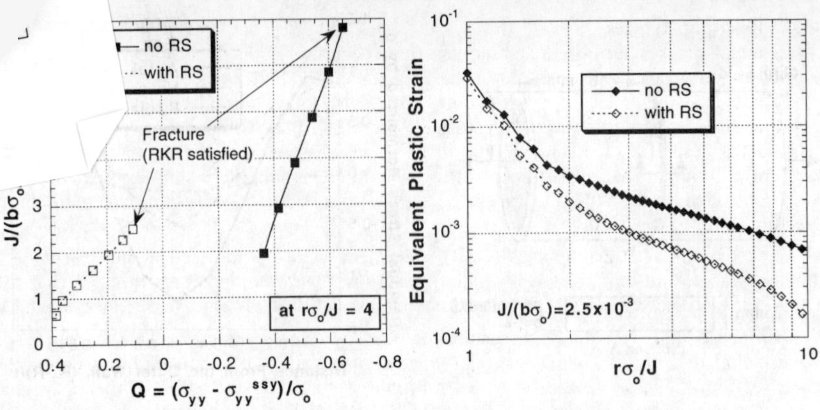

Figure 2 - (a) J-Q trajectories and (b) plastic strain for the shell

tip fields in a geometry and loading condition that would otherwise exhibit low constraint.

4 TRIAXIAL STRESS EFFECTS IN DUCTILE FRACTURE

This section discusses an experimental and computational investigation of residual stress effects on ductile fracture initiation in a high strength aluminum alloy. Residual stresses are introduced by local compression near the crack-tip. Results show that fracture predictions performed using the SMCS criterion predict the experimental trend of decreasing toughness with increasing local compression.

4.1 Geometry and material

A standard SE(B) specimen geometry is used, loaded in three point bending as shown in Figure 3(a). Experimental toughness measurements are made under various conditions. Two specimen thicknesses are used, corresponding to half- and full-plate thickness (12.5 and 25 mm). Nominal planar dimensions of these two specimen types were fixed at W = 25 mm and S/W = 4.

All specimens were removed in the TL orientation from a single 25 mm thick 7050 T7451 aluminum plate. 7050 is a high strength alloy resistant to stress corrosion cracking. It has low hardening (n ≈ 17), with a uniaxial yield strength of 531 Mpa (determined experimentally). The micromechanisms of fracture are ductile, although occurring at low energy. SMCS parameters found for this material in a previous study are: $\alpha = 4.2$, $\beta = 3.7$, and $l_d{*} = 0.15$ mm Hill (13).

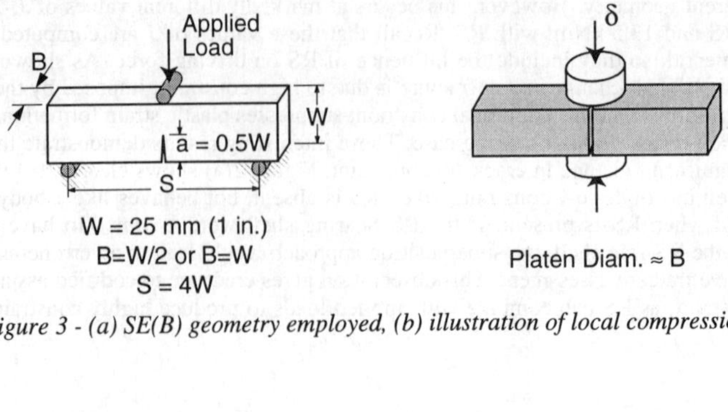

Figure 3 - (a) SE(B) geometry employed, (b) illustration of local compression

4.2 Residual stresses

Residual stresses are introduced into fracture specimens by local compression (LC). That is, two cylindrical platens are used to make indentations on both sides of the specimen on the W-S face, near the crack tip, as shown in Figure 3(b). LC is normally used to relieve weld residual stresses to allow fracture testing Towers (14), but it obviously produces its own triaxial RS field Hill (15). The amount of LC is usually stated as the permanent thickness reduction divided by original thickness, in percent. LC is relatively simple to perform and well controlled. In this study, LC provided a repeatable RS state, whose subsequent effect on fracture could be assessed.

Experimentally, full thickness (BxB) specimens were compressed about 1% using a 20 mm platen, and half-thickness (Bx2B) specimens were compressed from 1.2 to 2.5% using a 12 mm platen. LC was performed on notched SE(B)'s, prior to fatigue pre-cracking.

Computationally, residual stresses are included by direct simulation. That is, four steps were included in the FEM analysis. First, local compression was simulated by modeling the compression platen as a rigid body, in frictionless contact with the SE(B) specimen, and applying to it a given deformation. Second, the compression load was removed and the RS state obtained. Third, the crack was extended by node release to simulate pre-cracking. Finally, three-point loading was simulated. Results during this final step were used with the SMCS criterion to predict fracture. SMCS parameters are assumed independent of the LC process. That assumption is only valid over a small range of compression, as increasing plastic deformation will eventually alter microstructure and influence the fracture process.

4.3 Experimental procedures

Specimens were tested on a computer controlled, servo-hydraulic test frame, following procedures in ASTM E813. Digitally acquired load and mouth-opening data were reduced according to ASTM E399 to provide values of candidate initiation toughness, K_Q.

4.4 Results

Experimental results are plotted in Figure 4(a), showing the effect of LC on measured toughness. For the Bx2B specimens, LC reduces measured toughness about 6.7% per percent of LC applied. For the BxB specimen, LC has a greater effect and reduces toughness by about 17% per percent LC.

Computational results shown in Figure 4(a) agree with the experimental trends, but over-predict the effect of LC. The micromechanical approach predicts a toughness drop of 9.1% per percent LC applied for Bx2B specimens, and 23% for the BxB specimens.

The computational results allow insight into the reason for the toughness decrease caused by LC. *J-Q* results for three SE(B) specimen conditions discussed above are shown in Figure 4(b). Here we see that RS due to LC increases crack-tip stresses at a given *J*. The thicker specimens are subject to a higher degree of additional constraint at a lower level of LC. However, SMCS predicts fracture at roughly the same *J* in each specimen type, which suggests that the SMCS predictions are not highly dependent on the initial constraint conditions. (For reference, results of a simulation for a shallow crack specimen, with a/W = 0.15, are also shown in Figure 4(b). These show that SMCS predicts a large toughness change for a similar magnitude, but opposite sign, constraint change.) The toughness drop shown in Figure 4(a), then, must be due mainly to driving force, not constraint, especially for the thick specimen. This comparison of the RS effects on driving force and constraint in fracture can only be accomplished with the type of modeling discussed here. Therefore, these results demonstrate the usefulness of micromechanical modeling when considering fracture in RS-bearing structures. Further, the approach discussed here provides fracture predictions in good agreement with experimental results.

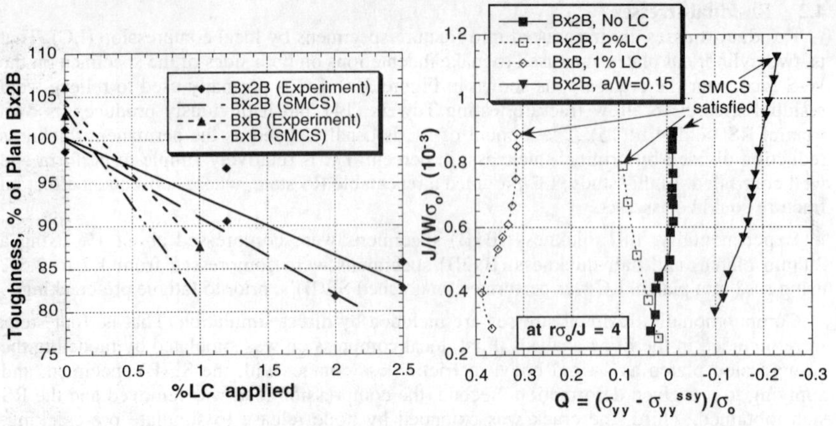

Figure 4 - The effect of LC: (a) Measured toughness, and (b) J-Q trend

5 DISCUSSION

This paper is intended to stimulate discussion regarding accepted methods of accounting for residual stresses in fracture prediction. Both computational and experimental results suggest a more thorough assessment of residual stress should be pursued, especially when the RS field is triaxial. Brevity here requires only a brief coverage of the requisite topics, and the interested reader should consult the references provided below.

6 REFERENCES

1. Mura T, 'Micromechanics of Defects in Solids', M. Nihoff (Dordrecht, Netherlands), 1987
2. Hill M R, 'Determination of Residual Stress Based on the Estimation of Eigenstrain', Ph.D. Thesis, Stanford University (1996)
3. Goldak J A, Patel B, et al, Adv Joining of Materials (AGARD CP-398) (1985) 1
4. Shih C F, Fat and Fract Mech, 29th Vol, ASTM STP 1332 (1999) 9
5. Ritchie R O, Server W L, Wullarert R A, Met Trans A 10 (1979) 1557
6. MacKenzie A C, Hancock J W, Brown D K, Eng Fract Mech 9 (1977) 167
7. Rice J R, Tracey D M, J Mech Phys Solids 17 (1969) 201
8. Panontin T L, Sheppard S D, Fat and Fract Mech, 26th Vol, ASTM STP 1256 (1995) 54
9. O'Dowd N P, Shih C F, J Mech Phys Solids 39 (1991) 989
10. O'Dowd N P, Shih C F, J Mech Phys Solids 40 (1992) 939
11. Panontin T L, Hill M R, Int J Fract 82 (1996) 317
12. Gunnert R, Proceedings of the Special Symposium on the Behavior of Welded Structures (1961) 164
13. Hill M R, Panontin T L, Manuscript in preparation for submission to Engineering Fracture Mechanics
14. Towers O L, Dawes M G, Elastic-Plastic Fracture Test Methods: The Users' Experience, ASTM STP 856 (1985) 23
15. Hill M R, Panontin T L, Fat and Fract Mech, 29th Vol, ASTM STP 1332 (1999) 154

SESSION 10B

RESIDUAL STRESS RELAXATION IN WELDED HIGH STRENGTH STEELS UNDER DIFFERENT LOADING CONDITIONS

Th. Nitschke-Pagel, H. Wohlfahrt
Welding Institute
Technical University Braunschweig
Germany

ABSTRACT

Investigations on welded joints of a high strength structural steel were carried out to observe the relaxation of residual stresses and microstructural changes under quasistatic tensile and compressive loading as well as during fatigue loading. The results of residual stress measurements by means of X-rays and diffraction line profile analyses in welded joints after different numbers of load cycles and under different load conditions reveal that tensile residual stresses with high initial magnitudes are reduced in first order due to quasistatic yielding during the first load cycle. Then the relaxation of the residual stresses increases linearily with the load stress. Under cyclic loading the relaxation of the residual stresses depends on the magnitude of the upper stress. An additional cyclic yielding leads to equivalent stresses calculated with the load stress and the two-dimensional residual stresses after higher number of load cycles, which are uniformly close to the cyclic yield strength of the base material.

1 INTRODUCTION

In literature much discussion is found on the influence of residual stresses on the fatigue behaviour of welded structures. Usually it is assumed that tensile residual stresses of the magnitude of the yield strength are generated at the weld toes. It is supposed, that the total amount of the load stresses and the residual stresses will exceed the yield strength during the first load cycle and therefore the residual stresses must be lowered by yielding so that the total amount of the residual stresses and the load stresses after the first cycle will be always as high as the yield strength /1/. It is well known, that a residual stress relaxation will occur if the load stress

$$\sigma^{LS} \geq R_e - \sigma^{RS} \text{ (quasistatic) or } \sigma^{LS} \geq R_{e,cyclic} - \sigma^{RS}$$

exceeds the yield strength (quasistatic loading) respectively the cyclic yield strength (cyclic loading) which is reduced by the initial residual stresses /2,5/. In case of a multiaxial state of the residual stresses the equivalent stresses must be taken into account. In low strength materials it is expected, that the residual stress relaxation is affected primarily by the yield strength of the material. Then the residual stresses after the first load cycle should be relatively constant but on a low level (fig.1). With increasing ultimate strength the yield strength increases more than the cyclic yield strength and therefore it is expected, that the residual stress relaxation due to static overloading decreases and a cyclic yielding leads to a constant residual stress relaxation during fatigue loading /3,4/. In steels with very high ultimate strengths it is assumed that the residual stresses will be stable. Several investigations on welded joints reveal, that especially in high strength steels where the fatigue strength probably depends significantly on the residual stresses, the tensile residual stresses due to welding are mostly much lower than the yield strength /12/. Nevertheless different changes of the

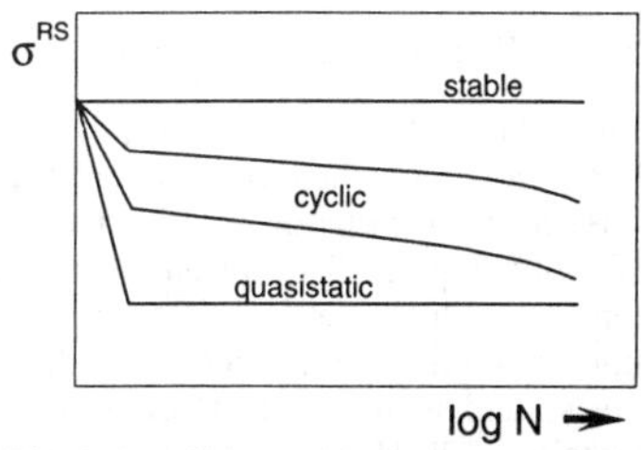

Fig.1 Possible residual stress relaxation characteristics due to fatigue loading /2/.

residual stresses and the microstucture can be detected under different load conditions even if the total amount of the load stresses and the residual stresses reaches neither the yield strength nor the cyclic yield strength /6/.

Investigations on welded joints of a high strength structural steel were carried out to observe the relaxation of residual stresses and microstructural changes under quasistatic tensile and compressive loading as well as during fatigue loading with different magnitudes of additionally applied mean stresses.

2 EXPERIMENTAL PROCEDURES

The investigations were carried out on welded joints of a quenched and tempered high strength structural steel (german grade S960QL, plate thickness 6 mm) with a yield strength of 1035 MPa. The weld seams were produced by TIG-welding with pulsed current without filler material (dummy seams) using a heat input of 10.13 kJ/cm. The welding speed was 0.2 m/min, the shielding gas was 99.95% Ar. All specimens were loaded transverse to the welding direction. The geometry of the specimens and the weld seam are given in fig.2.

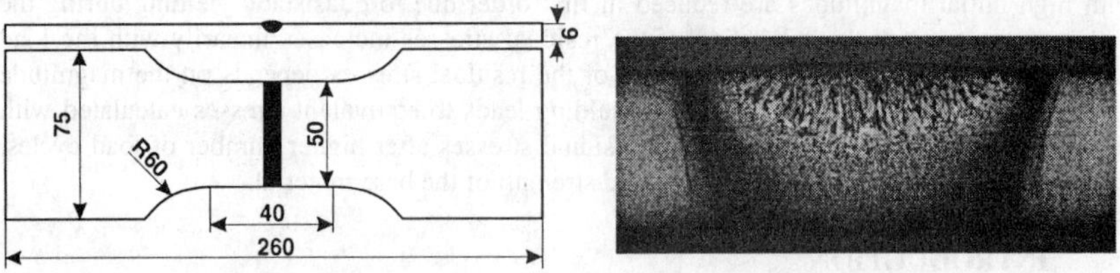

Figure 2 Specimen geometry and weld seam microstructure (overview), scale 5:1.

The longitudinal and the transverse residual stresses in the weldments were measured by means of X-rays. Therefore the diffraction lines of the {211}-lattice planes of the ferrite and the martensite were measured under 11 ψ-angles using CrK_α-radiation. The residual stresses were calculated with the $\sin^2\psi$-method. The X-ray profiles were analyzed with the modified single-line Voigt-method described in /7/, where the physical profiles (using an annealed C10 specimen as standard) were calculated with help of a Fast-Fourier-transformation. The specimens were loaded perpendicular to the weld seam quasistatically with compressive and with tensile load stresses in steps of ±100 MPa up to ±1000 MPa. Cyclic load experiments were performed under tensional loading with different stress amplitudes and stress ratios of $\kappa = -1$, $\kappa = -0.33$ and $\kappa = 0$. The residual stress relaxation under cyclic loading was examined with measurements after each load decade. The measurements were finished after 10^5 cycles respectively after fracture.

3 RESIDUAL STRESS RELAXATION DURING QUASISTATIC LOADING

Fig.3 shows the residual stress, the hardness and the half width distributions of the weldments before loading, where the residual stress distributions represent mean values and scatter bands after measurements on 27 specimens. The transverse residual stresses (e.g. in load direction) show the typical distribution after welding with a relatively high heat input. In the weld seam tensile residual stresses of 750 MPa (approximately 75% of the yield strength) are generated due to welding. With increasing distance from the weld centre line the residual stresses decrease and in the heat affected zone (HAZ) low compressive residual stresses of approximately – 120 MPa are found. As a consequence of the relatively low width of the specimens the magnitude of the longitudinal residual stresses is lower in the weld seam (450 MPa). The tensile residual stress peaks of 350 MPa in the base material, which are typical for joints welded with a relatively high heat input, are the equilibrium residual stresses generated during the phase transformation in the weld seam.

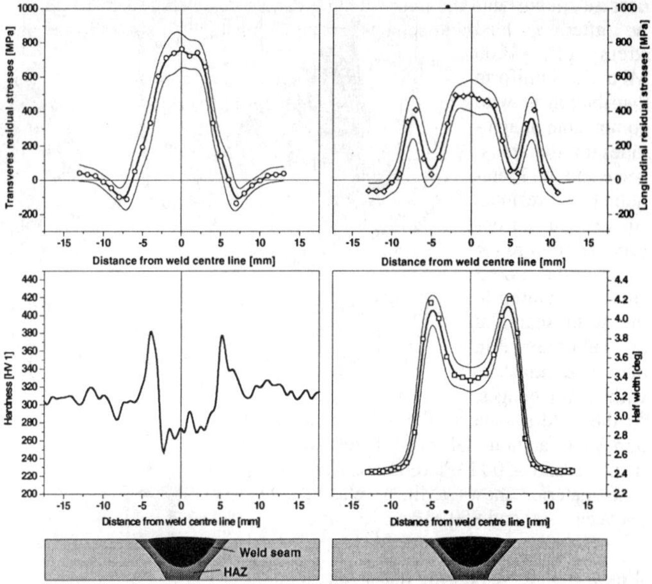

Fig. 3 Scatterbands of the residual stresses due to welding, hardness and half width distributions in welded joints of a quenched and tempered steel S960QL.

Figure 4 and figure 5 show the relaxation of very high initial welding residual stresses (load stress = 0) due to increasing quasistatic tensional (fig.4) and compressive (fig.5) load stresses. Under tension loading the transverse residual stresses in the weld seam (e.g. in loading direction) are reduced in a proportional relation to the increasing load stress. The longitudinal residual stresses are reduced in the weld seam from 500 MPa to approximately 350 MPa by a load stress of 100 MPa. Up to 700 MPa the longitudinal residual stresses in the weld seam are nearly constant. Higher load stresses cause a stronger relaxation of the longitudinal residual stresses. However the tensile residual stress peaks in the base material are lowered significantly after a load stress of 500 MPa. Under compressive loading the transverse residual stresses are reduced slightly and the longitudinal residual stresses are constant up to a load of –1000 MPa. However the longitudinal residual stress peaks in the base material are affected by the load stresses. From a load of –400 MPa they

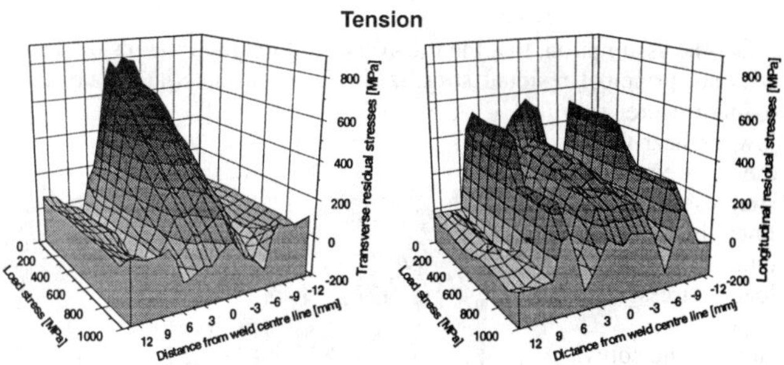

Fig. 4 Relaxation of the transverse (loading direction, left) and of the longitudinal residual stresses (right) in a welded joint of the steel S960QL during *tensional* quasistatic loading.

decrase constantly, after a load stress of –1000 MPa a uniform distribution with comparable magnitudes of the transverse and the longitudinal residual stresses can be observed. Figure 6 shows the σ–ε-curves measured in the weld seam, at the weld toe and in the base material with strain gauges. At the weld toe and in the weld seam plastification starts at nominal stress levels of 400 MPa (tension) and –500 MPa (compression), while the base material shows a linear elastic behaviour between –800 and 850 MPa.

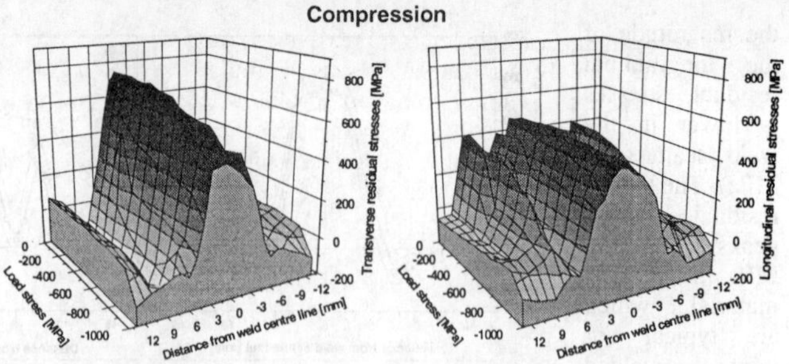

Fig. 5 Relaxation of the transverse (loading direction, left) and of the longitudinal residual stresses (right) in a welded joint of the steel S960QL during *compressive* quasistatic loading.

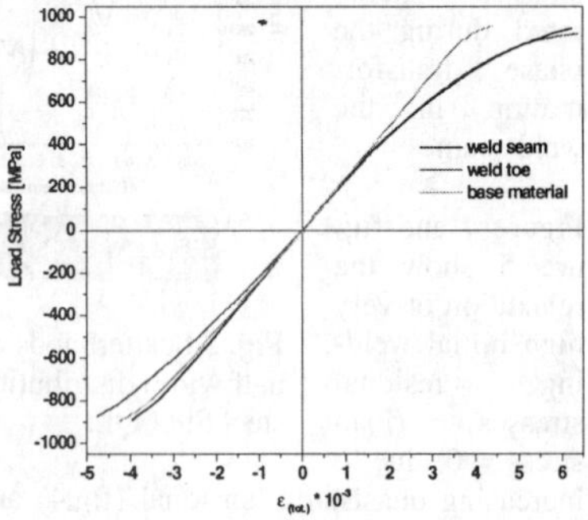

Fig. 6 σ–ε-curves during quasistatic loading of welded joints of the steel S960QL.

In fig 7 the equivalent stresses during quasistatic loading which have been calculated with the measured residual stresses and the load stresses after each load step according to V'Mises with

$$\sigma_V = \sqrt{\left(\sigma_t^{RS} + \sigma^{LS}\right)^2 + \sigma_l^{RS\,2} - \left(\left(\sigma_t^{RS} + \sigma^{LS}\right) \cdot \sigma_l^{RS}\right)}$$

under the assumption, that the transverse and longitudinal residual stress components $\sigma^{RS}{}_t$ and $\sigma^{RS}{}_l$ are principal residual stresses. In the base material, where the residual stresses before loading were very low or nearly zero the equivalent stresses increase linearly with the uniaxial tensile load stresses as expected. The slope of the equivalent stresses in the weld seam is lower due to the residual stress relaxation. At the highest load stresses the equivalent stresses are more uniform in

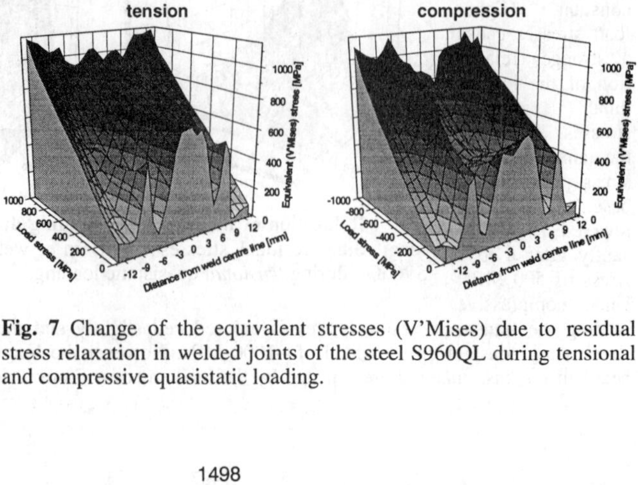

Fig. 7 Change of the equivalent stresses (V'Mises) due to residual stress relaxation in welded joints of the steel S960QL during tensional and compressive quasistatic loading.

the entire weld surface. Under compressive loading the distribution of the equivalent stresses is similar. However in the weld seam up to a load of –400 MPa the equivalent stresses decrease because the tensile residual stresses in the loading direction are compensated by the compressive load stresses.

The relaxation behaviour of the transverse and the longitudinal residual stresses in the weld seam are summarized in fig.8. The relaxation of the residual stress components is very inhomogenious but although the longitudinal residual stresses are not influenced between 100 and 700 MPa and strongly reduced by higher than 700 MPa the relaxation of both components results in a linear relation between the load stresses and the equivalent stresses.

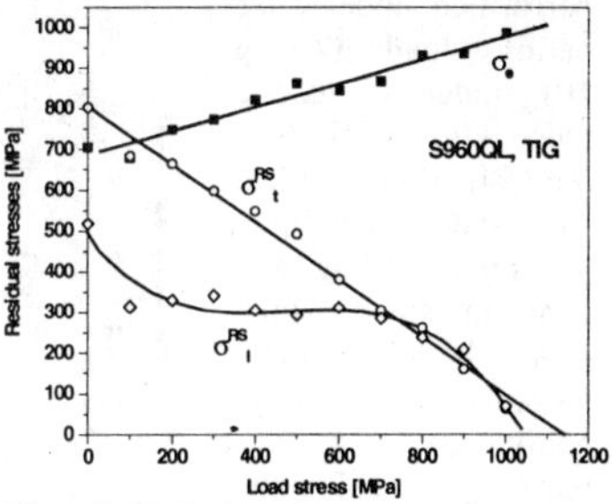

Fig. 8 Relation between the upper stresses and the residual stress relaxation after the first load cycle.

The relaxation of the macro residual stresses has nearly no influence on the stability of the microstructural parameters. As Fig. 9 shows, the half width distributions across the weld seam and the heat affected zone are relatively stable. A small decrease of the half widths in the weld seam occurs with load stresses of 400 and 800 MPa. With a load stress of 1000 MPa, which is close to the yield strength of the base material the half width in the weld seam is reduced significantly and in the base material the half widths increase due to cold hardening. The integral widths show the same characteristics. The change of the half and integral widths leads to a reduction of the domain sizes and therefore to an increasing dislocation density in the base material, however these micrustructural parmeters are stable in the weld seam and in the heat affected zone.

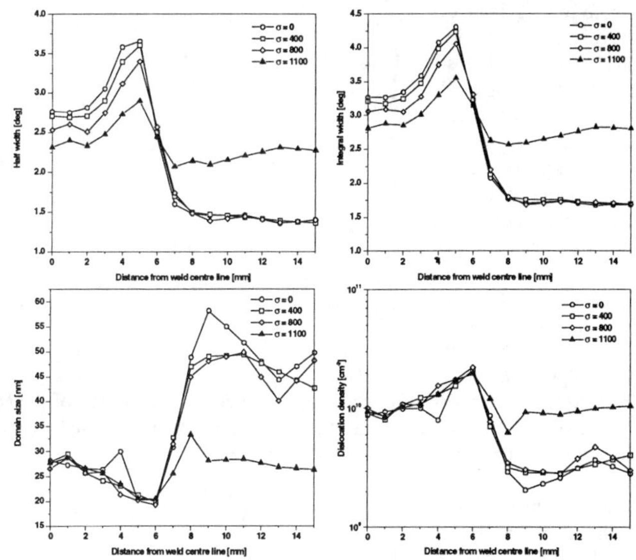

Fig. 9 Half widths, intergal widths, domain sizes and calculated dislocation densities after quasistatic loading of weldments of the steel S960QL.

4 RESIDUAL STRESS RELAXATION DURING CYCLIC LOADING

In fig. 10-12 the relaxation of the transverse residual stresses in the weld centre line during cyclic loading and the corresponding equivalent stresses are summarized. The load tests were

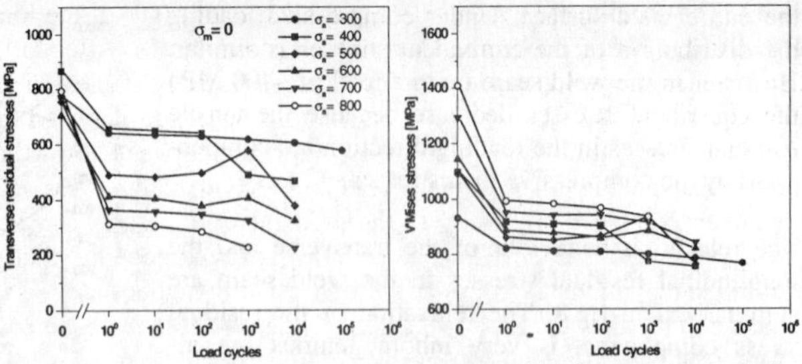

Fig. 10 Relaxation of the transverse residual stresses and the equivalent stresses in TIG-welded joints due to alternating loading.

performed under alternating loading (fig. 10), under a tensional mean stress of 50 % of the load amplitude (fig. 11) and under pure tensional loading with a mean stress which was as high as the load amplitude (fig.12). The equivalent stresses have been calculated with the residual stresses measured initially and after each load decade under addition of the different upper stresses to the transverse residual stress component.

Under alternating loading (fig.10) the strongest relaxation of the transverse residual stresses occur during the first load cycle. The reduction increases linearily with the stress amplitude. The relaxation during the following load cycles is relatively low and depends obviosly not on the magnitude of the load amplitude. The equivalent stresses show a uniform behaviour. After the first cycle the equivalent stress are inside a relatively small scatterband of 200 MPa with a magnitude between 800 and 1000 MPa. With higher number of load cycles the tendency can be observed, that the scatterband of the equivalent stresses becomes smaller due to the slight cyclic relaxation of the residual stresses. The mean value is very close to the yield strength of the base material.

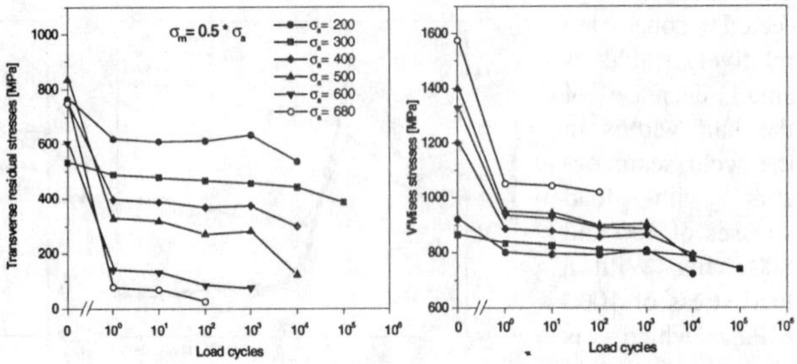

Fig. 11 Relaxation of the transverse residual stresses and the equivalent stresses in TIG-welded joints due to tensional loading.

The specimens tested with additionally applied mean stresses (fig.11 and 12) show the same characteristics like the specimens which were loaded without mean stresses. The residual stress reduction during the first load cycles increases with the magnitude of the upper

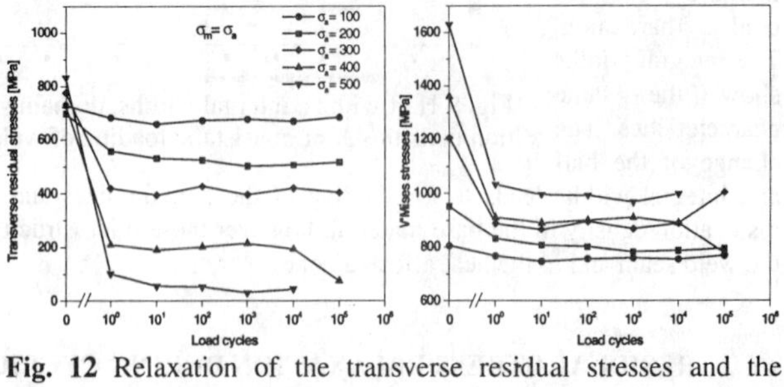

Fig. 12 Relaxation of the transverse residual stresses and the equivalent stresses in TIG-welded joints due to fully tensional loading.

stress. The specimens loaded with a mean stress of 50 % of the load amplitude (fig.11) show also a slight reduction during the following load cycles. After full tensional loading (fig.12) the residual stresses after the first cycle are relatively stable. The scatterband of the equivalent stresses seems not to depend on the loading conditions, and that is to say, after the first cycle their magnitudes are in all cases in a range between 750 MPa and 1050 MPa. The tendency, that higher upper stresses lead to a full residual stress relaxation and therefore the equivalent stresses correspond to the uniaxial load stresses can be observed. If the residual stress relaxation is a consequence of quasistatic overloading, that means that the theoretical value for the equivalent stress at the first cycle is higher than the yield strength, it should be expected, that after the first cycle all specimens should reach an equivalent stress of the magnitude of the yield strength. However at lower load amplitudes (e.g. at lower upper stresses) the equivalent stresses are significantly below the yield strength respectively the residual stress relaxation is obviously higher than expected.

A uniform evaluation of the observed residual stress relaxation behaviour is given by fig.13, where the initial transverse residual stresses are compared with the residual stresses after the first load cycle and after 10^3 load cycles. All values are related to the yield strength as well as the upper stresses S_{max}. The dotted line in fig.13 is the limit defined by the yield strength of the base material. It can be concluded, that in all cases, where the initial values are higher than the limit line a significant quasistatic residual stress relaxation should occur and all values below the limit should be stable. It can be seen, that high upper stresses lead to a residual stress relaxation after the first load cycle where the residual stresses are very close to the defined limit and after 10^3 cycles residual stresses with the corresponding limit values are generated. However in cases, where the limit is not exceeded, that is to say at lower load levels a significant relaxation occurs without a dependency on the number of load cycles.

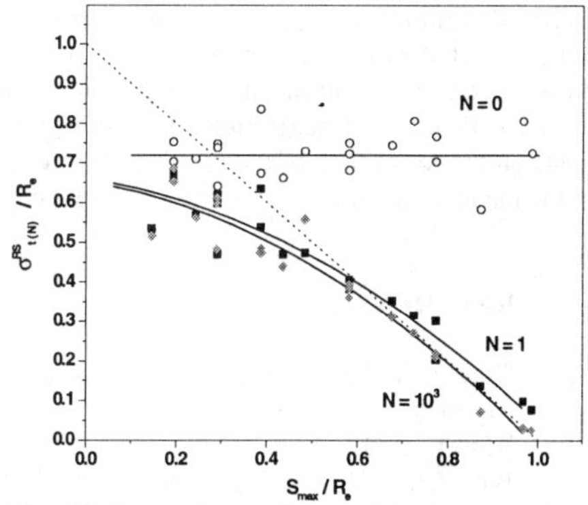

Fig. 13 Comparison of the residual stress relaxation due to quasistatic and due to cyclic loading.

Fig.14 shows a Bergström-Diagramm for the evaluation of the residual stress relaxation, where the two-dimensional residual stresses can be considered. The outer limit line (ellipsoid) is given by the uniaxial yield strength, the inner limit line by the cyclic yield strength. All values are related to the yield strength of the base material S960QL. In case of a two-dimensional stress state plastifications due to the load

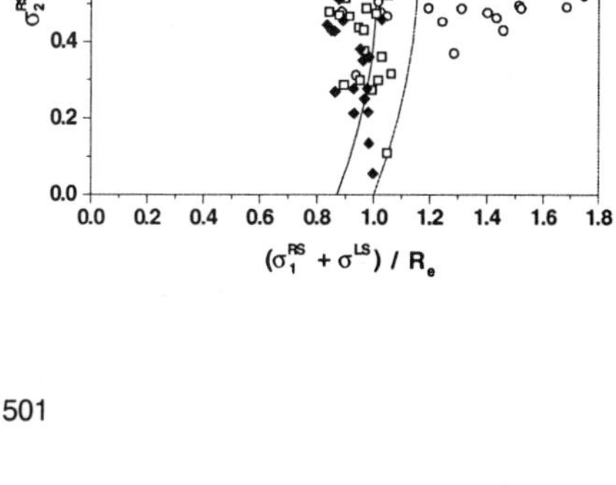

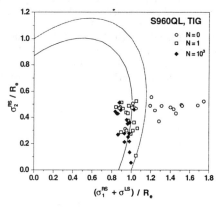

Fig. 14 Bergström-diagramm for the characterization of the relaxation of multiaxial residual stresses.

stresses must occur, when the total amount of the residual stresses and the load stress exceeds the limit lines. One can see, that for most of the investigated specimens the initial values exceed the given limits. The consequence is, that in case of a quasistatic residual stress relaxation the residual stresses must be reduced, so that the values are close to or below the limit given by the yield strength. As fig. 14 reveals the residual stresses are reduced stronger. After 10^3 cycles the values of the combined stresse are nearly as high or lower as the cyclic yield strength.

5 CONCLUSIONS

Investigations on a high strength steel S960QL have been carried out with the aim to evaluate the residual stress relaxation in weldments due to quasistatic and cyclic loading under consideration of the influence of mean stresses. The relaxation of high initial residual stresses in loading direction is a consequence of the effect, that the total amount of the residual stresses and the load stresses exceeds the yield strength during the first cycle. Therefore the residual stress relaxation is a quasistatic process. Further residual stress relaxations due to cyclic loading are very low and neglectible. The change in a two-dimensional residual stress state depends on the magnitude of the cyclic yield strength, where the reduction depends not strongly on the loading conditions, but on the magnitude of the upper stresses.

REFERENCES

[1] Gurney, T. R.: Fatigue of Welded Structures. 2nd Edition (1979), Cambridge University Press

[2] Vöhringer,O.:

[3] Wohlfahrt, H. in: Eigenspannungen: Entstehung - Messung - Bewertung, Band 2, DGM Informationsgesellschaft, 1983

[4] Hirsch, T.: PHD-Thesis TH Karlsruhe, 1983

[5] Vöhringer, O.: In: Eigenspannungen: Entstehung - Messung - Bewertung, Band 1, DGM Informationsgesellschaft, 1983

[6] Lachmann

[7] Burgahn, F.: PHD-Thesis TH Karlsruhe, 1994

[7] Bergström, J. et al.: In: Shot Peening, Proceedings of the 3rd International Conference on Shot Peening, DGM Informatiosgesellschaft, 1987, S. 221-230

[8] Lu, J., Flavenot, J. F.: In: Proc. of the 2nd Int. Conf. on Residual Stress, Nancy 1988, Elsevier, 1989, 784-790

[9] Bäumel, A: PHD-Thesis TH Darmstadt, 1991

[10] James, M. R., Morris, W. L.: Scripta Met. 17 (1983), 1101-1104

[12] Nitschke, Th.: PHD-Thesis TU Braunschweig, 1994

[13] Schulze, V.: PHD-Thesis TH Karlsruhe, 1993

RESIDUAL STRESSES IN ELECTRON BEAM WELDED NICKEL BASED SUPERALLOY RING

A N Ezeilo
MSX International,
Pipps Hill Business Park, Basildon SS14 3WF, UK

G A Webster
Imperial College of Science Technology and Medicine
Exhibition Road
London SW7 2BX, UK

ABSTRACT
Measurements have been made of the residual stresses generated by electron beam welding in a ring specimen, representative of a gas turbine compressor drum assembly. The ring was made of the nickel base superalloy Waspaloy and was designed to provide geometric constraint during the heating and cooling cycles as would be experienced by a real component. Measurements of lattice strain were made at the pulsed neutron source at the Rutherford Appleton Laboratory in the UK at two sections of the ring 90° apart; one in the 'slope-out' region where the weld was started and finished and one remote from this region. It has been found that a triaxial state of tension exists in the weld metal which decays away rapidly through the heat affected zone and that similar stress levels were obtained at both measuring locations. Maximum stresses approaching the tensile strength of the material were measured in the hoop direction across the weld at both locations. It was also observed that the maximum hoop residual stresses generated in the constrained ring are approximately 20% higher than those reported in unconstrained plate.

1. INTRODUCTION
Electron beam welding is used to join metals by concentrating a beam of high velocity electrons upon the surfaces to be joined. The power densities achieved are two orders of magnitude greater than can be obtained with conventional welding procedures. Electron beam welding offers significant advantages over conventional welding techniques. The advantages include the production of a weld with uniform chemical composition, low porosity and a reduced Heat Affected Zone (HAZ) producing a very high quality joint. This makes it very attractive in aero-engines where the lowest weight design solution is one in which individual compressor drums are welded together to form an assembly. For example in the Trent 800 series engines electron beam welding is employed in the latter stages of the compressor. However this welding process can produce undesirable tensile residual stresses which can impair fatigue performance unless a post weld heat treatment (PWHT) is employed to reduce their effects, Webster et al (1). In addition, geometric features and also changes in electron beam power, may influence the levels of residual stresses introduced.

There has been significant interest in the application of the neutron diffraction technique to the measurement of weld residual stresses (1-4). This is because neutrons can penetrate several centimeters into most metals, Allen et al (5), thus allowing stress with depth profiles to be obtained non-destructively for structural integrity assessments. A difficulty of the technique however, particularly in the case of welds, is the need to establish unstressed reference lattice strains for material across the weld necessary for the calculation of stress. This is of most concern in fusion welds where the use of dissimilar filler rod material can cause a gradient in chemical composition and microstructure across the weld, HAZ and parent materials and therefore a variation of the stress free lattice spacing with position through a weld, Winholtz (2). For an electron beam weld with no filler metal this is not a problem as a near homogenous weld is formed. Various studies have been undertaken of residual stresses introduced by electron beam welding in plate, Stone et al (3) and Braham et al (4). This paper describes measurements of residual stress which have been made in a specimen in the shape of a stiffened ring to represent a practical engineering component. It also investigates the influence of geometry on the levels of residual stress generated.

2. DESCRIPTION OF SPECIMEN

A diagram of the specimen is shown in fig 1. It was manufactured and supplied by Rolls Royce plc Derby. It was made of Waspaloy which is a nickel base superalloy with the chemical composition given in Table 1. The ring was fabricated in two halves, labelled **A** and **B** (fig 1b) which were joined together by an electron beam weld. A welding power of 1.44 kW and traverse velocity of 8.4 mm s^{-1} were employed. The specimen contained a 'slope out' region where a reduced beam power was used at the start and finish of the welding process. Measurements were made at positions marked **I** (slope out region) and **II** (90° away).

Table 1 Chemical composition of Waspaloy

Element	Ni	C	Cr	Co	Al	Mo	Ti	Zr	B
Mean Comp.	bal	0.08	19.5	13.5	1.3	4.3	3.0	0.06	0.006

3 MEASUREMENTS

The residual stress measurements were made using the purpose built stress diffractometer, ENGIN at ISIS at the Rutherford Appleton Laboratory in the UK, Johnson (6). ISIS is a pulsed neutron source producing a polychromatic beam of neutrons. The Time of Flight approach is used to analyse the diffraction data. The main features include a sample positioning device; focussing collimators and 2 detectors fixed at 90° from the incident neutron beam designated left and right hand detectors. The radial sollers define a gauge volume width along the line of the neutron beam of 1.4 mm (full width half maximum). Before the experiments were made the equipment was calibrated using a standard in-house procedure. This ensured a positioning accuracy of +/- 0.1 mm from the instrument and neutron beam focussing.

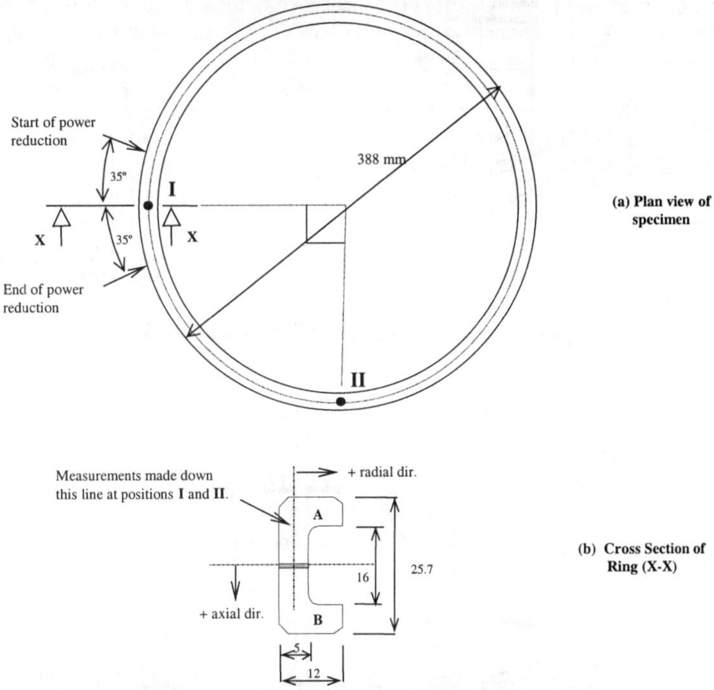

Figure 1 Dimensions of Electron Beam Weld Specimen
(all dimensions in mm)

The geometry of the specimen and the symmetry of the welding process suggested that the principal stress directions were in the hoop, radial and axial directions of the specimen. These were therefore identified as the measurement directions for which residual stresses were required. Strain measurements were made in the specimen in these directions at a number of axial positions at the midsection of the specimen (see fig 2a). Neutron absorbing masks were inserted in the incoming beam path to define suitable sampling volumes for adequate resolution of strain gradients. Hoop direction strain measurements were made using a 3 x 1 x 1.4 mm^3 sampling volume, with the 1mm width in the direction of the stress gradient (fig 2a). For radial and axial direction measurements the sampling volume was 10 x 1 x 1.4 mm^3 again orientated for optimum resolution (fig 2b). In order to measure strains in the hoop direction, the Right Hand Detector had to be removed to create sufficient space for mounting the specimen.

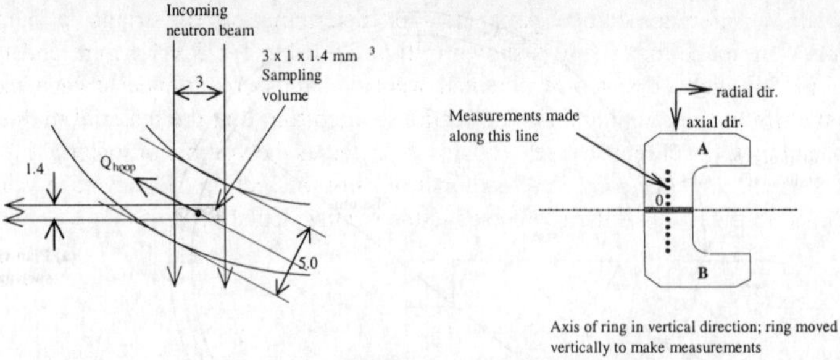

Figure 2a Layout of Specimen for Hoop Direction Measurements

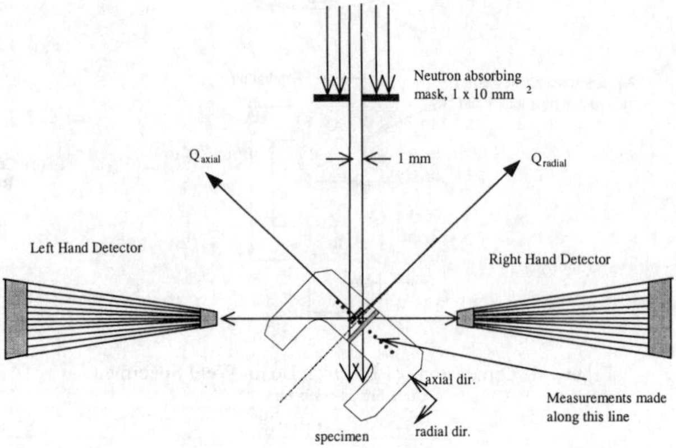

Figure 2b Layout of Specimen for Radial and Axial Direction Measurements

With the masking slits fully retracted, the incoming neutron beam had to traverse one section of the ring thickness in order to measure at the region of interest. In order to accurately position the specimen, neutron intensity measurements were made at the top surface and an entering curve was used to determine the position of the neutron beam precisely (fig 2a). This suggests a positioning accuracy of 0.1 mm of the specimen in the neutron beam. Confidence in positioning the specimen was further confirmed by comparing measurements of strain on either side of the weld line (not shown), which exhibited symmetry. Radial and axial direction strain measurements were made as shown in figure 2b using both the left and right hand detectors. In order to obtain a reference lattice parameter for determination of strains, a number of measurements were made in the rim as shown in figure 3 using 1 x 3 x 1.4 mm^3 and 1 x 10 x 1.4 mm^3 gauge volumes. d-spacings obtained were of similar magnitude at each measured point along the rim in the radial and axial directions suggesting that the material in this region is not influenced by the welding stresses. This is expected as the volume of material influenced by the weld is small in comparison with the dimensions of the section. The average value of d-spacing obtained in the rim was therefore used in the strain calculations.

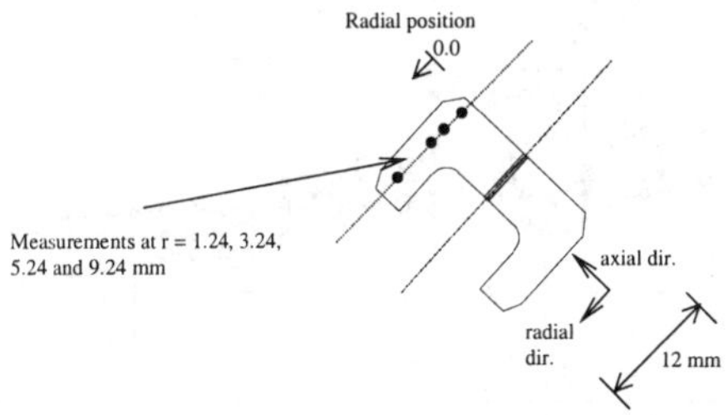

Figure 3 Layout of Specimen for Reference Measurements in the axial and radial directions

4. RESULTS and DISCUSSION

Because the radiation was polychromatic all the (hkl) reflections were obtained. A Pawley refinement analysis was used to interpret the results. Refinement of the neutron intensity spectrum involved the prediction of the strained lattice parameter by performing a least squares minimisation procedure on selected peaks from the measured spectrum. The predicted lattice parameter for strained material is then compared to the reference lattice parameter for "unstrained" material. Strain obtained in this manner is therefore the average value for the relevant crystal planes examined across the spectrum. Typical uncertainties in strain were +/- 80 $\mu\varepsilon$. The stresses were obtained from the expression below;

$$\sigma_{hoop} = \frac{E}{(1+\nu)(1-2\nu)}\left[(1-\nu)\varepsilon_{hoop} + \nu(\varepsilon_{radial} + \varepsilon_{axial})\right]$$

and similarly for the radial and axial direction stresses. In this equation E is the elastic modulus and ν Poissons ratio, which for Waspaloy were taken as 226 GPa and 0.3 respectively.

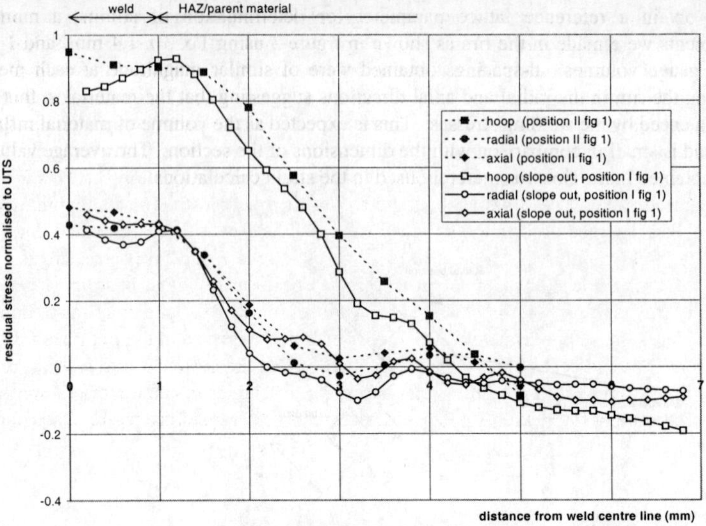

Figure 4 Residual Stress Distribution in Electron Beam Welded Ring

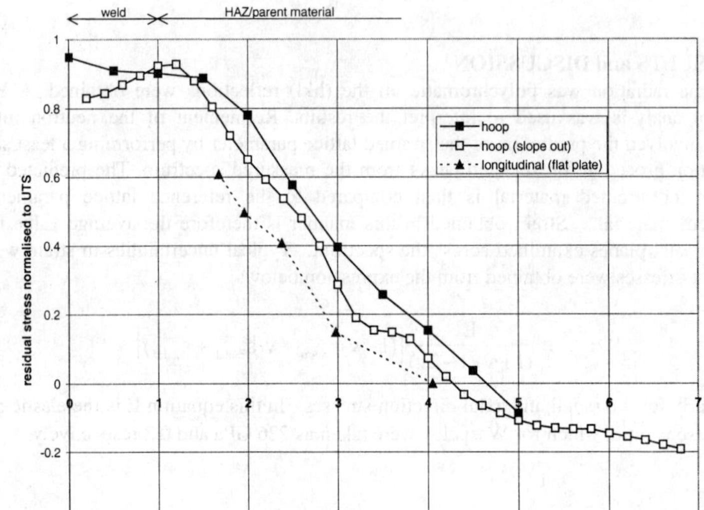

Figure 5 Comparison of Stresses in Electron Beam Welded Ring and Plate

Figure 4 shows the stresses in the 'slope out' region (I) and in the region of constant power (II), normalised to the UTS. The scatter in stress is typically +/- 45 MPa. These results show that the welding residual stresses are significant and decay within 2 weld widths of the weld centre line. In the region where the weld power was constant at 1.44 kW (II), a maximum stress of 95% of the UTS was measured at the weld centre line. Stresses start to decay at approximately 1.5mm away from this point over a distance of 3 mm. A similar distribution is observed at the slope out region (I) except that the stresses are about 100 MPa less than at location II. This lower hoop stress may be attributed to a slight annealing effect of the overlap weld pass. Figure 5 compares the residual stresses measured in the stiffened ring specimen with those generated in a flat plate under similar weld conditions, Stone et al (4). The plate investigated was a rectangular plate of 200 x 50 x 4.3mm dimensions containing an electron beam weld with a beam power of 1.8 kW and welding velocity of 8.4 mm s^{-1}. The results indicate that the maximum hoop stress measured in the ring is approximately 20% higher than that observed in the flat plate for the same distance from the weld centreline. It can be concluded that the stiffened ring restricts relaxation of the welding residual stresses during fabrication so that larger residual stresses are generated than are produced in a flat plate. A post weld heat treatment is therefore required to reduce these high stresses.

5. CONCLUSIONS

Residual stress measurements have been made in a stiffened Waspaloy ring containing an electron beam weld. Hoop, radial and axial direction stresses were obtained with maximum hoop stresses approaching the tensile strength of the material. Radial and axial direction stress profiles were similar with maximum values approximately half of the maximum hoop stress. Residual stress levels were constant in the weld and decayed over 3-4 mm after which the stresses become compressive. These results indicate that the constrained geometry restricts the relaxation of the residual stresses developed by the process when compared with stresses reported in flat plate. Also, reducing the beam power at the end of the welding process, has little influence on the residual stress profile for the conditions investigated.

6. ACKNOWLEDGEMENTS

The authors would like to thank the EPSRC and DERA for providing funding for this study (EPSRC project no. Ref:GR/L19942) and for the collaboration of Rolls-Royce in the project and their provision of the test specimen. They would also like to thank Mark Daymond of ISIS, for his advice and assistance in carrying out the measurements.

7. REFERENCES

[1] Webster G & Ezeilo A, 'Neutron scattering in engineering applications', *Physica B*, (1997).

[2] Winholtz R & Krawitz A, 'Depth probing of stress tensors using neutron diffraction' Proc. 4th Int. Conf. On Residual Stresses, (1994).

[3] Stone H, Withers P, Holden T, Roberts S, Reed R, 'Comparison of Three Different Techniques for Measuring the Residual Stresses in an Electron Beam – Welded Plate of Waspaloy', Metallurgical and Materials Trans A, Vol 30A, (1999).

[4] Braham C, Ceretti M, Coppola R, Lodini A, Nardi C, 'X-ray and Neutron Diffraction Study of Residual Stresses in Electron-Beam Welded F82H Modified Martensitic Steel for Fusion Reactors', Proc. 5th Int. Conf. On Residual Stresses, Linköping, Sweden (1997).

[5] Allen A, Andreani C, Hutchings M and Windsor C, 'Measurement of internal stress within bulk materials using neutron diffraction', NDT Int., (1981)

[6] Johnson M, PREMIS Final Technical Report, BriteEuram II Project No. 5129, Rutherford Appleton Laboratory Technical Report RAL-TR-96-068.

[7] Ezeilo A & Webster G, 'Neutron Diffraction Analysis of the Residual Stress Distribution in a Bent Bar', accepted for publication in the Journal of Strain Analysis (submitted Aug. 1999).

MEASUREMENT AND MODELLING OF RESIDUAL STRESSES IN THICK SECTION TYPE 316 STAINLESS STEEL WELDS

SK Bate[1], PJ Bouchard[2], PEJ Flewitt[3], D George[4], RH Leggatt[5] and AG Youtsos[6]
[1]AEA Technology, Risley, Warrington, Cheshire, WA3 6AT, UK
[2]British Energy, Barnett Way, Barnwood, Gloucester GL4 3RS, UK
[3]BNFL (Magnox), Berkeley Technology Centre, Berkeley, Glos. GL13 9PB, UK
[4]University of Bristol, Queens Building, University Walk, Bristol, BS8 1TR, UK
[5]TWI, Abington Hall, Abington, Cambridge CB1 6AL, UK,
[6]CEC Joint Research Centre, PO Box 2, 1755 ZG Petten, The Netherlands.

ABSTRACT

The spatial distribution of residual stress in a thick section girth weld (432 mm outside diameter, 65 mm thick) joining two ex-service AISI type 316H austenitic stainless steel forgings has been characterised by both measurement and modelling. Measurements of residual stress in two, nominally identical, fabricated components were carried out using diverse techniques including surface centre-hole drilling, deep hole drilling, neutron diffraction and X-ray diffraction. Finite element analyses, employing alternative simulation procedures and computer codes (ABAQUS and SYSWELD), were also used to predict the residual stresses in the components in the as-welded condition. This paper briefly describes the methods applied to measure and predict the residual stresses in the component. Comparison is then made between the measured and predicted as-welded stresses, to evaluate the application of FE methods for the modelling of residual stresses.

INTRODUCTION

Weld residual stresses have an important influence on the structural integrity of ageing plant. Tensile residual stresses increase the susceptibility of components to degradation mechanisms such as stress corrosion cracking or reheat cracking initiation, accelerate crack growth rates and generally reduce the defect tolerance of a structure. Bounding residual stress profiles for many weld types can be found in compendia for use in integrity assessments, for example (1). However, there is little published work characterising residual stresses in thick section (greater than 50mm) stainless steel girth welds in pipes and vessels, apart from measurements in a 68mm thick orbital TIG weld (2) and a more recent measurement study comparing residual stresses in a 63 mm thick girth from three different weld procedures (3).

Both analytical and experimental approaches for determining weld residual stresses have significant limitations. Finite element (FE) weld simulation procedures can be used (4), but the methods are inherently more complex than conventional stress analysis and many simplifications are often made; for example with material constitutive models and the use of two-dimensional representations to reduce computational requirements. Techniques for measuring residual stress vary in accuracy, spatial resolution, penetration below the surface, completeness of information, applicability to in-situ components, and cost. However, when analytical and experimental approaches are combined, and the results corroborate each other sufficiently well, the resulting residual stress distributions can be confidently used for accurate structural integrity assessments of safety-critical components.

This paper briefly describes the diverse methods applied to measure and predict the residual stresses in a thick section girth weld (432 mm outside diameter, 65 mm thick) austenitic stainless steel girth weld. Comparisons are then made between the measured and predicted as-welded stresses, to evaluate the application of FE methods for predicting residual stresses. The work described was carried out as part of the EC co-funded collaborative project 'Variation of Residual Stresses in Aged Components', VORSAC (5). The overall objective of VORSAC was to obtain a better understanding of the evolution of residual stresses and degradation phenomena in nuclear components during manufacture and service life, and to validate improved methods for modelling and measurement of residual stresses.

EXPERIMENTAL APPROACH

Three nominally identical girth-welded test specimens, designated components A, B and C, were fabricated from three pairs of ex-service steam headers. The header forgings' material was AISI type 316H austenitic stainless steel (service-aged 65,000 hours at 520-530°C). One end of each header was machined to form a J-preparation. Each pair of headers was then joined using a manual metal arc welding procedure with type 316L electrodes. A total of 42 weld passes were typically used: including 30 filler passes deposited side by side (with 5mm diameter electrodes), and one layer of four capping passes (with 4mm diameter electrodes). Fig. 2 shows a macro-graph of the MMA weld. The test components had an outer diameter of 432 mm, a measured thickness of about 65 mm, and were approximately 1m long, prior to machining to a length of 550mm to facilitate handling and neutron diffraction measurements. The final geometry of the fabricated components is illustrated in Fig. 1. The holes at top dead centre (TDC) of the component resulted from the removal of nozzles from the original headers. A slot was introduced in the weld at TDC of component A to facilitate neutron diffraction measurements (not shown).

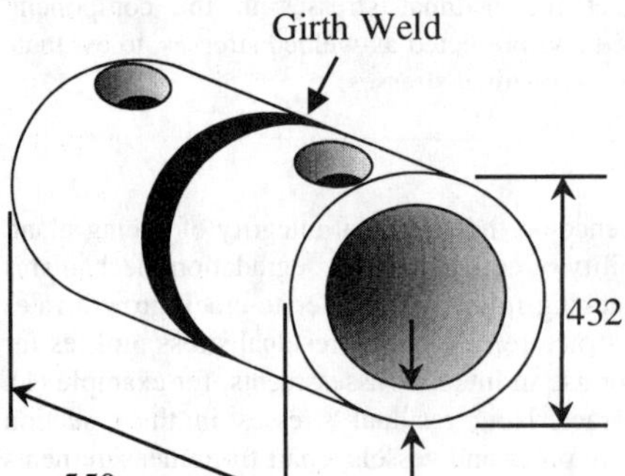

Figure 1 Sketch of Girth Welded Specimens

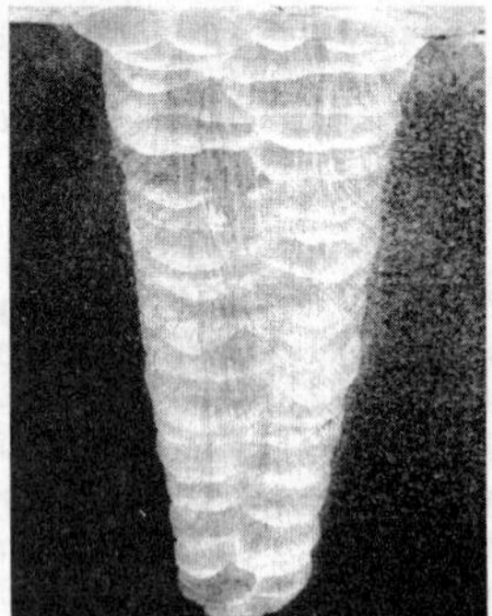

Figure 2 Macro-graph of Test Weld

The as-welded residual stresses in Components A and B were measured using diverse techniques (see below). Component C was cut-up and used for materials characterisation tests. Components A and B were subsequently used to investigate post-weld heat treatment (750°C for 2.5 hours) and thermal ageing effects (up to 8,400 hours at 550°C); the stress relaxation results are described in a companion paper (6).

MATERIAL CHARACTERISATION

Material characterisation tests were performed on samples cut from component C to underpin the VORSAC project FE weld simulation and stress relaxation (6) studies:

a) thermal properties of the base and weld materials up to melting point,
b) monotonic tensile properties for the base and weld materials up to melting point,
c) cyclic tensile properties for the base material up to 900°C.

The measured properties can be found in the VORSAC project final report (5). Parameters for a combined isotropic-kinematic hardening material model (Lemaitre-Chaboche type) were derived from the measured cyclic tensile test data for the Type 316H base material. A reasonable correspondence was obtained between computed hysteresis loops and the measured ones, although the first quarter cycles were somewhat inaccurate because the saturated cycle shape was used in the data fitting procedure.

RESIDUAL STRESS MEASUREMENTS

As-welded residual stresses in components A and B were measured at circumferential positions remote from TDC. Near-surface measurements of in-plane stresses were made using surface centre-hole drilling and X-ray diffraction techniques and through-wall stresses were characterised using the deep hole drilling method and neutron diffraction.

The surface centre-hole rosette gauge technique (7) is probably the most widely used method for in-situ weld residual stress measurements. Several measurements around the circumference were made at an axial distance of 50mm from the weld centre-line (i.e. in base material 26-30mm from the edge of the weld cap). No systematic circumferential variation in stress was found, although a scatter of ±33 MPa in measured stresses was observed. These stress variations could be associated with the accuracy of the surface hole drilling technique in the presence of large stress gradients, or be associated with a long range capping pass start/stop effect. Several measurements were made to characterise the distributions of residual stress along the outer surfaces of the components.

X-ray diffraction is an established technique for measurement of stresses to a depth of about 10μm with high spatial resolution. Measurements were made to characterise the as-welded residual stress distribution along the outer surfaces of components A and B, following careful surface preparation by electro-chemical polishing. Considerable scatter in the results is evident (Figs. 9 and 10), with stresses achieving much higher magnitudes than measured using other techniques. Two contributions to possible errors in the measurements were identified: diffraction peak overlap (owing to carbide precipitation) and variation of diffraction peak intensity with measurement angle (probably influenced by texture effects). Very high surface stresses (up to 1600 MPa) from X-ray measurements in type 316L stainless steel have been reported by (8), and attributed to an intensely work hardened layer at the surface. Skin effects are likely to be sensitive to the fabrication history (forging, quenching, welding etc.) and service ageing history. If present, such skin effects can completely mask the sub-surface stress distribution of structural significance.

The deep hole drilling method can measure in-plane residual stress variations through the wall of components greater than about 20 mm thick. The technique measures the average stress over an effective plan diameter of about 9 mm and shows good accuracy in validation tests, and thick section weld measurements (3). A principal direction of stress must be assumed and the method leaves a hole in the structure of about 26 mm diameter. Deep hole measurements were made at the weld centre-line of component A and in the heat affected zone (HAZ) of both components; that is at the edge of the weld cap (remote from the last pass side). The measured stresses are illustrated in Figs. 5-10.

Neutron diffraction measurements were performed at the large component neutron diffraction facility at the HFR, Petten, using a gauge volume of 1.8 cm^3. The apparent strains derived from these experiments varied by up to 3000 micro-strain in all three measurement directions. An attempt was made to quantify the real strains by reference to measurements of strain in 'stress-free' coupons destructively extracted from component A. However, it was found that there is a limiting thickness, above which very large pseudo-strains mask the real strain. This is mainly due to the attenuation the neutron beam experiences in long path measurements, and a currently not well understood background effect that shifts results towards pseudo-compression. Through obtaining reasonable results in the specimen radial direction up to 25 mm below the specimen surface it was established that the limiting wall thickness would have been about 50 - 55 mm in this case.

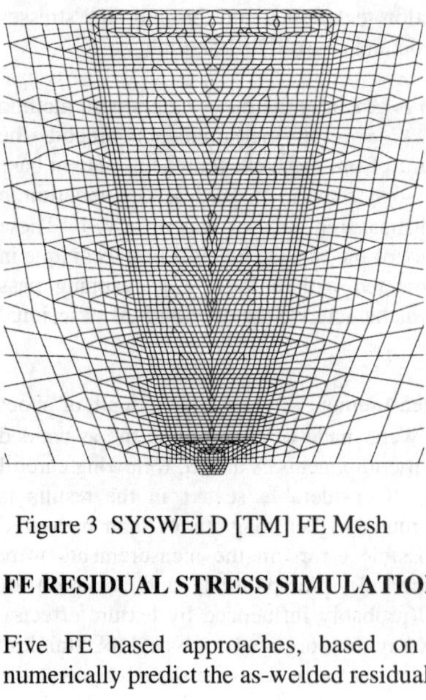

Figure 3 SYSWELD [TM] FE Mesh

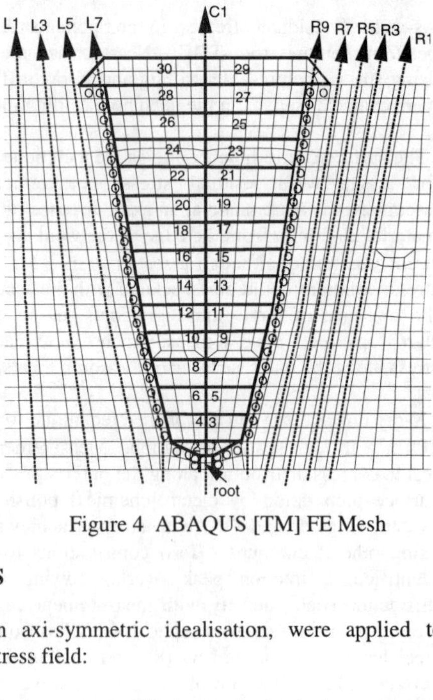

Figure 4 ABAQUS [TM] FE Mesh

FE RESIDUAL STRESS SIMULATIONS

Five FE based approaches, based on an axi-symmetric idealisation, were applied to numerically predict the as-welded residual stress field:

- SYSWELD TM-ISO: a thermo-mechanical approach with isotropic hardening using the FE code SYSWELD(11) where every deposited weld bead was simulated (see Fig. 3);
- ABAQUS TM-ISO: a thermo-mechanical approach with isotropic hardening in the FE code ABAQUS (10), where weld passes were 'lumped' (see Fig. 4);
- ABAQUS TM-KIN: a repeat thermo-mechanical lumped bead analysis with pure kinematic hardening of parent material;

- ABAQUS TM-MIX: a repeat analysis with a mixed isotropic-kinematic (Lemaitre-Chaboche type) hardening model for parent material; and
- ABAQUS M: a simplified approach (9) based on mechanical analysis alone using an elastic/perfectly plastic material model, where weld beads were thermally contracted in sequence.

Predicted weld residual stress distributions from the SYSWELD TM-ISO and ABAQUS TM-ISO simulations showed good general agreement with each other (see Figs. 5-10). Maximum tensile stresses from the SYSWELD TM-ISO analysis were higher than the ABAQUS TM-ISO results, partly because higher (estimated) parent monotonic yield strength properties were used in the former analysis. The SYSWELD TM-ISO model gave more detailed distributions of stress in the region of the weld root and weld cap because each weld pass was modelled rather than a bead lumping approach.

The mixed isotropic-kinematic hardening analysis (ABAQUS TM-MIX) predicted significantly lower magnitudes of residual stress in the HAZ and base material towards the outer surface than the TM-ISO simulations (Figs. 7-10). The results were judged reasonably accurate for plastically-cycled HAZ material up to about 15mm from the weld preparation, and along the outer surface up about ±50mm from the weld centre-line. Stresses beyond these limits were probably under-estimated because the mixed hardening material model was somewhat inaccurate for the first half (monotonic) loading cycle.

The kinematic hardening analysis (ABAQUS TM-KIN) results tended to lie between the mixed and isotropic cases. This is because both the kinematic and isotropic hardening models were based on the monotonic stress-strain properties, whereas the mixed hardening model simulated evolutionary cyclic hardening behaviour, which was too soft in the first cycle.

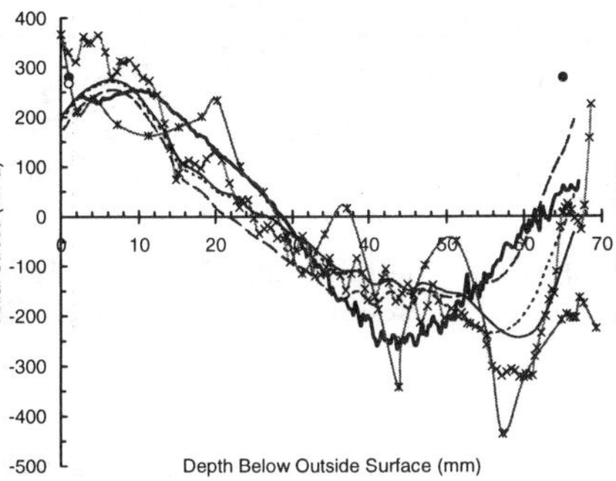

Figure 5 Measured and Predicted Axial Stresses at the Weld Centre-line

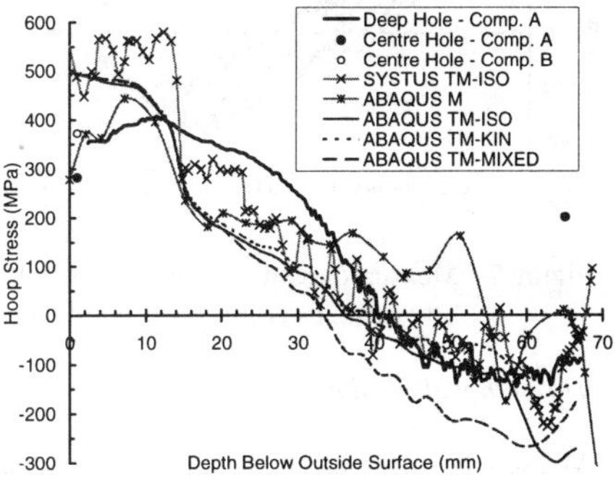

Figure 6 Measured and Predicted Hoop Stresses at the Weld Centre-line

COMPARISONS OF MEASURED AND PREDICTED STRESSES

Through-wall Residual Stresses at Weld Centre-line

Measured and predicted through-wall residual stresses at the weld centre-line are compared in Figs. 5 and 6. The use of mixed hardening for parent material (ABAQUS TM-MIX results) is seen to have a significant influence on stresses towards the inner half thickness of the weld, giving a better correlation with measured data in the axial direction but worse in the hoop. Both the SYSWELD TM and all the ABAQUS TM predicted hoop stresses are somewhat greater than measured towards the outer surface of the weld (outer 15mm). Measured and predicted maximum tensile stresses near the outer surface are summarised in Table I.

Method	Maximum Hoop Stress MPa	$\sigma/\sigma_{weld\ 1\%\ PS}$ [1]	Maximum Axial Stress MPa	$\sigma/\sigma_{weld\ 1\%\ PS}$ [1]
Deep hole measurements	407	0.91	254	0.57
Surface hole measurements	282	0.63	280	0.63
SYSWELD TM-ISO (FE)	580[2]	1.22[2]	365[2]	0.77[2]
ABAQUS TM-ISO (FE)	497	1.11	274	0.61
ABAQUS TM-MIX (FE)	493	1.11	254	0.57

[1] Measured monotonic $\sigma_{weld\ 1\%\ PS}$ = 446 MPa at 20 °C
[2] Estimated value of $\sigma_{weld\ 1\%\ PS}$ = 476 MPa used in SYSWELD analysis (prior to testwork)

Table I Maximum Measured and Predicted Tensile Stresses Near the Weld CL Outer Surface

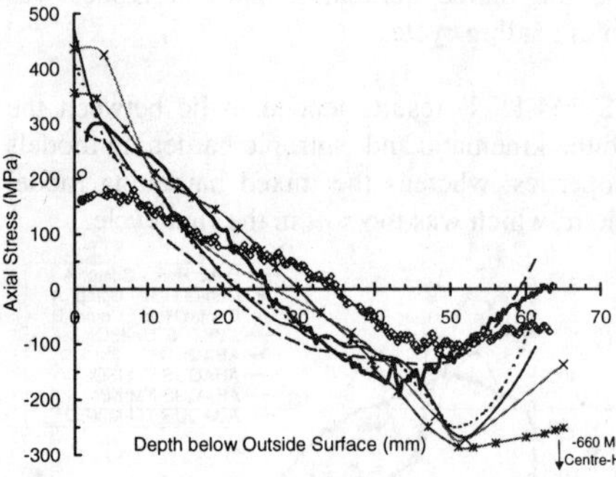

Figure 7 Measured and Predicted Axial Stresses, 20-24mm from Weld CL

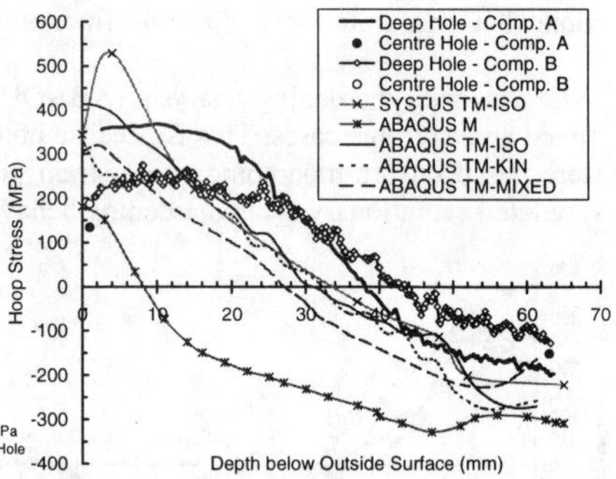

Figure 8 Measured and Predicted Hoop Stresses, 20-24mm from Weld CL

Through-wall Residual Stresses in HAZ

Measured and predicted through-wall residual stresses in the HAZ (20-24mm from the weld centre-line) are compared in Figs. 7 and 8. The measured deep hole results indicate significant differences in hoop and axial stress magnitudes between Components A and B, even though they were nominally fabricated to identical procedures. However, all the axial stress results are in broad agreement with each other (apart from one rogue surface hole measurement of –660 MPa). The predictions consistently suggest higher magnitudes of compressive stress than measured over the inner 20mm of the pipe, except for the ABAQUS TM-MIX results which show a good correlation with the deep hole measurements. Some variations in axial stress in the region of the weld cap are evident, but this is an area where the stresses vary rapidly owing to the influence of individual weld beads. The hoop stress results are also in broad agreement with each other, except for the simplified ABAQUS M results. The SYSWELD TM-ISO and ABAQUS TM numerical approaches appear to overestimate the hoop stresses in the vicinity of the outer weld cap, and under-estimate tensile stresses by about 100 MPa in the mid-thickness region. Maximum measured and predicted maximum tensile stresses in the HAZ near the outer surface are summarised in Table II.

Method	Maximum Hoop Stress		Maximum Axial Stress	
	MPa	$\sigma/\sigma_{base\ 1\%\ PS}$ [1]	MPa	$\sigma/\sigma_{base\ 1\%\ PS}$ [1]
Deep hole measurements	367	1.12	300	0.91
Surface hole measurements	180	0.55	210	0.64
SYSWELD TM-ISO (FE)	528[2]	1.32[2]	437[2]	1.10[2]
ABAQUS TM-ISO (FE)	415	1.27	471	1.44
ABAQUS TM-MIX (FE)	319	0.97	304	0.93

[1] Measured monotonic $\sigma_{base\ 1\%\ PS}$ = 328 MPa at 20 °C
[2] Estimated value of $\sigma_{base\ 1\%\ PS}$ = 399 MPa used in SYSWELD analysis (prior to testwork)

Table II Maximum Measured and Predicted Tensile Stresses Near the HAZ Outer Surface

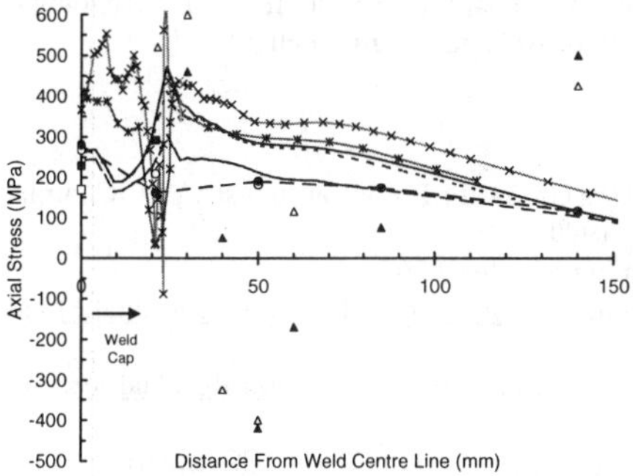

Figure 9 Measured and Predicted Axial Stresses along Outer Surface

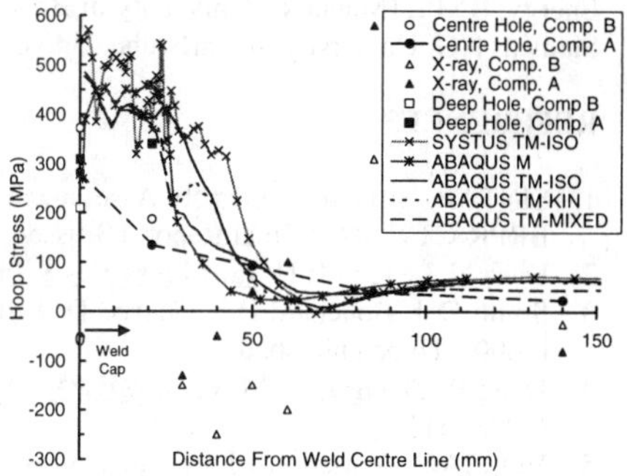

Figure 10 Measured and Predicted Hoop Stresses along Outer Surface

Outer Surface Residual Stresses

Measured and predicted residual stresses along the outer surface of the welded pipe are compared in Figs. 9 and 10. The analytical predictions of the stress distribution (shape) are in agreement with each other, apart from in the weld cap region where stresses vary rapidly owing to the influence of individual weld beads. However, the magnitudes of predicted stress are seen to be dependent on the material hardening model employed (also note that higher parent yield properties were used for the SYSWELD TM-ISO analysis). The ABAQUS TM-MIX results appear to give the best correlation with measurements, although the surface results from this analysis greater than ±50mm from the weld centre-line must be treated with caution. The other TM analyses predict axial and hoop stresses that are generally greater than the values measured using the surface centre-hole technique. The X-ray stress measurements from Components A and B show some degree of agreement with each other, but little apparent relation to the predictions or surface hole measurements. This is probably due to the skin effects discussed earlier.

CONCLUDING REMARKS

Overall, the thermo-mechanical FE weld simulations predicted similar through-wall and surface residual stress profiles that correlated reasonably well with deep hole and surface centre-hole stress measurements. The hardening behaviour was found to have a significant effect on predicted stress magnitudes; a mixed isotopic-kinematic model gave the lowest stresses that generally correlated more closely with measurements. If detailed distributions of residual stress in the region of the weld root and weld cap are required, individual weld beads should be modelled, rather than lumped passes. Use of X-ray diffraction to measure residual stresses in Type 316H stainless steel components is difficult, possibly owing to the presence of high near-surface stress gradients (skin effects). Background effects in long-path neutron strain measurements can introduce large compressive pseudo-strains that completely mask the real strain.

ACKNOWLEDGEMENTS

VORSAC was co-funded by the EC Nuclear Fission Safety Programme, the UK Health and Safety Executive and project partners. The work was performed by AEA Technology, British Energy, BNFL (Magnox), University of Bristol, TWI, Institute de Soudure, VTT Technology, Siemens AG, University of Karlsruhe, University of Ancona and JRC Petten.

REFERENCES

1. SINTAP, 'Structural Integrity Assessment Procedures for European Industry', EC Contract BRPR-CT95-0024 Final Report (Brussels), 1999
2. Faure F, Leggatt R H, Int J Press Ves & Piping 65 (1996) 265
3. Smith D J, Bouchard P J, George D, J Strain Analysis, Special Issue on Residual Stress (2000), To be published.
4. Dong P, Zhang J, Li M V, ASME PVP-Vol 373, Fatigue, Fracture and Residual Stresses (1998) 311
5. VORSAC, 'Variation of Residual Stresses in Ageing Components', EC Contract F14S-CT96-0040 Final Report (Brussels), 2000
6. Bouchard P J, Bate S K, Flewitt P E J, George D, Leggatt R H, Youtsos A G, Proc ICRS6. This volume.
7. ASTM E837-95, 'Standard test method for determining residual stresses by the hole drilling strain gage method', ASTM, 1995
8. Bouzina A, Braham C, Lédion J, Proc ICRS-5 (1997) 1060
9. Green D, Bate S, Proc ICRS5 (1997) 508
10. ABAQUS 5.8, Hibbitt, Karlsson & Sorensen Inc., 1997
11. SYSWELD Operating Instructions, 1998

VALIDATION OF RESIDUAL STRESS PREDICTIONS FOR A 19MM THICK J-PREPARATION STAINLESS STEEL PIPE GIRTH WELD USING NEUTRON DIFFRACTION

L.Edwards [1], G.Bruno[1,2], M.Dutta[1], P.J.Bouchard [3], K.L.Abbott [3], R. Lin Peng [4]
[1] Department of Materials Engineering, The Open University, Milton Keynes, UK
[2] Hahn-Meitner Institute, Berlin, Germany
[3] British Energy, Barnwood, Gloucester, UK.
[4] NFL, Studsvik, Sweden

ABSTRACT

This paper describes and interprets neutron diffraction measurements of residual strain and stress that were used to validate a finite element (FE) residual stress simulation for a 19mm thick, J-preparation manual metal arc girth weld in a stainless steel pipe of outer diameter 432mm. The measurements were performed on the instrument REST, at NFL in Studsvik (Sweden). The experimental requirements necessary to produce full 3-dimensional stress measurements in large (≈200Kg) components are discussed together with the importance of characterising any variations in stress free lattice parameter through the weld. Approaches to the latter problem include the interpretation of measurements on small cubes cut from a ring core specimen, and the use of effective values inferred from axial stress balance. Details of the finite element residual stress simulation for the girth weld are described and the predicted stress state compared with the measurements. The agreement between predictions and measurements is generally good, given the sensitivity of the stress field to local weld bead deposition effects.

INTRODUCTION

Tensile weld residual stresses generally have an adverse effect on component life. When detailed structural integrity assessments are performed by industry, upper bound weld residual stress distributions from published compendia (1) are generally used. However, for safety-related plant it is sometimes vital to thoroughly understand the complete residual stress field and how it influences crack initiation, crack growth and fracture processes. For example, the principal stress magnitude and multi-axial stress state are important factors affecting reheat crack initiation in stainless steel power plant operating at high temperatures (2).

FE methods are increasingly used to calculate residual stress distributions in multi-pass fusion welds by simulating both the thermal and mechanical response of the materials (3). They have the advantage of providing a detailed map of the full residual stress tensor. But residual stress modelling is inherently more complex than conventional stress analysis and many approximations have to be made. For example, the weld heat input must be idealised and the sequential addition of weld deposits modelled in both the thermal and mechanical analyses. Also two-dimensional representations are generally used to reduce computational requirements. So it is very important to independently validate predicted residual stress results and understand their limitations, before use in safety-critical structural integrity assessments.

defined, but the actual number of beads, and heat input chosen by the welder were unknown. An axi-symmetric ABAQUS [11] FE model of the girth weld was created. A thermal analysis was performed to predict transient temperatures for each consecutive weld pass, followed by an uncoupled mechanical analysis based on the temperature history. The deposition of weld beads was represented by sequentially adding blocks of new elements to the model. The weld filler metal was added at a temperature above melting point, and heat fluxes applied to represent typical weld heat inputs associated with 2.5mm, 3.25 mm and 4 mm diameter MMA electrodes. In the absence of fabrication data, two weld bead idealisations were examined: a thick bead model (14 passes), and a thin bead model (21 passes), see Figs. 7 and 8.

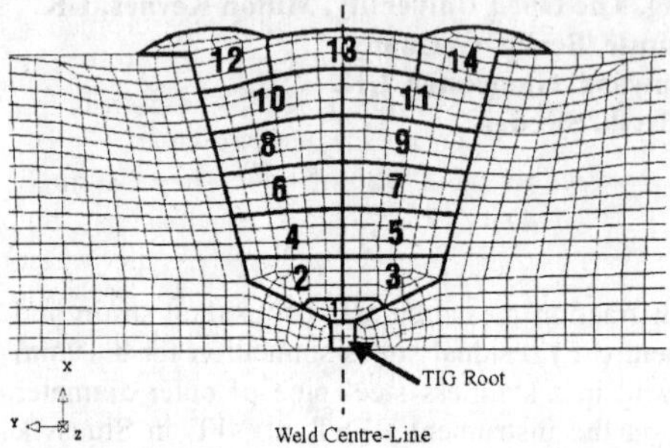

Figure 7: Finite element model (14 pass)

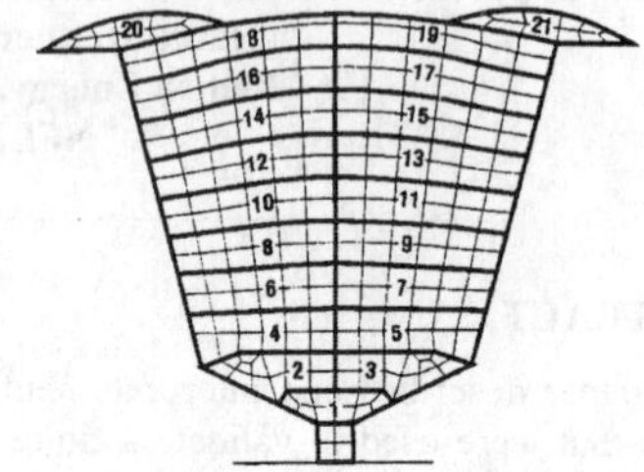

Figure 8: Finite element model (21 pass)

Temperature dependent material properties for the base and weld materials up to melting point were used. The room temperature 1% proof stress values for the base and weld materials were 280 MPa and 476 MPa respectively. An isotropic hardening model was employed for the base material with a saturation level defined by the 10% proof stress, and the weld metal was treated as elastic-perfectly-plastic at the 1% proof stress level. Some of modelling assumptions and their significance are reviewed in the discussion below.

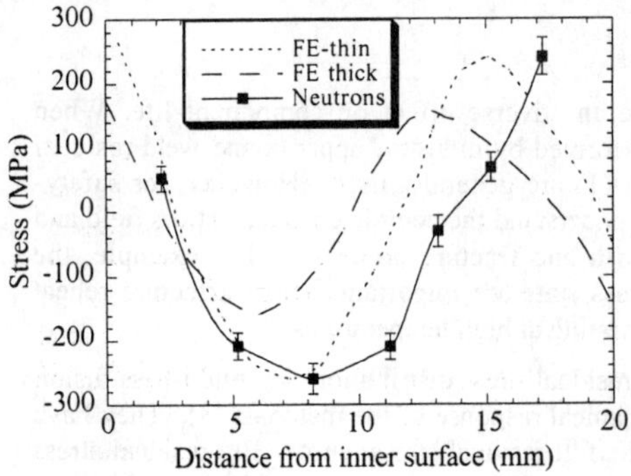

Figure 9: Measured and calculated HAZ Axial stresses

Figs. 9 and 10 illustrate the predicted residual stresses along a line in the heat affected zone about 12mm from the weld centre-line in the FE model, that is below the over-hang of the final capping pass (see Figs. 7 and 8). The shape of the hoop and axial stress profiles from the thick and thin bead models are similar, but the thick bead distributions are shifted towards the inner surface. The predicted axial and hoop stresses from the two models can differ by up to 150 MPa, at any given point through the thickness.

This effect is probably associated with the size and heat input (KJ/mm) of the final weld capping pass. The thin bead model results in higher magnitudes of peak stress: for example, axial values of about ± 250 MPa compared with ± 150 MPa from the thick bead

Derivation of Stresses (based on cube d_o measurements)

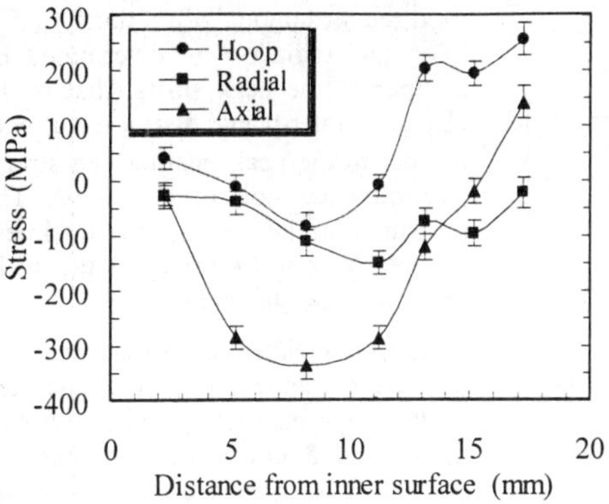

Figure 6 HAZ stresses based on cube d_o values

Given the symmetry of the component, it was assumed that the measured directions (axial, hoop and radial) were principal stress directions. A value of 193 GPa was used for the modulus of elasticity (E) and 0.3 for Poisson ratio (ν) to derive bulk stresses from the single peak (311) strain measurements. The calculated stresses through the thickness of the HAZ at 14mm from the weld centre-line are shown in Fig. 6. The magnitude of hoop stress is small over the inner half of the thickness, but rapidly increases towards the outer surface reaching a peak value of about 260 MPa at about 3 mm below the outer surface of the pipe. However, this outermost point is probably adjacent to the cap fusion boundary, as mentioned earlier. The axial stresses are generally in compression, again with the exception of the outermost point. The peak compressive value of 340 MPa is observed to be at about 8 mm away from the inner surface. The radial stresses are compressive in nature throughout the thickness.

Determining the Strain Free Reference (d_0) from a Stress Balance Condition

If the distribution of weld residual stresses is assumed to be axi-symmetric, an average value for d_0 through the thickness can be inferred from equilibrium. The axial stress-balance condition for the cylindrical geometry is expressed by:

$$\int_T \sigma_a r \mathrm{d}r = 0$$

where T is the thickness and r is the radius. This approach gives a d_0 of $1.08209 \pm 6 \times 10^{-5}$ Å for the HAZ measurements, which differs by $\approx 1.3 \times 10^{-6}$ Å (about twice the cubes measurement error) from the average cube d_o value. Axial and hoop stresses based on the stress-balance d_0 are shown in Figs 9 and 10. All components of stress (including radial) are shifted upwards by about ~50-100 MPa compared with the results shown in Fig. 6. The through-thickness radial stresses (not shown) are now close to zero. It should be noted that the cube measurements showed little variation in d_o through the thickness in the HAZ, which supports the assumption of a constant d_o value in the stress-balance method. The significance of the axi-symmetric assumption is discussed later.

FINITE ELEMENT WELD SIMULATION

The FE weld residual stress simulation was performed 'blind', that is prior to fabrication of the mock-up used for stress measurements. The geometry, materials and weld procedure were

MEASURED RESULTS

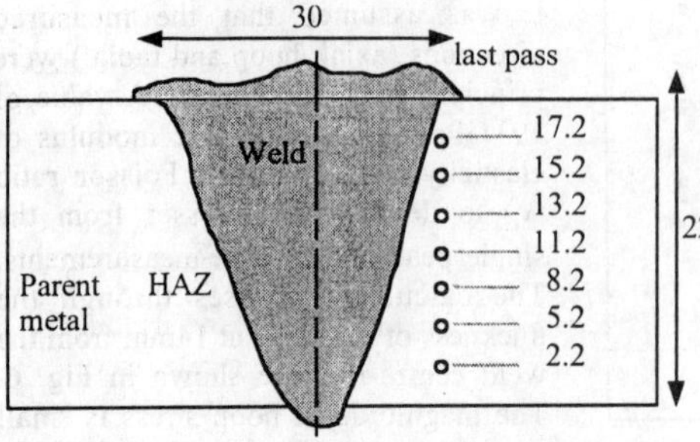

Figure 4: Measurement positions (under last pass)

The strain values at each measured point in three orthogonal directions (axial, hoop and radial) were determined by comparing the peak shifts (that is the change in inter-planar distance, Δd) with respect to the peak positions in strain-free reference cubes (or d_0 values). The measured strains through the thickness of the HAZ at 14mm from the weld centre-line are shown in Fig. 4.

The precise dimensions of the weld pool are not known at the measurement position, but microstructural analysis of the removed core suggests that the outermost HAZ measurement may lie near the edge of the weld cap fusion boundary.

Determination of the Stress Free Reference (d_0)

The determination of a suitable stress-free lattice parameter is often problematic in neutron measurements. This is particularly so with welds owing to the compositional gradients that can be found in the fusion zone and the HAZ. In order to assess the Stress Free Reference (d_0), small 3 x 3 x 3 mm^3 cubes were electro-discharge machined from a ring-core specimen removed from the HAZ at 150° around the circumference from the measurement location.

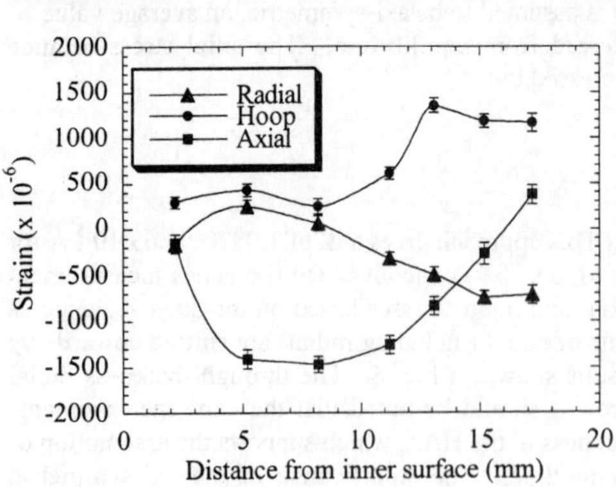

Figure 5 Measured HAZ (311) strains

Representative material from the weld pool, the HAZ and the parent material was sampled. Cubes from each region were scanned in axial and hoop directions from both sides (positive and negative) to minimise the errors arising from possible misalignment.

The averages of these d_0 values were found to be very similar in both the parent material and the HAZ, as previously seen in a type 316 weld (4,10). However, higher scatter was found in the average values in the weld pool.

hour at 1050°C followed by air cooling) to remove any remnant residual stresses. One end of each header was further machined to form a J-preparation, typically employed in steam raising plant butt welds. The matching sections were then welded by rotating the component. This minimised circumferential variations in heat input associated with the welding position. The root pass was made using the Tungsten Inert Gas (TIG) method. Subsequent passes were made by the MMA method using electrodes of varying size conforming to BS 2926 19.12.3 L B R. A summary of the deposition sequence and electrode sizes used is given in Fig. 1. The final welded component was 830 mm in length and weighed ≈190 kg. A neutron access slot ≈30 m m x 90 mm was machined near the edge of the weld at 70° from the measurement position to aid hoop direction counting times. A schematic drawing of the component is shown in Fig. 2.

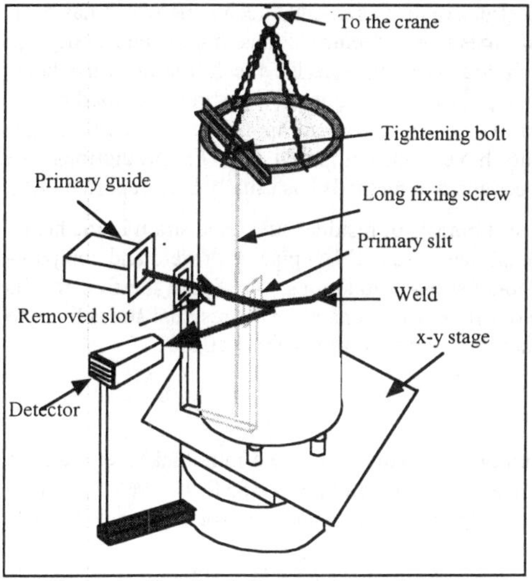

Figure 3: Sketch of the experimental set-up

Mounting and alignment of the large component within the limited space of the spectrometer was difficult. The pipe was suspended from a crane to reduce the load experienced by the positioning table. The pipe was upright for the hoop measurements and horizontal for the other two directions. The hoop measurements required the incoming beam to pass through the neutron access slot so the primary slit was placed inside the pipe, as shown in Fig. 3. The width of the primary slit was maintained (3 mm) for all measurements; but the height was 3 mm for the hoop direction and small reference cubes (d_0 measurements); 5 mm for the axial; and 10 mm for the radial measurements.

A double focusing monochromator is used at REST where both horizontal and vertical divergences play an important role in the resolution function, so calibration runs were required to assess the correct wavelength for each gauge volume used. The scattering angle for the chosen peak (311) at the selected wavelength of ≈1.76Å was ≈108.6°

The alignment and exact positioning of the component was performed using a telescope and neutron surface scanning (9). Through-thickness measurements were performed both in the weld and HAZ (see Fig. 4), but only the latter are reported here. At the measured position in the HAZ (14 mm from the weld centre-line), the local thickness was 22 mm owing to the presence of the weld cap. The gauge volume was always kept completely immersed in the material.

Runs	Current (A)	Electrode
1	90	2.4 mm
2-3	70	2.4 mm
4-5	120	3.2 mm
6-9	135	3.2 mm
10-12	155	4 mm
13-16	135	3.2 mm

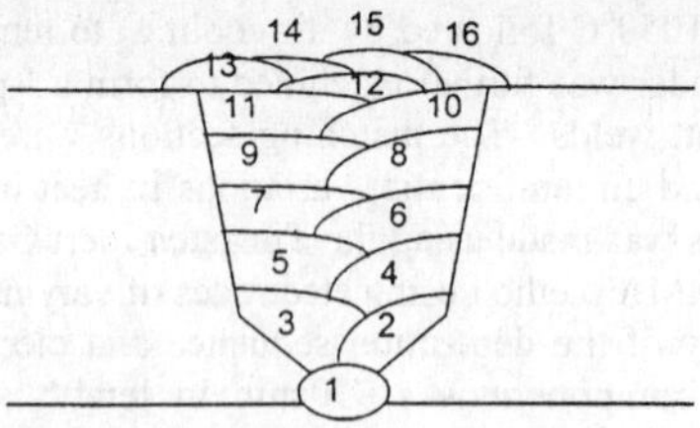

Figure 1 Welding data and sketch indicating weld bead sequence.

Neutron diffraction is an established non-destructive measurement technique which has been used to quantify residual stresses in welded pipes (4-8). Neutrons have high penetrability into most metallic materials. Moreover, the technique can characterize the full strain (and hence stress) tensor. This means that neutrons provide a unique non-destructive method for determining sub-surface residual stresses in welded industrial components. Residual stresses obtained from neutron strain measurements have been compared with FE predictions in a number of studies and good agreement between the two methods has usually been reported (4,5).

This paper describes neutron diffraction measurements of residual stress and strain in the heat affected zone (HAZ) of a stainless steel manual metal arc (MMA) pipe girth weld and compares the results with axi-symmetric FE weld residual stress simulations. These are the first results from a larger study examining the influence of off-set weld repairs on the residual stress field, to validate more complex FE simulations that take account of 3-dimensional effects.

EXPERIMENTAL DETAILS

Two ex-power station steam headers (432mm outside diameter by 63.5 mm thick) were used to fabricate the test component. The original material specification was ASME II: 1968 SA-182F-316H. The headers were bore-machined to a thickness of 19mm and then solution treated (for 1

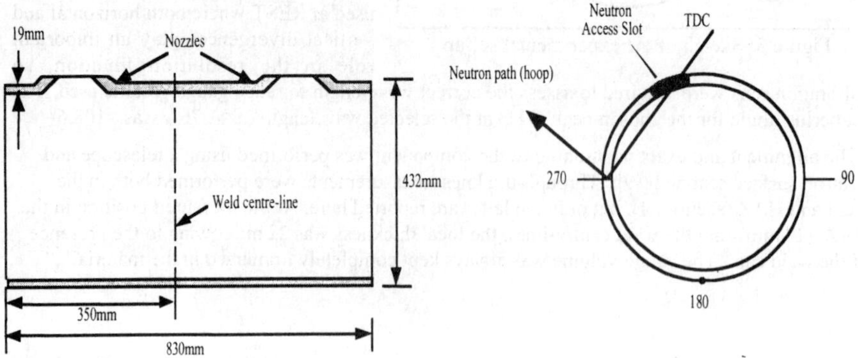

Figure 2 Schematic drawing of the welded component

model, and a hoop stress peak-to-peak range of 480 MPa compared with 340 MPa from the thick bead model. Predicted hoop stresses from both models exceed 500 MPa, which is substantially greater than the parent 1% proof stress at room temperature.

The high stresses are partly caused by multi-axial effects, although a more important factor is likely to be the isotropic hardening model used. Recent research (12) has shown that isotropic hardening tends to over-predict maximum tensile and compressive hoop residual stresses, whereas a mixed isotropic-kinematic hardening material model gave predictions which better matched measurements. Isotropic material hardening was chosen here to ensure a conservative prediction of the residual stress field for structural integrity assessments.

COMPARISON OF MEASURED AND FE RESULTS

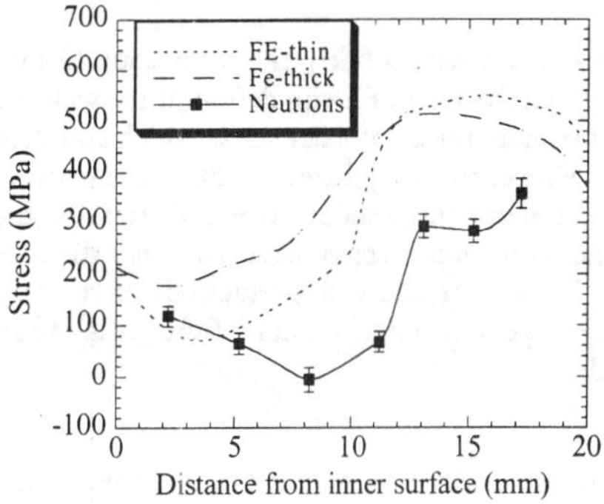

Figure 10: Measured and calculated HAZ Hoop stresses

The neutron diffraction results (based on stress balance d_o) for the HAZ are compared with the through-thickness stress profiles from the thick and thin weld bead simulations in Figs. 9 and 10. The measured axial residual stresses correlate closely with the thin bead model results over the inner half of the section thickness, and reasonably well over the outer portion. Note that the outermost measured point is less reliable owing to its suspected proximity to the weld fusion face. The shape of the measured hoop stress profile is similar to the FE predictions, but the magnitudes of stress are much lower; the peak measured value is 357 MPa compared with predictions exceeding 500 MPa. Again the thin bead model gives a better match.

DISCUSSION

The neutron results based on stress-balance were chosen to compare with the FE results for two reasons. First, because both the stress-balance and FE approaches assume an axi-symmetric distribution of weld residual stresses. Secondly, the stress-balance results gave measured stresses that were judged to be more realistic; that is they gave a peak compressive axial stress of lower magnitude (-260 MPa compared with –337 MPa), and radial stresses in the range ±73 MPa (i.e. less compressive).

Circumferential variations in girth weld residual stresses are not well understood and are difficult to quantify because of stress and measurement scatter effects. They can arise in small diameter, thin section girth welds (13,14). However, a 3-D weld simulation for a 16mm thick 800 mm diameter girth weld has shown negligible circumferential variations. Thin section small diameter girth welds are probably susceptible to 3-D effects because they provide a limited heat sink to the welding process and because the moving weld torch subtends a significant proportion of the circumference. An axi-symmetric distribution of weld residual stresses is a reasonable assumption for the present girth weld dimensions (19 mm, 432 mm OD).

The present FE stress results from the 21 weld pass model (Fig. 8) agree more closely with the neutron measurements, even though the mock-up was made with 16 passes. Two reasons for this can be inferred. First, low heat input electrodes were used for the mock-up capping passes (see Fig. 1), and these are more realistically represented in size and shape by the thin 21 bead model than by the thick 14 bead model (Fig. 7). Note that the position of the last weld cap pass has a dominant influence on the HAZ through-wall stress profiles and magnitudes in a 19mm girth weld (4). Secondly, beads might have been deposited in single thin layers (perhaps with some weaving) rather than side by side; this would effectively give a greater number of layers. These factors imply that a better prediction of residual stresses could be obtained by using macrographs of the actual weld to identify the pattern and sizes of weld passes and by using measured rather than estimated heat input data.

CONCLUDING REMARKS

The neutron diffraction method provides residual stresses with a fairly fine resolution (3 mm gauge volume dimensions), ideally suited to validation of detailed FE simulation of the welding process. The 'thin' bead FE model gives much higher magnitudes of axial stress which correlate more closely with the neutron measurements. However, hoop stresses have been over-estimated, probably owing to the use of an isotropic hardening model. It is inferred that the pattern and sizes of weld beads, and particularly the final capping pass, have a strong influence on the stress field in the 19mm thick girth weld. Thus more accurate predictions of residual stresses could be obtained by basing weld bead sizes/layers on a macrograph of the actual weld, and by using more realistic material hardening models.

ACKNOWLEDGEMENTS

This work is published by kind permission of British Energy Generation Ltd. The authors acknowledge the financial support of the EU through contract BRRT-CT97-5043.

REFERENCES

1. BS7910 1999, British Standards Institution, London.
2. Bradford R, *I Mech E Conf. Trans. Assuring It's Safe*, PEP Ltd., London, (1998) 287
3. Dong P, Zhang J, Li MV, PVP-Vol.373, 311-317, ASME 1998.
4. Edwards L, Bouchard P J, Dutta M, Fitzpatrick, M E, *I Mech E Conf. Trans Integrity of High Temperature Welds*, , PEP Ltd., London, (1998) 181
5. M. Nasstrom, P. J. Webster and J. Wang, Trends in Welding Research (1993) 109
6. X. L. Wang, E. A. Payzant, B. Taljat, C. R. Hubbard, J. R. Keiser and M. J. Jirinec, Mater. Sci. Engng, A232, (1997) 31
7. R. A. Winholtz and A. D. Krawitz, *Met. Trans., A265*, (1995) 1287
8 D. Brugnami, G. Bruno, M. Ceretti, F. Cernuschi, and L. Edwards, *Neutrons in Research and Industry*,, SPIE. 2867, (1997) 123
9. D.Q Wang and L.Edwards *Proc. ECRS4*, Ed. Denis, S., SFM, France, 1, 135-144.
10. P. J. Withers, *ISIS Experimental Report.* RB8230 (1997)
11. ABAQUS, Version 5.5, Hibbitt, Karlsson and Sorensen Inc
12. S K Bate, P J Bouchard, P E J Flewitt, D George, R H Leggatt and A G Youtsos, Proc. ICRS6. This volume.
13. E Keim, S. Fricke, and J. Schmidt al., ibid.
14. W. J. Shack, W. A. Ellingson and L. E. Pahis, EPRI NP-1413, (1980)

THREE DIMENSIONAL STRAIN MEASUREMENTS IN BULK MATERIALS WITH HIGH SPATIAL RESOLUTION

U. Lienert*, S. Grigull*, Å. Kvick*,
R.V. Martins*, and H.F. Poulsen**

*European Synchrotron Radiation Facility, BP 220, F-38043
Grenoble Cedex, France
**Risø National Laboratory, DK-4000, Roskilde, Denmark

ABSTRACT

A novel diffraction technique utilizing focussed high energy synchrotron radiation has been developed for local structural characterization within polycrystalline bulk materials. Three dimensional gauge volumes on the micrometer scale are obtained. The technique is non destructive and fast and therefore well suited for *in-situ* measurements during thermo-mechanical processing. The method is presented and the application to the measurement of macrostrains is discussed.

INTRODUCTION

Grains or subgrain domains may be considered as fundamental units of polycrystalline bulk materials subject to the degree of plastic deformation. The length scale of these fundamental units ranges from nano- to millimeters depending on the material and processing.
Macrostresses are defined as at least one dimensional averages over fundamental units whereas microstresses describe the deviations between the fundamental units. Meaningful changes of macrostresses arise on length scales which comprise many fundamental units parallel to dimensions of averaging. However, perpendicular to the averaging directions macrostrain gradients may exist on shorter length scale than given by the fundamental units. Many features within polycrystaline materials such as inclusions, cracks, grain size, or interfaces produce inhomogenities on the micrometer scale and may introduce macro- and microstresses on this length scale. None of the established non-destructive bulk strain scanning techniques provides sufficient spatial resolution to measure such strain fields.

Recently a novel diffraction technique has been developed that provides a three dimensional spatial resolution on the micrometer scale within polycrystalline bulk materials and therefore fills a wide gap between existing techniques, Lienert *et al.* (1, 2). The technique is non destructive and provides fast data acquisition making *in-situ* studies of thermo-mechanical processing possible. This paper focusses on the measurement of macrostrains, applications to the structural characterization of single grains are reported by Juul Jensen *et al.* (3).

The micrometer length scale becomes experimentally accessible by exploitation of the unique brilliance of high energy synchrotron radiation in combination with focussing optics. Two dimensional (2D) detectors reduce the data acquisition time by orders of magnitude. In collaboration with the Materials Research Department, Risø (Denmark), a dedicated experimental station has been constructed at the Materials Science Beamline ID11 of the European Synchrotron Radiation Facility (ESRF) in Grenoble (France). The station, referred to as the 3-Dimensional X-Ray Diffraction (3DXRD) Microscope, is now open for beamtime applications from external users.

PROPERTIES OF HIGH ENERGY X-RAYS

The 3DXRD microscope operates within an energy range from about 40 to 100 keV. Important consequences arise from the small scattering angles 2Θ which are typically 0.1 to 0.2 radians. Samples are therefore generally investigated in transmission geometry. As common to diffraction techniques, the lattice strain ε is deduced from measured peak shifts $\Delta 2\Theta$ by means of the Bragg equation

$$2d \sin\Theta = \lambda \tag{1}$$

where d is the strained lattice parameter, Θ denotes the Bragg angle and λ is the wavelength of the incoming beam. Because elastic strains are small eq. (1) is differentiated and for angle dispersive measurements (constant wavelength) one obtains

$$\varepsilon = \frac{d - d_0}{d_0} = -\frac{\Delta 2\Theta}{2\tan\Theta} \approx -\frac{\Delta 2\Theta}{2\Theta} \quad . \tag{2}$$

Application of eq. (2) requires the knowledge of the strain free lattice constant d_0, and appropriate elastic constants are needed to convert the strain to stress. These are common problems to diffraction techniques and are not discussed here. For practical purposes the $\tan\Theta$ in (2) may be approximated by Θ at high energies. It should be noted that peak broadening due to size effects or microstrain scales with the wavelength and does therefore not complicate the strain determination at small scattering angles. However, constraints arise from instrumental effects such as a beam divergence due to focussing or the absolute error of the measured scattering angle. These effects are discussed in subsequent sections.

The maximum sample thickness is limited by the absorption and typically a transmission of about 10 % still provides sufficient flux and signal-to-noise ratio. The absorption of X-rays is described by a linear attenuation coefficient which decreases roughly with the cube of the wavelength in the absence of absorption edges and increases with $Z^{4.5}$, Z being the atomic number. At 80 keV, 10 % transmission is obtained for 42 mm Al, 13 mm Ti or 5 mm Fe.

FOCUSSING OPTICS

Third generation high energy synchrotron facilities like the ESRF produce high energy X-rays of unprecedented brilliance. Intense beams of micrometer dimension can be prepared by broad band focussing optics. Bent Laue crystals and elliptically shaped multilayer mirrors have been developed to focus high energy X-rays, Schulze *et al.* (4) and Lienert *et al.* (5). A single element provides a line focus, and point focussing is achieved by combination of two elements. A line focus of 1.2 μm height and a point focus of 4×6 μm^2 were achieved. The focal spot size is mainly limited by shape errors of the optical elements and further progress is expected. The typical flux in the focal spot is 10^{11} to 10^{12} ph/sec.

The energy and divergence band width of the focussing optics can be tuned to a corresponding instrumental peak broadening $\Delta\Phi/(2\Theta)$ between 0.1% and 1%. Hence, the lattice strain $(d-d_0)/d_0$ can still be determined to one part in ten thousand if the peak center can be determined within 1% to 10% of the peak width.

EXPERIMENTAL SETUP

The experimental setup is sketched in Fig. 1. The main components are the focussing optics, a precision sample goniometer, an optional optical element that defines the longitudinal resolution, and a 2D detector.

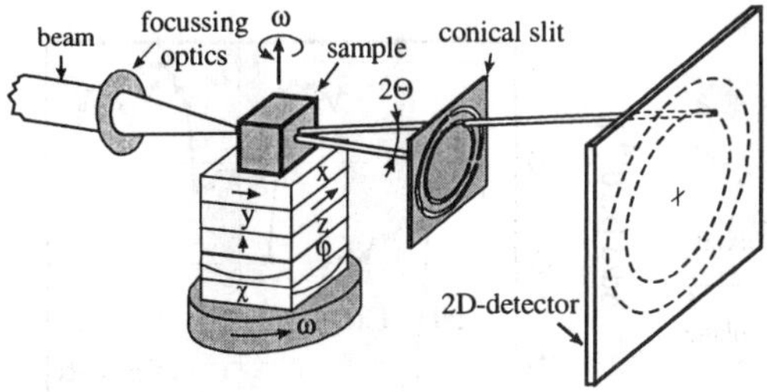

Fig.1: Sketch of the main components of the experimental setup. Distinct spots or continuous diffraction rings are observed on the 2D detector depending on the degree of the plastic deformation and the number of diffracting grains in the effective gauge volume.

The choice of an angle dispersive technique based on 2D detectors has important consequences on the design and operation of the instrument. A pixel number of 1000 by 1000 has proven to be sufficient for many cases, as the effective pixel number in a diffraction peak is increased by azimuthal integration. Spatial distortions can be corrected, but a high reproducibility is compulsory. Several complete diffraction rings can be captured simultaneously on the 2D detector due to the small scattering angles. As a consequence the biaxial strain state in a plane perpendicular to the beam and sections of pole figures may be extracted from a single exposure. Measurement of the complete strain tensor and complete texture characterization only requires sample rotation around a single axis perpendicular to the beam. Hence, only a high concentricity of the rotary table is required to retain the micrometer spatial resolution under sample rotation, as opposed to a small sphere-of-confusion of a Eulerian cradle setup. Typical exposure times of the 2D detector range from tenths of seconds to several seconds.

The actual sample goniometer is based on an air bearing rotary table to achieve the required concentricity. Positioning tables with high dynamical range, *i.e.* high resolution and high maximum speed, are being developed by a combination of incremental encoders and micro-stepping drives. This solution should enable high spatial resolution and averaging by sample oscillation. Samples up to 100 kg can be mounted (with restricted degrees of freedom). The list of auxiliaries includes a stress rig, a torsion cell, and furnaces.

STRAIN MAPPINGS TRANSVERSE TO THE BEAM

The transmission geometry sketched in Fig. 2 renders possible the direct exploitation of the transversal spatial resolution provided by the focussed beam. No further optical element is required between sample and 2D detector but in this case there is no spatial resolution along the beam. Furthermore, the position of scattering grains along the beam is coupled to the radial position of the observed diffraction spot on the 2D detector and an inhomogeneous distribution of scattering grains may be falsely interpreted as peak shifts. The magnitude of this effect is given by the ratio of the sample thickness to the sample-to-detector distance which can be increased by increasing the energy and the detector size. Within these limitations the technique provides a simple and powerful tool for one and two dimensional strain mappings.

As a case study, the depth dependent strain gradient in layered Cu/Ni structures was measured, Lienert *et al.* (5). Reported here are results on a structure consisting of two 90 µm thick electrodeposited Ni/Cu bilayers on a Cu substrate.

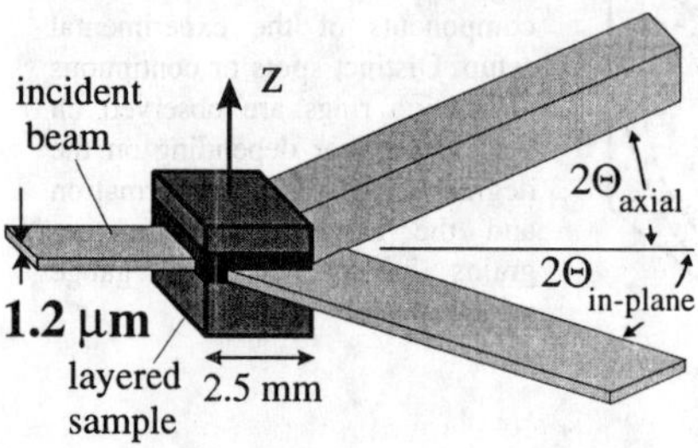

Fig. 2: Scattering geometry of the strain gradient mapping of layered structures. The samples were scanned in the z direction and the axial and in-plane diffraction angles were recorded simultaneously.

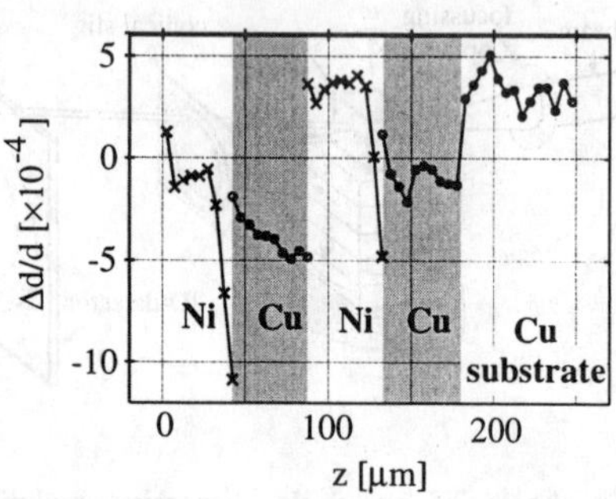

Fig. 3: Residual strain gradients in a structural Cu/Ni multilayer as a function of depth below the surface z. Plotted are the relative d-spacings of the axial 200 reflection. Note the steep gradients at the buried Ni/Cu interfaces.

90 keV X-rays were focussed to a line of 1.2 µm height. The samples were aligned with the interfaces parallel to the beam and scanned in a perpendicular direction obtaining a depth resolution of the same size as the focus height. The longitudinal resolution was not confined but the signal was averaged along the full sample thickness of 2.5 mm where the front and back surface regions contribute only a small amount. The measurement is therefore assumed to reflect true bulk properties. In this way strain gradients across the buried Cu/Ni interfaces were measured, which is not possible by other techniques. The actual strain gradient was recorded by measuring the position of the diffracted beams 2 m behind the sample. Steep strain (and texture) gradients were observed at the Cu/Ni interfaces, particularly within the Ni layers (Fig. 3). The grains within the Ni layers had sub-micron size giving a smooth signal. The strain gradients are suggested to be caused by recrystallisation processes during the electrodeposition.

For applications of the simple transmission geometry using unfocussed high energy X-rays and 2D detectors see *e.g.* Wanner & Dunand (6), Korsunsky *et al.* (7).

LONGITUDINAL SPATIAL RESOLUTION

A three dimensional gauge volume is obtained by the crossed beam technique placing a narrow triangulation slit behind the sample (Fig. 4). The gauge volume is defined by the intersection of the incident beam with the selected diffracted beams.

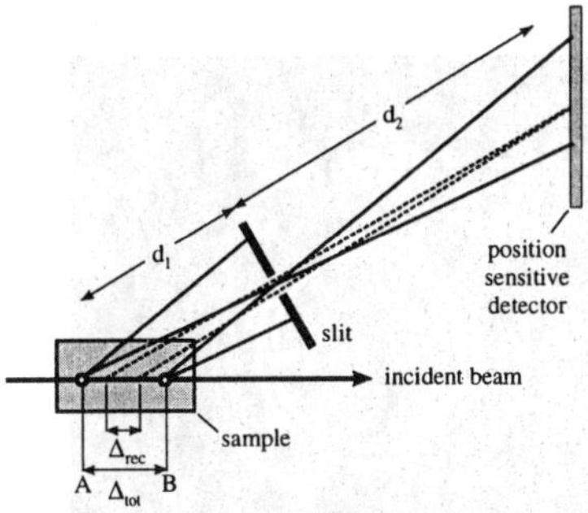

Fig. 4: Sketch of the crossed beam technique. The longitudinal gauge length parallel to the incoming beam is defined by a slit and a position sensitive detector. The finite divergence of the diffracted beams is indicated for local sample volumes A and B. Volume elements between A and B can contribute to the detected signal and constitute the total gauge length Δ_{tot} which increases with the distance d_1. The reconstructed gauge length Δ_{rec} (indicated by dashed lines) primarily depends on the slit gap as long as d_2 is sufficiently larger than d_1.

Due to the small scattering angles the longitudinal resolution is typically ten times larger than the transversal resolution. A good longitudinal resolution can therefore only be obtained for narrow transversal beam dimensions. The size of the samples or sample environment often prevent the slit from being placed close to the sample. Then, a coupling arises between the position and apparent strain of a diffracting grain. It has been demonstrated that this can be taken into account by an appropriate evaluation algorithm, Lienert *et al.* (8). The in-plane strain profile of a shot peened Al sample was measured both with the transversal and longitudinal gauge length. The shot peened Al sample consisted of two pieces of an area of 10 × 10 mm^2 and 5 mm thickness. Each plate was shot peened on one side and the plates were then mounted to form a 10 mm cube such that the shot peened surfaces faced each other resulting in an internal interface to cancel out both surface and absorption effects in strain measurements (9). Fig. 5 shows that the strain profiles agree apart from the expected resolution broadening.

Fig. 5: In-plane 311 strain profile of the shot peened Al sample. q indicates the scattering vector. Plotted are: (a) experimental reference profile (beam parallel to shot peened surfaces)(bold), (b) experimental profile from the reconstruction technique (beam perpendicular to the shot peened surfaces) (circles), and the experimental reference profile convoluted with a Gaussian resolution function of 100 μm FWHM (thin). The insets show the scattering geometry. The shot peened regions are hatched.

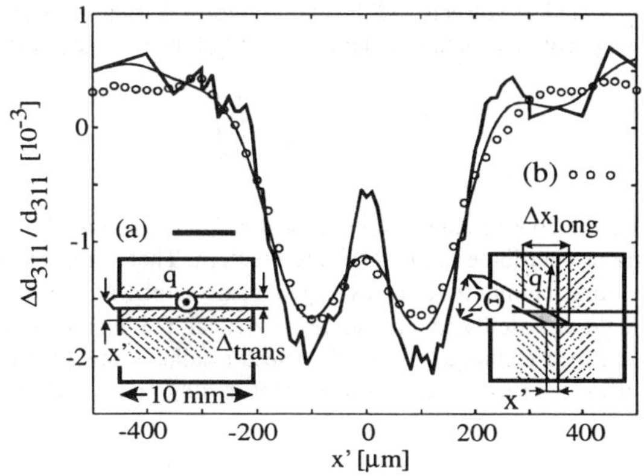

Furthermore, conical slit cells have been developed that enable the simultaneous observation of several diffraction rings from a gauge volume of about 20×20×200 μm^3, Nielsen *et al.* (10). Fig. 6 shows the diffraction pattern obtained from a local volume element within an AlSi alloy sample plastically deformed by torsion. The simple transmission geometry cannot be applied to the rotational symmetry of torsion deformation as integration along the incoming beam averages the strain profile to zero. Experimental details and strain profiles are given by Martins *et al.* (11).

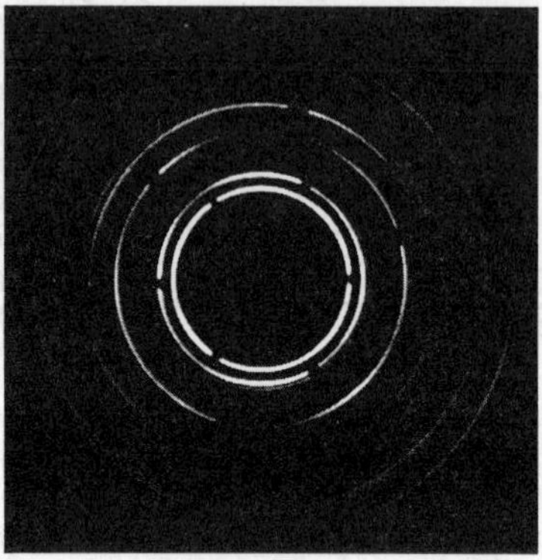

Fig. 6: Diffraction pattern as recorded on a 2D detector from a torsionally deformed AlSi alloy sample. A local scattering volume of 20×20×250 μm^3 was selected by a conical slit cell. The selected reflections are 111, 200, 220, 222, 331 and 422. The azimuthal intensity variation reflects the local texture. Distance pieces, used to assemble the conical slit, can be seen as dark segments in the rings.

Grain averaging

Finally, we address the question under what circumstances meaningful macrostrains can be measured with narrow gauge volumes. The answer will depend on the grain size, texture, geometry of the macrostrain field, nature of existing microstrains, and degree of plastic deformation within the actual sample system. A detailed discussion is beyond the scope of this paper but it seems worthwhile to give rough estimations as differences of orders of magnitude arise due to the use of 2D detectors as compared to diffraction techniques with fixed scattering vector.

As a starting point we consider a gauge volume V_g = 20×20×200 μm^3 which can be confined by a conical slit cell and averaging over a certain number of grains, lets say N > 500. The gauge volume contains at least N grains of an average grain diameter d_{av} of

$$d_{av} = \sqrt[3]{\frac{V_g}{N}} \qquad (3)$$

For the chosen parameters we obtain d_{av} = 5.4 μm. We now estimate how many of these grains contribute to the diffraction pattern. Therefore, we assume random orientation, *i.e.* no texture, and introduce an average mosaic spread $\Delta\omega_{gr}$ of the grains. Furthermore, the sample might be oscillated around axes vertical the incoming beam by an amount $\Delta\omega_{osc}$. The described technique using 2D detectors allows the simultaneous observation of n = 5 full diffraction rings. The fraction of contributing grains is approximately given by

$$\frac{\Delta M}{M}=\sum_{1}^{n}\frac{m_{hkl}}{2}\left(\Delta\omega_{gr}+\Delta\omega_{osc}\right)\approx\frac{nm(\Delta\omega_{gr}+\Delta\omega_{osc})}{2} \quad (4)$$

m_{hkl} is the multiplicity factor which is approximated by its average m being 14 for the conical slit cell. A sample oscillation up to $\Delta\omega_{osc}$ = 0.1 rad = 6 deg, *i.e.* of the order of the scattering angle, does not increase the transversal gauge length substantially. Even for rather perfect grains with $\Delta\omega_{gr} << \Delta\omega_{osc}$, eq. (4) gives ΔM/M = 3.5 which means that several reflections are observed per grain. If point detectors are used the fraction of observed grains is typically two orders of magnitude smaller requiring a correspondingly larger gauge volume.

Texture and a triaxial microstrain state can be taken into account by measurements at different angular sample settings around an axis perpendicular to the beam. Grains with a mosaic spread larger than the above oscillation range are in general strongly plastically deformed and it is then questionable if averaging over grains is still appropriate or if averaging should take place over the smaller cell blocks.

The gauge volume may be further increased by a translational oscillation in cases where the macrostrain field is homogeneous in at least one direction. We conclude that macrostrain fields should be measurable with the given gauge volume within most materials of grain size below about 10 μm or strongly plastically deformed materials. Finally, it is noted that continuous diffraction rings are not required to obtain meaningful macrostrains. An evaluation procedure of 'spotty' diffraction rings was suggested by Wanner and Dunand (6).

CONCLUSION

A novel diffraction technique has been developed that enables local strain measurements within polycrystalline bulk materials. The technique is based on the combination of high energy synchrotron radiation, focussing optics and two dimensional detectors. Three dimensional gauge volumes on the micrometer scale are achieved at high data acquisition rates. Fast mappings of the complete strain tensor become feasible due to the simultaneous measurement of biaxial strain states. Therefore, a large gap between existing techniques is filled.

The scope of the technique is illustrated by case studies. Routine operation requires adapted instrumentation and software, which is under development. It should be noted that the synchrotron radiation source, focussing optics, and two dimensional detectors are steadily improving. Hence, further improvement of the space, time, and momentum resolution is expected.

We also anticipate the development of three dimensional imaging as demonstrated by micro-tomography. Combining diffraction and imaging on the same instrument would provide the same type of advantages as the electron microscope does, but applied to bulk materials.

ACKNOWLEDGEMENTS

The authors acknowledge the contribution from L. Margulies towards further progress of the project. Support for this work was provided by the Danish Reseach Councils, STVF and SNF (via Dansync).

---

1. Lienert U., Poulsen H.F. and Kvick Å., Proceedings of 40th AIAA Structures, Structural Dynamics, and Materials Conference (St. Louis, MO, USA), 1999, no. A99-24795, p. 2067-2075

2. Lienert U., Poulsen H.F., Martins R.V., Kvick Å., Proceedings of the ECRS-5 conference, 28-30 Sept. 1999, (Noordwijkerhout, The Netherlands), eds. Böttger A.J., Delhez R. and Mittemeijer E.J., J. Mat. Sci. Forum, to be printed

3. Juul Jensen D, Kvick Å, Lauridsen E.M., Lienert U., Margulies L., Nielsen S.F. and Poulsen H.F., to be published in the Proceedings of the MRS 1999 Fall Meeting, *Applications of synchrotron radiation techniques to materials science*, Boston, MA

4. Schulze C., Lienert U., Hanfland M., Lorenzen M., and Zontone F., J. Synchrotron Rad. **5** (1998) p. 77-81

5. Lienert U., Schulze C., Honkimäki V., Tschentscher T., Garbe S., Hignette A., Horsewel A., Lingham M., Poulsen H. F., Thomsen N. B. and Ziegler E., J. Synchrotron Rad. **5** (1998) p. 226-231

6. Wanner A. and Dunand D.C., to be published in the Proceedings of the MRS 1999 Fall Meeting, *Applications of synchrotron radiation techniques to materials science*, Boston, MA

7. Korsunsky A.M., Wells K.E. and Withers P.J., Scripta Materialia **39** (1998) p. 1705-1712

8. Lienert U., Martins R., Grigull S., Pinkerton M., Poulsen H.F., Kvick Å., to be published in the Proceedings of the MRS 1999 Fall Meeting, *Applications of synchrotron radiation techniques to materials science*, Boston, MA

9 Webster P.J., Vaughan G.B.M., Mills G. and Kang W.P., Mater. Sci. Forum vol. 278-281 (1998) p. 323

10. Nielsen S.F., Wolf A., Poulsen H.F., Ohler M., Lienert U., Owen R.A., J. of Synchrotron Rad., to be printed

11 Martins R.V., Grigull S., Lienert U., Margulies L., and Pyzalla A., these proceedings